ANATOMY AND PHYSIOLOGY

DIANA CLIFFORD KIMBER

CAROLYN E. GRAY, A.M.

CAROLINE E. STACKPOLE, M.A.

Fifteenth Edition by

LUTIE C. LEAVELL, M.A., M.S.
Civilian Consultant, U.S. Army Nurse Corps, Walter Reed Institute of Research, Washington, D.C. Formerly, Lecturer, University of Pennsylvania School of Nursing, Philadelphia ; Clinical Professor, Graduate School of Nursing, New York Medical College, New York. Professor Emeritus of Nursing Education, Teachers College, Columbia University, New York

MARJORIE A. MILLER, M.S.
Associate Professor of Science (Physiology), Cornell University–New York Hospital School of Nursing, New York. Formerly, Instructor of Nursing Education (Physiology), Teachers College, Columbia University, New York

With the assistance of

FLORENCE M. CHAPIN, M.A., M.S. Assistant Professor of Science (Anatomy and Physiology), University of Pennsylvania School of Nursing, Philadelphia. Formerly, Instructor of Nursing Education (Physiology), Teachers College, Columbia University ; Assistant Professor (Surgical Nursing, Anatomy), Cornell University–New York Hospital School of Nursing, New York

ANATOMY AND PHYSIOLOGY

15th edition

THE MACMILLAN COMPANY, NEW YORK
COLLIER-MACMILLAN LIMITED, LONDON

Second printing, 1967

Earlier editions: Text-book of Anatomy and Physiology for Nurses *by Kimber, copyright,* 1893, *by Macmillan and Co., and copyright,* 1902, *by The Macmillan Company;* Text-book of Anatomy and Physiology for Nurses *by Kimber and Gray, copyright* 1909, 1914, 1918, *by The Macmillan Company;* Text-book of Anatomy and Physiology *by Kimber and Gray, copyright,* 1923, 1926, *by The Macmillan Company;* Textbook of Anatomy and Physiology *by Kimber and Gray, copyright,* 1931, *by The Macmillan Company;* Textbook of Anatomy and Physiology *by Kimber, Gray, and Stackpole, copyright,* 1934, 1938, 1942, *by The Macmillan Company;* Textbook of Anatomy and Physiology *by Kimber, Gray, Stackpole, and Leavell, copyright,* 1948, 1955, *by The Macmillan Company;* Anatomy and Physiology *by Kimber, Gray, Stackpole, and Leavell,* © 1961, *by The Macmillan Company.*
Copyright renewed: 1930, 1937, *by Mary J. Kimber;* 1946, 1951, 1954, 1959, *by Theresa Buell;* 1962, 1966, *by Lutie C. Leavell.*

Library of Congress catalog card number: 66-25281

The Macmillan Company, New York

Collier-Macmillan Canada, Ltd., Toronto, Ontario

Printed in the United States of America

Preface

DURING THE PAST decade, in keeping with the accelerated pace of research in the biological and physical sciences, there has been considerable expansion in the scope of most high school science courses. Accordingly, students are now entering college and nursing school with a much better understanding of both general and human biology. This fact has influenced the selection and organization of materials for this fifteenth edition of *Anatomy and Physiology*; in short, the authors have attempted to build rather than to repeat. We continue to believe that the integrated study of anatomy and physiology, with each subject giving immediate meaning to the other, is conducive to better understanding and to an appreciation of the interlocking relationships of structure and function.

Although many chapters have been completely rewritten or rearranged, every effort has been made to retain the over-all organization and clarity of style that characterized previous editions. There are now four, rather than five, units; the elimination of one unit has resulted from the integration of the material on skin and appendages with the chapter on tissues, as well as the correlation of the discussions of temperature regulation and control with those of metabolism and the nervous system. In the section on the nervous system, the instructor will note additional evidence of change: the chapter on sensation now includes pain and referred pain, and special and somatic sensation; the structure and function of the autonomic nervous system have been elaborated upon and placed in a separate chapter.

In the chapter on muscles, the authors have attempted to correlate blood supply and, in particular, nerve distribution to muscles; we are hopeful that this arrangement will help the student to think primarily in terms of muscle function, rather than anatomical location. New material will be found in the sections on cell physiology; this includes revised discussions of cell structure, enzymes, hormones, vitamins, and electrolytes. There are entirely new chapters dealing with the maturation of reproductive cells and fertilization, and with embryonic development.

New charts and tables have been added to clarify difficult concepts. New diagrams, many in color, have increased the number of figures from 409 to 426. In addition, several electron micrographs will be found in Chapters 2 and 25. The Paris nomenclature, adopted in 1955 and modified in 1960, is used throughout. Questions for discussion will be found at the close of each chapter; they are intended to be thought provoking and to aid the student in applying the principles and facts of physiology and functional anatomy.

This textbook can be supplemented by the Leavell-Chapin-Miller *Workbook and Laboratory Manual in Anatomy and Physiology*, Fourth Edition, 1964, published by The Macmillan Company. Also available from Macmillan are revised editions, 1966, of the *Teacher's Guide* and the *Test Manual to Accompany Anatomy and Physiology*. A set of Kodachrome (Medichrome) slides, series MH2, which were selected or made by the authors, can be obtained from the Clay-Adams Company of New York City.

Grateful acknowledgment is made to Mrs. Barbara Finneson, who prepared all the new linecut illustrations; to Dr. James L. German, III, of Cornell University Medical College, who supplied the chromosome map; to Dr. George Palade of Rockefeller University, who provided the electron micrographs of the cell; to several dozen teachers of undergraduate courses in anatomy and physiology, who made many helpful suggestions concerning content and organization of material; and to our students, past and present, who have been a constant source of inspiration. We also wish to thank 15 medical-school faculty members, all experts in particular areas of modern physiology, who reviewed the total manuscript and offered constructive comments and criticisms. In particular, we are indebted to Miss Joan C. Zulch, medical editor of The Macmillan Company, for her loyal support and help.

                                                                                      L. C. L.
                                                                                      M. A. M.

Contents

Unit III The Structural and Functional Relationships for Correlation and Coordination of Internal Activities. Metabolism

Unit IV The Structural and Functional Relationships for Human Reproduction and Development

The Body as a Whole: Structural and Functional Relationships and Organization

CHAPTER 1

Anatomy, Physiology, The Anatomical Position, Body Regions

THE HUMAN ORGANISM has the ability to observe his environment and its changes, to respond to stimuli in a purposeful manner, to think and make judgments. These abilities are all part of the processes called life and are dependent on the efficient functioning of the cells and tissues of the body. How these life processes are brought about in the human is the subject of this book; basic understandings are presented in this chapter.

Understanding one's self and others is essential to a happy life as well as a healthful one. The structure and functioning of the body are an integral part of this understanding; thus the study of anatomy and physiology can help those in every walk of life. More particularly—as a basis for understanding the sick individual, what is wrong, what can be done to help him return to his normal, healthy state—the study of anatomy and physiology is a necessity for those in the medical sciences.

Both anatomy and physiology are divisions of a larger science, *biology*, which deals with the acquisition and organization of knowledge about living things, plant and animal. Anatomy is the study of the parts of the living organism and their relationship to each other; physiology is the study of the way these parts accomplish their function—the multiple activities involved in the life of the organism. It is impossible to separate completely these two areas of study, and the fullest understanding of each comes from an understanding of the other.

Anatomy belongs to that group of biological sciences known as *morphology*, the group which deals with structure and spatial relationships, the way bodies are built, the kinds of material used, and the architecture of the entire organism. There are many specialties, for example:

Gross anatomy is the science of macroscopic structure, that which can be seen with the unaided eye.

Comparative anatomy is the study of animal structure, the similarities and differences among various orders or species of animals.

Systemic anatomy gives attention to the structure of areas of the body with similar function, e.g., circulatory and respiratory systems.

Regional anatomy, on the other hand, considers regions of the body, such as the head and the extremities, and all the systems in that particular region.

Developmental anatomy is the study of the embryonic and later development of body structures. In its widest sense *embryology* means the science of growth from the one-cell stage to the adult, but the term frequently is restricted to mean the period of growth and development before birth. This period is followed by the postnatal development of infancy, childhood, adolescence, and early, middle, and late maturity. Development can be studied much more vigorously from the standpoint of physiology.

Pathological anatomy has to do with structural changes in disease, their location, and their regional effects. The term *pathology* may be used in connection with anatomy, histology, physiology, etc., and is concerned with deviations from the normal state.

Histology is the study of the minute structure that can be seen only with the aid of lenses, and therefore is often called *microscopic anatomy*, or microanatomy. It makes clear the structure and activities of cells, their arrangement in tissues, and the manner in which tissues are built into organs.

Similar to anatomy, the science of physiology has many specialties, two of which are of interest here.

Human physiology gives attention to all the functions and activities occurring in the human.

Cellular physiology is the study of the individual cells themselves, as they live out on a small scale all the activities that characterize the larger organism—respiration, excretion, absorption of food, movement, etc.

The state of constancy or *homeostasis* found in the body fluids is a prerequisite to healthy functioning of the cell and of the human. The composition of fluids within and around the cell depends on the adequate supply of nutrients and the removal of waste products from its environment according to the varying general and local needs of the body cells in their steady state of flux.

These sciences and others, including psychology and sociology, can be grouped as the *biological sciences*, having to do with living things, as contrasted with the *physical sciences*, represented by mathematics, physics, and the like. The branches of science are closely related and tend to overlap, particularly as more knowledge is gathered in each.

GENERAL STRUCTURE OF THE BODY

An anatomical characteristic of all *vertebrate animals* is their vertebral column giving support to the body. In actuality the body is a tube (the *body wall*) enclosing a tube (the gastrointestinal tract), the cavity between the two tubes being the body cavity, or *celom*.

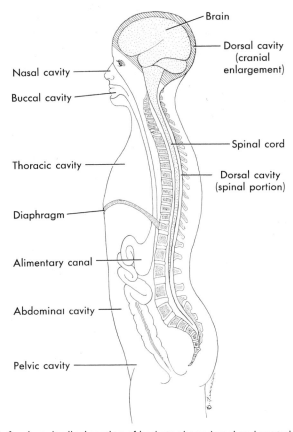

Figure 1–1. Longitudinal section of body to show dorsal and ventral body cavities.

Cavities. There are several cavities within the body. The thoracic and abdominal cavities are separated by the diaphragm; the dorsal cavity lies within the dorsal body wall and the ventral cavity lies in front of it. Some of the cavities are more open, such as the orbital, nasal, and buccal cavities.

The celom, or *body cavity,* is a *ventral cavity,* and it is enclosed by the body wall. This wall is composed of skin, connective tissues, bone, muscles, and serous membrane. In mammals, during embryonic life this cavity becomes subdivided by a dome-shaped, musculomembranous partition, the *diaphragm,* into the thoracic and abdominal cavities. The pericardial cavity is also developed embryologically from the celom.

5

The thoracic cavity, or *chest*, contains the trachea, the bronchi, the lungs, the esophagus, nerves, the heart, and the great blood and lymph vessels connected with the heart. It also contains lymph nodes and the thymus gland.

The thoracic cavity is lined with pleura and is divided into right and left

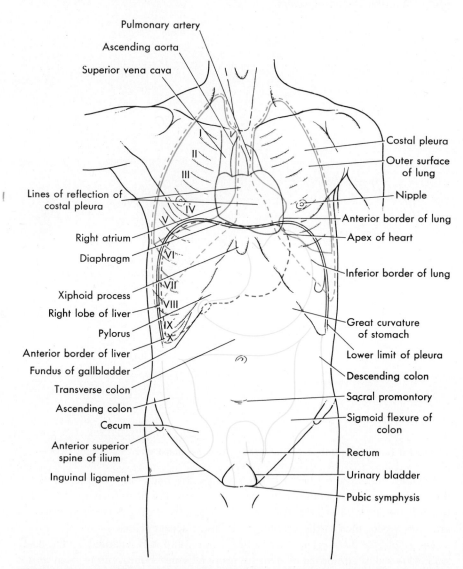

Figure 1–2. Projection outlines of the thoracic and abdominal organs on the anterior surface of the trunk. (*Continuous red*) Outline of heart, superior vena cava, ascending aorta, pulmonary artery; (*continuous blue*) two lungs; (*dotted blue*) boundaries of pleural cavities; (*dotted red*) liver and fundus of gallbladder; (*yellow*) stomach and parts of large intestine; (*black*) dome of diaphragm and lower edge of spleen. (Modified from Toldt.)

pleural cavities, each containing a lung. The other thoracic organs lie in the *mediastinum* between these pleural cavities (Fig. 1–5).

The abdominal cavity contains the stomach, liver, gallbladder, pancreas, spleen, kidneys, and small and large intestines. It may be divided into nine regions, as seen in Figure 1–6.

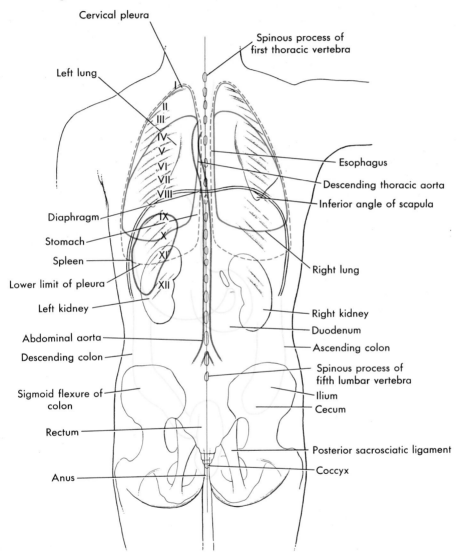

Figure 1–3. Projection outlines of the thoracic and abdominal organs on the posterior surface of the trunk. (*Red*) Outline of descending thoracic aorta, abdominal aorta, and spleen; (*continuous blue*), two lungs; (*dotted blue*) boundaries of pleural cavities; (*yellow*) stomach, duodenum, parts of large intestine; (*black*) dome of diaphragm and two kidneys. (Modified from Toldt.)

The pelvic cavity is that portion of the abdominal cavity lying below an imaginary line drawn across the prominent crests of the hipbones. It is more completely bounded by bony walls than the rest of the abdominal cavity. It is divided by a narrow bony ring, the pelvic inlet, into the greater, or false, pelvis above and the lesser, or true, pelvis below. The greater, or false, pelvic cavity is the lower part of the peritoneal cavity and contains parts of the organs listed for the abdominal cavity. The lesser, or true, pelvis contains the bladder, rectum, and some of the reproductive organs. Study Figures 1–1, 1–2, and 1–3.

The dorsal cavity is within the *dorsal body wall*. It contains the brain and spinal cord. The dorsal cavity is a continuous bony cavity formed by the cranial bones and the vertebrae, and it is lined by the meninges of the brain and spinal cord.

A survey of the skeleton shows small cavities in the skull, in addition to the cranial cavity, which, for the sake of simplicity in study, are included here.

The orbital cavities contain the eyes, the optic nerves, the muscles of the eyeballs, and the lacrimal apparatus.

The nasal cavity contains the structures forming the nose (p. 516).

The buccal cavity, or *mouth cavity*, contains the tongue and teeth.

BODY REGIONS

Owing to the fact that man walks erect and the majority of other mammals go on all fours, confusion sometimes arises in the use of terms which describe corresponding parts of man and other animals. To avoid this confusion, anatomists have given these terms arbitrary significance.

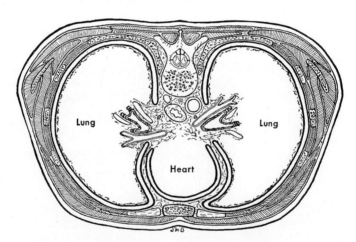

Figure 1–4. Diagram of a cross section of the body in the thoracic region. The mediastinum occupies the space between the lungs and extends from the sternum to the vertebrae (p. 529). (Modified from Toldt.)

The Anatomical Position. In describing the body, anatomists always consider it as being in the erect position with the face toward the observer, the arms hanging at the sides, and the palms of the hands turned forward. All references to location of parts assume the body to be in this position.

Textbooks of human anatomy use both *dorsal* and *posterior* for the side containing the backbone, and *ventral* or *anterior* for the opposite side. Comparative anatomists call the head end of an animal or man *anterior*, the opposite end *posterior*, the side containing the backbone *dorsal*, and the opposite side *ventral*. The head end is spoken of as *cranial* or *superior*, and the opposite end as *caudal* or *inferior*. A part above another part is described as superior to it. A part below another is said to be inferior.

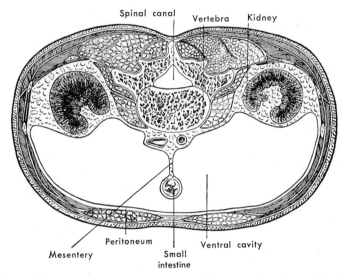

Figure 1–5. Diagrammatic transverse section of the body to show abdominal part of ventral cavity and spinal part of dorsal cavity.

General Anatomical Terms. *Sagittal plane* is the dorsoventral plane dividing the body into right and left sides. It is usually used in the sense of a *midsagittal plane* dividing the body into right and left halves. A *coronal* or *frontal plane* divides the body into ventral and dorsal parts. A *transverse plane* divides the body into cranial and caudal parts. The parts nearest the midsagittal plane are *medial* (mesial); those farthest from this plane are *lateral*. A *horizontal plane* is parallel to the horizon, and the term should be used only in relating the individual to his environment. If the term is used solely in relation to the individual, it indicates a transverse plane, since the individual is supposed to be in the anatomical position.

Internal and *external* are reserved almost entirely for describing the walls of cavities or of hollow viscera.

Proximal is used to describe a position near the origin of any part. *Distal* is used to describe a position distant, or farthest away, from the source of any part. Thus we speak of the proximal end or of the distal end of a finger.

Parietal (Latin, *paries*, a wall) is used to describe the walls enclosing the body cavity or surrounding the organs.

Visceral (Latin, *viscus*, an organ) is applied to the organs within the body cavities.

Peripheral pertains to the outside or surface of a body or an organ.

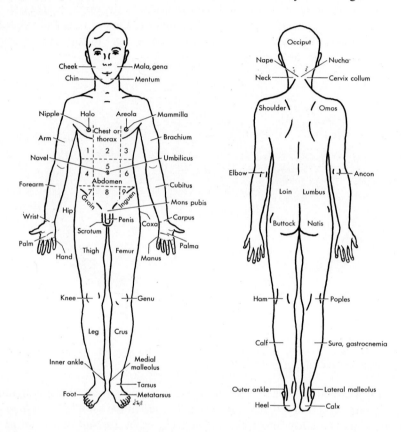

Figure 1–6. The anatomical position and regional names. Latin on one side and English on the other side.

QUESTIONS FOR DISCUSSION

1. Discuss the anatomical characteristics of all vertebrate animals.
2. Stand in the anatomical position and use each of the following terms correctly in relation to parts of the body:

ventrodorsal   superior-inferior

caudal-cranial   parietal-visceral

external-internal   proximal-distal

3. Name the body cavities and list the organs in each cavity.

SUMMARY

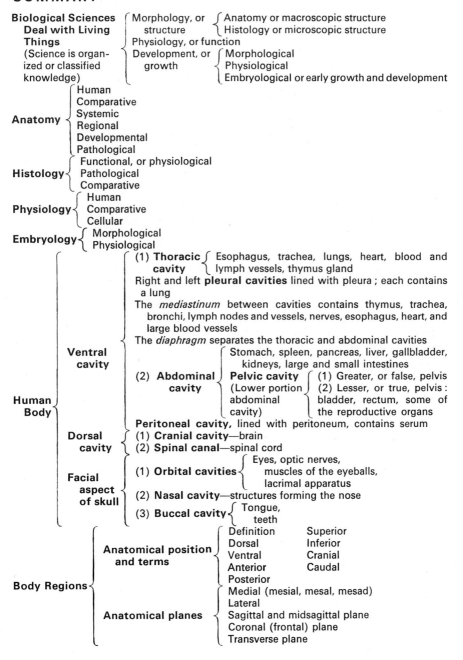

Biological Sciences Deal with Living Things (Science is organized or classified knowledge)
- Morphology, or structure
  - Anatomy or macroscopic structure
  - Histology or microscopic structure
- Physiology, or function
- Development, or growth
  - Morphological
  - Physiological
  - Embryological or early growth and development

Anatomy
- Human
- Comparative
- Systemic
- Regional
- Developmental
- Pathological

Histology
- Functional, or physiological
- Pathological
- Comparative

Physiology
- Human
- Comparative
- Cellular

Embryology
- Morphological
- Physiological

Human Body

Ventral cavity
- (1) **Thoracic cavity** Esophagus, trachea, lungs, heart, blood and lymph vessels, thymus gland

  Right and left **pleural cavities** lined with pleura ; each contains a lung

  The *mediastinum* between cavities contains thymus, trachea, bronchi, lymph nodes and vessels, nerves, esophagus, heart, and large blood vessels

  The *diaphragm* separates the thoracic and abdominal cavities
- (2) **Abdominal cavity** (Lower portion abdominal cavity)
  - Stomach, spleen, pancreas, liver, gallbladder, kidneys, large and small intestines
  - **Pelvic cavity**
    - (1) Greater, or false, pelvis
    - (2) Lesser, or true, pelvis : bladder, rectum, some of the reproductive organs

  Peritoneal cavity, lined with peritoneum, contains serum

Dorsal cavity
- (1) **Cranial cavity**—brain
- (2) **Spinal canal**—spinal cord

Facial aspect of skull
- (1) **Orbital cavities** Eyes, optic nerves, muscles of the eyeballs, lacrimal apparatus
- (2) **Nasal cavity**—structures forming the nose
- (3) **Buccal cavity** Tongue, teeth

Body Regions

Anatomical position and terms
- Definition
- Dorsal
- Ventral
- Anterior
- Posterior
- Medial (mesial, mesal, mesad)
- Lateral
- Superior
- Inferior
- Cranial
- Caudal

Anatomical planes
- Sagittal and midsagittal plane
- Coronal (frontal) plane
- Transverse plane

2

The Body as an Organized Whole: Systems, Organs, Tissues, Cells

THE CELL is the structural and physiological, as well as the developmental, unit of the body. It is desirable, however, to begin the study of the body with an analysis of it into its component parts—the systems, organs, tissues, unit patterns, and cells.

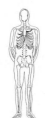

A system is an arrangement of organs closely allied to one another and concerned with the same functions (see Figs. 2–1 to 2–8).

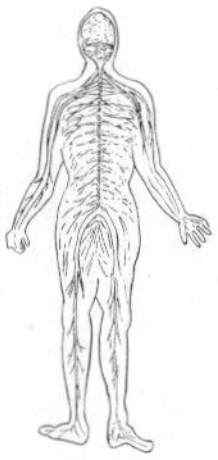

The skeletal system consists of bones of the body and connective tissues which bind them together.

Main functions: support, protection , and motion.

The muscular system consists of striated muscles (e.g., biceps muscle) and nonstriated muscles (e.g., muscle coats of the stomach).

Fig 2–1

Fig. 2–3

Main functions: to cause movement by contracting and to maintain static skeletal and postural support.

The nervous system consists of the brain, the spinal cord, ganglia, nerve fibers, and their sensory and motor terminals (e.g., motor end-plates on striated muscle). These are grouped into two integrated systems—the *somatic* and the *visceral* systems.

Main functions: to correlate the afferent nerve impulses in the sensory centers and to coordinate the nerve impulses

Fig. 2–2

in the motor centers, thus acquainting the organism with

Fig. 2–4

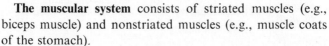

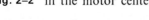

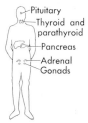

Pituitary
Thyroid and parathyroid
Pancreas
Adrenal
Gonads

Fig. 2–5

Fig. 2–7

the environment and integrating the nerve impulses into appropriate or adaptive responses. The nervous system contains centers for sensation, emotion, thinking, and many other functions.

The vascular, or **circulatory, system** consists of the heart, the blood vessels and blood, and the lymphatic vessels and lymph.

Main functions: to supply necessary nutrients and to remove cell secretions and excretions, thus helping to maintain the constancy of fluids around and inside all cells at all times (homeostasis).

The endocrine system includes the thyroid gland, parathyroids, pituitary body, adrenals, portions of the glands with ducts, such as the islands of Langerhans in the pancreas, portions of the ovaries and testes, and the thymus gland.

Fig. 2–8

Main function: to contribute to the body fluids specific substances which affect the activity of cells, organs, and tissues.

The respiratory system consists of the nose, pharynx, larynx, trachea, bronchi, and lungs.

Fig. 2–6

Main functions: to provide oxygen and get rid of excess carbon dioxide.

The digestive system consists of the alimentary canal and the accessory glands, i.e., the salivary glands, the pancreas, and the liver.

Main functions: to receive, digest, and absorb food, and eliminate some wastes.

The excretory system consists of the urinary organs, i.e., the kidneys, ureters, bladder, urethra, and also the respiratory and digestive systems and the skin.

Main function: to eliminate the waste products that result from cell activity.

The reproductive system consists of the testes, seminal vesicles, penis, urethra, prostate, and bulbourethral glands in the male; the ovaries, uterine tubes, uterus, vagina, and vulva in the female.

All these systems are closely interrelated and dependent on each other. Although each forms a unit especially adapted for the performance of some function, that function cannot be performed without the cooperative activity of the other systems; for instance, the skeleton does not support unless assisted by the muscular, nervous, circulatory, and other systems. It is the function of the body fluids and the nervous system to integrate the work of the systems.

An organ is a member of a system and is composed of tissues associated in performing some special function for which it is especially adapted. Systems are made up of *organs* with a corresponding division of labor and special adaptation of the organ to its particular share of the work of the system. For example, the urinary system consists of the following organs: (1) two kidneys, which form the urine from the blood; (2) two ureters, ducts which convey the urine from the kidneys to the bladder; (3) the bladder, a reservoir for the reception of urine; and (4) the urethra, a tube through which the urine passes from the bladder and is finally voided. The interdependence of these organs is obvious, and differences in structure suggest differences in function in the work of the system.

Tissues. The organs can be analyzed into component *tissues*. For example, the stomach is composed of columnar epithelial tissue, smooth muscle tissue, connective tissue, serous tissue, nerves, blood, and lymph.

Microscopic study of tissues reveals the fact that tissues are made up of smaller units, or cells. Each tissue is a group of cells with more or less intercellular material. The intercellular material varies in amount and in composition and in many cases determines the nature of the tissue, as, for instance, in the case of the bone.

Unit Pattern. Study of the tissues that compose the organs shows that the tissues are arranged in an orderly way.

A *unit pattern*, or *functional unit*, can be defined approximately as the smallest aggregate of cells which, when repeated many times, composes an organ. It can be said that these unit patterns are simple, minute, and repeated a vast number of times to form the organ. If the liver is studied in this way, it will be seen that the lobules (smallest macroscopic units) are composed of *chains of cells* with their definite supply paths of blood and lymph and bile capillaries. This arrangement gives an *enormous area*, for the volume of cells and body fluid concerned, over which the cells and circulatory fluids can be brought into diffusion relations and shows an orderly arrangement of blood and lymph tubes and nerve fibers throughout the organ.

These units can be studied as to structure (the shape, size, kinds, and arrangement of cells composing them, their grouping in the organ, orderly supply of blood and lymph vessels and nerve fibers). Some have been dissected out from the organs of lower organisms and can be worked with singly in experiments. Some have been cultured on nutrient media outside the bodies of animals, and their activities have been observed and studied.

Some of these units are probably better known in terms of their physiology, as, for instance, the reflex arc. Most of these reflex arcs are too long to be traced easily with the microscope, but at the same time they are too fine to be seen with the naked eye. They were known as functional units before they were *seen* as unit patterns. Most reflex arcs are today traced by function rather than by the microscope (e.g., the exact distribution of most of the *individual fibers* of the sciatic nerve has not been worked out objectively).

Today we are far from understanding completely the interrelationship between the cell's structure and its functioning, and the manner in which this structure controls development of the cell, the organ, and the organism. However, our knowledge has greatly increased in the past decade as a result of research investigations made possible by scientific advances such as the phase and electron microscopes and others in the field of electronics.

CELLS—COMPOSITION, STRUCTURE, AND ACTIVITIES

Cells are the physiological and structural units of the body. It is therefore necessary to understand their activities and structure. Low down in the scale of life there are simple animals consisting of one cell. The unicellular animals carry on the biological functions that are essential to life. These biological functions are movement, respiration, digestion, absorption, circulation, excretion, irritability (response to environment), and reproduction. As with the ameba, a typical one-cell animal, the life of each individual cell in the body is dependent on its ability to carry on these biological functions.

Higher in the scale of life are animals that consist of a greater number of cells. The human being may be described as a multicellular animal consisting of an enormous number of cells and intercellular material which the cells have made. In multicellular animals, individual cells are often remote from air, food, and the excreting organs and must rely upon the circulating fluids to carry oxygen and food to them and waste matters from them. The systems of the body represent an adaptation and specialization of groups of cells to carry on the biological activities for the body as a whole.

Form or Shape of Cells. Cells differ (markedly in some cases) in their size and shape; however, they are, in general, extremely minute and not visible to the naked eye.

Figure 2–9 shows cells of various shapes. A is a "shapeless" cell—the ameba. At the right, outlines of an ameba in pseudopodial motion are shown, in A^1 from above and in A^2 from the side; the straight line represents the *edge* of a microscope slide. B shows a typical plant cell with a cell wall of cellulose giving it fixed shape, with somewhat angled corners.

C^1 shows a spherical white blood cell, at left seen in face view, at right in profile view. C^2 shows at left a face view of a red blood cell; at right, edge views of a few red cells. C^3 shows side views of two cylindrical cells. C^4 shows a surface view of a flat (squamous) cell, the folded-over edge showing its thickness. C^5 shows a very irregular cell.

D^1 shows an abundance of intercellular material between cells (as seen in areolar connective tissue); D^2 shows two cells with very little intercellular material between the cells (represented by the black line).

E^1 shows the shape which soft living cells (e.g., fat cells) assume when lightly pressed together (as in adipose connective tissue); E^2 shows how the microscope would show this cell if focused at plane $a \ldots b$.

As a generalization, it can be said that for a *given volume* spherical cells have least surface area, and that the more irregular the cell, the greater is its surface area. For example, irregular connective tissue cells and nerve cells expose an enormous surface area to body fluids (for a given volume of cell contents) as compared with cylindrical or columnar cells, or the disk-shaped red blood cells.

The surface area–volume ratio in cells of various shapes is conspicuous as it concerns nerve cells, which contain relatively little metaplasm (e.g. stored food)

15

and may have very long, exceedingly fine processes (fibers); this means an enormous area in relation to the volume of protoplasm concerned. This surface area is in contact with circulating lymph in the perineural lymph spaces, and hence the protoplasm of the cell has abundant opportunity to get supplies (e.g., food) in relation to its need. Or consider a *piece* of nerve fiber 25 mm long and less

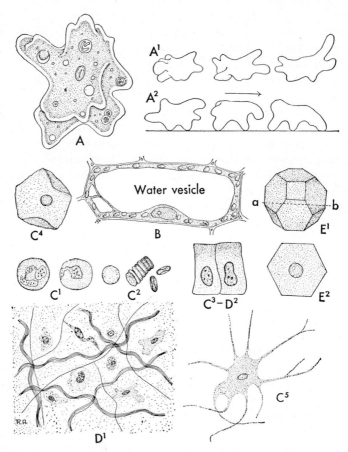

Figure 2–9. Diagrams of cells of many shapes as they would appear under the microscope. Description in text. The cells are not drawn to any scale.

than 0.01 mm in diameter in terms of surface area–volume ratio! This is one of the many items in favor of the membrane theory of the nerve impulse (p. 237).

Size of Cells. The factors that determine the sizes of cells are unknown, though much experimental work has been done in this field, and several theories have been proposed. However, cells, with few exceptions, are minute. The average diameter of a red blood cell is about 0.0075 mm, and it is about one fourth as thick. A striated muscle cell may be an inch or more long, but the diameter is seldom over 0.05 mm. The total length of the peripheral and central processes of a spinal sensory nerve fiber may reach from the toe to the medulla. In a tall person, then, it may be more than 4 or 5 ft long, but the diameter of the

Figure 2–10. Size of cells. (*A*) Voluntary muscle cell magnified in width 200 times and represented as cut off at *C*. At this magnification it would be about 200 in. long. (*B*) Red blood cell, also magnified about 200 times.

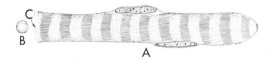

nerve fiber would probably be less than 0.01 mm. If all the processes of this nerve cell, divested of their sheaths, were wrapped closely around the cell body, the total volume of the cell would still be minute. Figure 2–11 shows that for a given volume of protoplasm, the greater the number of cells composing it, the greater

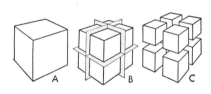

Figure 2–11. Diagrams to illustrate increased proportion of total surface area to total volume on fragmenting an object. *A* is a cube 2 in. on a side. *B* shows planes in which it may be cut to produce the eight cubes shown in *C*. Each of these eight cubes is 1 in. on a side. The total area of *A* is 24 sq in. The total area of the eight cubes in *C* is 48 sq in. The volume of material in *A* and *C* is the same, 8 cu in.

will be the surface area. (*Specific surface*, ratio of surface area to volume, is high.) As a generalization, it can be said that the protoplasm of the body is so partitioned in minute cells as to expose to the tissue fluid around the cells a truly enormous surface area for the volume of protoplasm itself.

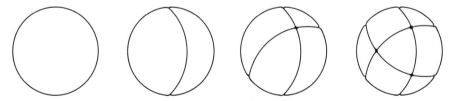

Figure 2–12. Animal cells* are more nearly spheres than cubes. A group of eight small cells having the same volume as one large cell will expose to body fluids very much more diffusion area than the large cell.

$$*4\pi R^2 = \text{area of a sphere} \quad 4/3\pi R^3 = \text{volume of a sphere}$$

The ratio of nuclear volume to cytoplasmic volume is in many cells somewhat the same, the volume of the nucleus being from about $\frac{1}{25}$ to $\frac{1}{50}$ the volume of the cytoplasm. In young cells with a high metabolic rate, the nucleus is relatively large. In position the nucleus is usually near the most active (chemically) part of the cell. These are indications of the fact that the activities of the cell can be carried on only within certain small limits of size. Since the surface area of the nucleus increases only in the ratio of the square, while the cell volume of cytoplasm and the nucleus increase in the ratio of the cube, the area of contact between nucleus and cytoplasm does not keep pace with their growth in volume; hence, the efficiency of the nucleus in relation to cell activities decreases markedly. This may be one of the important factors in limiting the sizes of cells.

The Constituents of Protoplasm.   Chemical analysis of the human body has shown that it contains the following *chemical elements:*

Oxygen	(O)	Form 96% of total weight of body	65.0%
Carbon	(C)		18.0
Hydrogen	(H)		10.0
Nitrogen	(N)		3.0
Sulfur	(S)		0.25
Calcium	(Ca)		2.2
Phosphorus	(P)		0.8–1.2
Potassium	(K)		0.35
Chlorine	(Cl)		0.15
Sodium	(Na)		0.15
Magnesium	(Mg)		0.05
Iron	(Fe)		0.004
Iodine	(I)		0.00004
Silicon	(Si)	Very minute amounts	
Fluorine	(F)		

Traces of Cu, Mn, Co; perhaps traces of Ni, Ba, Li.

In the human body free oxygen, hydrogen, and nitrogen have been found in the blood and intestines, but the bulk of these elements, as well as of all the others, exists in the form of complex compounds which are constituents of the cells and body fluids. The compounds are divided into two classes, organic and inorganic.

The *organic compounds* found in protoplasm are proteins, carbohydrates, and lipids. Wherever found in living organisms, these compounds are fundamentally similar.

In addition to this universal similarity, the proteins, carbohydrates, and lipids of each species of plant or animal possess distinctive characteristics. The essential chemical elements are present in varying absolute quantities, in varying relative quantities, and in varying combinations. The essential elements in proteins are carbon, hydrogen, oxygen, and nitrogen, and in some also sulfur and phosphorus; in carbohydrates and lipids the essential elements are carbon, hydrogen, and oxygen. The body ingests these proteins, carbohydrates, and lipids. They are split up into simpler compounds (i.e., carbohydrates into simple sugars, lipids into an alcohol and fatty acids, proteins into amino acids), which are carried by the blood and lymph to the cells, where they are reconverted into carbohydrates, lipids, and proteins having the distinctive characteristics of those found in the human body. These may then be stored in the cells, or utilized for making protoplasm or for supplying energy. A more complete discussion will be found in Chapters 20 and 21.

The *inorganic compounds* exist in cells partly as dissolved salts and partly in combination with the organic compounds. In chemical analyses of cells, the *mineral elements* remain either wholly or largely in the ash when the cells are incinerated; hence, they are grouped as the *ash constituents*. Only small amounts of these elements are needed, but they are essential parts of cells.

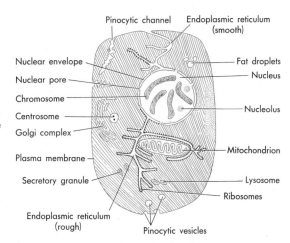

Figure 2–13. Diagram of typical cell showing structures visible under electron microscope.

Water is the most abundant constituent of tissues and constitutes about two thirds of body weight and more than 70 to 75 per cent of nonbony body weight. It is difficult to obtain the normal water content of an isolated living cell. One estimate gives it at from 85 to 92 per cent of the weight of the cell. It is evident that water is by far the predominant constituent of protoplasm. As will be seen later, this is true also of the body fluids—blood, lymph, and tissue fluid—which differ from protoplasm in many respects to only a slight degree.

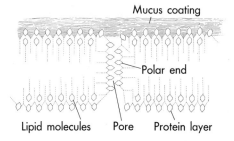

Figure 2–14. Diagram of molecular arrangement of cell membrane.

Structure of the Cell. A cell is a microscopic unit of living substance called protoplasm contained within a double-layered envelope, the *cell membrane*, or *plasma membrane*. The membrane has long been of interest since through it must pass all the materials the cell needs as well as any secretions of the cell; yet it must be of sufficient consistency to retain the *cytoplasm*, the protoplasm outside the nucleus. It is thought to be composed of lipid and protein molecules arranged in a double layer with the protein molecules outside.

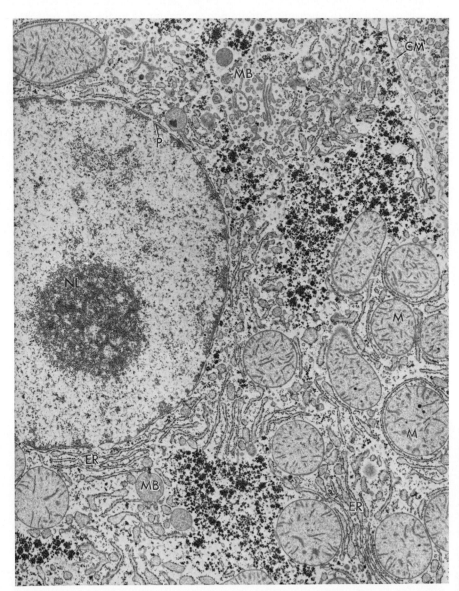

Figure 2–15. Liver cell of newborn rat showing nucleolus (*NL*); nucleus and nuclear membrane with several pores, one of which is labelled *P;* endoplasmic reticulum (*ER*); microbodies (*MB*); several mitochondria at lower right, two of which are labelled *M;* glycogen particles, which are visible as aggregated black dots. A portion of the cell membrane (*CM*) is visible at upper right. × 8,400. (Courtesy of Dr. George Palade, Rockefeller University, New York.)

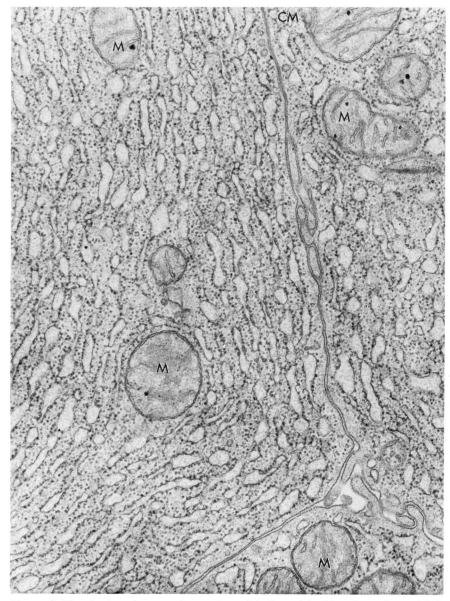

Figure 2–16. Portion of pancreatic exocrine cell (guinea pig) with cell membrane (*CM*) separating it from two adjacent cells visible to the right and in the lower right-hand corner. Endoplasmic reticulum is shown; several mitochondria (*M*) are seen in cross section. × 32,000. (Courtesy of Dr. George Palade, Rockefeller University, New York.)

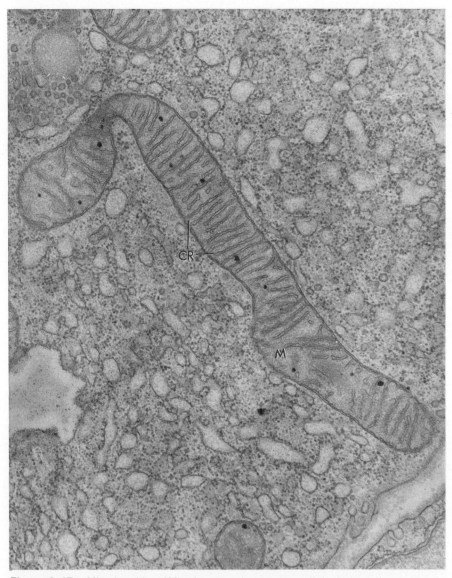

Figure 2–17. Mitochondrion (*M*) of pancreatic exocrine cell (guinea pig), seen longitudinally. Note infolding of inner membrane to form cristae (*CR*). × 30,000. (Courtesy of Dr. George Palade, Rockefeller University, New York.)

Cytoplasm contains a variety of structures—*organelles*, organized living material, and *inclusions*, lifeless and often temporary material, such as pigment granules, secretory granules, and nutrients such as protein and carbohydrate particles—material which will be utilized by the cell in its life processes, or excreted.

The organelles comprise the *mitochondria*, the *Golgi complex* or *apparatus*, the *centrioles, endoplasmic reticulum* and *ribosomes, lysosomes*, and in some cells *fibrils*.

Mitochondria vary in number from a few to several hundred, depending on the type of cell, appearing as rod-shaped or round structures which change shape as cell activity varies. They are concentrated in areas of greatest cell activity, e.g.,

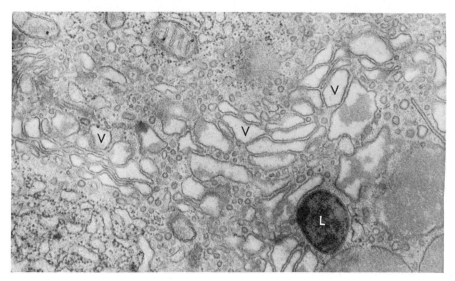

Figure 2–18. Golgi region of pancreatic exocrine cell (guinea pig). Clear areas are large vacuoles (*V*). A lysosome is visible as the dark granular body (*L*). × 30,500 (Courtesy of Dr. George Palade, Rockefeller University, New York.)

near the surface of actively secreting gland cells, in muscle cells near the motor end-plates, and in nerve cells near the nodes. The surface is a double-layered membrane, whose inner surface is extensively infolded. The mitochondria contain a variety of enzymes for energy-releasing chemical reactions in the cell.

The *Golgi complex*, most noticeable in secretory cells, appears as parallel arrangements of membrane and small vacuoles, somewhat like flattened bags, lying near the centrioles. It functions in regard to concentrating the cell secretion.

The *centrioles* are two in number in most cells, lying near the nucleus, and are important in cell division—orienting the spatial arrangement of chromosomes prior to division of the cell into two parts. In reality the centriole, or centrosome, is cylindrical in appearance with nine longitudinally arranged fibers plus two in the center. (It is of interest that this same arrangement of fibers is found in cilia and the tail of spermatozoa.)

Endoplasmic reticulum is found within many areas of cytoplasm as a network of vesicles. These are pairs of parallel membranes with which are associated dark-staining granules, the *ribosomes*, known to contain ribonucleic acid (RNA). In certain cells ribosomes are present without the endoplasmic reticulum. Since they are the site of protein synthesis, they are crucial elements in the cell. The term *microsome* refers to small fragments of the endoplasmic reticulum.

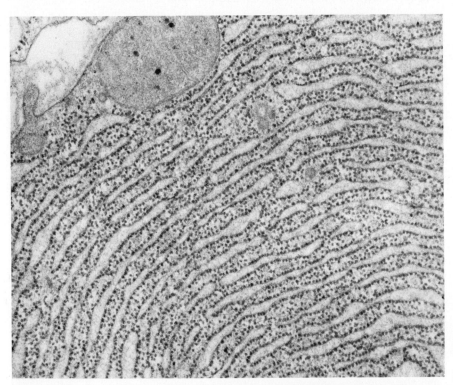

Figure 2–19. Endoplasmic reticulum of pancreatic exocrine cell (guinea pig). Ribosomes are seen as dark "beads" along the membranes as well as lying free and unattached. × 41,500. (Courtesy of Dr. George Palade, Rockefeller University, New York.)

Lysosomes are seen as "droplets" within the cell which are of different consistency from the rest of the cytoplasm. Separation of these droplets by centrifugation and chemical analysis indicates that various digestive enzymes are contained within the lysosomal membrane at the edge of the "droplet." Thus, cytoplasm is protected from digestion by the enzymes; at the same time ingested nutrients coming into contact with the lysosome can be acted on. Larger molecules may be broken down to smaller ones which the cell can use.

Distinct granules termed *microbodies* are found in liver and kidney cells. Their exact function is not understood, but they are known to contain certain enzymes (e.g., catalase, which causes the release of oxygen from hydrogen peroxide).

Fibrils are found in many cells and are prominent in muscle and nerve cells. The myofibrils in muscle cells are contracting units. Neurofibrils are hairlike processes arranged in a network throughout nerve cell bodies and processes. It is possible that they lend support to the cell; other function is not known.

The most noticeable structure within the cell is the *nucleus*—usually one in each cell, although some liver cells contain two, and skeletal muscle cells contain multiple numbers. Protoplasm of the nucleus is given a special name, *karyoplasm*; it is surrounded by a nuclear membrane—a double-layered membrane which has openings or pores at intervals, through which materials pass from the nucleus to the cytoplasm and vice versa. The nucleus contains a more densely staining particle called the *nucleolus*, which is very large in growing cells and disappears entirely during the process of cell division. In addition to the nucleoli, the nucleus contains *chromatin*—a combination of protein and *deoxyribonucleic acid* (DNA). The chromatin is transformed during cell division from its granular arrangement to one of long strands, called *chromosomes*—the particles within cells that control the transmission of characteristics from parent to child, or from one cell to daughter cells.

Nucleic acids derive their name from the fact that they were first identified in the nucleus; however, they are found in the cytoplasm as well. These molecules are immense in relation to others, e.g., a molecule of water or of sugar. Like a coiled ladder, the nucleic acid molecule is made up of repeating units that are basically almost identical. The unit is termed a *nucleotide*, each of which contains a sugar (with five carbon atoms), a phosphate group, and one of the following organic substances called "bases": adenine, guanine, cytosine, thymine, and uracil. In the case of DNA the sugar is deoxyribose; the bases are adenine, guanine, cytosine, and thymine. In RNA the sugar is ribose; the bases are adenine, guanine, cytosine, and uracil. The nucleotides are fastened to each other in a particular fashion—the phosphate group of one attaching to the sugar of the next, forming the backbone of the molecule with the "bases" projecting outward from it. A DNA molecule contains a double array of these backbones, and the bases from each half attach to the bases of the other half—thus the base attachments form the steps of the ladder and the sugar-phosphate links form the sides. The bases pair themselves; adenine on either side always combines with thymine on the other; cytosine combines with guanine. A sequence of four different bases on one side will give a complementary sequence on the other. Current biochemical experiments with bacteria indicate that it is the sequence of bases in DNA—the order in which they are arranged—which contains the genetic information and is responsible for transmission of this information. Prior to cell division, the DNA molecule splits in half lengthwise—each half synthesizing its opposite half so that two DNA molecules result. In fact, the entire chromosome, including the protein portion, doubles. Certain drugs used in the treatment of cancer act by preventing the normal synthesis of DNA molecules.

RNA differs from DNA in that it is usually a single strand and is characteristically found in the cytoplasm, although lesser, varying amounts are found in the nucleus, depending on the activity of the cell. There are several forms of RNA—some much smaller than others. *Messenger* RNA is synthesized in the nucleus under the direction of DNA; it moves out into the cytoplasm and usually

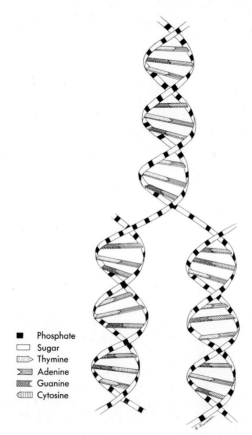

■ Phosphate
▢ Sugar
▧ Thymine
▨ Adenine
▨ Guanine
▨ Cytosine

Figure 2–20. Diagram of DNA molecule showing replication.

attaches to the ribosomes, where it acts as a template or plan for formation of a particular type of protein. In some cells the RNA does not attach to ribosomes but is free within the cytoplasm. *Transfer* RNA is a small molecule which attaches to amino acids present in the cytoplasm and aids in their transfer to the ribosome and in the attachment of the amino acid in its appropriate position so that the particular protein molecule will be formed. Formation of such a larger molecule from smaller ones requires energy, and the amino acids acquire energy prior to their transfer to the ribosome. This energy is obtained from adenosine triphosphate. (See p. 645.) The influence of RNA on cell functioning is crucial since it controls protein synthesis. Much of the cell is protein as well as the enzymes that control the chemical activities of the cell.

Activities of Cells. Living cells are active—performing a variety of chemical reactions as well as being physically active. Activities exhibited by cells are:

1. Motion. This involves two forms of movement:

a. Ameboid movement consists in the pushing outward by the cell of protoplasmic processes, called *pseudopodia*. These pseudopodia may be slowly retracted, they may be bent, or the contents of the cell may flow slowly or rapidly

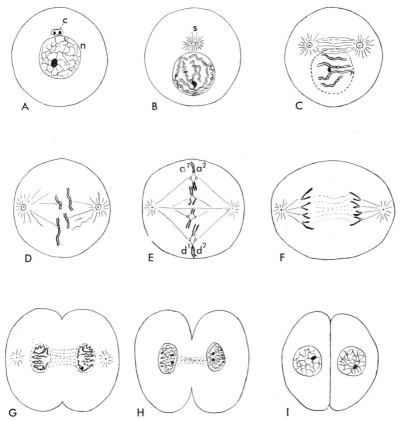

Figure 2–21. Diagrams to show mitosis. The cell is presumed to have four chromosomes. (*A*) Resting cell with nucleus (*n*) and centrosome (*c*); a nucleolus and network of chromatin are shown in the nucleus. (*B*) Spindle fibers (*s*) forming; a chromatin thread, or *spireme*, is breaking into chromosomes. (*C*) Nuclear membrane disappearing, *chromosomes* shown dividing *lengthwise* into halves. (*D*) Chromosomes shorter and thicker, staining power increased. (*E*) Chromosomes arranged on the *spindle*, the two halves of each chromosome opposite each other at a^1 and a^2, d^1 and d^2, etc. (*F*) Chromosomes moving toward the poles of the spindle. (*G*) Cell beginning to divide. (*H*) Cell division continued. (*I*) Cell division complete. *A-C* called prophase; *C-D* called metaphase; *E-G* called anaphase; *G-I* called telophase. (Modified from *The Cell in Development and Heredity*, by E. G. Wilson, The Macmillan Company.)

into them and change both the shape and position of the cell. By a repetition of this process, the cell may move slowly about, so that an actual locomotion takes place, e.g., ameboid or pseudopodial movement of white blood cells.

b. Ciliary movement is the whipping motion exhibited by short, protoplasmic processes called *cilia*, which project from the surface of some epithelial cells. This motion serves to propel particles and secretions along the surface of the membrane, e.g., secretions in the respiratory tract.

2. Irritability is that property which enables a cell to respond to stimuli (change in its environment). If the stimulus received by a cell is strong enough, it is conducted throughout the protoplasm of the cell, and the cell responds. The response may take the form of an increase of some kind of activity, such as motion, or growth, or it may take the form of a decrease of these activities. If the response is an increased activity, the protoplasm is said to be *excited;* if the response is a decreased activity, the protoplasm is said to be *inhibited.*

3. Respiration. Each cell coming in contact with oxygen absorbs it. During this absorption some of the cell contents are oxidized, and, as a result of this oxidation, energy is liberated, and carbon dioxide is formed and given off by the cell to its liquid environment. This is known as cellular respiration.

4. Circulation. This consists of a "streaming" of the protoplasm within the cell. In plant cells and protozoa, where this streaming is sometimes conspicuous, it is often called *cyclosis.* By this means nutritive material and oxygen may be distributed gradually to all parts of the protoplasm, and the waste substances are gradually brought to the surface of the cell for elimination.

5. Use of Nutrients. Each cell can absorb and convert into its own proto-plasm certain materials (foods) that are nonliving; in this way the protoplasm is maintained and may undergo repair, and the cell may grow. Foods can also be oxidized to yield energy and to regulate body functions. The general term *metabolism* summarizes the activities each living cell carries on. The changes that involve the building up of living material within the cell have received the general name of *anabolic* changes, or *anabolism;* those that involve the breaking down of such material into other and simpler products are known as *catabolic* changes or *catabolism;* the sum of all the anabolic and catabolic changes proceeding within the cell is spoken of as the *metabolism* of the cell. These chemical changes are always more marked as the activity of the cell is hastened by warmth, electrical or other stimulation, or the action of certain drugs.

6. Excretion and Secretion. Excretion refers to the ability of the cell to ex-trude waste products from within. If the extruded material is a useful substance such as a hormone or gastric juice, the extruded material is termed a secretion. The process may be by diffusion or by the functioning of excretory vacuoles in some cells, such as in the ameba.

7. Cell Division. In all living organisms, each cell grows and produces other cells. Since the cells of the body are constantly wearing out and leaving the body in the excretions, the need for constant reproduction of cells is apparent. Cells usually divide by indirect cell division, called also *karyokinesis* or *mitosis.* In mitosis the nucleus passes through a series of changes, illustrated in Figure 2–21. It will be noted that the chromatin, which at first (*A*) exists as granules in the nucleus, becomes (*C*) definite bodies, the chromosomes. Each chromosome duplicates itself during interphase and separates (*E*), and one of each pair of chromosomes thus formed moves to the poles of the spindles (*F* and *G*) so that when the cell divides, each daughter cell has a complete set of chromosomes. The chromosomes in the daughter cells unwind, so that the daughter cells are like the parent cell except in size. As indicated earlier in the chapter, the nucleic acid portion of the chromosome is thought to be responsible for transmission of genetic information from one generation to the next. During the resting stage between cell divisions, the chromosomes double so that the cell will be prepared for the next division. The "genes" of the chromosome are probably (according to research with bacteria) portions of the DNA molecule—the sequence of the bases in a particular portion. Evidence for this lies in the fact that DNA controls (through RNA synthesis) the formation of all enzymes within the cell. The types of enzymes present, in turn, control the make-up of the cell and the activities it is capable of performing.

Some cells are thought to divide directly, or by *amitosis*. In direct division the cell elongates, the nucleus and cytoplasm become constricted in the center, and the cell divides, forming two cells which grow to the size of the original cell.

QUESTIONS FOR DISCUSSION

1. Mary Ann is sitting before the mirror carefully combing her hair, turning her head from side to side. Her brother is in the kitchen mopping up the milk he accidentally spilled. What systems of the body are involved in these activities? Which systems are interrelated in their functioning? Explain.
2. Explain the arrangement of cells in relation to unit patterns and to tissue fluid.
3. Contrast the physiological activities of the human body and those of the individual cell.
4. How does cell activity influence the growth and development of a child?
5. Explain the structure and functions of DNA and RNA.
6. What are organelles? Name them and give their function.

SUMMARY

System. An arrangement of organs, closely allied and concerned with the same function
Systems found in the human body :

Skeletal	Endocrine
Muscular	Respiratory
Nervous	Digestive
Vascular, or circulatory	Excretory
Reproductive	

Organ. A physiological unit composed of two or more tissues associated in performing some special function

Tissue. A group of cells with varying amount of intercellular material

Functional Unit, or Unit Pattern

- **Definition** — Smallest aggregate of cells (with intercellular material) which when repeated many times composes an organ
- **Examples**
  - Lung or pulmonary unit
  - Nephron
  - Chain or cord of cells
  - Haversian system
  - Reflex arc
- **No names for others** — Example ... villus and gland of duodenum with portion of wall behind them (duodenal unit)
- **Distribution of blood and lymph vessels and nerve fibers** — In orderly way following unit pattern, giving great diffusion area between cells and body fluids for volumes concerned
- **Anatomy and physiology of functional unit**
  - They can be studied as to structure—anatomy
  - They can be studied as to their activities—physiology

The Cell Theory — Since intercellular material is thought to be made by the cells, a fundamental generalization in biology is that the cell is the unit of structure, of function, and of development of the body.

Difference in Cells

- **Size** } In general, microscopic in size
- **Arrangement**
  - Very little intercellular material between cells, e.g., epithelium
  - A great deal of intercellular material between cells, e.g., areolar connective tissue

Constituents of Protoplasm

- Organic compounds contain carbon
  - Carbohydrates
  - Lipids
  - Proteins
- **Proteins contain** — Carbon, Hydrogen, Oxygen, Nitrogen, Sulfur, Phosphorus
- **Carbohydrates contain** — Carbon, Hydrogen, Oxygen
- **Lipids contain** — Carbon, Hydrogen, Oxygen
- **Inorganic substances** — Sulfur, Phosphorus, Chlorine, Sodium, Potassium, Calcium, Magnesium, Iodine, Iron, Silicon, Traces of others
- **Water**
  - Most abundant constituent of { Cells, Intercellular material
  - More than two thirds of weight of body
  - More than 75% of nonbony body weight
  - Estimated 85–92% of weight of cell

Cell Structure

- **Protoplasm**
  - **Cytoplasm**
    - Organelles
    - Centrioles
    - Endoplasmic reticulum
    - Ribosomes
    - Lysosomes
    - Ribonucleonic acid (RNA)
    - Microsome
    - Microbodies
    - Vacuoles

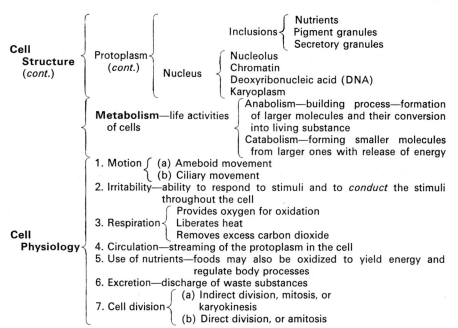

Cell Structure *(cont.)*

Protoplasm *(cont.)*

Nucleus

Inclusions
- Nutrients
- Pigment granules
- Secretory granules

- Nucleolus
- Chromatin
- Deoxyribonucleic acid (DNA)
- Karyoplasm

Metabolism—life activities of cells
- Anabolism—building process—formation of larger molecules and their conversion into living substance
- Catabolism—forming smaller molecules from larger ones with release of energy

Cell Physiology

1. Motion
   - (a) Ameboid movement
   - (b) Ciliary movement
2. Irritability—ability to respond to stimuli and to *conduct* the stimuli throughout the cell
3. Respiration
   - Provides oxygen for oxidation
   - Liberates heat
   - Removes excess carbon dioxide
4. Circulation—streaming of the protoplasm in the cell
5. Use of nutrients—foods may also be oxidized to yield energy and regulate body processes
6. Excretion—discharge of waste substances
7. Cell division
   - (a) Indirect division, mitosis, or karyokinesis
   - (b) Direct division, or amitosis

CHAPTER 3

Physiology of the Cell

CELLS are the building blocks of tissues, and of organs within the body. In order to maintain their healthy state they must have a constant supply of nutrients, as well as a constant removal of metabolic products from the cell. There is therefore a steady streaming of these materials across the cell membrane to and from the liquid environment immediately surrounding the cell, and into and out of the blood stream. All the physiological activities of the cell, such as movement and irritability, are closely interrelated to the chemical and physical reactions within the cell.

Cells are in contact with one another and with the blood stream, in some cases very intimately and tightly packed together as with muscle cells. At other times the arrangement is rather loose with relatively much material between the cells, or between the cells and the capillaries—the tiny blood vessels from which materials move to the cells.

**Concentration of Major Electrolytes in
Cellular and Interstitial Fluid**

	Cell Fluid	Tissue Fluid
Na^+	10 mEq/l	146 mEq/L
K^+	150	4
Ca^{++}		2.5
Mg^{++}	40	1.5
HCO_3^-		30
Cl^-		115
HPO_4^-	140	2
SO_4^-		1
Organic acids$^-$		5
Protein$^-$	40	1

With the exception of dense connective tissue and bone, the intercellular, or interstitial, material is a viscous solution which is in general similar to cytoplasm—containing inorganic chemicals, proteins, carbohydrates, and lipids— the primary difference being one of kind of protein present and of amounts of the various chemicals present. The accompanying chart illustrates the difference in mineral make-up between the fluid within the cell and that without the cell. In some tissues fibers are embedded within the *matrix*, or background substance of intercellular material.

Physically cytoplasm and intercellular material are emulsions containing *ions* (electrically charged particles) and noncharged particles dissolved or suspended in water. Several advantages accrue from the fact that water is the universal solvent in animal tissue.

Following are some of the characteristics of water that make it significant as the most abundant constituent of all body cells:

1. The solvent power of water is great. No other substance can compare with water in relation to the kinds of substances which can be dissolved in it and the great and varied concentrations that can be obtained.

2. The ionizing power of water is high; hence, the great number and many kinds of solute molecules yield large numbers of varied ions.

3. Water has a high specific heat. This means that it can hold more heat with less change of temperature than most substances; hence, the heat produced by cell metabolism makes comparatively little change in the temperature of the cell.

4. The heat-conducting power of water is high (for liquids). This means that the heat produced in the cells can pass to body fluids even if the temperature of the cell is barely above that of the fluid around the cell, which likewise can hold this heat with comparatively little rise in temperature and pass it on with little change in temperature to the blood and finally to the skin.

5. The latent heat of evaporation of water is high. Owing to the high latent heat of evaporation, a maximum of heat is taken from the skin for the evaporation of perspiration—about 0.5 large calorie per gram of water evaporated.

6. Another significant characteristic of water as a constituent of the cell is its high surface tension. Because of this any immiscible liquid with which it comes in contact must expose to it the minimum of surface. The substances which dissolve in water lower its surface tension, since dilute concentrations especially have a tendency to lower surface tensions, and because of the great solvent capacity of water, the surface tension of water can be lowered greatly and by a great variety of substances. This permits the area of contact of the immiscible liquids to be enormously increased. Also, it is known that any dissolved substances which do lower surface tension will accumulate or be *adsorbed* at the surface of contact of the immiscible liquids.

The particles of material dispersed throughout protoplasm vary in size and may be dissolved, as in the case of glucose, or merely suspended in the case of fat droplets in the cytoplasm. Particles whose diameters is less than 0.1 mμ are dissolved in water and are said to form true solutions; whereas particles 0.1 to

1 mμ in diameter are termed colloidal particles and form colloidal solutions. Colloids may be individual molecules of large size, e.g., protein, or groups of molecules. Other characteristics of colloids that are important in cell physiology include:

1. They can take up large quantities of water and hold it within the cell.
2. Owing to their large size they do not diffuse readily.
3. They adsorb other substances at their interphase, or surface.
4. They possess electrical charges which contribute to chemical activity.

Sometimes in experimental work cells behave as *sols*, that is, as solutions in which the continuous phase is water, the colloidal particles of proteins and lipoids being dispersed in it. Sometimes they behave as *gels*, in which the protein

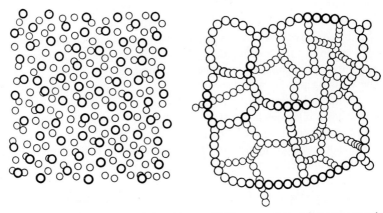

Figure 3–1. Colloidal particles of the sol state (*left*) are separated from one another like islands in a lake. Such a sol is therefore a continuous liquid and flows easily. When the particles stick together in interlacing strands in the gel state (*right*), the mass is more comparable to lakes separated by strips of land. Such a gel, then, is a spongy solid and, though soft, holds its shape. (Courtesy of Dr. Ralph W. Gerard and Harper & Row.)

molecules form networks enclosing areas of water between them. It has been said of protoplasm that its characteristics are like those of a reversible sol-gel colloidal system. "Hence to speak of protoplasm as a liquid or as a solid has little meaning."[1] (Fig. 3–1.)

It can be seen that these characteristics of water and colloids lend great stability to the cell but at the same time allow many diverse chemical changes to take place, varied products being formed and broken down with minute changes in kinds and concentration of ions, temperature, etc. The characteristics of water form the basis of a chemical equilibrium always tending to completeness but never quite reaching it, because from the "lymph bathing the cell" (tissue fluid) small quantities of these varied substances in dilute solution are always entering the cell, and small quantities of varied cellular products in dilute solu-

---

[1] R. Chambers, "The Micromanipulation of Living Cells" in *The Cell and Protoplasm.* Publication No. 14 of the American Association for the Advancement of Science.

tion are always leaving the cell, the whole bringing about the smooth, slowly acting dynamic equilibrium characteristic of the physiology of cells. The cell is to be regarded as a highly organized or integrated unit engaged in ceaseless chemical activities. These activities are dependent on the continuous reception of substances from the so-called *internal environment* (tissue fluid) and the continuous elimination of substances to this tissue fluid. The circulatory liquids continually bring substances from the supply organs, which obtain them from the *external environment*, and continuously take eliminated substances to the eliminating organs for final removal to the external environment. Keeping the cell environment constant, within a narrow range, as regards oxygen, nutrients, acidity, and temperature is critical for optimum cell functioning. All organs of the body participate in this activity in varying degrees. The term "homeostasis" was coined by Walter B. Cannon[2] and refers to the over-all processes of maintaining optimum internal environmental conditions.

The physical processes that govern the movement of materials across the cell membrane are only partially understood at present. However, four processes seem to be important—diffusion, osmosis, active transport, and pinocytosis.

Diffusion. The term *diffusion* is applied to the spreading or scattering of molecules of gases or liquids. When two gases are brought into contact, the continual movement of the molecules of gas will soon produce a uniform mixture. If a solution of salt is placed in a receptacle and a layer of water poured over it, there will be a mingling of salt molecules and water molecules, producing a solution of uniform composition.

Molecular movement of particles is random; however, they will move in greater number toward the area where they are fewer in number, that is, from an area of greater concentration to one of lesser concentration (of that particular substance). Eventually an equilibrium will be reached in which all areas of the solution are identical. In the case of the salt solution, there will be the same number of salt molecules relative to water molecules in all parts of the solution. Oxygen moves from the blood into the fluid around the cell and into the cell as a result of diffusion. The amount of oxygen in the blood is much greater than that in the cell. Therefore, it moves to the area of lesser concentration. In this instance a static equilibrium is never reached, but a dynamic equilibrium is kept constant. Oxygen supply to the cell is continually replenished owing to movement of blood through the circulatory system; the oxygen is continually used in metabolic processes once it enters the cell.

Osmosis. The usual definition of osmosis is the movement of solvent particles, such as water molecules, through a membrane. If a saline solution and water are separated by a membrane permeable to water, the water molecules will pass through the membrane to the salt solution, thereby raising the level of the latter. Theoretically, molecules of liquid are constantly in motion, a permeable membrane offering no resistance to their passage, and therefore the movement of water particles is in both directions; but the water molecules will travel in

---

[2] Walter B. Cannon, American physiologist (1871–1945).

greater numbers per unit of time from the place where their concentration is highest to where it is lowest. If the concentration of the water particles on both sides of the membrane is the same, in a given time equal numbers of particles will travel in each direction, and equilibrium will be reached. If the concentrations of water molecules are kept constant by the addition of water molecules on one side and the removal of water molecules on the other, equilibrium will be prevented, and the movement of the water molecules from a constant source to a constant place of disappearance will be continuous.

Osmotic pressure is determined by the *number* of particles of solute dissolved in a particular solution. The more particles in solution, the greater the osmotic pressure of that solution and the greater is its "pull" for water. In other words, water moves toward the area of greater osmotic pressure. It is important to remember that the particles in solution are the critical factor in determining osmotic pressure. A solution made from an ionizing substance (e.g., sodium chloride) will have a greater osmotic pressure than the one containing an equal amount of nonionizing substance such as glucose.

In physiology the osmotic characteristics of different solutions are often determined by the way in which they affect the red cells of the blood. In other words, their effect is compared with that of the blood serum. If red cells are subjected to contact with any fluid other than normal serum, they may remain unchanged or they may shrink or swell. If they remain unchanged, the solution is said to have the same osmotic characteristics as the blood serum and is called *isotonic*. If they shrink, the solution has higher osmotic characteristics than that of the blood serum and is called *hypertonic*. If they swell, the solution has lower osmotic characteristics than that of the blood serum and is called *hypotonic*.

Sometimes the word *dialysis* is used for the diffusion of molecules of the soluble constituents (solutes) through a permeable membrane. If two solutions of unequal concentration are separated by a membrane which is permeable to the solute, a greater number of solute particles will pass from the more concentrated solution to the less concentrated, per unit of time. The diffusing particles may be ions, molecules, or small molecular aggregates. Many substances in solution may pass to and fro through membranes, so that two liquids separated by a permeable membrane and originally unlike in composition may, by the action of diffusion, come to have the same composition.

Active Transport. It is obvious that diffusion and osmosis alone cannot explain entirely the movement of particles into the cell. Clearly the cell membrane controls selectively which materials enter and whether or not they remain inside. When materials are transported across the cell membrane against a concentration gradient, that is, in a direction opposite to what would be expected from the principles of diffusion and osmosis, energy is utilized and oxygen is consumed by the cell. This process is therefore termed active transport of the substance, as opposed to *passive* transport as in diffusion or osmosis during which cell energy is not expended. It is possible that there are carriers to aid in transportation of certain materials into the cell, or out of the cell, as in the case of sodium which is present in large amounts outside the cell but not inside. Support for this theory is based on the fact that certain enzymes are known to be present just inside the cell membrane.

Pinocytosis. Material enters cells by the process of pinocytosis—indentation of cell membrane and cytoplasm so that channels form, permitting entrance of molecules and minute droplets of fluid from the exterior. The channel seals off, forming small vacuoles within the cytoplasm.

When a substance moves across the cell membrane, the membrane is said to be permeable to that particular substance. Size of the particle is important—if it is too large (over 7 angstrom units), it cannot enter and the cell is impermeable to it. This leads to the belief that there are pores in the membrane too small for the electron microscope to identify. Ionic charge also influences cell permeability. The positive charge on the outside of the membrane tends to repel positively charged ions.

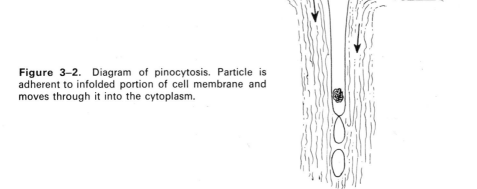

Figure 3–2. Diagram of pinocytosis. Particle is adherent to infolded portion of cell membrane and moves through it into the cytoplasm.

Enzyme Action. Materials that enter the cytoplasm have potential value to the cell (1) as a source of energy, (2) as building blocks for the parts of the cell itself, if it is growing or dividing, and (3) as building blocks for cell secretions, e.g., hormones and digestive enzymes.

Utilization of nutrients is possible only through chemical reactions—the step-by-step breaking down of large molecules to smaller, or building small molecules into larger ones. These chemical reactions are many and varied and require the presence of enzymes, termed *endoenzymes*, to differentiate them from enzymes which are secreted from the cell and act outside the cell (exoenzymes), e.g., the digestive enzymes.

Characteristics of Enzyme Action. In general, all enzymes are influenced by temperature, pH, and the presence of the appropriate *substrate*, or initial substance which is being changed in the chemical reaction. When the temperature or pH of the fluid in which the enzyme is found is not at optimum levels, the enzyme action is slowed down, or it may be completely ineffective. Endoenzymes

act best at body temperature and at the pH of the cytoplasm and body fluids·
A given enzyme can catalyze only one type of reaction, or sometimes only
one particular reaction. For the metabolic reaction to occur, the substrate molecule must come into contact with the specific enzyme. Because the enzyme molecule
is large and the substrate molecule is small, there must be a relatively great
number of substrate molecules in order to ensure activity. It is believed that there
is a specific configuration for each enzyme and its substrate. Thus a particular
enzyme and its substrate 'must possess shapes that complement each other.
Inhibitors of enzymes, such as certain metals, perhaps act by interfering with
this complementary shape, or by attaching to the site on the molecule which will
react, e.g., to accept the hydrogen atom in the case of dehydrogenases.

The accompanying chart lists important classes of enzymes and their actions.
Many of the biological reactions are reversible, the enzyme influencing the
speed of both the forward and the reverse reaction, operating to bring about
equilibrium.

Endoenzyme Classification

Name	Action
I. Hydrolases :	Split molecules into smaller ones through utilization of H_2O
(a) Esterases :	Split ester linkages of acids and alcohols
cholinesterase	Split acetylcholine to acetic acid and choline
lipases	Split fats to fatty acids and glycerol
phosphatases	Split phosphate group from phosphoric acid esters
pyrophosphatases	Split phosphate group from high-energy phosphate compounds
nucleases	Split nucleic acids to nucleotides
(b) Carbohydrases :	Break down polysaccharides and other compounds with similar chemical bonding
amylases	{ Split glycogen to glucose / Split starch to maltose, then to glucose
hyaluronidase	Splits hyaluronic acid, cement substance between cells
(c) Proteases :	Split peptide linkages of proteins and peptides
carboxypeptidases	Split terminal peptide bond to free amino acids from protein one by one
proteinases	Split proteins by attacking interor peptide bonds
II. Phosphorylases :	Split molecule by addition of phosphate radical
muscle phosphorylase	Phosphate + glycogen $\rightleftarrows$ glucose phosphate
III. Oxidation-reduction enzymes	
(a) Dehydrogenases	Oxidation of a compound by removal of $2H^+$
(b) Oxidases	Addition of oxygen to a compound
IV. Transferases	Transfer a radical from one compound to another
(a) Transaminases	Transfer NH_2^-
(b) Hexokinases	Transfer phosphate from adenosine triphosphate to glucose
V. Decarboxylases	Remove CO_2 from a compound without oxidation
(a) Carbonic anhydrase	Carbonic acid $\rightleftarrows$ CO_2 and H_2O
VI. Hydrases	Remove H_2O from a molecule
VII. Isomerases	Move radical from one part of molecule to another
VIII. Condensing enzymes	Transfer acetyl radical from acetyl coenzyme A into the citric acid cycle

Note that the -ase ending indicates an enzyme and the prefix indicates its action (e.g.,
transaminase) or its substrate (e.g., amylase).

Endoenzymes are found in the active form within the cell. This is not true of *exoenzymes*, those that act outside the cell, for these are usually secreted in an inactive form and must be activated by another substance or the pH of the environment before they can catalyze the particular chemical reaction. The inactive form is known as *zymogen* or *proenzyme*. Activation of the proenzyme is believed to involve a chemical change, such as the removal of a small group from the molecule and exposure of the active site of the enzyme.

In some cases the action of an enzyme is helped by, or perhaps is dependent upon, the presence of some other substance. An example of this activity is the interaction of bile salts and lipase on fat digestion. The bile salts emulsify fat droplets, thereby increasing the surface area available for enzyme activity. These cases of *coactivity* are to be distinguished from activation by the fact that the combination may be made or unmade. For example, in a mixture of bile salts and lipase, the bile salts may be removed by dialysis. In activation, on the contrary, the active enzyme cannot be changed back to the inactive zymogen.

Nature of Enzymes. Most enzymes are proteins of high molecular weight, hence cannot diffuse across cell membranes. Some enzymes, such as pepsin and trypsin, appear to be simple proteins; others resemble the conjugated proteins in that they function with a nonprotein component known as a *coenzyme*. The importance of vitamins is becoming increasingly evident as more is learned about enzyme activity within the cells. The B-complex vitamins in particular are known to form parts of the molecules of various enzymes involved in energy release. These are discussed more fully in Chapter 20.

The Cells and Tissue Fluid

All cells lie in a liquid environment called tissue fluid. This fluid serves as the only medium of exchange between blood plasma and the cells. Substances needed by cells for maintenance, growth, and repair diffuse from the plasma to the tissue fluid and on into the cell. The products of cell metabolism or other cell activity diffuse into the tissue fluid and enter either the blood or lymph capillaries.

The name *tissue fluid* covers all fluids *not* in the blood vascular system, the lymph vascular system, the great spaces of the body, or the cells themselves. The body fluids may be grouped as follows:

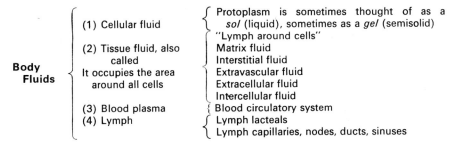

Body Fluids

(1) Cellular fluid — { Protoplasm is sometimes thought of as a *sol* (liquid), sometimes as a *gel* (semisolid)

(2) Tissue fluid, also called It occupies the area around all cells — { "Lymph around cells" / Matrix fluid / Interstitial fluid / Extravascular fluid / Extracellular fluid / Intercellular fluid

(3) Blood plasma — { Blood circulatory system

(4) Lymph — { Lymph lacteals / Lymph capillaries, nodes, ducts, sinuses

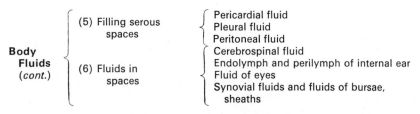

Body
Fluids
(*cont.*)

(5) Filling serous spaces

{ Pericardial fluid
  Pleural fluid
  Peritoneal fluid

(6) Fluids in spaces

{ Cerebrospinal fluid
  Endolymph and perilymph of internal ear
  Fluid of eyes
  Synovial fluids and fluids of bursae, sheaths

Sources of Tissue Fluid. The walls of the capillaries are thin, and some of the fluid passes out into the spaces between the tissue cells. *Tissue fluid* is derived from the plasma of the blood mainly by diffusion and by capillary hydrostatic pressure. There is sometimes assumed an active secretory process on the part of the endothelial cells of the capillaries.

Points of view differ in regard to classifying the liquids concerned in the exchange of material between the blood and the tissue cells. In general, the lymph vessels form a closed system, and the name *lymph* should be applied to the fluid within the vessels only; the fluid outside the vessels, in the tissue spaces, should be called *tissue fluid*. In this discussion the name *lymph* is restricted to the fluids found in the lymph vessels. In the different spaces of the body, e.g., the pericardial, pleural, and peritoneal cavities, it is serous; in the spaces of the cerebrum and spinal cord it is cerebrospinal fluid, and in joints it is synovial fluid. Lacteals are lymph vessels in the small intestine. During digestion, they are filled with *chyle*, a milk-white fluid composed mainly of emulsified fat.

Formation of Tissue Fluid. Tissue fluid is formed from plasma by the process of diffusion and filtration. There is difference in pressure within the blood capillary and in the tissue spaces surrounding the capillary. For instance, at the arterial end of the capillary the hydrostatic pressure is about 30 mm Hg and in the tissue spaces surrounding the capillary the pressure is much lower. Since the pressure is highest within the capillary, fluid and other substances are driven from the capillary into the tissue spaces. Another force that must be considered is the protein osmotic pressure formed by the plasma proteins, which act as a "pulling" force to hold fluids within the vessels as well as to "attract fluids in." This opposing force prevents undue loss of fluid from the capillaries.

At the venous end of the capillary, hydrostatic pressure is about 15 mm Hg. This means that the difference in pressure within the capillary and in the tissue spaces is not as great as at the arterial end. It is also conceivable that as blood moves through the capillary network and fluid is lost to the tissue spaces, plasma protein concentration is slightly raised, and hence the "pulling force" is increased so that water and crystalloids re-enter the capillaries readily, but colloids, along with water and crystalloids, enter the lymph capillaries. Increases in hydrostatic pressure within the capillaries from any cause will interfere with return of substances to the lymphatics or capillaries and will result in excess accumulation of tissue fluid, or edema.

There are two important exceptions to the capillary pressure figures used in the preceding discussion. These exceptions are the capillaries of the lungs and of the kidneys. Hydrostatic pressure in the lung capillaries is approximately 6 mm Hg; thus fluid does not move out of the capillary as it does in other tissue of the body. In the kidney, glomerular hydrostatic pressure is 60–70 mm Hg, which acts to force an increased amount of fluid from the capillary in the first step of urine formation.

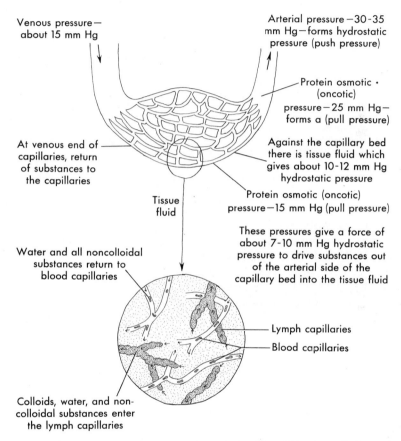

Venous pressure—about 15 mm Hg

Arterial pressure—30-35 mm Hg—forms hydrostatic pressure (push pressure)

Protein osmotic (oncotic) pressure—25 mm Hg—forms a (pull pressure)

At venous end of capillaries, return of substances to the capillaries

Against the capillary bed there is tissue fluid which gives about 10-12 mm Hg hydrostatic pressure

Tissue fluid

Protein osmotic (oncotic) pressure—15 mm Hg (pull pressure)

These pressures give a force of about 7-10 mm Hg hydrostatic pressure to drive substances out of the arterial side of the capillary bed into the tissue fluid

Water and all noncolloidal substances return to blood capillaries

Lymph capillaries

Blood capillaries

Colloids, water, and non-colloidal substances enter the lymph capillaries

Figure 3–3. Detail of capillary bed showing relationship of blood capillaries to lymph capillaries and return of substances to the blood stream. By this process the amount of tissue fluid is kept constant. Since all lymph vessels eventually enter lymph nodes before emptying into the blood stream, what would occur if the returning lymph could not reach the blood stream? What might be some of the causes?

The composition of tissue fluid is similar to that of blood plasma. It is a colorless or yellowish fluid possessing an alkaline reaction, a salty taste, and a faint odor. When examined under the microscope, it is seen to consist of cells floating in a clear liquid. Its resemblance to the plasma is indicated in the table below. In consequence of the varying needs and wastes of different tissues at different times, both the tissue fluid and blood must vary in composition in different parts of the body. But the loss and gain are so fairly balanced that the average composition is pretty constantly maintained. The composition of the fluids in the serous, cerebrospinal, and synovial cavities, and that of the fluids of the eye and ear, vary.

Comparison of Blood and Tissue Fluid

Blood	Tissue Fluid
Specific gravity about 1.055	Specific gravity varies between 1.015 and 1.023
Contains erythrocytes	May contain a few erythrocytes
Contains white cells	Granulocyte count lower, lymphocyte count higher
Contains blood platelets	Does not contain blood platelets
A high content of blood proteins	A lower content of blood proteins
A low content of waste products	A higher content of waste products
A high content of nutrients	A lower content of nutrients
Normally—clots quickly and firmly	Clots slowly, and clot is not firm
Relatively high in colloidal protein	Relatively low in colloidal protein ; globulin practically absent

Water, glucose, salts, same concentration in both

Function of Tissue Fluid. The tissue fluid bathes all cells of the body. It delivers to the cells the material they need to maintain functional activity and picks up and returns to the blood the products of this activity. These products may be simple waste or materials capable of being made use of by some other tissue. There is thus a continual interchange going on between the blood and the tissue fluid. This interchange is effected by means of *diffusion*.

The tissue fluid becomes altered by the metabolic changes of the tissues which it bathes. There are three different fluids separated by the moist membranes which form the walls of the blood vessels and lymphatics—the blood inside the capillary walls, the tissue fluid in the tissues outside the walls of the blood vessels, and the lymph in the lymph channels. Some of the constituents of the blood pass into the tissue fluid; some of the constituents of the tissue fluid pass into the blood directly, and some into the lymphatics. Water and noncolloidal substances are returned to the blood capillaries; colloidal substances as well as water and noncolloidal substances enter the lymphatics. Diffusion of this kind is dependent on differences in concentration of diffusible particles of any substance on the two surfaces of the diffusion membranes.

Tissue fluid is also closely related to physiological integration. As cells become active, varying needs must be met in relation to supplies and the products of metabolism. Experimental work has shown that as use of oxygen increases, the number of open capillaries in the muscle increases, the capillary diameter increases, the total area of the capillary bed increases, the volume of blood in the muscle increases, the distance of the farthest cell from a capillary decreases, and the difference in oxygen pressure inside and outside the capillary decreases. There are also other changes, such as increased temperature, and velocity of blood flow.

If cellular metabolism is increased when muscular effort is increased, there is produced in the cells an increased quantity of metabolites, carbon dioxide, and other substances to be eliminated, as well as pH change. Thus the chemical activity of the muscle cells may be a factor, and probably the chief factor, controlling the amount and distribution of blood through the muscle. This is an automatic control—the graded need to get and to give off brings about the graded means (variable blood flow) to do so accurately. If maximum blood supply does not bring sufficient oxygen and remove metabolites fast enough, oxygen hunger, followed by fatigue, results.

This automatic control for optimum distribution of blood in relation to muscular effort involves adjustment of pulse rate, pulse volume, general and local peripheral resistance, respiratory rate, and respiratory volume, and, in fact, an adjustment of all body functions. This control is brought about by the effects of variations in chemical equilibrium on the tissues themselves, or by the local changes in chemical equilibrium and the influence of the nervous system on the distant organs concerned.

This indicates the relative functions of blood plasma and tissue fluid. The blood brings (and takes away) substances. The volume of blood per minute in the muscle, the capillary area for diffusion, etc., are constantly varied. To the muscle cells the blood is the source of supplies, kept relatively high in concentration because circulation keeps blood in motion. Blood and tissue fluid are also the place of disappearance of products of metabolism which are kept relatively low in concentration.

In the cells the supplies are used and wastes produced.

The tissue fluid stands between the two. It is a fluid that moves very slowly and is separated both from the blood and from the cell contents, which it closely resembles chemically and physically, by diffusion membranes. In the cell the rate of change of chemical equilibriums, controlled by catalysts, constantly uses supplies and produces wastes; the blood constantly brings supplies and carries off wastes. The tissue fluid mediates this transfer and makes it possible for large amounts of substances to be transported and used with relatively small differences in concentration of soluble constituents in any of the body fluids.

This, together with the fact that blood returning from all tissues is *mixed in the heart* and hence all tissues receive the same blood, is probably the basis of all *physiological integration*.

QUESTIONS FOR DISCUSSION

1. Discuss the relationship between cells and tissue fluid and explain how tissue fluid is formed.
2. What are the characteristics of water and colloids that make them so important in physiology?
3. Differentiate between protein osmotic and hydrostatic pressure.
4. What is the difference between active and passive transport across cell membranes?
5. Name the classes of endoenzymes and discuss their function.

SUMMARY

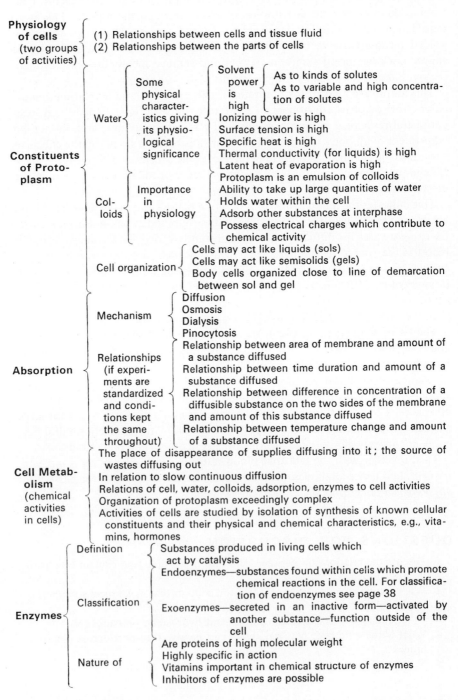

Physiology of cells (two groups of activities)
(1) Relationships between cells and tissue fluid
(2) Relationships between the parts of cells

Constituents of Protoplasm

Water — Some physical characteristics giving its physiological significance
- Solvent power is high
  - As to kinds of solutes
  - As to variable and high concentration of solutes
- Ionizing power is high
- Surface tension is high
- Specific heat is high
- Thermal conductivity (for liquids) is high
- Latent heat of evaporation is high

Colloids — Importance in physiology
- Protoplasm is an emulsion of colloids
- Ability to take up large quantities of water
- Holds water within the cell
- Adsorb other substances at interphase
- Possess electrical charges which contribute to chemical activity

Absorption

Cell organization
- Cells may act like liquids (sols)
- Cells may act like semisolids (gels)
- Body cells organized close to line of demarcation between sol and gel

Mechanism
- Diffusion
- Osmosis
- Dialysis
- Pinocytosis

Relationships (if experiments are standardized and conditions kept the same throughout)
- Relationship between area of membrane and amount of a substance diffused
- Relationship between time duration and amount of a substance diffused
- Relationship between difference in concentration of a diffusible substance on the two sides of the membrane and amount of this substance diffused
- Relationship between temperature change and amount of a substance diffused

Cell Metabolism (chemical activities in cells)
- The place of disappearance of supplies diffusing into it; the source of wastes diffusing out
- In relation to slow continuous diffusion
- Relations of cell, water, colloids, adsorption, enzymes to cell activities
- Organization of protoplasm exceedingly complex
- Activities of cells are studied by isolation of synthesis of known cellular constituents and their physical and chemical characteristics, e.g., vitamins, hormones

Enzymes

Definition
- Substances produced in living cells which act by catalysis

Classification
- Endoenzymes—substances found within cells which promote chemical reactions in the cell. For classification of endoenzymes see page 38
- Exoenzymes—secreted in an inactive form—activated by another substance—function outside of the cell

Nature of
- Are proteins of high molecular weight
- Highly specific in action
- Vitamins important in chemical structure of enzymes
- Inhibitors of enzymes are possible

Enzymes
(cont.)
{ Characteristics { Act best at body temperature
of   { Require medium of definite pH
             { Action is specific and may be reversible.

(1) Cellular   { Protoplasm is sometimes thought of as a sol (liquid),
fluid   { sometimes as a gel (semisolid)

(2) Tissue fluid { Intercellular
also called   { Matrix fluid

It occupies the   { Interstitial fluid
area around   { Extravascular fluid
all cells   { Extracellular fluid
                    { Intercellular fluid

(3) Blood plasma { Blood circulatory system

(4) Lymph   { Lymph lacteals
                { Lymph capillaries, nodes, ducts, sinuses

The Cells
and Body
Fluids

(5) Filling serous { Pericardial fluid
cavities   { Pleural fluid
                   { Peritoneal fluid

Location   { Surrounding all cells
                { Occupies the spaces of loose (areolar) connective tissue
                {   and all other tissues

Source   { Diffused from blood plasma
                { Diffused from cellular materials
                { Cell membrane is a two-way filtering and diffusion mem-
                {   brane between all cells and tissue fluid, including capil-
                {   lary cells

Composition { Chemically and physically similar to blood plasma and
                { protoplasm

Function   { Go-between for blood and lymph and cells

CHAPTER 4

The Tissues of the Body

MICROSCOPIC ANATOMY refers to the study of any structure under the microscope. Histology limits microscopic anatomy to the study of tissues. It is concerned with structural characteristics of cells and groups of cells as arranged to form tissues; hence a knowledge of the structure and activities of cells forms the basis of histology. The structure and function of the tissues are closely related. An understanding of structure will clarify function and help to build the foundation for physiology.

The kinds of tissues of which the body is formed are comparatively few, and some of these, although apparently distinct, have so much in common in their structure and origin that only four distinct tissues are usually recognized:

1. The epithelial tissues   3. The muscular tissues
2. The connective tissues   4. The nerve tissues

For convenience and to avoid repetition, muscle tissues are discussed with the muscles and the nerve tissues with the nervous system.

THE EPITHELIAL TISSUES

Epithelial tissues are composed of cells held firmly together by the viscous intercellular cement. The cells are generally arranged so as to form a membrane covering the external surfaces and lining the internal parts of the body; hence they are called boundary tissues. Epithelial tissues are devoid of blood vessels and are nourished by the fluid which passes to the cells by way of the inter-cellular substance. The general functions of epithelial tissues are protection, excretion, secretion, absorption, and the reception of stimuli.

Epithelial tissues may be classified as:

From a functional point of view they may be classified as:

1. Forming membranes $\begin{cases} \text{covering} \\ \text{lining} \end{cases}$

2. Forming glandular tissue

Squamous epithelium is so called because the cells on the free surface are flattened, scalelike, and fitted together to form a mosaic.

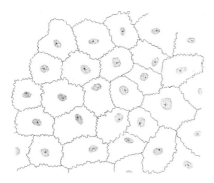

Figure 4–1. Simple squamous epithe-lium, surface view.

Figure 4–2. Diagram of endothelium, surface and sectional views. Seen in the wall of a capillary.

Simple squamous epithelium consists of one layer of flat scalelike cells. The edges of these cells are usually serrated. The nucleus, located in the center of the cell, is oval or spherical, causing a bulging of the cytoplasm. It forms smooth surfaces and secretes a serous fluid to lubricate them. It is found lining the alveoli of the lungs, in the crystalline lens of the eye, in the membranous laby-rinth of the inner ear, and in portions of the uriniferous tubules and rete testis. These tissues are derived from the ectoderm and entoderm[1] and are called true *epithelium*.

A tissue similar in structure is found lining the heart and the blood and lymph vessels, and forming the capillary networks. This tissue is derived from

[1] Often spelled *endoderm*.

the mesoderm and is called *endothelium*. Mesothelium is the name given to this tissue where it lines the serous cavities and covers visceral organs.

Another tissue somewhat similar in structure is called *mesenchyme* and is found lining the perilymph chambers of the ear, the cavities of the eyeball, and the spaces between the dura and the pia of the brain and cord.

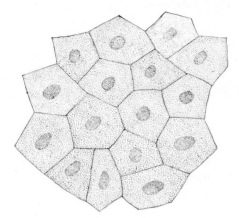

Figure 4–3. Stratified squamous epithelium, surface view.

Stratified squamous epithelium consists of several layers of cells which differ in shape. The cells of the deepest layer are cylindrical, the next are many-sided, and those nearest the surface are flattened and scalelike. The deep or basal cells

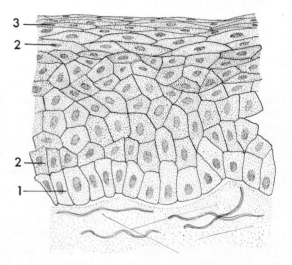

Figure 4–4. Stratified squamous epithelium, sectional view. Seen in the skin. Note areolar connective tissue underneath it. (1) Cylindrical layer, (2) transitional layers, (3) flat, or squamous, layers of cells.

rest on modified connective tissue called *basement* membrane. The deeper cells of a stratified epithelium are separated from one another by a system of channels, which are bridged across by numerous protoplasmic threads. They are continually multiplying by cell division, and as the new cells which are thus produced in the deeper parts increase in size, they compress and push outward those previously formed. In this way cells which were at first deeply seated are gradually shifted outward, becoming dehydrated, shrinking, and growing harder as they are forced away from their contact with underlying body fluids and approach the surface. The older superficial cells are being continually rubbed off, and new ones continually rise up to replace them. Hence, when injured, this tissue has great capacity for repair.

Function. Stratified squamous epithelium is a protective tissue. It protects the body in many ways. It covers the body, forming the epidermis, and is found wherever the ectoderm folds in from the outside, e.g., mouth, nose, and anus. It prevents loss of body fluids and contains structures for the reception of stimuli.

Transitional Epithelium. This tissue is somewhat like stratified squamous epithelium, because it is composed of several layers of cells. The deepest cells

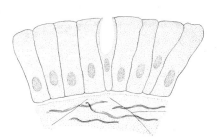

Figure 4–5. Columnar epithelium, sectional view. Note one goblet cell.

Figure 4–6. Columnar epithelium, sectional view, showing tall, slender cells.

are polyhedral in shape, whereas the superficial cells are more flattened. The cells are soft and pliable and adjust to environmental influences which either increase or decrease the surface area. Thus the membrane is adjusted to the content of the organ. It is found in the pelvis of the kidney, ureters, bladder, and part of the urethra. When the bladder is empty the five or six layers of cells are evident, but when it is distended there are only two or three layers of cells.

Columnar Epithelium. In plain columnar epithelium the cells have a cylindrical shape and are set upright on the surface which they cover. Epithelium consisting of only one layer of prismatic cells constitutes the simple columnar variety.

The broad base rests on basement membrane. The nucleus is oval and located near the base of the cell. Numerous mitochondria are present. The distal part of these cells usually contains inclusions such as zymogen in the form of granules.

Columnar epithelium is found in its most characteristic form lining the stomach, small and large intestines, digestive glands, and gallbladder. (See Chap. 17 for glands.)

The chief functions of columnar epithelium are the secretion of digestive fluids and absorption of digested food and fluids.

An important modification of columnar epithelial cells is seen in the *goblet cells*. These cells assume a chalice form, resulting from an accumulation of mucoid secretion. Goblet cells may be regarded as unicellular glands. They are numerous in the mucosa of the small and large intestine and in the respiratory tract.

The mucus protects the membrane in many ways. After discharge of secretion, the cell repeats its secretory activity.

Ciliated Columnar Epithelium. In some areas the free surface of columnar epithelium is provided with microscopic, threadlike processes which carry on ciliary motion. These minute processes, the *cilia*, are prolongations of the cell protoplasm. The motion of an individual cilium may be compared to the lashlike motion of a short-handled whip, the cilium being rapidly bent in one direction and recovering slowly. The motion does not involve the whole of the ciliated

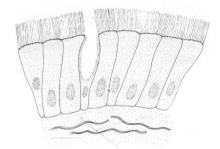

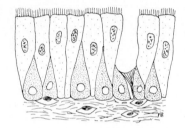

Figure 4–7. Ciliated columnar epithelium, sectional view. Note one goblet cell.

Figure 4–8. Pseudostratified ciliated epithelium. All of the cells reach the basement membrane; some cells do not reach the free surface. One goblet cell is shown.

surface at the same moment but is performed by the cilia in regular succession, giving rise to the appearance of a series of waves traveling along the surface. Since they all move in one direction, a current of much power is produced.

Function. The function of cilia is motion, to impel secreted fluids and other materials along the surfaces from which they extend and to prevent the entrance of foreign matter into cavities.

Ciliated epithelium is found in the respiratory tract from the nose to the end of the bronchial tubes (with the exception of the pharynx and vocal cords), in the uterine tubes and the upper part of the uterus in the female, and in the efferent ducts of the testes in the male.

Pseudostratified Epithelium. In the trachea and larger bronchi the ciliated cells are narrow and tall. Between these are cells that do not reach the surface. These nonciliated cells function in the repair of ciliated epithelium in these areas. Numerous mucus-secreting goblet cells are found in ciliated epithelium.

Neuroepithelium (sensory) contains the end organs of nerve fibers. For example, in the epithelium lining of the nose two kinds of cells develop—olfactory and supporting cells. The olfactory cells send their axons into the brain, where they come into relation with other neurons in the olfactory tract. The olfactory epithelium is thus a neuroepithelium; its sensory cells are nerve cells. They are derived from the ectoderm. The cells of the organ of Corti, the taste buds, and the retina are other examples of neuroepithelium.

Functions. The function of the sensory cells is sensation, and the term *supporting* describes the function of the others.

MEMBRANES

In combination with the underlying connective tissue, epithelium forms *membranes*. The word *membrane* in its broadest sense is used to designate any thin expansion of tissues. In the commonest sense, the word *membrane* is used to denote an *envelope* or *lining* made up of tissues. The underlying connective tissue forms a stratum of closely woven fibers which permits a variable amount of stretching but prevents an expansion which may separate the epithelial cells.

Classification of Membranes

The chief membranes of the body are classified as serous, synovial, mucous, and cutaneous.

Serous membranes are thin, transparent, strong, and elastic. The surfaces are moistened by a self-secreted serous fluid. They consist of simple squamous epithelium and a layer of areolar connective tissue which serves as a base. Since the epithelium is derived from mesoderm, it is called *mesothelium.*

Serous membranes are found (1) lining the body cavities and covering the organs which lie in them, and (2) forming the fascia bulbi and part of the membranous labyrinth of the ear.

1. Lining the Body Cavities and Covering the Organs Which Lie in Them. With one exception, these membranes form closed sacs, one part of which is attached to the walls of the cavity which it lines—the *parietal* portion—while the other is reflected over the surface of the organ or organs contained in the cavity and is named the *visceral* portion of the membrane. In this way the viscera are not contained within the sac but are really placed outside of it; and some of the organs (e.g., lung) may receive a complete, while others (e.g., kidney) receive only a partial, investment.

The free surface of a serous membrane is smooth and lubricated; in this group the free surface of one part is applied to the corresponding free surface of some other part, only a small quantity of fluid being interposed between the surfaces. The organs situated in a cavity lined by a serous membrane, being themselves also covered by it, can thus glide easily against the walls of the cavity or upon each other, their motions being rendered smoother by the lubricating fluid.

This class of serous membranes includes (*a*) the two *pleurae*, which cover the lungs and line the chest, (*b*) the *pericardium*, which covers the heart and lines the

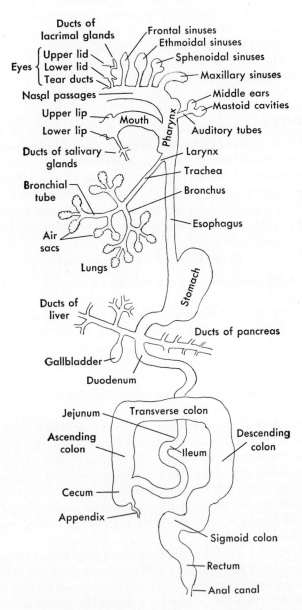

Figure 4–9. Diagram showing continuity of the gastropulmonary mucous membrane.

outer fibrous pericardium, and (*c*) the *peritoneum*,[2] which lines the abdominal cavity and covers its contained viscera and the upper surface of some of the pelvic viscera.

2. *Lining the Vascular System.* This is the internal coat of the heart, blood vessels, and lymph vessels. It is called endothelium.

3. *Forming the Fascia Bulbi and Part of the Membranous Labyrinth of the Ear.*

(*a*) Between the pad of fat in the back of the orbit and the eyeball is a serous sac—the fascia bulbi—which envelops the eyeball from the optic nerve to the ciliary region and separates the eyeball from the bed of fat on which it rests.

(*b*) The membranous labyrinth of the ear has somewhat the same general form as the bony cavities in which it is contained.

Function. The function of the membranes is mainly protective; and this protection is accomplished in many ways, as, for example, by secreting serum which covers its surface, supplying the lubrication for organs as they move over each other.

Synovial membranes are membranes associated with the bones and muscles. They consist of an outer layer of fibrous tissue and an inner layer of areolar connective tissue with loosely arranged collagenous and elastic fibers, connective tissue cells, and fat cells. There is no definite cellular layer at the inner surface. Synovial membranes secrete *synovia*, a viscid, glary fluid that resembles the white of egg, and contain hyaluronic acid.

They are divided into three classes: (1) articular, (2) mucous sheaths, and (3) bursae mucosae.

1. *Articular synovial membranes* line the articular capsules of the freely movable joints.

2. *Synovial sheaths* (mucous sheaths) are elongated closed sacs which form sheaths for the tendons of some of the muscles, particularly the flexor and the extensor muscles of the fingers and toes. They facilitate the gliding of the tendons in the fibro-osseous canals.

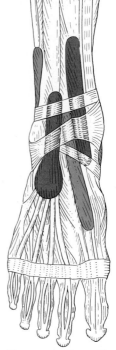

Figure 4–10. The anterior annular ligament of the ankle and the synovial membranes of the tendons beneath it. Artificially distended.

3. *Synovial bursae* (bursae mucosae) are simple sacs interposed to prevent friction between two surfaces which move upon each other. They may be subcutaneous, submuscular, subfascial, or subtendinous. The large bursa situated over the patella is an example of a subcutaneous bursa. Similar, though smaller, bursae are found over the olecranon, the malleoli, the knuckles, and other prominent parts.

[2] The peritoneal cavity in the female is an exception to the rule that serous membranes form perfectly closed sacs, since it communicates with the uterine (*fallopian*) tubes at their ovarian ends.

The function of synovial membranes is the same as that of serous membranes. Both the serous and the synovial membranes are derived from the mesoderm.

The mucous membranes may be grouped in two great divisions: (1) gastro-pulmonary and (2) genitourinary. Mucous membranes secrete *mucus*, a watery fluid containing *mucin* (a glycoprotein), salts, and other substances.

1. *The gastropulmonary mucous membrane* lines the alimentary canal, the air passages, and the cavities communicating with them. It is continuous from the edges of the lips and nostrils, extends through mouth and nose to the throat, throughout the length of the alimentary canal to the anus. At its origin and termination it is continuous with the external skin. It also extends throughout the trachea, bronchial tubes, and air sacs. From the interior of the nose the membrane extends into the frontal, ethmoid, sphenoid, and maxillary sinuses,

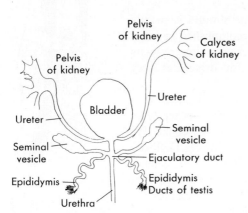

Figure 4–11. Diagram showing continuity of mucous membrane in the male genitourinary pathway.

also into the lacrimal passages, becoming the conjunctival membrane over the fore part of the eyeball and inside of the eyelids on the edges of which it meets the skin. A prolongation of this membrane extends on each side of the upper and back part of the pharynx, forming the lining of the auditory eustachian tube.[3] This membrane also lines the salivary, pancreatic, and biliary ducts and the gallbladder.

2. *The genitourinary mucous membrane* lines the bladder and the urinary tract from the interior of the kidneys to the orifice of the urethra; it lines the ducts of the testes, epididymis, and seminal vesicles; it lines the vagina, uterus, and uterine (fallopian)[4] tubes.

A study of Figures 4–11 and 4–12 will make this plain.

Structure of Mucous Membrane. A mucous membrane is usually composed of three layers of tissue: (1) epithelium, (2) a supporting lamina propria, and (3) a thin, usually double, layer of smooth muscle.

1. EPITHELIUM is the surface layer. It may be stratified squamous, as in the

[3] Bartolommeo Eustacchio, Italian anatomist (1520–1574).
[4] Gabriel Falloppius, Italian anatomist (1523–1562).

throat; columnar, as in the stomach and intestine where it is secretory or absorptive; or ciliated, as in the respiratory tract.

2. THE LAMINA PROPRIA is formed by connective tissue with fine interlacing fibers. It contains fibroblasts and macrophages. It may contain plasma cells and lymphocytes; many blood and lymph capillaries are present. It supports the epithelium and connects it with the muscularis layer.

3. THE MUSCULARIS MUCOSAE is usually a double layer of smooth muscle fibers held together by elastic tissue. The muscle fibers of the inner layer are circularly arranged, and in the outer layer, longitudinally. This layer is not present in the trachea.

The mucous membranes are attached to the parts beneath them by loose connective tissue, in this case called *submucous* connective tissue. This differs greatly in quantity as well as in consistency in different parts. The connection is in some cases close and firm, as in the cavity of the nose. In other instances, especially in cavities subject to frequent variations in capacity, like the esophagus

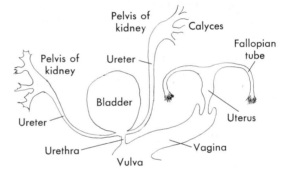

Figure 4–12. Diagram showing continuity of mucous membrane in the female genitourinary pathway.

and the stomach, it is lax. When such a cavity is narrowed by contraction of its outer coats, the mucous membrane is thrown into folds, or *rugae*, which disappear again when the cavity is distended. In certain parts the mucous membrane forms permanent folds that cannot be effaced, and these project conspicuously into the cavity which it lines. The best example of these folds is seen in the small intestine, where they are called *circular folds* (valvulae conniventes), which increase the area of absorbing surface for the products of digestion. In some locations the free surface of mucous membrane contains minute glands or is covered with papillae or villi.

Functions of Mucous Membranes. The functions of mucous membranes are protection, support of blood vessels and lymphatics, and provision of a large amount of surface for secretion and absorption.

A mucous membrane protects by forming a lining for all the passages that communicate with the exterior, i.e., those passages subject to contact with foreign substances which are introduced into the body and with waste materials which are expelled from the body. The mucus secreted is a thicker and more viscid liquid than either serum or synovia and, by coating the surface, lessens the irritation from food, waste materials, or secreted substances. This is especially true in the stomach and duodenum where mucus protects the membrane against the highly acid secretion of hydrochloric acid. The cilia of the respiratory tract also assist in protection. They keep up an incessant motion and thus carry mucus toward the outlet of these passages. Dust and foreign materials usually become entangled in the mucus and are forced out with it.

The redness of mucous membranes is due to their abundant supply of blood. The small blood vessels which convey blood to the mucous membranes divide in the submucous tissues and send smaller branches into the corium, where they form a network of capillaries just under the basement membrane. The lymphatics also form networks in the corium and communicate with larger vessels in the submucous tissue below.

The projections of mucous membrane, such as the circular folds, covered with glands and villi as they are, increase enormously the surface area of the membrane for secretion and absorption and enable the membrane to carry more blood vessels and lymphatics.

Cutaneous membrane or integument refers to membrane that covers the body and is commonly spoken of as skin.

THE SKIN AND APPENDAGES

Most of our contacts with the environment are through the skin. Since living cells must be surrounded with fluid, the contact of the body with the air is made by means of dead cells. These dead cells form a protective covering for the living cells. The living cells of the inner layers of the skin are constantly pushed to the outside, shrinking and undergoing progressive chemical changes which cement them firmly together and render them waterproof. In this way a tissue-fluid environment is maintained for living cells although man lives in an air environment.

The Skin

The skin has many functions. It covers the body and protects the deeper tissues from drying and injury. It protects from invasion by infectious organisms. It is important in many ways in temperature regulation. It contains end organs of many of the sensory nerve fibers by means of which one becomes aware of items of the environment. It acts as an accessory mechanism for tactile and pressure corpuscles. In the skin fat, glucose, water, salts such as sodium chloride, and fluid accumulate in the tissues. The skin has excretory functions, eliminating water with the various salts which compose perspiration, and the dead cells themselves become an important way of eliminating many salts. It is an important light screen for the underlying living cells. It also has absorbing powers. It will absorb oily materials placed in contact with it. The skin doubtless has many other functions.

Skin *area* is especially important when an individual is burned. The following figures give the approximate areas of the body.

Head and neck 6 per cent; trunk 38 per cent (anterior trunk and genitals 20 per cent, posterior trunk 18 per cent). Upper extremities 18 per cent (arms 13.5 per cent, hands 4.5 per cent). Lower extremities 38 per cent (thighs including buttocks 19 per cent, legs 12.6 per cent, feet 6.4 per cent).

The rule of nine gives the relative distribution of total body surface area.

Head and neck	9%
Anterior trunk	18%
Posterior trunk	18%
Upper extremity (9 × 2)	18%
Lower extremity (18 × 2)	36%
Perineum	1%
Total 100%	

Skin consists of two distinct layers: (1) epidermis, cuticle; (2) dermis, corium, or cutis vera.

The epidermis is a stratified squamous epithelium, consisting of a variable number of layers of cells. It varies in thickness in different parts, being thickest on the palms of the hands and on the soles of the feet, where the skin is most exposed to friction, and thinnest on the ventral surface of the trunk and the inner surfaces of the limbs. It forms a protective covering over every part of the true skin and is closely molded on the papillary layer of the corium. The external surface of the epidermis is marked by a network of ridges caused by the size and arrangement of the papillae beneath. Some of these ridges are large and correspond to the folds produced by movements, e.g., at the joints; others are fine and intersect at various angles, e.g., upon the back of the hand. Upon the palmar surface of the fingers and hands and the soles of the feet, the ridges serve to increase resistance between contact surfaces and therefore prevent slipping. On the tips of the fingers and thumbs these ridges form distinct patterns which are peculiar to the individual and practically never change, hence the use of fingerprints for purposes of identification.

From without inward four regions of the epidermis are named: the *stratum corneum*, the *stratum lucidum*, the *stratum granulosum*, and the *stratum germinativum (mucosum)*.

The three outer layers consist of cells which are practically dead and are constantly being shed and renewed from the cells of the *stratum germinativum*. In the *stratum corneum* the protoplasm of the cells has become changed into a protein substance called *keratin*, which acts as a waterproof covering. The reaction is acid; and many kinds of organisms, when placed upon the skin, are destroyed, presumably by the effect of the acidity. Underneath this is the *stratum lucidum*, a few layers of clear cells.

The *stratum granulosum* is formed by two or three layers of flattened cells that are cells in transition between the stratum germinativum and the horny cells of the superficial layers.

The *stratum germinativum* consists of several layers of cells. The cells of the deepest layer are columnar in shape and are sometimes called the *stratum mucosum*. The growth of the epidermis takes place by multiplication of the cells of the germinative layer. As they multiply, the cells previously formed are pushed upward toward the surface. In their upward progress these cells undergo a chemical transformation, and the soft protoplasmic cells become converted into the flat scales which are constantly being rubbed off the surface of the skin. The pigment in the skin is found in greatest amount in the cells of the stratum germinativum. No blood vessels pass into the epidermis, but fine nerve fibers lie between the cells of the inner layers.

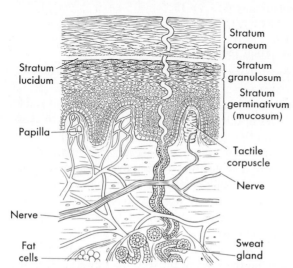

Figure labels: Stratum corneum; Stratum lucidum; Stratum granulosum; Stratum germinativum (mucosum); Papilla; Tactile corpuscle; Nerve; Nerve; Fat cells; Sweat gland

Figure 4–13. Diagram of a section of the skin to show its structure. The epidermis consists of the strata corneum, lucidum, granulosum, and germinativum (mucosum). The corium lies below the epidermis.

The corium (derma) is a highly sensitive and vascular layer of connective tissue. It contains numerous blood vessels, lymph vessels, nerves, glands, hair follicles, and papillae and is described as consisting of two layers: the *papillary*, or *superficial, layer*, and the *reticular*, or *deeper, layer*.

The surface of the *papillary*, or *superficial*, layer is increased by protrusions in the form of small conical elevations, called papillae, whence this layer derives its name. They project up into the epidermis, which is molded over them. The papillae consist of small bundles of fibrillated tissue, the fibrils being arranged parallel to the long axis of the papillae. Within this tissue is a loop of capillaries; and some papillae, especially those of the palmar surface of the hands and fingers, contain *tactile corpuscles*, which are numerous where the sense of touch is acute.

The *reticular*, or *deeper*, layer consists of strong bands of fibrous tissue and some fibers of elastic tissue. These bands interlace, and the tiny spaces left by their interlacement are occupied by adipose tissue and sweat glands. The reticular layer is attached to the parts beneath by a subcutaneous layer of areolar connective tissue, which, except in a few places, contain fat. In some parts, as on the front of the neck, the connection is loose and movable; in other parts, as on the palmar surface of the hands and the soles of the feet, the connection is close and firm. In youth the skin is both extensile and elastic, so that it can be stretched

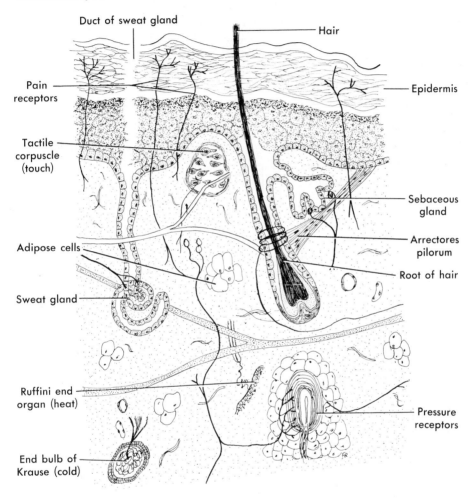

Figure 4–14. Diagram of skin showing receptors for pain, pressure, touch, heat, and cold.

and wrinkled and return to its normal condition of smoothness. As age advances, the elasticity is lessened, and the wrinkles tend to become permanent.

Blood Vessels and Lymphatics. The arteries which supply the skin form a network in the subcutaneous connective tissue and send branches to the papillae, the hair follicles, and the sudoriferous glands. The capillaries of the skin are so numerous that when distended they are capable of holding a large proportion of the blood contained in the body. The amount of blood they contain is dependent on their caliber, which is regulated largely by the vasomotor nerve fibers.

There is a superficial and a deep network of lymphatics in the skin. These communicate with each other and with the lymphatics of the subcutaneous connective tissue.

Nerves. The skin contains the peripheral terminations of many nerve fibers and receptors. These fibers may be classified as follows:

1. Motor nerve fibers, including the vasoconstrictors and vasodilators distributed to the blood vessels, and motor nerve fibers distributed to the arrector muscles (arrectores pilorum).

2. Receptors concerned with the temperature sense, which terminate in *cold receptors* (end organs of Krause, Fig. 8–6) and *receptors for warmth* (possibly the end organs of Ruffini).

3. Receptors concerned with touch and pressure, which terminate in *touch* (Meissner's corpuscles and free nerve endings around hairs and skin) and *pressure receptors* (pacinian corpuscles). (See Chap. 8, Fig. 8–6.)

The Appendages of the Skin

The appendages of the skin are the nails, the hairs, the sebaceous glands, the sudoriferous, or sweat, glands, and their ducts.

The nails (ungues) are composed of clear, horny cells of the epidermis, joined so as to form a solid, continuous plate upon the dorsal surface of the terminal phalanges. Each nail is closely adherent to the underlying corium, which is modified to form what is called the bed, or *matrix*. The body of the nail is the part that shows. The hidden part, in the nail groove, is called the root. The *lunule* is the crescent-shaped white area which can be seen on the part nearest the root. The nails appear pink except at the *lunule* because blood in the capillary bed shows through.

The nails grow in length by multiplication of the soft cells in the stratum germinativum at the root. The cells are transformed into hard, dry scales, which unite to form a solid plate; and the nail, constantly receiving additions, slides forward over its bed and projects beyond the end of the finger. When a nail is thrown off by suppuration or torn off by violence, a new one will grow in its place provided any of the cells of the stratum germinativum are left.

The hairs (pili) are growths of the epidermis, developed in the hair follicles, which extend downward into the subcutaneous tissue. The part which lies within the follicle is known as the root, and that portion which projects beyond the surface of the skin is called the shaft. The hair is composed of:

Cuticle, a single layer of scalelike cells which overlap.

Cortex, a middle portion, which constitutes the chief part of the shaft, formed of elongated cells united to form flattened fibers which contain pigment granules in dark hair and air in white hair.

Medulla, an inner layer composed of rows of many-sided cells, which frequently contain air spaces. The fine hairs covering the surface of the body and the hairs of the head do not have this layer.

The root of the hair is enlarged at the bottom of the follicle into a bulb which is composed of growing cells and fits over a vascular papilla which projects into the follicle. Hair has no blood vessels but receives nourishment from the blood vessels of the papilla.

Growth of Hair. Hair grows from the papilla by multiplication of its cells (matrix cells). These cells become elongated to form the fibers of the fibrous portion, and as they are pushed to the surface, they become flattened and form the cuticle. If the scalp is thick, pliable, and moves freely over the skull, it is favorable to the growth of hair. A thin scalp that is drawn tightly over the skull tends to constrict the blood vessels, lessen the supply of blood, and cause atrophy of the roots of the hair by pressure; in such cases massage of the head loosens the scalp, improves the circulation of the blood, and usually stimulates the growth of the hair. The hairs are constantly falling out and constantly being replaced. In youth and early adult life not only may hairs be replaced, but there may be an increase in the number of hairs by development of new follicles. When the matrix cells lose their vitality, new hairs will not develop.

With the exceptions of the palms of the hands, the soles of the feet, and the last phalanges of the fingers and toes, the whole skin is studded with hairs. The hair of the scalp is long and coarse, but most of the hair is fine and extends only a little beyond the hair follicle.

Arrector (Arrectores Pilorum) Muscles. The follicles containing the hairs are narrow pits which slant obliquely upward, so that the hairs they contain lie slanting on the surface of the body. Connected with each follicle are small bundles of involuntary muscle fibers called the *arrector muscles.* They arise from the papillary layer of the corium and are inserted into the hair follicle below the entrance of the duct of a sebaceous gland (Fig. 4–14). These muscles are situated on the side toward which the hairs slope, and when they contract, as they will under the influence of cold or fright, they straighten the follicles and elevate the hairs, producing the roughened condition of the skin known as "gooseflesh." Since the sebaceous gland is situated in the angle between the hair follicle and the muscle, contraction of the muscle squeezes the sebaceous secretion out from the duct of the gland. This secretion aids in preventing too great heat loss.

Glands in the Skin. *Sebaceous glands* occur everywhere over the skin surface with the exception of the palms of the hands and the soles of the feet. They are abundant in the scalp and face and are numerous around the apertures of the nose, mouth, external ears, and anus. Each gland is composed of a number of epithelial cells and is filled with larger cells containing fat. These cells are cast off bodily, their detritus forms the secretion and new cells are continuously formed. Occasionally the ducts open upon the surface of the skin, but more frequently they open into the hair follicles. In the latter case, the secretion from the gland passes out to the skin along the hair. Their size is not regulated by the length of the hair.

Some of the largest sebaceous glands are found on the nose and other parts of the face, where they may become enlarged with accumulated secretion. This retained secretion often becomes discolored, giving rise to the condition commonly known as blackheads. It also provides a medium for the growth of pus-producing organisms and consequently is a common source of pimples and boils.

Sebum is the secretion of the sebaceous glands. It contains fats, soaps, cholesterol, albuminous material, remnants of epithelial cells, and inorganic salts. It serves to protect the hairs from becoming too dry and brittle, as well as from becoming too easily saturated with moisture. Upon the surface of the skin it forms a thin protective layer, which serves to prevent undue absorption or evaporation of water from the skin. This secretion keeps the skin soft and pliable. An accumulation of this sebaceous matter upon the skin of the fetus furnishes the thick, cheesy, oily substance called the *vernix caseosa*.

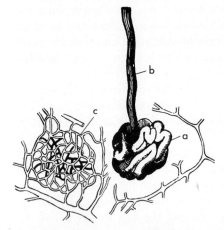

Figure 4–15. Coiled end of a sweat gland. (*a*) The coiled end, (*b*) the duct, (*c*) network of capillaries, inside which the sweat gland lies.

Sudoriferous, or *sweat, glands* are abundant over the whole skin but are largest and most numerous in the axillae, the palms of the hands, the soles of the feet, and the forehead. Each gland consists of a single tube, with a blind, coiled end which is lodged in the subcutaneous tissue. From the coiled end the tube is continued as the excretory duct of the gland up through the corium and epidermis and finally opens on the surface by a pore. Each tube is lined with secreting epithelium continuous with the epidermis. The coiled end is closely invested by capillaries, and the blood in the capillaries is separated from the cavity of the glandular tube by the thin membranes which form their respective walls.

Perspiration, or Sweat. Pure sweat is very dilute and practically neutral. When gathered from the skin, it contains fragments of cells and sebum and has a pH range of 5.2 to 6.75. Perspiration contains the same inorganic constituents as the blood, but in lower concentration. The chief salt is sodium chloride. The organic constituents in sweat include urea, uric acid, amino acids, ammonia, sugar, lactic acid, and ascorbic acid. Any factor which affects the composition of blood may also alter the composition of sweat. Sulfonamides are present after administration. Immune substances may also be present.

Under ordinary circumstances, the perspiration that the body is continually throwing off evaporates from the surface of the body without one's becoming aware of it and is called *insensible perspiration*. When more sweat is poured upon the surface of the body than can be removed at once by evaporation, it appears on the skin in the form of drops, and is then spoken of as *sensible perspiration*.

The amount secreted during 24 hours varies greatly. It is estimated to average about 480 to 600 ml (16 to 20 oz), but may be increased to such an extent that even more than this may be secreted in an hour.

ACTIVITY OF THE SWEAT GLANDS. Special secretory nerve fibers are supplied to the glandular epithelium of the sweat glands. The activity of these glands is supposed to be the result either of direct stimulation of the nerve endings in the glands or of indirect stimulation through the sensory fibers of the skin. The usual cause of profuse sweating is a high external temperature or muscular exercise. It is known that the high temperature acts upon the sensory cutaneous nerves, possibly the heat fibers, and stimulates the sweat fibers indirectly.

PHYSIOLOGY OF THE SWEAT GLANDS. While perspiration is an excretion, its value lies not so much in the elimination of waste matter but in the loss of body heat by the evaporation of water. Each gram of water requires about 0.5 Cal for evaporation, and this heat comes largely from the body. This loss of heat helps to balance the production of heat that is constantly taking place. When the kidneys are not functioning properly, and the blood contains an excessive amount of waste matter, the sweat glands will excrete some of the latter, particularly if their activity is stimulated. In the condition known as uremia, when the kidneys secrete little or no urine, the percentage of urea in perspiration rises.

Ceruminous Glands. The skin lining the external auditory canal contains modified sweat glands called *ceruminous* glands. They secrete a yellow, pasty substance resembling wax, which is called cerumen. An accumulation of cerumen deep in the auditory canal may interfere with hearing.

THE CONNECTIVE TISSUES

The connective tissues differ in appearance but are alike in that the cellular elements are relatively few and the intercellular material is relatively abundant. They serve to connect and support the other tissues of the body, and with few exceptions they are highly vascular. The intercellular substance determines the physical characteristics of the tissue. The connective tissues may be classified as:

A. Embryonal tissue

B. Connective tissues proper
    Loose connective
    Adipose
    Liquid tissue—see Chapter 12
    Reticular
    Elastic
    Fibrous

C. Cartilage
  Hyaline
  Fibrous
  Elastic

D. Bone
  Compact
  Cancellous

A. Embryonal Tissue

In the development of connective tissue from the mesoderm, the cells unite to form a network. The cytoplasm increases rapidly, with a resulting differentiation into cells and a semifluid intercellular substance. This embryonal tissue is abundant in the embryo. It represents a stage in the development of connective tissue. Some of the mesodermal cells migrate into spaces between the primary germ layers and form a diffuse network of embryonal connective tissue called mesenchyme. Some cells have short processes and exhibit ameboid activity. These are known as wandering cells and are the precursors of macrophages. Normally embryonal tissue does not occur in the adult but is found in connective tissue repair after injuries and in certain pathological growths. Embryonal tissue, in which the ground substance is rich in mucin, is called *mucous connective tissue.* Wharton's jelly,[5] in the umbilical cord, and the vitrous body of the eye is mucous connective tissue.

B. Adult Connective Tissue

1. Loose Connective Tissue. Loose, irregularly arranged connective (areolar) tissue is composed of cells separated from one another by a semifluid ground

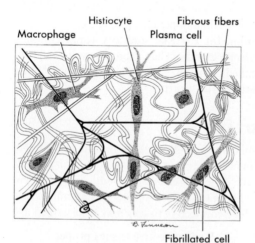

Histiocyte   Fibrous fibers
Macrophage   Plasma cell

Fibrillated cell

Figure 4–16. Loose connective tissue (highly magnified). The fibrous fibers are in wavy bundles; the elastic fibers form an open network. The ground substance, or matrix, in which the cells and fibers lie is tissue fluid. About 11 per cent of the body fluid lies in this tissue.

substance, or *matrix.* Lying in this ground substance is an irregular network of silvery-white collagenous fibers and light elastic fibers. These fibers are the predominant characteristic of the tissue. The microscopic appearance of this tissue

[5] Wharton, English anatomist (1610–1673).

is shown in Figure 4–16. Note the semiliquid ground substance, the cells, the fibrous fibers, and the elastic fibers lying in it. Hyaluronic acid is present in many connective tissues. It has the capacity to bind water in the tissues and is an important factor for changes in viscosity and permeability of the ground substance in the tissue.

Collagenous fibers are composed of an albuminoid protein called collagen. Collagen, when boiled in water, yields gelatin. A collagenous fiber is composed of many minute wavy fibrils lying parallel and held together by cement. The fibrils frequently separate into groups extending in different directions. These fibrils are flexible but possess great tensile strength. Elastic fibers are homogenous, branch freely, and are composed of a protein called elastin.

This tissue is soft and pliable, and when fresh it is transparent. It plays an important part in the exchange of substances between blood plasma and tissue cells.

The Cells of Connective Tissues. The cells found in connective tissue include:

1. THE FIBROBLASTS. These are most numerous and are large, flat branching cells with many processes. They play a part in the formation of the collagenous fibers. It is believed that they also form ground substance. After tissue injury, these cells enlarge and become active in forming fibers.

2. THE HISTIOCYTES OR MACROPHAGES. These are irregularly shaped cells with short processes. They are also found in the sinusoids of the liver, lymph organs, and bone marrow. The histiocytes are phagocytic and function in normal physiological processes. They also have great phagocytic capacity under such conditions as inflammatory processes.

3. THE PLASMA CELLS. These are small round or irregular-shaped cells found in greatest numbers in all connective tissues but especially in the connective tissue of the alimentary mucous membrane and great omentum. There is evidence that they may be derived from special cells in the thymus and are distributed to other tissues shortly after birth. Plasma cells are the actual formers of circulating antibodies.

4. THE MAST CELLS in loose connective tissue are most numerous along blood vessel beds. They form the anticoagulant heparin. *Histamine* is also liberated from these cells in allergic and inflammatory reactions. Recent evidence shows that mast cells contain serotonin which functions as a vasoconstrictor at the site of injury.

5. BLOOD CELLS. Lymphocytes, neutrophils, monocytes, and eosinophils from the blood and lymph move in and out of this tissue.

Function. Loose connective tissue serves to connect the various tissues of an organ. Nerves, blood vessels, lymph vessels, and cells lie in it. It is found under the skin (subcutaneous), under the mucous membranes (submucous), and filling in the spaces around the blood vessels and nerves. Moreover, it is continuous throughout the body, and from one region it may be traced into any other, however distant.

The matrix of this tissue is frequently called tissue fluid and in most areas of the body is spoken of as the *internal environment*. Speaking generally, it is this tissue that delivers supplies from the blood to the cells and delivers wastes from the cells to the blood and lymph. It stores water, salts, and glucose temporarily.

The connective tissue matrix and cells play an important role during inflammatory processes and in the repair of tissue.

2. Adipose Connective Tissue. This tissue is areolar connective tissue in which many of the cells are filled with fat. Adipose tissue exists very generally

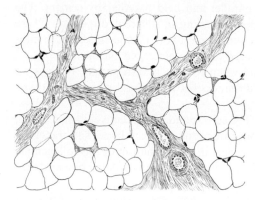

Figure 4–17. Diagram of a thin section of adipose connective tissue. (Low magnification.) Note fibers close together in strands containing blood vessels and a few cells. The adipose cells are crowded together.

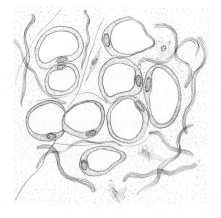

Figure 4–18. Diagram of a thin section of adipose connective tissue (highly magnified). Note adipose cells, matrix, fibrous fibers, elastic fibers, connective tissue. The white centers of the adipose cells represent fat. Excess fat adds to the work of the heart.

throughout the body, accompanying the still more widely distributed areolar connective tissue in most parts in which the latter is found. It is found chiefly:

Underneath the skin, in the subcutaneous layer.

Beneath the serous membranes or in their folds, e.g., omentum.

Collected in large quantities around certain internal organs, especially the kidneys, helping to hold them in place.

Covering the base and filling up furrows on the surface of the heart.

As padding around the joints.

In the marrow of the long bones.

Function. Adipose tissue has many functions, among which are: (1) to constitute an important reserve food, which when needed can be returned to the cells by the blood and oxidized, thus producing energy—adipose tissue stores more calories of energy-producing substance than any other tissue in the body volume concerned; (2) to serve as a jacket or covering under the skin and, being a poor conductor of heat, to reduce the loss of heat through the skin; (3) to support and protect various organs, e.g., the kidneys; and (4) to serve to fill up spaces in the tissues, thus supporting delicate structures such as blood vessels and nerves.

3. Liquid Tissue. Blood and lymph may be classified as liquid tissue. They consist of cells and an intercellular substance, which is liquid. (See Chap. 12.)

4. Reticular[6] Tissue. Reticular tissue is a variety of loose connective tissue with a network, or reticulum, of fibrous fibers. The cells are thin and flat and are

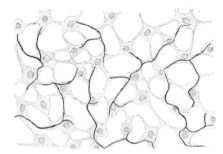

Figure 4–19. Diagram of reticular tissue as seen in a thin section of a bit of lymph node. (Highly magnified.) This tissue forms the framework of lymph tissue.

wrapped around the fibers. It can also be described as a meshwork of stellate cells forming minute cavities in which lymph cells are found. It forms the framework of lymphoid tissue.

Lymphoid or adenoid[7] tissue is reticular tissue in which the meshes of the network are occupied by lymph cells. This is the most common variety of reticular tissue.

Function. Reticular tissue forms a supporting framework in the lymph nodes in bone marrow, and in muscular tissue. It is also present in the spleen, in the mucous membrane of the gastrointestinal tract, and in the lungs, liver, and kidneys.

5. Elastic Connective Tissue. This tissue is loose connective tissue in which the elastic fibers predominate. It consists of a ground substance containing cells with a few fibrous fibers and a predominance of elastic fibers which branch freely. They give it a yellowish color.

Function. Elastic tissue is extensile and elastic. It is found:

Entering into the formation of the lungs and uniting the cartilages of the larynx.

In the walls of the arteries, the trachea, bronchial tubes, and vocal folds.

[6] Reticulum (Latin *reticulum*, "a small net").
[7] Adenoid (Greek *aden*, "a gland," and *eidos*, "resemblance").

In a few elastic ligaments and between the laminae of adjacent vertebrae (ligamenta flava, ligamentum nuchae).

6. Fibrous Connective Tissue.   This tissue is loose connective tissue in which the fibrous fibers predominate. It consists of a ground substance in which there

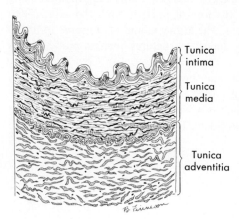

Tunica intima

Tunica media

Tunica adventitia

Figure 4–20.   Elastic connective tissue as seen in a thin section of the wall of a large artery (highly magnified.) The elastic fibers appear as short, black lines in the tunica media.

are cells and wavy, collagenous fibers, which cohere very closely and are arranged side by side in bundles which have an undulating outline. The matrix between the bundles contains cells arranged in rows, but the cells are not a prominent feature of this tissue.

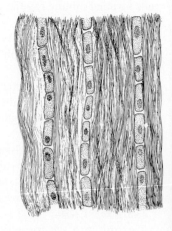

Figure 4–21.   Fibrous connective tissue as seen in a thin, longitudinal section of a tendon (highly magnified). Fibrous fibers and cells lying in a matrix (white).

Fibrous tissue is silvery-white, strong, and tough, yet perfectly pliant; it is almost devoid of extensibility and is very sparingly supplied with nerves and blood vessels.

Function. Fibrous connective tissue is part of the supporting framework of the body. It forms:

1. LIGAMENTS, strong flexible bands, or capsules, of fibrous tissue that help to hold the bones together at the joints.

2. TENDONS or SINEWS, white glistening cords or bands which serve to attach the muscles to the bones.

3. APONEUROSES, flat, wide bands of fibrous tissue which connect one muscle with another or with the periosteum of bone.

4. MEMBRANES containing fibrous connective tissue found investing and protecting different organs of the body, e.g., the heart and the kidneys.

5. FASCIAE. The word *fascia* (Latin) means a band or bandage. It is most frequently applied to sheets of fibrous connective tissue which are wrapped around muscles and serve to hold them in place. Fasciae are divided into two groups, (*a*) superficial fascia and (*b*) deep fasciae.

(*a*) Superficial fascia, composed of subcutaneous areolar connective tissue, forms a nearly continuous covering beneath the skin. It varies in thickness and usually permits free movement of the skin on the subjacent parts.

Infection of the superficial fascia is called *cellulitis.* In this loose, areolar connective tissue infection spreads readily, and it is difficult to keep it from extending to surrounding areas.

(*b*) Deep fasciae are sheets of white, fibrous tissue, enveloping and binding down the muscles, also separating them into groups. The term *fasciae* usually designates the *deep fasciae.* Subcutaneous areolar tissue is rarely called by the name *fascia,* though it is correctly classed as such.

C. Cartilage

Cartilage, the well-known substance called *gristle,* is firm, tough, and flexible. When a very thin section is examined with a microscope, it is seen to consist of groups of cells in a mass of intercellular substance called the matrix. According to the texture of the intercellular substance, three principal varieties can be distinguished: (1) hyaline, or true, cartilage; (2) fibrocartilage; (3) elastic cartilage.

1. Hyaline Cartilage. Comparatively few cells lying in fluid spaces or lacunae are embedded in an abundant quantity of intercellular substance. This substance appears as a bluish-white glossy or homogeneous mass. It is made up of collagenous fibrils forming a feltlike matrix. These fibers are similar to those found in fibrous connective tissue.

Hyaline cartilage covers the ends of the bones in the joints, forming articular cartilage; it forms the ventral ends of the ribs as the costal cartilages.

In these situations the cartilages are in immediate connection with bone and may be said to form part of the skeleton; hence they are frequently described as skeletal cartilages. Hyaline cartilage also enters into the formation of the nose, larynx, trachea, bronchi, and bronchial tubes.

Function. In covering the ends of the bones in the joints, the articular cartilages provide the joints with a thick, springy coating which gives ease to motion. In forming part of the bony framework of the thorax, the costal cartilages impart flexibility to its walls.

In the embryo a type of hyaline cartilage, known as embryonal cartilage, forms the matrix in which most of the bones are developed.

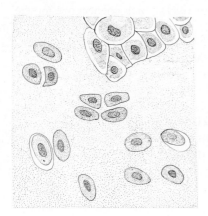

Figure 4–22. Hyaline cartilage as seen in a thin section (highly magnified). Some cells are shrunken to show that they lie in fluid spaces. Matrix is stippled.

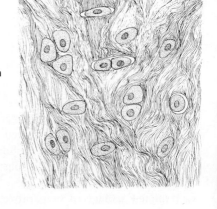

Figure 4–23. Fibrous cartilage as seen in a thin section (highly magnified).

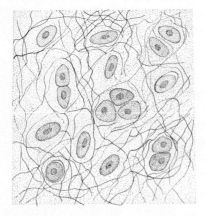

Figure 4–24. Elastic cartilage as seen in a thin section (highly magnified).

2. Fibrous Cartilage. The intercellular substance is pervaded with bundles of white fibers, between which are scattered cartilage cells. It closely resembles fibrous tissue. The encapsulated cells frequently lie in rows with the bundles of collagenous fibers between them.

Fibrocartilage is found joining bones together, the most familiar instance being the flat round disks or symphyses of fibrocartilage connecting the bodies of the vertebrae and the symphysis pubis between the pubic bones. In these cases the part in contact with the bone is always hyaline cartilage, which passes gradually into fibrocartilage. It forms the interarticular cartilage of other joints. In the center of the intervertebral disks there is a softened mass called the *nucleus pulposus.* Herniation of this mass may occur into the spinal canal.

Function. Fibrocartilage serves as a strong, flexible connecting material between bones and is found wherever great strength combined with a certain amount of rigidity is required.

3. Elastic Cartilage. The intercellular substance is pervaded with a large number of elastic fibers which form a network. In the meshes of the network the cartilage cells are found. This form of cartilage is found in the epiglottis, cartilages of the larynx, auditory tube, and external ear.

Function. It strengthens and maintains the shape of these organs and yet allows a certain amount of change in shape.

Cartilage is not supplied with nerves and very rarely with blood vessels. *Perichondrium*, a moderately vascular fibrous membrane, covers and nourishes cartilage except where it forms articular surfaces. Perichondrium also functions in the repair process of injured cartilage. When injured, the area is invaded by the perichondrial tissue, which is gradually changed into cartilage. Regeneration of cartilage is slow and may not take place in some instances. With the aging process, cartilage loses its translucency and bluish-white color and appears cloudy. Calcification may occur along with degenerating changes of the cartilage cells.

D. Bone, or Osseous Tissue

Bone is connective tissue in which the intercellular substance is rendered hard by being impregnated with mineral salts, chiefly calcium phosphate and calcium carbonate. The mineral salts, or inorganic matter, constitute about two thirds of the weight of bone. The organic matter, consisting of cells, blood vessels, and cartilaginous substance, constitutes about one third. The inorganic matter can be dissolved out by soaking a bone in dilute acid, or the organic matter may be driven off by heat. In both cases the shape of the bone will be preserved. Bone freed from inorganic matter is called *decalcified.* It is a tough, flexible, elastic substance, so free from stiffness that it can be tied in a knot. Bone free from organic matter is white and so brittle that it can be crushed in the fingers.

Structure of Bone. On sectioning a bone, it will be seen that in some parts it consists of slender fibers and lamellae which form a structure resembling latticework, whereas in others it is dense and close in texture, appearing like ivory.

There are two forms of bony tissue: (1) the *cancellous*, or *spongy*; and (2) the *dense*, or *compact*.

All bone is porous, the difference between the two forms being a matter of degree. The *compact* tissue has fewer spaces and is always found on the exterior of a bone, whereas the *cancellous* has larger cavities and more slender intervening bony partitions and is found in the interior of a bone. The relative quantity of these two kinds of tissue varies in different bones and in different parts of the same bone, depending on the need for strength or lightness. The

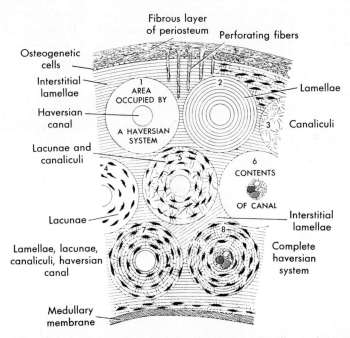

Figure 4–25. Diagram of a cross section of osseous tissue. Details are drawn to a very much larger scale than the complete drawing. A small part of a *transverse section* of a long bone is shown. At the uppermost part is the periosteum, covering the outside of the bone; at the lowermost part is the medullary membrane, lining the marrow cavity. Between these is compact tissue, consisting largely of a series of haversian systems, each being circular in outline and perforated by a central canal, left blank in the canals of five of the systems in this illustration, and represented in color in two. The *first* circle shows the area occupied by a system. The *second* shows the layers of bony tissue, or lamellae, arranged around the central canal.

In the *third*, fine dark radiating lines represent canaliculi, or lymph channels. In the *fourth*, dark spots arranged in circles between the lamellae represent lymph spaces, or lacunae, which contain the bone cells. In the *fifth*, the central canal, lacunae, and canaliculi, which connect the lacunae with each other and with the central canal, are shown.

The *sixth* shows the contents of the canal: artery, veins, lymphatics, and areolar tissue. The *seventh* shows the lamellae, lacunae, canaliculi, and haversian canal. The *eighth* shows a complete haversian system.

Between the systems are interstitial lamellae, only a few of which show lacunae. The periosteum is made up of an outer fibrous layer and an inner osteogenetic layer, so called because it contains bone-forming cells, or osteoblasts. (Modified from Gerrish.)

shafts of the long bones are made up almost entirely of compact tissue, except that they are hollowed out to form a central canal, the medullary canal, which is lined by a vascular tissue called the medullary membrane.

Marrow is of two distinct kinds, red and yellow.

Red marrow consists of a small amount of connective tissue that acts as a support for a large number of blood vessels; a large number of marrow cells, or *myelocytes*, which resemble the white blood cells; a small number of fat cells; a number of cells called *erythroblasts*, from which the red blood cells are derived; and *giant cells* (*osteoclasts*) found in both kinds of marrow but more abundant in the red marrow. Red marrow is found in the articular ends of the long bones, mainly femur and humerus, and in the cancellous tissue. (See Chap. 12 for red blood cell formation.)

Yellow marrow consists of connective tissue containing numerous blood vessels and cells. Most of the cells are fat cells; only a few are myelocytes. It is found in the medullary canals of the long bone and extends into the spaces of the cancellous tissue and the haversian[8] canals. It is thought that in the adult the neutrophilic, eosinophilic, and basophilic white cells of the blood are formed in the marrow tissue from its myelocytes.

Periosteum. All bones are covered, except at their cartilaginous extremities, by a membrane called periosteum. It consists of an outer layer of connective tissue and an inner layer of fine fibers which form dense networks. In young bones the periosteum is thick, vascular, and closely connected with the epiphyseal cartilages. Later in life the periosteum is thinner and less vascular.

Endosteum. The marrow cavities and haversian canals are lined with a membrane called *endosteum*. During bone growth it is formed by a delicate layer of connective tissue. Beneath it lies a layer of osteoblasts. After growth ceases, the cells become flattened and the two layers are indistinguishable. A stimulus for bone formation, such as an injury, activates these cells.

Blood Vessels and Nerves. Unlike cartilage, the bones are plentifully supplied with blood. If the periosteum is stripped from a fresh bone, many bleeding points representing the canals (Volkmann's[9]) through which the blood vessels enter and leave the bone are seen. These blood vessels proceed from the periosteum to join the system of haversian canals. Around the haversian canals the lamellae are disposed, and lying between them, arranged in circles, are found the lacunae which contain the bone cells. Radiating from one lacuna to another and toward the center are the canaliculi. Following this scheme, it will be seen that the innermost canaliculi run into the *haversian canals*; thus, direct communication is established between the lymph in these canals and the cells in the lacunae surrounding the haversian canals.

Bone cells or *osteocytes* are located in the almond-shaped cell spaces or lacunae. Their cytoplasmic processes project into the canaliculi. Before imprisonment in the lacunae they were the osteoblasts, or bone-forming cells, of

[8] Clopton Havers, English anatomist (1650–1702).
[9] Alfred Wilhelm Volkmann, German physiologist (1800–1877).

the matrix. They are arranged in single rows on surfaces of growing bone. *Osteoclasts* are found on surfaces of bone where reabsorption takes place. They have numerous mitochondria.

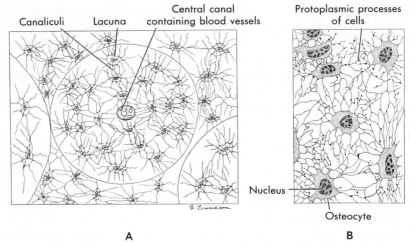

Figure 4–26. Diagram of thin cross section of compact bone. *A* is one complete haversian system. *B*. Osteocytes with their protoplasmic processes (highly magnified).

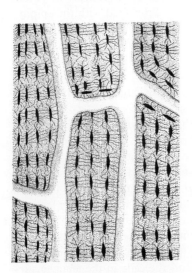

Figure 4–27. Bony tissue as seen in a thin longitudinal section of a bone (highly magnified). Haversian canals light in color, lacunae and canaliculi black.

The marrow in the body of a long bone is supplied by one large artery (sometimes more) called the *medullary* or *nutrient* artery, which enters the bone at the nutrient foramen, situated in most cases near the center of the body, and perforates the compact tissue obliquely. It sends branches upward and downward, which ramify in the marrow and enter the adjoining bony tissue. The twigs of these vessels anastomose with the arteries of the compact and cancellous tissue. In this way the whole substance of the bone is penetrated by intercommunicating blood tubes. In most of the flat and in many of the short spongy bones, larger apertures give entrance to vessels which pass to central parts of the bone and correspond to nutrient arteries of long bones. Veins emerge with or apart from arteries.

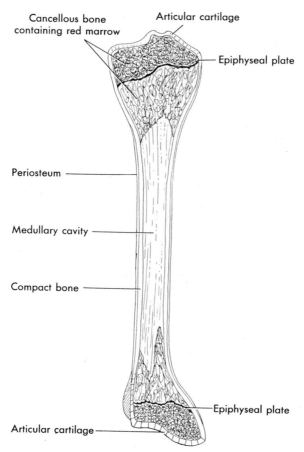

Figure 4–28. Diagram of longitudinal section of a long bone. Note the cancellous tissue at the ends and the epiphyseal plates.

Lymphatic vessels have been traced into the substance of bone and accompanying the blood vessels in the haversian canals. The periosteum is well supplied with nerves, which accompany the arteries into the bone. These nerve fibers form a plexus around the blood vessels. The nerve fibers include afferent myelinated and autonomic unmyelinated fibers.

Development of Bones. In the early embryo some bones, such as those forming the roof and sides of the skull, are preformed in membrane; others, such as those of the limbs, are preformed in cartilage. Hence two kinds of ossification occur, the intramembranous and the intracartilaginous.

Intramembranous Ossification. Before the cranial bones are formed, the brain is covered by inner meningeal membranes, a middle fibrous membrane, and an outer layer of skin. The fibrous membrane occupies the place of the future bone. From it periosteum and bone are formed. It is composed of fibers and bone-forming cells called *osteoblasts* in a matrix, or ground substance. When bone begins to form, a network of spicules radiates from a point or center of ossification. The spicules develop into fibers. Calcium salts are deposited in the fibers and matrix, enclosing some of the osteoblasts in minute spaces, called lacunae. As the fibers grow out, they continue to calcify and give rise to fresh bone spicules. Thus, a network of bone is formed, the meshes of which contain the blood vessels and a delicate connective tissue crowded with osteoblasts. The bony network thickens by the addition of fresh layers of bone formed by the osteoblasts, and the meshes are correspondingly encroached upon. Successive layers of bony tissue are deposited under the periosteum, so that the bone increases in thickness and presents the structure of compact bone on the outer and inner surfaces with a layer of soft, spongy, cancellous tissue between. The cancellous tissue between the layers, or tables, of the skull is called the *diploe*. Ossification of the bones of the skull is not complete at birth. At the site of the future union of two or more bones, membranous areas persist and are called fontanels.

Intracartilaginous, or Endochondral, Ossification. By the end of the second month the skeleton of the embryo is preformed in cartilage. Soon after this, ossification begins. The first step in intracartilaginous ossification is that the cartilage cells at the center of ossification enlarge and arrange themselves in rows. Following enlargement, calcium salts are deposited in the matrix between the cells, first separating them and later surrounding them so that all nutriment is cut off, resulting in their atrophy and disappearance. The membrane called *perichondrium*, which covers the cartilage, assumes the character of periosteum. From this membrane grow cells which are deposited in the spaces left by the atrophy of the cartilage cells. These two processes, destruction of cartilage cells and the formation of bone cells to replace them, continue until ossification is complete. The number of centers of ossification varies in differently shaped bones. In most of the short bones ossification begins at a point near the center and proceeds toward the surface. In the long bones, there is first a center of ossification for the body called the *diaphysis* and one or more centers for each extremity called *epiphyses*. Ossification proceeds from the diaphysis toward the epiphyses and from the epiphyses toward the diaphysis. As each new portion is ossified, thin layers of cartilage continue to develop between the diaphysis and epiphyses; and during the period of growth these outstrip ossification. When this ceases, the growth of a bone stops.

Ossification begins soon after the second month of intrauterine life and continues well into adult life. Such bones as the sternum, the sacrum, and the hip-bones do not unite to form single bones until the individual is well beyond 21 years of age.

From this brief discussion two points of practical interest stand out: (1) the bones of the newborn infant are soft and largely composed of cartilage; (2) since the process of ossification is going on continually, the proper shape of the cartilage should be preserved in order that the shape of the future bone may be normal. Therefore it is obvious that a young baby's back should be supported, and a child should always rest in a horizontal position. The facility with which bones may be molded and become misshapen is seen in the bowlegs of children. However, the softness of the skeleton of a child accounts for the fact that the many jars and tumbles experienced in early life are not as injurious to the cartilaginous frame as they would be to a harder structure.

Numerous experiments have demonstrated that the proper ossification and growth of bone depend upon (1) adequate amounts of calcium and phosphorus in the food and (2) chemical substances which enable the bone cells to utilize calcium and phosphorus. The chemical substances may be vitamins derived from food or a hormone, such as thyroxin, derived from the internal secretion of the thyroid gland and the parathyroid hormone. Low-calcium content of the blood may be caused by inadequate calcium in the diet, by poor absorption of calcium, or by too rapid excretion of it in the feces. Milk contains well-balanced proportions of calcium and phosphorus; hence the dietary rule of a quart of milk each day for every child.

Normal healthy bone is under constant change as it is reabsorbed and repaired continuously. There are special cells called *osteoclasts* found along the edges of bone and there is evidence that they may be active in the process of bone reabsorption, or on the other hand, the osteoclast may be merely the result of reabsorption.

Hormonal Influences on Bone

Somatotropin (STH) of the anterior pituitary influences growth of all tissues, especially bone growth. When the epiphyses of the long bones have united with the bone shafts, growth of bone ceases.

Thyroxin increases osteoclastic activity, more than it increases osteoblastic activity.

Hyperactivity of *adrenocortical hormones* will cause protein mobilization from the organic matrix of bone, thereby decreasing it.

Parathyroid hormone is essential for normal osteoclastic activity and the deposition of calcium and phosphate in bone tissue.

Estrogens cause increased osteoblastic activity—for this reason, after puberty, bone rate of growth becomes rapid for several years. They also cause rapid uniting of the epiphyses with the shafts of long bone. Estrogens have a broadening effect on the pelvis.

Testosterone causes bones to thicken and deposit calcium salts, thereby increasing the total quantity of the matrix.

Rickets. Rickets is a condition in which the mineral metabolism is disturbed so that calcification of the bones does not take place normally. The bones remain soft and become misshapen, resulting in bowlegs and malformations of the head, chest, and pelvis. Liberal amounts of calcium and phosphorus in food, and vitamin D, found in fish-liver oils and in significant amounts in egg yolk, whole milk, butter, fresh vegetables, etc., are important factors in the cure and prevention of rickets. Exposure to sunshine, especially irradiation of the skin, helps also in the optimal use of calcium and phosphorus in the body.

Three types of rickets are recognized as due to chemical deficiency of the blood. The first, or so-called low-phosphorus rickets, is caused by a subnormal content of phosphate ions in the blood. This is the commonest type, sometimes called true rickets, and is characterized by histological changes resulting in large joints, deformed bones of the cranium, chest, and spine and a condition in which beadlike deposits occur at the ends of the ribs. The second type is characterized by deformed bones of the head, trunk, and limbs and is frequently accompanied by tonic muscular spasms (tetany) lasting for considerable periods of time. It is sometimes called low-calcium rickets or a "ricketslike condition." The third type is one in which both calcium and phosphorus are below normal and is characterized by progressive porosity of the bones. A deficiency of vitamin C interferes with the function of the osteoblasts and their formation of organic intercellular substance. Individuals, especially women past middle life, frequently suffer from impaired skeletal maintenance, and the bones become relatively more fragile. This condition is called *osteoporosis*. There is some evidence that certain hormones may in part contribute to the condition.

Fracture is a term applied to the breaking of a bone. It may be either partial or complete. As a result of the greater amount of organic matter in the bones of children, they are flexible, bend easily, and do not break readily. In some cases the bone bends like a bough of green wood. Some of the fibers may break, but not the whole bone, hence the name *green-stick fracture*. The greater amount of inorganic matter in the bones of the aged renders the bones more brittle, so that they break easily and heal with difficulty.

Regeneration of Bone. A fracture is usually accompanied by injury to the periosteum and tissues causing hemorrhage and destruction of tissue.

Fibroblasts and capillaries grow into the blood clot, forming granulation tissue. The plasma and white cells from the blood exude into the tissues and form a viscid substance, which sticks the ends of the bone together. This exudate into which the fibroblasts and capillaries grow is called *callus*. Usually bone cells from the periosteum and calcium salts are gradually deposited in the callus, which eventually becomes hardened and forms new bone. Occasionally the callus does not ossify, and a condition known as *fibrous union* results. The periosteum is largely concerned in the process of repair. If a portion of the periosteum is stripped off, the subjacent bone may die, whereas if a large part of the whole of a bone is removed and the periosteum at the same time is left intact, the bone will wholly or in great measure be regenerated.

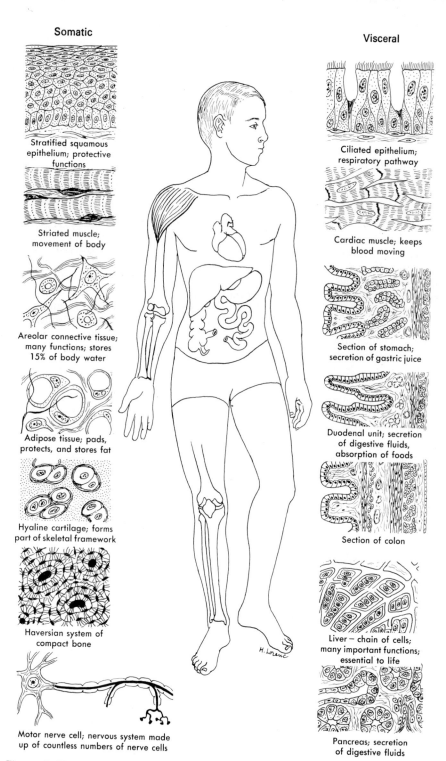

Somatic

Stratified squamous epithelium; protective functions

Striated muscle; movement of body

Areolar connective tissue; many functions; stores 15% of body water

Adipose tissue; pads, protects, and stores fat

Hyaline cartilage; forms part of skeletal framework

Haversian system of compact bone

Motor nerve cell; nervous system made up of countless numbers of nerve cells

Visceral

Ciliated epithelium; respiratory pathway

Cardiac muscle; keeps blood moving

Section of stomach; secretion of gastric juice

Duodenal unit; secretion of digestive fluids, absorption of foods

Section of colon

Liver — chain of cells; many important functions; essential to life

Pancreas; secretion of digestive fluids

H. Lorenc

Figure 4–29. Diagram showing some unit patterns and tissue relationships of the body as a whole.

79

TISSUE REPAIR

Repair of tissues takes place continually under the normal process of living. Some tissues are subject to more wear and tear than others, such as, for example, those in the skin. The stratified squamous epithelium of the skin is constantly being subjected to varying degrees of friction and will respond to meet immediate needs. This might be shown by thickening, callus formation, or a blister, depending on the rapidity of the friction. When subjected to greater friction, sudden contact with sharp, dull, or blunt objects, the tissues are damaged or there may be tissue loss.

Some tissues are repaired easily and quickly, such as surface epithelium, connective tissue, and liver cells. Others repair more slowly; others, as typified by bone, must have parts kept in alignment and immobilized until repair is completed. Periosteum must be present for bone regeneration, muscle tissue has least ability for repair, and nerve cells destroyed by injury or infection do not regenerate.

Repair of Epithelial Tissues. Both the epithelial cells and underlying connective tissue cells have capacity for cell division and repair. The response to injury depends on the extent of the injured surface. There is usually rapid cell multiplication of the surface layer. Mitosis is decreased for the first few days but soon exceeds the normal rate. When injury is more extensive, the underlying tissue cells divide and migrate by a sort of ameboid movement into the injured area. There is formation of tonguelike processes which grow into the area and finally the surface layer of cells multiplies and they migrate over the injured surface, reforming the surface layer of cells.

Primary Repair. Primary repair takes place in "clean" wounds, such as, for instance, incisions, cuts, and the like, when infection is not present. If the injury simply involves the skin, the deep layer of stratified squamous epithelium divides longitudinally, the cells "push up," and the wound is rapidly and completely restored to normal. If the area is larger, the underlying connective tissue cells, the fibroblasts, take part in the repair process.

If the area of skin loss is great, fluid exudes from the capillaries; it dries and seals the open tissue, and a "scab" forms. Epithelial cells proliferate at the edges and continue to grow over the area until it is covered. If skin loss involves a large area, skin grafting is done to hasten the process.

When the deeper tissues are involved, if the edges of the wound are brought together with sutures, as, for example, in operative incisions, there is outpouring of serous fluid into the wound, and a coagulum is formed which seals the wound. The coagulum contains leukocytes and tissue fragments. In 24 to 36 hours, fibroblasts of connective tissue and the *endothelial* cells of the capillaries are multiplying rapidly. The newly formed cells remain along the edges of the wound, and by the third day new vascular buds are present. These grow across the wound along with connective tissue formation.

By the fourth or fifth day, fibroblast activity is markedly evident. Collagenous fibers are rapidly formed, and capillaries sprout and extend across the wound, holding the edges firmly together. Later the fibers shorten and scar tissue is reduced to a minimum.

Secondary Repair. In large open wounds with more or less tissue loss, the area is filled in by a process of building up "granulation tissue." Each granulation represents a minute vascular area consisting of newly formed, vertically upstanding blood vessels which are surrounded by young connective tissue and wandering cells of different kinds.

The surface has a characteristic pebbly appearance. The connective tissue cells, the fibroblasts, increase in number; collagenous fibers are proliferated by them, and eventually the wound closes.

Granulation tissue secretes a fluid which has definite bactericidal properties. Its defense characteristics include hyperemia, which is more or less marked, active exudation, and marked local leukocytosis.

The amount of scar tissue formed is in relation to tissue damage. It is important that parts of the body undergoing extensive tissue repair (such as, for example, burned areas involving the chest and neck, the chest after radical mastectomy, and the like) be kept in alignment, immobile at first, and in some instances stretched. Active movement should be encouraged early so that, as new tissues are formed, contracture from scar formation will not result. Every effort should be directed toward preventing or minimizing disfigurement.

At times, as when large areas of skin are destroyed by burns, considerable blood plasma is lost, with its contained proteins, electrolytes, and other substances. This may result in disturbance of fluid balance. It is, therefore, important that fluids be replaced by artificial means until the tissues themselves can prevent such loss by coagulation and initial wound healing response.

It is known that glucocorticoids have an anti-inflammatory action. However, the exact mechanism of action is not understood. If given in large doses, it diminishes the inflammatory process and inhibits the formation of granulation tissue.

Conditions Favorable to Wound Healing. Nutrition plays an important role in the healing process. The tissues need plenty of protein for repair, hence the need for protein-rich diets.

The vitamins play an important part in wound healing, as well as resistance to and prevention of infection. It is believed that *vitamin A* is important for repair of epithelial tissues, especially the maintenance of epithelial integrity of the respiratory pathway. There is no conclusive evidence that vitamin A has anti-infective or wound-healing properties when applied in ointments. However, reports of controlled experiments on animals show that ointments containing vitamins A and D shortened the healing time.

Vitamin B. Thiamine, nicotinic acid, and riboflavin are important from the viewpoint of the general well-being of the individual as a whole, and specifically in relation to metabolism, vigor, appetite, relief of pain in some instances, and integrity of selective epithelial areas.

Vitamin C. The normal production and maintenance of intercellular substance as well as cement substances of the connective tissues, especially collagen formations and the integrity of capillary walls, are directly dependent upon vitamin C. In wound healing by granulation, new capillaries must sprout and fibroblasts must grow; to meet the increased demands, vitamin C is essential.

Vitamin D is essential for the normal absorption of calcium from the intestine; so possibly it aids in the healing of fractures. A low serum calcium level stimulates parathormone production, which increases excretion of phosphorus at the kidney and tends to raise serum calcium.

Vitamin K. Vitamin K functions in wound healing from the viewpoint of helping to maintain the normal coagulability of the blood.

On the whole, tissues heal faster and leave less visible scars in the young than in the aged. This perhaps is due to the fact that in the young the tissues are soft, pliable, and in a constant state of growth; and in comparison to the aged or older age group cells multiply more rapidly.

Normally tissue repair takes place so readily and is so commonplace that thought is not given to it. Tissues may remain dormant for years, then suddenly become actively growing tissues in a response to stimulus. It is believed the stimulus is almost certainly chemical in nature, which appears to be liberated by the degenerating cells. When part of a tissue is removed, this in itself initiates regeneration and forms the basis of the theory that disturbance of *spatial equilibrium* is an important factor. Another theory suggests the coaptation theory—that cells of a tissue have common affinity due to highly specialized specific stereochemical bonds which exist at cell surfaces. If the bonds are disrupted, it provides a stimulus for proliferation of tissue activity.

The *leukocytes* have a specific function in relation to tissue repair. They are attracted to areas of injury, perhaps in response to the chemical liberated. The monocytes are especially active in the repair of tissue, possibly providing nutritive and building materials of protein and lipoid character.

Tissue Transplants.   In the human, transplants of tissue from one part of the body to another are accepted because they are part of the same body and are said to be *autologous*. The tissues of identical twins are also autologous because they are from the same fertilized egg so that the tissues have the same tissue proteins. The transplanted cells survive only when nutrients and oxygen can reach the cells from the surrounding tissue fluid. Fraternal twins do not come from the same fertilized ovum and are genetically different; hence each has different tissue proteins and they are said to be *homologous*.

Each individual has a different genetic structure and therefore different protein structure so that when tissues are transplanted from one person to another, *antibodies* are formed in the *recipient* against the foreign tissue proteins which are antigenic, and destruction of the cells of the transplant results. However, the many tissues used for transplants from "tissue banks" such as bone, tendons, blood vessels, nerves, and fascia survive because of the large amount of connective tissue and the relatively small numbers of cells. The transplanted tissue serves as a temporary bridge which functions as a substitute for the destroyed tissue and stimulates regeneration of tissue in the recipient. In some instances the recipient for fresh tissue transplants is subjected to radiation to destroy his ability to form antibodies against the donor's tissue proteins. Antibody-blocking drugs, antimetabolites, and glucocortoids are also used to prevent antibody formation by the recipient.

Successful corneal transplants have been done for many years. It has been thought that since the cornea is normally avascular and does not contain lymphocytes, it is different from other tissues. Recent studies show that the surface epithelium is regenerated by the recipient so that the transplanted cornea is covered in a few days. Regeneration of the endothelium takes longer, and the connective tissue cells are slowly replaced. Research today is vigorous in relation to *organ* transplants, and a certain degree of success is reported in the transplantation of the kidney.

Summary—Tissue Repair

Name of Tissue	Repair Process
Stratified squamous epithelium	Thickens in response to slow friction. Forms blister in response to rapid friction. Readily repaired. Basal layer of cells divides by mitosis, the cells migrate upward, forming a tonguelike process which grows over the denuded area. If large areas are denuded, skin grafts may be necessary

Modified forms
  Cornea
  Conjunctiva
	When injured, the cells of the cornea form scar tissue. Conjunctiva is repaired readily

Simple squamous In kidney and small ducts	Considerable ability for repair. Repair in some areas may result in abnormal shape of cells
Mesothelium In serous cavities	Destruction by inflammatory processes frequently results in the formation of fibroblasts which form scar tissue
Endothelium All blood vessels and lymphatic capillaries	In capillaries, cells have ability to multiply rapidly. In all tissue repair, capillaries are formed by an outgrowth of former capillaries

Plain columnar epithelium
  Glands of stomach and intestine
  Ducts of many glands
	Secretory cells are replaced occasionally. They multiply or the underlying cells replace surface cells. If large areas are destroyed, scar tissue results

Goblet cells	Readily replaced
Cuboidal cells of liver	Liver cells have great power of regeneration
Ciliated columnar epithelium	Small injuries are repaired by mitotic division. Large areas repaired by underlying cell layers or connective-tissue cells
Loose connective tissue	Blood oozes or flows into wound; clot forms, edges of wound are glued together, capillaries sprout, fibroblasts multiply rapidly. Collagenous and elastic fibers are formed quickly and invade area
Adipose tissue	Regeneration rapid
Elastic connective tissue	Good blood supply to tissue. Tissue repaired by fibroblasts and invasion of elastic and fibrous fibers
Fibrous connective tissue Ligaments, tendons, and fascial sheaths	Scant blood supply to tissue except in fibrous membranes. Repair process slow but complete Periosteum and dura mater—blood supply good, repair depends upon the connective tissue Repair limited to a few cells

Muscle
  Striated
  Smooth
  Cardiac
	Regeneration limited, healing takes place by scar formation. In pregnant uterus cells increase in size. Limited cell multiplication
	Do not regenerate. Repair by scar tissue

Cartilage
  Hyaline
  Elastic
  Fibrous
	Healing of cartilage is by repair of the surrounding connective tissue called perichondrium. Degenerative changes frequently occur as age advances

Summary—Tissue Repair (*cont.*)

Name of Tissue	Repair Process
Bone	All bone is surrounded by periosteum, which is richly supplied with blood, lymph, and nerves. Bone is readily repaired if the periosteum is present. Deformations will not occur if good approximation is maintained. Cells under the periosteum proliferate and form a splint of cartilage around the fractured ends. Cells at the edges become osteoblasts and form bone
Nerve tissue	Nerve cells when injured are *not* replaced. Nerve fibers when severed from the cell body die. Myelinated nerve fibers will grow into the sheath if the neurilemma is present

QUESTIONS FOR DISCUSSION

1. Mr. X. had second-degree burns of all of his chest, abdomen, and arms and first-degree burns of all of his face and neck. Orders included: give plasma, 1,000 ml, and electrolytes with dextrose by vein; record fluid intake and output each hour; give medication ordered for pain; and apply dressings; Foley catheter is to be kept in place.

   a. What percentage of the body received first-degree burns? Second-degree burns?
   b. What receptors are involved? What is the reason for so much pain?
   c. What fluids are being lost from the body? How do you know?
   d. Give reasons for giving each of the fluids by vein.
   e. Are the sweat glands involved?
   f. What problems must the nurse be alert for during the healing process of the skin before and after skin grafting is done?
   g. Why must fluid intake and output be measured each hour? Why must the catheter be kept in place?
   h. One pint of blood was ordered on the fifth day. Explain why.

2. Explain the relationship between tissue repair and nutrition?

SUMMARY

Classification { The epithelial tissues   The muscular tissues
tissues   { The connective tissues   The nerve tissues
Epithelial Tissues. Boundary tissues composed of cells and a minimum of intercellular substance

Classification of Epithelial Tissues {
  Squamous {
    Simple—one layer of flat cells {
      Mesothelium and endothelium—derived from mesoderm
      Epithelium—derived from ectoderm and entoderm
    }
    Stratified—several layers of cells
  }
  Columnar {
    Plain—cylindrical cells, upright on surface
    Ciliated—threadlike processes at free end
  }
  Neuroepithelium
}

Functions
- (1) *Protection.* Some varieties are specially modified so as to form protective membranes. Example—skin
- (2) *Motion.* This is seen in the cilia
- (3) *Absorption.* This is particularly well seen in the digestive tube
- (4) *Secretion.* Every secreting organ contains epithelial cells. Mucous and serous membranes are examples of secreting membranes
- (5) *Special sensation.* The organs of the special senses contain epithelial cells. Examples—eye, ear, nose, etc.

Membranes
- **Definition** — Any thin expansion of tissues that serves as a lining or covering
- **Varieties**
  - (1) Serous membranes
  - (2) Synovial membranes
  - (3) Mucous membranes
  - (4) Cutaneous membrane

Serous Membranes

Consist of
- (1) Simple squamous epithelium
- (2) A thin layer of connective tissue

Derived from the mesoderm and called mesothelium

Found lining closed cavities or passages that do not communicate with the exterior. They are moistened by serum

Three Classes
- Lining the body cavities and covering the organs which lie in them
  - Pleurae—cover the lungs and line the chest
  - Pericardium—covers the heart and lines the outer fibrous pericardium
  - Peritoneum—covers the abdominal and the top of some of the pelvic organs, lines the abdominal cavity
- Lining the vascular system
  - Heart
  - Blood vessels
  - Lymphatics
- Forming the fascia bulbi and part of the membranous labyrinth of the ear

Functions —Protection
- (1) Furnishes a cover or lining for viscera and vascular system
- (2) Secretes serum, a lubricant

Synovial Membranes

Consist of thin serous tissue associated with bones and muscles

Three Classes
- Articular synovial membranes } Surround cavities of movable joints
- Mucous sheaths—form sheaths for tendons
- Bursae mucosae—Sacs interposed between two surfaces which move upon each other

Functions
- Furnish a lining or cover
  - Joints
  - Tendons
  - Sacs under skin, muscles, and tendons
- Furnish a secretion—synovia—which acts as a lubricant

Mucous Membranes

Found lining passages that communicate with the exterior and are protected by mucus

Two Divisions
- Gastropulmonary
  - Alimentary canal
  - Air passages
  - Cavities communicating with both alimentary canal and air passages
- Genitourinary
  - Urinary tract
  - Generative organs

Consist of
- (1) Epithelium
  - Stratified
  - Columnar
  - Ciliated
- (2) Basement membrane, a layer of flat cells, etc.
- (3) Stroma — Loose connective tissue, which contains blood vessels
- (4) Muscularis mucosae—thin layer of muscular tissue which is not always present

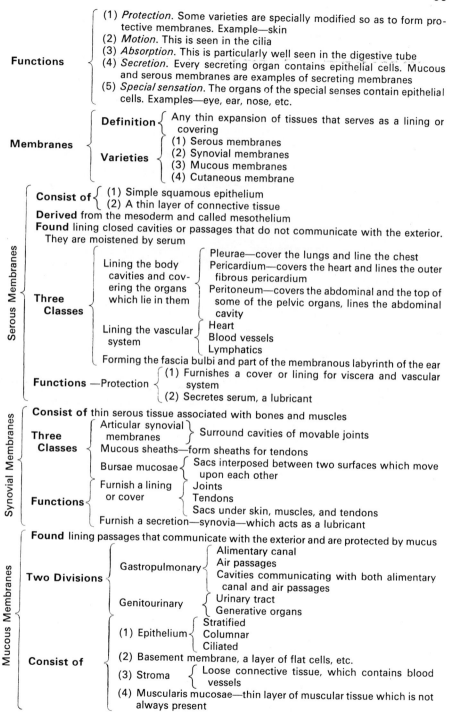

Mucous Membranes—(cont.)

Projections
- Rugae—temporary folds { Esophagus / Stomach }
- Circular folds—permanent folds of mucous membrane found in small intestine
- Papillae—conical processes of mucous membrane best seen on tongue. Contain blood vessels and nerves
- Villi—tiny threadlike projections of the mucous membrane of small intestine

Functions
- Protection { Secretion of mucus / Action of cilia }
- Support for network of blood vessels
- Absorption and Secretion { Various modifications increase the surface }

Cutaneous Membrane
- Forms the skin
- Covers the body
- Serves to protect underlying tissues
- Prevents loss of body fluids
- Contains structures for the reception of stimuli

Skin

Functions
- (1) Covers the body
- (2) Protects the deeper tissues from { Drying, injury / Invasion by infectious organisms }
- (3) Important factor in heat regulation
- (4) Contains the end organs of many sensory nerves
- (5) It has limited excretory and absorbing power

Consists of

Epidermis is a stratified epithelium
- (1) Stratum corneum
- (2) Stratum lucidum
- (3) Stratum granulosum } Practically dead cells being constantly shed and renewed from the stratum germinativum
- (4) Stratum germinativum } Soft protoplasmic cells that are constantly multiplying by cell division

Corium is a layer of connective tissue
- (1) Papillary layer—papillae are minute conical elevations of the corium. They contain looped capillaries, and some contain termination of nerve fibers called tactile corpuscle
- (2) Recticular layer } Bands of fibrous and elastic tissue which interlace, leaving tiny spaces which are occupied by adipose tissue and sweat glands

Blood vessels. The arteries form a network in the subcutaneous tissue and send branches to papillae and glands of skin. Capable of holding a large proportion of total amount of blood in body

Lymphatics. There is a superficial and a deep network of lymphatics in the skin

Nerve fibers
- (1) Motor fibers to blood vessels and arrector muscles
- (2) Fibers concerned with temperature sense
- (3) Fibers concerned with sense of touch and pressure
- (4) Fibers stimulated by pain
- (5) Secretory fibers which are distributed to the glands

Appendages
- Nails, hairs
- Sebaceous glands, sudoriferous glands

Nails
- Consist of clear, horny cells of epidermis
- Corium forms a bed, or matrix, for nail
- Root of nail is lodged in a deep fold of the skin
- Nails grow in length from soft cells in stratum germinativum at root

Hairs (Pili)
- The hairs grow from the roots
- The roots are bulbs of soft, growing cells contained in the hair follicles
- Hair follicles are little pits developed in the corium

Hairs (Pili) *(cont.)*
- Stems of hair extend beyond the surface of the skin, consist of three layers of cells: (1) cuticle, (2) cortex, and (3) medulla
- Found all over body, except
  - Palms of the hands
  - Soles of the feet
  - Last phalanges of the fingers and toes
- Arrector muscles are attached to corium and to each hair follicle. Contraction pulls hair up straight, drags follicles upwards, forces secretion of sebaceous glands to surface, and forces blood to interior

Sebaceous Glands
- Compound alveolar glands, the ducts of which usually open into a hair follicle but may discharge separately on the surface of the skin
- Lie between arrector muscles and hairs
- Found over entire skin surface except
  - Palms of hands
  - Soles of feet
- Secrete *sebum*, a fatty, oily substance, which keeps the hair from becoming too dry and brittle, the skin flexible, forms a protective layer on surface of skin, and prevents undue absorption or evaporation of water from the skin

Sweat Glands
- Tubular glands, consist of single tubes with the blind ends coiled in balls, lodged in subcutaneous tissue, and surrounded by a capillary plexus. Secrete sweat and discharge it by means of ducts which open exteriorly

Sweat
- Watery, colorless, turbid liquid, salty taste, distinctive odor, and usually an acid reaction: pH is 5.2 to 6.75
- Contains the same inorganic constituents as the blood but in lower concentration
- Average quantity, about 16–20 oz in 24 hours
- Amount increased by
  - (1) Increased temperature or humidity of the atmosphere
  - (2) Dilute condition of blood
  - (3) Exercise
  - (4) Pain
  - (5) Nausea
  - (6) Mental excitement or nervousness
  - (7) Dyspnea
  - (8) Use of diaphoretics, e.g., pilocarpine, physostigmine, nicotine
  - (9) Various diseases, such as tuberculosis, acute rheumatism, and malaria
- Amount decreased by
  - (1) Cold
  - (2) Voiding a large quantity of urine
  - (3) Diarrhea
  - (4) Certain drugs, e.g. atropine and morphine
  - (5) Certain diseases

Activity of Sweat Glands due to
- (1) Direct stimulation of nerve ending in sweat glands
- (2) Indirect stimulation through sensory nerves of the skin
- (3) Influenced by external heat, dyspnea, muscular exercise, strong emotions, and the action of various drugs

Function of Sweat
- Importance not in elimination of waste substances in perspiration, but elimination of **heat** needed to cause evaporation of perspiration
- When kidneys are not functioning properly, sweat glands will excrete waste substances, particularly if stimulated

Ceruminous Glands
- Modified sweat glands
- Found in skin of external auditory canal
- Secrete cerumen, a yellow, pasty substance, like wax

Connective Tissues. Tissues composed of cells with much intercellular substance, which is derived from the cells

Character-
istics
{
Cellular element at a minimum, intercellular element abundant
Intercellular material determines characteristic of the tissue
Serves to connect and support other tissues
With the exception of cartilage, they are highly vascular
}

Varieties
{
A. Embryonal
B. Connective tissue proper
    1. Loose connective   4. Reticular
    2. Adipose   5. Elastic
    3. Liquid   6. Fibrous
C. Cartilage
D. Bone
}

A. Embryonal Tissue. Represents a stage in development of connective tissue. Consists of cells and a primitive intercellular ground substance. When ground substance is rich in mucin, it is called mucous connective tissue

B. Connective Tissue Proper
    Loose Connective Tissue. Formed by interlacing of wavy bundles of fibrous fibers and some straight elastic fibers with cells lying in the ground substance
    Function. Connects, insulates, forms protecting sheaths, and is continuous throughout the whole body
    Fluid matrix is called tissue fluid
    Fluid matrix, often called internal environment, serves as a medium for transfer of supplies from blood and lymph vessels to cells, and wastes from cells to blood and lymph. Stores water, salts, glucose, etc.
    Adipose Tissue. Modification of areolar tissue, with cells filled with fat. Distribution quite general but not uniform

Function
{
1. Forms a reserve food to be drawn upon in time of need
2. Prevents the too rapid loss of heat
3. Serves to protect and support delicate organs
}

    Liquid Tissues. Cells in a liquid intercellular substance, e.g., blood and lymph
    Reticular Tissue. Areolar tissue with a network of fibrous fibers. Cells wrapped around fibers
    Lymphoid Tissue. Reticular tissue with meshes of network occupied by lymph cells
    Function. Reticular tissue forms a supporting framework in many organs, e.g., lymph nodes, bone marrow, and muscular tissue. Reticular tissue is present in the spleen, mucous membrane of the gastrointestinal tract, lungs. liver, and kidneys
    Elastic Tissue. Consists of cells with few fibrous fibers and a predominance of elastic fibers
    Function. It is extensible and elastic. Found in blood vessels, air tubes, larynx, vocal folds, and lungs, ligamenta flava, ligamentum nuchae
    Fibrous Tissue. Formed of wavy bundles of fibrous fibers only, with cells in rows between bundles; very strong and tough but pliant
    Function. Is found in form of ligaments, tendons, aponeuroses, protecting sheaths, and fasciae

C. Cartilage. Cartilage consists of a group of cells in a matrix. It is firm, tough, and elastic, covered and nourished by perichondrium

Varieties
{
1. **Hyaline cartilage** { Articular / Costal } Skeletal
2. **Fibrocartilage**
3. **Elastic cartilage**
}

D. **Bone, or Osseous Tissue.** Bone is connective tissue in which the intercellular substance derived from the cells is rendered hard by being impregnated with mineral salts

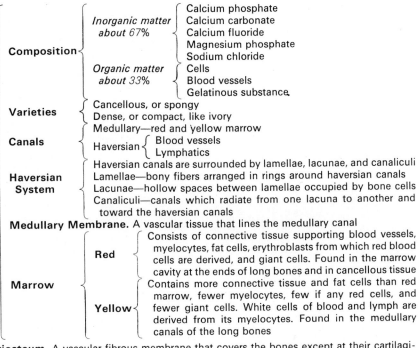

Bone, or Osseous Tissue

Composition

Inorganic matter about 67%
Calcium phosphate
Calcium carbonate
Calcium fluoride
Magnesium phosphate
Sodium chloride

Organic matter about 33%
Cells
Blood vessels
Gelatinous substance

Varieties
Cancellous, or spongy
Dense, or compact, like ivory

Canals
Medullary—red and yellow marrow
Haversian { Blood vessels / Lymphatics

Haversian System
Haversian canals are surrounded by lamellae, lacunae, and canaliculi
Lamellae—bony fibers arranged in rings around haversian canals
Lacunae—hollow spaces between lamellae occupied by bone cells
Canaliculi—canals which radiate from one lacuna to another and toward the haversian canals

Medullary Membrane. A vascular tissue that lines the medullary canal

Marrow

Red
Consists of connective tissue supporting blood vessels, myelocytes, fat cells, erythroblasts from which red blood cells are derived, and giant cells. Found in the marrow cavity at the ends of long bones and in cancellous tissue

Yellow
Contains more connective tissue and fat cells than red marrow, fewer myelocytes, few if any red cells, and fewer giant cells. White cells of blood and lymph are derived from its myelocytes. Found in the medullary canals of the long bones

Periosteum. A vascular fibrous membrane that covers the bones except at their cartilaginous extremities and serves to nourish them. Important in the reunion of broken bone and growth of new bone

Blood Vessels. Twigs of nutrient artery in medullary canal anastomose with twigs from haversian canals, and these in turn anastomose with others which enter from periosteum. Nerves accompany arteries into bone

Development of Bone
In the embryo bones are preformed in membrane and in cartilage
Ossification { Intramembranous / Intracartilaginous, or endochondral
Dependent upon { Adequate amounts of calcium and phosphorus in food / Vitamins and hormones

Rickets
A **disturbance** of mineral metabolism
Prophylaxis, or Prevention { Adequate amounts of calcium and phosphorus in food / Vitamin D supplied by fish oils, egg yolk, milk, butter, fresh vegetables, direct sunlight
Types { True rickets / "Ricketslike condition" / Sometimes called osteoporosis

The Structural and Functional Relationships for Correlation and Coordination of External Activities

CHAPTER 5

Skeleton: Bones and Sinuses of Head, Trunk, Extremities

THE BONES are the principal organs of support and the passive instruments of locomotion. They form a framework of hard material to which the skeletal muscles are attached. This framework affords attachment for the soft parts, maintains them in position, shelters them, helps to control and direct varying internal pressures, gives stability to the whole body, and preserves its shape. The bones form joints which may be movable. Here the bones act as levers for movement. Certain blood cells are formed in red bone marrow.

The adult skeleton consists of 206 named bones.

Cranium	8	
Face	14	
Ear { Malleus 2 / Incus 2 / Stapes 2 }	6	
Hyoid	1	206
The spine, or vertebral column (sacrum and coccyx included)	26	
Sternum and ribs	25	
Upper extremities	64	
Lower extremities	62	

This list does not include the sesamoid[1] and wormian[2] bones. Sesamoid bones

---

[1] Ses'amoid (Greek *sesamon*, a "seed of the sesamum," and *eidos*, "form," "resemblance").
[2] Olaus Wormius, Danish anatomist (1588–1654).

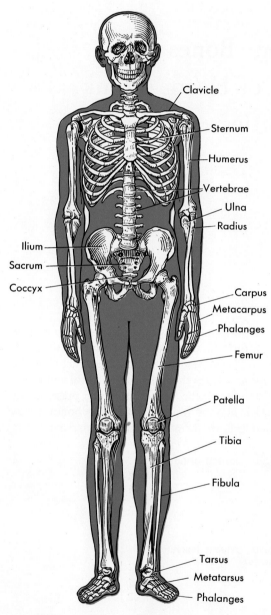

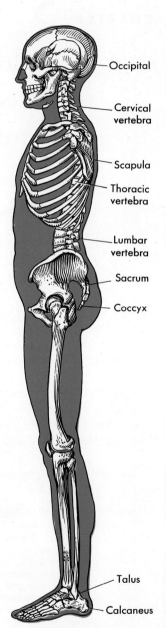

Figure 5–1. The human skeleton, front view.

Figure 5–2. The human skeleton, side view.

are found embedded in the tendons covering the bones of the knee, hand, and foot. Wormian bones are small isolated bones which occur in the course of the cranial sutures, most frequently the lambdoid suture.

Classification. The bones may be classified according to their shape into four groups: (1) *long*, (2) *short*, (3) *flat*, and (4) *irregular*.

A *long bone* consists of a shaft and two extremities. The shaft is formed mainly of compact bone tissue, this compact tissue being thickest in the middle, where the bone is most slender and the strain greatest, and it is hollowed out in the interior to form the *medullary canal*. The extremities are made of cancellous tissue, with only a thin coating of compact tissue, and are more or less expanded for greater convenience of mutual connection and to afford a broad surface for muscular attachment. All long bones are more or less curved, which gives them greater strength. They are found in the arms and legs, e.g., humerus.

The *short bones* are irregularly shaped. Their texture is spongy throughout, except at their surface, where there is a thin layer of compact tissue. The short bones are the 16 bones of the carpus, the 14 bones of the tarsus, and the two patellae.

Where flat bones are found there is need for extensive protection or the provision of broad surfaces for muscular attachment. The bony tissue expands into broad or elongated flat plates which are composed of two thin layers of compact tissue, enclosing between them a variable quantity of cancellous tissue, e.g., occipital bone.

The *irregular bones*, because of their peculiar shape, cannot be grouped under any of the preceding heads. A vertebra is a good example. The bones of the ear are so small that they are described as *ossicles*.

Processes and Depressions. The surface of bones shows projections, or *processes*, and depressions, called *fossae* or *cavities*. Qualifying adjectives or special names may be used to describe them. Both processes and depressions are classified as (1) *articular*—those serving for connection of bones to form joints, and (2) *nonarticular*—those serving for the attachment of ligaments and muscles.

Processes

Process. Any marked bony prominence
Condyle. A rounded or knucklelike process
Tubercle. A small rounded process
Tuberosity. A large rounded process
Trochanter. A very large process
Crest. A narrow ridge of bone
Spine, or *spinous process*. A sharp, slender process
Head. A portion supported on a constricted part, or *neck*

Cavities

Fissure. A narrow slit
Foramen. A hole or orifice through which blood vessels, nerves, and ligaments pass
Meatus, or *canal*. A long, tubelike passageway
Sinus[3] and *antrum*. Applied to cavities within certain bones
Groove, or *sulcus*. A furrow
Fossa. A depression in or upon a bone

[3] The term *sinus* is also used in surgery to denote a narrow tract through tissues, leading from the surface down to a cavity, and sometimes it refers to a large vein.

DIVISIONS OF THE SKELETON

The bones of the body may be divided into two main groups:

The Axial Skeleton	(1) Head or skull {	Cranium	8
		Face	14
	(2) Hyoid		1
	(3) Trunk {	Vertebrae—child 33, adult 26	
		Sternum	1
		Ribs	24
Appendicular Skeleton {	(4) Upper		64
	(5) Lower		62

The head, or **skull,** rests upon the spinal column and is composed of the cranial and facial bones. It is divisible into *cranium*, or *brain case*, and *anterior region*, or *face*.

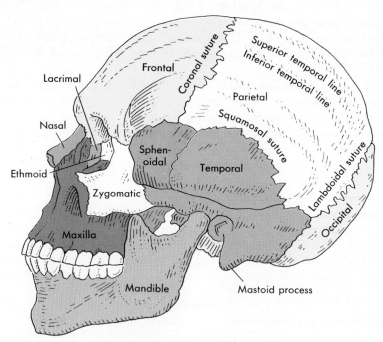

Figure 5–3. Side view of the skull.

Bones of the Cranium

Occipital, base of skull	1	
Parietal, crown	2	
Frontal, forehead	1	
Temporal, ear region	2	8
Ethmoid, between cranial and nasal cavities	1	
Sphenoid, base of brain and back of orbit	1	

The occipital bone is situated at the back and base of the skull. The internal surface is deeply concave and presents many eminences and depressions for parts of the brain. The *foramen magnum* is a large opening in the inferior portion of the bone for the transmission of the medulla oblongata where it narrows to join the spinal cord. At the sides of the foramen magnum on the external surface it has two processes called condyles, which articulate with the atlas.

The external surface is convex and presents midway between the summit of the bone and the foramen magnum a projection—the external occipital protuberance—which can be felt through the scalp. From this a median ridge—the external occipital crest—leads to the foramen magnum. The protuberance and

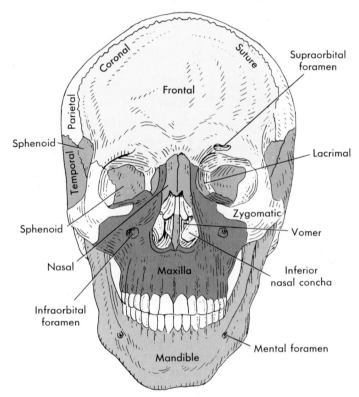

Figure 5–4. Front view of the skull.

crest give attachment to the ligamentum nuchae (Fig. 5–24, p. 111). Two curved lines extend laterally from the protuberance. To these lines and the expanded plate behind the foramen magnum—the squama—several muscles are attached.

The parietal bones, right and left, form by their union the greater part of the sides and roof of the skull. The external surface is convex and smooth; the internal surface is concave and presents eminences and depressions for lodging the convolutions of the brain, and numerous furrows for the ramifications of arteries supplying blood to the dura mater, which covers the brain.

The frontal bone forms the forehead and part of the roof of the orbits and of the nasal cavity. The arch, formed by part of the frontal bone over the eye, is sharp and prominent and is known as the supraorbital margin. Just above the supraorbital margins are hollow spaces, the *frontal sinuses*, that are filled with air and open into the nose. In the upper and outer angle of each orbit are two depressions called lacrimal fossae, in which lie the lacrimal glands, which secrete tears. At birth the bone consists of two pieces, which later become united along the middle line by a suture that runs from the vertex of the bone to the root of the nose. This suture usually becomes obliterated within a few years after birth.

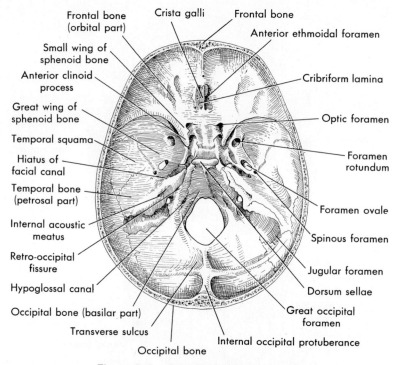

Frontal bone (orbital part)
Crista galli
Frontal bone
Anterior ethmoidal foramen
Small wing of sphenoid bone
Anterior clinoid process
Cribriform lamina
Great wing of sphenoid bone
Optic foramen
Temporal squama
Hiatus of facial canal
Foramen rotundum
Temporal bone (petrosal part)
Internal acoustic meatus
Foramen ovale
Retro-occipital fissure
Spinous foramen
Hypoglossal canal
Jugular foramen
Occipital bone (basilar part)
Dorsum sellae
Transverse sulcus
Great occipital foramen
Occipital bone
Internal occipital protuberance

Figure 5–5.   Base of the skull, interior view.

The temporal bones,[4] right and left, are situated at the sides and base of the skull. They are divided into five parts, the squama, the petrous, mastoid, and tympanic parts, and the styloid process.

The *squama*, a thin, expanded portion, forms the anterior and upper part of the bone. A curved line, the temporal line or supramastoid crest, runs backward and upward across its posterior part. Projecting from the lower part of the squama is the long, arched, zygomatic process, which articulates with the temporal process of the zygomatic bone.

The *petrous* portion is shaped like a pyramid and is wedged in at the base of

[4] Named temporal from the Latin *tempus*, "time," as it is on the temples that the hair first becomes gray and thin.

the skull between the sphenoid and occipital bones. The internal ear, the essential part of the organ of hearing, is contained in a series of cavities in the petrous portion. Between the squamous and the petrous portions is a socket, called the mandibular fossa, for the reception of the condyle of the mandible.

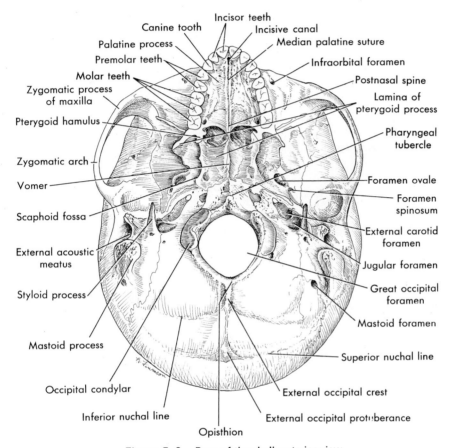

Figure 5–6. Base of the skull, exterior view.

The *mastoid* portion projects downward behind the opening of the meatus. It is filled with a number of connected spaces, called mastoid cells or sinuses, which contain air and communicate with the cavity of the middle ear. Inflammation of the lining of these sinuses is known as mastoiditis. The bony partition between the mastoid cells[5] and the brain is thin. A danger in mastoiditis is that the infection may penetrate the bone, reach the meninges or coverings of the brain and cause meningitis. The purpose in operating is to bring about external drainage to prevent the infection reaching the meninges.

[5] *Cells.* Histologically, the word *cell* refers to one of the component units of the body, such as an epithelial cell. Occasionally it refers to such minute chambers as mastoid cells.

The *tympanic* portion is a curved plate of bone below the squama and in front of the mastoid process. It forms a part of the acoustic meatus leading to the internal ear.

The *styloid* is a slender, pointed process that projects downward from the undersurface of the temporal bone. To its distal part are attached ligaments and some of the muscles of the tongue.

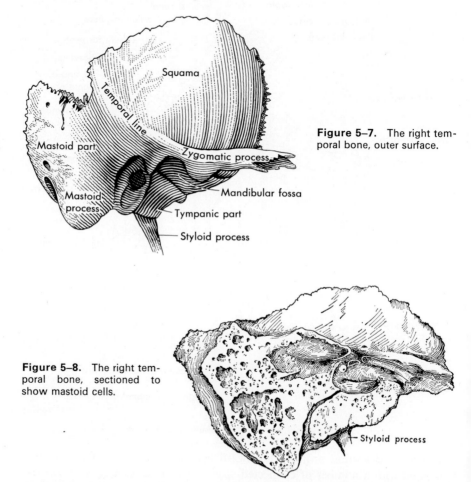

Figure 5–7. The right temporal bone, outer surface.

Figure 5–8. The right temporal bone, sectioned to show mastoid cells.

The ethmoid bone is a light, cancellous bone consisting of a horizontal or cribriform plate, a perpendicular plate, and two lateral masses, or labyrinths. The horizontal plate forms the roof of the nasal cavity and closes the anterior part of the base of the cranium. It is pierced by numerous foramina, through which the olfactory nerve fibers pass from the mucous membrane of the nose to the olfactory bulb. Projecting upward from the horizontal plate is a smooth, triangular process called the *crista galli* (cock's comb), which serves for the attachment of the *falx cerebri* (Fig. 14–18, p. 425). Descending from the horizontal plate is the perpendicular plate, which helps to form the upper part of the nasal septum. On either side, the lateral masses form part of the orbit and part

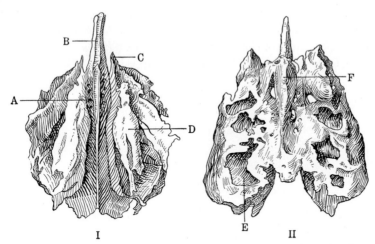

Figure 5–9. The ethmoid bone. (*I*) Undersurface, (*II*) upper surface showing ethmoid cells. (*A*) Horizontal plate showing foramina, (*B*) perpendicular plate, (*C*) ala, (*D*) labyrinth or lateral mass, (*E*) ethmoid cell, (*F*) crista galli.

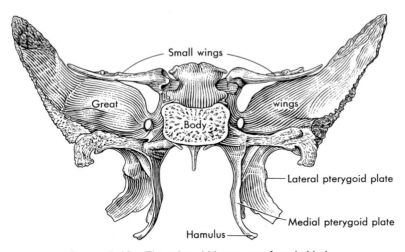

Figure 5–10.   The sphenoid bone, seen from behind.

of the corresponding nasal cavity. The lateral masses contain a number of thin-walled cavities, the ethmoidal cells or sinuses, which communicate with the nasal cavity. Descending from the horizontal plate on either side of the septum are two processes of thin, cancellous, bony tissue, the superior and middle conchae.

  The sphenoid is an important bone, situated at the anterior part of the base of the skull. It binds the other cranial bones together. In form it resembles an airplane with extended wings and consists of a body, two great and two small wings extending transversely from the sides of the body, and two pterygoid processes which project downward. The body is joined to the ethmoid in front and the occipital behind. It contains cavities called sphenoidal sinuses, which communicate with the nasopharynx. The upper portion of the body presents a fossa with anterior and posterior eminences. This is called the *sella turcica*, from its resemblance to a Turk's saddle. The *hypophysis cerebri* is lodged in the sella turcica.

Bones of the Face

Nasal	2
Vomer	1
Inferior nasal concha (inferior turbinates)	2
Lacrimal	2
Zygomatic (malar)	2
Palatine (palate)	2
Maxilla (upper jaw)	2
Mandible (lower jaw)	1

14

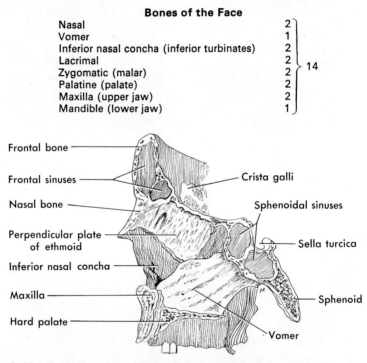

Figure 5–11. Sagittal section of face a little to the left of the middle line, showing the vomer and its relations. Note also frontal and sphenoidal sinuses.

The nasal bones are two small oblong bones placed side by side at the middle and upper part of the face, forming by their junction the upper part of the bridge of the nose, the lower part being formed by the nasal cartilages.

The vomer is a single bone placed at the lower and back part of the nasal cavity, forming part of the central septum of the nasal cavity. It is thin and varies in different individuals, being frequently bent to one or the other side, thus making the nasal chambers of unequal size.

The inferior nasal conchae are situated in the nostril on the outer wall of each side. Each consists of a layer of thin, cancellous bone curled upon itself like a scroll. They are below the superior and middle conchae of the *ethmoid bone*.

Structural deviations and abnormal conditions of these bones and the membranes covering them are involved in some of the more common nasal abnormalities.

The lacrimal bones are situated at the front part of the inner wall of the orbit and somewhat resemble a fingernail in form, thinness, and size. They are named lacrimal because they contain part of the canal through which the tear duct runs.

The zygomatic, or **malar, bones** form the prominence of the cheeks and part of the outer wall and floor of the orbits. A long, narrow, and serrated process of each malar bone, called the temporal process, projects backward and articulates with the zygomatic process of the temporal bone, thus forming the zygomatic arch of each side.

Figure 5–12. The lacrimal bone.

Palatine Bones. Each one is shaped somewhat like an L and consists of a horizontal part, a vertical part, and three processes, the pyramidal, orbital, and sphenoidal processes. They are situated at the back part of the nasal cavity between the maxillae and the pterygoid processes of the sphenoid and help to form (1) the back part of the roof of the mouth, (2) part of the floor and outer wall of the nasal cavities, and (3) a very small portion of the floor of the orbit.

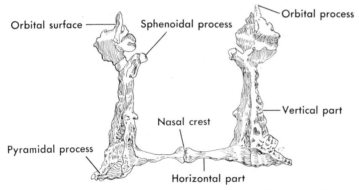

Figure 5–13. The two palatine bones in their natural position, viewed from behind.

The maxillae, or **upper jawbones,** are two in number, right and left, and form by their union the whole of the upper jaw. Each bone assists in forming (1) part of the floor of the orbit, (2) the floor and lateral wall of the nasal cavities, and (3) the greater part of the roof of the mouth.

Each consists of a body and four processes. The body of the bone contains a large cavity known as the *antrum of Highmore,* or *maxillary sinus,* which opens into the nose. The alveolar process is excavated into cavities varying in depth and size according to the teeth they contain. The palatine process projects medialward from the nasal surface of the bone and forms part of the floor of the nose and the roof of the mouth. Before birth these bones usually unite to form one bone. When they fail to do so, the condition known as cleft palate results.[6]

The mandible, or **lower jawbone,** is the largest and strongest bone of the face and consists of a curved horizontal portion, the body, and two perpendicular portions, the rami. The superior or alveolar border of the body is hollowed out into cavities for the reception of the teeth. Each ramus has a condyle which articulates with the mandibular fossa of the temporal bone and a coronoid process which gives attachment to the temporal muscle and some of the fibers of the

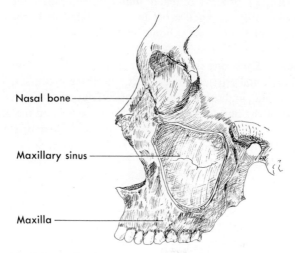

Nasal bone

Maxillary sinus

Maxilla

Figure 5–14. The left maxilla. Outer surface cut away in part to show maxillary sinus, or antrum.

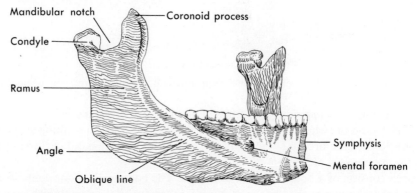

Mandibular notch

Coronoid process

Condyle

Ramus

Angle

Symphysis

Mental foramen

Oblique line

Figure 5–15. The mandible, viewed from the right and a little in front.

[6] In its simplest form cleft palate is a divided uvula. In a more severe form the cleft extends through the soft palate, the posterior part of the hard palate may be involved, or the cleft may extend through the maxilla between the teeth. It may affect one or both sides and may be complicated with a cleft in the lip (harelip or cleft lip).

buccinator. The deep depression between these two processes is called the mandibular notch. The mental foramen, which is just below the first molar tooth, serves as a passageway for the inferior dental nerve, which is a terminal branch of the mandibular nerve, which in turn is a branch of the fifth, or trigeminal, nerve. Branches of the inferior dental nerve supply the molar and premolar teeth of the lower jaw.

At birth the mandible consists of two parts, which join at the symphysis in front and form one bone, usually during the first year. It undergoes several changes in shape during life, due mainly to the first and the second dentition and to the loss of teeth in the aged with the subsequent absorption of that part of the bone which contained them.

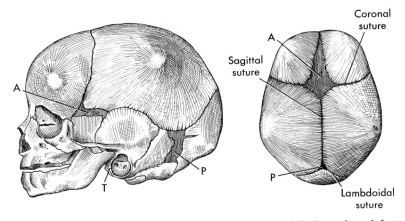

Figure 5–16. (*Left*) Skull of newborn infant, side view. (*A*) Anterolateral fontanel, (*P*) posterolateral fontanel, (*T*) tympanic ring. (Modified from Toldt.) (*Right*) Same, seen from above. (*A*) Anterior fontanel, (*P*) posterior fontanel. (Modified from Toldt.)

The Skull as a Whole. The cranium is a firm case, or covering, for the brain. Four of the eight bones (occipital, two parietal, and frontal) which form this bony covering are flat bones and consist of two layers of compact tissue, the outer one thick and tough, the inner one thinner and more brittle. The base of the skull is much thicker and stronger than the walls and roof; it presents a number of openings, or foramina, for the passage of the cranial nerves, blood vessels, and other structures.

The bones of the cranium, most of which are thin and flat, begin to develop in early fetal life. Ossification of these bones is gradual and takes place from ossification centers, generally near the center of the future completed bones. Ossification is not complete at birth; hence, membrane-filled spaces are found between the bones. These spaces are called fontanels.

The Fontanels. At birth there may be many of these fontanels. The shape and location of six of them are quite constant.

The *anterior*, or *bregmatic*, is the largest and is a lozenge-shaped space between the angles of the two parietal bones and the two segments of the frontal bone. Normally this fontanel closes at about 18 months of age.

In abnormal conditions the fontanel may close much earlier or much later. In cases of retarded brain growth, called microcephalus, it closes early. In hydrocephalus the increased internal pressure may cause it to remain open. In rickets and cretinism which are not yielding to treatment it may not close until much later.

The *posterior,* or *occipital, fontanel* is much smaller in size and is a triangular space between the occipital and two parietal bones. Usually this closes by an extension of the ossifying process a few months after birth.

There are two *anterolateral,* or *sphenoidal, fontanels* at the junction of the frontal, parietal, temporal, and sphenoid bones. They are quite small and usually close by the third month after birth.

There are two *posterolateral,* or *mastoid, fontanels* at the junction of the parietal, occipital, and temporal bones. They decrease in size but usually do not close entirely until the second year.

The membranous tissue between the cranial bones at the sutures and fontanels allows more or less overlapping during birth processes, thus reducing the diameters of the skull. This is called *molding* and accounts for the elongated shape of the head of a newborn infant, particularly if the labor has been long.

The Sinuses of the Head.   Four air sinuses communicate with each nasal cavity: the frontal and the ethmoidal open into the nasal cavity; the sphenoidal

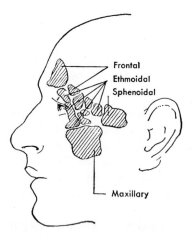

Frontal
Ethmoidal
Sphenoidal

Maxillary

Figure 5–17.   Sinuses projected to the surface of the face. All except the maxillary sinus are near the central line of the skull when viewed from the front.

See also Figure 5–8 for mastoid cells, Figure 5–9 for ethmoid cells, Figure 5–11 for sphenoidal and frontal sinuses, Figure 5–14 for maxillary sinuses.

opens into the nasopharynx; and the maxillary, or antrum of Highmore, opens on the lateral wall of each nasal passage. The mucous membrane which lines the nose also lines these sinuses, and inflammation of this membrane may extend into any of them, causing *sinusitis.* The mastoid cells are comparable to the sinuses and are lined by an extension of the same mucous membrane that lines the sinuses.

At birth the skull is proportionately larger than other parts of the skeleton, and the facial portion is small. The small size of the maxillae and mandible, the noneruption of the teeth, and the small size of the sinuses and nasal cavities account for the smallness of the face. With the eruption of the first teeth there is an enlargement of the face and jaws. This enlargement is much more pronounced

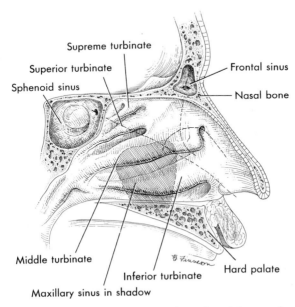

Supreme turbinate

Superior turbinate

Sphenoid sinus

Frontal sinus

Nasal bone

Middle turbinate

Inferior turbinate

Hard palate

Maxillary sinus in shadow

Figure 5–18.   Diagram of sinuses and openings into nasopharynx.

after the eruption of the second set of teeth. Usually the skull becomes thinner and lighter in old age, but occasionally the inner table hypertrophies, causing an increase in weight and thickness (pachycephalia). The most noticeable feature of the skull in the aged is the decrease in the size of the maxillae and mandible, resulting from the loss of the teeth and the absorption of the alveolar processes.

The hyoid bone is shaped like a horseshoe and consists of a central part called

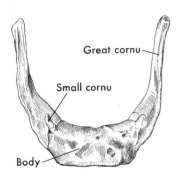

Great cornu

Small cornu

Body

Figure 5–19. The hyoid bone, seen from above. (Modified from Toldt.)

the body and two projections on each side called the greater and lesser cornua. It is suspended from the styloid processes of the temporal bones and may be felt in the neck just above the laryngeal prominence (Adam's apple). It supports the tongue and gives attachment to some of its numerous muscles.

The Trunk

The bones which enter into the formation of the *trunk* consist of the *vertebrae*, *sternum*, and *ribs*.

The vertebral column is formed of a series of bones called vertebrae and in a man of average height is about 71 cm long (28 in.). In youth the vertebrae are 33 in number:

Cervical, in the neck	7	⎫
Thoracic, or dorsal, in the thorax	12	⎬ Movable, or true, vertebrae
Lumbar, in the loins	5	⎭
Sacral, in the pelvis	5	⎱
Coccygeal, in the pelvis	4	⎰ Fixed, or false, vertebrae

In the three upper portions of the spine the vertebrae are separate and movable throughout life. Those found in the sacral and coccygeal regions are firmly united in the adult, so that they form two bones, five entering into the sacrum and four into the terminal bone, or coccyx; because of their union the number of vertebrae in the adult is 26.

The vertebrae differ in size and shape, but in general their structure is similar. Seen from above, as in Figure 5–23, page 111, they consist of a body from which two short, thick processes, called the pedicles, project backward, one on each side to join with the laminae which unite posteriorly and form the vertebral, or neural, arch. This arch encloses the spinal foramen. Each vertebra has several processes: four articular, two to connect with bone above, two to connect with bone below; two transverse, one at each side where the pedicle and lamina join; and one spinous process, projecting backward from the junction of the laminae.

Cervical Vertebrae. The bodies of the cervical vertebrae are smaller than the thoracic, but the arches are larger. The spinous processes are short and are often cleft in two, or bifid. Each transverse process is pierced by a foramen (foramen transversarium) through which nerves, a vertebral artery, and a vein pass.

The first and second cervical vertebrae differ considerably from the rest. The first, or *atlas*, so named from supporting the head, is a bony ring consisting of an anterior and posterior arch and two bulky lateral masses. Each has a superior and inferior articular surface. Each superior surface forms a cup for the corresponding condyle of the occipital bone and thus makes possible the backward and forward movements of the head. The bony ring is divided into an anterior and posterior section by a transverse ligament. The posterior section of this bony ring contains the spinal cord, and the anterior, or front, section of the ring contains the bony projection which arises from the upper surface of the body of the second cervical vertebra, the *epistropheus*, or *axis*. This bony projection, the *odontoid* process, forms a pivot; and around this pivot the atlas rotates when the head is turned from side to side. The atlas carries the skull, to which it is firmly articulated.

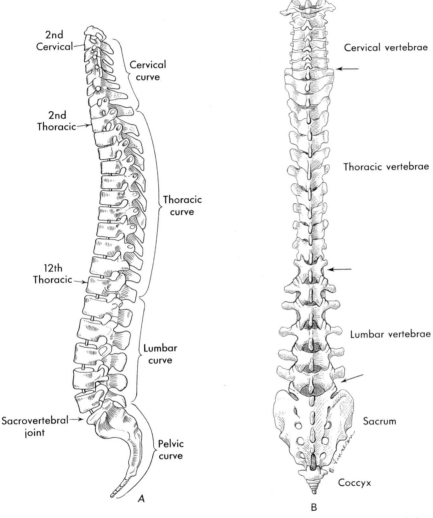

2nd Cervical

Cervical curve

2nd Thoracic

Thoracic curve

12th Thoracic

Lumbar curve

Sacrovertebral joint

Pelvic curve

A

Cervical vertebrae

Thoracic vertebrae

Lumbar vertebrae

Sacrum

Coccyx

B

Figure 5–20. The vertebral column. (*A*) Left lateral view showing curves, (*B*) dorsal view.

Thoracic, or Dorsal, Vertebrae. The bodies of the thoracic vertebrae are larger and stronger than those of the cervical and have a facet or demifacet for articulation with the heads of the ribs. The transverse processes are longer and heavier than those of the cervical, and all except those of the eleventh and twelfth vertebrae have facets for articulation with the tubercles of the ribs. The spinous processes are long and are directed downward.

Lumbar Vertebrae. The bodies of the lumbar vertebrae are the largest and heaviest in the whole spine. The processes are short, heavy, and thick.

The sacrum is formed by the union of the five sacral vertebrae. It is a large wedge-shaped bone firmly connected with the hipbones. The pelvic side is concave and relatively smooth and convex and irregular dorsally. It is marked by four transverse ridges. At the ends of the ridges there are four pairs of pelvic

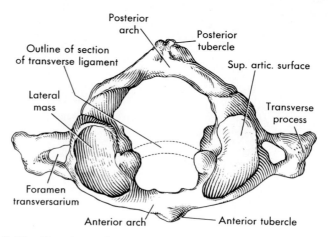

Figure 5–21. The atlas, or first cervical vertebra. (Modified from Gray's *Anatomy*.)

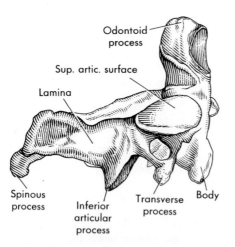

Figure 5–22. The epistropheus, or axis, seen from the right side. (Modified from Gray's *Anatomy*.)

sacral foramina which communicate with the four pairs of dorsal foramina through which nerves and blood vessels pass. The sacral canal contains the lower part of the cauda equina of the spinal cord, spinal membrane, and fat. **The coccyx** is usually formed of four small segments of bone and is the most rudimentary part of the vertebral column.

The *intervertebral disks* are disks of fibrocartilage interposed between the

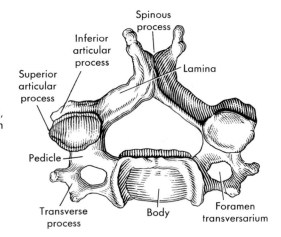

Figure 5–23. A cervical vertebra, viewed from above. (Modified from Gray's *Anatomy*.)

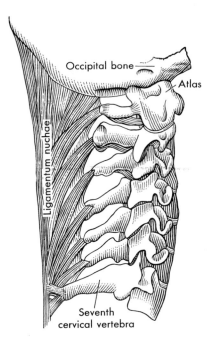

Figure 5–24. The ligamentum nuchae, seen from the right side. (Modified from Henle.)

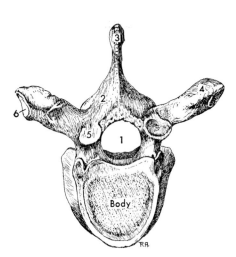

Figure 5–25. Sixth thoracic vertebra, seen from above. (1) Spinal foramen, (2) lamina, (3) spinous process, (4) transverse process, (5) superior articular process, (6) facet for tubercle of rib. (Modified from Toldt.)

bodies of adjacent vertebrae from the axis to sacrum. They vary in size and thickness in different regions, being thickest in the lumbar region. They are attached below and above by a thin layer of hyaline cartilage which covers the surfaces of the bodies of the vertebrae. The *nucleus pulposus* is a soft, pulpy elastic and compressible substance centrally located within each disk. Embryologically the remnants of the notochord become incorporated into the intervertebral disk and persist as the nucleus pulposus. The disk as a whole permits flexibility of the vertebral column and the nucleus pulposus functions as an important shock absorber.

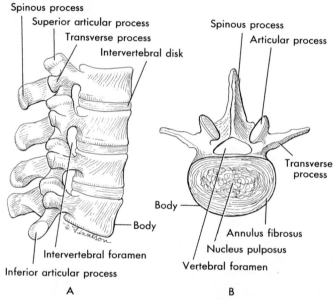

Figure 5–26. (*A*) Diagram of several vertebrae with intervertebral disks between the vertebrae. (*B*) Viewed from above. Note nucleus pulposus.

Structure of Vertebral Column. The bodies of the vertebrae, which are piled one upon another, form a strong, flexible column for the support of the cranium and trunk and provide articular surfaces for the attachment of the ribs. The arches form a hollow cylinder for the protection of the spinal cord. Viewed from the side, the vertebral column presents four curves, which are alternately convex and concave. The two concave ones, named thoracic and pelvic, are called primary curves because they exist in fetal life and are designed for the accommodation of viscera. The two convex ones, named cervical and lumbar, are called secondary, or compensatory, curves because they are developed after birth. The cervical curve begins its development when the child is able to hold up his head (at about three or four months) and is well formed when he sits upright (at about 19 months). The lumbar develops when the child begins to walk (from 12 to 18 months).

The joints between the bodies of the vertebrae are slightly movable, and those between the arches are freely movable. The *bodies* are connected (1) by disks of fibrocartilage placed between the vertebrae; (2) by the *anterior longitudinal ligament*, which extends along the anterior surfaces of the bodies of the vertebrae from the axis to the sacrum; and (3) by the *posterior longitudinal ligament*, which

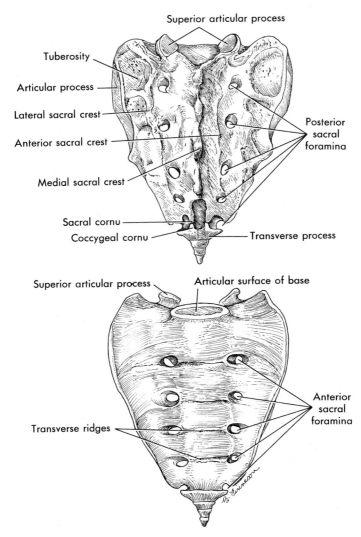

Figure 5–27. The sacral bone. (*A*) Posterior view. (*B*) Anterior view. (Modified from Pansky and House.)

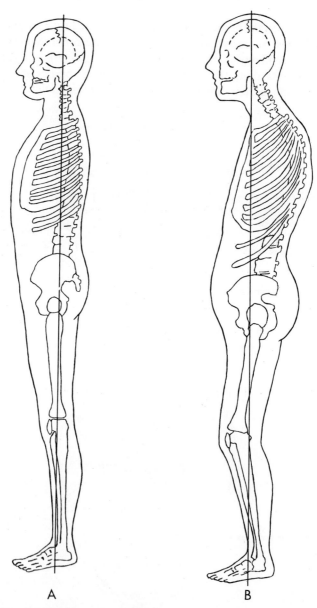

A   B

Figure 5–28. (*A*) Skeletal form of a person with good body mechanics, (*B*) skeletal form of a person with poor body mechanics. (Courtesy of the Children's Bureau, U.S. Department of Health, Education, and Welfare.)

is inside the vertebral canal and extends along the posterior surfaces of the bodies from the axis to the sacrum.

The *laminae* are connected by broad, thin ligaments called the *ligamenta flava* (*ligamenta subflava*).

The *spinous processes* are connected at the apexes by the supraspinal ligament, which extends from the seventh cervical vertebra to the sacrum. It is continued upward as the *ligamentum nuchae*, which extends from the protuberance of the occiput to the spinous process of the seventh cervical vertebra. In some of the lower animals the ligamentum nuchae serves to sustain the weight of the head, but in man it is rudimentary.

Adjacent spinous processes are connected by interspinal ligaments which extend from the root to the apex of each process and meet the ligamenta flava in front and the supraspinal ligament behind. The *transverse processes* are connected by the intertransverse ligaments, which are placed between them.

The spinal curves confer a considerable amount of springiness and strength upon the spinal column, and the elasticity is further increased by the ligamenta flava and the disks of fibrocartilage. These pads also mitigate the effects of concussion arising from falls or blows. The vertebral column is freely movable, being capable of bending forward freely, backward and from side to side less freely. Certain exercises increase the flexibility of the spine to a marked degree. In the cervical and thoracic regions a limited amount of rotation is possible.

Posture. The weight of the body should rest evenly on the two hip joints. A perpendicular dropped from the ear should fall through shoulder, hip, and ankle (Fig. 5–28). In this position the chest is up, the head is erect, the lower abdominal muscles are retracted, and the body is well balanced and functioning efficiently.

As a result of postural habits, injury, or disease, the normal curves may become exaggerated and are then spoken of as *curvatures*. If the thoracic curve is exaggerated, it is called *kyphosis* or humpback; if the exaggeration is in the lumbar region, it is called *lordosis* or hollow back. If the curvature is lateral, i.e., toward one side, it is called *scoliosis*. Lateral curvature is usually to the right side, because even in normal people there is often a slight curve toward the right in the thoracic region.

It occasionally happens that the laminae of a vertebra do not unite and a cleft is left in the arch (*spina bifida*). As a result the membranes and the spinal cord itself may protrude, forming a "tumor" on the child's back. This most often occurs in the lumbosacral region, though it may occur in the thoracic or cervical region.

The Thorax

The thorax is a bony cage formed by the sternum and costal cartilages, the ribs, and the bodies of the thoracic vertebrae. It is cone-shaped, being narrow above and broad below, flattened from before backward and shorter in front than in back. In infancy the chest is rounded and the width from shoulder to shoulder and the depth from the sternum to the vertebrae are about equal. With growth the width increases more than the depth. The thorax supports the bones of the shoulder girdle and upper extremities and contains the principal organs of respiration and circulation.

The sternum, or **breastbone,** is a flat, narrow bone about 6 in. long, situated in the median line in the front of the chest. It develops as three separate parts. The upper part is named the *manubrium;* the middle and largest part, the *body,* or *gladiolus;* the lowest portion, the *ensiform,* or *xiphoid, process.* On both sides of the manubrium and body are notches for the reception of the sternal ends of the

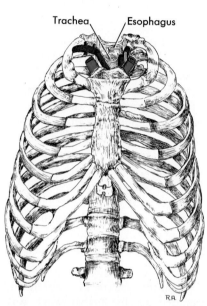

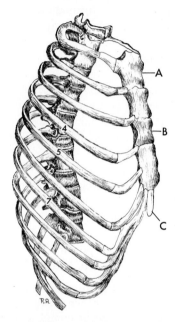

Figure 5–29. Bones of thorax, seen from the front. Lying in the superior aperture of the "thoracic basket," note: esophagus (close to vertebral column), trachea, vagus nerves (*yellow*), arteries (*red*), veins (*blue*). (Modified from Toldt.)

Figure 5–30. Bones of thorax, seen from right side. Between the fourth and fifth ribs note articulation of the head and tubercle of the seventh rib. (*A*) Manubrium, (*B*) body showing articular notches of ribs and lines of union of parts of body, (*C*) xiphoid process.

upper seven costal cartilages. The xiphoid process has no ribs attached to it but affords attachment for some of the abdominal muscles.

At birth the sternum consists of several unossified portions, the body alone developing from four centers. Union of the centers in the body begins at about puberty and proceeds from below upward until at about 25 years of age they are all united. Sometimes by 30 years of age, more often after 40, the xiphoid process becomes joined to the body. In advanced life, the manubrium may become joined to the body by bony tissue. Posture, activity (play, work), and diet have much to do with shaping the sternum and the thoracic cavity.

The ribs (costae), 24 in number, are situated 12 on each side of the thoracic cavity. They are elastic arches of bone consisting of a body, or shaft, and two extremities, the posterior, or vertebral, and the anterior, or sternal. Each rib is connected with the thoracic vertebra by the head and tubercle of the posterior extremity. The head fits into a facet formed on the body of one vertebra or formed by the adjacent bodies of two vertebrae;[7] the tubercle articulates with the transverse processes. Strong ligaments surround and bind these articulations but permit slight gliding movements.[8]

The anterior extremities of each of the first seven pairs are connected with the sternum in front by bars of hyaline cartilage called costal cartilages. They are called *vertebrosternal* or *true ribs*. The remaining five pairs are termed *false ribs*.

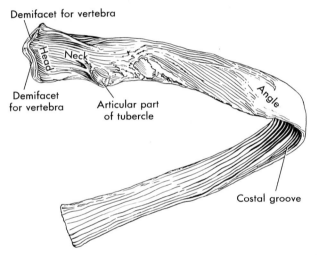

Figure 5–31. A central rib of the right side, viewed from behind. (Modified from Gray's *Anatomy*.)

Of these, the upper three, eighth, ninth, and tenth, are attached in front to the costal cartilages of the next rib above. These are the *vertebrochondral ribs*. The two lowest are unattached in front and are termed *floating* or *vertebral ribs*.

The convexity of the ribs is turned outward, giving roundness to the sides of the chest and increasing the size of its cavity; each rib slopes downward from its posterior attachment, so that its sternal end is considerably lower than its vertebral. The lower border of each rib is grooved for the accommodation of the intercostal nerves and blood vessels. The spaces left between the ribs are called the *intercostal spaces*. The red marrow of the sternum and ribs is one of the principal sites of red blood cell formation.

[7] The heads of the first, tenth, eleventh, and twelfth ribs each articulate with a single vertebra. The heads of the remaining ribs articulate with facets formed by the bodies of two adjacent vertebrae.
[8] In the eleventh and twelfth ribs the articulation between the tubercle and the adjacent transverse process is missing.

The Extremities

The appendicular skeleton consists of the appendages of the skeleton, namely, the upper and lower extremities.

Bones of the Upper Extremities

Shoulder Girdle	Clavicle, or collarbone	2
	Scapula, shoulder blade	2
Upper Limb	Humerus, arm bone	2
	Ulna, elbow bone	2
	Radius, small bone of forearm	2
	Carpus, wrist (ossa carpi)	16
	Metacarpus, body of hand	10
	Phalanges, 2 in thumb, 3 in each finger	28

64

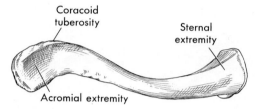

Figure 5–32.   The right clavicle, seen from above.

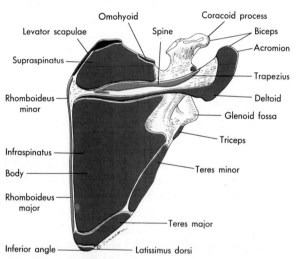

Figure 5–33.   The right scapula, dorsal surface. (*Red*) Origin of muscles, (*blue*) insertion of muscles.

The two clavicles and the two scapulae form the *shoulder girdle*, which is incomplete in front and behind. The clavicles articulate with the sternum in front but behind the scapulae are connected to the trunk by muscles only. The shoulder girdle serves to attach the bones of the upper extremities to the axial skeleton.

The clavicle, or **collarbone,** is a long bone with a double curvature, which is placed horizontally at the upper and anterior part of the thorax, just above the first rib. It articulates with the sternum by its inner end, which is called the sternal extremity. Its outer, or acromial, end articulates with the scapula. In the female, the clavicle is generally less curved, smoother, shorter, and more slender than in the male. In those persons who perform considerable manual labor, which brings the muscles connected with this bone into constant action, it acquires considerable bulk.

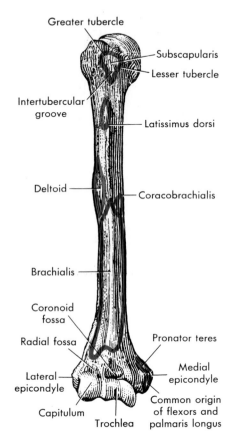

Figure 5–34. The right humerus, or arm bone, ventral view. (*Red*) muscle origins, (*blue*) insertions.

Greater tubercle

Subscapularis

Lesser tubercle

Intertubercular groove

Latissimus dorsi

Deltoid

Coracobrachialis

Brachialis

Coronoid fossa

Radial fossa

Pronator teres

Lateral epicondyle

Medial epicondyle

Capitulum

Common origin of flexors and palmaris longus

Trochlea

The **scapula,** or **shoulder blade,** is a large flat, triangular bone situated on the dorsal aspect of the thorax between the second and seventh ribs. It is unevenly divided on its dorsal surface by a prominent ridge, the spine of the scapula, which terminates in a large triangular projection called the *acromium process*, which articulates with the clavicle. Below the acromion process, at the head of the shoulder blade, is a shallow socket, the *glenoid cavity*, which receives the head of the humerus.

The humerus, or arm[9] bone, is the longest and largest bone of the upper extremity. Its upper end consists of a rounded head joined to the shaft by a constricted neck and of two eminences, called the *greater* and *lesser tubercles,* between which is the intertubercular (bicipital) groove. The constricted neck

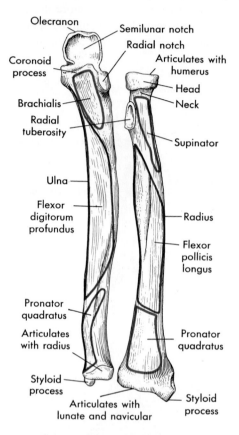

Olecranon
Semilunar notch
Radial notch
Coronoid process
Articulates with humerus
Brachialis
Head
Radial tuberosity
Neck
Supinator
Ulna
Flexor digitorum profundus
Radius
Flexor pollicis longus
Pronator quadratus
Articulates with radius
Pronator quadratus
Styloid process
Articulates with lunate and navicular
Styloid process

Figure 5–35. Anterior view of the bones of the left forearm. (*Red*) Muscle origins, (*blue*) insertions.

above the tubercles is called the *anatomical neck,* and that below the tubercles the *surgical neck,* because it is so often fractured. The head articulates with the glenoid cavity of the scapula. The lower end of the bone is flattened from before backward and ends below in an articular surface which is divided by a ridge into a lateral eminence called the *capitulum* and a medial portion called the *trochlea.* The capitulum is rounded and articulates with the depression on the head of the radius. The trochlea articulates with the ulna. Above these surfaces on the lateral and medial aspects are projections called *epicondyles.*

The ulna, or elbow bone, is the largest bone of the forearm and is placed at the

[9] Anatomically, the word *arm* is reserved for that part of the upper limb which is above the elbow; between the elbow and wrist is the forearm; below the wrist are the hand and fingers.

medial side of the radius. Its upper extremity shows two processes and two con-
cavities; the larger process forms the prominence of the elbow, called the *olecranon process*. The smaller process is called the *coronoid process*. The trochlea
of the humerus fits into the semilunar notch (greater sigmoid cavity) between
these two processes. The radial notch (lesser sigmoid cavity) is on the lateral side
of the coronoid and articulates with the radius. The lower end of the ulna is
small and ends in two eminences; the larger head articulates with the fibrocartilage disk which separates it from the wrist; the smaller is the styloid process,
to which a ligament from the wrist joint is attached.

The radius is placed on the lateral side of the ulna and is shorter and smaller
than the ulna. The upper extremity presents a head, a neck, and a tuberosity.

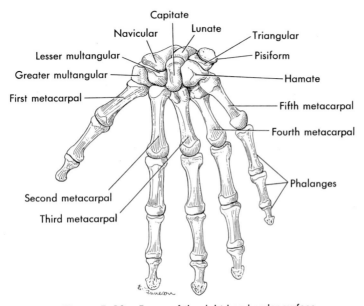

Figure 5-36. Bones of the right hand, volar surface.

The head is small and rounded and has a shallow, cuplike depression on its
upper surface for articulation with the capitulum of the humerus. A prominent
ridge surrounds the head, and by means of this it rotates within the radial notch
of the ulna. The head is supported on a constricted neck. Beneath the neck on
the medial side is an eminence called the *radial tuberosity*, into which the tendon
of the biceps brachii muscle is inserted. The lower end has two articular surfaces,
one below, by which it articulates with the navicular and lunate bones of the
wrist, and the other at the medial side, called the *ulnar notch*, by which it articulates with the ulna. Fracture of the lower third of the radius is called *Colles'
fracture*.[10]

The carpus, or **wrist**, is composed of eight small bones (ossa carpi), united by

[10] Abraham Colles, Irish surgeon (1773–1843).

ligaments; they are arranged in two rows and are closely joined together, yet by the arrangement of their ligaments allow a certain amount of motion. They afford origin by their palmar surface to most of the short muscles of the thumb and little finger and are named as follows:

Proximate, or Upper Row		Distal, or Lower Row	
(1) Navicular (scaphoid)	1	(5) Greater multangular (trapezium)	1
(2) Lunate (semilunar)	1	(6) Lesser multangular (trapezoid)	1
(3) Triangular (cuneiform)	1	(7) Capitate (os magnum)	1
(4) Pisiform	1	(8) Hamate (unciform)	1

8

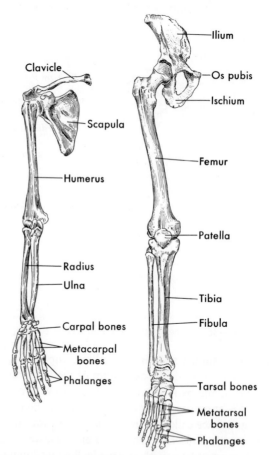

Figure 5–37. Comparison of bones of the upper and lower extremities. (Modified from Toldt.)

Metacarpus, or Body of Hand. Each metacarpus is formed by five bones (ossa metacarpalia), numbered from the lateral side. The bones are curved longitudinally, convex behind, concave in front. They articulate at their bases with the second row of carpal bones and with each other. The heads of the bones articulate with the bases of the first row of the phalanges.

The phalanges are the bones of the fingers, 14 in number in each hand, three for each finger and two for the thumb. The first row articulates with the metacarpal bones and the second row of phalanges; the second row articulates with the first and third; the third articulates with the second row.

Bones of the Lower Extremities

Hipbones, ossa coxae or ossa innominata	2	
Femur, thighbone	2	
Patella, kneecap	2	
Tibia, shinbone, 2 } leg	4	62
Fibula, small bone of calf, 2 }		
Tarsus, ossa tarsi	14	
Metatarsus, sole and lower instep	10	
Phalanges, 2 in great toe, 3 in others	28	

The two hipbones, which articulate with each other in front, form an arch called the *pelvic girdle.* This arch is completed behind by the sacrum and the coccyx, forming a rigid and complete ring of bone called the *pelvis.* The pelvis attaches the lower extremities to the axial skeleton.

The bones of the lower extremities correspond in general to those of the upper extremities and bear a rough resemblance to them, but their function is different. The lower extremities support the body in the erect position and are therefore more solidly built, and their parts are less movable than those of the upper extremities.

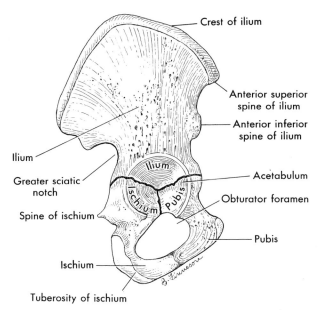

Figure 5–38.   The hipbone, showing the union of ilium, ischium, and os pubis in the acetabulum.

The hipbone, os coxae, or **os innominatum,** is a large, irregularly shaped bone which, with that of the opposite side, forms the sides and front wall of the pelvic cavity. In youth it consists of three separate parts. In the adult these have become united, but it is usual to describe the bone as divisible into three portions: (1) the *ilium* (pl., *ilia*), or upper, expanded portion forming the prominence of the hip; (2) the *ischium* (pl., *ischia*), or lower strong portion; (3) the *pubis* (pl., *pubes*), or portion helping to form the front of the pelvis. These three portions of the bone meet and finally ankylose in a deep socket, called the *acetabulum* (cotyloid cavity), into which the head of the femur fits. Other points of special interest to note in the hipbones are:

1. The processes formed by the projection of the crest of the ilium in front, called the *anterior superior iliac spine* and the *anterior inferior iliac spine*. The former is a convenient landmark in making anatomical and surgical measurements.

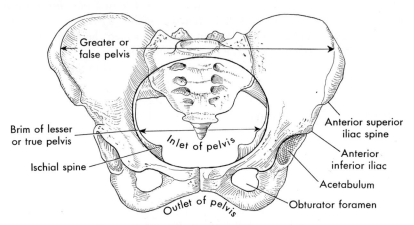

Figure 5–39. The female pelvis, ventral view.

2. The largest foramen in the skeleton, the *obturator foramen*, situated between the ischium and pubis.

3. The articulation formed by the two pubic bones in front, called the *symphysis pubis*, serving as a convenient landmark in making measurements.

The pelvis, so called from its resemblance to a basin, is strong and massively constructed. It is composed of four bones, the two hipbones forming the sides and front, the sacrum and coccyx completing it behind, and is divided by a narrowed bony ring into the greater, or false, and the lesser, or true, pelvis. The narrowed bony ring which is the dividing line is spoken of as the *brim of the pelvis.*

The greater pelvis is the expanded portion situated above the brim, bounded on either side by the ilium; the front is filled by the walls of the abdomen. *The lesser pelvis* is below and behind the pelvic brim, bounded on the front and sides by the pubes and ischia and behind by the sacrum and coccyx. It consists of an inlet, an outlet, and a cavity. The space included within the brim of the pelvis is called the superior aperture, or inlet; and the space below, between the tip of the coccyx behind and the tuberosities of the ischia on either side, is called the inferior aperture, or outlet. The cavity of the lesser pelvis is a short, curved canal, deeper on the posterior than on its anterior wall. In the adult it contains part of the sigmoid colon,[11] the rectum, bladder, and some of the reproductive organs. The bladder is behind the symphysis pubis; the rectum is in the curve of the sacrum and coccyx. In the female the uterus, tubes, ovaries, and vagina are between the bladder and the rectum.

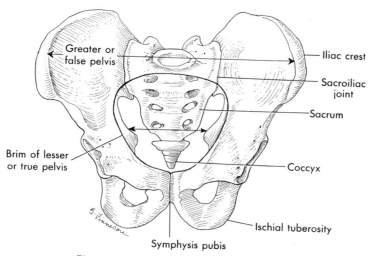

Figure 5–40. The male pelvis, ventral view.

The female pelvis differs from that of the male in those particulars which render it better adapted to pregnancy and parturition. It is more shallow than the male pelvis but relatively wider in every direction. The inlet and outlet are larger and more nearly oval, the bones are lighter and smoother, the coccyx is more movable, and the subpubic arch is greater than a right angle. The subpubic angle in a male is less than a right angle.

The femur, or **thighbone,** is the longest bone in the body. The upper end consists of a rounded head with a constricted neck, and of two eminences, called the greater and lesser *trochanters.* The head articulates with the cavity in the hipbone, called the acetabulum. The lower extremity of the femur is larger than the upper, is flattened from before backward, and is divided into two large eminences, or *condyles,* by an intervening notch. The condyles are called lateral and medial, and the intervening notch is the *intercondyloid fossa.* The lower end of the femur articulates with the tibia and the patella. In the erect position it is not vertical, being separated from its fellow by the entire breadth of the pelvis. The

[11] The sigmoid colon is freely movable and may be displaced into the abdominal cavity.

bone inclines gradually downward and inward, so as to approach its fellow below to bring the knee joint near the line of gravity of the body. The degree of inclination is greater in the female than in the male.

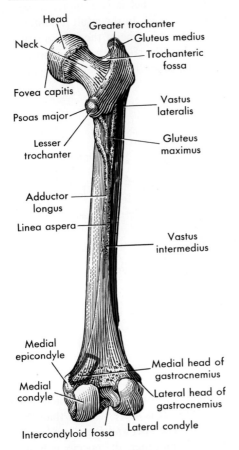

Head
Neck
Greater trochanter
Gluteus medius
Trochanteric fossa
Fovea capitis
Psoas major
Lesser trochanter
Adductor longus
Linea aspera
Vastus lateralis
Gluteus maximus
Vastus intermedius
Medial epicondyle
Medial condyle
Medial head of gastrocnemius
Lateral head of gastrocnemius
Intercondyloid fossa
Lateral condyle

Figure 5–41. The right femur, or thigh-bone, dorsal aspect. (*Red*) Muscle origins, (*blue*) insertions.

The patella, or **kneecap**, is a small, flat, triangular, sesamoid bone developed in the tendon of the quadriceps femoris muscle and placed in front of the knee joint. It articulates with the femur and is surrounded by large, fluid-filled bursae.

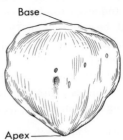

Base

Apex

Figure 5–42. The right patella, anterior surface.

The tibia, or **shinbone,** lies at the front and medial side of the leg.[12] The upper extremity is expanded into two lateral eminences with the sharp intercondyloid eminence between them. The lateral eminences are called medial and lateral condyles. The superior surfaces are concave and receive the condyles of the femur. The lower extremity is much smaller than the upper; it is prolonged downward on its medial side into a strong process, the *medial malleolus,* which

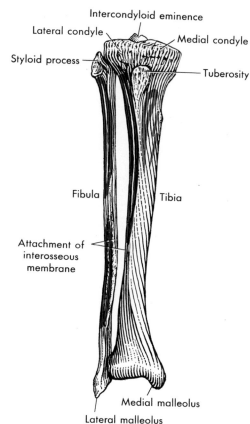

Figure 5–43. The bones of the right leg, ventral surface. (*Red*) Muscle origins, (*blue*) insertions.

Intercondyloid eminence

Lateral condyle

Styloid process

Medial condyle

Tuberosity

Fibula

Tibia

Attachment of interosseous membrane

Medial malleolus

Lateral malleolus

forms the inner prominence of the ankle. At the same lower extremity is the surface for articulation with the talus, which forms the ankle joint. The tibia also articulates with the lower end of the fibula. In the male the tibia is vertical and parallel with the bone of the opposite side, but in the female it has a slightly oblique direction lateralward, to compensate for the oblique direction of the femur medialward.

The fibula is situated on the lateral side of the tibia, parallel with it. It is smaller than the tibia and, in proportion to its length, is the most slender of all

[12] Generally speaking, the lower extremity is called the leg. Anatomically, the word *leg* is reserved for that part of the lower extremity between the knee and the ankle. Above the knee is the thigh.

the long bones. Its upper extremity consists of an irregular quadrant head by means of which it articulates with the tibia, but it does not reach the knee joint. The lower extremity is prolonged downward into a pointed process, the *lateral malleolus*, which lies just beneath the skin and forms the outer anklebone. The lower extremity articulates with the tibia and the talus. The talus is held between the lateral malleolus of the fibula and the medial malleolus of the tibia. A fracture of the lower end of the fibula with injury of the lower tibial articulation is called a *Pott's*[13] *fracture.*

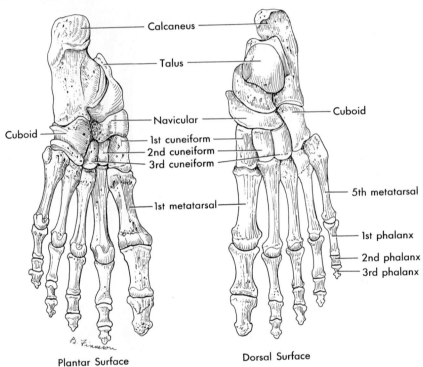

Calcaneus

Talus

Navicular

Cuboid

Cuboid

1st cuneiform
2nd cuneiform
3rd cuneiform

5th metatarsal

1st metatarsal

1st phalanx

2nd phalanx
3rd phalanx

Plantar Surface

Dorsal Surface

Figure 5–44. Bones of the left foot.

Tarsus. The seven tarsal bones, namely, the calcaneus, talus, cuboid, navicular, and the first, second, and third cuneiforms, differ from the carpal bones in being larger and more irregular. The largest and strongest of the tarsal bones is called the *calcaneus*, or *heel bone;* it serves to transmit the weight of the body to the ground and forms a strong lever for the muscles of the calf of the leg.

The metatarsus, or **sole and instep of the foot,** is formed by five bones which resemble the metacarpal bones of the hand. Each bone articulates with the tarsal bones by one extremity and by the other with the first row of phalanges.

[13] Percivall Pott, English surgeon (1714–1788).

The tarsal and metatarsal bones are so arranged that they form two distinct arches; the one running from the calcaneus to the heads of the metatarsal bones on the inner (medial) side is called the *longitudinal arch*, and the other across the foot in the metatarsal region is called the *transverse arch*. The arches of the foot are completed by strong ligaments and tendons. The foot is strong, flexible, resilient, and able to provide the spring and lift for the activities of the body.

These arches may become weakened and progressively broken down, a condition known as flatfoot. This condition is thought to be due to prenatal conditions, dietary or hormone disturbances, improper posture, weight or fatigue conditions, or the wearing of shoes ill-fitting in last or size.

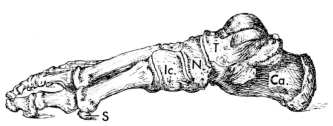

Figure 5–45. Inner side of right foot. (*Ca*) Calcaneus, (*T*) talus or astragalus, (*N*) navicular, (*1c*) first cuneiform, (*S*) sesamoid. (Toldt.)

Phalanges. Both in number and general arrangement they resemble those in the hand, there being two in the great toe and three in each of the other toes.

QUESTIONS FOR DISCUSSION

1. What are the functions of the bones?
2. Which bones articulate with the femur, humerus, scapula, and the atlas?
3. What is the anatomical relationship of the nerves, blood vessels, and lymphatics to the skeleton?
4. Discuss the structure and function of the intervertebral disk and nucleus pulposus.

SUMMARY

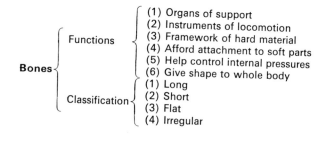

Bones
— Functions
  (1) Organs of support
  (2) Instruments of locomotion
  (3) Framework of hard material
  (4) Afford attachment to soft parts
  (5) Help control internal pressures
  (6) Give shape to whole body
— Classification
  (1) Long
  (2) Short
  (3) Flat
  (4) Irregular

TABLE OF THE BONES

Bones of the Head

CRANIUM		FACE	
Occipital	1	Nasal	2
Parietal	2	Vomer	1
Frontal	1	Inferior nasal concha (inf. turb.)	2
Temporal	2	Lacrimal	2
Sphenoid	1	Zygomatic (malar)	2
Ethmoid	1	Palatine (palate)	2
	—	Maxilla	2
	8	Mandible	1
			—
			14

Fontanels	Anterior	1
	Posterior	1
	Anterolateral	2
	Posterolateral	2
Sinuses Opening into Nasal Cavity	Frontal	
	Ethmoidal	
	Sphenoidal	
	Maxillary	
Ear	Malleus	2
	Incus	2
	Stapes	2
		—
		6

Described with ear (Chap. 11)

Hyoid bone in the neck   1

Bones of the Trunk

		CHILD	ADULT	
Vertebrae	Cervical	7	7	
	Thoracic	12	12	
	Lumbar	5	5	
	Sacral	5	1	
	Coccygeal	4 = 33	1 = 26	
Ribs			24	
Sternum			1	
			—	
			51	

Intervertebral Disks { Disks of fibrocartilage interposed between the bodies of vertebrae from axis to sacrum

Bones of the Upper Extremity

Clavicle	1	Greater multangular (trapezium)	1
Scapula	1		
Humerus	1	Lesser multangular (trapezoid)	1
Ulna	1		
Radius	1	Capitate (os magnum)	1
Carpus		Hamate (unciform)	1
Navicular (scaphoid)	1	Metacarpus	5
Lunate (semilunar)	1	Phalanges	14
Triangular (cuneiform)	1		—
Pisiform	1		32
		32 × 2 =	64

130

Bones of the Lower Extremity

Hipbone (os coxae)	1	Third cuneiform	
Femur	1	(external cuneiform)	1
Patella	1	Second cuneiform	
Tibia	1	(middle cuneiform)	1
Fibula	1	First cuneiform	
Tarsus		(internal cuneiform)	1
Calcaneus (os calcis)	1	Metatarsus	5
Talus (astragalus)	1	Phalanges	14
Cuboid	1		—
Navicular (scaphoid)	1		31
		31 × 2 =	62

COMPARISON OF FEMALE AND MALE PELVIS

Bone	FEMALE	MALE
Sacrum	Slender	Heavier and rough
Symphysis	Broad, less curved	Narrow, more curved
Major pelvis	Shallow	Deeper
Minor pelvis	Narrow	Wide
	Shallow and wide, capacity great	Deeper and narrower, capacity less
Great sciatic notches	Wide	Narrow
Superior aperture	Oval	Heart-shaped

CHAPTER 6

Arthrology: Joints or Articulations

ALL BONES have articulating surfaces so that various body movements may be accomplished. These surfaces form joints or articulations, some of which are freely movable, others slightly movable or immovable. All types are important for smooth, coordinated movements of the body.

Structure of Joints. The articulating surfaces of the bones are sometimes separated by a thin membrane, sometimes by strong strands of connective tissue, or fibrocartilage, and in the freely moving joints are completely separated. Strong ligaments extend over the joints or form capsules, which ensheathe them. Tendons of muscles also extend over the joints.

Classification.[1] Joints are classified according to the amount of movement of which they are capable.

1. *Synarthroses*, or immovable joints.

2. *Amphiarthroses*, or slightly movable joints.

3. *Diarthroses*, or freely movable joints. In this kind of joint, cartilage or fibrous tissue is placed between the bones, uniting them or covering the opposed surfaces.

Synarthroses, or Immovable Joints. The bones are connected by fibrous tissue or cartilage. There are four varieties of these joints. They are listed in the summary on page 140. The bones of the cranium and the face (with the exception of

[1] A more complete classification of joints is given in the summary at the end of this chapter.

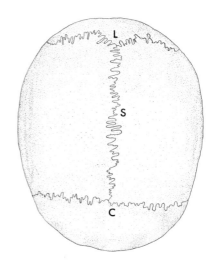

Figure 6–1. A toothed, or dentated, suture seen on the top of the skull. (*L*) Lambdoidal suture, (*S*) sagittal suture, (*C*) coronal suture.

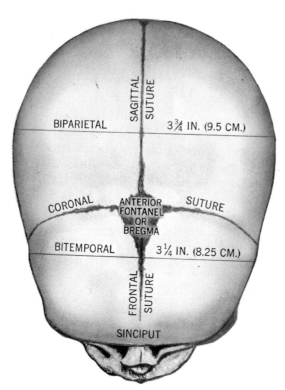

Figure 6–2. Diameters and landmarks of the fetal skull, upper surface. (Modified from Edgar.)

the lower jaw) have their adjacent surfaces applied in close contact, with only a thin layer of fibrous tissue between them. In most of the cranial bones union is by a series of interlocked processes and indentations which form the *sutures*. The three most important sutures are (1) *coronal*, uniting the frontal and parietal bones; (2) *lambdoid*, uniting the parietal and occipital bones; and (3) *sagittal*, which begins at the base of the nose, extends along the middle line on the top of the crown, separates the frontal bone into two parts and the parietal bones from each other, and ends at the posterior fontanel. That portion of the sagittal suture which separates the frontal bone into two parts is often called the frontal *suture*. The junction of the sagittal and coronal sutures is called the *bregma*; the junction of the sagittal and lambdoid sutures is called the *lambda*.

Amphiarthroses, or slightly movable joints, include two varieties: (1) the symphysis and (2) the syndesmosis.

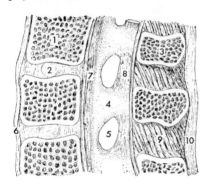

Figure 6–3. Diagram of two intervertebral symphyses, seen in a longitudinal section through three segments of the vertebral column. (*1*) Body of vertebra, (*2*) intervertebral cartilaginous disk, (*3*) spinous process, (*4*) spinal canal, (*5*) intervertebral foramen, (*6*) anterior longitudinal ligament, (*7*) posterior longitudinal ligament, (*8*) ligamentum flavum, (*9*) interspinous ligament, (*10*) supraspinous ligament.

SYMPHYSIS. In this form of articulation the bony surfaces are joined together by broad, flattened disks of fibrocartilage, as in the articulations between the bodies of the vertebrae. These intervertebral disks being somewhat compressible and extensile, the spine can be moved to a limited extent in every direction. In the pelvis the articulations between the two pubic bones (symphysis pubis) (Fig. 5–40, p. 125) and between the sacrum and ilia (sacroiliac articulation) are slightly movable. The pubic bones are united by a disk of fibrocartilage and by ligaments. In the sacroiliac articulation the sacrum is united more closely to the ilia, the articular surfaces being covered by cartilage and held together by ligaments.

The fibrocartilage between these joints (symphysis pubis and sacroiliac) becomes thickened and softened during pregnancy and allows a certain limited motion which is essential to a normal birth.

SYNDESMOSIS. In this type of articulation the bony surfaces are united by an interosseous ligament, as in the lower tibiofibular articulation.

Diarthroses, or freely movable joints, include most of the joints in the body. The adjacent ends of the bones are covered with hyaline cartilage and are surrounded by a fibrous *articular* capsule which is strengthened by ligaments and lined with synovial membrane. Tendons of muscles also pass over these joints. These joints have been classified as follows:

1. GLIDING JOINTS permit gliding movement only, as in the joints between the carpal bones of the wrist, between the tarsal bones of the ankle, and between the articular processes of the vertebrae. The articular surfaces are nearly flat, or one may be slightly convex. This type of movement is to some extent common to all movable joints.

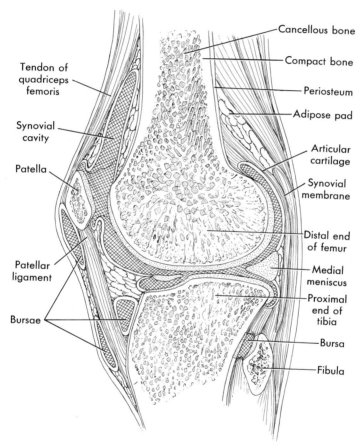

Figure 6–4. Longitudinal section of a hinge joint—the knee. (Modified from Ham.)

2. HINGE JOINTS allow angular movement in one direction, like a door on its hinges. The articular surfaces are of such shape as to permit motion in the forward and backward plane. These movements are called flexion and extension and may be seen in the joint between the humerus and ulna, in the knee and ankle joints, and in the articulations of the phalanges.

Although the knee joint is described as a hinge joint, it is actually much more complicated. There is the articulation between each condyle of the femur and the corresponding meniscus and the condyle of the tibia, and the articulation between the femur and the patella. The bones are held together by the articular capsule and ten ligaments. (See Fig. 6–5.) There are two menisci, the medial and the lateral; they are crescent-shaped structures of fibrocartilage; the surfaces are smooth and covered with synovial membrane. The upper surfaces are concave

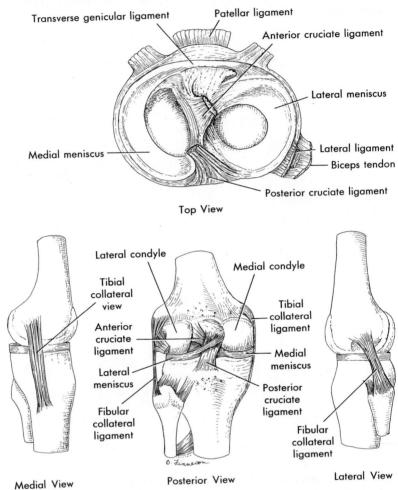

Figure 6–5. Ligaments of the knee. (Modified from Pansky and House.)

and in contact with the femur; the lower surfaces are flat and rest upon the head of the tibia. The peripheral border of each one is thick and convex and attached to the inside of the joint capsule. The inner border is thin, concave, and unattached. The function of the menisci is to deepen the surfaces of the head of the tibia for articulation with the condyles of the femur.

3. CONDYLOID JOINTS admit of an angular movement in two directions. When

an oval-shaped head, or condyle, of bone is received into an elliptical cavity, it is said to form a condyloid joint, e.g., the wrist joint. Movements permitted in this form of a joint include flexion, extension, adduction, abduction, and circumduction but no axial rotation.

4. SADDLE JOINTS are like condyloid joints in providing for angular movement in two planes, but the structure is different. The articular surface of each of the articular bones is concave in one direction and convex in another, at right angles to the former. The metacarpal bone of the thumb is articulated with the greater multangular bone of the carpus by a saddle joint. The movements at these joints are the same as in condyloid joints.

5. PIVOT JOINTS are joints with a rotary movement in one axis. In this form a ring rotates around a pivot, or a pivotlike process rotates within a ring being

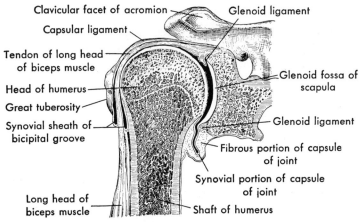

Figure 6–6. Diagram of the shoulder joint. Shallow ball-and-socket joint. (Modified from Toldt.)

formed of bone and cartilage. In the articulation of the axis and atlas, the front of the ring is formed by the anterior arch of the atlas and the back by the transverse ligament. The odontoid process of the axis forms a pivot, and around this pivot the ring rotates, carrying the head with it. In the proximal articulation of the radius and ulna, the head of the radius rotates within the ring formed by the radial notch of the ulna and the annular ligament. The hand is attached to the lower end of the radius, and the radius, in rotating, carries the hand with it; thus, the palm of the hand is alternately turned forward and backward. When the palm is turned forward or upward, the attitude is called *supination*; when backward or downward, *pronation*.

6. BALL-AND-SOCKET JOINTS have an angular movement in all directions and a pivot movement. In this form of joint a more or less rounded head lies in a cuplike cavity, as the head of the femur in the acetabulum and the head of the humerus in the glenoid cavity of the scapula. The shoulder joint is the most freely movable joint in the body.

Movement. Bones thus connected are capable of four different kinds of movement, which rarely occur singly but usually in combination, which produce great variety.

1. *Gliding movement* is the simplest kind of motion that can take place in a joint, one surface moving over another without any angular or rotatory move-

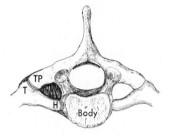

Figure 6–7. Diagram of gliding joints between the head of a rib and the body of a vertebra, and also between the tubercle of a rib and the transverse process of a vertebra. (*H*) Head of rib, (*T*) tubercle of rib, (*TP*) transverse process.

ment. The costovertebral articulations permit a slight gliding of the heads and tubercles of the ribs on the bodies and transverse processes of the vertebrae.

2. *Angular movement* occurs only between long bones, and by it the angle between two bones is either increased or diminished. It includes flexion, extension, abduction, and adduction.

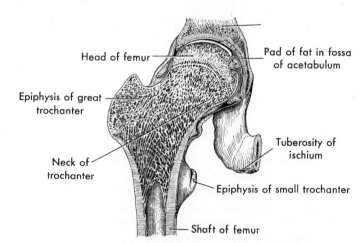

Figure 6–8. Diagram of the hip joint. Section of a ball-and-socket joint. (Modified from Toldt.)

(A) FLEXION. A limb is flexed when it is bent, e.g., bending the arm at the elbow.

(B) EXTENSION. A limb is extended when it is straightened out, e.g., straightening the arm; hence, the reverse of flexion.

(C) ABDUCTION. This term means drawn away from the middle line of the body, e.g., lifting the arm away from, or at right angles to, the body.

(D) ADDUCTION. This term means brought to, or nearer, the middle line of the body, e.g., bringing the arm to the side of the body.

Both abduction and adduction have a different meaning when used with reference to the fingers and toes. In the hand abduction and adduction refer to an imaginary line drawn through the middle finger, and in the foot, to an imaginary line drawn through the second toe.

3. *Circumduction* means that form of motion which takes place between the head of a bone and its articular cavity, when the bone is made to circumscribe a conical space by rotation around an imaginary axis, e.g., swinging the arms or legs.

4. *Rotation* means a form of movement in which a bone moves around a central axis, often an imaginary one, without undergoing any displacement from this axis, e.g., rotation of the atlas around the odontoid process of the axis.

Complete rotation, as of a wheel, is not possible in any joints of the body, as such motion would tear asunder the vessels, nerves, muscles, etc.

Sprain. A wrenching or twisting of a joint accompanied by a stretching or tearing of the ligaments or tendons is called a sprain.

Dislocation. If, in addition to a sprain, the bone of a joint is displaced, the injury is called a dislocation.

Ankylosis. Immobility and consolidation of a joint.

QUESTIONS FOR DISCUSSION

1. How are joints classified? Give an example of each.
2. A frequent knee injury to football players involves ligaments and the menisci of the knee. Explain the menisci and give their location and structure.
3. What is the soft spot felt on a baby's head? What is its function? What becomes of this as the baby develops?
4. After injury to a knee, there may be considerable swelling. What structure of the knee is affected?

SUMMARY

Joints or Articulations—connections existing between bones

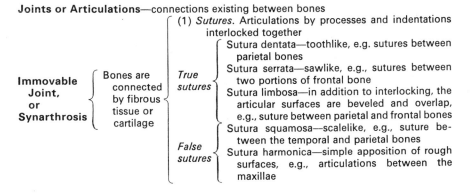

Immovable Joint, or Synarthrosis — Bones are connected by fibrous tissue or cartilage

(1) *Sutures.* Articulations by processes and indentations interlocked together

True sutures
Sutura dentata—toothlike, e.g. sutures between parietal bones
Sutura serrata—sawlike, e.g., sutures between two portions of frontal bone
Sutura limbosa—in addition to interlocking, the articular surfaces are beveled and overlap, e.g., suture between parietal and frontal bones

False sutures
Sutura squamosa—scalelike, e.g., suture between the temporal and parietal bones
Sutura harmonica—simple apposition of rough surfaces, e.g., articulations between the maxillae

Immovable Joint or Synarthrosis (*cont.*) — Bones are connected by fibrous tissue or cartilage (*cont.*)

(2) *Schindylesis*. A thin plate of bone is received in a cleft or fissure of another bone, e.g., the reception of the vomer in the fissure between the maxillae and between the palatine bones

(3) *Gomphosis*. A conical process fits into a socket, e.g., roots of teeth into the alveoli of the maxillae and mandible

(4) *Synchondrosis*. Temporary joint. Cartilage between bones ossifies in adult life, e.g., between the occipital and sphenoid

Slightly Movable Joint, or Amphiarthrosis — Bones are connected by disks of cartilage or interosseous ligaments

(1) *Symphysis*. The bones are united by a plate or disk of fibrocartilage of considerable thickness

(2) *Syndesmosis*. The bony surfaces are united by an interosseous ligament, as in the lower tibiofibular articulation

Movable Joint, or Diarthrosis —
(1) Hyaline cartilage covering adjacent ends of the bones
(2) Fibrous capsule strengthened by ligaments
(3) Synovial membrane lining fibrous capsule

(1) *Arthrodia*. Gliding joint; articulates by surfaces which glide upon each other

(2) *Ginglymus*. Hinge, or angular, joint; moves backward and forward in one plane

(3) *Condylarthrosis*. Condyloid joint; ovoid head received into elliptical cavity

(4) *Reciprocal Reception*. Saddle joint; articular surfaces are concavoconvex

(5) *Trochoides*. Pivot joint; articulates by a process turning within a ring or by a ring turning around a pivot

(6) *Enarthrosis*. Ball-and-socket joint; articulates by a globular head in a cuplike cavity

Movement —
(1) Gliding movement
(2) Angular — Flexion, Extension; Adduction, Abduction
(3) Circumduction
(4) Rotation

7

Muscular Tissue:
Physiology of Contraction,
Levers, Skeletal Muscles

MOTION is an important activity of the body which is made possible by special development of the function of contractility in muscle tissue. Motion in this sense includes not only movements of the entire body or parts of the body from place to place, but those of breathing, the beating of the heart, movements of the parts of the alimentary canal and its glands, and movements of the other viscera, including those of the blood and lymph vessels.

All physiological activities are closely related to motion brought about by contraction of muscle. Consider the effect of the contraction (change in shape) of the enormous number of muscle cells so intimately related as they are to all the other tissue cells of the body, for instance, in supplying gland cells with the requisite materials for the manufacture of their secretion; in making it possible for them to empty this secretion into cavities or fluids of the body, in stirring up the tissue fluid and moving it about in relation to supplying all cells, e.g., nerve cells or the muscle cells themselves, with a continuous source of supplies at low concentration, and removing their wastes constantly.

MUSCULAR TISSUE

In the human, muscular tissue constitutes 40 to 50 per cent of the body weight. **Special characteristics** of muscle tissue are irritability (excitability),

141

contractility, extensibility, and elasticity. *Irritability*, or *excitability*, is the property of receiving stimuli and responding to them. All cells possess this property. The response of any tisse to stimulation is to perform its special function, which, in the case of muscular tissue, is contraction. *Contractility* is the property which enables muscles to change their shape and become shorter and thicker. This property is characteristic of all protoplasm but is more highly developed in muscular tissue than in any other. *Extensibility* of a living muscle cell means that it can be stretched, or extended; and *elasticity* means that it readily returns to its original form when the stretching force is removed.

Types of Muscle Tissue

Muscle tissue is composed, as is every other tissue, of cells and intercellular substance. The cells become elongated and are termed *fibers*. The intercellular

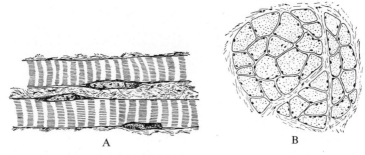

A   B

Figure 7–1. Striated muscle cells. (*A*) Parts of two cells seen in longitudinal section showing sarcolemma, sarcoplasm, nuclei, cross striations. Note that each cell lies in connective tissue. (*B*) Three bundles (fasciculi) of cells seen in cross section. Note sarcoplasm, nuclei, and connective tissue between cells and around fasciculi.

substance consists of a small amount of cement, which holds the cells to the framework of loose connective tissue in which they are embedded.

Muscular tissue may be classified according to its structure or location:

STRUCTURE	LOCATION
Striated, or cross-striped	Skeletal
Nonstriated, or smooth	Visceral
Indistinctly striated	Cardiac

Striated, or **cross-striped, muscular tissue** is called striated because of the parallel cross stripes, or *striae*, which characterize its microscopic appearance. It is called *skeletal* because it forms the muscles which are attached to the skeleton, *somatic* because it helps to form the body wall, and *voluntary* because the movements accomplished are in most instances under conscious control. It is composed of spindle-shaped fibers, or cells, which may be 1 to 40 mm long and from 0.01 to 0.15 mm in diameter. These fibers consist of a tubular sheath, or *sarcolemma*, which encloses a soft, contractile substance. On the inner surface of the sarcolemma many nuclei are seen. Microdissection shows cross-striped fibrils (myofibrils) which are closely packed together and run lengthwise through the entire fiber. Fluid material, called *sarcoplasm*, surrounds the *myofibrils*. The individual fibers show variation in length, width, and number of nuclei, and in the relative amount of myofibrils and sarcoplasm present in them. The electron micrographs show that the myofibrils are marked by alternating light and dark bands. The dark bands are called anisotropic (A) bands and the light, isotropic

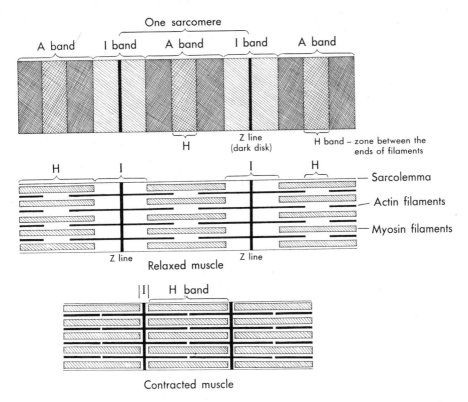

Figure 7–2. Diagram illustrating detail of structure of skeletal muscles and changes that occur during contraction. Note that the I band shortens considerably during contraction.

(I) bands. Each I band is bisected by a thin, dark disk or line called the Z line. The combination of an A and I band is called a sarcomere. The H band is the zone between the ends of the filaments.

The sarcoplasm contains a Golgi complex, numerous mitochondria, endoplasmic reticulum, a few ribosomes, and glycogen. The mitochondria are found beneath the sarcolemma, around the nuclei and in the sarcoplasm between the myofibrils, and in the neuromuscular junctions. Contraction of the muscle fiber is evidently based on the sliding together of the myofilaments in the sarcomeres. The muscle fiber becomes shorter and broader, but the total length of the A band remains constant except in extreme contractions, when it shortens, producing thick myosin filaments against the Z band. The I band shortens markedly during contraction.

Each myofibril is composed of myosin and actin. Another protein, tropomyosin, is bound with actin to form actin-tropomyosin. These are the large protein molecules that are responsible for muscle contraction. Two types of fibers are found, *red* and *white*. Probably each skeletal muscle contains some fibers of each type; but, in general, rapid movements are carried out by muscles in which white fibers predominate, while the slower movements are executed by those in which red fibers predominate.

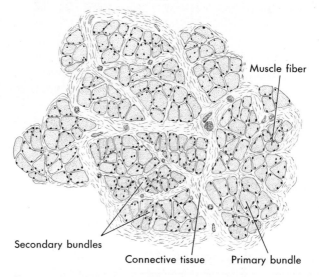

Figure 7–3.   Cross section of a bit of muscle trunk. The fibers are surrounded by connective tissue. Bundles of fibers are surrounded by wider areas of connective tissue. Primary bundles form secondary bundles surrounded by still wider areas of connective tissue.

The muscle fibers lie closely packed, forming primary bundles, or *fasciculi*. Loose connective tissue forms a supporting framework, penetrating between the fibers and surrounding the small bundles, grouping them into larger bundles. It also surrounds the larger bundles and forms a covering for the entire muscle trunk, which is called *fascia*. This connective tissue carries an intricate network of blood and lymph tubes and nerves, so that every muscle fiber is supplied with nerve endings and surrounded by tissue fluid.

Each skeletal muscle is a separate organ having its own sheath of connective tissue, called *epimysium*. The muscles vary in length from about 1 mm to nearly 60 cm (24 in.) and are diverse in form. In the trunk they are broad, flattened, and expanded, forming the walls of the cavities which they enclose. In the limbs they form more or less elongated spindles or straps. A typical muscle consists of a body and two extremities.

ORIGIN AND INSERTION.   Skeletal muscles in general pass over joints, some of which are movable, some immovable. If the joint is movable, it is convenient to speak of the origin and insertion of the muscle. The *origin* is the end attached to the relatively less movable bone, and the *insertion* is the attachment to a bone moving in the ordinary activity of the body. The origin alone is fixed in a small number of muscles such as those of the face, many of which are attached by one end to a bone and by the other to skin. A muscle increases in diameter as it contracts lengthwise, pulling the attachments at each end nearer to each other.

Tendons and *aponeuroses* attach muscles to bones. As the end of a muscle is approached, the connective-tissue framework of the muscle increases in quantity

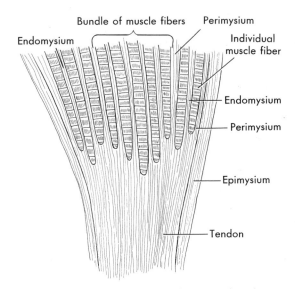

Figure 7–4.   Diagram of a muscle-tendon junction.

and usually extends beyond the muscle fibers as a dense white cord, or *tendon*, or as a flattened tendon, or *aponeurosis*. The tendons are cablelike in that they are exceedingly strong, inextensible, and at the same time flexible.

Fasciae, as previously stated, are sheets of connective tissue by which most muscles are closely covered. They not only envelop and bind down the muscles but also separate them into groups. Such groups are named according to the parts of the body where they are found—cervical fascia, thoracic fascia, abdominal fascia, pelvic fascia. Individual fasciae are frequently given the names of the muscles which they envelop and bind down, such as pectoral fascia. In the vicinity of the wrist and ankle, parts of the deep fascia become blended into tight transverse bands, or *annular* ligaments, which serve to bind down the tendons close to the bones.

It is important to realize the continuity of the connective tissues of the body. Tendons, ligaments, and fasciae blend with periosteum; tendons and fasciae serve as ligaments; tendons lose themselves in fasciae; and tendons of some muscles serve as fasciae for others.

The function of skeletal muscle is to operate the bones of the body, thereby producing motion.

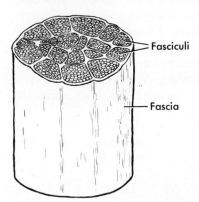

Fasciculi

Fascia

Figure 7–5. A section of voluntary muscle trunk composed of fasciculi covered with fascia.

Skeletal muscle enables one by body gesture or facial expression to show pleasure or displeasure; the ability to speak, to hear, to see are all dependent upon muscle activity.

Nonstriated, or **smooth, muscular tissue** is so called because it does not exhibit cross stripes, or striae. It is called *visceral* because it forms the muscular portion

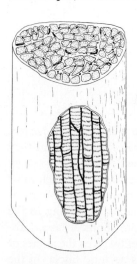

Figure 7–6. A single fasciculus of striated muscle fibers. At the top the fibers are shown cut across, each fiber being surrounded with connective tissue. The bundle of cells is wrapped with fascia. In one area the fascia is cut off to show the muscle fibers and a part of the capillary network surrounding the fibers.

of the visceral organs. The cells are usually arranged in two main layers: the inner, thick, *circular coat* and the outer, thin, *longitudinal coat*. The motions caused by it are involuntary; usually we are not conscious of them. This tissue is composed of spindle-shaped cells each containing a single large nucleus. The cells are 0.015 to 0.5 mm long and 0.002 to 0.02 mm in diameter, and the coats are surrounded by a network of connective tissue which carries lymph, blood tubes, and nerves. In contrast with the skeletal muscle, smooth muscle contracts more slowly but possesses greater extensibility and maintains a state of contraction, or tonus (p. 149). The cells of smooth muscle seem to be connected by fibrils

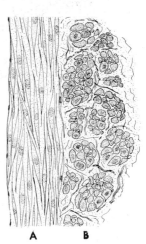

Figure 7–7. Longitudinal section of a visceral organ to show smooth muscle tissue. (*A*) In longitudinal section, (*B*) in cross section. Note that there is a little connective tissue between the cells and that the cells are arranged in bundles.

Figure 7–8. An injected longitudinal section of the wall of a visceral organ to show blood vessels. (*A*) In longitudinal section, (*B*) in cross section. Note that the blood vessels run in the same general direction as the muscle fibers. In *B* the blood vessels are in groups lying between the muscle bundles rather than between the muscle cells. Outside of organ is at left in Figures 7–7 and 7–8.

which extend from cell to cell holding them close together. There are nerve endings about smooth muscle cells, but motor end-plates have not been demonstrated. In general, smooth muscle is innervated by both sympathetic and parasympathetic fibers, but it is not under precise nerve control as is skeletal muscle.

It is probable that impulses are transmitted by a chemical agent, or by mechanical pull exerted by one cell in contraction serving as a stimulus for other cells. Blood supply is not as abundant as in cardiac and striated muscle.

Functions of Smooth Muscle. The walls of all visceral organs, including blood tubes, contain smooth muscle cells. It is the function of these cells to produce such changes in shape and size as occur in these organs. An example is peristalsis of the alimentary canal.

Cardiac muscle tissue forms the heart. The myofibrils are similar to those in skeletal muscle, but transverse striations are less distinct, and the cells are smaller and the mitochondria are more abundant. Each cell has a large, oval,

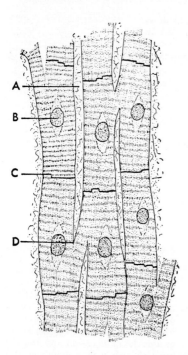

Figure 7–9. Diagram of a thin section of cardiac muscle tissue. (*A*) Connective tissue between cells, (*B*) nucleus, (*C*) intercalated disks, (*D*) branching of a cell.

centrally placed nucleus. The cells fit tightly together. Electron micrographs show that cardiac muscle is composed of elongated branching cells which are irregular at their junctions. Intercalated disks are dark-stained cross bands located at cell junctions. Their irregular course gives a "step formation" appearance. The electron micrographs indicate that the intercalated disks are the membranes of adjacent cells. The cells are surrounded by a close network of fine collagenous fibers, blood, and lymph capillaries. The rhythm of the heartbeat is presumably preserved by means of this "network" nature of cardiac muscle over which impulses may pass. Cardiac muscle has little or no capacity for regeneration of fibers. After injury, healing is accomplished by scar formation.

PHYSIOLOGY OF CONTRACTION

Tone is a property of muscle whereby a steady, partial contraction varying in degree is maintained. The fundamental mechanism whereby *tone*, or *tonus*, is produced is not fully understood, but physiologically it is known to be due to nerve impulses. By means of tonic contraction in skeletal muscles, posture is maintained for long periods with little or no evidence of fatigue. Absence of fatigue is brought about mainly by means of different groups of muscle fibers contracting in relays, giving alternating periods of rest and activity for a given muscle-fiber group. In man the antigravity skeletal muscles (retractors of neck, extensors of the back, etc.) exhibit the highest degree of tonus. In an unconscious person the body collapses if these antigravity muscles are completely relaxed. During sleep, tone is at a minimum.

The tone of skeletal muscles gives them a certain firmness and maintains a slight, steady pull upon their attachments; it also functions in the maintenance of a certain pressure upon the contents of the abdominal cavity. Both the rapidity and the smoothness of movement depend on tone. In fractures the overriding of the broken ends of the bone is often due to the contractions of the muscles because of this property of tonicity.

Both visceral and cardiac muscle exhibit tonus even when isolated from the nervous system. This is probably due to the plexuses of nerve cells and fibers distributed through them. The maintenance of normal blood pressure is partly dependent upon the tone of the muscles in the walls of the small arteries. Likewise, digestion is dependent upon the tone of the muscles of the stomach and intestines. Although the tone of visceral and cardiac muscles is inherent in them, it is probably also under chemical control similar to that for striated muscle. The fact that tonus varies according to the general condition of health, and under certain conditions such as during abnormally high concentration of carbon dioxide disappears altogether, indicates the influence of environmental conditions upon it. It is possible that tonic changes are the result of variation in hydrogen ion concentration acting directly upon the muscle fibers.

Muscle contraction is concerned with the tone of the protoplasm of muscle cells, first the tone of individual muscle cells themselves, then the integrated tone of muscle cells in individual muscles. This tone is maintained by the chemical and physical composition of tissue fluids and by the nervous system. The cerebellum makes the final adjustments needed for *muscle groups* to act together, though muscle tone is maintained through centers in the spinal cord or brain.

Excitation (Stimulation). A muscle is excitable because the muscle fibers composing it are excitable. All protoplasm possesses the property of *excitability*. Any force which affects this excitability is called a *stimulus*. Physiologically, a stimulus represents a change in the environment of the muscle cells. Protoplasm also possesses the property of *conductivity*, and when stimulated at one point the response may travel through the cell. The response is the specialized one which is characteristic for the tissue stimulated; in muscles it is contraction. Normally,

149

the muscles (muscle trunks, such as gastrocnemius) are stimulated by impulses conveyed to them by nerve fibers.

As the motor nerve fiber approaches the muscle fiber, it loses its myelin sheath. The unmyelinated fiber divides into terminal ramifications which make profuse and close contact with a specialized part of the muscle sarcoplasm called the neuromuscular junction. When the nerve impulse reaches the nerve terminal, acetylcholine is released and diffuses into the end-plate. Acetylcholine becomes attached to the end-plate receptor, and local end-plate electrical potential is produced. Eventually the surface membrane of the muscle fiber is depolarized, the muscle fibers set up a propagated muscle action potential, and the muscle responds. An enzyme cholinesterase also formed in the motor end-plate rapidly destroys acetylcholine at the area of release. Various stimuli may serve to inhibit

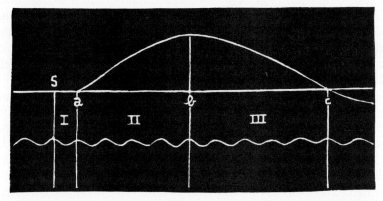

Figure 7–10. Diagram curve of a simple contraction of a muscle. *S* indicates the time when the stimulus enters the muscle. Phase I (*S* to *a*), the *latent period*, in isolated frog muscle lasts about 0.01 second. Phase II (*a* to *b*), the *period of contraction*, lasts about 0.04 second. Phase III (*b* to *c*), the *period of relaxation*, lasts about 0.05 second. From crest to crest of the wavy line below represents an interval of 0.01 second. The apparatus for recording a muscle contraction is shown in Figure 7–11.

muscular activity as well as to excite it. Other forms of stimuli, such as mechanical, thermal, chemical, and electrical, are used in experimental work with muscles and are called *artificial stimuli*. A common source of stimulation is electricity because it is available and convenient, easily controlled as to strength and speed of application, and least destructive to the tissues stimulated. While muscles are within the body or when isolated from the body, they can be excited by artificial stimuli applied to their nerves or to the muscles directly.

Muscles are supplied with two types of nerve fibers—*sensory* fibers, conveying to the central nervous system the state of contraction of the muscle, and *motor* fibers, conveying impulses from the central nervous system to the muscles, controlling their contraction. If a motor nerve is severed or the center in the brain or cord is damaged, no stimulus is carried to the muscle, and its function is lost.

When a sensory nerve is severed, no stimuli are carried from the sensory end organ to the central nervous system, and sensation is thereby lost.

Conditions of Contraction. Skeletal muscles contract quickly and relax promptly. In sharp contrast to this, the contractions of visceral muscle coats develop slowly, are maintained for some time, and fade out slowly. The contraction of a skeletal muscle is the result of stimuli discharged by the nerve fibers innervating it. If one of these contractions is analyzed, it will be found that there is a brief period after the muscle is stimulated before it contracts. This is called the *latent period* and is followed by a *period of contraction*, which in turn is followed by a *period of relaxation* (Fig. 7–10). It has been demonstrated experimentally that if electrical stimuli are applied to a muscle, for instance to the gastrocnemius muscle of the frog, and the contractions are recorded on a moving drum, the contractions will vary in strength (in height on the drum

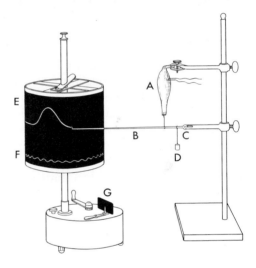

Figure 7–11. Record made by a contracting muscle. (*A*) Muscle extending from clamp to writing lever, (*B*) writing lever, hinged at *C* and counterweighted at *D*, (*E*) revolving smoked drum, on which the point of the writing lever draws a line, (*F*) time record—from crest to crest of a wave may be 0.01 second, (*G*) fan for regulating speed. A muscle attached to the lever draws a line on the moving surface. When the muscle contracts, the lever is raised ; and when the muscle relaxes, the lever falls. The drum is called a kymograph.

record) depending on certain factors: (1) the strength of the stimulus, (2) the speed of application of the stimulus, (3) the duration of the stimulus, (4) the weight of the load, and (5) the temperature. In general, the stronger the stimulus up to a certain maximum, the stronger the contraction will be, i.e., the greater the number of single cells which will contract. Strongest contractions result from stimuli of moderate duration. Some load is necessary in order to get the best response, but increase of load beyond the optimum decreases the height of contraction. Muscles do their best work at a certain optimum temperature. For man this is about 37° C (98.6° F) body temperature. If the temperature is raised much above this, the muscle loses its excitability and becomes functionally depressed, entering finally the state of heat rigor, i.e., a condition of permanent shortening.

Response to Stimuli. It has been found by laboratory studies that if the stimulus applied to a single muscle fiber is strong enough to produce a response, it will give a contraction which is maximal, no matter what the strength of the stimulus. This is the all-or-none law. This means that each muscle fiber gives a maximal response or none at all under the conditions of the experiment. Fatigue and varying conditions of nutrition may alter the cell's response, but increasing the strength of the stimulus will not change the response.

The weakest stimulus which when applied over a reasonable period will cause contraction of the fiber under specified conditions is called the *minimal stimulus*. Any stimulus weaker than this is known as *subminimal (subliminal)*. Two subminimal stimuli (each too weak in itself to cause contraction of the muscle fiber) may, when applied in rapid succession, by their combined forces be equivalent to a minimal stimulus and the cell will respond. This phenomenon is called *summation of stimuli*.

The unit of measure used in studying the excitability or irritability of any tissue is the *chronaxie*. The chronaxie of a cell is the shortest duration of time that a stimulus of twice minimal (rheobasic) strength must be applied to evoke a response.

When a muscle trunk is stimulated to contract many times in succession, the contractions for a time become progressively increased in extent, resulting in a record which shows a staircase effect. This effect is probably determined by an increase in irritability brought about by metabolic wastes formed during the first few contractions. As these metabolic products increase, irritability is decreased, and the contractions diminish progressively in extent until fatigue develops to a point where the muscle fails to respond. From this staircase phenomenon it is judged that activity of muscles is at first physiologically beneficial to the extent that irritability of muscular tissue is thereby increased.

If a second stimulus occurs during the apex of contraction from the first stimulus, the resulting height of contraction will be maximal. This is known as *summation of contractions*. If, however, the second stimulus occurs during a certain period of time after the accomplishment of the first contraction, there will be no second contraction. During this exceedingly brief lapse of time, known as the *absolute refractory period*, the muscle will not respond to any stimulus, however strong. This is followed by the *relative refractory period*, often called the *period of depressed excitability*, during which the muscle gradually regains its irritability.

If stimuli are applied to a muscle in such rapid succession that each occurs before the fibers have relaxed from the one preceding, the cells will remain in a state in which no relaxation is apparent. Such sustained contraction is called *tetanus*. Probably all voluntary acts, even the simplest, have tetanic contractions as their basis, and they are especially to be noted in such continued muscular work as holding the body erect or in carrying a load. Postural tonus is believed to be the result of a slight state of tetanic contraction of skeletal muscles due to fiber summation.

Types of Contractions. When a muscle trunk contracts and a weight is lifted, the muscle becomes shorter and thicker, but its tone remains the same. Since the tone of the fibers is not altered, such contractions are called *isotonic*. If the muscle is compelled to contract against some weight which it cannot lift, the tension in the fibers increases, but the muscle length remains unaltered. Since the length of the fibers is unchanged, such contractions are called *isometric*. Contraction of a skeletal muscle is usually of the isotonic type, but complexities of muscular activity involve the coordinated development of both isometric and isotonic contractions in the different fibers of a muscle trunk.

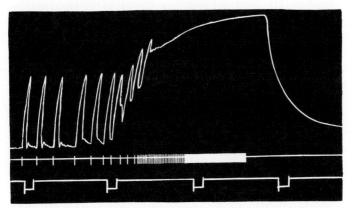

Figure 7–12. Tetanus in skeletal muscle. When stimuli are applied to a muscle at a gradually increasing rate of frequency (indicated by signal), the individual muscle twitches blend together so that, when the stimuli are applied in very rapid succession, a smooth, sustained contraction results. Ordinary muscle movements are of this tetanic nature. Note that the height of contraction is greater in tetanus than in a single twitch. (A. J. Carlson and V. Johnson, *The Machinery of the Body.* Courtesy of the University of Chicago Press.)

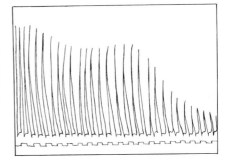

Figure 7–13. Record of muscular fatigue of finger. A weight is lifted by a finger by means of a cord which runs over a pulley. The writing lever is attached to the weight and writes on a moving drum. The apparatus is called an ergo-graph.

Contraction in Skeletal Muscles. The height of contraction of a skeletal muscle is in direct proportion to the strength of the stimulus applied. This is not a contradiction of the all-or-none law. It is explained by the fact that voluntary muscle cells are separate units insulated from each other by connective tissue. On account of environmental conditions the minimal stimulus of these separate fibers may vary. Thus, the minimal stimulus of a skeletal muscle trunk is one which evokes contraction from a single fiber; the maximal stimulus is one which will cause the contraction of every fiber present. A skeletal muscle trunk varies in this respect from the heart muscle, which responds as a unit to any stimulus which will contract a single cardiac cell. It will be recalled that cardiac muscle is a "network" of cells and that the rhythmic action of the heart is brought about by the contraction of these cells in unison.

The immediate cause of muscular contraction is not known, although there is evidence that *diffusion* and physical characteristics of *colloidal* conditions may help to explain it. The chemical reactions known to be associated with it seem to follow contraction rather than to produce it.

There are two phases in the contraction of muscle fibers: the *contractile phase* for which energy must be provided, and the *recovery phase* during which the fiber returns to resting state. The direct source of energy for muscle contraction is from reactions involving adenosine triphosphate (ATP), a compound which is rich in chemical energy. During the recovery period this substance is promptly reformed by reaction with creatine phosphate, which is stored in muscle cells. Both contraction and relaxation of muscle can occur under anaerobic conditions with lactic acid made at the expense of muscle glycogen. However, to maintain adenosine triphosphate and creatine phosphate within the cell, energy is supplied primarily by oxidation of glycogen to carbon dioxide and water through reactions for which oxygen is essential.

Chemical Changes During Muscle Contraction

The active parts of striated muscle are composed of very minute fibers which contain the proteins actin and myosin surrounded by a very thin membrane. In resting muscle this membrane is polarized by the ions distributed on either side of the membrane. When the nerve impulse stimulates the muscle cells, waves of excitation pass over the fibers; the concentrations of potassium, sodium, and chloride ions change; and the muscle contracts. During the recovery period, the cell returns to its resting state. For these activities energy must be supplied within the cell.

Contraction of muscle involves combination of myosin and actin to form a complex known as actomyosin. This complex reacts with adenosine triphosphate (ATP) releasing phosphate in the cell and leaving adenosine diphosphate (ADP), myosin functioning as a catalyst. This reaction provides energy for the contraction of muscle.

Actomyosin + ATP→ADP-Actomyosin + Phosphate + Energy

Relaxation of muscle, which follows contraction, is accompanied by resynthesis of adenosine triphosphate in reaction with creatine phosphate; some

ADP + Creatine phosphate → Creatine + ATP

energy must be used in this synthesis. It has been observed that creatine phosphate, which is stored in muscle cells, is used in the course of muscle activity in direct quantitative relation to the work done by the cell. In fatigued muscle, as the store of creatine phosphate is exhausted, the concentration of adenosine triphosphate is reduced, and the rate of muscle relaxation slows down and finally ceases.

Contraction and relaxation of muscles are also influenced by the varying ion concentrations within the cells and interstitial fluids. Magnesium and calcium are essential for normal response of skeletal muscle fibers to the nerve impulse. A lack of calcium ions increases irritability and may cause tetany (generalized tonic skeletal muscle contraction). Magnesium has the opposite effect, because it has a sedative action on the neuromuscular junction. The fibers also respond to changes in hydrogen ion concentration; an increase in hydrogen ions favors relaxation, a decrease favors contraction.

Source of Energy for Muscle Activity. Production of energy in muscle cells is at the expense of stored glycogen. The initial reactions, which involve the breaking down of the large carbohydrate units to smaller units, pyruvic acid and lactic acid, are known as glycogenolysis. These reactions are catalyzed by enzymes and do not involve oxygen. They result in a small net gain of adenosine triphosphate within the cell. It is believed that lactic acid is transported to the surface of the muscle cell by the sarcoplasmic reticulum. Lactic acid then escapes into the blood stream and is borne to the liver where it is converted to glycogen and stored. In the muscle cell lactic acid may be used to reform pyruvic acid, which can be oxidized to carbon dioxide and water.

The major *source* of energy for *resynthesis* of ATP, hence for the activity of muscle cells, comes through the reactions that involve oxygen. When oxygen supply is adequate, the production of lactic acid is inhibited and pyruvic acid enters the citric acid cycle—the common pathway for terminal oxidation of carbohydrate, fat, and amino acids—with the production of carbon dioxide and water. The greater part of the energy product comes from the transfer of electrons from hydrogen to oxygen through the citric acid cycle (p. 644) to form water. Much of this energy is captured by enzymes and used in the synthesis of ATP; some energy is liberated as heat. The reactions with oxygen make available from 10 to 12 times as much energy as do the anaerobic reactions. Muscles operating under anaerobic conditions use six to eight times as much glycogen to do the same amount of work as could be accomplished under aerobic conditions.

Heat Formation. Initial heat is produced by several different processes. (1) *Heat of activation and maintenance.* Heat is liberated by the chemical processes that change the muscle from a relaxed to an active state, regardless of whether the muscle shortens or not. (2) *Heat of shortening* is caused by the shortening process. During contraction, if the muscle is prevented from shortening, no heat will result. Heat of shortening is believed to result from increased rate of energy liberation in the muscle fibers as the actin-tropomyosin filaments slide over the myosin filaments. (3) *Heat of relaxation* is produced by release of potential energy from the muscle when it relaxes.

Summary of Some of the Chemical Changes Taking Place in Muscle Cells in Relation to Contraction

1. ATP-actomyosin → ADP-actomyosin + Phosphate ion + Energy
2. Phosphocreatine + ADP → Creatine + ATP

Pyruvic acid → Carbon dioxide + Water + Energy

3. Glycogen ↗ ↓ ↑ ↘

Lactic acid + Energy

4. Lactic acid → Re-formed into glycogen in liver cells

Oxygen Debt. During moderate exercise little or no lactic acid accumulates in the muscle cells, but with vigorous exercise the oxygen demand may be greater than the oxygen supply to the cells. Lactic acid accumulates in blood and cells. This produces the condition known as *oxygen debt*. The anaerobic process is stimulated, with its attendant demand for glycogen, lessened synthesis of ATP, and depletion of creatine phosphate. This causes fatigue and the physiological demand for rest. The length of time is variable for meeting oxygen needs and restoration to normal concentration of cell components. Almost all reactions in living cells are catalyzed by enzymes; therefore, maintenance of enzymes is of physiological importance. Several members of the vitamin-B group have been identified as essential in the functioning of enzymes and enzyme systems.

Fatigue and Exercise. In muscles undergoing contraction, the first effect of the formation of carbon dioxide and lactic acid is to increase irritability; but if a muscle is continuously stimulated, the strength of contraction becomes progressively less until the muscle refuses to respond (Fig. 7–13). This is true fatigue and is caused, in part at least, by anoxia and the toxic effects of metabolites (carbon dioxide, acid phosphate, lactic acid) which accumulate during exercise. The loss of nutritive materials may also be a factor in fatigue, but recent conceptions stress the accumulation of metabolites.

In moderate exercise the system is able to eliminate these substances readily. After prolonged contractions a period of rest may be necessary to furnish opportunity for the blood to carry the fatigue substances to the excretory organs and nutritive material and oxygen to the muscle. Probably it is chiefly lactic acid which brings on fatigue by disturbing the hydrogen ion concentration of the cell fluids, thus inhibiting the enzyme action which is responsible for further breakdown of glycogen. It has been demonstrated that injection of the blood of a fatigued animal into a rested one will promptly bring on signs of fatigue.

If fatigue is carried on to the point of absolute exhaustion, the cells do not recover. The protein constituents of the fibers coagulate, exhibiting the phenomenon known as *rigor mortis*. Rigor mortis occurs in muscles from 10 minutes to seven hours after death.

The body is susceptible to other fatigue than that of muscles. Most easily fatigued of all are the synapses next the junctions between nerves and muscle fibers, then the muscles themselves. It must not be thought that the state which is ordinarily recognized as fatigue is entirely physiological. The sense of fatigue is very complex and is often associated with various mental states.

Exercise stimulates circulation and thereby brings about a change in conditions for cells in all locations throughout the body. This great stirring-up effect of exercise brings fresh blood to all the arterioles, and the local pressure as well as the fluid environment of all cells is changed. Exercise has been shown to increase the size, strength, and tone of the muscle fibers. Massage and passive exercise may, if necessary, be used as a partial substitute for exercise. While physical recreation is desirable for aiding metabolic processes, continued use of fatigued muscles is injurious if, during such conditions, the muscles exhaust their glycogen supply and utilize the protein of their own cells. Under normal conditions it is the sensation of fatigue which protects us from such extremes.

MUSCLES AND THE BONY LEVERS

Levers. Direct muscular contraction alone is not generally responsible for bodily motions. Intermediate action of bony levers is usually essential. In the

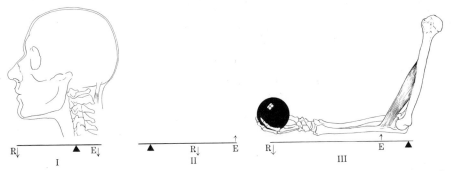

Figure 7–14. Diagram of simple levers. Note insertion of muscle in relation to fulcrum and resistance. The effort is applied at the place of insertion of muscle to the bone. The ▲ represents the fulcrum, (*R*) the resistance, (*E*) the effort, (*arrows*) the direction of motion. There are no levers of the second class in the body. See discussion in text.

body, cooperative functioning of bones and muscles forms levers. A knowledge of levers gives a basis for understanding the principles underlying good posture and the movements of the body.

A *simple lever* is a rigid rod which is free to move about on some fixed point or support called the *fulcrum*. It is acted upon at two different points by (1) the *resistance* (*weight*), which may be thought of as something to be overcome or balanced, and (2) the *force* (*effort*) which is exerted to overcome the resistance. In the body bones of varying shapes are levers, and the resistance may be a part of the body to be moved or some object to be lifted or both of these. The muscular effort is applied to the bone at the insertion of the muscle and brings about the motion or work.

For example, when the forearm is raised, the elbow is the fulcrum, the weight of the forearm is the resistance, and the pull due to contraction of the biceps muscle is the effort.

Levers act according to a law which may be stated thus: When the lever is in equilibrium, the effort times the effort arm equals the resistance times the resistance arm ($E \times EA = R \times RA$).

The "resistance arm" is the perpendicular distance from the fulcrum to the line of action of the resistance (weight). The "effort arm" is the perpendicular distance from the fulcrum to the line of action of the effort (force).

For example, if the distance from the effort to the fulcrum is the same as the distance from the resistance to the fulcrum, an effort of 5 lb will balance a resistance of 5 lb.

Levers may be divided into three classes according to the relative position of the fulcrum, the effort, and the resistance. In levers of the *first class* the fulcrum lies between the effort and the resistance, as in a set of scales. In this type of lever the resistance is moved in the opposite direction to that in which the effort is applied. In the body when the head is raised, the facial portion of the skull is the resistance, moving upon the atlanto-occipital joint as a fulcrum, while the muscles of the back produce the effort.

In levers of the *second class* the resistance lies between the fulcrum and the effort and moves, therefore, in the same direction as that in which the effort is applied, as in the raising of a wheelbarrow. There are no levers of the second class in the body. An example of the second-class lever frequently cited is the human foot, when the body is raised on tiptoe, the point of contact with the earth being considered the fulcrum. The pull exerted through the tendon of Achilles in this case is greater than the weight of the body acting at the ankle joint. Hence this is *not* a lever of the second class.

In levers of the *third class* the effort is exerted between the fulcrum and the resistance. Levers in which the resistance arm is thus longer than the effort arm produce rapid delicate movements wherein the effort used must be greater than the resistance. The flexing of the forearm is a lever of this type, as are most of the levers of the body. The *law of levers* applies in the maintenance of correct posture. The head held erect in correct standing posture rests on the atlas as a fulcrum, with little or no muscular effort being exerted to maintain this position. The head in this position is in the "line of gravity" which passes through the hip joints, knee joints, and the balls of the feet (Fig. 5–28, p. 114). When the shoulders are stooped and head is bent forward, constant muscular effort is exerted against the pull of gravity on the head.

SKELETAL MUSCLES

Skeletal muscles are arranged in groups with specific functions to perform: flexion and extension, external and internal rotation, abduction and adduction. For example, in flexing of the elbow, several muscle groups are involved in varying degrees. The *agonists*, or prime movers, give power for flexion; the opposing group, the *antagonists*, contribute to smooth movements by their power to maintain tone yet relax and give way to movement of the flexor group. Other groups of muscles act to hold the arm and shoulder in a suitable position for action and are called *fixation* muscles. The *synergists* are muscles which assist the agonists (prime movers) and reduce undesired action or unnecessary movement. Activity of these opposing muscle groups is coordinated in relation to degree of tension exerted. When tension of the flexor muscles is increased, the tone of the extensor muscles is decreased; movement is controlled and position is maintained against varying degrees of pressures or pulls.

Each muscle has motor and sensory nerve fibers and is well supplied with arteries, capillaries, veins, and lymphatics. The synergic units are believed to have a complex reciprocal innervation because they receive both inhibitory and excitatory impulses which effect the muscle tension needed for any specific movement. The cerebellum plays an important role in muscle activity because it regulates muscle tension necessary for the proper maintenance of equilibrium and posture; it coordinates skilled movement initiated at cortical levels and regulates muscular tension essential for all fine muscle movements.

Almost all the skeletal muscles occur in pairs. A few single muscles situated in the median line represent the fusion of two muscles. Only a few of the over 600 muscles of the body are included in this chapter. They are arranged in relation to function.

Many skeletal muscles bear two names, one Latin and the other English, e.g., obliquus externus abdominis and external abdominal oblique. Sometimes a muscle has more than one Latin name, e.g., psoas magnus and psoas major, vastus intermedius and vastus crureus. Frequently a muscle has no well-known English name, e.g., levatores costarum; sometimes the English name is the one that is best known, e.g., deltoid instead of deltoideus.

Muscles of Expression

Epicranial	Platysma
Corrugator	Risorius
Buccinator	The quadrati labii
Zygomatic	Mentalis
Triangularis	The nasal muscles
	Orbicularis oris

This group of muscles enables one to express pleasure, pain, disgust, disdain, contempt, fear, anger, sadness, surprise, or other emotional states.

The epicranial, or **occipitofrontalis,** may be considered as two muscles—the occipital, which covers the back, or occiput, of the head, and the frontal, which covers the front of the skull. The two muscles are held together by a thin aponeurosis extending over and covering the whole of the upper part of the cranium. The occipital takes its origin from the occipital bone and the mastoid portion of the temporal bone and is inserted into the aponeurosis. The frontal takes its origin from the aponeurosis and is inserted into the tissues in the region of the eyebrows.

Action. The frontal portion of this muscle is the more powerful; by its contraction the eyebrows are elevated and the skin of the forehead is thrown into

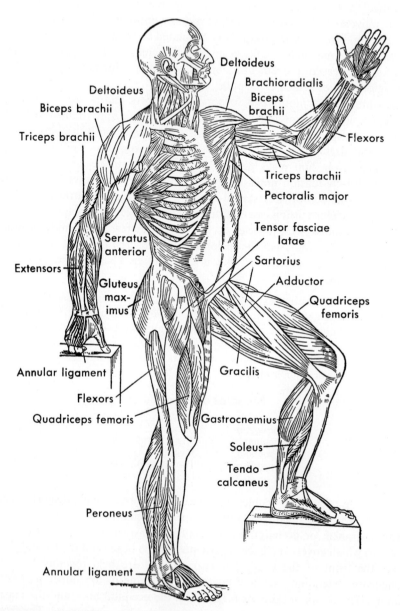

Figure 7–15. The human body, showing muscles (right side and front). (Courtesy of William Wood & Company.)

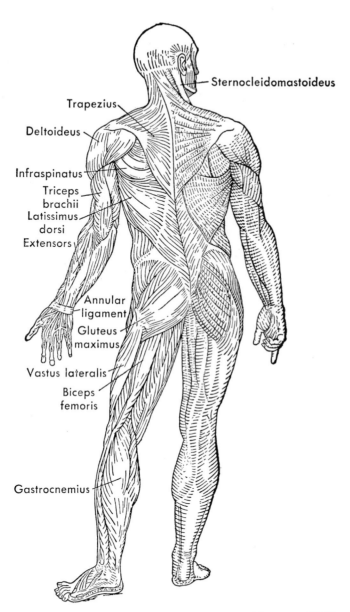

Sternocleidomastoideus

Trapezius

Deltoideus

Infraspinatus

Triceps
brachii

Latissimus
dorsi

Extensors

Annular
ligament

Gluteus
maximus

Vastus lateralis

Biceps
femoris

Gastrocnemius

Figure 7–16. The human body, showing muscles (back). (Courtesy of William Wood & Company.)

transverse wrinkles and thereby expresses surprise. The occipital portion draw the scalp backward.

The corrugator muscle wrinkles the skin of the forehead vertically as in frowning. It has its origin from the medial end of the superciliary arch and is inserted into the skin of the forehead.

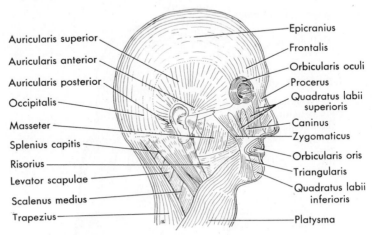

Figure 7–17. The superficial muscles of the head and neck.

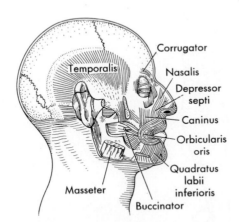

Figure 7–18. The temporal and deep muscles about the mouth.

The buccinator (trumpeter's muscle) arises from the alveolar processes of the maxilla and mandible. The fibers converge toward the angle of the mouth and are inserted into the orbicularis oris. It forms the principal muscle of the cheeks and lateral wall of the oral cavity.

Action. It compresses the cheek during mastication, keeping the food under pressure of the teeth.

The zygomatic arises from the zygomatic bone and descends obliquely to its insertion into the orbicularis oris muscle. It pulls the angles of the mouth upward and backward as in smiling or laughing.

The **triangularis** is a broad, flat muscle which arises from the oblique line of the mandible. The fibers converge and are inserted in the orbicularis oris muscle. It depresses the angle of the mouth.

The **platysma** (broad sheet muscle) arises from the skin and fasciae, covering the pectoral and deltoid muscles, and is inserted in the mandible and muscles about the angle of the mouth.

Action. It depresses the mandible and draws down the lower lip and angle of the mouth and wrinkles the skin of the neck.

The **risorius** has its origin in the fascia over the masseter muscle and passes horizontally forward and is inserted into the skin at the angle of the mouth. When contracted strongly, it gives an expression of strain and tenseness.

The **quadratus labii superioris** is a thin quadrangular muscle with three heads. The angular head arises in the upper part of the maxilla and passes obliquely downward, dividing into two slips. One of these is inserted into the greater alar cartilage and skin of the nose and the other into the orbicularis oris muscle. The infraorbital head arises from the lower margin of the orbit; the zygomatic head has its origin in the zygomatic bone. Both of these are inserted into the orbicularis oris muscle. It elevates the upper lip. Contraction of the infraorbital head gives expression of sadness. When the whole muscle contracts it gives an expression of disdain and contempt.

The **quadratus labii inferioris** is a small quadrilateral muscle which extends from the oblique line of the mandible upward and medialward and is inserted into the skin of the lower lip and the orbicularis oris muscle. It draws the lower lip downward, as in the expression of irony.

The **mentalis** is a short, thick muscle which has its origin in the incisive fossa of the mandible and is inserted into the skin of the chin. The mentalis protrudes the lip and wrinkles the skin of the chin, which expresses disdain or doubt.

The **nasal muscles** vary in size and strength in different individuals, and one or more may be absent.

The nasalis, depressor septi, and the posterior and anterior dilator naris are small muscles about the nasal openings which *constrict and enlarge the apertures of the nares.* The procerus covers the nasal bones and lateral nasal cartilage and is inserted into the skin over the lower part of the forehead between the eyebrows. It draws down the medial angle of the eyebrows and produces transverse wrinkles over the bridge of the nose.

The **orbicularis oris** (ring-shaped muscle of the mouth) consists of numerous layers of muscular fibers which surround the opening of the mouth and pass in different directions. Some of the fibers are derived from other facial muscles which are inserted into the lips; some fibers of the lips pass in an oblique direction from the under surface of the skin through the thickness of the lips to the mucous membrane; other fibers connect the maxillae and septum of the nose above with the mandible below.

Action. It causes compression and closure of the lips in various ways, e.g., tightening the lips over the teeth, contracting them, or causing pouting or protrusion of one or the other.

Nerve Supply. The trigeminal nerve distributes sensory fibers to the face. Motor branches are from the facial nerve.

Movement of the Eye and Lid

Movement of the eyeball is controlled by six muscles. The orbit contains seven muscles; six of them are attached to the eyeball, arranged in three opposing pairs.

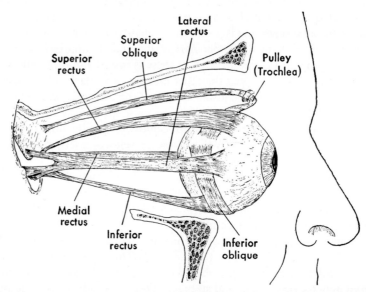

Figure 7–19. The extrinsic muscles of the eyeball in the right orbit. Note tendinous insertions of superior and inferior oblique muscles between the superior and lateral recti.

The four recti muscles, called, respectively, superior, inferior, medial, and lateral, arise at the apex of the orbital cavity. Each muscle passes forward in the position which its name indicates and is inserted into the eyeball.

The two oblique muscles are called, respectively, superior and inferior. The superior oblique arises from the apex of the orbit and courses forward to the upper and inner angle of the orbit, where it passes through a ring of cartilage; then it bends at an acute angle, passes around the upper part of the eyeball, and is inserted between the superior and lateral recti. The inferior oblique arises from the orbital plate of the maxilla and passes around the under portion of the eyeball to its attachment between the superior and lateral recti.

Action. The four recti acting singly turn the corneal surface of the eye upward, downward, inward, or outward, as their names suggest. The action of the two oblique muscles is somewhat complicated, but their general tendency is to roll the eyeball on its axis. These muscles do not act singly but rather cooperatively and with a high degree of coordination.

The levator palpebrae superioris (lifter of the upper lid) arises from the apex of the orbit, passes forward, and is inserted into the tarsal cartilage of the upper lid.

Action. It raises the upper lid and opens the eye.

The orbicularis oculi (circular muscle of the eye) arises from the nasal portion of the frontal bone, from the frontal process of the maxilla, and from a short, fibrous band, the medial palpebral (tarsal) ligament. It spreads lateralward, forming a broad, thin layer which occupies the eyelid, and is inserted at the union of the upper and lower lids at the outer side of the eye. This is called the palpebral portion. A broader, thicker part, called the orbital portion, surrounds the circumference of the orbit and spreads over the temple and downward on the cheek; its fibers form a complete ellipse, the upper ones being inserted in the frontalis muscle.

Action. It serves as a sphincter muscle of the eyelids. The action of the palpebral portion is involuntary. It closes the lids gently as in sleep or blinking. The orbital portion is under the control of the will. The action of the entire muscle is to close the lids forcibly, drawing the parts toward the inner angle and tightening the brow. It is the antagonist of the levator palpebrae superioris.

Nerve Supply. The external recti muscles are supplied by the abducens nerve; the superior oblique, by the trochlear; all the other muscles of the eyeball are supplied by the oculomotor nerve.

Branches of the ophthalmic division of the internal carotid artery supply the eyeball. Venous return is by the superior ophthalmic vein.

Muscles Concerned with Mastication

The muscles of mastication are the masseter (chewing muscle), the temporal (temple muscle), the internal pterygoid, and the external pterygoid.

The masseter arises from the zygomatic process and adjacent portions of the maxilla and is inserted into the angle and lateral surface of the ramus of the mandible.

The temporal (temporalis) arises from the temporal fossa of the skull and the deep surface of the temporal fascia by which it is covered. It is inserted into the coronoid process of the mandible.

The internal pterygoid (pterygoideus internus) arises from the medial surface of the lateral pterygoid plate, the pyramidal process of the palatine bone, and the tuberosity of the maxilla. The fibers pass downward, lateralward, and backward, to be inserted into the ramus of the mandible.

The external pterygoid (pterygoideus externus) is a short, thick muscle which arises by two heads, an upper from the zygomatic surface of the great wing of the sphenoid and a lower from the lateral surface of the pterygoid plate. The fibers extend backward and are inserted in front of the neck of the condyle of the mandible and into the articular disk of the joint between the temporal and mandible bones.

ACTION. The masseter, temporal, and internal pterygoid raise the mandible against the maxillae. The posterior fibers of the temporal retract the mandible.

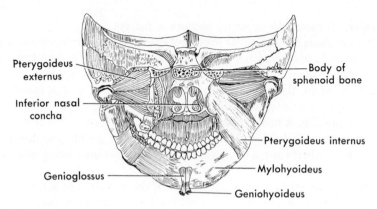

Figure 7–20. The pterygoid muscles viewed from behind, the back portion of the skull having been removed.

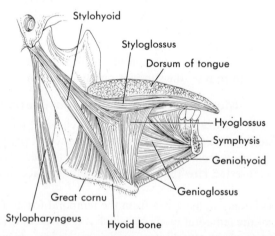

Figure 7–21. The muscles of the tongue viewed from the right side.

The external pterygoid assists in opening the mouth, and the internal and external pterygoids acting together cause the lower jaw to protrude, so that the lower teeth are projected in front of the upper. The internal and external pterygoids of one side produce lateral movements of the jaw such as take place during the grinding of food.

Movement of the Tongue. The muscles of the tongue are concerned with speaking, mastication, and swallowing. They are divided into right and left paired groups by a fibrous septum which is attached below to the hyoid bone. In each side there are two sets of muscles; the *extrinsic* have their origin outside the tongue, and the *intrinsic* are contained within it. Two extrinsic muscles are the genioglossus and the styloglossus.

The genioglossus arises by a short tendon from the inner surface of the mandible at the symphysis and spreads out in a fanlike form. It is attached by a thin aponeurosis to the hyoid bone, and the fibers are inserted the whole length of the under surface of the tongue, in and at the side of the mid-line.

ACTION. It thrusts the tongue forward, retracts it, and also depresses it.

The styloglossus has its origin in the styloid process of the temporal bone and is inserted in the whole length of the side and under part of the tongue.

ACTION. It draws the tongue upward and backward.

Nerves of the Tongue.

Motor—hypoglossal (twelfth cranial nerve)
General sensation—branch of fifth cranial nerve
Taste ⎰ anterior two thirds of tongue—branch of seventh cranial nerve
　　　⎱ posterior third of tongue—branch of ninth cranial nerve

During general anesthesia these, together with all the other muscles, become relaxed, and it is necessary to press the angle of the lower jaw upward and forward in order to prevent the tongue from falling backward and obstructing the larynx.

Movement of the Head

FLEXION	EXTENSION
Sternocleidomastoid	Splenius capitis
	Semispinalis capitis
	Longissimus capitis

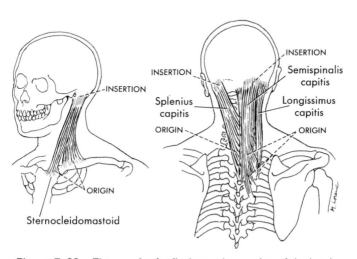

Figure 7–22. The muscles for flexion and extension of the head.

The atlanto-occipital articulation permits flexion and extension of the head. Movement occurs between the condyles of the occipital bone and the superior articular surfaces of the atlas, and a backward and forward movement occurs as in nodding of the head. When movement takes place at the vertical axis, the head is rotated to the right when the muscles on the right side contract and rotated to the left when those on the opposite side contract.

The sternocleidomastoid (sternocleidomastoideus) muscle is named from its origin and insertion. It arises by two heads from the upper part of the sternum and the inner border of the clavicle and is inserted by a strong tendon into the mastoid portion of the temporal bone. This muscle is easily recognized in thin persons by its forming a cordlike prominence obliquely situated along each side of the neck.

Action. When one muscle acts alone, it draws the head toward the shoulder of the same side and rotates the head, pointing the chin upward to the opposite side. Both muscles acting together flex the head in a forward direction, and in forced inspirations they assist in elevating the thorax. If one of these muscles is either abnormally contracted or paralyzed, deformity called *torticollis*, or wryneck, results.

Nerve Supply. Motor, spinal accessory, sensory branches of second and third cervical nerves.

The splenius capitis arises from the lower half of the ligamentum nuchae and from the spinous process of the seventh cervical vertebra and the upper three or four thoracic vertebrae. The fibers extend upward and lateralward and are inserted into the outer part of the occipital bone and into the mastoid process of the temporal bone, under the sternocleidomastoid muscle.

Action. When both muscles act together, the head is pulled backward in extension. Acting alone, the head is rotated to the same side.

The semispinalis capitis arises from the transverse processes of the upper six thoracic vertebrae and from the articular processes of the four lower cervical vertebrae and is inserted between the superior and inferior nuchal lines of the occipital bone.

Action. When both muscles contract, the head is extended; acting alone, the head is rotated toward the same side.

Nerve Supply. Lateral branches of the posterior divisions of second, third, and fourth cervical nerves.

The longissimus capitis arises by tendons from the transverse processes of the upper four thoracic vertebrae and is inserted into the posterior margin of the mastoid process.

Action. When both muscles contract, the head is extended; when the muscle acts alone, the head is bent to the same side and the face is rotated toward that side.

Also see trapezius muscle for action on the head.

Nerve Supply. Branches of the dorsal division of the middle and lower cervical nerves.

Movement of the Vertebral Column

FLEXION	EXTENSION
Quadratus lumborum	Sacrospinalis

Forward and backward movement of the spine is limited in the thoracic region, but movement is free in the lumbar region, particularly between the fourth and fifth lumbar vertebrae.

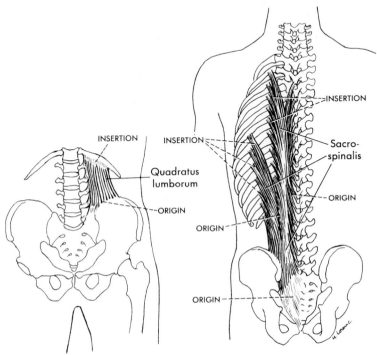

Figure 7–23. The muscles producing movement of the vertebral column in the lumbar region.

The quadratus lumborum is a rectangular muscle which forms part of the posterior wall of the abdominal cavity. It arises from the posterior part of the crest of the ilium and the iliolumbar ligament and is inserted into the lower border of the twelfth rib and upper four lumbar vertebrae.

Action. Acting together, the two muscles flex the spine at the lumbar vertebrae.

Nerve Supply. Direct branches from the first, third, or fourth lumbar nerves.

The sacrospinalis (erector spinae) arises from the lower and posterior part of the sacrum, from the posterior portion of the iliac crests, and from the spines of the lumbar and the lower two thoracic vertebrae. The fibers form a large mass of muscular tissue, which splits in the upper lumbar region into three columns, namely, a lateral, the *iliocostalis*, an intermediate, the *longissimus*, and a medial, the *spinalis*. Each of these consists from below upward of three parts.

These muscles are attached to the ribs and vertebrae at different levels all the way up the back to the occipital bone and the mastoid process of the temporal bone. As the muscle climbs up the back, it does not relinquish one foothold before it establishes another. The result is not merely a continuity of structure but an overlapping, as one segment begins back of the insertion of the segment below it.

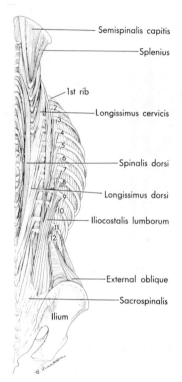

Semispinalis capitis

Splenius

1st rib

Longissimus cervicis

Spinalis dorsi

Longissimus dorsi

Iliocostalis lumborum

External oblique

Sacrospinalis

Ilium

Figure 7–24. Diagram showing location of the deep muscles of the back.

Action. It serves to maintain the vertebral column in erect posture against gravity.

Nerve Supply. Lateral branches—posterior divisions of the spinal nerves.

Movement of the Shoulder Girdle

ELEVATION	DEPRESSION
Levator scapulae	Pectoralis minor
Rhomboideus major	Subclavius
Rhomboideus minor	Trapezius (lower fibers)
Trapezius (upper fibers)	

The levator scapulae arises from the upper four or five cervical vertebrae. It is inserted into the vertebral border of the scapula between the medial angle and the root of the spine.

Action. As the name suggests, it lifts the angle of the scapula.

Nerve Supply. Anterior branches of the third and fourth cervical nerves.

The rhomboideus major arises from the spines of the first four or five thoracic vertebrae and is inserted into the vertebral border of the scapula between the root of the spine and the inferior angle.

The rhomboideus minor arises from the lower part of the ligamentum nuchae and from the spinous processes of the last cervical and the first thoracic vertebrae. It is inserted into the vertebral border of the scapula at the root of the spine.

Action. The rhomboidei carry the inferior angle of the scapula backward and upward and thus produce a slight rotation.

Nerve Supply. Branches of the fifth cervical nerves.

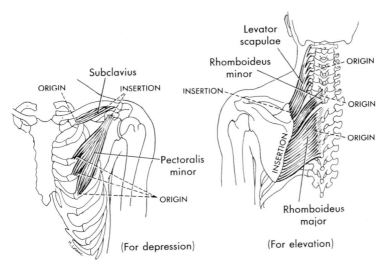

Figure 7–25. Opposing muscle groups that elevate and depress the shoulder girdle.

The pectoralis minor is underneath and entirely covered by the pectoralis major. It arises from the upper margins and outer surfaces of the third, fourth, and fifth ribs near their cartilages and is inserted into the coracoid process of the scapula.

Action. It depresses the point of the shoulder and rotates the scapula downward. In forced inspiration the pectoral muscles help in drawing the ribs upward and expanding the chest.

Nerve Supply. Nerve fibers from the seventh and eighth cervical nerves.

The subclavius arises from the junction of the first rib and its cartilage and is inserted into a groove on the under surface of the clavicle.

Action. The subclavius depresses the shoulder, i.e., carries it downward and forward.

Nerve Supply. Branches from the fifth and sixth cervical nerves.

The trapezius, so called because right and left together make a large diamond-shaped sheet, arises from the occipital bone, the ligamentum nuchae, and the spinous processes of the seventh cervical and the 12 thoracic vertebrae. From this extended line of origin the fibers converge to their insertion in the clavicle, the acromion process, and the spine of the scapula. It is a very large muscle and covers the other muscles of the upper part of the back and neck, also the upper portion of the latissimus dorsi.

Action. If the upper end is fixed, the shoulder is raised, as in shrugging the shoulder or carrying weights on the shoulder. If the shoulders are fixed, contractions of both muscles will draw the head backward; if only one muscle contracts, the head is drawn to that side.

Nerve Supply. Motor, spinal accessory; sensory, branches of second, third, and fourth cervical nerves.

FORWARD MOVEMENT   BACKWARD MOVEMENT
(*abduction*)   (*adduction*)
Serratus anterior   Trapezius

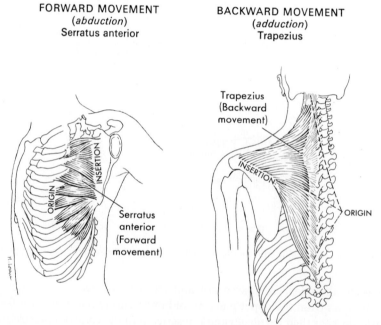

Figure 7–26. Opposing muscles that abduct and adduct the shoulders.

The **trapezius** muscle is described above in relation to elevation and depression of the shoulder girdle. When the whole muscle acts together the scapulae are drawn toward the spine (adduction). At the same time the scapulae are rotated, raising the point of the shoulder or the glenoid cavity upward.

The serratus anterior (serratus magnus) arises from the outer surfaces and superior borders of the upper eight or nine ribs and from the intercostals between them. The fibers pass upward and backward and are inserted in various portions of the ventral surface of the vertebral border of the scapula.

Action. Since its origin is on the chest wall, it moves the scapula forward away from the spine (abduction), as in the act of pushing. It also moves the scapula downward and inward toward the chest wall.

Nerve Supply. Anterior branches of the fifth, sixth, and seventh cervical nerves.

Muscles Having Opposing Action at the Joints
Movement of the Humerus

The shoulder joint is a ball-and-socket joint held by ligaments and tendons. The head of the humerus fits into the shallow glenoid cavity of the scapula. This permits free movement of flexion, extension, abduction, adduction, and rotation.

FLEXION	EXTENSION
Coracobrachialis	Teres major

ABDUCTION	ADDUCTION
Deltoid	Pectoralis major
Supraspinatus	

EXTERNAL ROTATION	INTERNAL ROTATION
Infraspinatus	Latissimus dorsi
Teres minor	

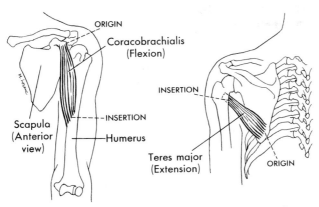

Figure 7–27. Opposing muscles that flex and extend the humerus.

The coracobrachialis is located at the upper and medial part of the arm. It has its origin on the coracoid process of the scapula and is inserted into the middle and medial surface of the humerus.

Action. It carries the arm forward, as in flexion. It also assists in adduction of the arm.

Nerve Supply. Branches from brachial plexus.

Teres major is a thick, flat muscle that has its origin on the dorsal side of the axillary border of the scapula and is inserted into the crest of the lesser tubercle of the humerus.

Action. It extends the humerus, drawing it downward. It also helps to adduct and rotate the arm medially.

Nerve Supply. Branches of subscapular nerve (fifth, sixth, and seventh cervical nerves).

The Deltoid. The deltoid is a thick triangular muscle which covers the shoulder joint. It arises from the clavicle, the acromion process, and the spine of the scapula and is inserted into the lateral side of the body of the humerus.

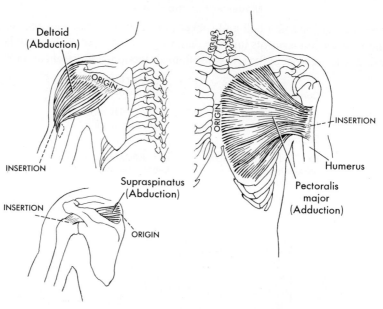

Figure 7–28. Muscles having opposing action for abduction and adduction of the humerus.

Action. Abduction—raises the arm from the side, so as to bring it at right angles to the trunk.

Nerve Supply. Branches of axillary nerve fibers (from the fourth, fifth, and sixth cervical nerves).

The supraspinatus muscle has its origin from the fossa above the spine of the scapula. The muscle passes over the shoulder joint and is inserted into the highest facet of the greater tubercle of the humerus.

Action. It assists the deltoid in abduction of the arm.

Nerve Supply. Branches from the suprascapular nerve, derived from the fifth cervical nerve.

The Pectoralis Major Muscle. The pectoralis major is a large fan-shaped muscle that covers the upper and front part of the chest. It arises from the anterior surface of the sternal half of the clavicle, the anterior surface of the sternum, the cartilages of the true ribs, and the aponeurosis of the external oblique. The fibers converge and form a thick mass, which is inserted by a flat tendon into the crest of the greater tubercle of the humerus.

Action. If the arm has been raised by the abductors, the pectoralis major, acting with other muscles, draws the arm down to the side of the chest. Acting alone, it adducts and draws the arm across the chest, and also rotates it inward.

Nerve Supply. From lateral and medial anterior thoracic nerves (derived from fifth, sixth, seventh, and eighth cervicals, and first thoracic).

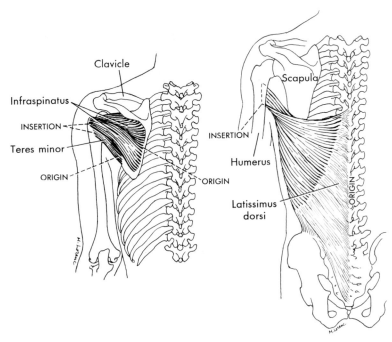

Figure 7–29. The muscles having opposing action for rotation of the humerus. (*A*) Muscles for external rotation, (*B*) muscles for internal rotation.

The infraspinatus muscle has its origin from the infraspinatus fossa on the back of the scapula and is inserted into the middle facet of the greater tubercle of the humerus.

Action. It rotates the humerus outward.

Nerve Supply. From suprascapular nerve, derived from fifth and sixth cervical nerves.

The teres minor is a long, narrow muscle that has its origin from the axillary border of the scapula and is inserted into the lowest facet of the greater tubercle of the humerus.

Action. It functions with the infraspinatus to rotate the humerus outward.

Nerve Supply. Branches of axillary nerve derived from the fifth cervical nerve.

The latissimus dorsi is a flat, broad muscle that has its origin from a broad aponeurosis which is attached to the spinous processes of the lower six thoracic vertebrae, the spinous processes of the lumbar vertebrae, the spine of the sacrum, the posterior part of the crest of the ilium, and from the outer surface of the lower four ribs. Its fibers converge and form a flat tendon which is inserted into the bottom of the intertubercular groove of the humerus.

Action. It rotates the arm inward. It also extends and adducts the humerus.

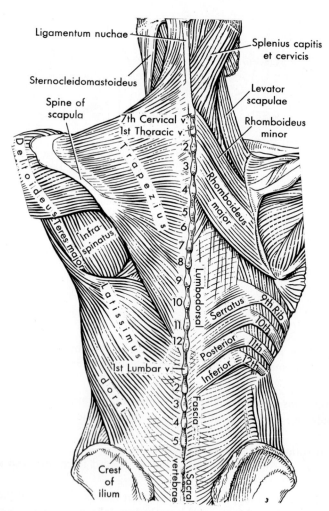

Figure 7–30. Diagram showing the anatomical relations of some of the muscles of the shoulders and back. (Modified from Gray's *Anatomy*.)

Nerve Supply. Long subscapular nerve derived from sixth, seventh, and eighth cervical nerves.

Movement Between the Humerus and Ulna

FLEXION	EXTENSION
Brachialis	Triceps
also	
Biceps brachii	
Brachioradialis	

The brachialis muscle has its origin on the lower half of the anterior surface of the humerus and is inserted into the tuberosity of the ulna and by tendinous bands into the coronoid process.

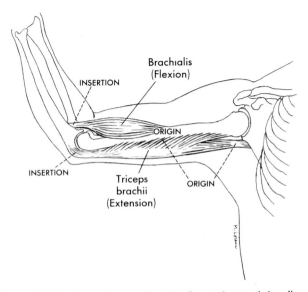

Figure 7–31. Opposing muscles that flex and extend the elbow.

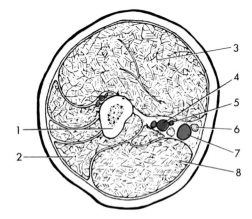

Figure 7–32. Transverse section through the middle of the right upper arm as seen from above. (1) Humerus, (2) brachialis muscle, (3) triceps muscle, (4) brachial artery, (5) companion vein, (6) ulnar nerve, (7) basilic vein, (8) biceps muscle.

Action. It is a strong flexor of the forearm.

Nerve Supply. Branches of the musculocutaneous nerve (branches from fifth and sixth cervical nerves).

The triceps (triceps brachii) arises by three heads, the long head from the infraglenoid tuberosity of the scapula and the lateral and medial heads from the posterior surface of the body of the humerus, the lateral head above the medial. The muscle fibers terminate in two aponeurotic laminae, which unite above the elbow and are inserted into the olecranon of the ulna.

Action. The triceps is the great extensor of the forearm and is the direct antagonist of the brachialis.

Nerve Supply. Radial nerve (sixth, seventh, and eighth cervical nerves).

Movement at the Radioulnar Joint
(Movement of the Hand)

SUPINATION	PRONATION
Biceps brachii	Pronator teres
Supinator (brevis)	Pronator quadratus

The biceps (biceps brachii) arises by two heads. The long head arises from a tuberosity at the upper margin of the glenoid cavity, and the short head from the coracoid process. These tendons are succeeded by elongated bodies which are separate until within a short distance (7 cm) of the elbow joint, where they unite and terminate in a flat tendon, which is inserted into the tuberosity of the radius.

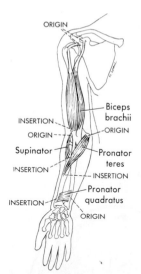

Action. As the biceps contracts, the radius turns outward, supinating the hand. It also flexes the forearm and its long head helps to hold the head of the humerus in the glenoid cavity, thus stabilizing the shoulder joint.

Nerve Supply. Nerve fibers from fifth and sixth cervical nerves, via musculocutaneous nerve.

The supinator (brevis) muscle has its origin on the lateral epicondyle of the humerus and ridge of the ulna and is inserted into the dorsal and lateral margin of the tuberosity and oblique line of the radius.

Action. Supination of the hand.

Figure 7–33. Opposing muscles that supinate and pronate the hand (right arm).

Nerve Supply. Deep radial nerve (fifth, sixth, and seventh branches of cervical nerves).

The pronator teres has two heads of origin, the humeral or larger head and the ulnar. It arises from the medial epicondyle of the humerus and the coronoid process of the ulna. It is inserted into the middle of the lateral surface of the body of the radius.

Action. Pronation of the hand.

Nerve Supply. Branch of median nerve (sixth and seventh cervical nerves).

The pronator quadratus is a small flat, rectangular muscle extending across the lower part of the radius and ulna. It arises from the ulna and is inserted on the radius.

Action. Pronation of the hand.

Nerve Supply. Volar interosseous (sixth, seventh, and eighth cervical nerves and first thoracic).

Movement of the Wrist

FLEXION	EXTENSION
Flexor carpi radialis	Extensor carpi radialis longus
Flexor carpi ulnaris	Extensor carpi ulnaris

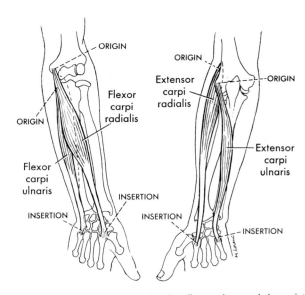

Figure 7–34. Opposing groups of muscles that flex and extend the wrist (left hand).

The flexor carpi radialis muscle arises from the medial epicondyle of the humerus, and its tendon is inserted into the base of the second metacarpal bone.

Action. Flexion of the hand and helps to abduct it.

Nerve Supply. Branches of median nerve (sixth, seventh, and eighth cervical nerves).

The flexor carpi ulnaris muscle arises from the medial epicondyle of the humerus and the upper part of the dorsal border of the ulna. It is inserted into the pisiform bone.

Action. Flexion of the hand and helps to adduct it.

Nerve Supply. Branches of ulnar nerve (seventh and eighth cervical nerves, and first thoracic).

Extensor carpi radialis longus arises from the lower third of the lateral supracondylar ridge of the humerus and is inserted on the dorsal side of the base of the radial side of the second metacarpal bone.

Action. It extends and abducts the hand.

Nerve Supply. Deep radial nerve.

Extensor carpi ulnaris arises from lateral epicondyle of the humerus and is inserted into the base of the fifth metacarpal bone.

Action. It extends and adducts the hand.

Nerve Supply. Deep radial nerve (sixth, seventh, and eighth cervical nerves).

Movement of the Fingers
(A Few of the Muscles)

FLEXION	EXTENSION
Flexor digitorum profundus	Extensor digitorum communis
Flexor digitorum sublimis	

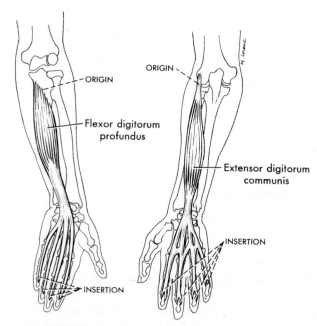

Figure 7–35. Opposing muscles that flex and extend the fingers (left hand).

Nerve Supply. Branches of median nerve (seventh and eighth cervical nerves and first thoracic). See page 213 for details of origin and insertion.

Movement of the Thumb
(A Few of the Muscles)

FLEXION	EXTENSION
Flexor pollicis longus	Extensor pollicis longus
ABDUCTION	ADDUCTION
Abductor pollicis longus	Adductor pollicis obliquus
	Adductor pollicis transversalis

Nerve Supply. Branches of deep radial nerve. Nerve supply of adductor muscle group: deep ulnar nerve. See page 213 for details of origin and insertion.

The diaphragm is a dome-shaped, musculofibrous partition which forms the convex floor of the thoracic cavity and the concave roof of the abdominal cavity.

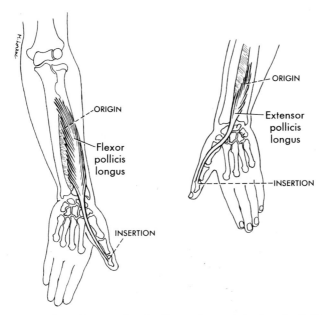

Figure 7–36.   Opposing muscles that flex and extend the thumbs (left hand).

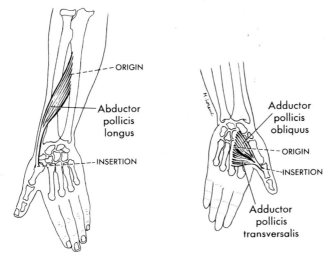

Figure 7–37.   The muscles concerned with adduction and abduction of the thumb (left hand).

The peripheral muscular fibers arise from the lower circumference of the thorax and are inserted into a central tendon. The fibers are grouped according to their origin into three parts: the *sternal*, which arise from the back of the xiphoid process: the *costal*, which arise from the cartilages of the lower six ribs on either

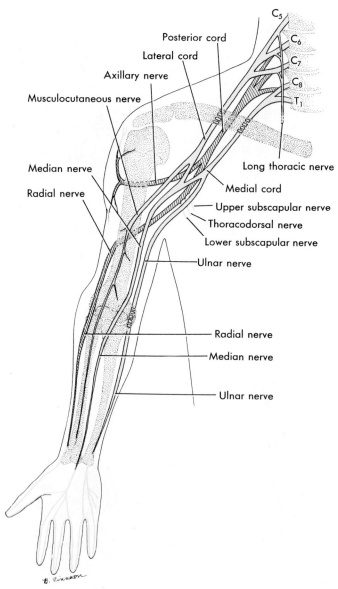

Figure 7–38. Diagram illustrating the brachial plexus and distribution of nerves. Note their relation to bone (right arm).

side; the *lumbar*, which arise from the *lumbocostal arches* and the lumbar vertebrae by two pillars, or *crura*. The *lumbocostal arches* are tendinous arches, one
of which extends from the body to the transverse process of the first or second
lumbar vertebra; the other arch extends from the transverse process of the first

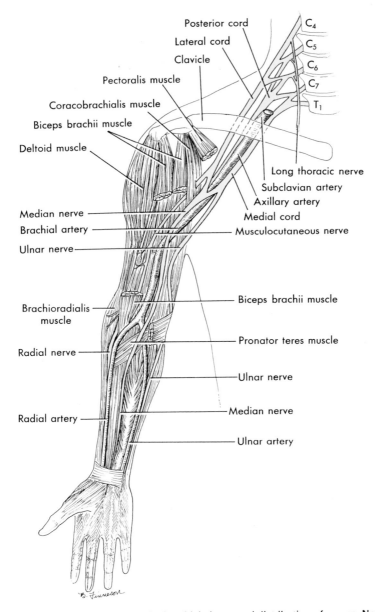

Figure 7–39. Diagram illustrating the brachial plexus and distribution of nerves. Note their
relation to arteries and to muscles (right arm).

lumbar vertebra to the last rib. *Crura* (singular, *crus*) are tendinous slips. The right crus arises from the bodies of the upper three lumbar vertebrae, and the left, from the bodies of the upper two. The fibers converge toward the central portion, which is aponeurotic and serves for the insertion of the muscular portion.

The diaphragm has three large openings: the esophageal, for the passage of the esophagus, some esophageal arteries, and the vagus nerves; the aortic, for the passage of the aorta, the azygos vein, and the thoracic duct (strictly speaking, behind the diaphragm); the vena caval, for the passage of the inferior vena cava and some branches of the right phrenic nerves. The upper, or thoracic, surface of the diaphragm is highly arched; the heart is supported by the central ten-

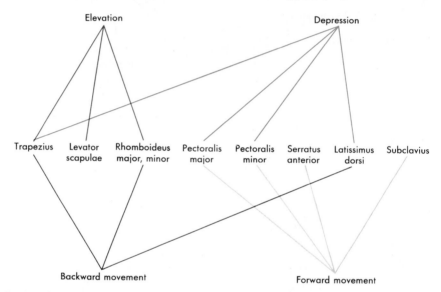

Figure 7–40. Summary of muscle action at the shoulder girdle illustrating multiple functions of muscles.

dinous portion of the arch, the right and left lungs by the lateral portions, the right portion of the arch being slightly higher than the left. The lower, or under, surface of the diaphragm is deeply concave and covers the liver, stomach, pancreas, spleen, and kidneys.

Action. The diaphragm is the principal muscle of inspiration. When the muscular portion contracts, the central tendon is pulled downward, so that the vertical diameter of the thorax is increased.

Nerve Supply. Supplied by branches of phrenic nerve (third, fourth, and fifth cervical nerves).

In forcible acts of expiration and in efforts of expulsion from the thoracic and abdominal cavities, the diaphragm and all the other muscles which tend to depress the ribs and those which compress the abdominal cavity concur in powerful action

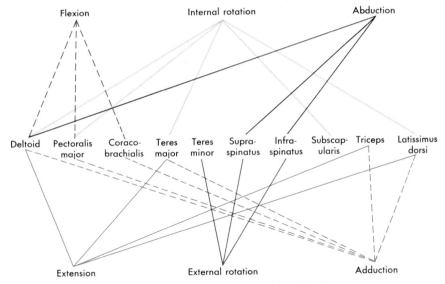

Figure 7–41.   Summary of muscle action of the humerus.

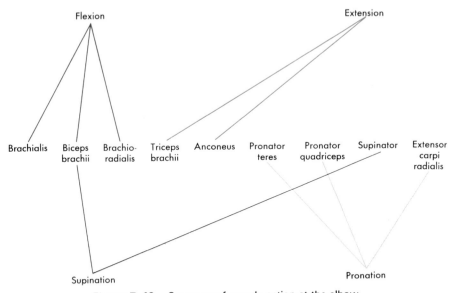

Figure 7–42.   Summary of muscle action at the elbow.

to empty the lungs, to fix the trunk, and to expel the contents of the abdominal viscera. Thus it follows that the action of the diaphragm is of assistance in expelling the fetus from the uterus, the feces from the rectum, the urine from the bladder, and the contents from the stomach in vomiting.

The intercostal muscles (intercostales) are found filling the spaces between the ribs. Each muscle consists of two layers, one external and one internal; and as there are 11 intercostal spaces on each side and two muscles in each space, it follows that there are 44 intercostal muscles. The fibers of these muscles run in opposite directions.

The external intercostals (intercostales externi) extend from the tubercles of the ribs behind to the cartilages of the ribs in front, where they end in membranes which connect with the sternum. Each arises from the lower border of a rib and is inserted into the upper border of the rib below. The direction of the fibers is obliquely downward.

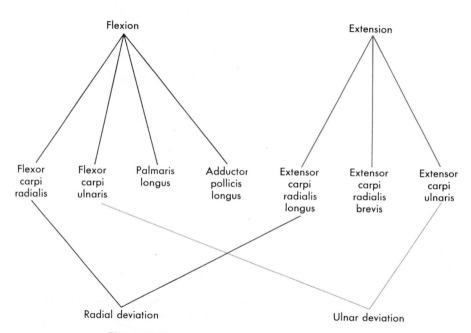

Figure 7–43. Summary of muscle action at the wrist.

The internal intercostals (intercostales interni) extend from the sternum to the angle of the ribs and are connected with the vertebral column by thin aponeuroses. Each arises from the inner surface of a rib and is inserted into the upper border of the rib below. The direction of the fibers is obliquely downward and opposite to the direction of the external intercostals.

Action. Investigators disagree as to the functions of the intercostal muscles. One authority states that the external and internal intercostals contract simultaneously and prevent the intercostal spaces from being pushed outward or drawn inward during respiration. Another classes the external ones as inspiratory and the internal ones as expiratory.

Nerve Supply. Intercostal nerves.

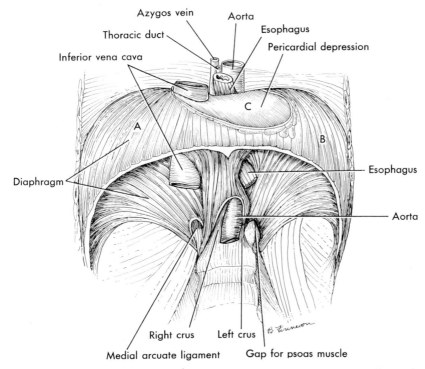

Azygos vein   Aorta
Thoracic duct   Esophagus
Inferior vena cava   Pericardial depression
Diaphragm
Esophagus
Aorta
Right crus   Left crus
Medial arcuate ligament   Gap for psoas muscle

Figure 7–44.   Frontal view of the diaphragm. It is slightly elevated at *A* by the liver and at *B* by the stomach.

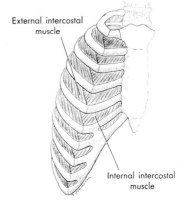

External intercostal
muscle

Internal intercostal
muscle

Figure 7–45.   The intercostal muscles of the right thorax.

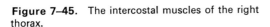

The levatores costarum are 12 small muscles which arise from the transverse processes of the vertebrae from the seventh cervical to the eleventh thoracic. They pass obliquely downward and lateralward like the external intercostals. Each one is inserted into the outer surface of the rib, just below the vertebrae from which it takes origin.

Action. These muscles raise the ribs, increasing the thoracic cavity (inspiratory), and rotate the vertebral column.

Nerve Supply. Intercostal nerves. The first intercostal muscle, eighth cervical nerve.

The Abdominal Muscles

The external, or **descending, oblique** (obliquus externus) is the strongest and most superficial of the abdominal muscles. It arises from the external surface of the lower eight ribs. The fibers from the lowest ribs pass downward and are inserted into the anterior half of the iliac crest; the middle and the upper fibers

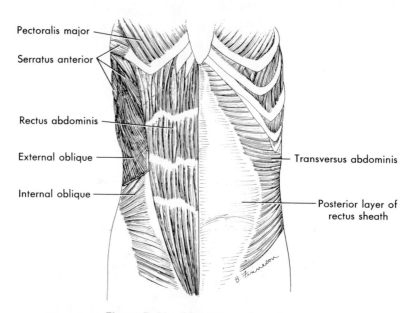

Figure 7–46. The abdominal muscles.

pass downward and forward and terminate in the broad aponeurosis which, meeting its fellow of the opposite side in the linea alba, covers the whole of the front of the abdomen. Between the anterior superior iliac spine and the pubic tubercle, the aponeurosis forms a thick band which is called the *inguinal ligament* (*Poupart's ligament*).

The internal, or **ascending, oblique** (obliquus internus) lies just beneath the external oblique. It arises from the inguinal ligament, the crest of the ilium, and the lumbodorsal fascia. The fibers are inserted into the costal cartilages of the lower four ribs, the linea alba (by means of an aponeurosis), and the crest of the pubis. At the lateral border of the rectus, the aponeurosis divides into two layers, which continue forward, one in front of and the other behind the rectus muscle; they reunite at the linea alba and thus form a sheath for the rectus.

The **transversus** (transversalis) muscle is just beneath the internal oblique. The fibers arise from the lower six costal cartilages, the lumbodorsal fascia, the anterior three quarters of the iliac crest, and the lateral third of the inguinal ligament. The greater part of its fibers have a horizontal direction and end in front in a broad aponeurosis, which is inserted into the linea alba and the crest of the pubic bone.

The **rectus abdominis** is a long, flat muscle, consisting of vertical fibers, situated at the front part of the abdomen and enclosed in the fibrous sheath formed by the aponeuroses of the internal oblique, external oblique, and transversus muscles. It arises from the pubic bone and the ligaments covering the front of the symphysis pubis and is inserted into the cartilages of the fifth, sixth, and seventh ribs. The linea alba, a narrow strip of connective tissue, lies between the two rectus muscles.

Action of the Abdominal Muscles. When these muscles contract, they compress the abdominal viscera and constrict the cavity of the abdomen, in which action they are much assisted by the descent of the diaphragm.

This action assists in expiration. When the diaphragm contracts, the abdominal muscles relax; when the diaphragm relaxes, the abdominal muscles contract. When the abdominal muscles are contracted they assist in parturition, defecation, micturition, and emesis. They also bend the thorax forward. When the muscles of only one side contract, the trunk is bent toward that side.

Nerve Supply. All of these muscles are supplied by branches of the seventh through twelfth thoracic nerves.

The linea alba is a tendinous line in the middle of the abdomen formed by the blending of the aponeuroses of the two oblique and the transversus muscles of both sides. It stretches from the xiphoid process to the symphysis pubis. It is a little broader above than below; and a little below the middle it is widened into a flat, circular space, in the center of which is situated the umbilicus. The pyramidalis muscle increases the tension of the linea alba. It arises from the front of the pubis and is inserted into the linea alba halfway between the umbilicus and the pubis. It is in front of the rectus, within the same sheath.

The Inguinal Canal. Parallel to, and a little above, the inguinal ligament is a tiny canal about 4 cm (1½ in.) long, called the inguinal canal. The internal opening of the canal is called the *abdominal inguinal ring* and is situated in the fascia of the transversus muscle, halfway between the anterior superior spine of the ilium and the symphysis pubis. The canal ends in the *subcutaneous inguinal ring*, which is an opening in the tendon of the external oblique just above and lateral to the crest of the pubis. This canal transmits the spermatic cord in the male and the round ligament of the uterus in the female.

Weak Places in the Abdominal Walls. The abdominal inguinal and the subcutaneous inguinal rings, described above, the umbilicus, and another ring situated just behind the inguinal ligament, called the *femoral ring*, are often the seat of *hernia*.

Hernia, or rupture, is a protrusion of a portion of the contents of a body cavity, and in this instance would mean a protrusion of a portion of the intestine or mesentery through one of these weak places. If it occurs in the umbilicus, it is called *umbilical hernia;* in the inguinal rings, *inguinal hernia;* and in the femoral ring, *femoral hernia.* Conditions which favor hernia are (1) lifting, coughing, etc., which greatly increase the pressure of the abdominal contents against the body wall, and (2) lack of tone of the ventral abdominal wall, which comes about in old age or as the result of illness. The inguinal canal is larger in the male than in the female; hence inguinal hernia is more common in the male than in the female.

Movement of the Femur

The hip joint is a ball-and-socket joint. The head of the femur fits into the deep cup-shaped cavity of the acetabulum (Fig. 6–8, p. 138), held by strong ligaments, yet permitting free movement.

FLEXION	EXTENSION
Psoas major	Gluteus maximus
Iliacus	

ABDUCTION	ADDUCTION
Gluteus medius	Adductor magnus
Tensor fasciae latae	Adductor longus
	Adductor brevis

OUTWARD ROTATION	INWARD ROTATION
Piriformis	Gluteus minimus (anterior part)
Quadratus femoris	Gluteus medius (anterior part)
Obturators	

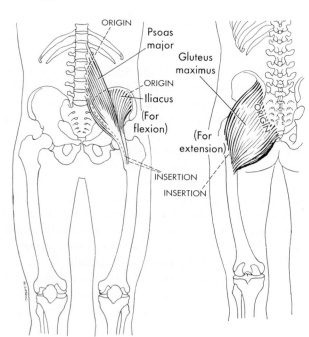

Figure 7–47. The muscles having opposing action for flexion and extension of the femur.

The psoas major (magnus) is a long, powerful muscle that arises from the bodies and transverse processes of the last thoracic and all the lumbar vertebrae with the included intervertebral cartilages. It extends downward and forward, then downward and backward, to its insertion in the small trochanter of the femur.

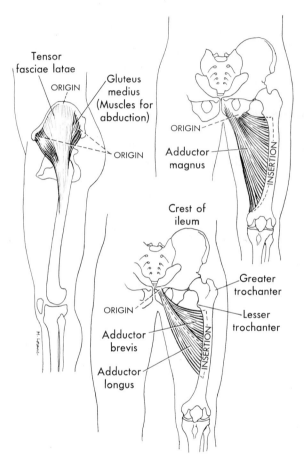

Figure 7–48. The muscles having opposing action for adduction and abduction of the thigh.

The iliacus arises from the iliac crest and fossa. The fibers converge and are inserted into the lateral side of the tendon of the psoas major and the body of the femur below and in front of the lesser trochanter. The relation of this muscle to the psoas major is well shown in Figure 7–47.

Action. The psoas major and iliacus act as one muscle to flex the thigh on the pelvis.

Nerve Supply. Second and third lumbar.

The gluteus maximus is a large, powerful muscle that arises from the posterior fourth of the iliac crest, the posterior surface of the lower part of the sacrum, the side of the coccyx, and the aponeuroses of the sacrospinalis and the gluteus medius. It is inserted into the fascia lata and the gluteal ridge, a prolongation of the upper end of the linea aspera of the femur. The thigh muscles are covered by a heavy cylindrical fascia—the fascia lata—which extends from the highest margin of the thigh to the body prominences around the knee and helps form the capsular ligament of the knee joint. It varies in thickness. In the region of the gluteus maximus and the tensor fasciae latae, it splits into two layers.

Action. It opposes the action of the iliopsoas muscle. It extends the femur and rotates it outward.

Nerve Supply. Inferior gluteal.

Gluteus medius and minimus lie under the maximus on the lateral side of the hip joint.

The gluteus medius arises from the outer surface of the ilium between the crest of the ilium and the posterior gluteal line and is inserted by a strong flat tendon into the lateral surface of the great trochanter.

Action. It abducts the thigh and rotates it inward.

Nerve Supply. From sacral plexus.

The gluteus minimus arises from the outer surface of the ilium and is inserted into the anterior surface of the great trochanter.

Action. It rotates the femur inward, opposing the muscles of outward rotation.

Nerve Supply. Superior gluteal.

The tensor fasciae latae has its origin from the anterior outer part of the crest of the ilium and iliac spine and is inserted into the iliotibial band of the fascia lata.

Action. When the foot is lifted off the ground, it abducts, flexes, and medially rotates the thigh. When the foot is on the ground it flexes and abducts the pelvis and laterally rotates it.

Nerve Supply. Superior gluteal.

Adduction. The three adductor muscles, magnus, longus, and brevis, have origin on the pubic bone and are inserted into the linea aspera of the femur. The *magnus* is large and triangular in shape, has its origin on the inferior ramus of the pubis and ischium, and is inserted the full length of the linea aspera. The *longus* is triangular in shape, has its origin on the front of the pubis, and is inserted into the middle third of the linea aspera. The *brevis* arises from the outer surface of the inferior ramus of the pubis and is inserted into the upper part of the linea aspera.

Action. These muscles are powerful adductors of the femur.

Nerve Supply. Obturator nerve.

The piriformis is a flat pyramid-shaped muscle that arises from the front of the sacrum and passes out of the pelvis through the great sciatic notch to be inserted into the upper border of the great trochanter.

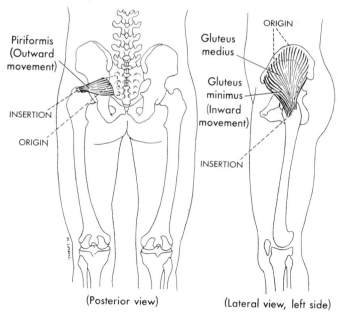

Piriformis
(Outward movement)

INSERTION

ORIGIN

ORIGIN

Gluteus medius

Gluteus minimus
(Inward movement)

INSERTION

(Posterior view)

(Lateral view, left side)

Figure 7–49. Opposing muscles for rotation of the thigh. Other outward rotators are not shown.

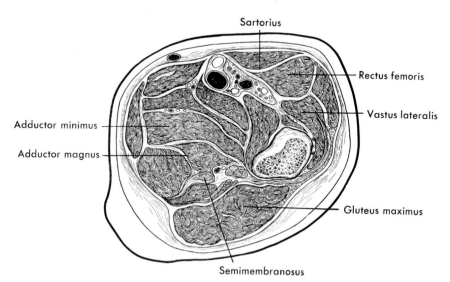

Sartorius

Rectus femoris

Vastus lateralis

Adductor minimus

Adductor magnus

Gluteus maximus

Semimembranosus

Figure 7–50. Transverse section through the right thigh at the level of the small trochanter viewed from above. (Modified from Toldt.)

Action. It abducts the femur and rotates it outward.

The quadratus femoris is a flat quadrilateral muscle that arises from the upper part of the tuberosity of the ischium and is inserted into the upper part of the linea quadrata of the femur.

Action. Outward rotation.

Nerve Supply. Branches from lumbosacral plexus.

The external obturator muscle is a flat triangular muscle that arises from the margin of bone around the obturator foramen and from the outer surface of the obturator membrane. The fibers pass backward, upward, and laterally and end in a tendon that is inserted into the trochanteric fossa of the femur.

Action. Outward rotation of the femur and support of the floor of the pelvis.

Nerve Supply. Obturator nerve.

The following muscles also externally rotate the thigh:

The obturator internus arises from the inner surface of the anterolateral wall of the pelvis, and the greater part of the obturator foramen, and the pelvic surface of the obturator membrane. It is inserted in the fore part of the medial surface of the greater trochanter.

Action. It brings about external rotation of the thigh.

Nerve Supply. Branches of obturator nerve.

The gemellus superior arises from the ischial spine and edge of the lesser sciatic notch. It is inserted in the fore part of the medial surface of the great trochanter.

The gemellus inferior arises from the upper and inner border of the tuberosity of the ischium. It is inserted with the gemellus superior.

Action. They act with the obturator internus.

Nerve Supply. Branches of sacral plexus.

Movement at the Knee Joint

The knee joint has been described as a modified hinge joint, but is really more complicated in character. The condyles of the femur articulate with the condyles of the tibia. The two semilunar rings of fibrocartilage, called the lateral and medial menisci, deepen the articulation. There is also the articulation between the femur and patella. Many ligaments surround and securely hold the joint.

FLEXION	EXTENSION
Biceps femoris	Quadriceps femoris
Semitendinosus	Rectus femoris
Semimembranosus	Vastus lateralis
Popliteus	Vastus medialis
Gracilis	Vastus intermedius
Sartorius	

The biceps femoris arises by two heads, the long head from the tuberosity of the ischium and the short head from the linea aspera of the femur. It is inserted into the lateral side of the head of the fibula and the lateral condyle of the tibia.

Nerve Supply. Branches of tibial nerve.

The semitendinosus arises from the tuberosity of the ischium and is inserted into the upper part of the medial surface of the body of the tibia.

Nerve Supply. Branches of sciatic nerve.

The semimembranosus arises from the tuberosity of the ischium and is inserted on the medial condyle of the tibia.

The tendons of insertion of these muscles are called the hamstrings; hence the muscles are often called the hamstring muscles.

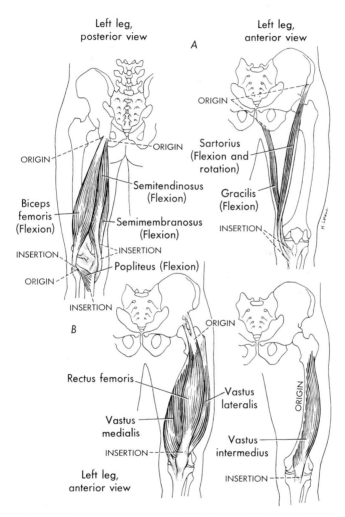

Figure 7–51. (*A*) The muscles concerned with flexion of the knee. The gracilis also adducts the thigh, and the sartorius assists in flexion and lateral rotation of the thigh. (*B*) The quadriceps femoris muscle for extension of the knee.

Action. They flex the leg upon the thigh and extend the thigh. When the knee is flexed, the semitendinosus and semimembranosus rotate the leg inward.

Nerve Supply. Branches of sciatic and tibial nerves.

The popliteus is a thin, flat, short muscle that is located behind the knee joint.

It arises from the lateral condyle of the femur and is inserted into the posterior surface of the body of the tibia.

Action. The popliteus assists in flexing the leg upon the thigh and rotates the tibia inward.

Nerve Supply. Posterior tibial nerve.

The gracilis is a long, slender muscle on the inner side of the thigh. It arises from the symphysis pubis and the pubic arch and is inserted into the medial surface of the tibia below the condyle.

Action. It assists in flexion of the leg and in adduction of the thigh.

Nerve Supply. Branches of obturator nerve.

The sartorius is a long muscle that extends obliquely across the front of the thigh. It arises from the anterior superior spine of the ilium and is inserted into the upper part of the medial surface of the body of the tibia.

Action. It flexes the leg upon the thigh and the thigh upon the pelvis; it also rotates the thigh outward.

Nerve Supply. Femoral nerve.

The quadriceps femoris (quadriceps extensor) is a four-headed muscle covering the front and sides of the thigh. Each head is described as a separate muscle.

1. *The rectus femoris* arises by two tendons, one from the anterior inferior iliac spine, the other from a groove above the brim of the acetabulum.

2. *The vastus lateralis* (vastus externus) arises by a broad aponeurosis from the great trochanter and the linea aspera of the femur.

3. *The vastus medialis* (vastus internus) arises from the medial lip of the linea aspera.

4. *The vastus intermedius* (crureus) arises from the ventral and lateral surfaces of the body of the femur.

The fibers of these four muscles unite at the *lower* part of the thigh and form a strong tendon, which is inserted into the tuberosity of the tibia. The tendon passes in front of the knee joint, and the patella is a sesamoid bone developed in it.

Action. The quadriceps femoris extends the leg, and the rectus femoris portion flexes the thigh.

Nerve Supply. Femoral nerve.

Movement of the Foot

The ankle is a hinge joint. It is formed by the articulation of the tibia, the malleolus of the fibula, and the convex surface of the talus. Movement here gives flexion (dorsiflexion), or foot bent toward the anterior part of the leg, and extension (plantar flexion), or downward movement of the foot. Inversion (supination), or turning the foot in, and eversion (pronation), or turning the foot out, also take place at the joint.

PLANTAR FLEXION	DORSIFLEXION
Gastrocnemius	Tibialis anterior
Soleus	Peroneus tertius
Tibialis posterior	

The **gastrocnemius and soleus** form the calf of the leg. The gastrocnemius arises by two heads from the medial and lateral condyles of the femur. The soleus arises from the back of the head of the fibula and the medial border of the tibia. The direction of both is downward, and they are inserted into a common tendon, the tendo calcaneus (tendo achillis), which is the thickest and strongest tendon in the body. The tendon is about 15 or 16 cm long and starts about the middle of the leg. The tendon receives muscle fibers on its anterior surface almost to the end. It is inserted into the calcaneus, or heel bone.

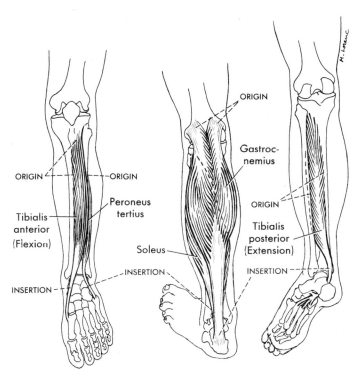

Figure 7–52. The muscles having opposing action for flexion and extension of the ankle.

Action. The gastrocnemius and soleus extend or plantar flex the foot at the ankle joint, and the gastrocnemius flexes the femur upon the tibia.

Nerve Supply. Tibial nerve.

The **tibialis posterior** (posticus) arises from the aponeurotic septum, between the tibia and the fibula, and from the adjoining parts of these two bones. It is inserted into the undersurface of the navicular bone and gives off fibers which are attached to the calcaneus, the three cuneiforms, the cuboid, and the second, third, and fourth metatarsal bones.

Action. It extends the foot at the ankle joint. Acting with the tibialis anterior, it inverts the foot, i.e., turns the sole of the foot upward and medialward.

Nerve Supply. Branches of tibial nerve.

The tibialis anterior (anticus) arises from the lateral condyle and upper portion of the lateral surface of the body of the tibia and is inserted into the under-surface of the first cuneiform bone and the base of the first metatarsal.

Action. It flexes the foot at the ankle joint and with the tibialis posterior raises the medial border of the foot or inverts the foot.

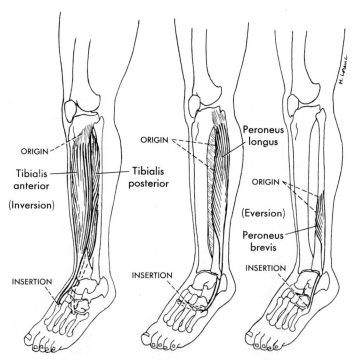

Figure 7–53. Opposing muscles for inversion (supination) and eversion (pronation) of the foot.

The peroneus tertius has its origin from the anterior part of the lower third of the fibula and is inserted on the base of the fifth metatarsal bone.

Action. It flexes and everts the foot.

The peroneus longus arises from the head and the lateral surface of the body of the fibula. The terminal tendon passes under the cuboid bone, crosses the sole of the foot obliquely, and is inserted into the lateral side of the first metatarsal and first cuneiform bones.

Action. It extends and everts the foot and helps to maintain the transverse arch.

The peroneus brevis arises from the lower portion of the lateral surface of the body of the fibula and is inserted into the fifth metatarsal bone.

Action.   Acting with the peroneus longus, it extends the foot upon the leg and everts the foot.

The Muscles of the Foot.   The leg muscles have important relations with the foot; hence, they are called extrinsic foot muscles. The muscles within the foot proper are called the intrinsic foot muscles. There are many small intrinsic muscles which are important in all movements of the foot and in maintaining the arches of the foot.

Nerve Supply.   All of the above muscles are supplied by branches of deep peroneal nerve.

Movement of the Toes

FLEXION	EXTENSION
Flexor hallucis longus	Extensor hallucis longus
Flexor digitorum longus	Extensor digitorum longus

Nerve Supply.   Flexor group, branches of tibial nerve. Extensor group, branches of the deep peroneal. Please see page 217 for details of origin and insertion.

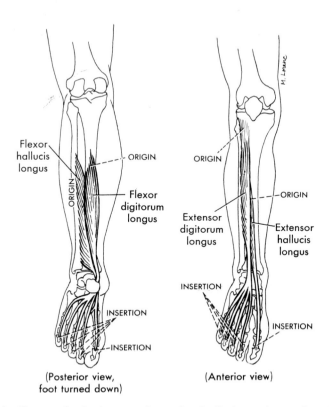

(Posterior view,
foot turned down)

(Anterior view)

Figure 7–54.   The muscles having opposing action for flexion and extension of the toes.

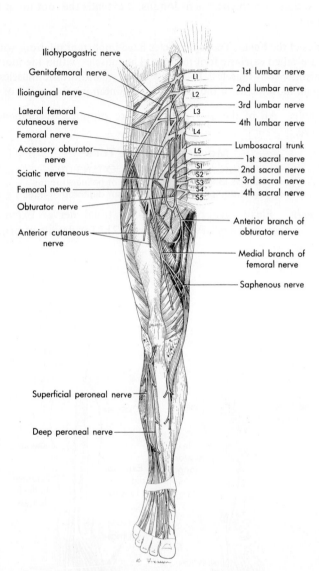

Figure 7–55. Diagram illustrating the lumbosacral plexus and distribution of nerves. Note their relation to muscles (right leg).

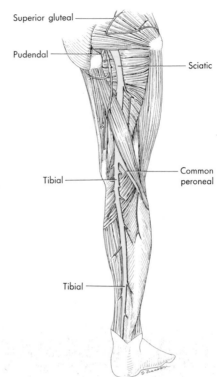

Figure 7–56. Nerve supply to right lower extremity, posterior view.

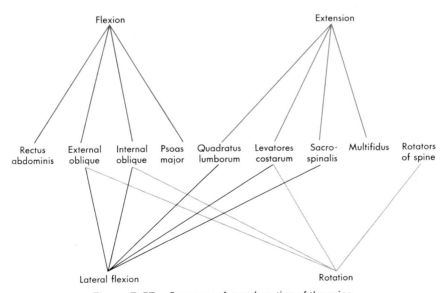

Figure 7–57. Summary of muscle action of the spine.

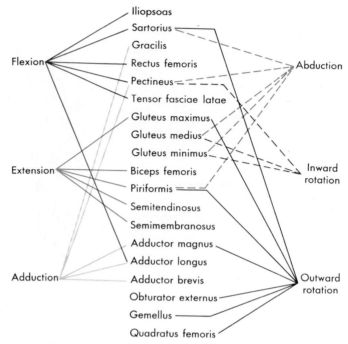

Figure 7–58.   Summary of muscle action of the hip.

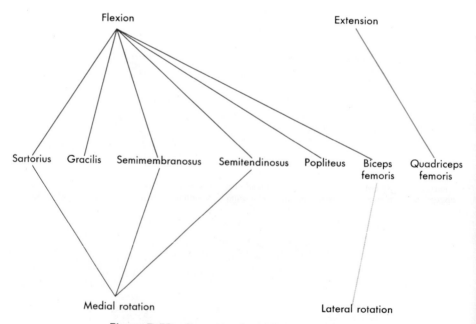

Figure 7–59.   Summary of muscle action at the knee.

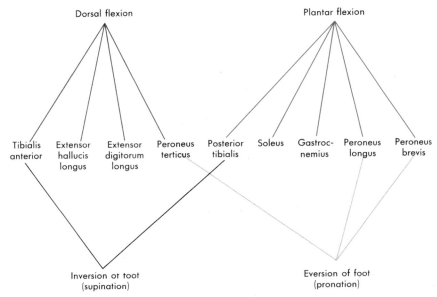

Figure 7–60. Summary of muscle action at the ankle and foot.

QUESTIONS FOR DISCUSSION

1. What groups of muscles are used in the following activities:
   a. Combing the hair?
   b. Climbing stairs?
   c. Turning the face over the right shoulder?
   d. Standing on tiptoe?

2. Why is it important for you to know the location and function of the larger muscles and the relationship of nerves and blood vessels to them?

3. What is the role of ATP during muscle contraction?

4. Distinguish between isometric and isotonic contraction of striated muscle.

5. Explain how an individual can exercise muscles while lying in bed.

6. What three principles of body mechanics should be observed in bending, lifting, and walking? Explain why.

7. In contraction of the biceps muscle in opening a door, what is occurring in the muscle cells in relation to:

   a. Myosin?   d. Oxygen?
   b. Actin?   e. ATP?
   c. The sarcomeres?

SUMMARY

The movements of the body are dependent upon the contractions of muscular tissue

Characteristics of Muscular Tissue
(1) Irritability or excitability—property of receiving stimuli and responding to them
(2) Contractility—muscle becomes shorter, thicker, because the cells do
(3) Extensibility—muscle can be stretched, i.e., property of individual cells
(4) Elasticity—muscle readily returns to original shape

Classification
(1) Striated, skeletal
(2) Nonstriated, visceral
(3) Indistinctly striated, cardiac

Muscular Tissue
Cells become elongated and are called fibers
Intercellular substance between fibers
Connective tissue—supporting framework
Well supplied with nerves and blood and lymph vessels

Striated { Cross-striped Skeletal
(1) Marked with transverse striae
(2) Movements accomplished by it are voluntary
(3) Attached to skeleton
(4) Muscle fibers are long and spindle-shaped
(5) Connective-tissue framework carries blood vessels and nerves
(6) Origin—more fixed attachment
(7) Insertion—more movable attachment
(8) Origin in periosteum of bone or intervening tendon
(9) Insertion either by tendons or aponeuroses
(10) Muscles closely covered by sheets of fasciae
(11) Deep fasciae form annular ligaments in vicinity of wrist and ankle

Function. To operate the bones of the body, producing motion

Nonstriated { Smooth Visceral
(1) Not marked with transverse striae
(2) Movements accomplished by it are involuntary
(3) Found in walls of blood vessels and viscera
(4) Composed of spindle-shaped cells that contain one large nucleus, cells held together by fibrils
(5) Connective-tissue framework carries blood vessels and nerves

Function. To cause visceral motion

Cardiac { Striated Involuntary Visceral
(1) Striated, but not distinctly
(2) Not under control of will
(3) Cells are elongated and branching
(4) Cells grouped in bundles
(5) Connective tissue forms a supporting framework

Function. To cause contraction, thereby ejecting blood from the heart

Physiology of Contraction

Tone
Steady, partial contraction existing under normal conditions
Gives skeletal muscles firmness and a slight, sustained pull upon attachments
Both visceral and cardiac muscle exhibit tonus even when isolated from body

Excitation (stimulation)
A property of all protoplasm
Stimulus—a change in the environment of the cell
Conductivity—a property of protoplasm by which responses are brought about
Artificial stimuli—pressure, temperature, electrical, etc.
Nerve fibers {
Sensory, convey to central nervous system the state of contraction of a muscle
Motor, convey impulses from central nervous system to the muscles and control their contraction

Physiology of Contraction *(cont.)*

Conditions of contraction

Latent period—time between stimulation and contraction
Period of contraction
Period of relaxation

Factors influencing contraction
(1) Strength of stimulus—the stronger (up to a certain maximum) the stimulus, the stronger the contraction of muscle trunk
(2) Duration of stimulus
(3) Weight of load—increase of load decreases the height of contraction
(4) Temperature—optimum is 37° C (98.6° F)

Response to stimuli

All-or-none law—contraction of muscle cell is maximal or none at all for the conditions
Minimal stimulus—the weakest stimulus which will give contraction
Subminimal stimulus—any stimulus weaker than minimal
Summation of stimuli—the combined forces of subminimal stimuli which result in contraction
Chronaxie—the shortest duration of time that a stimulus of twice minimal strength must be applied to evoke a response
Summation of contraction—a maximal contraction resulting from a second stimulus occurring during apex of contraction from the first
Absolute refractory period—the time between the accomplishment of a contraction and the reception of the next stimulus
Tetanus—sustained contraction resulting from rapid succession of stimuli

Types of contractions

Isotonic—muscle shortens and thickens but its tone is not altered
Isometric—tension increases but length of muscle is unaltered

Contraction in skeletal muscle

Voluntary muscle cells are separate units, in contrast to heart muscle, which responds as a unit

Phases in contraction
Contraction
ATP — ADP + Energy. Oxygen not required. Glycogen converted to lactic acid and energy
Recovery
ATP resynthesized from ADP and phosphocreatine. Oxygen needed. Lactic acid oxidized or converted to glycogen by liver cells
During contraction changes occur in ionic concentrations of sodium, potassium, chloride, calcium, and magnesium ions also necessary

Fatigue and exercise

Oxygen debt—when oxygen demand exceeds oxygen supply, lactic acid accumulates
Formation of carbon dioxide at first increases irritability of muscles
Continuous contraction brings about accumulation of waste products, causing fatigue
Moderate exercise aids in getting rid of these waste products
Rigor mortis—fatigue carried to point beyond possible recovery. Protein constituents of muscle fibers coagulate
Fatigue is complex
Other cells than muscles show fatigue
Associated with various mental states
Exercise brings change in conditions (new blood, etc.) for all cells of body. May increase size, strength, and tone of muscle fibers

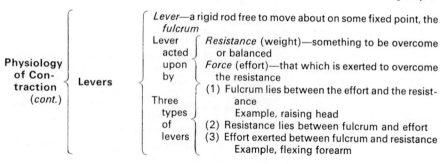

Physiology of Con- traction (*cont.*) — Levers

- *Lever*—a rigid rod free to move about on some fixed point, the *fulcrum*
- Lever acted upon by
  - *Resistance* (weight)—something to be overcome or balanced
  - *Force* (effort)—that which is exerted to overcome the resistance
- Three types of levers
  - (1) Fulcrum lies between the effort and the resistance
    - Example, raising head
  - (2) Resistance lies between fulcrum and effort
  - (3) Effort exerted between fulcrum and resistance
    - Example, flexing forearm

SUMMARY: FUNCTIONALLY IMPORTANT MUSCLES

	NAME OF MUSCLE	ORIGIN	INSERTION	FUNCTION
	Epicranial, or Occipitofrontalis { Occipital	Occipital bone	Aponeurosis—top of skull	Draws the scalp backward
	{ Frontal	Aponeurosis—top of skull	Tissues of the eyebrows	Elevates the eyebrows, causes transverse wrinkles of forehead
	Corrugator	Medial end superciliary arch	Skin of forehead	Wrinkles the skin of the forehead vertically as in frowning
	Buccinator	Alveolar processes of maxilla and mandible	Orbicularis oris muscle	Compresses the cheeks, brings them in contact with the teeth
	Zygomatic	Zygomatic bone	Orbicularis oris muscle	Draws angle of the mouth backward and upward as in laughing
	Triangularis	Oblique line of the mandible	Orbicularis oris muscle	Depresses angle of the mouth
	Platysma	Skin and fascia of the pectoral and deltoid muscles	Mandible and muscles about the angle of the mouth	Depresses the mandible and draws down the lower lip
Facial Expression	Risorius	Fascia over the masseter muscle	The skin of the angle of the mouth	Retracts angle of the mouth, produces an unpleasant grinning expression
	Quadratus labii superioris Angular head Infraorbital head Zygomatic head	Upper part of frontal process of the maxilla Lower margin of the orbit Zygomatic bone	Alar cartilage, skin of nose and upper lip Upper lip Orbicularis oris muscle	Elevates upper lip, angular head dilates the naris Gives expression of sadness
	Quadratus labii inferioris	Oblique line of the mandible below canine and premolar teeth	Skin of lower lip and orbicularis oris muscle	Draws lower lip downward and lateralward as in the expression of irony
	Caninus	Canine fossa of maxilla	Orbicularis oris muscle	Produces the nasolabial furrow
	Mentalis	Incisive fossa of mandible	Skin of chin	Raises and protrudes lower lip, expresses doubt and disdain
	Orbicularis oris	Facial muscles and partition between nostrils and maxillae	Lips and mandible	Closes the lips, sphincter of mouth

NAME OF MUSCLE		ORIGIN	INSERTION	FUNCTION
Facial Expression (*Continued*)	Procerus	Tendinous fibers from fascia, lower part of nasal bones	Skin over lower part of forehead between the 2 eyebrows; its fibers blend with those of the frontalis	Draws angle of eyebrows down and produces transverse wrinkles over bridge of nose
	Depressor septi	Incisive fossa of maxilla	Septum and ala of nose	Draws ala of nose downward, constricting aperture of naris
	Dilator naris posterior Dilator naris anterior	Margin—nasal notch of maxilla and lesser alar cartilage	Skin—margin of nostril	Enlarges aperture of naris
Movement of Eye and Lids	Superior rectus	Apex of orbit	Upper and central portion of eyeball	Rolls the eyeball upward
	Inferior rectus	Apex of orbit	Lower and central portion of eyeball	Rolls the eyeball downward
	Medial rectus	Apex of orbit	Midway on inner side of eyeball	Rolls the eyeball inward
	Lateral rectus	Apex of orbit	Midway on outer side of eyeball	Rolls the eyeball outward
	Superior oblique	Apex of orbit	Eyeball—between superior and lateral recti	Rotates eyeball on its axis, directs cornea downward and lateralward
	Inferior oblique	Orbital plate of the maxilla	Eyeball—between superior and lateral recti	Rotates eyeball on its axis, directs cornea upward and lateralward
	Levator palpebrae superioris	Apex of orbit	Tarsal cartilage of upper lid	Elevates upper lid and opens eye
	Orbicularis oculi	Nasal portion of frontal bone, frontal process of maxilla, and a short, fibrous band, the medial palpebral ligament	Palpebral portion is inserted into lateral palpebral raphe Orbital portion surrounds orbit—upper fibers blend with the frontalis muscle	Palpebral portion closes the lids as in blinking. This action is involuntary Entire muscle closes lids forcibly

NAME OF MUSCLE		ORIGIN	INSERTION	FUNCTION
Mastica-tion	Masseter	Zygomatic process and adjacent portions of maxilla	Ramus of mandible	Raises the mandible and closes the mouth
	Temporal	Temporal fossa	Coronoid process of mandible	Raises the mandible and closes the mouth, draws the mandible backward
	Internal pterygoid	Pterygoid plate, palatine, and maxilla	Ramus of mandible	Raises the mandible and closes the mouth
	External pterygoid	Pterygoid plate and great wing of sphenoid	Condyle of mandible	Moves the jaw forward and sideways, helps to open the mouth
Move-ment of Tongue	Genioglossus	Symphysis of mandible	Hyoid bone and under surface of tongue	Thrusts the tongue forward, retracts it, and also depresses it
	Styloglossus	Styloid process of temporal bone	Whole length of side and under part of tongue	Draws the tongue upward and backward
Movement of Head: Flexion	Sternocleidomastoid	Sternum and clavicle	Mastoid portion of temporal bone	Each muscle acting alone draws the head toward shoulder of same side; both acting together flex the head on the chest or neck
	Splenius capitis	Lower half ligamentum nuchae spinous processes of the seventh and upper 4 thoracic vertebrae	Outer part of occipital bone and mastoid process	When both muscles act together, head is pulled back. Acting alone, head is rotated to same side
Extension	Semispinalis capitis	Transverse processes of upper 6 thoracic and 4 lower cervical vertebrae	Occipital bone	Both muscles acting together, head is extended. Acting alone, head is rotated to the same side
	Longissimus capitis	Transverse processes of upper 4 thoracic vertebrae	Mastoid process	Same as above
Movement of Vertebral Column: Flexion	Quadratus lumborum	Iliac crest and the iliolumbar ligament	Twelfth rib and transverse processes of 4 upper lumbar vertebrae	Acts as a muscle of inspiration by holding outer edge of diaphragm steady, and flexes the spine

Movement of Vertebral Column (cont.)

NAME OF MUSCLE	ORIGIN	INSERTION	FUNCTION

Extension
Sacrospinalis
 Lateral column
   Iliocostalis { lumborum / dorsi / cervicis
 Intermediate column
   Longissimus { dorsi / cervicis / capitis
 Medial column
   Spinalis { dorsi / cervicis / capitis
	Lower and posterior part of sacrum, posterior portion of iliac crests, spines of the lumbar and lower two thoracic vertebrae	Series of attachments to ribs and vertebrae all the way up the back to the occipital bone and mastoid process of temporal bone	Serves to maintain the vertebral column in the erect posture

Movement of Shoulder Girdle:

NAME OF MUSCLE	ORIGIN	INSERTION	FUNCTION
Trapezius (upper fibers)	Occipital bone, ligamentum nuchae, spinous process of the seventh cervical and the spinous processes of 12 thoracic vertebrae	Clavicle, acromion process, and spine of scapula	If upper end is fixed, shoulder is raised If shoulders are fixed, both muscles draw head backward Contraction of whole muscle retracts the scapula and braces back the shoulder
Elevation Rhomboideus major	Spines of first 4 or 5 thoracic vertebrae	Vertebral border of scapula	Carry the inferior angle of the scapula backward and upward and thus produce slight rotation
Rhomboideus minor	Ligamentum nuchae and spinous processes of last cervical and first thoracic vertebrae	Vertebral border of scapula	
Levator scapulae	First 4 cervical vertebrae	Vertebral border of scapula	Lifts the angle of the scapula

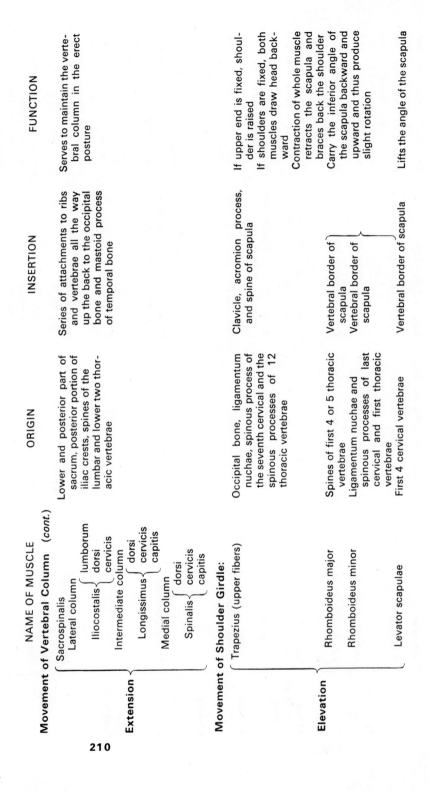

	NAME OF MUSCLE	ORIGIN	INSERTION	FUNCTION
Movement of Shoulder Girdle *(cont.)*				
Depression	Pectoralis minor	Upper margins and outer surfaces of third, fourth, and fifth ribs	Coracoid process of scapula	Depresses the shoulder and rotates the scapula downward
	Subclavius	Junction of first rib and its cartilage	Groove on under surface of clavicle	Carries the shoulder downward and forward
	Trapezius (lower fibers)			
Backward Movement (adduction)	Trapezius	As above		
Forward Movement (abduction)	Serratus anterior	Surfaces and superior borders of upper 8 or 9 ribs	Various portions of the ventral surface of scapula	Carries scapula forward and raises vertebral border as in pushing ; assists deltoid in raising the arm
Movement of Humerus :				
Flexion	Coracobrachialis	Coracoid process of scapula	Mesial surface of humerus	Flexes the arm at shoulder
Extension	Teres major	Dorsal surface, lower part scapula	Crest of lesser tubercle of humerus	Adduction and rotation of arm
Abduction	Deltoideus	Clavicle, acromion process, and spine of scapula	Lateral side of the body of the humerus	Abducts the arm
	Supraspinatus	Supraspinous fossa of scapula	Greater tubercle of humerus	Abducts the arm
Adduction	Pectoralis major	Clavicle, sternum, cartilages of true ribs, and external oblique	Crest, greater tubercle of humerus	It adducts and draws the arm across the chest, also rotates it inward
External Rotation	Infraspinatus	Infraspinous fossa of scapula	Greater tubercle of humerus	Outward rotation of arm
	Teres minor	Axillary border of scapula	Greater tubercle of humerus	Outward rotation of arm
Internal Rotation	Latissimus dorsi	Lower 6 thoracic vertebrae, lumbar and sacral vertebrae, crest of ilium, and lower 3 or 4 ribs	Intertubercular groove of humerus	Lower fibers help to depress scapula Depresses the humerus, draws it backward, and rotates it inward
	Subscapularis	Subscapular fossa of scapula	Lesser tubercle of humerus	Inward rotation of arm

NAME OF MUSCLE	ORIGIN	INSERTION	FUNCTION
Movement of the Elbow:			
Flexion			
Brachialis	Lower half of front of humerus	Tuberosity of ulna and coronoid process	Flexes the forearm
Biceps brachii	Long head from tuberosity at upper margin of glenoid cavity Short head from coracoid process of scapula	Tuberosity of the radius	Flexes the elbow and supinates the hand
Brachioradialis	Supracondylar ridge of humerus	Styloid process of radius	Flexes the elbow joint, assists in bringing hand into supine position
Extension			
Triceps brachii	Long head from infraglenoid tuberosity of scapula, lateral and medial heads from body of humerus	Olecranon of the ulna	Great extensor muscle of forearm
Anconeus	Lateral epicondyle of humerus	Side of olecranon and dorsal surface of ulna	Assists the triceps in extending the forearm
Movement of the Hand:			
Supination			
Biceps brachii	As on page 178		
Supinator (brevis)	Lateral epicondyle of humerus and radial ligament of elbow	Dorsal and lateral surfaces of body of radius	Assists the biceps in bringing hand into supine position
Pronation			
Pronator teres	Humerus and ulna	Body of the radius	Rotates radius upon ulna, renders the hand prone
Pronator quadratus	Pronator ridge on body of ulna	Volar surface of body of radius	Rotates the radius upon the ulna
Movement of Wrist:			
Flexion			
Flexor carpi radialis	Medial epicondyle of humerus	Base of second metacarpal bone	Flexes and abducts the wrist
Palmaris longus	Medial epicondyle of humerus	Transverse carpal ligament and palmar aponeurosis	Flexes the wrist joint, assists in flexing the elbow
Flexor carpi ulnaris	Humerus and ulna	Pisiform, hamate, and fifth metacarpal	Flexor and abductor of wrist, assists in bending elbow

NAME OF MUSCLE	ORIGIN	INSERTION	FUNCTION
Movement of Wrist (*cont.*)			
Extension			
Extensor carpi radialis longus	Supracondylar ridge of humerus	Dorsal surface of base of second metacarpal	Extends the wrist and abducts the hand
Extensor carpi radialis brevis	Lateral epicondyle of humerus	Dorsal surface of base of third metacarpal bone	Extends the wrist; may abduct the hand
Extensor carpi ulnaris	Lateral epicondyle of humerus and dorsal border of ulna	Ulnar side of fifth metacarpal bone	Extends the wrist
Movement of the Fingers:			
Flexion			
Flexor digitorum sublimis	Humerus, radius, and ulna	Second phalanges of the four fingers	Flexes the middle and proximal phalanges, assists in flexing the wrist and elbow
Flexor digitorum profundus	Volar and medial surfaces of body of ulna	Bases of the last phalanges	Flexes the phalanges
Extensor digiti quinti proprius	From tendon of extensor digitorum communis	Tendon of extensor digitorum communis on dorsum of first phalanx of little finger	Extends the little finger
Extension			
Extensor digitorum communis	Lateral epicondyle of humerus	Second and third phalanges of fingers	Extends the phalanges, then the wrist, finally the elbow
Extensor indicis proprius	Dorsal surface of body of ulna	The tendon of extensor digitorum communis	Extends the index finger
Movement of Thumb:			
Flexion			
Flexor pollicis longus	Volar surface of body of radius	Distal phalanx of thumb	Flexes the phalanges of thumb
Extension			
Extensor pollicis longus	Dorsal surface of body of ulna	Base of last phalanx of thumb	Extends terminal phalanx of thumb
Extensor pollicis brevis	Dorsal surface of body of radius	Base of first phalanx of thumb	Extends proximal phalanx of thumb
Abduction			
Abductor pollicis longus	Dorsal surface of body of ulna	Radial side of base of first metacarpal bone	Carries thumb laterally from the palm of the hand
Adduction			
Adductor pollicis obliquus	Capitate bone bases of second and third metacarpals	Ulnar side, base of first phalanx of thumb	Adduct the thumb, bring thumb toward the palm
Adductor pollicis transversus	Base, distal two thirds, volar surface of the third metacarpal bone	Ulnar side, base of first phalanx of the thumb	

Muscles of Respiration

NAME OF MUSCLE	ORIGIN	INSERTION	FUNCTION
Diaphragm	Lower circumference of the thorax	A central aponeurotic tendon	Principal muscle of inspiration, modifies size of chest and abdominal cavity; aids in expulsion of substances from body
External intercostals	Arise from lower border of a rib	Upper border of rib below	Elevates ribs, increases anteroposterior and transverse diameters of thorax
Levatores costarum	Transverse process of vertebrae from seventh cervical to the eleventh thoracic	Outer surface of the rib just below vertebrae from which it arises	Act as rotators and lateral flexors of the vertebral column; may be inspiratory muscles
Internal intercostals	Arise from inner surface of a rib	Upper border of rib below	Decrease thoracic diameters by lowering the ribs
External, or descending, oblique	External surface of lower 8 ribs	Anterior half of iliac crest and broad aponeurosis, meeting its fellow of opposite side in linea alba	Compresses the abdominal viscera
Internal, or ascending, oblique	Inguinal ligament, crest of the ilium, and the lumbodorsal fascia	Lower 4 ribs, linea alba, and crest of pubis	Compresses the abdominal viscera
Transversus abdominus	Lower 6 costal cartilages, lumbodorsal fascia, iliac crest, and lateral third of the inguinal ligament	Linea alba and crest of the pubis	Compresses the abdominal viscera
Rectus abdominis	Pubic bone and ligaments covering front of symphysis pubis	Costal cartilages of fifth, sixth, and seventh ribs	Compresses the abdominal viscera
Levator ani	Posterior surface of body of pubic bone, spine of ischium, and obturator fascia	Side of the coccyx and a fibrous band which extends between the coccyx and anus	Helps to form pelvic floor, constricts the lower end of rectum and vagina

Inspiration
Expiration
Support Pelvic Floor

NAME OF MUSCLE	ORIGIN	INSERTION	FUNCTION
Muscles of Respiration *(cont.)*			
Support Pelvic Floor *(Cont'd)* { Coccygeus	Spine of the ischium	Coccyx and the sides of the sacrum	Helps to form pelvic floor
Psoas minor			
External obturator			
Movement of Femur:			
Flexion { Psoas major	Bodies and transverse processes of last thoracic and all the lumbar vertebrae	Small trochanter of femur	Flexes thigh on pelvis
Iliacus	Iliac fossa	Tendon of the psoas major and body of the femur	Acts with psoas major
Extension Gluteus maximus	Iliac crest, sacrum, side of coccyx, and aponeurosis of sacrospinalis	Fascia lata and gluteal ridge of femur	Extends the femur and rotates it outward
Abduction { Gluteus medius	Outer surface of ilium and gluteal aponeurosis covering it	Lateral surface of greater trochanter	Abduction of thigh and inward rotation
Tensor fasciae latae	Anterior crest and spine of ilium	About one third of way down thigh in fascia lata	Tightening of the fascia lata, abduction and inward rotation of thigh
Adduction { Adductor longus	Front of pubis		
Adductor brevis	Outer surface of inferior ramus of pubis	Linea aspera of femur	Adduct, flex, and rotate thigh outward
Adductor magnus	Inferior ramus of pubis and tuberosity of ischium		
Outward Rotation { Piriformis	Anterior surface of sacrum	Upper border of great trochanter	Supports floor of pelvis, rotates thigh outward
Quadratus femoris	Tuberosity of ischium	Upper part of linea quadrata	External rotation of thigh
Internal obturator	Inner surface of anterolateral wall of obturator foramen and obturator membrane	Fore part of medial surface of greater trochanter	External rotation of thigh

NAME OF MUSCLE	ORIGIN	INSERTION	FUNCTION
Movement of Femur (cont.)			
Outward Rotation			
External obturator	Margin of bone around the obturator foramen and obturator membrane	Tendinous insertion into trochanteric fossa	Supports floor of pelvis, external rotation of thigh
Gemelli	Act with obturators		
Inward Rotation			
Gluteus medius (anterior part)	Outer surface of ilium	Anterior border of greater trochanter	Abduction of thigh and inward rotation
Gluteus minimus (anterior part)			
Movement of Knee Joint:			
Flexion			
Biceps femoris	Tuberosity of ischium, linea aspera of femur	Head of fibula and lateral condyle of tibia	Flex the leg upon the thigh and extend the thigh
Semitendinosus	Tuberosity of ischium	Medial surface of body of tibia	
Semimembranosus	Tuberosity of ischium	Medial condyle of tibia	Assists in flexing leg upon thigh, rotates tibia medially
Popliteus	Lateral condyle of femur	Posterior surface of body of tibia	
Gracilis	Symphysis pubis and pubic arch	Medial surface of tibia below condyle	Adducts the thigh, flexes the leg
Sartorius	Anterior superior spine of ilium	Upper medial surface of body of tibia	Flexes the leg upon the thigh and the thigh upon the pelvis
Plantaris	Linea aspera of femur, popliteal ligament	Calcaneus	Accessory to the gastrocnemius
Extension			
Quadriceps femoris arises by 4 heads:			
(1) Rectus femoris	Anterior inferior iliac spine and brim of acetabulum	Unite and form tendon which is inserted into tuberosity of tibia	Extends the leg upon the thigh; rectus portion flexes the thigh
(2) Vastus lateralis	Great trochanter and linea aspera of femur		
(3) Vastus medialis	Medial lip of linea aspera		
(4) Vastus intermedius	Anterior and lateral surfaces of body of femur		

NAME OF MUSCLE	ORIGIN	INSERTION	FUNCTION
Movement of the Foot:			
Gastrocnemius	Medial and lateral condyles of femur	Calcaneus, or heel bone	The gastrocnemius flexes the femur upon the tibia, the gastrocnemius and soleus together extend the foot at the ankle joint
Soleus	Head of tibia and fibula and medial border of tibia		
Tibialis posterior	Shaft of tibia and fibula and interosseous membrane	Under surface of navicular bone, calcaneus, 3 cuneiforms, the cuboid, second, third, and fourth metatarsals	Extends the foot at the ankle joint
Peroneus longus	Head and lateral surface of body of fibula	Lateral side of first metatarsal and first cuneiform	Extends and everts the foot, helps to maintain transverse arch
Peroneus brevis	Lateral surface of body of fibula	Fifth metatarsal bone	Extends the foot
Tibialis anterior	Lateral condyle and upper portion of body of tibia	Under surface of first cuneiform and base of first metatarsal	Flexes the foot at the ankle joint and, with the tibialis posterior, inverts the foot
Peroneus tertius	Lower third of fibula	Base of fifth metatarsal bone	Dorsiflexes the foot
Movement of the Toes:			
Flexor hallucis longus	Distal two thirds of posterior surface of fibula	Base of last phalanx of great toe	Flexes the great toe
Flexor digitorum longus	Posterior surface of body of tibia	By 4 tendons into last phalanges of 4 outer toes	Flexes the phalanges and extends the foot
Extensor hallucis longus	Anterior surface of fibula	Distal phalanx of great toe	Extend the phalanges of the toes and flex the foot upon the leg
Extensor digitorum longus	Lateral condyle of tibia and anterior surface of fibula	Second and third phalanges of 4 lesser toes	

217

Movement of the Toes (cont.)

NAME OF MUSCLE	ORIGIN	INSERTION	FUNCTION
Extensor digitorum brevis	Calcaneus and cruciate ligament	By 4 tendons—phalanges of medial 4 toes	Extends the phalanges of the medial 4 toes
Flexor digitorum brevis	Medial process tuberosity of calcaneus	Phalanges of second, third, and fourth toes	Flexes the toes
Abductor hallucis	Medial process tuberosity of calcaneus	Tibial side of base of first phalanx, great toe	Abducts the great toe
Abductor digiti quinti	Lateral process tuberosity of calcaneus	Fibular side of first phalanx of fifth toe	Abducts the little toe
Quadratus plantae	Calcaneus and plantar ligament	Tendon of flexor digitorum longus	Assists flexor digitorum longus in flexing the toes
Lumbricales	Tendons of flexor digitorum longus	Dorsal surface of phalanges of lateral 4 toes	Extends the last phalanges of the toes and flexes the first

Other Muscles Functioning in Toe Movement

NAME OF MUSCLE	ORIGIN	INSERTION	FUNCTION
Flexor hallucis brevis	Cuboid and cuneiform	First phalanx of great toe	Flexes the toe
Adductor hallucis Oblique head	Bases of second, third, and fourth metatarsal bones and ligaments	Side of base of first phalanx of great toe	Adducts and aids flexing of the great toe
Transverse head	Plantar metatarsophalangeal ligaments of third, fourth, and fifth toes	Side of base of first phalanx of great toe	Holds head of metatarsal bones together
Flexor digiti quinti brevis	Base of fifth metatarsal bone	Base of first phalanx of the fifth toe	Flexes the little toe, draws its metatarsal bone downward and medialward
Interossei dorsales	Metatarsal bones and ligaments	Phalanges of the second, third, and fourth toes	Abducts these toes
Interossei plantares	Metatarsal bones and ligaments	First phalanges of toes	Adducts the third, fourth, and fifth toes

DISTRIBUTION TO A FEW MUSCLES

SPINAL NERVES		PLEXUSES FORMED	SOME MAIN NERVES	DISTRIBUTION TO A FEW MUSCLES
Cervical	1			
	2	Cervical plexus C2–C4	Branches from plexus	To muscles of occipital triangle; Skin and muscles of cervical region and neck; trapezius, etc.
	3		Phrenic nerve (chiefly C4)	Motor to diaphragm
	3		Branches from plexus	Deltoid Supraspinatus; Pectoralis Infraspinatus; Rhomboides Biceps
	4	Brachial plexus C5–T1	Median and ulnar nerve	Flexor carpi radialis Flexor carpi ulnaris; Flexor digitorum sublimis Flexor digitorum profundus; Flexor pollicis longus Flexor pollicis brevis; Pronators
	5			
	6			
	7		Radial nerve	Triceps Extensor carpi radialis; Brachialis Extensor carpi ulnaris; Brachioradialis Extensor pollicis; Supinator Extensor indicis proprius; Extensor digitorum
	8			
Thoracic	1			
Thoracic	1–12		Intercostal nerves	Levatores costarum Back muscles; Intercostal muscles; Abdominal muscles
Lumbar	1		Femoral nerve	Iliopsoas Quadriceps femoris; Sartorius Knee
	2	Lumbosacral T12–S3	Ventral branches of L5–S2	External rotators of thigh
	3			
	4		Obturator nerve	Gracilis, adductor muscles
	5		Gluteal nerve	Gluteal muscles
Sacral	1		Sciatic nerve	Biceps femoris (long head); Semitendinosus; Semimembranosus
	2	Lumbosacral T12–S3	Medial and posterior popliteal and tibial nerves	Posterior tibial Flexor digitorum; Gastrocnemius Flexor hallucis longus; Soleus Small muscles of foot; Plantaris
	3			
	4		Lateral popliteal and anterior tibial nerves	Biceps femoris (short head); Anterior tibialis; Extensor digitorum longus and brevis; Extensor hallucis longus; Peroneus longus, brevis, tertius
	5			
Coccygeal	1			Muscles over coccyx

8

The Nervous System:
Parts of the Nervous System,
Neurons, Receptors,
Effectors, The Reflex Arc
and Response,
Nerve Impulses

THE VARIED ACTIVITIES of the body are regulated with respect to each other by the general chemical composition of body fluids, including hormones, and by the nervous system. Through the nervous system rapid coordination of the functions of widely separated cells is brought about in cooperation with the body fluids at these distant points. It is also through this medium that acquaintance with the environment is possible.

THE NERVOUS SYSTEM

The parts of the nervous system can be classified in many ways. A simple classification is into brain, spinal cord, and nerves (Fig. 8–1). Another classification follows:

Nervous System
- Central
  - Brain
  - Spinal cord
- Peripheral (cranial and spinal nerves)
  - (1) Connections of "centers" in the central nervous system with the body wall by cranial and spinal nerve fibers. *The somatic* (pertaining to body wall), *or* **cerebrospinal**, *system*
  - (2) Connections of "centers" in the central nervous system with the viscera by **visceral fibers**

Nervous System (cont.)	Peripheral (cranial and spinal nerves) (cont.)	(a) Nerve fibers from the brain and sacral spinal cord. *The craniosacral, or parasympathetic, system*
		(b) Nerve fibers from the thoracolumbar region of the spinal cord and autonomic ganglia. *The thoracolumbar (thoracicolumbar), or sympathetic, system*

The cerebrospinal system is also known as the somatic, craniospinal, or voluntary nervous system. It includes (1) those parts of the brain which are

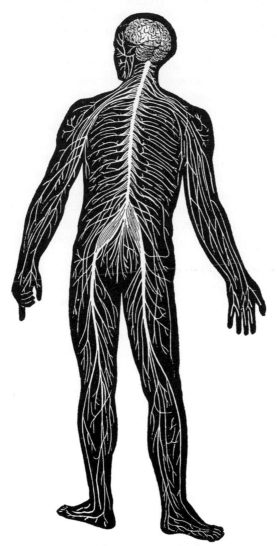

Figure 8–1. Diagram illustrating the brain, spinal cord, and spinal nerves.

concerned with consciousness and mental activities; (2) the parts of the brain, spinal cord, and the nerve fibers, both sensory and motor, that control the skeletal muscles; and (3) the end organs, receptors and effectors, of the body wall.

The autonomic system is also known as the visceral or involuntary system because, unlike the cerebrospinal system, it is not under voluntary control. It includes all parts of the nervous system that innervate the smooth muscles of the blood vessels and the viscera, the heart, and the glands.

The efferent (motor) autonomic system is subdivided into (1) the craniosacral, or parasympathetic, and (2) the thoracolumbar, or sympathetic, divisions. Throughout the body the efferent visceral fibers are found in all the spinal nerves and in most of the cranial nerves with the somatic fibers. The afferent (sensory) fibers of both the somatic and autonomic systems have their cell bodies in the spinal ganglia and enter the cord through the dorsal root.

Although the autonomic and somatic nervous systems are anatomically and functionally independent, their activities are closely integrated both centrally and peripherally. Visceral receptors are capable of initiating somatic activity, and somatic receptors can elicit visceral activity. (See Chap. 10.)

Nerve tissue like other tissue is composed of cells, but these cells differ from other cells in both structure and function. Some nerve cells, or neurons, have long, threadlike projections of their protoplasm which may extend to lengths of 2 to 4 ft, the nerve fiber. The unique functional aspects of neurons are (1) irritability (excitability), or the ability to respond to changes in their environment; and (2) conductivity, or the ability to transmit nerve impulses to other cells.

Neuroglial tissue consists of cells called *glial* cells, which give off numerous processes that extend in every direction and intertwine among the neurons forming a supporting and protecting framework through the brain and cord. Neuroglia is derived from ectoderm. Neuroglia includes the *ependymal* cells, which are found in the choroid plexus and the central canal of the spinal cord. Three types of neuroglia cells can be distinguished as neuroglia proper, or glia. *Astrocytes*, or spider cells, are of two varieties: (1) The *protoplasmic* astrocytes have a large nucleus, abundant cytoplasm, and numerous protoplasmic processes. Many of these are attached to blood vessels and to the pia mater. Some of the smaller protoplasmic astrocytes lie close to the bodies of neurons and are called *satellite* cells. (2) The *fibrous* astrocytes have long, thin smooth branched processes. These cells are frequently found attached to blood vessels by means of their processes. The *oligodendrocytes* resemble the astrocytes. They are smaller and have fewer processes which do not branch. These cells are found in rows along nerve fibers.

Microglial cells are found in both gray and white matter of the nervous system. They are very small, multipolar cells of mesodermal origin. Their function under normal conditions is not clear; however, they function as phagocytic cells when nerve tissue is damaged.

Neurons

Nerve cells are called *neurons* (neurones).[1] Neurons develop from embryonic cells called *neuroblasts*. They vary greatly in size, shape, manner of branching, and number of processes but consist of a cell body and processes. The nervous system consists of an enormous number of neurons. Connective tissue containing blood and lymph vessels penetrates between the cells and forms protective membranes covering all parts of the system.

The cell body of a nerve cell, or perikaryon, consists of a mass of granular cytoplasm surrounding a nucleus. The nucleus, spherical in shape, with a well-defined membrane, is usually centrally placed. Scattered throughout the cytoplasm are the mitochondria and other usual cell constituents, including the

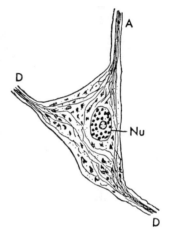

Figure 8–2. Cell body of a nerve cell. (*A*) Axon, (*D, D*) dendrites. (*Nu*) Nucleus with contained nucleolus. The lines represent fibrils in the protoplasm of the cell; the dark spots represent Nissl, or chromophilic, granules. Note the absence of Nissl granules at the base of the axon. This area is known as the axon hillock. (Modified from Opitz.)

Golgi apparatus. Running through the cytoplasm and processes of the nerve cell is an arrangement of fine fibrils called *neurofibrils*. They form a reticulum in the cell body and dendrites and axons. Scattered throughout the cell body and the protoplasm of the larger dendrites is a substance which stains deeply with basic dyes, such as methylene blue. It is called Nissl,[2] or chromophilic, substance and contains ribonucleic acid. The quantity is variable, depending on the fatigue of the cell. The quantity varies from time to time within any one cell. A cell will have less Nissl substance after prolonged activity than after inactivity. This loss of chromophilic substance (chromatolysis) is especially evident following injury to the nerve fiber.

The bodies of nerve cells vary greatly in size. The granule cells of the cerebellum have a diameter of 4 or 5 μ,[3] whereas the large motor cells of the ventral

[1] Cowdry classifies nerve cells into *primitive cells* (as in the myenteric plexus) and *neurons*, which form synapses.

[2] Franz Nissl, German neurologist (1860–1919). Nissl substance is called chromophilic (color-loving) because it takes stains readily. In many nerve cells this substance appears as granules, known as the Nissl, chromophilous, or tigroid bodies.

[3] The micron (symbol μ) equals $^1/_{1000}$ of a millimeter (0.001).

column of the cord may be 125 to 130 μ in diameter. The cells of the lateral columns and of the autonomic ganglia are of medium size.

The cell processes are given off from the cell body. These processes are named dendrites and axons. They differ in many ways.

From the viewpoint of structure they are called dendrites and axons. From the viewpoint of function they are called afferent and efferent.

Dendrites are usually short, rather thick protoplasmic projections of the cell

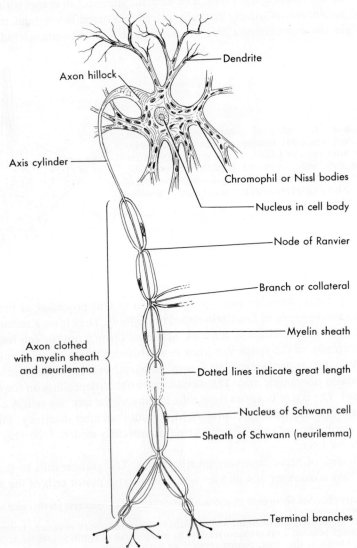

Figure 8–3. Diagram of a motor neuron from the ventral gray area of the spinal cord.

body. They have a rough outline, diminish in caliber as they extend farther from the cell body, and branch in a treelike manner. The number of dendrites varies.

Axons may be long, slender protoplasmic projections of the cell body and in some instances attain a length equal to more than half that of the whole body. They have a smooth outline and diminish very little in caliber. They give off one or more minute branches called *collaterals.* Usually a neuron has only one axon. These axons as they extend away from the cell body may become surrounded with sheaths called myelin. Myelinated fibers appear white. If the fibers lack a sheath, they are called nonmyelinated and appear gray.

The function of the neuron is to generate the nerve impulse, when suitably stimulated, and to convey this impulse to other cells. The structure is such that normally the neuron conducts in only one direction. Consequently each neuron possesses a distinct polarity, and the general arrangement of neurons depends in a large measure upon the connections which they establish with each other for functional purposes. The cell body is the source of energy and affords nutriment to its processes, as is evidenced by the fact that if a nerve fiber is cut, the part separated from the cell body undergoes chromatolysis and dies.

Classification of Neurons. Neurons are classified in many ways. One anatomical classification is based on the number of processes they possess.

1. Bipolar cells are somewhat oval in shape, and from the two poles nerve processes are given off. They are found in the vestibular and cochlear ganglia of the ear. In the ganglia of the dorsal roots of the spinal nerves, so-called unipolar cells give off a single T-shaped process, which rapidly divides. During the early stages of development they are bipolar cells, which gradually develop into the *unipolar* or *pseudounipolar* cells.

2. Multipolar cells possess numerous processes, which correspond to the number of angles or poles possessed by the cell body. It is in the large motor cells of this group that the difference between axons and dendrites is recognized. This group includes, in addition to the motor cells of the spinal cord, the pyramid-shaped cells of the cerebral cortex and the flask-shaped cells of Purkinje[4] found in the cortex of the cerebellum. The pyramidal cells give off branching dendrites from each angle and one axon from the middle of the base. Each cell of Purkinje gives off a single axon from its base and from the apex gives off dendrites, which branch abundantly. A functional classification of neurons is based on the role they perform. Neurons which carry impulses from the periphery to the center are described as *afferent* or *sensory.* The cell bodies of this type of neuron are often at some distance from their terminals. Neurons which carry impulses from the central nervous system to the periphery are described as *efferent* or *motor* if they cause motion, or *secretory* if they cause secretion. The cell bodies of this type of neuron are close to the central end of the fiber. Certain neurons carry impulses from the afferent neurons to the efferent neurons and are designated as *central, connecting, internuncial, intercalated,* or *association cells.*

[4] Johannes Evangelista von Purkinje, Bohemian physiologist (1787–1869).

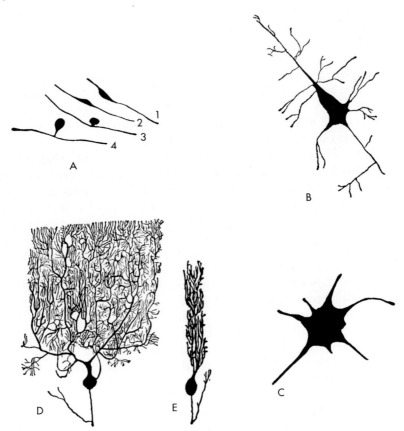

Figure 8–4. Types of neurons. (*A*) Cell of dorsal root ganglion; *1, 2, 3, 4* show how it gradually develops into a unipolar cell. (*B*) Pyramidal cell of cerebral cortex. (*C*) Motor cell of spinal cord. (*D* and *E*) Purkinje cells of cerebellum, (*E*) profile view.

Figure 8–5. Diagram to show coiling of a Schwann cell around an axon. Myelin will form in the clear areas between the layers of Schwann cell cytoplasm. (Modified from Crosby, Humphrey, and Lauer.)

Myelinated Fiber. Microscopic studies of myelinated fibers show them to consist of three parts:

1. A central core, or *axis cylinder*, is the cell process containing cytoplasm, or *axoplasm*, flowing from the cell body, surrounded by cell membrane. Mitochondria are abundant in the axoplasm.

2. Immediately surrounding the axis cylinder is a covering of a semifluid, fatty substance called the *myelin sheath*. It is to this fatty material that myelinated nerve fibers owe their white color. This fatty material, cholesterol and phospholipid, is found in concentric rings separated by the flattened layers of cell membrane from the cytoplasmic extensions of the Schwann, or sheath, cell. At the time that myelin is forming around the axis cylinder, the Schwann cell surrounds it and folds one edge of cytoplasm over the other in a continually spiralling or "jelly roll" fashion, the nucleus remaining at the surface. The myelin layer may be thick or thin; it serves as an electrical insulator and helps determine the speed with which the nerve impulse is transmitted. The thicker the myelin, the faster the impulse travels.

3. External to the myelin sheath is a thin membrane forming the outer covering called the *neurilemma*. In actuality it is the outer coil of cytoplasm of the Schwann cell.

At regular intervals along the course of the myelinated nerve fibers, the myelin sheath is interrupted, and the neurilemma is brought close to the axis cylinder. These constrictions (some 80 to 200 μ apart) are the *nodes of Ranvier*.[5] Interruption of the myelin sheath at the nodes permits sites for ion exchange between the extracellular fluid and the axoplasm. This is probably important for the nutrition of the fiber, but it is indispensable for the transmission of the nerve impulse. Branching of the nerve fiber takes place at the nodes. In each internodal segment the neurilemma contains one *Schwann* cell, which plays a particularly important role during degeneration and regeneration when nerve fibers are cut off from their cell bodies (Fig. 9–17, p. 263). Myelinated fibers found within the brain and spinal cord differ from those of the peripheral nerves in that the neurilemma is absent. Oligodendrocytes which lie between the nerve fibers may perform the same function embryologically as the Schwann cells in forming the myelin sheath.

Nonmyelinated nerve fibers (fibers of Remak[6]) differ from myelinated nerve fibers in the great reduction or absence of the myelin sheath, the fiber being directly invested with the neurilemma. Owing to the absence of the myelin sheath they present a gray or yellow color. Amyelinated fibers are delicate processes of small nerve cells. Most of the cells of the sympathetic ganglia and the small cells of the cerebrospinal ganglia give rise to amyelinated fibers. In the absence of myelin insulation, the conduction of the nerve impulse is very much slower.

Nerve fibers may be grouped in three general groups—the fine fibers (amyelinated and slightly myelinated) having a diameter between 2 and 4 μ, the

[5] Louis Antoine Ranvier, French histologist (1835–1922).
[6] Robert Remak, German physiologist (1815–1865).

medium fibers varying in diameter from 4 to 10 μ, and the large fibers having a diameter from 10 to 20 μ. Many functional characteristics of nerve fibers can be correlated with the axon diameter. In general fine, nonmyelinated nerves need stronger stimuli to excite them and conduct impulses less rapidly than the larger myelinated fibers.

Synapse. Each neuron is a separate and distinct unit. The fine branches of the axon of one neuron seem to interlace with the dendrites of, or lie on the surface of, another neuron, forming a synapse. At the synapse the two neurons involved come into functional contact. There is no protoplasmic continuity of the neurons across the synapse, but there is contact of the terminals, or synaptic knobs, of the axon of one neuron and the cell bodies or dendrites of other neurons. This implies something in the way of a thin "surface layer" or membrane separating the cells, which may act to raise the resistance (threshold) to nerve impulses or may set up fresh nerve impulses.

End organs are the peripheral structures related to nerve fibers. (1) They are sensory, or receptor, if associated with afferent fibers, or (2) effector, or motor, if associated with efferent fibers.

Receptor end organs may be classified as to location into those of epithelium, of connective tissue, and of muscle. The receptor end organs of connective tissue may be *free* or *encapsulated.*

Many receptors are surrounded by capsules of connective tissue and are said to be *encapsulated.* Here the comparatively coarse nerve fiber lies in a semiliquid substance enclosed by a connective-tissue capsule. The myelin sheath is lost; the neurofibrils form a network which shows varicosities. Tactile, bulbous, articular, lamellar, and cylindrical forms are found. The corpuscles of Pacini,[7] Meissner,[8] Ruffini,[9] Krause,[10] the neuromuscular bundle (spindles), and tendon spindles (neurotendinous organs) belong to this group.

MECHANORECEPTORS

1. *Tactile Corpuscles of Meissner* (touch receptor) are ellipsoidal, encapsulated structures found in groups on the skin of the fingertips, lips, and orifices of the body and the nipples. These receptors are stimulated mechanically and adapt rapidly to environment, e.g., we become unaware of clothing.

2. *Pacinian Corpuscles* (Pressure Receptors). These receptors are large and have a lamellated structure similar to an onion. They are numerous in the subcutaneous tissues and tissues around joints and tendons. They respond to firm pressure and are quickly adapting. Their afferent fibers are heavily myelinated.

THERMORECEPTORS

1. *End Bulbs of Krause* (Cold Receptors). These are found in the skin, conjunctiva, lips, and tongue and in the sheaths of nerves. In structure they resemble tactile receptors but are more spherical. Their afferent fibers are heavily myelinated.

---

[7] Filippo Pacini, Italian anatomist (1812–1883).
[8] Georg Meissner, German anatomist and physiologist (1829–1905).
[9] Angelo Ruffini, Italian anatomist (1864–1929).
[10] Wilhelm Krause, German anatomist (1833–1910).

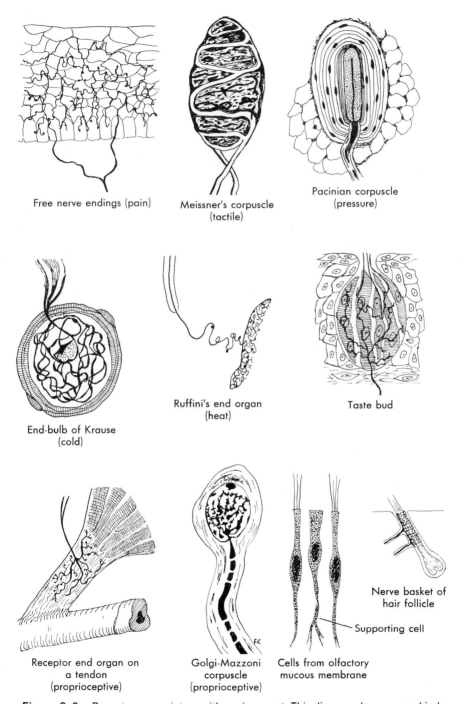

Free nerve endings (pain)

Meissner's corpuscle
(tactile)

Pacinian corpuscle
(pressure)

End-bulb of Krause
(cold)

Ruffini's end organ
(heat)

Taste bud

Receptor end organ on
a tendon
(proprioceptive)

Golgi-Mazzoni
corpuscle
(proprioceptive)

Cells from olfactory
mucous membrane

Nerve basket of
hair follicle

Supporting cell

Figure 8–6. Receptors acquaint us with environment. This diagram shows many kinds.

2. *Ruffini End Organs* (Warm Receptors). They are found in all areas of the skin. For structure see Figure 8–6.

UNENCAPSULATED RECEPTORS. Free unencapsulated nerve endings function as receptors for pain (nocuous stimuli). These receptors can subserve sensations of touch and temperature as well as pain. In the epidermis many of the nerve fibers lose their myelin sheaths, gradually becoming arborized into neurofibrils which ramify between the cells in varying degrees of complexity. Many of these neurofibrils show minute varicose expansions along their courses and at their ends, which are on the surfaces of cells. Free endings of this kind are found in the sclera and cornea of the eye, in the areolar connective tissue or serous and mucous membranes, on muscles and tendons, and in the periosteum of bone.

It must be remembered that all sensations may be experienced even from regions that are devoid of morphologically specific receptor end organs. Hence, specificity of sensation cannot be accounted for in terms of specific receptors. However, in skin areas where morphologically specific receptors are found, sensation is most acute. Absolute thresholds are lowest, differential thresholds are smallest, localization is precise, two-point discrimination is keen, receptive fields are narrow, and small degrees of temperature are recognized.

PROPRIOCEPTORS include receptors located on muscles, tendons, and joints. These are the Golgi and pacinian corpuscles in ligaments and receptor end organs on tendons. They respond to and give awareness and information as to position and movement of a joint or part of the body.

MUSCLE SPINDLES. Muscle spindles are extremely important receptors but it is now believed that their afferent information is not projected to the cortex. Hence, muscle spindles are not concerned with muscle "sensation."

Muscle spindles are 7 to 8 mm long; they lie parallel with muscle fibers. They are found throughout muscle and especially deep in muscle. There are two recognized receptor structures within each muscle spindle: the primary endings and the secondary endings. Both respond to stretch. It is the central connection of the afferent fibers that gives the receptors their respective functional significance.

CHEMORECEPTORS. *Taste buds* of the tongue and mouth are stimulated by dissolved molecules. These are discussed in Chapter 11.

Olfactory Cells. Olfactory cells of the high nasomucous membrane detect and respond to chemical substances in the air. These functions are discussed in Chapter 11.

The cells of the *aortic* and *carotid bodies* respond to altered oxygen and carbon dioxide tensions of arterial blood and pH changes in arterial blood. These functions are discussed in Chapter 18.

Photosensitive Receptors. These receptors are the rods and cones of the retina and respond to light. Their function is discussed in Chapter 11.

Effectors are striated, smooth, or cardiac muscle cell or glandular cells. Motor end-plates or myoneural junctions are elevations of sarcoplasmic areas of striated muscle cells where the rather coarse myelinated nerve fibers lose their myelin sheaths, pass through the sarcolemma, and ramify through the nucleated elevations of sarcoplasm as hypolemmal endings. The whole structure, some 0.04 to 0.06 mm in diameter, is the motor end-plate. *Visceral motor nerve endings* are called cardiomotor, visceromotor, vasomotor, pilomotor, and secretory. In cardiac and smooth muscle, the nerve fibers form arborizations with beaded surfaces and ends. The ends are thought to be hypolemmal, penetrating the surface of the cells. The motor fibers to glands ramify between the cells ending on their surfaces.

Ganglion. *Ganglion* is an aggregate of neural cell bodies outside of the brain and cord. The cell bodies of the visceral and somatic sensory nerves lie in the dorsal root ganglia. The (postganglionic) cell bodies of the visceral efferent nerves lie in the sympathetic and parasympathetic ganglia of the autonomic nervous system. (See Chap. 11.) The cell bodies of spinal ganglia are usually round with a large nucleus. The cytoplasm contains neurofibrils and a network of chromatin-staining material. The cells are surrounded by a single layer of flattened non-nervous cells called capsule or satellite cells. The dorsal root ganglia cells are bipolar. One branch passes into the spinal nerve and continues to the receptor. The other branch passes inward via the dorsal root to the posterior gray column of the same side of the cord. In general the ganglia cells of the autonomic system are similar to those of the cerebrospinal ganglia, but instead of being bipolar they are multipolar; they are smaller and not always surrounded by capsules.

Nucleus. An aggregate of nerve cell bodies within the central nervous system, the fibers of which go to form one anatomical nerve or a tract within the brain or spinal cord, is called a *nucleus*, e.g., the facial nucleus or nucleus of the facial nerve, basal nuclei.

Center. A group of neurons and synapses regulating a certain function is called a *center*. It may be either a nucleus or a ganglion, as these terms refer to an anatomical entity and the term *center* refers to a functional entity. For instance, the rate of respiration is regulated by a *center* in the medulla oblongata, and odor is interpreted by a *center* in the cerebrum. A center may receive information over sensory fibers from a wide variety of receptors. The center then acts like a computer in analyzing and weighing the incoming signals. The response of the center may be a "sensation" or a motor response adjusted appropriately to coordinate all the sensory information. Usually the fibers, which connect the centers with the organs they control, do not extend all the way to the organs but terminate in masses of gray matter which serve as *relay stations*, where they synapse with other neurons that carry impulses onward, possibly to one or more relay stations or directly to the organs. There may be one or several relay stations. In any such series, the neuron first to be stimulated is called the *neuron of the first order*, and the succeeding neurons are called neurons of the second, third, and fourth order, etc.

Gray and White Matter. The cell bodies of neurons and many of their processes and synapses are grouped together into gray matter. *Gray matter* is found in the cortex and other nuclei of the brain and in the core of the spinal cord. It also composes the nuclei and ganglia and the unmyelinated nerve fibers.

The myelinated processes of cell bodies are grouped together into nerves and tracts of brain and cord, forming the *white matter*. It will therefore be seen that the gray matter contains the cell bodies and the synapses where the adjusting of sensory to motor neurons takes place, forming the *collecting and distributing stations*. The white matter is made up of nerve fibers. The white matter of the brain and cord and the myelinated nerves also contain many amyelinated nerve fibers. Groups of nerve fibers in the spinal cord and brain are called *tracts*, e.g., pyramidal tract and ascending tracts.

Nerves. A nerve fiber consists of an axis cylinder with its coverings. A bundle of these fibers enclosed in a tubular sheath is called a *funiculus*. A nerve may

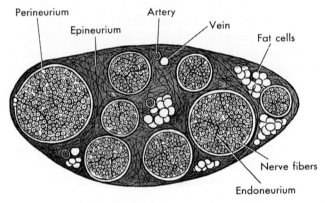

Figure 8–7. Transverse section of the sciatic nerve of a cat. This nerve consists of eight bundles (funiculi) of nerve fibers. Each bundle has its own wrappings (perineurium); and all the bundles are embedded in connective tissue (epineurium) in which arteries, veins, and fat cells can be seen. See Figure 8–3 for the structure of a nerve fiber.

consist of a single funiculus or of many funiculi collected into larger bundles. Between the individual fibers is connective tissue called *endoneurium*, which serves to bind the fibers together into funiculi. Connective tissue called *perineurium* surrounds each funiculus in the form of a tubular sheath, and all the funiculi are held in a connective-tissue covering called the *epineurium*. The capillaries of the blood vessels supplying a nerve penetrate the perineurium and either run parallel with the fibers or form short transverse connecting vessels. Fine autonomic nerve fibers (vasomotor) accompany these capillaries. Considerably more than 75 per cent of a nerve is composed of nonnervous substance —more than 50 per cent of it is loose connective tissue, blood vessels, and more than 25 per cent is myelin.

The nerves branch frequently throughout their courses, and these branches often meet and fuse with one another or with the branches of other nerves; yet each fiber always remains distinct. The nerve is thus merely an association of individual fibers which have very different activities and which function independently of one another. Most nerves are *mixed nerves* containing both sensory and motor fibers. The arrangement of nerve fibers in a nerve trunk can be seen in a cross section of a nerve (Fig. 8–7).

The nerve fibers in a nerve have various diameters. The sciatic nerve of the frog consists of more than 8,000 fibers, more than two thirds of which are amyelinated. The diameters of the fibers of the ventral root of the sciatic nerve range up and down from 14 μ. In general, it has been found that large fibers are heavily myelinated, originate from large cells, and extend to specialized somatic structures, e.g., motor fibers to striated muscle cells. Nerves as a rule contain all sizes of fibers.

The Reflex Arc and Response

The unit pattern, or functional unit of the nervous system is the *reflex arc*. The response that it initiates is the reflex response. A short reflex consists of a sensory, a connecting, and a motor neuron with sensory and motor end organs. Figure

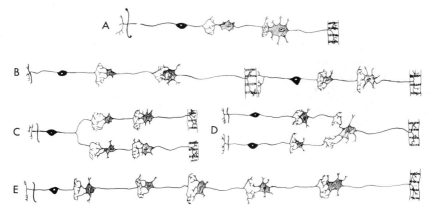

Figure 8–8. Reflex arcs or circuits. (*A*) Reflex arc of three cells—sensory cell body, *black*; connecting cell body, *striped*; motor cell body, *dotted*. (*B*) A short chain reflex of two simple reflex arcs in sequence. (*C*) One sensory cell connected with two motor cells. (*D*) Two sensory cells connected with one motor cell. (*E*) A long simple reflex arc in which there are four connecting cells between the sensory cell and the motor cell.

8–8 shows possible types of linkages of reflex arcs. *A* shows a unit pattern of three neurons; *B*, two reflex arcs in sequence; *E*, a reflex arc in which four connecting neurons extend between the sensory and motor neurons. *C* and *D* show how one receptor can send nerve impulses into two (or many) effectors and how two (or many) receptors can send nerve impulses into one effector. Each part of the reflex arc has its own function in carrying out the reflex response.

The Reflex Response. When an appropriate stimulus is applied to the receptor ending of the sensory neuron, an impulse is initiated which passes along the afferent process to the spinal cord where it synapses with a connecting neuron, which when excited transmits the impulse to the next synapse. Finally a motor neuron is excited, and the nerve impulse is conducted down the efferent fiber, across the peripheral synapse to the muscle or gland cell. Between the simplest form of involuntary activity and the higher activities that involve consciousness, memory, or control are many types of reactions. Reflexes may be classified in many ways:

Stereotyped Reflexes. These depend upon a sensory neuron, a central neuron, and a motor neuron. Stimulation of the sensory neuron results in response by a

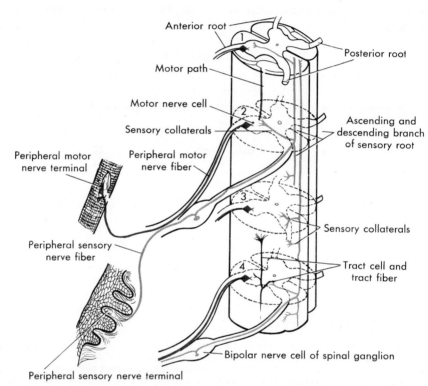

Figure 8–9. Motor (*red*) and sensory (*blue*) conduction paths and reflex arcs of the spinal cord. (Modified from Toldt.)

muscle. Examples of such simple reflexes are the winking reflex caused by an object striking or appearing as if it would strike the cornea, the swallowing re-action due to food on the back of the tongue, avoiding reactions due to tickling, pricking, the application of heat or cold. The presence, absence, and strength of these reflexes are of value in diagnosis of diseases of the nervous system, because in general they are direct, rapid, stereotyped, and persistent and are modified or inhibited only with difficulty.

Neurologists have developed special tests for such reflexes as the *wink*, *pupillary*, and *patellar* reflex. Patellar reflex is the name given to the jerk of the foot caused by tapping upon the patellar ligament while the leg is crossed, or suspended across the edge of a table or chair. The impulses generated in muscle spindles are conveyed to the sciatic center and thence to the quadriceps femoris muscle, which contracts and extends the leg. The varying intensity of this reflex is indicative of the irritability of the entire nervous system. Injuries to the spinal cord may abolish this reflex entirely. Lesions of the higher centers increase its intensity.

Reflexes Involving the Spinal Cord. Some of the reflexes that involve the spinal cord are: (1) those concerned with withdrawal from harmful stimuli, called *flexion reflexes;* walking involves the flexion reflexes; (2) the *extensor* or *stretch reflex*, such as the knee jerk and those concerned with posture and muscle-tone maintenance; (3) the *scratch reflex* or responses to local irritation.

Some spinal cord reflexes are very complex and involve many segments of the spinal cord. In some instances cord reflexes involve the viscera, as in the reflex that empties the bladder. Afferent nerve impulses from the bladder enter the sacral and lumbar regions of the cord over internuncial neurons to the efferent neurons and the bladder is emptied. At the same time sensory impulses travel to higher brain levels and provide for the conscious sensations of, for example, a full bladder.

The reason a reflex may be involuntary yet conscious is that at the same time impulses continue over collaterals to internuncial neurons to the sensory areas of the brain.

Reflexes Involving the Brain Stem and Cerebellum. These involve neurons extending up into the brain stem and cerebellum. These reactions are more complex, less stereotyped, and more readily modified and varied, and, as a rule, involve wider regions of the body. Many of the muscular coordinations concerned with walking, running, etc., are examples of reactions of this kind. The heart, blood vessels, and respiration are regulated by reflex centers in the medulla. Application of heat to an arm or leg causes dilatation of the blood vessels and may also produce sweating by way of reflex circuits through the brain.

When the swallowing reflex is initiated, other reflexes inhibit respiration.

Reflexes Involving the Diencephalon. In a cold environment the receptors of the skin convey impulses to the hypothalamus and the skeletal muscles are reflexly stimulated through efferent fibers so that shivering occurs.

Reflexes Involving the Cerebral Cortex. In the cerebral cortex the possibilities of a wide range of connections between the receptor and effector mechanisms of the body are almost limitless. The reactions often involve many widely different regions of the body. The simple withdrawal of a finger from a prick is an example of a stereotyped reflex. If at the same time one cries out, there is an example of involvement of the brain stem. If in addition one deliberately moves away, there is an example of a reflex involving the cerebrum.

Physiology of the Reflex Arc

Receptor Stimuli. If nerve impulses are to be initiated at the receptors, the stimuli must be adequate and at least minimal. By an *adequate stimulus* is meant the *kind* of change to which the receptor is sensitive. For fiber terminals about the hair follicles the adequate stimulus is mechanical (bending of hairs). This is true also for receptors connected with muscle spindles, tendons, and joints. The adequate stimulus for some end organs is temperature change (for corpuscles of Krause, cold; for corpuscles of Ruffini, warmth); for some the change is brought about by chemical agents (as in taste buds, olfactory cells); for some the adequate stimulus is photochemical (as in the retina). A *minimal* (*threshold*) stimulus refers to the least change which can excite the receptor and produce a response in the effector. This varies greatly in receptor end organs. Subminimal stimuli are below threshold level, but, if repeated at very short intervals, subminimal stimuli may summate and produce nerve activity.

Intensity of stimulus determines the degree of change at the receptor and is reflected in the frequency (number per second) of the impulses initiated. With increase in intensity of stimulus, the frequency of discharge from the receptor increases; also, the more rapid the increase in intensity of stimulus, the more frequent the discharges from the receptor to the nerve fiber.

Adaptation. When an appropriate stimulus is applied to a receptor, the receptor is excited, and nerve impulses are generated and conducted to the central nervous system by the afferent nerve fiber. The number of impulses resulting from a given stimulus depends upon two things: (1) the strength and duration of the stimulus and (2) the inherent properties of the receptors. Some receptors continue to elicit action potentials for as long as the stimulus endures. Other receptors discharge only at the time the stimulus is applied and soon cease discharging, even though the stimulus continues. The former are classed as *slowly adapting* receptors; the latter are *rapidly adapting*. Slowly adapting receptors provide neural information to the central nervous system about steady state conditions. Rapidly adapting receptors report to the nervous system primarily about changes in conditions. For example, receptors at the base of hairs discharge at the moment the hair is bent but promptly cease discharging even though the hair remains in the bent position. Only movement of the hair is signalled to the central nervous system. In contrast, muscle spindles are slowly adapting. If a muscle is stretched, its muscle spindles increase their discharge rate for the entire duration of the stretch. Hence, the muscle spindle is said to be slowly adapting. It reports to the nervous system on the static length of a muscle and not on just the change in length.

The Nerve Fiber and Nerve Impulse. Nerve fibers possess the properties of *irritability* and *conductivity*. Once the nerve impulses are started from the receptor along the fiber, each impulse is like every other impulse; they vary only in frequency and number. The impulses carried by sensory nerve fibers, such as the optic fibers, are similar to those carried by motor nerve fibers. In one instance there is a visual sensation and in the other contraction of a muscle. The difference in result is due to the optic nerve fibers ending in a visual center in the cerebrum and the motor nerve fibers ending in a muscle. In this connection physiologists speak of the "doctrine of specific nerve energies." Regardless of how an optic fiber is stimulated, the subjective sensation will be visual. The nature of the sensation resulting from a given type of stimulus depends upon *what* nerve fibers are excited, not upon *how* they are excited. Normally, impulses start at the receiving end organ of a nerve fiber, but it is possible to induce them at any part of the nerve fiber. When this happens, the brain projects the resulting sensation to the part containing the receptors of the fibers stimulated. This may explain why patients who have suffered an amputation refer the pain to the part that has been removed; the pressure of the surgical dressings or of new tissue on the

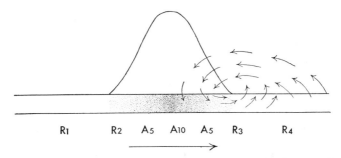

Figure 8–10.   Diagram of frog's motor nerve axon. Shaded region between R_2 and R_3 is occupied by the excitation wave. Excitation beginning at R_3 has reached its maximum at A_{10} and has subsided at R_2. Small arrows indicate direction of *bioelectric current*. Between R_3 and R_4 its intensity is sufficient to excite the fiber. Excitation is thus always being initiated in advance of the area of excitation. The *curve* represents the microvoltage of the bioelectric current, highest at A_{10}. (R. S. Lillie, *Protoplasmic Action and Nervous Action*. Courtesy of the University of Chicago Press.)

nerve fibers excites nerve impulses that are interpreted as having been initiated at the original receptors. Of the many theories that have been advanced to explain the nerve impulse, the membrane theory is most firmly held today.

The axoplasm within the nerve cell differs in ionic concentrations as compared with the fluid outside the cell. In particular, the concentration of potassium ions is higher and the concentration of sodium ions is lower inside than outside the cell. These differences in ionic concentrations are basic to the establishment of a potential difference across the cell membrane, a "membrane potential." In the resting cell the outside is positively charged as compared with the inside. Thus the membrane is said to be polarized and to have a resting membrane potential. It requires a continuous expenditure of metabolic energy in the form of ATP to pump sodium out of the cell. The large ionic concentration differences and the large electrical gradient between the inside and outside of the cell provide a reservoir of potential energy which is readily available for the nerve impulse. When stimulation occurs, normal impermeability to sodium is abruptly but only temporarily lost, sodium enters the cell rapidly for a very short period of time. This inward movement of sodium causes a reversal of the membrane potential, and the outside of the membrane is now negative as compared with the inside and with other points along the membrane. The sodium influx is followed by a rapid outward movement of potassium ions which returns the membrane potential to its resting level. Thus, an action potential has been generated. When one part of the membrane is undergoing the action potential, a small electric current flows from the excited region to the resting region next to it, which in turn undergoes the action potential. Thus, the impulse moves or is conducted along the nerve fiber. The generation of the nerve impulse and its transmission occur within fractions of a second, and the impulse is an electrical change which can be measured in millivolts.

Transmission of Impulses at the Neuromuscular Junction. A nerve impulse is not electrically transmitted across synapses. Transmission of the nerve impulse from the nerve fiber to the skeletal muscle occurs at a specialized region called the neuromuscular junction.

Details of how the nerve impulse is transmitted at this synapse are better understood than for the synapses within the central nervous system. The action potential in the nerve fiber causes the release of acetylcholine which diffuses across the synapse and depolarizes the muscle cell membrane sufficiently to produce a muscle action potential. The muscle action potential in turn excites contraction. The acetylcholine is rapidly hydrolyzed by the enzyme cholinesterase, and the muscle membrane once again repolarizes. Acetylcholine is also known to be the chemical transmitter at some of the synapses in the autonomic nervous system. Nerve impulses move in both directions from a point of stimulation, but normally nerve fibers are *stimulated at their ends*—sensory nerve fibers at their peripheral ends (receptors) and motor fibers from cell bodies which are centrally located.

In the body *the nerve impulse in nerve fibers* is considered to be a self-propagated disturbance (wave of electrical negativity) which, when initiated at the end organ, travels along the fiber by virtue of local electrical changes. Therefore variations of electrical change (*action potentials*) in nerve fibers during excitation and conduction are used to study the characteristics of nerve impulses.

Studied in this way, *the excitability of nerve fiber shows three periods*—the absolute refractory, the relative refractory, and the normal period.

The *absolute refractory period* is the short period following a stimulus during which the nerve fiber is inexcitable. This period makes it impossible for a fiber continuously to respond to stimuli from a receptor. There is, therefore, a "rhythmical discharge" of nervous impulses from receptor to nerve fiber rather than a continuous flow, hence the expression "nervous impulses." Small nerve fibers have longer refractory periods than large fibers.

The *relative refractory period* follows the absolute refractory period. During this time the nerve fiber gradually resumes its excitability and finally returns to the normal period.

Threshold Value of Stimulus. As stated, the intensity of the stimulus at the receptor end of a fiber must reach threshold value before it can excite the fiber. During the *relative refractory period* the stimulus must be stronger than during the *normal phase.*[11] The smaller the fiber, the higher the threshold value of the stimulus must be to produce excitation.

Frequency of nerve impulses usually varies directly with the strength of the stimulus. *Velocity* of conduction of nerve impulses varies with diameter of nerve fiber, the thicker fibers conducting more rapidly than the finer fibers.

Amplitude of the action potential is related to the diameter of the nerve fiber but not to the strength of the stimulus. In general nerve fibers with large axons have higher "spikes" (action potentials) than small axons. Any stimulus strong enough to excite provokes a spike which is independent of the strength of the stimulus. This is known as the all-or-none law, which states that fibers give a

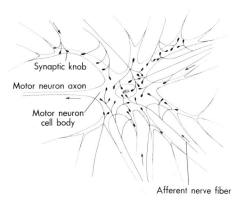

Figure 8–11. Diagram of a motor neuron cell body with dendrite connections from other neurons.

Synaptic knob

Motor neuron axon

Motor neuron cell body

Afferent nerve fiber

maximum response to a stimulus or none at all. An increase in the strength of stimulus does not alter the amplitude of the action potential but it may increase the number of action potentials (the frequency of discharge).

Fatigue of nerve fibers is practically impossible if oxygen and glucose supply is adequate, which is usually the case in normal physiology. While a fiber is conducting, there is first given off a small amount of "initial" heat, and this is followed by "recovery" heat, which is 10 to 30 times as much as initial heat and is given off slowly. This implies chemical changes which in some respects seem to be similar to the metabolic changes in other cells, e.g., glucose oxidation.

Physiology of Nerves and Tracts. Nerves are composed of nerve fibers of various diameters, and most nerves contain both sensory and motor nerve fibers. It has been said that, in general, the larger the fiber, the lower its threshold stimulus, the more rapidly is the excitatory process set up, the shorter is the chronaxie (see p. 152), the greater is the velocity of nerve impulses, the shorter is the refractory period, the greater the strength of the "charges" set up in it, etc.

---

[11] A period of hyperexcitability or supernormal phase occurs, according to Adrian, only when the pH of perifiber fluid is lower than that of plasma.

Nerve fibers have been classified into A, B, and C groups on the basis of their size and activities. The velocity in the A group is about 100 m per second. To this group belong large motor fibers (8 to 18 μ diameter), fibers to skeletal muscle, and fibers from muscle receptors. The fibers of the B group are preganglionic autonomic fibers with conduction velocities of about 10 to 20 m per second, and those of the C group are pre- and postganglionic myelinated and afferent amyelinated fibers with conduction rates of 0.3 to 1.6 m per second. The relation of size to activity is not as clear in the B and C groups as in the larger fibers of the A group. The ventral roots of spinal nerves are composed largely of A-group fibers, whereas the dorsal roots contain fibers of all groups.

Synapses and the Nerve Impulse.   Synapses are found in gray matter of brain, spinal cord, and ganglia. Conduction at synapses differs from that along nerve fibers. The chief differences are:

1. Conduction at the synapse is slower than conduction along a nerve fiber. This suggests that there are some time-consuming events occurring at the synapse.

2. There is greater variability in the ease of transmission.

3. Summation and inhibition occur at the synapses.

4. The refractory period is more highly variable.

5. The synapses are more readily susceptible to fatigue and are more easily affected by anesthetics and drugs.

6. In regions containing many synapses, the blood supply is very rich, which suggests more active metabolism.

7. A nerve fiber is capable of transmitting an impulse either to or from the cell body, but at the synapse the nerve impulse can pass in only one direction, which is from the axon of one neuron to the dendrite of another. In this way a synapse appears to function as a factor in establishing the *polarity* of neurons.

It is at the synapse that conditions determine where the nerve impulse is to go; for instance, in *C*, Figure 8–8, the nerve impulse from a receptor may go to the upper muscle, to the lower muscle, to both, or to neither, depending probably on conditions at the synapse and cell bodies. Thus groups of synapses and cell bodies are often called *adjustors* or centers.

Spreading of Impulses.   All parts of the nervous system are bound together by connecting pathways. Some of these pathways are long, well-defined bundles of fibers connected in a way to facilitate uniform and definite responses to stimulation. Other pathways are diffuse, poorly integrated, and not well adapted to conduct impulses for long distances. Incoming impulses have many pathways open to them. Usually the varying resistance offered at different available synapses prevents their too wide diffusion, and the formation of pathways reinforces this limitation. However, a strong stimulus may produce a great spreading of impulses through the gray matter; and in extreme cases efferent impulses may be sent to all the muscles, causing contractions and resulting in convulsions. In early life spreading of impulses occurs much more readily than in later years, which accounts for the fact that conditions which cause marked muscular contractions or convulsions in a child often cause only mild contractions or a chill in adults. In some cases weak stimuli may cause marked spreading. It is thought that (1) certain drugs such as strychnine and caffeine affect the synapses and render the passage of impulses easier; (2) some toxins produce a state of abnormal irritability or sensitiveness; and (3) there may be a summation of mild stimuli at the synapses caused by various irritations.

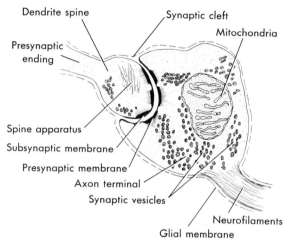

Figure 8–12. Diagram of an electron micrograph of an axodentritic synapse in the cerebral cortex. (Modified from Strong and Elwyn.)

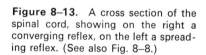

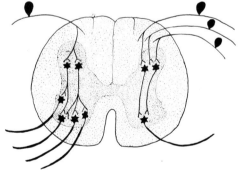

Figure 8–13. A cross section of the spinal cord, showing on the right a converging reflex, on the left a spreading reflex. (See also Fig. 8–8.)

Convergence of impulses. Nerve impulses from many receptors may converge to one effector mechanism over a nerve fiber which becomes the *final common path.* Each muscle is thus connected with a number of receptors, and it follows that the stimulation of two receptors will produce a more vigorous response than the stimulation of one; three will be more effective than two, etc. The energy of one impulse is added to the energy of other impulses activated at the same time, when all have more or less open pathways to a common effector.

Facilitation. After repetition of a reflex act, its establishment becomes increasingly easy, and the reaction time lessens, within limits. This is known as facilitation and is the basis of habit formation and conditioned reflexes.

Reaction Time. This term is applied to the time elapsing between the application of a stimulus and the beginning of a response. Reaction time varies in different individuals and in the same individual under different conditions, depending upon the strength of the stimulus (the stronger the stimulus, the more prompt the response), the nature of the stimulus (e.g., the response to sound is more prompt than that to light), and the number of synapses through which impulses are transmitted. The number of synapses determines to some extent the length of time required for response.

It is sometimes stated that the time required for conduction within the nerve centers may be 12 times as great as that required for conduction along the sensory and motor nerve fibers. The time within the center varies, depending upon (1) the strength of the stimulus, and (2) the condition of the nerve centers, the time being lengthened by any condition, such as fatigue, that lessens the irritability of the center.

The *speed* at which a nerve impulse travels along a nerve fiber varies in different varieties of fibers but is estimated to be about 80 to 120 m (393 ft) per second in a myelinated nerve fiber in man. In general, the speed of the nerve impulse varies with the diameter (or cross-sectional area) of the fiber. The velocity of the nerve impulse over any nerve refers to the velocity over the largest fibers of that nerve.

Automatic Action. Some of the nerve centers are in a state of constant stimulation due to some unknown inherent property and to substances contained in the circulating blood which are constantly acting upon them. In consequence they are constantly discharging impulses to the organs they innervate. The centers controlling respiration and the action of the heart are of this type and are described as automatic.

Inhibition. One tends to think of activation of a neuron and production of the impulse as resulting in action, e.g., stimulation of a second neuron, stimulating muscles to contract or glands to secrete. This is not always the case; some neurons are inhibitory, and their activities prevent the second neuron from discharging. It is interesting that an electrical impulse which seems identical in all neurons can in one neuron stimulate and in another inhibit. Recent experiments with neurons of the central nervous system indicate that inhibition is related to ionic membrane permeability as is excitation. However, when an inhibitory neuron is stimulated, as the impulse reaches the synapse, instead of lowering the permeability of the second neuron, so that sodium moves into the cytoplasm, the opposite occurs; the membrane permeability to potassium of the second neuron is increased, and the cell, instead of being depolarized, is *hyperpolarized,* the inside becomes even more negative with respect to the outside and is, therefore, less excitable (or inhibited).

Inhibitory neurons are primarily located in the central nervous system (although some autonomic neurons are inhibitory). The spinal cord has many fibers which descend from cells in the inhibitory areas of the brain. When a motor neuron affecting skeletal muscle action receives an impulse from these fibers, the result is inhibition or decreased excitability of the motor neuron. A good example is relaxation of flexor muscles of the arm when extensor muscles contract—one set of motor neurons is inhibited when the other set is stimulated and vice versa. All reflexes can be inhibited as well as stimulated. Spreading and convergence of impulses, facilitation, and inhibition make a wide range and greater variety of reactions possible. Physiological conditions at the synapses are important in relation to the ease and direction of the traveling of the nerve impulses over these reflex mechanisms.

Reflexes whose adjusting mechanism is in the spinal cord may be inhibited by centers in the cerebrum. Micturition is an example. Micturition is probably brought about as a spinal reflex, the stimulus starting from receptors in the bladder itself, so that when the bladder is filled, it automatically empties itself. By training in early infancy, this reflex may be inhibited from the cerebrum, so that micturition takes place only under voluntary control. The same is true of defecation. These are examples of "modulated" primitive reflexes. If the conducting paths to the cerebrum are interrupted, the spinal reflex may resume control, resulting in involuntary micturition and defecation.

Effectors, or the ends of motor fibers, are discussed on page 230.

Energy Production. Energy must be provided within the nerve cells not only for transmission of the nerve impulse, but also for synthesis of highly specific compounds which contribute to the structure of these cells. It is well established that the primary source of energy for the cells of the nervous system is through the oxidation of glucose. About one quarter of the oxygen used throughout the body is delivered to these cells. Study of the arterial and venous circulation to the brain indicates a very direct relation between the uptake of glucose and of oxygen. Moreover, all of the enzymes required for oxidation of glucose are found within the nerve cells. Very little glycogen is stored; consequently they are largely dependent upon glucose of the blood for energy production. Dependence of brain cells on carbohydrate metabolism is illustrated by the fact that the first symptoms of hypoglycemia are reflected in the nervous system; in insulin shock unconsciousness may result. The cells are also very sensitive to oxygen shortage and prolonged deprivation of oxygen results in permanent damage to nerve cells.

Fatigue in the Nervous System. Fatigue in nerve cells may occur at the synapses in the anterior horn cells, in the sympathetic chain, or at the neuromuscular junction. Fatigue does not readily occur in nerve fibers. Various authorities state that a normal neuron, when stimulated, first increases in size (owing to increased metabolism), but that long-continued activity decreases the size of the cell bodies and reduces the granular material of the cytoplasm and the chromatic material of the nucleus. If the fatigue is not excessive, a period of rest will restore the cells to a normal condition. Nerve fatigue is induced by both mental and muscular work.

Sensation of fatigue (more psychological than relating to the nervous system per se) is favored by poor health and mental conflict of any kind, such as sorrow, anger, worry, fear. Conscious effort to keep the attention concentrated induces fatigue. Work done under compulsion, as from a sense of duty, results more readily in fatigue than when interest is the driving motive.

Constant irritation such as eyestrain, abnormal conditions of the feet, prolonged distention of the intestine with feces such as occurs in chronic constipation—in fact anything that causes pain or a continued sense of discomfort brings about conditions in the nervous system similar to those caused by fatigue.

It is often stated that change of activity is equivalent to rest. It is questioned whether this is true of mental activity; but it may be true of muscular activity, and the explanation offered is that when nervous stimuli are altered, new pathways and new groups of muscles are called into play. For example, a person who is tired of housework may go out of doors and walk, because the fresh air, changed environment, and different thoughts serve as new stimuli, travel different brain paths, and throw into activity different groups of muscles.

QUESTIONS FOR DISCUSSION

1. Name and discuss the structure and function of each part of the neuron.
2. Where are myelinated and nonmyelinated fibers located? Differentiate between nerve fibers of the brain and cord and those in peripheral nerves.
3. What is an appropriate stimulus for receptors that are:
   a. In the skin?
   b. On muscles and tendons?
   c. Chemoreceptors?
4. What is the relationship between fatigue and reaction time?
5. In an acute stress situation, might reaction time be increased or decreased? Explain.

SUMMARY

The nervous system cooperates with the body fluids in coordinating activities of the body

Classification of parts of the nervous system (p. 220)

Neurons
- Consist of
  - Cell body, or cyton, source of energy and affords nutrient
  - Cell processes
    - *Dendrites*, short, thick, rough outline, branch freely
    - *Axons*, long, smooth, few branches
- Function, to receive impulses and convey them to other cells
- Classification based on number of processes
  - Bipolar cells
  - Multipolar cells
- Classification based on functions
  - Afferent (receptor, sensory) carry impulses from periphery to center
  - Efferent (effector, motor) carry impulses from center to periphery

Neurons (cont.)

Nerve fibers

Myelinated, white
Consist of:
- Axis cylinder
- Medulla, or myelin sheath
- Neurilemma, or sheath of Schwann

Function of myelin sheath is insulation, and it possibly plays part in chemical processes involved in the production of nerve impulses

Nodes of Ranvier, constriction, myelin sheath absent, branching of fiber, permit rapid conduction velocity

Nonmyelinated, gray or yellow
Myelin sheath reduced or absent

Synapse, probably interlacing of branches of axon of one neuron with dendrites and cell bodies of another neuron; no protoplasmic continuity

End Organs

(1) Receptor

Mechano-receptors
- Tactile corpuscles   Touch receptors
- Pacinian corpuscles   Pressure receptors

Thermo-receptors
- End bulbs of Krause—cold receptors
- Ruffini end organs—warm receptors

Unencapsulated receptors
- Free nerve endings for pain

Proprioceptors
- On muscles, tendons, joints—give awareness and information as to position and movement

Muscle spindles
- Lie parallel with muscle fibers
- Respond to stretch

Chemoreceptors
- Taste buds—tongue and mouth
- Olfactory cells high in nasomucous membrane
- Cells of the aortic and carotid bodies
- Respond to altered oxygen and carbon tensions of arterial blood and to the pH of arterial blood

Photosensitive receptors
- Rods and cones of the retina

(2) Motor, or effector
- Motor end-plates
- Visceral motor nerve endings

Nucleus, a group of the cell bodies within the central nervous system, the fibers of which form one anatomical nerve, or tract, within the brain or cord

Ganglion, a group of the cell bodies of several neurons outside the central nervous system

Center, a group of neurons regulating a certain function; may be either a nucleus or a ganglion

Nerves

(1) **Funiculus,** a bundle of fibers enclosed in a tubular sheath
(2) **Endoneurium,** connective tissue between the individual fibers
(3) **Perineurium,** connective tissue surrounding each funiculus
(4) **Epineurium,** connective tissue covering several funiculi

Reflex Arc, structural unit of nervous system
Reflex Response, functional unit of nervous system

Reflex Arc and Response

Classification of activities or reactions

(1) Stereotyped reflexes such as withdrawal of finger from prick
(2) Involving neurons extending up into brain stem and cerebellum, such as crying out when finger is pricked
(3) Involving neurons in the cerebral cortex, such as dressing of wound after finger is pricked

Reflex Arc and Response (*cont.*)

Receptor end organs
(1) May be simple fiber ends, or these ends may be surrounded by accessory structures
(2) *Stimuli* are physical or chemical changes in the immediate environment
(3) Changes in environment are converted into a rhythmical succession of nervous impulses

Receptor stimuli
(1) *Adequate* stimulus, the *kind* of physical or chemical change to which the receptor is sensitive
(2) *Minimal* stimulus, the *least* change that can excite a receptor
(3) *Subminimal* stimulus, a stimulus below the threshold level which fails to excite
(4) *Intensity* of stimulus, probably related to the degree of change at the receptor and reflected in the frequency of impulses initiated

Adaptation
Adaptation of end organs varies in relation to the speed with which they reach approximate equilibrium with their environment
(1) *Slow* adaptation, long trains (sequences) of nerve impulses issue from end organs in response to prolonged stimulation
(2) *Rapid* adaptation, short trains of impulses issue from end organs even though stimulus is prolonged

The nerve impulse
(1) All impulses of similar nature whether carried by sensory or motor nerves
(2) Self-propagated disturbance
(3) Excitability of nerve fiber shows three periods
    (*a*) Normal period or phase,
    (*b*) Absolute refractory period, a short period during which the nerve fiber is inexcitable to any stimulus regardless of strength
    (*c*) Relative refractory period, period of less excitability than normal phase—stronger than normal stimulus required to excite
(4) Frequency of nerve impulse varies with the strength of the stimulus
(5) Velocity of conduction of nerve impulse varies with diameter of fiber
(6) Amplitude of nerve impulse is inherent property of cell
(7) Spreading of impulses greater in early life

Automatic action (constant stimulation) of some nerve centers due to inherent property and to substances in blood

Reaction time, time elapsing between application of a stimulus and beginning of response

Depends upon
(1) *Strength* of stimulus
(2) *Nature* of stimulus
(3) *Number* of synapses through which impulses are transmitted

Fatigue of nerve cells
When first stimulated neurons increase in size
Long-continued activity
    Decreases size of cell bodies
    Reduces granular material of cytoplasm
    Reduces chromatin of nucleus

Due to
Accumulation of waste products
Exhaustion of nutritive material of cell

Result—resistance at synapse increased

CHAPTER **9**

The Spinal Cord and Spinal Nerves, The Brain and Cranial Nerves

RECEPTORS are stimulated by alterations in their environment. Thus, physical energies are converted into nerve impulses which speed along the sensory fibers of the peripheral nerves; these afferent fibers enter the spinal cord and either terminate or ascend to the medulla or thalamus. Other cells convey the impulses to various parts of the brain for interpretation. Impulses which begin in the brain are conveyed by efferent fibers down the spinal cord where they terminate around the large motor cells in the ventral gray of the cord. The fibers of these cells form the motor components of the peripheral nerves. Thus the spinal cord serves to connect the brain with peripheral nerve processes, receptors, and motor end organs.

THE SPINAL CORD

A brief sketch of the lower animals, characterized as segmental, is helpful in understanding the structure and functions of the spinal cord. Segmental animals are made up of a number of smaller units which may be capable of leading an independent existence. This is made possible by the fact that each segment possesses separate circulatory, digestive, excretory, and nervous systems, so that the segments may be separated without endangering or seriously impairing their life processes. As far as the nervous system is concerned, each segment of these animals is equipped with a centrally placed ganglion from which nerve fibers

247

extend in all directions to the different tissues of the segment. A stimulus applied to its surface is soon followed by movement or some other motor response. The nervous elements allotted to each segment are arranged in the form of reflex circuits, their centers being located in a central ganglion. The life of the animal as a whole, however, requires a certain *correlation* between the activites of its different segments and a *subordination* of the latter to the functional necessities of the whole. This end is attained, first, by intermediary neurons which unite the successive ganglia with one another and, second, by a hyperdevelopment of the head ganglion which thus gains a directing control over the other segments.

A nervous system of this kind is reflex in its nature and forms the basal stem around which the nervous system as it appears in the highest animals is eventually developed. The head ganglion is comparable to the brain and the segmental ganglia, to the spinal cord, and from these parts the afferent and efferent fibers arise.

The spinal cord is lodged within the spinal canal of the vertebral column. It consists of gray and white matter extending from the foramen magnum of the skull, where it is continuous with the medulla oblongata, to about the second lumbar vertebra.

The spinal cord diminishes slightly in size from above downward and presents two spindlelike enlargements—the cervical enlargement (level of fourth cervical to second thoracic vertebrae) and the lumbar enlargement (level of tenth thoracic, widest at twelfth thoracic), which dwindles as the *conus medullaris* ending at the level of the first or second lumbar vertebra, where it gives rise to the nonnervous threadlike *filum terminale*. The filum terminale punctures the dura mater at the level of the second sacral vertebra and terminates on the first coccygeal vertebra (Fig. 9–2). At these enlargements the nerves supply the arms and legs, respectively. Since the spinal cord ends opposite the first and second lumbar vertebrae, the roots of the lumbar, sacral, and coccygeal nerves must have a means of reaching their proper intervertebral foramina. Hence these nerves descend in the dural sac along with the filum terminale. This bundle of fibers is known as the cauda equina, as it resembles a horse's tail. The average length of the cord is about 45 cm (18 in.). It is incompletely divided into lateral halves by a ventral fissure and a dorsal sulcus, the ventral fissure dividing it in the middle line in front and the dorsal sulcus in the middle line behind. Because of these fissures only a narrow bridge of the substance of the cord connects its two halves. This bridge, the *transverse commissure*, is traversed throughout its entire length by a minute *central canal*, which opens into the fourth ventricle at its upper end and, at its lower, terminates blindly in the filum terminale.

Meninges, or Membranes. The spinal cord does not fit as closely into the spinal canal as the brain does into the cranial cavity but is suspended within the canal. It is protected by three membranes and nourished not only by the arterial supply to the spinal cord, but also by the cerebrospinal fluid which circulates between the membranes, especially in the subarachnoid space. These membranes are continuous with the membranes covering the brain and are called by the

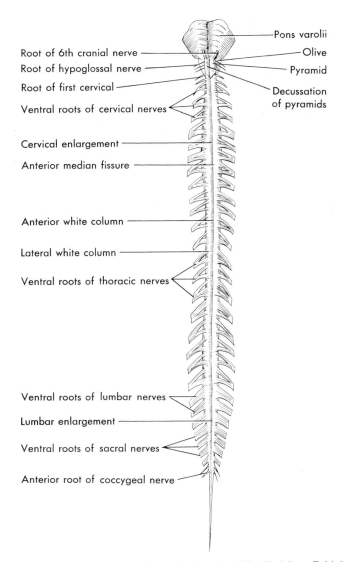

Root of 6th cranial nerve
Root of hypoglossal nerve
Root of first cervical
Ventral roots of cervical nerves
Cervical enlargement
Anterior median fissure
Anterior white column
Lateral white column
Ventral roots of thoracic nerves
Ventral roots of lumbar nerves
Lumbar enlargement
Ventral roots of sacral nerves
Anterior root of coccygeal nerve

Pons varolii
Olive
Pyramid
Decussation of pyramids

Figure 9–1. Ventral view of the spinal cord. (Modified from Toldt.)

same names, the *pia mater* closely investing the cord, the *arachnoid mater*, and the *dura mater* outside. The spinal fluid serves to moisten and lubricate the cord and protect it against changing pressures and mechanical damage.

Structure of the Cord. The cord consists of gray and white matter. The gray matter consists of nerve cells and nerve fibers held together by neuroglia. The white matter consists of nerve fibers embedded in a network of neuroglia. The gray and white matter are supported by connective tissue and are well supplied with blood and lymph vessels. The blood supply is from the anterior spinal artery and from a succession of small arteries which enter the spinal canal through the intervertebral foramina; these branches are derived from the vertebrals, the intercostals, and the arteries in the abdomen and pelvis.

The *gray matter* is in the interior surrounding the central canal and on cross section appears to be arranged in the form of the letter H. The transverse bar on the H is called the *gray commissure* and connects the two lateral masses of gray matter. On each side the gray matter presents a ventral, or anterior, and a dorsal,

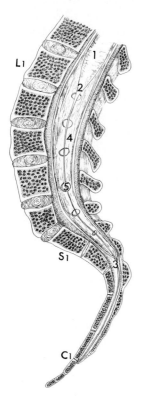

Figure 9–2. Longitudinal section of the vertebral column, showing the end of the spinal cord. (*1*) Beginning of conus, (*2*) end of conus and beginning of filum terminale; (*3*) filum punctures dura, (*4*) spinal canal, (*5*) foramen for exit of spinal nerve, (C_1) first coccygeal vertebra, (L_1) first lumbar vertebra, (S_1) first sacral vertebra.

Figure 9–3. The conus, filum terminale, and cauda equina. (Modified from Toldt.)

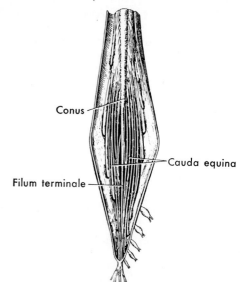

or posterior, column.[1] The former is short and bulky, whereas the latter is long and slender. The ventral column contains the cell bodies from which the efferent (motor) fibers of the spinal nerves arise. These nerves pass out through openings in the meninges and the intervertebral foramina. The lateral aspect of the ventral column contains cell bodies which give rise to the efferent fibers of the white *rami communicantes*, or preganglionic fibers, which travel outside the vertebral column. Preganglionic fibers are efferent, myelinated fibers (*white rami*) which

---

[1] This text uses *ventral* and *anterior* for the front aspect, *dorsal* and *posterior* for the back, and *columns* for what were formerly described as *horns* of the gray matter. For each of the three major divisions of the white matter of each half of the cord, *funiculus* instead of *column* is used.

pass from the spinal cord by the way of the ventral column and end around the cells of the sympathetic ganglia. From the cells of the ganglia, nonmyelinated postganglionic fibers go to the various visceral effector organs, i.e., smooth muscle, cardiac muscle, and glands. Some pass back to the spinal nerves and form the *gray rami.* The dorsal column contains cell bodies from which afferent, ascending fibers go up to higher levels of the spinal cord (usually on the opposite side), and to the brain. The fibers of the spinal nerves entering the cord form synapses with

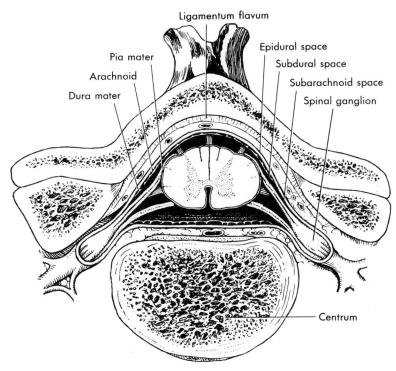

Figure 9–4. Transverse section of spinal cord and vertebra to show their relative positions. Note dorsal root ganglia lying in the intervertebral foramina and the dorsal and ventral roots in the spinal canal. The spinal nerve is shown outside the vertebra, with branches to the dorsal body wall, ventral body wall, and viscera.

the neurons in these columns. The gray matter also contains a great number of connecting (or internuncial) neurons which serve for the passage of impulses (1) from the dorsal to the ventral roots of the spinal nerves, (2) from one side of the cord to the other, and (3) from one segment of the cord to another.

The *white matter,* composed of variably myelinated fibers, is arranged around and between the columns of gray matter; the proportion of gray and white varies in different regions of the cord. On each side the white matter may be said to consist of three portions, or funiculi, namely, a ventral, a lateral, and a dorsal funiculus. Each funiculus is in turn divided into smaller segments, or fasciculi.

Some of these funiculi consist of fasciculi made up of fibers which are *ascending*, or sensory (ascending tracts). They serve as pathways to the brain for impulses entering the cord over afferent fibers of spinal nerves. Other funiculi

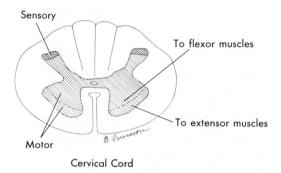

Figure 9–5. Diagram showing location of cell bodies of motor neurons to flexor and extensor muscles.

consist of fasciculi which are *descending*, or motor (descending tracts). They transfer impulses from the brain to the motor neurons of the spinal nerves. They begin in the gray matter of the brain, descend, and terminate in the gray matter of the cord, e.g., Figures 9–6 and 9–7. Other funiculi (white in Fig. 9–7) are made

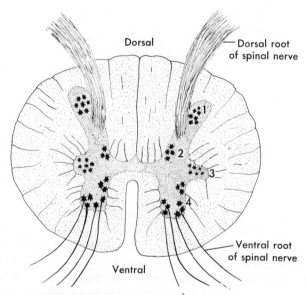

Figure 9–6. Cross section of the spinal cord to show some of the groups of nerve cells. (*1*) Dorsal column cells, (*2*) Clarke's column cells, (*3*) lateral column cells, (*4*) ventral column cells.

up chiefly of short ascending and descending fibers beginning in one region of the spinal cord and ending in another.

The funiculi in the dorsal portion are chiefly ascending. Injury to these funiculi will interfere with the passage of sensory impulses and possibly (depending on location and extent of injury) result in loss of sensation in the parts from which the passage of impulses is blocked.

Locomotor ataxia, or *tabes dorsalis,* is a degeneration of the posterior fasciculi and posterior columns of the cord, resulting in disturbances of muscle and joint sensation, interference with reflexes, and consequently with movements such as walking. *Anterior poliomyelitis,* or infantile paralysis, is a viral inflammation of the anterior areas of gray matter and results in paralysis of the muscles supplied with motor nerves from the diseased portion of the cord.

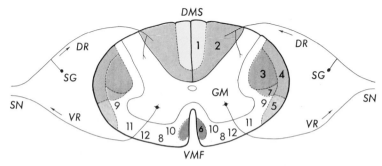

Figure 9–7. Diagram to show general location of some of the conduction paths as seen in a transverse section of the spinal cord. (*DMS*) Dorsal median sulcus, (*DR*) dorsal root, (*GM*) gray matter, (*SG*) spinal ganglion, (*SN*) spinal nerve, (*VMF*) ventral median fissure, (*VR*) ventral root. (*1*) Fasciculus gracilis (tract of Goll), (*2*) fasciculus cuneatus (tract of Burdach), (*3*) lateral cerebrospinal fasciculus (crossed pyramidal tract), (*4*) dorsal spinocerebellar fasciculus, (*5*) ventrolateral spinocerebellar fasciculus (Gowers' tract), (*6*) ventral cerebrospinal fasciculus (direct pyramidal tract), (*7*) rubrospinal tract, (*8*) ventral spinothalamic tracts, (*9*) lateral spinothalamic tracts, (*10*) vestibulospinal tracts, (*11*) tectospinal tracts, (*12*) olivospinal tracts.

Physiology of the Spinal Cord. It is an important center of reflex action for the trunk and limbs, and consists of the principal conducting paths to and from the higher centers in the cord and brain. The spinal cord may be regarded as consisting of more or less independent segments. Each segment is related by afferent and efferent nerve fibers to its own definite segmental area of the body, as well as to the segments above and below. However, it is obvious from the large amount of spinal cord space devoted to ascending and descending tracts that the brain exerts an important controlling influence over all segments.

The Pathways of the Cord

Ascending Pathways of the Cord

1. Of the Dorsal Portion of the Spinal Cord (Fasciculus Gracilis and Cuneatus).

(A) Fasciculus Gracilis. The fibers of fasciculus gracilis are medially placed in the dorsal part of the cord and are made up of long ascending fibers from the sacral, lumbar, and lower thoracic dorsal ganglia. These fibers terminate around cells in the nucleus gracilis in the low medulla. The fibers from the cells in the nucleus gracilis cross to the opposite side (sensory decussation), ascend, and

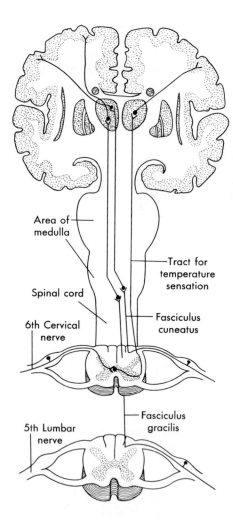

Area of medulla

Spinal cord

6th Cervical nerve

5th Lumbar nerve

Tract for temperature sensation

Fasciculus cuneatus

Fasciculus gracilis

Figure 9–8. Ascending tracts, three shown. Fasciculus (tract) gracilis, concerned with proprioceptor impulses from lower part of body; fasciculus cuneatus, concerned with proprioceptor impulses from upper part of body; and spinothalamic fasciculus, concerned with pain and temperature sensations.

terminate in the thalamus. The cells in the thalamus send fibers to the post-central gyrus of the cortex (sensory area).

The peripheral fibers of these dorsal root ganglia form the general sensory proprioceptive fibers of the peripheral nerves from the lower extremity and lower part of the trunk.

(B) Fasciculus Cuneatus. The fibers of fasciculus cuneatus are more laterally placed in the dorsal part of the cord and are made up of long ascending fibers from the upper thoracic and cervical ganglia. These fibers terminate around cells in the nucleus cuneatus in the medulla. The fibers from the cells of the nucleus cuneatus cross to the opposite side, ascend, and terminate in the thalamus. *Both* of these pathways conduct impulses from proprioceptors (on muscles, tendons, and joints) that give rise to sensations of movement and position. Other impulses conducted are for spatial discrimination, for more exact tactile localization, for vibratory sensations, and for two-point discrimination.

The peripheral fibers of these dorsal ganglia form the sensory fibers of the peripheral nerves from the upper extremity, trunk, and neck.

2. The spinothalamic pathways arise from large cells in the dorsal column of the gray matter of the cord. Most of the fibers cross in the cord and ascend in the white matter of the opposite side as the lateral and ventral spinothalamic pathways (Fig. 9–7, areas *8* and *9*). These fibers eventually terminate in the thalamus. The lateral spinothalamic pathway conveys impulses of pain and temperature; the ventral fibers convey impulses of touch and pressure. The cells in the cord receive impulses from sensory fibers of the peripheral nerves.

3. The dorsal spinocerebellar pathways arise from cells in the medial gray of the cord (Clarke's column) and pass to the white of the cord of the same side (Fig. 9–7, area *4*) and ascend to the medulla. Here they form the inferior cerebellar peduncle and terminate in the cortex of the cerebellum. This pathway conveys impulses from all parts of the body, especially from the trunk and lower extremity.

The ventral spinocerebellar pathway arises from cells in the intermediate gray of the cord. Most of the fibers cross in the cord. They all ascend in the cord (Fig. 9–7, area *5*) and reach the cerebellum via the superior cerebellar peduncle. These fibers convey proprioceptive impulses from all parts of the body.

Both of the spinocerebellar pathways convey impulses from receptors in muscles, tendons, and joints to the cerebellum. This enables the cerebellum to exert its synergizing and regulative tonic influence upon all voluntary muscles. Both of these pathways are composed of two neurons, the dorsal root ganglion cells and the cell bodies located in the spinal cord.

Descending Pathways of the Cord

1. The Crossed Pyramidal Pathways—motor (corticospinal). The fibers arise from the large pyramidal cells in the precentral gyrus of the cerebral cortex and other adjacent areas. They converge and descend through the internal capsule, midbrain, pons, and medulla. As they descend, fibers are given off to the motor nuclei of the cranial nerves. In the medulla the majority of the fibers cross to the opposite side (pyramidal decussation) and descend as the crossed pyramidal pathway (Fig. 9–7, area *3*).

2. The Uncrossed Pyramidal Pathways. The remaining fibers do not cross but descend on the same side as the direct pyramidal pathway (Fig. 9–7, area *6*); some, but not all, fibers cross to the opposite side just before terminating. All pyramidal fibers terminate around the large motor cells in the ventral gray of the cord and convey impulses which bring about volitional movements, especially fine individual movements that are essential for developing motor skills. The fibers are large and heavily myelinated. Myelinization begins before birth and is not complete until about the third year.

3. *Extrapyramidal Pathways.*

(A) THE VESTIBULOSPINAL PATHWAY originates from cells in the vestibular nucleus of the medulla and descends uncrossed in the cord and terminates around

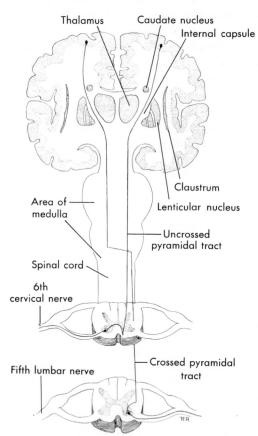

Figure 9–9. Descending tracts, two shown. The lateral corticospinal tract (crossed pyramidal) and the ventral corticospinal tract (direct pyramidal). These tracts contain motor fibers to skeletal muscles.

the large motor cells in the ventral gray of the cord (Fig. 9–7, area *10*). Since the vestibular nucleus receives fibers from the vestibular portion of the eighth nerve and from the cerebellum, the tract conveys impulses from the middle ear and cerebellum which exert a tonic influence on the muscles of the extremities and trunk, thus helping to maintain equilibrium and posture.

(B) THE RUBROSPINAL PATHWAY originates from cells in the red nucleus of the midbrain. The fibers cross and descend in the cord and terminate around cells in the dorsal part of the ventral gray of the cord of the thoracic region. The red nucleus relays impulses from the cerebellum and vestibular apparatus to the motor nuclei of the brain stem and spinal cord, and in this way the coordination of reflex postural adjustments is possible.

(c) THE TECTOSPINAL PATHWAYS originate from cells in the colliculi of the midbrain. The fibers cross and descend in the cord to terminate around cells in the ventral gray. The fibers convey impulses which mediate reflex activity of the muscles of the head and neck in response to optic stimuli and perhaps auditory stimuli. (Fig. 9–7, area *11*.)

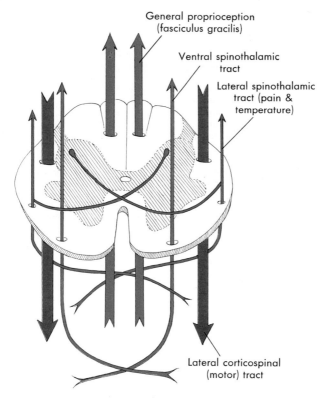

Figure 9–10. Diagram showing location of major afferent and efferent spinal tracts and the direction of impulse. Hemisection of the cord on the right side would cause what symptoms?

(D) THE OLIVOSPINAL PATHWAY originates from cells in the olivary nucleus of the medulla and perhaps other higher centers and terminates around cells in the ventral gray of the upper part of the cord (Fig. 9–7, area *12*). The olivary nucleus receives impulses from and sends impulses to the cerebellum.

The impulses from all of these descending pathways eventually reach the voluntary muscles via the large motor cells in the ventral gray of the cord, and exert regulatory control over reflex responses and volitional movements.

4. There are also descending fibers in the cord that innervate smooth muscle, cardiac muscle, and glandular epithelium. The hypothalamus is the chief coordinating center of the autonomic system. The hypothalamus is under control of the thalamus and higher autonomic centers of the cortex. The fibers descend from the hypothalamus in a rather diffuse manner and terminate around autonomic cells in the ventrolateral gray of the cord.

In addition to the long descending and ascending fiber tracts, there are short fiber tracts connecting neighboring segments that form part of the intrinsic reflex mechanisms of the spinal cord.

THE SPINAL NERVES

There are 31 pairs of spinal nerves, arranged in the following groups, and named for the region of the vertebral column from which they emerge:

Cervical	8 pairs
Thoracic	12 pairs
Lumbar	5 pairs
Sacral	5 pairs
Coccygeal	1 pair

The first cervical nerve arises from the medulla oblongata and leaves the spinal canal between the occipital bone and the atlas. The other cervical spinal nerves

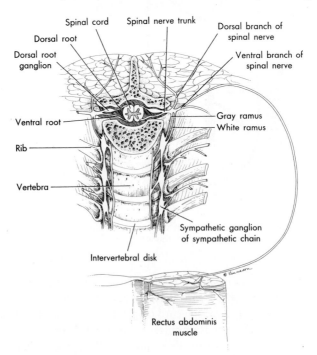

Figure 9–11. Diagram of spinal nerve branching, relationship to spinal cord, sympathetic ganglia, and vertebral column. (Modified from Pansky and House.)

arise from the spinal cord, and each leaves the spinal canal through an intervertebral foramen above the vertebra whose number it bears, e.g., the seventh
thoracic nerve emerges through the foramen between the sixth and seventh

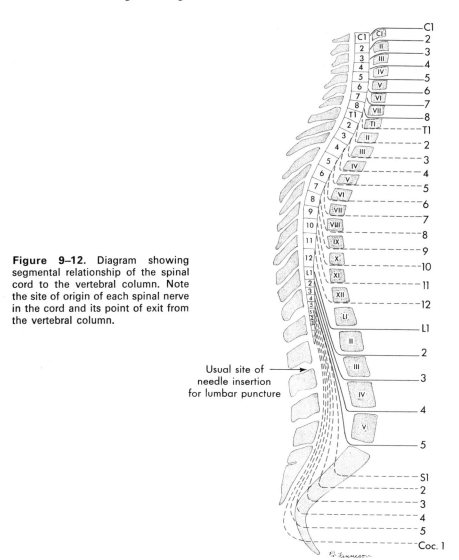

Figure 9–12. Diagram showing segmental relationship of the spinal cord to the vertebral column. Note the site of origin of each spinal nerve in the cord and its point of exit from the vertebral column.

Usual site of
needle insertion
for lumbar puncture

vertebrae. The eighth spinal nerve emerges from the vertebral column below the
seventh cervical vertebra. All the other spinal nerves emerge from the cord
below the vertebra whose number it bears. The coccygeal nerve passes from the
lower extremity of the canal.

Mixed Nerves. The spinal nerves consist mainly of myelinated nerve fibers and are called mixed nerves because they contain both motor and sensory fibers. Each spinal nerve has two roots, a ventral root and a dorsal root. The fibers of the ventral root *arise from nerve cells comprising the gray matter* in the ventral column and convey motor impulses from the spinal cord to the periphery.

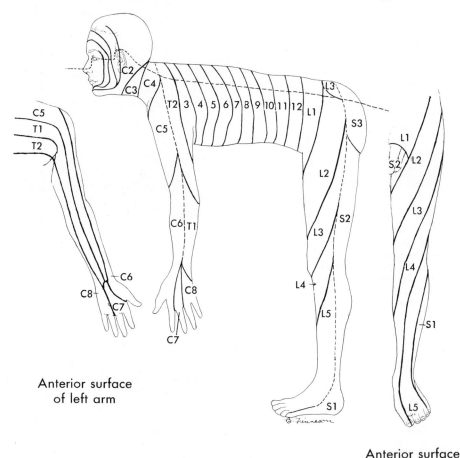

Anterior surface
of left arm

Anterior surface
of left leg

Figure 9–13.   Distribution of spinal nerves. (Modified from Pansky and House.)

The fibers of the dorsal root arise from the *cells composing the enlargement,* or *ganglion,* of the dorsal root situated in the openings between the arches of the vertebrae. These cell bodies give off a single fiber which divides in a T-shaped manner into two processes. One extends to a sensory end organ of the skin or of a muscle, tendon or joint. The other extends into the spinal cord, forming the dorsal root of a spinal nerve.

The fibers that enter the cord directly do not pass into the gray matter immediately; some extend upward and some downward in the white matter before doing so. Sooner or later they all enter the gray matter of the spinal cord or brain, where they form synapses with central or motor neurons.

The ventral roots have their origin within the spinal cord and contain motor fibers. The dorsal roots have their origin outside the cord, i.e., in the spinal ganglia, and contain sensory fibers. The fibers of these two roots are collected into one bundle and form a spinal nerve just before leaving the canal through the intervertebral openings.

Distribution of Terminal Branches of the Spinal Nerves. After leaving the spinal column, each spinal nerve divides into three main branches known as the meningeal, or recurrent (distributed to the meninges), the dorsal, and the ventral. The dorsal branches supply the muscles and skin of the back of the head, neck, and trunk. The ventral branches supply the extremities and parts of the body wall in front of the spine. There is a fourth, or visceral, branch, present only in nerves from the first thoracic to the third lumbar. These connect with the sympathetic ganglia by means of fibers which pass from the nerve to the ganglia and vice versa (the white and gray rami, see pp. 303, 304). Extending from the sympathetic

Figure 9–14. The four branches of a typical thoracic spinal nerve. (*1*) Meningeal, or recurrent, branch, (*2*) dorsal branch, (*3*) ventral branch, (*4*) visceral branch, (*a*) gray ramus, (*b*) white ramus, (*AG*) autonomic ganglion, (*DR*) dorsal root of spinal nerve, (*G*) gray matter, (*VR*) ventral root of spinal nerve, (*W*) white matter.

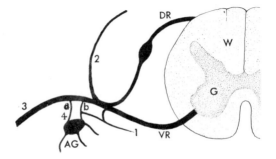

ganglia to their final distribution are the autonomic nerves. These nerves form plexuses called the cardiac, the celiac or solar, the hypogastric, the pelvic, and the enteric. Some nerve fibers from the sympathetic ganglia return to and are distributed with the spinal nerve to supply sweat glands, arrector pili muscles, and the smooth muscle of all blood vessels.

After the nerves emerge from the cord, a plexus is formed in the cervical, brachial, lumbar, and sacral segments from which the peripheral nerves are formed.

The Cervical Plexus. This plexus is formed by the ventral branches of the first four cervical nerves. The second, third, and fourth nerves divide into an upper and a lower branch; these in turn unite to form three loops from which peripheral nerves are distributed. There is communication between these nerves and the hypoglossal, vagus, and accessory cranial nerves to the head and neck musculature.

The Brachial Plexus. This plexus is formed by the union of the ventral branch of the last four cervical and the first thoracic nerves. See Figure 9–15 for fiber communications and nerves formed. There are three main cords formed, the lateral, medial, and posterior. Important nerves formed are the median, ulnar, and radial nerves which supply the upper extremities.

The Lumbar Plexus. This plexus is formed by a few fibers from the twelfth thoracic and the anterior primary divisions of the first four lumbar nerves. Figure 9–16 illustrates the communications and distribution of the fibers to the muscles. The largest nerves formed are the femoral and obturator nerves.

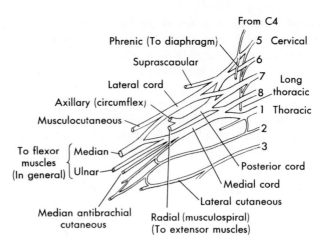

Figure 9–15. Diagram of the brachial plexus, showing distribution of some of the larger nerves. See page 183 for distribution of the nerves.

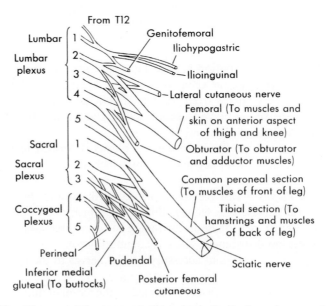

Figure 9–16. Diagram of lumbosacral plexus and distribution of some of the larger nerves. See page 200 for distribution of the nerves.

The Sacral Plexus. This plexus is formed by a few fibers from the fourth lumbar nerve, all of the fifth, and the first, second, and third sacral nerves. Figure 9–16 illustrates the intercommunication of these fibers and the great nerves formed. The largest is the great sciatic, which supplies the muscles of the lower extremity.

In the thoracic region a plexus is not formed, but the fibers pass as intercostal nerves out into the intercostal spaces to supply the intercostal muscles, the upper abdominal muscles, and the skin of the abdomen and chest.

Names of Peripheral Nerves. Many of the larger branches given off from the spinal nerves bear the same name as the artery they accompany or the part they supply. Thus, the radial nerve passes down the radial side of the forearm in company with the radial artery; the intercostal nerves pass between the ribs in company with the intercostal arteries. An exception to this is the two sciatic nerves, which pass down from the sacral plexus, one on each side of the body near the

Figure 9–17. Degeneration of spinal nerves and nerve roots after section. (*A*) Section of nerve trunk beyond the ganglion. (*B*) Section of anterior root. (*C*) Section of posterior root. (*D*) Excision of ganglion. (*a*) Anterior root, (*p*) posterior root, (*g*) ganglion. *Black* indicates the portion of the nerve that degenerates after section.

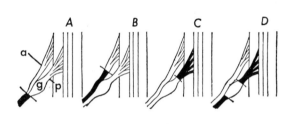

center of each buttock and the back of each thigh, to the popliteal region, where each divides into two large branches which supply the legs and feet. Motor branches from these nerves pass to the muscles of the legs and feet, and sensory branches are distributed to the skin of the lower extremities.

Degeneration and Regeneration of Nerves. Since the cell body is essential for the nutrition of the whole cell, it follows that if the processes of a neuron are cut off, they will suffer from malnutrition and die. If, for instance, a spinal nerve is cut, all the peripheral part will degenerate, because the fibers have been cut off from their cell bodies. The divided ends of a nerve that has been cut across readily reunite by cicatricial tissue; that is, the connective-tissue framework unites, but the cut ends of the fibers themselves do not unite. On the contrary, the peripheral or severed portion of the nerve fiber begins to degenerate, its medullary sheath breaks up into a mass of fatty molecules and is gradually absorbed, and finally the central fiber also disappears. In regeneration, many new fibers start to grow out from the central end of the severed axon. If one of these "growth sprouts" makes a successful penetration into the peripheral end of the neurilemma, all other growth sprouts wither and die. The successful sprout continues to grow toward the end organ and is destined to become the new functional new fiber. In time it will become surrounded with a myelin sheath. The Schwann cells of peripheral fibers play an important part in both the degeneration and regeneration of the cut fiber. Restoration of function in the nerve may not occur for several months, during which time it is presumed the new nerve fibers are slowly

Cerebrum. Memory, association, personality. Synthesizes sensory impressions into perceptions. Highest level of somatic motor control. Receives impulses from and sends impulses to all lower levels.

Midbrain. Contains many nuclei for control of ocular reflexes, eye movement, higher postural reflex actions. Motor nuclei of cranial nerves III and IV. Nuclei for control of many visceral activities.

Cerebellum. Vestibular and postural reflexes, equilibrium and orientation in space. Helps to maintain muscle tone and regulate muscle coordination.

Pons. Relay station from lower to the higher centers. Contains nuclei for cerebro-cerebellar relay of impulses. Nuclei and pathways for regulation of skeletal muscle tones. Contains nuclei for cranial nerves V, VI, VII, and VIII. Connects both halves of the cerebellum.

Medulla. Contains nuclei of many cranial nerves. Location of many vital centers. Contains nuclei for relaying sensory impulses to higher centers. Contains fiber tracts for all ascending and descending impulses.

Cord. Only means by which impulses from the periphery can reach higher centers, and impulses from higher centers can reach the periphery. Contains neurons that form ascending sensory pathways. Receives incoming sensory fibers and their impulses. Centers for intersegmental and segmental reflexes.

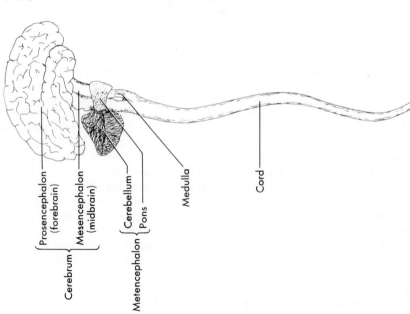

Prosencephalon (forebrain)

Mesencephalon (midbrain)

Cerebrum

Metencephalon { Cerebellum Pons

Medulla

Cord

Figure 9–18. Diagram of the divisions of the central nervous system.

finding their way along the course of those which have been destroyed. Since the nerve fibers of the brain and cord have little or no neurilemma, regeneration after injury does not occur.

THE BRAIN

The brain is the largest and most complex mass of nervous tissue in the body. It is contained in the cranial cavity and comprises five fairly distinct connected parts: the cerebrum, the midbrain, the cerebellum, the pons varolii,[2] and the medulla oblongata.

In early embryonic life the brain, or encephalon, consists of three hollow vesicles:

1. Cephalic, or prosencephalon (forebrain)
2. Mesencephalon, or midbrain
3. Caudal, or rhombencephalon (hindbrain)

During growth the cerebral hemispheres, their commissures, and the first, second, and third ventricles are developed from the forebrain; the corpora quadrigemina, the cerebral peduncles, and the cerebral aqueduct (a tubular connection between the third and fourth ventricles) are developed from the midbrain; the medulla oblongata, the pons varolii, the cerebellum and the included fourth ventricle are developed from the hindbrain.

The weight of the brain in the adult male is about 1,380 gm (48.6 oz); in the adult female, about 1,250 gm (44 oz). The weight of the brain is an indication of growth, which in early life depends upon the enlargement of the cells and their processes, the myelination of the nerve fibers, and an increase in the amount of neuroglia. The brain grows rapidly up to the fifth year and in general ceases to grow much beyond about the twentieth year. In advanced age the brain gradually loses weight.

The development of the brain is not only a matter of growth but also a matter of forming new functional pathways, i.e., new synapses and a permanent modification of the synapses that are functionally active during various forms of activity. The nature of the brain protoplasm and the use to which it is put determine to some extent the length of time during which development may continue. Mental exercise keeps the brain active and capable of development, just as exercising a muscle tends to prevent atrophy or loss of function.

Parts of the Brain

For convenience, the brain may be studied from its embryological development. These include the forebrain, midbrain, and hindbrain, which are further subdivided:

1. **The Forebrain** (prosencephalon)
   (a) Cerebral hemispheres (telencephalon), with the lateral ventricles. Each

[2] Constanzo Varolio, Italian anatomist (1543–1575).

hemisphere includes the cerebral cortex, basal nuclei, rhinencephalon (olfactory portion).

(*b*) The diencephalon (connects cerebral hemispheres with midbrain, and forms the walls of the third ventricle). The diencephalon has four major parts: (1) the epithalamus, (2) the thalamus and the metathalamus, (3) the hypothalamus, and (4) the subthalamus.

2. The Midbrain (mesencephalon)—connects the forebrain with the hindbrain.

(*a*) Ventral part—cerebral peduncles, which are the massive bundles of fibers extending from the border of the pons varolii to the optic tract where they disappear into the substance of the forebrain.

(*b*) Dorsal part—includes the corpora quadrigemina (superior and inferior colliculi).

3. The Hindbrain (rhombencephalon)

(*a*) Metencephalon—cerebellum, pons.

(*b*) Myelencephalon, or medulla oblongata.

The Forebrain

The Hemispheres. *The cerebrum* is by far the largest part of the brain. It is egg-shaped and fills the whole of the upper portion of the skull. The entire surface, both upper and under, is composed of layers of gray matter and is called the cortex. The bulk of the white matter in the interior of the cerebrum consists of small fibers running in three principal directions: (1) from above downward—*projection fibers*, connecting the cerebrum with other parts of the brain and spinal cord; (2) from the front backward—*association fibers*, connecting gyri on the same side of the cerebrum; and (3) from side to side—*commissural fibers*, connecting the right and left sides of the cerebrum. The fibers link the different parts of the brain together and connect the brain with the spinal cord (Figs. 9–25 and 9–30). There are also autonomic fibers that link the brain with the spinal cord.

Fissures and Convolutions. In early life the cortex of the cerebrum is comparatively smooth, but as time passes and the brain develops, the surface becomes covered with furrows, which vary in depth. The deeper furrows are called *fissures*, the shallow ones, *sulci*, and the ridges between the sulci are called *gyri* or *convolutions*. The fissures and sulci are infoldings of gray matter; consequently the more numerous and deeper they are, the greater is the amount of gray matter. The number, length, and depth of these fissures and sulci and the prominence and sizes of the convolutions vary. The cortex on the top of the convolutions is thick but thins out toward the floor or the fissures and sulci.

The Cerebral Fissures. There are five important fissures which are landmarks.

1. *The longitudinal cerebral fissure*—the cerebral hemispheres are separated by a deep vertical longitudinal fissure. The separation is incomplete in front and behind, but in the middle portion it extends to the corpus callosum, a wide band of commissural fibers which unite the two hemispheres. In the posterior region

the cerebrum overlaps the thalamus, midbrain, and cerebellum. A process of the dura mater extends down into this fissure and separates the two cerebral hemispheres. It is called the *falx cerebri*, because it is narrow in front and broader behind, thus resembling a sickle in shape, and contains important venous sinuses between its two layers.

2. The *transverse fissure* is between the cerebrum and the cerebellum. A process of the dura also extends into this fissure and covers the upper surface of the cerebellum and the undersurface of the cerebrum. It is called the *tentorium cerebelli* and also contains important venous sinuses.

3. *Central sulcus*, or *fissure of Rolando*
4. *Lateral cerebral fissure*, or *fissure of Sylvius*
5. *Parieto-occipital fissure*

There is one of each in each hemisphere. For location see Figure 9–20.

Lobes of the Cerebrum. The longitudinal fissure divides the cerebrum into two hemispheres, and the transverse fissure divides the cerebrum from the cerebellum. The three remaining fissures, assisted by certain arbitrary lines, divide

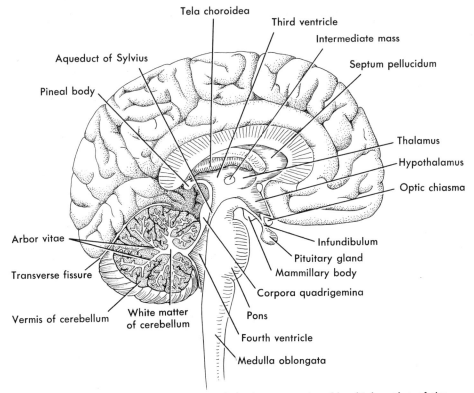

Figure 9–19. Brain stem, cerebellum, and cerebrum seen in midsagittal section of the brain. (Modified from Pansky and House.)

each hemisphere in five lobes. With one exception these lobes are named from the bones of the cranium under which they lie; hence they are known as: (1) *frontal lobe*, (2) *parietal lobe*, (3) *temporal lobe*, (4) *occipital lobe*, and (5) the *insula* (*island of Reil*).

The frontal lobe is that portion of the cerebrum lying in front of the central sulcus and usually consists of four main convolutions on the convex side.

The parietal lobe is bounded in front by the central sulcus and behind by the parieto-occipital fissure.

The temporal lobe lies below the lateral cerebral fissure and in front of the occipital lobe. There are three horizontal convolutions: the superior, middle, and inferior gyri.

The occipital lobe occupies the posterior extremity of the cerebral hemisphere. There is no marked separation of the occipital lobe from the parietal and temporal lobes that lie to the front, but when the surface of the longitudinal cleft is

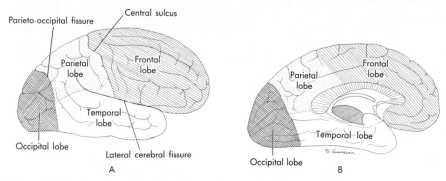

Figure 9–20.   Lobes of cerebrum. (*A*) Lateral view. (*B*) Medial view—brain stem removed.

examined, the parieto-occipital fissure serves as a boundary anteriorly for the occipital lobe.

The insula (island of Reil[3]) is not seen when the surface of the hemisphere is examined, for it lies within the lateral cerebral fissure, and the overlying convolutions of the parietal and frontal lobes must be lifted up before the insula may be seen. The medial surface of the brain may be seen after it has been divided in the midsagittal plane and the brain stem removed. See Figure 9-20.

Ventricles of the Brain.   The brain contains cavities called *ventricles*. The *two lateral ventricles* are situated one in each of the cerebral hemispheres under the mass of white fibers called the corpus callosum, which connects the two hemispheres. The *basal nuclei* of the brain are in the floor of the lateral ventricles. The cavity of the lateral ventricles is large and may become overdistended with cerebrospinal fluid in certain pathological conditions.

The *third ventricle* is behind the lateral ventricles but connected with each one

[3] Johann Christian Reil, Dutch physiologist (1759–1813).

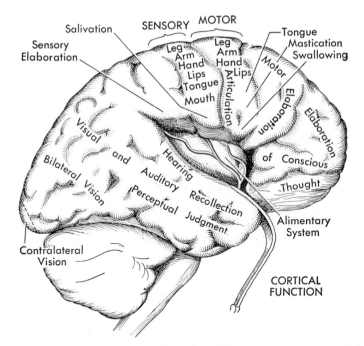

Figure 9–21. Cortical function. This illustration will serve as a summary restatement of conclusions, some hypothetical (e.g. the elaboration zones), others firmly established. The suggestion that the anterior portion of the occipital cortex is related to both fields of vision rather than to one alone is derived from the results of stimulation. (W. Penfield and T. Rasmussen, *The Cerebral Cortex of Man*. Courtesy of The Macmillan Company.)

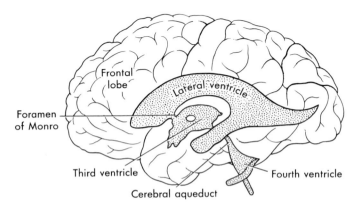

Figure 9–22. Diagram showing ventricles of the brain. Side view.

by means of small openings called the foramina of Monro.[4] The *fourth ventricle* is in front of the cerebellum, behind the pons varolii and the medulla. The third communicates with the fourth by means of a slender canal called the *aqueduct* of the cerebrum (aqueduct of Sylvius[5]). In the roof of the fourth ventricle there is an opening called the foramen of Magendie.[6] In the lateral wall there are two openings called the foramina of Luschka. By means of these three openings, the ventricles communicate with the subarachnoid space, and the cerebrospinal fluid can circulate from one to the other. The so-called fifth ventricle is not a portion of the general cavity—not a true ventricle. It is a narrow space in front of the third, having no connection with the other ventricles.

Physiology of Cerebrum. In the higher vertebrates the cerebrum constitutes a larger proportion of the central nervous system than in the lower forms. It is especially large in animals that are capable of profiting by experience; the areas which govern all our mental activities—reason, intelligence, will and memory—are located in the cerebrum. It is on the main stream to consciousness, the interpreter of sensations (correlation), the instigator and coordinator of voluntary acts and it exerts strong control (both facilitating and inhibiting) over many reflex acts which originate as involuntary. Laughing, weeping, micturition, defecation, and many other acts might be cited as examples of the latter.

Consciousness and memory are two areas of cerebral activity which encompass much or all of its other more specific activities. The conscious brain is kept aware of environmental changes by way of afferent nerve impulses and responds appropriately. The unconscious brain fails to respond to these changes; only very basic physiological activities and reflexes persist during unconsciousness. For example, the cardiovascular and respiratory systems continue to function.

There seems to be no specific control center for consciousness, although the hypothalamus and the reticular area of the brain stem are known to play an important role. Sedatives which produce sleep act by interfering with the transmission of impulses to the cortex from those deeper brain areas. Sleep is similar to unconsciousness in that both conditions involve an unawareness of surroundings; however, one can be aroused easily from sleep but not from unconsciousness.

Memory and learning are activities of the cortex, although other cerebral areas are involved. For example, sensory impulses from the eye or ear are transmitted to the appropriate cortical areas, so that at a later date they may be recalled—for pleasure or interpretation and thought. Somehow the initial impulses cause a change in neurons or neural connections so that at a later date activation of some of these neurons causes a memory to be presented. What the exact change may be is an intriguing enigma.

Localization of Brain Function. As the result of numerous experiments on animals and close observation of the effects of electrical stimulation of the cere-

---

[4] Alexander Monro (Primus), Scottish anatomist (1697–1767).
[5] Franciseus Sylvius, Dutch physician (1614–1672).
[6] François Magendie, French physiologist (1783–1855).

bral cortex on human individuals and clinical results of cerebral disease, physiologists have been able to localize certain areas in the brain which control motor, sensory, and other activities. Some knowledge has been gained concerning the areas in the cerebrum which are concerned with the higher mental activities. In no case, however, is the control of a function limited to a single center, for practically all mental processes involve the discharge of nervous energy from one center to another. All parts of the cerebrum are connected. Change in the nervous activity of any part alters the excitability of the whole. Any activity, therefore, is the result of all the changes throughout the whole of the cortex. No one area

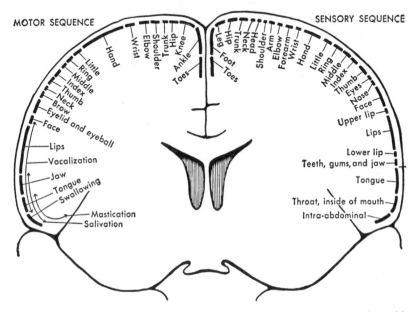

Figure 9–23. Cross section of the cerebrum through the sensorimotor region with the motor and sensory sequences indicated. The lengths of the solid bars represent an estimate of the average relative cortical areas from which the corresponding responses were elicited. (W. Penfield and T. Rasmussen, *The Cerebral Cortex of Man.* Courtesy of The Macmillan Company.)

acts alone to govern a particular function. As Herrick[7] says, such areas "are merely nodal points in an exceedingly complex system of neurons which must act as a whole in order to perform any function whatsoever."

Names of Areas. The portions of the cerebrum which govern muscular movement are known as *motor areas*, those controlling sensation as the *sensory areas*, and those connected with the higher faculties, such as reason and will, as *association areas*.

Motor Area. The surface of the brain involved in the function of movement is the precentral gyrus of the frontal lobe, i.e., the gray matter immediately in

[7] C. J. Herrick, *An Introduction to Neurology.*

front of the central sulcus. The large pyramidal cells whose fibers form cortico-spinal pathways are located in the precentral gyrus and arranged so that motor cells for toe movement are located in the lowest area on the medial side of the cortex and motor cells for face movement are located near the lateral cerebral fissure. A study of Figures 9–21 and 9–23 illustrates the arrangement of both motor and sensory areas.

Sensory Area. The somatic sensory area occupies the part of the cortex behind the central sulcus and can be divided into regions like those of the motor area just in front of the sulcus. The *visual area* is situated in the posterior part of the occipital lobe and the *auditory area*, in the superior part of the temporal lobe.

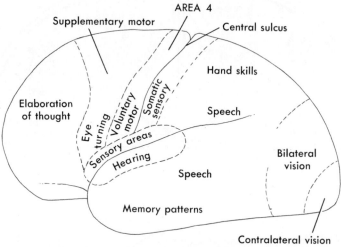

Figure 9–24. Functional areas of cerebral cortex. (Modified from Penfield and Rasmussen.)

The area for the sense of *taste* has been located deep in the fissure of Sylvius near the island of Reil. See Figure 9–21 for *alimentary system* areas. The area concerned with interpretation of the sense of smell is located on the medial aspect of the temporal lobe (uncus).

The *motor speech* area is located in the frontal lobe, anterior to the laryngeal area in the premotor region of the motor cortex. It is known as Broca's area. The temporal speech region is believed to be concerned with choice of thoughts to be expressed, and the parietal region, concerned with choice of words used in the expression of thoughts. In right-handed persons the area is more fully developed in the left hemisphere; and in left-handed persons, in the right hemisphere. The basis of language is a series of memory pictures. The mind must know and recall the names of things in order to mention them; it must have seen or heard things in order to describe them and to have learned the words to express these ideas. Even this is not enough. All these factors must work together under the influence of the center for articulate speech, which, as seen in Figure

9–24, is in close connection with those for the larynx, tongue, and the muscles of the face. Injury to these centers results in some form of inability to speak (aphasia), to write (agraphia), or to understand spoken words (word deafness) or written words (word blindness). It is customary, therefore, to distinguish two types of aphasia, i.e., motor and sensory. By *motor aphasia* is meant the condition of those who are unable to speak although there is no paralysis of the muscles of articulation. By *sensory aphasia* is meant the condition of those who

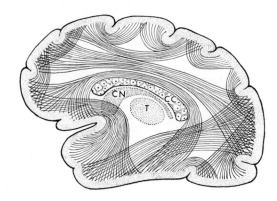

Figure 9–25. Section of brain, showing association fibers connecting the gyri and commissural fibers connecting the two sides of the brain. The commissural fibers are cut across and appear as dots. The myelin sheaths surrounding these fibers appear as white areas. (*CC*) Corpus callosum, (*CN*) caudate nucleus, (*T*) thalamus.

are unable to understand written, printed, or spoken symbols of words, although the sense of vision and that of hearing are unimpaired. These centers are really memory centers, and aphasia is due to loss of memory of words, meaning of words seen or heard, or formation of letters.

Association Areas. The motor and sensory areas form, so to speak, small islands which are surrounded on all sides by cerebral tissue in which as yet no definite functions have been localized. These regions are designated as association areas and are made up of association fibers which connect motor and sensory areas. Animals that are capable of acquiring habits and conditioned reflexes have a greater development of these areas. It is thought that the association areas are plastic and register the effects of individual experience.

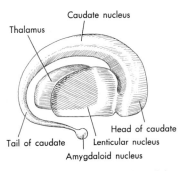

Thalamus

Caudate nucleus

Head of caudate

Tail of caudate

Lenticular nucleus

Amygdaloid nucleus

Figure 9–26. The basal nuclei.

After removal of the cerebrum, any animal becomes a simple reflex animal. In other words, all its actions are then removed from volition and consciousness. All responses that depend upon memory of acquired and inherited experience are lost.

The Basal Nuclei—Location and Physiology. Located deep within the cerebral hemispheres are masses of gray matter called the basal nuclei, which consist of four nuclei located near the thalamus. These are the caudate, the lentiform (made up of putamen and globus pallidus), the amygdaloid, and the claustrum. The *internal capsule* contains corticospinal, corticobulbar, and sensory fibers. The anterior limb lies between the caudate and lentiform nuclei, and the posterior limb lies between the thalamus and lentiform nuclei. (The lentiform and caudate nuclei plus that portion of the internal capsule are called the corpus striatum.) (See Fig. 9–27 for specific location of fibers.)

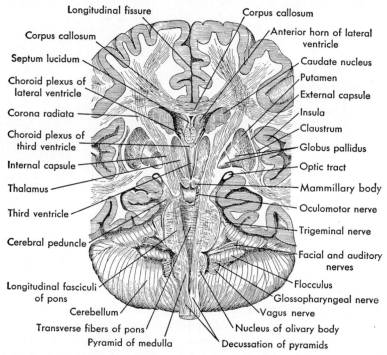

Figure 9–27.   Section of brain to show basal nuclei, internal capsule, pons, and medulla. (Modified from Toldt.)

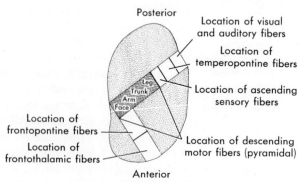

Figure 9–28.   Horizontal section through the basal nuclei to illustrate the location of the various fiber components of the left internal capsule.

The basal nuclei are all interconnected with many fibers; some are connected as well to the thalamus and hypothalamus. The *functions* are not clear, but there is clinical evidence that the basal nuclei play an important role in extrapyramidal control of motor activities.

The thalamus, subthalamus, substantia nigra, and red nucleus function in close association with these nuclei.

The Caudate Nucleus and Putamen	Regulates gross intentional movements of the body that are performed *unconsciously* through pathways into the globus pallidus and thalamus to the cerebral cortex and finally downward into the spinal cord via the cortico-spinal and extrapyramidal spinal pathways. The motor cortex controls *conscious* specific fine movements
Globus Pallidus	Is concerned with regulation of muscle tone essential for intended, specific movements of the body. It is believed that it can also excite the cerebral cortex
The Subthalamic Nuclei	Are concerned with various rhythmical motions such as walking and running
The Red Nucleus	Receives impulses from the dentate nucleus of the cerebellum and from the caudate nucleus and putamen. It sends fibers down into the spinal cord. It is concerned with movements of the head and upper trunk. It is necessary for reflexes concerned with righting oneself in space
The Substantia Nigra	Receives many fibers from other basal nuclei. It is believed to function in controlling associative movements

Degenerative changes cause disturbances of motor activity, such as tremor, involuntary movement, and muscular rigidity. Rupture of blood vessels in or near the internal capsule is a frequent occurrence. Patients having suffered such a cerebral vascular accident may become hemiplegic (paralyzed on one side).

The Rhinencephalon. This comprises all portions of the cerebral hemispheres concerned with reception and integration of olfactory impulses, and regulation of motor activities in response to olfactory stimuli. The olfactory lobe, or bulb, receives fibers from the olfactory nerve. The olfactory tract distributes the fibers to the cortical olfactory areas. The hippocampus represents the cortical part of the olfactory system of most importance. There are connections with the hypothalamus that are concerned with visceral reflexes.

The Mammillary Bodies. These are two small, round nuclear masses situated below the floor of the third ventricle and behind the optic chiasma. They receive fibers from the olfactory areas of the brain and from ascending pathways, and send fibers to the thalamus and to other brain nuclei. They form relay stations for olfactory fibers and are concerned with olfactory reflexes.

The Diencephalon

The Thalamus. The thalamus is a large bilateral, oval structure located above the midbrain. It receives all sensory impulses either directly or indirectly from all parts of the body with the exception of olfactory sensations. It also receives impulses from the cerebellum, cerebral cortex, and many nuclei. The thalamus contains many nuclei concerned with specific functions. The medial and lateral geniculate bodies known as the metathalamus are parts of the thalamus which relay auditory and visual reflexes.

The Thalamic Nuclei Connections

Impulses from	
Touch receptors Pressure receptors Joint receptors Temperature receptors Pain receptors	Are received by cells in the posteroventral nucleus of the thalamus. With the possible exception of the pain impulse, these impulses are relayed to the postcentral gyrus in parietal lobe cortex for interpretation
Olfactory sensations	Are relayed to the thalamus via the mammillary bodies to the cortex
Taste fibers	Are finally projected to the thalamus from the geniculate ganglion and are relayed to the postcentral cortex close to the face area
Auditory fibers	Are projected from the cochlear nuclei and inferior colliculi to the thalamus and from there relayed to the temporal cortex
Visual fibers	Are projected to the lateral geniculate bodies of the thalamus and from there relayed to the calcarine cortex

Some of the impulses received by the thalamus are associated, some are synthesized and sorted out, and some are simply relayed to specific areas of the cerebral cortex. In this way it is evident that the thalamus functions as a sensory integrating center of great physiological importance. Bodily well-being or malaise is believed to be interpreted by the thalamus rather than by the cortex. Appreciation of part of temperature, crude touch, and pain is possible even though the sensory cortex is destroyed. Through connections with the hypothalamus influence is exerted on both visceral and somatic activities.

The Hypothalamus. The hypothalamus lies below the thalamus and forms part of the lateral walls and floor of the third ventricle. It is thought that the hypothalamus is intimately related to the following visceral activities.

METABOLISM and WATER BALANCE. Recent investigations have shown that cells in the supraoptic and paraventricular nuclei secrete an antidiuretic hormone (ADH). This hormone reaches the posterior pituitary via the nerve fibers of these cells. The function of ADH is the control of water balance of the body by controlling reabsorption of water in the kidney tubule. Carbohydrate and fat metabolism are also in some way regulated through the hypothalamus. Certain disorders involving the hypothalamus produce obesity.

AUTONOMIC NERVOUS CONTROL. The hypothalamus is the main subcortical center for regulation of both parasympathetic and sympathetic activities. (See pp. 310–11 for discussion.) There is evidence that there is a center in the hypothalamus for controlling emotional states and sleep.

SLEEP-WAKING MECHANISMS. Impulses carried along pathways to the cortex, connected with the thalamus and posterior hypothalamus, influence sleep and wakefulness. It is now evident that the hypothalamus plays a part in changes in the state of consciousness.

REGULATION OF BODY TEMPERATURE. The hypothalamus contains centers that function as a "thermostat" to maintain the internal temperature of the body. Studies show that, when the nude body is exposed to dry air temperature as low as 10°C (50°F) or as high as 71.1°C (160°F) for several hours, there is little variation in internal temperature. When blood temperature is above normal, the parasympathetic centers in the hypothalamus are stimulated, and reflexes are established for heat loss. When blood temperature is below normal, the sympathetic centers in the hypothalamus are stimulated and reflexes are established for heat conservation. It is the reciprocal functioning of these two centers that maintains the body temperature with slight variations at about 37°C (98.6°F).

RELEASING FACTORS. It is believed that there are areas in the hypothalamus that secrete substances that reach the anterior pituitary via the hypothalamic-portal system and function as releasing factors for the anterior pituitary hormones.

FOOD INTAKE. Two centers in the hypothalamus regulate the amount of food ingested. The "feeding center" in the lateral hypothalamus is presumably stimulated by hunger sensations and the over-all need for food (such as accompanies starvation) since electrical stimulation of this area causes eating of whatever food is available to the animal (appetizing or not). The "satiety center" in the medial hypothalamus is stimulated when the animal has taken in enough food. Electrical stimulation of the satiety center inhibits the feeding center, and the animal abruptly stops eating. Destruction of this nucleus, on the other hand, produces animals who eat until they are too obese to move. They always "feel hungry" because there is no satiety center to inhibit the feeding center.

The Reticular Formation. The reticular formation is composed of large and small nerve cells and an intricate system of interlacing fibers which run in all directions. It begins in the upper part of the spinal cord and extends upward where it terminates in the diencephalon. The reticular cells receive collaterals from all the great ascending pathways and nuclei. Efferent impulses are sent to both higher and lower brain centers. It is believed to be essential for control of cortical activities such as initiation and maintenance of alert wakefulness, hence has been called the activating system. It can be stimulated by impulses from all peripheral sense organs. It exerts some sort of a regulatory action on the brain and cord by either excitation or inhibition of certain activities, such as spinal cord reflexes, or voluntary movements. Muscle tone and smooth, coordinated muscle activity are dependent upon this system. Its function is not to relay a specific impulse or message but simply to arouse the brain for action. Any stimulus reaching the reticular formation alerts the cortex to a state of wakefulness so that, when a specific stimulus reaches a specific cortical center, it may be identified and action may result, as, for example, being wakened by a loud noise or other unusual environmental condition. Impulses through the reticular system can be blocked by hypnotic drugs; thus, emotional response to environmental stress is reduced. Injury or disease to the system results in permanent unconsciousness.

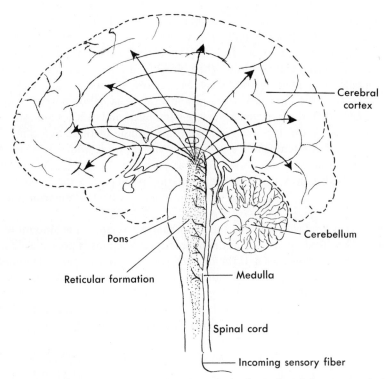

Figure 9–29. Section of brain showing the reticular formation. It is composed of inter-lacing fibers and nerve cells which form the central core of the brain stem. Incoming fibers from the spinal tracts send collaterals into the reticular formation. *Arrows* indicate the general arousal of higher brain centers which the reticular area controls.

The Midbrain

The midbrain (mesencephalon) is a short, constricted portion which connects the pons and cerebellum with the hemispheres of the cerebrum. It is directed upward and forward and consists of (1) a pair of cylindrical bodies called the cerebral *peduncles*, which are made up largely of the descending and ascending fiber tracts from the cerebrum above, the cerebellum, medulla, and spinal cord below; (2) four rounded eminences, called the *corpora quadrigemina* (Fig. 9–19) which contain important correlation centers and also nuclei concerned with motor coordination; and (3) an intervening passage or tunnel, the cerebral aqueduct (aqueduct of Sylvius), which serves as a communication between the third and fourth ventricles.

The Brain Stem. The pons, the medulla, and the midbrain containing the cerebral and cerebellar peduncles, corpora quadrigemina, red nucleus, etc., are frequently called the brain stem. (See Fig. 9–19.)

The Hindbrain (Rhombencephalon)

The Cerebellum and Its Functions. The cerebellum occupies the lower and posterior part of the skull cavity. It is below the posterior portion of the cerebrum, from which it is separated by the *tentorium cerebelli*, a fold of the dura mater, and behind the pons and the upper part of the medulla. It is oval in form, constricted in the center, and flattened from above downward. The constricted central portion is called the *vermis*, and the lateral expanded portions are called the *hemispheres*.

The surface of the cerebellum consists of gray matter and is not convoluted

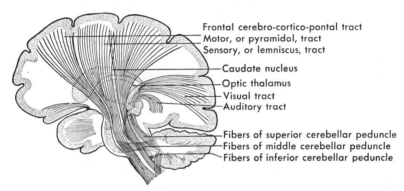

Frontal cerebro-cortico-pontal tract
Motor, or pyramidal, tract
Sensory, or lemniscus, tract

Caudate nucleus
Optic thalamus
Visual tract
Auditory tract

Fibers of superior cerebellar peduncle
Fibers of middle cerebellar peduncle
Fibers of inferior cerebellar peduncle

Figure 9–30. Dorsoventral section of brain, showing some of the fiber tracts from the spinal cord to the cerebral cortex. Fiber tracts to cerebellum are also shown.

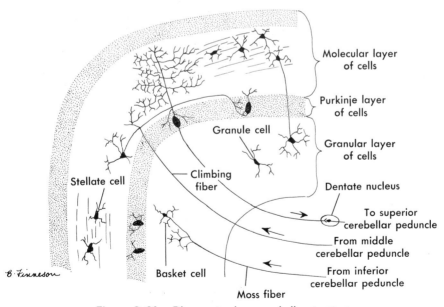

Molecular layer
of cells

Purkinje layer
of cells

Granule cell

Granular layer
of cells

Climbing
fiber

Stellate cell

Dentate nucleus

To superior
cerebellar peduncle

From middle
cerebellar peduncle

Basket cell

From inferior
cerebellar peduncle

Moss fiber

Figure 9–31. Diagram to show cerebellar structure.

but is traversed by numerous furrows, or sulci. The gray matter contains cells from which fibers pass to form synapses in other areas of the brain and cells with which fibers entering the cerebellum from other parts of the brain form synapses.

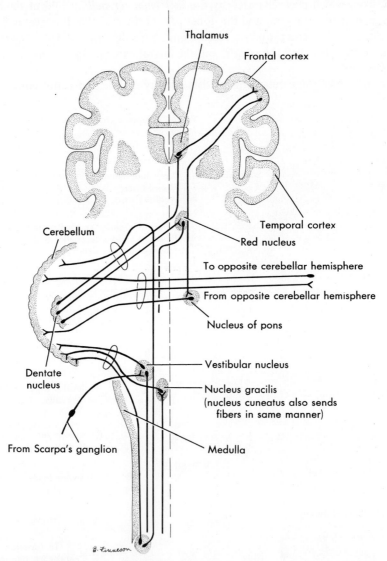

Figure 9–32. Connections of cerebellum with spinal cord and cerebrum.

The cerebellum is connected with the cerebrum by the *superior peduncles*, with the pons by the *middle peduncles*, and with the medulla oblongata by the *inferior peduncles* (Fig. 9–30). These peduncles are bundles of fibers. Impulses from the motor centers in the cerebrum, from the semicircular canals of the inner ear, and from the muscles enter the cerebellum by way of these bundles. Outgoing impulses are transmitted to the motor centers in the cerebrum, down the cord, and thence to the muscles.

The cerebellum receives tactile, proprioceptive, auditory, visual and cortical, and pontine impulses. It sends nerve impulses into all the motor centers of the body wall and helps to maintain posture and equilibrium and the tone of the voluntary muscles. It modifies the stretch reflexes. Movements elicited by spinal reflexes are also modified. The dentate nucleus is large and receives most of the fibers from Purkinje cells and relays the impulses to the thalamus. From there impulses are sent on to the frontal motor cortex.

There are other smaller nuclei that relay impulses to the reticular formation of the midbrain and to the red nucleus. None of the activities of the cerebellum comes into consciousness. In man, injury to the cerebellum results in muscular weakness, loss of tone, and inability to direct the movements of the skeletal muscles. There may be difficulty in walking due to inability to control the muscles of the legs or difficulty in talking due to lack of coordination of the muscles moving the tongue and jaw. The area of the body affected is determined by the location and extent of the injury to the cerebellum. Only parts of the body on the same side as the injury to the cerebellum are involved; if both sides of the cerebellum are injured, the lack of muscle tone and coordination may be so great that the person is helpless.

The pons varolii is situated in the front of the cerebellum between the midbrain and the medulla oblongata. It consists of interlaced transverse and longitudinal white fibers intermixed with gray matter. The transverse fibers are those derived from the middle peduncles of the cerebellum and serve to join its two halves. The longitudinal fibers connect the medulla with the cerebrum. In it also are the nuclei of all or a part of the fibers of the fifth, sixth, seventh, and eighth cranial nerves.

Physiology. The pons is a bridge of union between the two halves of the cerebellum and a bridge between the medulla and the midbrain. The fifth (trigeminal) nerve emerges from the side of the pons near its upper border. The sixth (abducent), seventh (facial), and eighth (statoacoustic) nerves emerge in the superficial furrow which separates the pons from the medulla (Fig. 9–34, p. 286). (There is a pneumotaxic center in the pons that participates in the regulation of respiration.)

The medulla oblongata (spinal bulb) is continuous with the spinal cord, which, on passing into the cranial cavity through the foramen magnum, widens into a pyramid-shaped mass which extends to the lower margin of the pons. Externally, the medulla resembles the upper part of the spinal cord, but the internal structure is different. All of the afferent and efferent tracts of the spinal cord are represented in the medulla, and many of them decussate, or cross, from one side to the other, whereas others terminate in the medulla. The nerve cells of the medulla are grouped to form *nuclei*, some of which are centers in which the cranial nerves arise. The motor fibers of the glossopharyngeal and of the vagus nerves, also the cranial portion of the accessory nerves, arise in the *nucleus ambiguus*. The hypoglossal nerve arises in the *hypoglossal nucleus*. Some of the nuclei are relay stations of sensory tracts to the brain, e.g., the *nucleus gracilis* and *nucleus cuneatus*. Some serve as centers for the control of bodily functions, e.g., the *cardiac, vasoconstrictor*, and *respiratory centers*.

Physiology. The medulla serves as an organ of conduction for the passage of impulses between the cord and the brain. It contains (1) the cardiac, (2) the vasoconstrictor, and (3) the respiratory centers and controls many reflex activities.

THE CARDIAC INHIBITORY CENTER consists of a bilateral group of cells lying in the medulla at the level of the nucleus of the *vagus nerve*. The fibers from this center accompany the vagi to the heart and unite with the cardiac branches from the thoracolumbar nerves to form the *cardiac plexus* (Fig. 13–12, p. 393) which envelops the arch and ascending portion of the aorta. From the cardiac plexus the heart receives *inhibitory fibers*. It is believed this center constantly discharges impulses which tend to hold the heart to a slower rate than it would assume if this check did not exist. The activity of the heart is also affected by impulses from the *cardiac sympathetic nerves*, which increase the rate of the heartbeat and are called accelerator nerves. The inhibitory and accelerator fibers are true antagonists having opposing effects upon the heart.

THE VASOCONSTRICTOR CENTER consists of a bilateral group of cells in the medulla. Fibers from these cells descend in the cord, and at various levels form synapses with spinal neurons in the lateral columns of gray matter. The spinal neuron serves as a preganglionic vasoconstrictor fiber, which terminates in a sympathetic ganglion. The path is further continued by a postganglionic fiber. The center and the fibers are in a state of constant activity and can be excited or inhibited reflexly through sensory nerves. One must conceive of different cells in this center being connected by definite vasoconstrictor paths with different parts of the body, e.g., the intestines or the skin. Further, the different parts of the center may be acted upon separately. The vasoconstrictor center is tonically or continuously active. This spontaneous activity is increased (facilitated) or decreased (inhibited) by different impulses. The fibers which, when stimulated, cause an excitation of the vasoconstrictor center, resulting in peripheral vasoconstriction and rise of arterial pressure, are called *pressor fibers*. The fibers which, when stimulated, cause an opposite effect, i.e., decrease the activity of the center, resulting in peripheral vasodilatation and fall of arterial pressure, are called *depressor fibers*.

Vasodilator fibers are efferent fibers which, when stimulated, cause an active relaxation of the smooth muscles of the arteries in the region supplied. Such fibers have been demonstrated in the facial and glossopharyngeal nerves, in some sympathetic nerves, and in the pelvic nerves. Vasodilators are not in a state of tonic activity nor is their activity controlled by the vasoconstriction center in the medulla.

THE RESPIRATORY CENTER consists of a bilateral group of cells located in the medulla. The results of various experiments tend to support the belief that the respiratory center is automatic, that is, it possesses an inherently rhythmic activity. It is very responsive to reflex stimulation. It is thought that the respiratory center is in connection with the sensory fibers of most cranial and spinal nerves and with many pathways between the cerebrum and the medulla. Stimulation of any of the sensory nerves of the body (e.g., by a dash of cold water, by unusual sights or sounds) or emotional states may alter respiration. The effect of the sensory nerves upon the activity of the respiratory center may be to alter the rate or the depth of the respiration. Sensory fibers which alter the activity of the cardiac and vasoconstrictor center may also affect the respiratory center. Changes in the oxygen and carbon dioxide tension of blood can have profound effects on respiration.

Inasmuch as normal respiration consists of an active inspiration and a passive expiration, it has been suggested that the respiratory center should be called the inspiratory center. However, we do have active expirations independent of the respirations proper, as in coughing, laughing, or the straining of defecation, micturition, or parturition, and as an integral part of the respirations in dyspnea. In dyspnea the coordinated activity of the expiratory muscles suggests the possibility of an expiratory center.

In addition to the control of respiration and circulation, many other reflex activities are effected through the medulla by means of the vagus and other cranial nerves, which originate in this region. Such reflex activities are sneezing, coughing, vomiting, winking, and the movements and secretions of the alimentary canal.

Meninges. The brain and spinal cord are enclosed within *three* membranes. These are named from without inward: the dura mater, arachnoid mater, and pia mater.

The dura mater is a dense membrane of fibrous connective tissue containing a great many blood vessels. The cranial and spinal portions of the dura mater differ and are described separately, but they form one complete membrane. The *cranial dura mater* is arranged in *two* layers which are closely connected except where they separate to form sinuses for the passage of venous blood. The outer, or endosteal, layer is adherent to the bones of the skull and forms their internal periosteum. The inner, or meningeal, layer covers the brain and sends numerous prolongations inward for the support and protection of the different lobes of the brain. These projections also form sinuses that return the blood from the brain, and sheaths for the nerves that pass out of the skull. The *spinal dura mater* forms a loose sheath around the spinal cord and consists of only the *inner layer* of the dura mater; the outer layer ceases at the foramen magnum, and its place is taken by the periosteum lining the vertebral canal. Between the spinal dura mater and the arachnoid mater is a potential cavity, the *subdural cavity*, which contains only enough fluid to moisten their contiguous surfaces.

The arachnoid mater is a delicate fibrous membrane placed between the dura mater and the pia mater. The cranial portion invests the brain loosely and, with the exception of the longitudinal fissure, it passes over the various convolutions and sulci and does not dip down into them. The spinal portion is tubular and surrounds the cord loosely. The *subarachnoid space*, between the arachnoid mater and the pia mater, contains a spongy connective tissue forming trabeculae and is filled with cerebrospinal fluid.

The pia mater is a vascular membrane consisting of a plexus of blood vessels held together by fine areolar connective tissue. The cranial portion invests the

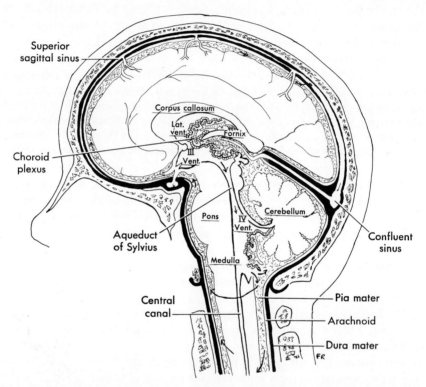

Figure 9–33. Diagram showing relationship of brain and cord to meninges. The choroid plexus forms the cerebrospinal fluid. (Modified from *The Principal Nervous Pathways*, 4th ed., by Andrew T. Rasmussen, The Macmillan Company.)

surface of the brain and dips down between the convolutions. The spinal portion is thicker and less vascular than the cranial. It is closely adherent to the entire surface of the spinal cord and sends a process into the ventral fissure.

Blood Supply. For blood supply to the brain and venous return, see pages 415 and 424.

The Cerebrospinal Fluid. The meningeal membranes and the spaces filled with fluid form a pad enclosing the brain and cord on all sides. Cerebrospinal fluid is secreted and diffused from the blood by the ependymal cells which cover the *choroid plexuses* of the ventricles. The choroid plexuses are highly vascular folds or processes of the pia mater, which are found in the ventricles. The capillary network is intricate and resembles other cerebral capillaries. These differ greatly in their selective permeability from those in other parts of the body. The choroid plexus capillaries are covered by thick, highly differentiated cells that have the structure needed for *active* transport. After filling the lateral ventricles, the cerebrospinal fluid escapes by the foramen of Monro into the third ventricle and thence by the aqueduct into the fourth ventricle. From the fourth ventricle the fluid is poured through the medial foramen of Magendie and the two lateral foramina of Luschka[8] into the subarachnoid spaces and reaches the cisterna magna. From the cisterna magna the cerebrospinal fluid may pass down the spinal canal within the subarachnoid space where it circulates around and upward and finally enters the venous circulation. From the cisterna magna this fluid also bathes all parts of the brain. From the subarachnoid spaces it is absorbed through the villi of the arachnoid mater, which project into the dural venous sinuses; a small amount passes into the perineural lymphatics of the cranial and spinal nerves. Experimentally, it has been found that dyes added to the cerebrospinal fluid travel along the course of certain cranial nerves, especially the olfactory. This loophole affords an opportunity for the entry of infection from the nasal cavities to the cerebral cavity.

The cerebrospinal fluid is highly variable in quantity, which is usually given as from 80 to 200 ml. It is colorless, alkaline, and has a specific gravity of 1.004 to 1.008. It consists of water with traces of protein, some glucose, and electrolytes, as in blood plasma, a few lymphocytes, and some pituitary hormones. The cerebrospinal fluid serves to keep the brain and spinal cord moist, lubricates them, and protects them from varying pressures. If the membranes of the brain or cord are inflamed, there is usually a change in the normal characteristics of the fluid.

Infection and inflammation of the meninges of the brain will quickly spread to those of the cord. Such inflammation results in increased secretion, which, as it collects in a confined bony cavity, gives rise to symptoms of pressure, such as headache, slow pulse, slow respirations, and partial or complete unconsciousness. Cerebrospinal fluid may be removed by lumbar puncture. The needle by which the fluid is withdrawn is usually inserted between the third and fourth lumbar vertebrae (Fig. 9-12) (thus below the end of the cord) into the subarachnoid space on the right side, the patient usually lying on his left side, with knees drawn up in order to arch the back, so as to separate the vertebrae. The fluid, or exudate, will contain the products of the inflammatory process and the organisms causing it. Lumbar puncture is used for (1) diagnosis of meningitis, syphilis, increased intracranial pressure, cerebral hemorrhage, and intracranial tumors; and (2) therapeutic effect: (*a*) to relieve pressure in meningitis, hydrocephalus, and convulsions in children; and (*b*) rarely for the introduction of sera, such as antimeningitis serum, or drugs.

---

[8] Hubert von Luschka, German anatomist (1820-1875).

THE CRANIAL NERVES—THEIR STRUCTURE, LOCATION, AND FUNCTION

Twelve pairs of cranial nerves emerge from the undersurface of the brain and pass through the foramina in the base of the cranium. They are classified as motor, sensory, and mixed nerves (Fig. 9–34). For simplicity one nerve of each pair is described.

The origin of the cranial nerves is comparable to that of the spinal nerves. The motor fibers of the spinal nerves arise from cell bodies in the ventral columns of

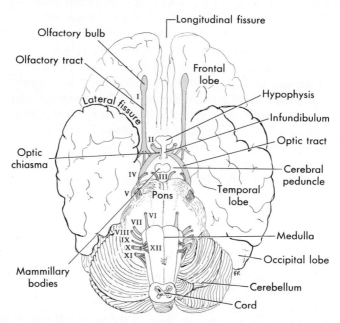

Figure 9–34. Undersurface of brain showing cerebrum, cerebellum, the pons, and medulla; note the infundibulum to which the pituitary, or hypophysis, is attached. The numerals indicate the cranial nerves. Note the olfactory bulb and tract, mammillary bodies, and the optic chiasma.

the cord, and the sensory fibers arise from cell bodies in the ganglia outside the cord. The motor cranial nerves arise from cell bodies within the brain, which constitute their *nuclei of origin*. The sensory cranial nerves arise from groups of nerve cells outside the brain. These cells may form ganglia on the trunks of the nerves, or they may be located in peripheral sensory organs, such as the nose and eyes. The central processes of the sensory nerves run into the brain and end by arborizing around nerve cells which form their *nuclei of termination*. The nuclei of origin of the motor nerves and the nuclei of termination of the sensory nerves are connected with the cerebral cortex.

Numbers and Names. The cranial nerves are named according to the order in which they arise from the brain, and also by names which describe their nature, function, or distribution.

I. Olfactory	Sensory	VII. Facial	Mixed
II. Optic	Sensory	VIII. Statoacoustic	Sensory
III. Oculomotor	Motor	IX. Glossopharyngeal	Mixed
IV. Trochlear	Motor	X. Vagus	Mixed
V. Trigeminal	Mixed	XI. Accessory	Motor
VI. Abducens	Motor	XII. Hypoglossal	Motor

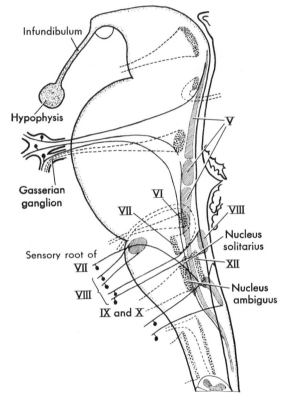

Figure 9–35. Brain stem; lateral view showing hypophysis and the nuclei of origin of some of the cranial nerves. (Modified from Toldt.)

I. The olfactory nerve is the special nerve of the sense of smell. It arises from the central or deep processes of the olfactory cells of the nasal mucous membrane, where its fibers form a network (Fig. 11–7) and are then collected into about 20 branches, which pierce the cribriform plate of the ethmoid bone in two groups and form synapses with the cells of the olfactory bulb. From the olfactory bulb other fibers extend inward to centers in the cerebrum.

II. The optic nerve is the special nerve of the sense of sight. It consists of fibers derived from ganglionic cells in the retina. These cells are third in the series of neurons from the receptors to the brain.

III. The oculomotor nerve arises from a nucleus in the floor of the cerebral aqueduct. It supplies motor fibers to four of the extrinsic muscles of the eyeball, namely, the superior rectus, inferior rectus, medial rectus, and inferior oblique. Parasympathetic fibers supply the two intrinsic muscles of the eyeball, namely, the ciliaris and the sphincter pupillae. This nerve is associated with the ciliary ganglion located in the back part of the orbit.

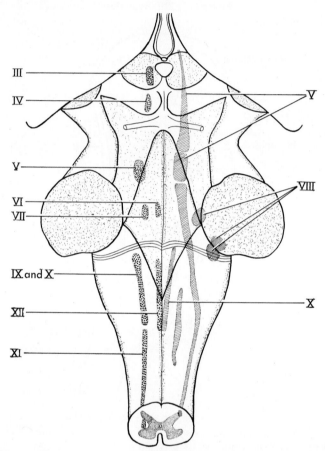

Figure 9–36. Dorsal view of brain stem, showing nuclei of origin of the cranial nerves. Sensory nuclei are striped and shown on the right. Motor nuclei are dotted and shown on the left. (Modified from Toldt.)

IV. The trochlear nerve arises from a nucleus in the floor of the cerebral aqueduct. It supplies motor fibers to the superior oblique muscle of the eye.

V. The trigeminal, or *trifacial, nerve* is the largest cranial nerve and the chief sensory nerve of the face and head. The motor fibers extend to the muscles of mastication. It emerges from the brain by a small motor and a large sensory root. The fibers of the motor root arise from two nuclei, a superior, located in

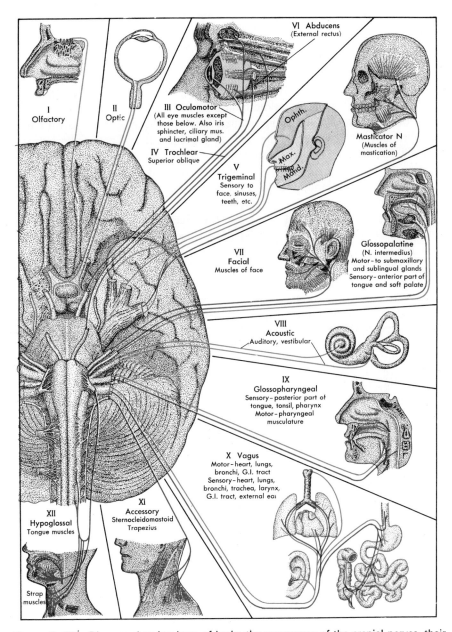

Figure 9–37. Diagram showing base of brain, the emergence of the cranial nerves, their distribution to the structures, and the functions with which they are concerned. *Blue—sensory; red—motor.* (Reproduced from full-color illustration in *Ciba Collection of Medical Illustrations*, Vol. 1, "Nervous System." Courtesy of Ciba Pharmaceutical Products, Inc., Summit, N.J.)

the cerebral aqueduct, and an inferior, located in the upper part of the pons. It is uncertain whether the fibers from the superior nucleus are motor or sensory. The fibers of the sensory root arise from cells in the trigeminal ganglion (semilunar, or gasserian), which lies in a cavity of the dura mater near the apex of the petrous portion of the temporal bone. The fibers from the two roots coalesce into one trunk and then subdivide into three large branches: (1) the ophthalmic, (2) the maxillary, and (3) the mandibular.

THE OPHTHALMIC BRANCH is the smallest and is a sensory nerve. It divides into three branches—the lacrimal, the frontal, the nasociliary—and communicates with the oculomotor, the trochlear, and the abducens. It supplies branches to the cornea, ciliary body, and iris; to the lacrimal gland and conjunctiva; to part of the mucous membrane of the nasal cavity; to the skin of the eyelid, eyebrow, forehead, and nose.

THE MAXILLARY, the second division of the trigeminal, is also a sensory nerve. It divides into many branches, which are distributed to the dura mater, the forehead, the lower eyelid, the lateral angle of the orbit, the upper lip, the gums and teeth of the upper jaw, and the mucous membrane and skin of the cheek and of the nose.

THE MANDIBULAR is the largest of the three divisions of the trigeminal. It is both a sensory and a motor nerve; it divides into many branches which are distributed to the temple, the pinna of the ear, the lower lip, the lower part of the face, the teeth and gums of the mandible, and the muscles of mastication. It also supplies the mucous membrane of the anterior part of the tongue with the lingual nerve.

VI. The abducens nerve arises in a small nucleus lying beneath the floor of the fourth ventricle. It is a motor nerve and supplies fibers to the lateral rectus muscle of the eye.

VII. The facial nerve is a mixed nerve, consisting of motor and sensory fibers. The motor fibers arise from a nucleus in the lower part of the pons. The sensory fibers arise from the geniculate ganglion on the facial nerve. The single process of the ganglionic cells divides in a T-shaped manner into central and peripheral fibers. The central fibers pass into the medulla oblongata and end in the terminal nucleus of the glossopharyngeal nerve. The peripheral fibers form the sensory root and emerge from the brain with the motor root. Behind the ramus of the mandible the facial nerve divides into many branches. Motor fibers are supplied to the muscles of the face, part of the scalp, the pinna, and muscles of the neck. Vasodilator fibers are supplied to the submaxillary (submandibular) and sublingual glands. Sensory fibers are supplied to the anterior two thirds of the tongue (taste), and a few to the region of the middle ear.

VIII. The statoacoustic nerve is a sensory nerve and contains two distinct sets of fibers, which differ in their origin, destination, and function. One set of fibers is known as the *cochlear nerve*, or nerve of hearing. These fibers originate in the spiral ganglion of the cochlea. The other is the *vestibular nerve*, or nerve for the maintenance of equilibrium. The fibers originate in the vestibular ganglion of the internal auditory meatus (Fig. 11–14, p. 329).

IX. The glossopharyngeal nerve contains both sensory and motor fibers and is distributed, as its name indicates, to the tongue and pharynx. The sensory fibers arise from the superior and petrous ganglia, which are situated on the trunk of the nerve, the former in the jugular foramen, the latter in the petrous portion of the temporal bone. The motor fibers arise from the nucleus ambiguus, common to this and the tenth nerve, which is situated in the medulla. This nerve supplies sensory fibers to the mucous membrane of the fauces, tonsils, pharynx, and the posterior third of the tongue, giving the sense of taste. It also supplies motor fibers to the muscles of the pharynx and secretory fibers to the parotid gland.

X. The vagus nerve has a more extensive distribution than any of the other cranial nerves, since it passes through the neck and thorax to the abdomen. It is a mixed nerve. Its motor fibers arise from the nucleus ambiguus. These fibers supply the muscles of the pharynx, larynx, trachea, heart, esophagus, stomach, small intestine, pancreas, liver, spleen, ascending colon, and kidneys. The heart is supplied with inhibitory fibers, and the gastric and pancreatic glands with secretory fibers. Its sensory fibers arise from cells of the jugular ganglion and from the ganglion nodosum located on the trunk of the nerve. The sensory fibers are distributed to the mucous membrane of the larynx, trachea, lungs, esophagus, stomach, intestines, heart, gallbladder, and aortic body.

XI. The accessory nerve is a motor nerve, consisting of two parts, an internal branch (cranial part) and an external branch (spinal part). The internal branch arises from the nucleus ambiguus in the medulla, and its fibers are distributed to the pharyngeal and superior laryngeal branches of the vagus. The external branch arises from the spinal cord as low as the fifth cervical nerve, ascends, enters the skull through the foramen magnum, is directed to the jugular foramen, through which it passes, and descends to the sternocleidomastoid and trapezius muscles. Some fibers are distributed in the vagus nerve.

XII. The hypoglossal nerve arises from the hypoglossal nucleus in the medulla. It is a motor nerve supplying the muscles of the tongue and hyoid bone.

QUESTIONS FOR DISCUSSION

1. Differentiate between the symptoms caused by a crush injury to the vertebra at the level of the fourth lumbar and an injury that involved the tenth thoracic vertebra.
2. Explain the symptoms resulting from an injury that hemisected the spinal cord at the tenth thoracic, left side.
3. An individual has had a cerebral accident that involves the lenticular artery and causes pressure on the internal capsule on the right side.
   a. Where will there be loss of motor function? Explain.
   b. What additional problems and/or symptoms would be present if the accident had involved the left side of the brain?

4. Name and discuss five functions of the hypothalamus.
5. Which part of the brain receives practically all the incoming sensory impulses? Explain what happens to these impulses.
6. Explain the arousal mechanism of the brain.
7. Differentiate between the symptoms of an upper and a lower motor neuron lesion.

SUMMARY

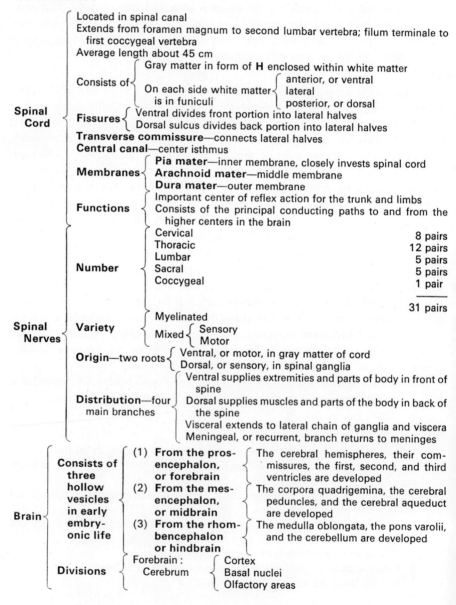

Spinal Cord
- Located in spinal canal
- Extends from foramen magnum to second lumbar vertebra; filum terminale to first coccygeal vertebra
- Average length about 45 cm
- Consists of
  - Gray matter in form of **H** enclosed within white matter
  - On each side white matter is in funiculi
    - anterior, or ventral
    - lateral
    - posterior, or dorsal
- **Fissures**
  - Ventral divides front portion into lateral halves
  - Dorsal sulcus divides back portion into lateral halves
- **Transverse commissure**—connects lateral halves
- **Central canal**—center isthmus
- **Membranes**
  - **Pia mater**—inner membrane, closely invests spinal cord
  - **Arachnoid mater**—middle membrane
  - **Dura mater**—outer membrane
- **Functions**
  - Important center of reflex action for the trunk and limbs
  - Consists of the principal conducting paths to and from the higher centers in the brain

Spinal Nerves
- **Number**
  - Cervical   8 pairs
  - Thoracic   12 pairs
  - Lumbar   5 pairs
  - Sacral   5 pairs
  - Coccygeal   1 pair
  - ————
  - 31 pairs
- **Variety**
  - Myelinated
  - Mixed
    - Sensory
    - Motor
- **Origin**—two roots
  - Ventral, or motor, in gray matter of cord
  - Dorsal, or sensory, in spinal ganglia
- **Distribution**—four main branches
  - Ventral supplies extremities and parts of body in front of spine
  - Dorsal supplies muscles and parts of the body in back of the spine
  - Visceral extends to lateral chain of ganglia and viscera
  - Meningeal, or recurrent, branch returns to meninges

Brain
- Consists of three hollow vesicles in early embryonic life
  - (1) From the prosencephalon, or forebrain
    - The cerebral hemispheres, their commissures, the first, second, and third ventricles are developed
  - (2) From the mesencephalon, or midbrain
    - The corpora quadrigemina, the cerebral peduncles, and the cerebral aqueduct are developed
  - (3) From the rhombencephalon or hindbrain
    - The medulla oblongata, the pons varolii, and the cerebellum are developed
- **Divisions**
  - Forebrain: Cerebrum
    - Cortex
    - Basal nuclei
    - Olfactory areas

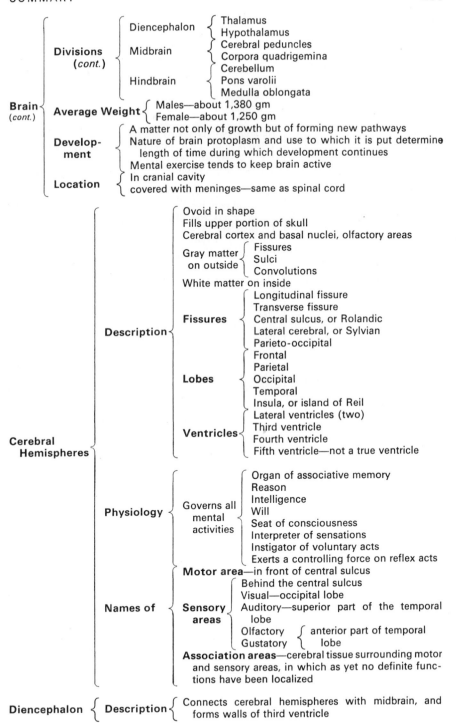

Brain *(cont.)*

Divisions *(cont.)*
- Diencephalon
  - Thalamus
  - Hypothalamus
- Midbrain
  - Cerebral peduncles
  - Corpora quadrigemina
- Hindbrain
  - Cerebellum
  - Pons varolii
  - Medulla oblongata

Average Weight
- Males—about 1,380 gm
- Female—about 1,250 gm

Development
- A matter not only of growth but of forming new pathways
- Nature of brain protoplasm and use to which it is put determine length of time during which development continues
- Mental exercise tends to keep brain active

Location
- In cranial cavity
- covered with meninges—same as spinal cord

Cerebral Hemispheres

Description
- Ovoid in shape
- Fills upper portion of skull
- Cerebral cortex and basal nuclei, olfactory areas
- Gray matter on outside
  - Fissures
  - Sulci
  - Convolutions
- White matter on inside
- **Fissures**
  - Longitudinal fissure
  - Transverse fissure
  - Central sulcus, or Rolandic
  - Lateral cerebral, or Sylvian
  - Parieto-occipital
- **Lobes**
  - Frontal
  - Parietal
  - Occipital
  - Temporal
  - Insula, or island of Reil
- **Ventricles**
  - Lateral ventricles (two)
  - Third ventricle
  - Fourth ventricle
  - Fifth ventricle—not a true ventricle

Physiology
- Governs all mental activities
  - Organ of associative memory
  - Reason
  - Intelligence
  - Will
  - Seat of consciousness
  - Interpreter of sensations
  - Instigator of voluntary acts
  - Exerts a controlling force on reflex acts

Names of
- **Motor area**—in front of central sulcus
- **Sensory areas**
  - Behind the central sulcus
  - Visual—occipital lobe
  - Auditory—superior part of the temporal lobe
  - Olfactory — anterior part of temporal lobe
  - Gustatory
- **Association areas**—cerebral tissue surrounding motor and sensory areas, in which as yet no definite functions have been localized

Diencephalon

Description
- Connects cerebral hemispheres with midbrain, and forms walls of third ventricle

Diencephalon (*cont.*)

Physiology
- Auditory and visual reflexes
- Sensory integration
- Regulation of autonomic nervous system, water balance, sleep-waking, body temperature, appetite

Areas
- Thalamus
- Hypothalamus
- Metathalamus
- Epithalamus

Reticular Formation

Description
- Network of interlacing cells and fibers
- Extends from upper spinal cord to diencephalon

Physiology
- Alerts cortex to wakefulness
- Sends efferent impulses to higher and lower centers

Midbrain

Description
- Short, constricted portion connects pons and cerebellum with the hemispheres of the cerebrum
- Consists of
  - Pair of cerebral peduncles
  - The corpora quadrigemina
  - The cerebral aqueduct
- Contains nuclei of the III and IV cranial nerves

Cerebellum

Description
- Oval in form, constricted in center
- Central portion called vermis
- Lateral portions called hemispheres
- Gray matter on exterior
- White matter in interior
- Connected with cerebrum by superior peduncles
- Connected with pons by middle peduncles
- Connected with medulla by inferior peduncles

Physiology
- Participates in the coordination and integration of posture and all voluntary movements

Pons Varolii

Description
- Situated between the midbrain and the medulla oblongata. Consists of interlaced transverse and longitudinal white fibers mixed with gray matter
- Connects two halves of cerebellum and also medulla with cerebrum

Physiology
- Contains nuclei of trigeminal, abducens, facial, and statoacoustic nerves
- Participates in the regulation of respiration

Medulla Oblongata

Description
- Pyramid-shaped mass, upward continuation of cord. Sensory and motor tracts or spinal cord represented. Many of them cross from one side to the other in the medulla; some end in medulla
- Gray matter forms nuclei

Physiology
- Nuclei serve as
  - Centers in which cranial nerves arise, centers for control of bodily functions
  - Relay stations of sensory tracts to brain
- Vital centers
  - Cardiac center
  - Vasoconstrictor center
  - Respiratory center
- Controls such reflex activities as
  - Sneezing
  - Coughing
  - Vomiting
  - Winking
  - Movements and secretions of alimentary canal

Meninges, or Membranes, of Brain and Cord

- **Cranial dura mater**—arranged in two layers. Outer layer adherent to bones of skull; inner layer covers the brain
- **Spinal dura mater**—consists of only the inner layer, forms a loose sheath around the cord
- **Arachnoid mater**—serous membrane placed between the dura mater and pia mater of both brain and cord
- **Cranial pia mater**—vascular membrane, invests brain and dips down into crevices and depressions, forms choroid plexuses
- **Spinal pia mater**—is closely adherent to cord and sends a process into the anterior fissure,

Cerebrospinal Fluid

- Found in subarachnoid space and ventricles of the brain
- Formed by choroid plexuses of the ventricles from blood
- Clear, limpid fluid, specific gravity 1.004 to 1.008
- Quantity variable, 80–200 ml
- Contains traces of protein, glucose, salts, lymphocytes, and pituitary hormones
- **Physiology** { Nutritive medium for nerve cells / Acts as a shock absorber

SUMMARY OF THE CRANIAL NERVES

NAME	NUCLEI OF ORIGIN AND TERMINATION	DISTRIBUTION	PHYSIOLOGY
I. Olfactory (sensory)	Central or deep process of olfactory bulb	Nasal mucous membranes	Sense of smell
II. Optic (sensory)	Ganglionic cells of retina	Retina of eye	Sense of sight
III. Oculomotor (motor)	Nucleus in floor of cerebral aqueduct	Superior, inferior, and medial recti; inferior oblique, ciliaris, and sphincter pupillae muscles	Muscle contraction, eye movements
IV. Trochlear (motor)	Nucleus in floor of cerebral aqueduct	Superior oblique muscle of eye	Muscle contraction, eye movements
V. Trigeminal (sensory and motor)	Fibers of sensory root arise from the semilunar ganglion, which lies in cavity of dura mater near the apex of the petrous portion of the temporal bone. Fibers of the motor root arise from superior and inferior nuclei in pons. Fibers from the two roots coalesce into one trunk and then subdivide into (1) the ophthalmic, (2) the maxillary, and (3) the mandibular	(1) Ophthalmic distributes nerves to cornea, ciliary body, iris, lacrimal gland, conjunctiva, part of the mucous membrane of the nasal cavity, skin of the forehead, eyelid, eyebrow, and nose	Sensation
		(2) Maxillary distributes nerves to the dura mater, forehead, lower eyelid, lateral angle of orbit, upper lip, gums and teeth of upper jaw, mucous membrane, and skin of cheek and nose	Facial Sensation
		(3) Mandibular distributes branches to the temple, auricle of ear, lower lip, lower part of face, teeth and gums of mandible and muscles of mastication. Lingual nerve to mucous membrane of anterior part of tongue	Sensation and motion. Some fibers of VII reach the anterior tongue via lingual branch of V (taste)
VI. Abducens (motor)	Nucleus beneath floor of fourth ventricle	Lateral rectus muscle of the eye*	Eye movements
VII. Facial (sensory and motor)	Sensory fibers arise from the geniculate ganglion on the facial nerve	Distributes nerves to the anterior two thirds of the tongue (taste) and a few to the region of the middle ear	Sense of taste
	Motor fibers arise from a nucleus in the lower part of the pons	Distributes nerves to the muscles of the face, part of the scalp, the auricle, and muscles of the neck	Facial movements
		Vasodilator fibers are distributed to the submaxillary and sublingual glands	Secretion

296

Nerve	Origin	Distribution	Function
VIII. Statoacoustic (sensory) Two sets of fibers	*Cochlear* from bipolar cells in the spiral ganglion of the cochlea	To the organ of Corti	Sense of hearing
	Vestibular from bipolar cells situated in upper part of the outer end of the internal auditory meatus	To the semicircular canals	Equilibrium
IX. Glossopharyngeal (sensory and motor)	*Sensory* fibers arise from the superior and petrous ganglia, situated on the trunk of the nerve, the former in the jugular foramen, the latter in the petrous portion of the temporal bone	Distributes sensory nerves to mucous membrane of fauces, tonsils, pharynx, and posterior third of tongue; carotid sinus and body	Sense of taste. Sense blood pressure and blood gas tensions
	Motor fibers arise from nucleus ambiguus in the medulla	Distributes motor fibers to the muscles of the pharynx, and secretory fibers to the parotid gland	Motion. Secretion
X. Vagus (sensory and motor)	*Sensory* fibers arise from jugular ganglion and ganglion nodosum situated on trunk of nerve after it passes through the jugular foramen	Distributes sensory nerves to the mucous membrane of the larynx, trachea, lungs, esophagus, stomach, intestines, gallbladder, aortic sinus, and body	Sensory impulses which initiate cardiovascular and respiratory reflexes. Sense blood pressure and blood gas tension
	Motor fibers arise from nucleus ambiguus in the medulla	Distributes motor nerves ot larynx, esophagus, stomach, small intestine, and part of the large intestine. Distributes inhibitory fibers to heart. Distributes secretory fibers to gastric and pancreatic glands	Muscle contraction. Secretion
XI. Accessory Nerve, or Spinal Accessory (consists of two parts, cranial and spinal) (motor)	*Cranial* fibers arise from nucleus ambiguus in the medulla	Distributes fibers to the pharyngeal and superior laryngeal branches of the vagus	Muscle contraction
	Spinal fibers arise from spinal cord as low as the fifth cervical nerve	Distributes nerves to the sternocleidomastoid and trapezius muscles. Some fibers are distributed with vagus	Muscle contraction
XII. Hypoglossal (motor)	Arises from the hypoglossal nucleus in the medulla	Distributes nerves to the muscles of the tongue	Muscle contraction

* Fibers from nucleus of third nerve communicate with nucleus of sixth nerve to coordinate the activity of the lateral rectus and medial rectus of the two sides. This coordination is effected by fibers in the medial longitudinal fasciculus.

CHAPTER **10**

The Autonomic Nervous
System: Its Structure
and Function

THE CENTRAL nervous system is concerned with control and response to environmental changes. There is purposeful, planned response to environmental needs; action is controlled.

The autonomic nervous system controls internal environment, such as, for example, control of heart action, adjustment of circulation to meet body needs, secretion of digestive juices, and peristaltic activity. There is also a personal non-intellectual response to environment, such as, for example, emotional reaction to a given situation, which in turn may affect physiological functioning.

The division of the nervous system into the cerebrospinal system and the visceral system is based on a difference in function and not on an actual anatomical separation. The *visceral* system is both afferent and efferent in function. This system possesses a certain independence of the cerebrospinal system. It regulates and controls vital activities. There is no consciousness of these activities, except as they contribute in a general way to a sense of well-being. Most of the centers controlling these processes are located within the central nervous system; but there is coordination of cellular activities even within the walls of the viscera, and this intraorgan integration helps to control such activities as gastrointestinal motility and secretion, cardiac output, sweating, urinary output, arterial blood pressure, and many other physiological processes. Some autonomic functions are almost completely controlled by the central nervous system; others are only partly controlled by the central nervous system. Some visceral

298

functions can be performed quite independently of any nervous control. The heart muscle contracts automatically; some of the glands are excited to secretion by chemical substances in the blood, such as, for instance, the secretion of pancreatic fluid due to the stimulus of the hormone *secretin*. Even though such activities are not directly dependent upon the nervous system, they may be regulated or modulated by the nervous system, because in all visceral functions the nonnervous and the nervous cooperate in a most intimate way.

In the autonomic (efferent visceral) system two neurons connect the central nervous system and the end organ. The fiber of a neuron lying in the *central nervous system* extends to an *autonomic* ganglion and synapses on the dendrites or cell body of an autonomic neuron. The fiber of the second neuron passes from the ganglion to the effector to be innervated. The fiber of the first neuron is called the *preganglionic fiber*, the fiber of the second neuron is called the *postganglionic fiber*.

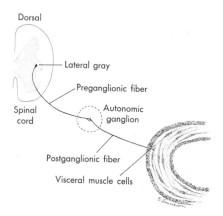

Figure 10–1. Diagram showing the relationship of the preganglionic and postganglionic neurons of the autonomic nervous system.

The Craniosacral, or Parasympathetic, System. This system includes all the fibers that arise from the midbrain (tectal autonomics), from the medulla and pons (bulbar autonomics), and from the sacral region of the cord (sacral autonomics).

The *tectal autonomics* arise from nuclei in the midbrain, send preganglionic fibers with the oculomotor nerve into the orbit, and pass to the ciliary ganglion, where they terminate by forming synapses with motor neurons whose axons (postganglionic fibers) proceed as the short ciliary nerves to the ciliary muscle of the eye and to the pupillary sphincters.

The *bulbar autonomics* arise from nuclei in the medulla and pons and emerge in the seventh, ninth, and tenth cranial nerves. Fibers from the seventh nerve are distributed to lacrimal, nasal, submaxillary, and sublingual glands. Fibers from the ninth nerve are distributed to the parotid gland. Fibers from the tenth nerve are distributed to the heart, lungs, esophagus, stomach, the small intestine, proximal half of the colon, gallbladder, liver, and pancreas.

Some of the fibers of the vagus nerve are distributed to the skeletal muscles of the larynx and pharynx from the nucleus ambiguus. The vagus also carries important afferent nerve fibers from pressor receptors in arteries and stretch receptors of the lungs to the medulla.

The sacral autonomics include autonomic fibers which emerge from the spinal cord. Neurons of the second, third, and fourth and sometimes the first sacral

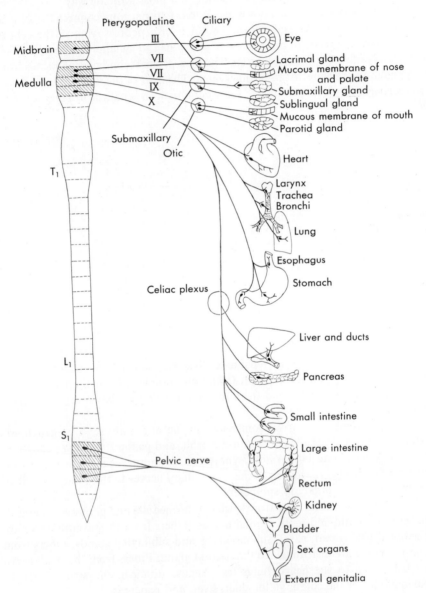

Figure 10–2. Craniosacral autonomic system.

spinal nerves send fibers to the pelvis, where they form the pelvic nerve, which sends fibers to the pelvic plexus, from which postganglionic fibers are distributed to the pelvic viscera. Motor fibers pass to the smooth muscle of the descending colon, rectum, anus, bladder, and reproductive organs. Vasodilator fibers are distributed to the organs and to the external genitals.

Thoracolumbar, or Sympathetic, System. This includes (1) small neurons in

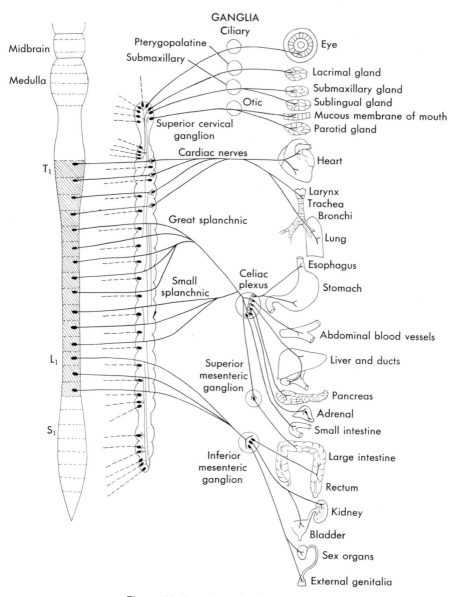

Figure 10–3. Thoracolumbar autonomic system.

the gray lateral columns of the thoracic and lumbar regions of the cord giving rise to preganglionic fibers; (2) the sympathetic ganglia and their postganglionic fibers—the lateral chain of the sympathetic trunk; and (3) the great prevertebral plexuses. Postganglionic fibers may arise either from a ganglion in the lateral chain or from a ganglion in one of the great plexuses.

The sympathetic centers of the spinal cord are composed of groups of cells lying in the lateral columns of the gray matter of the cord from the first thoracic

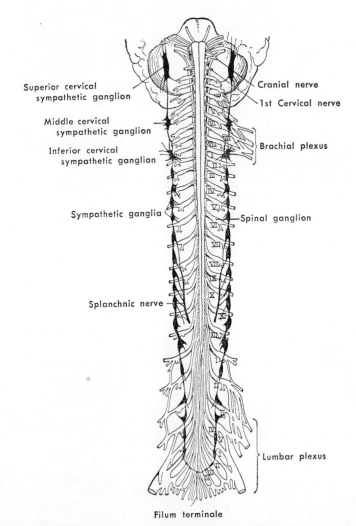

Superior cervical
sympathetic ganglion

Middle cervical
sympathetic ganglion

Inferior cervical
sympathetic ganglion

Sympathetic ganglia

Splanchnic nerve

Cranial nerve

1st Cervical nerve

Brachial plexus

Spinal ganglion

Lumbar plexus

Filum terminale

Figure 10–4. Diagram of spinal cord, spinal nerves, the right and left chains of autonomic ganglia. At the top the medulla is seen, with some of the cranial nerves. The cerebellum is seen behind the medulla at the sides, and behind the cerebellum the cerebrum is shown at the sides. (From Huxley, after Allen Thomson.)

to lumbar two or three. They give rise to preganglionic fibers which make their first termination in one of the sympathetic ganglia.

The sympathetic ganglia (Fig. 10–4) consist of paired chains of ganglia which lie along the ventrolateral aspects of the vertebral column, extending from the base of the skull to the coccyx. They are grouped as cervical, thoracic, lumbar, and sacral, and, except in the neck, they correspond in number to the vertebrae against which they lie: •

CERVICAL	THORACIC	LUMBAR	SACRAL
3 pairs	10–12 pairs	4 pairs	4–5 pairs

The sympathetic ganglia are connected with each other by nerve fibers called gangliated cords, and with the spinal nerves by branches which are called *rami*

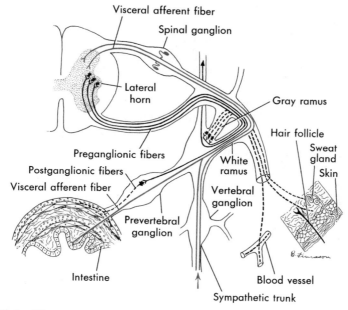

Figure 10–5. Diagram showing origin of sympathetic preganglionic and postganglionic fibers and their distribution.

communicantes. In the thoracic and lumbar regions these communications consist of two rami, a white ramus and a gray ramus (Fig. 10–5).

The white rami fibers are *myelinated fibers* passing between the central nervous system and the sympathetic ganglia. The gray rami fibers are nonmyelinated fibers that are the axons of cells in the sympathetic ganglia and are distributed chiefly with the peripheral branches of all the spinal nerves to the periphery.

The White Rami Fibers. The cell of origin of these fibers lies in the lateral gray of the spinal cord from the first thoracic (T_1) to the second or third (L_2 or L_3). The fibers leave by way of the anterior root with the peripheral nerves. They leave the peripheral nerve by way of the white rami and enter the sympathetic ganglia, where they may terminate around a sympathetic postganglionic neuron or may pass up or down in the sympathetic chain for some distance before ending around a sympathetic neuron. These are the fibers that form the connection in the sympathetic chain.

The fibers from T_1 to T_5 (preganglionic) emerge from the cord and synapse in the sympathetic ganglia. The fibers of the sympathetic cells in the ganglia (postganglionic fibers) are distributed to the heart and to blood vessels.

The fibers from T_6 to T_{12} form the splanchnic nerves. These preganglionic fibers pass through the sympathetic ganglia and terminate in the celiac ganglia (solar plexus). The postganglionic fibers are distributed to the esophagus, stomach, intestine as far as the proximal colon, liver, and gallbladder.

The fibers from L_1 to L_3 form the *preganglionic* fibers that terminate in the inferior mesenteric ganglia. The *postganglionic* fibers are distributed to the distal part of the colon, rectum, and genitourinary organs.

The gray rami fibers have their cells of origin in the sympathetic ganglia and are distributed by the spinal nerves to arteries, arterioles (vasoconstrictors), veins, venules, sweat glands, and pilomotor muscles (Fig. 10–5).

The fibers to the blood vessels, glands, and walls of the viscera are distributed by various sympathetic ganglia. For the head region the fibers, after entering the sympathetic chain, pass upward and end in the *superior cervical ganglion;* from this ganglion postganglionic fibers emerge by the various plexuses that arise from this ganglion.

The great plexuses of the thoracolumbar system consist of ganglia and fibers derived from the lateral chain ganglia and the spinal cord. They are situated in the thoracic, abdominal, and pelvic cavities, and are named the cardiac, celiac, mesenteric, lumbar, and sacral plexuses.

1. THE CARDIAC PLEXUS is situated at the base of the heart, lying on the arch and the ascending portion of the aorta.

2. THE CELIAC PLEXUS (solar plexus) is situated behind the stomach, between the suprarenal glands. It surrounds the celiac artery and the root of the superior mesenteric artery. It consists of two large ganglia and a dense network of nerve fibers uniting them. It receives the greater and lesser splanchnic nerves of both sides and some fibers from the vagi, and gives off numerous secondary plexuses along the neighboring arteries. The names of the secondary plexuses indicate the arteries which they accompany and the organs to which they distribute branches.

Phrenic	Superior gastric	Spermatic
Hepatic	Suprarenal	Superior mesenteric
Splenic	Renal	Abdominal aortic
		Inferior mesenteric

These nerves form intricate networks, and any one organ may receive branches from several nerves. This increases the number of pathways and connections between the organs.

3. THE MESENTERIC PLEXUS is situated in front of the last lumbar vertebra and

the promontory of the sacrum. It is formed by the union of numerous filaments which descend on either side from the aortic plexus and from the lumbar ganglia; below, it divides into the lumbar and sacral plexuses.

The Enteric System. This system includes the myenteric (Auerbach's[1]) and submucous (Meissner's[2]) plexuses of the digestive canal. They extend from the upper level of the esophagus to the anal canal. The myenteric plexus is situated between the longitudinal and circular muscular coats. The submucous plexus lies in the submucosa. These plexuses are intimately connected with each other (Fig. 10–6).

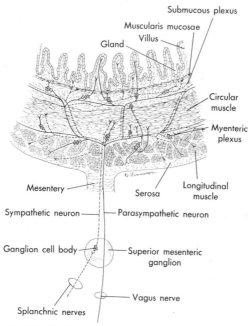

Figure 10–6. Distribution of autonomic neurons to the enteric system.

Physiology of the Autonomic System. The autonomic system innervates (1) all plain muscular tissue in the body, (2) the heart, and (3) the glands. The ganglia serve as relay stations for many of the impulses passing from the midbrain, pons, and medulla, or spinal cord, or they may act independently of these influences.

In general, most organs have a double autonomic innervation, one from the thoracolumbar system and one from either the cranial or the sacral autonomic system. The functions of these two systems are usually antagonistic. With the exception of nicotine, which paralyzes all autonomic ganglia, most drugs which act on the autonomic system affect principally either the craniosacral system, as do atropine, pilocarpine, and physostigmine, or the thoracolumbar system, as do epinephrine,

[1] Leopold Auerbach, German anatomist (1828–1897).
[2] Georg Meissner, German anatomist and physiologist (1829–1905).

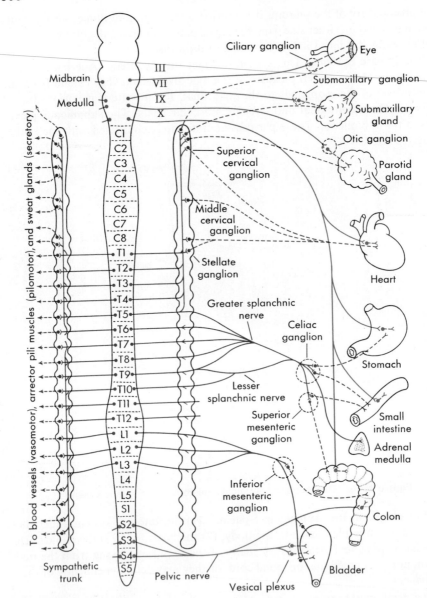

Figure 10–7. Diagrammatic representation of some of the chief conduction pathways of the autonomic nervous system. For clarity, the nerves to blood vessels, arrector pili muscles, and sweat glands are shown on the left side of the figure and the pathways to other visceral structures only on the right side. The sympathetic division is shown in red, the parasympathetic in blue. *Solid lines* represent preganglionic fibers; *broken lines* represent postganglionic fibers. (Modified from *Bailey's Textbook of Histology*, 13th ed., revised by P. E. Smith and W. M. Copenhaver. Courtesy of The Williams and Wilkins Company.)

Analysis of Figure 10–7

Fibers from the various ganglia are distributed to organ listed in center column

PARASYMPATHETIC—BLUE FIBERS		Name of Part	THORACOLUMBAR—RED FIBERS	
Nucleus of Origin of Preganglionic Cell	Postganglionic Cell Bodies, Peripheral Ganglia		Postganglionic Cell Bodies, Peripheral Ganglia	Nucleus of Origin of Preganglionic Cell Body
Edinger-Westphal nucleus, midbrain	Ciliary ganglion	Eye, iris, ciliary muscle	Superior cervical sympathetic, no fibers to ciliary muscle	Lateral gray of cord, T_1–T_2 or T_3
Superior salivatory nucleus in pons	Pterygopolatine ganglion	Lacrimal glands	Superior and middle cervical sympathetic ganglia	Lateral gray of cord, T_1–T_2
Superior salivatory nucleus in pons	Submandibular ganglion	Submaxillary, submandibulary glands	Superior and middle cervical sympathetic ganglia	Lateral gray of cord, T_1–T_3 or T_4
Inferior salivatory nucleus in medulla	Otic ganglia	Parotid glands	Superior and middle cervical sympathetic ganglia	Lateral gray of cord T_1–T_3 or T_4
Dorsal motor nucleus of vagus	Ganglia of pulmonary plexus	Lungs and bronchi	Inferior cervical and T_1–T_5 sympathetic ganglia	Lateral gray of cord, T_1–T_5
Dorsal motor nucleus of vagus	Intracardiac ganglia of the atria	Heart	Superior, middle, and inferior cervical sympathetic ganglia and T_1–T_6 sympathetic ganglia	Lateral gray of cord, T_1–T_6
Dorsal motor nucleus of vagus	Myenteric and submucous plexuses	Esophagus	Sympathetic ganglia T_1–T_3	Lateral gray of cord, T_1–T_6
Dorsal motor nucleus of vagus	Myenteric and submucous plexuses	Stomach, small intestine, and transverse colon	Celiac and superior mesenteric ganglia	Lateral gray of cord, T_5–L_{11}
Autonomic nucleus of the lateral gray of cord, S_2–S_4	Ganglia of myenteric, submucous and hemorrhoidal plexuses	Descending colon, rectum, and internal sphincter	Lumbar and inferior mesenteric sympathetic ganglia	Lateral gray of cord, T_{12}–L_3
Autonomic nucleus of the lateral gray in cord, S_2–S_4	Ganglia of vesical branches of internal iliac artery	Urinary bladder and internal urethral sphincter	Lumbar and inferior mesenteric sympathetic ganglia	Intermediolateral gray of cord, T_{12}–L_2
Autonomic nucleus of the lateral gray in cord, S_2–S_4	Ganglia along branches of aorta and internal iliac arteries	Reproductive organs	Lumbar, sacral, and inferior sympathetic ganglia	Intermediolateral gray of cord, T_{10}–L_2

ergotoxine, and cocaine. There are new drugs that block the transmission of impulses from the preganglionic neurons to the postganglionic neurons. All of these interfere with the transmission of impulses in both the parasympathetic and sympathetic systems to varying degrees. These drugs are used in the treatment of high blood pressure and intestinal hyperactivity.

The coordinated activities of the autonomic system and the suprarenal glands are referred to by Cannon[3] as the "sympatheticoadrenal system" which contributes to homeostasis of the body. For this reason Cannon refers to the autonomic system as the interofective division of the nervous system and to the voluntary (central and somatic) nervous system as the exterofective division.

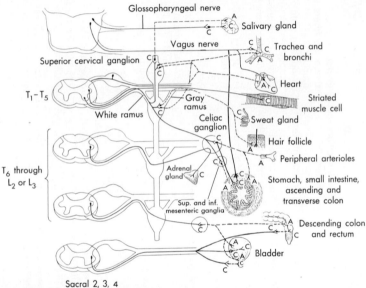

Figure 10–8. Diagram of autonomic nervous system showing cholinergic (*C*) and adrenergic (*A*) nerve endings.

Neural Transmission. The action of nerve impulses at their ends, either on muscle, on gland, or at a synapse, is the release of a chemical substance or mediator. These substances[4] are acetylcholine and predominantly norepinephrine, rather than epinephrine (Adrenaline). On this basis autonomic fibers have been classed by H. H. Dale[5] as cholinergic and adrenergic fibers.

Nerve impulses in preganglionic fibers cause the release from vesicles in the nerve endings of a chemical transmitter which diffuses across the synaptic cleft and produces permeability changes in the membrane of the next cell. The transmitter is rapidly hydrolyzed by an appropriate enzyme. It is also known that all

---

[3] W. B. Cannon, *The Wisdom of the Body.*
[4] O. Loewi demonstrated that vagus inhibition of the heart is due to acetylcholine and that cardiac acceleration is due to epinephrine and norepinephrine.
[5] H. H. Dale and W. Feldberg, *Journal of Physiology,* 1934.

preganglionic fibers of both parasympathetic and sympathetic systems release the transmitter acetylcholine. Hence, preganglionic fibers are called "cholinergic." All parasympathetic postganglionic fibers are also cholinergic. The enzyme that hydrolyzes acetylcholine is cholinesterase. Most sympathetic postganglionic fibers release norepinephrine (formerly noradrenalin) and are called "adrenergic." Monamine oxidase is the enzyme that rapidly destroys norepinephrine.

The thoracolumbar system is strongly stimulated by pain and unpleasant excitement such as anger, fear, or insecurity. The animal responses to anger and fear are fight and flight, and the conditions brought about by stimulating the thoracolumbar system are such as to favor these responses; i.e., the bronchial tubes are relaxed and rapid breathing is rendered easier; the constriction of the blood vessels in the stomach and intestines and the increased heart action deliver more blood to the skeletal muscles and thus provide them with the extra oxygen and nutrients needed for increased muscular activity; the supply of glucose from the liver is also increased, thus providing for greater production of energy. Increased activity of sweat glands produces perspiration. If the environmental conditions permit the evaporation of this excess perspiration, body temperature will be maintained more nearly constant. All these responses are closely connected with the suprarenal glands, which secrete epinephrine and norepinephrine. The amount of secretion is increased when the thoracolumbar system is stimulated.

In acute stress situations the physiological response is to prepare the body for fight and flight. However, it must be remembered that in certain stressful situations physiological response may be mainly either sympathetic or parasympathetic or a combination of both. Excessive response to environmental conditions of portions of either of these divisions of the autonomic nervous system may predispose the individual to physiological disorders classified by some physicians as psychovisceral diseases. Such changes may include a great variety of physiological disorders, a few of which are hypertension, peptic ulcers, colitis, and headache.

Afferent Visceral Fibers. The afferent fibers of many receptors in the viscera carry impulses from receptors in the organs to the spinal cord and brain. These impulses travel over both the sympathetic and parasympathetic fibers. The afferent fibers of the vagus, with cell bodies located in the nodosal ganglion, are distributed to heart, lungs, and other viscera of the thoracic and abdominal cavity. The pelvic nerve also carries afferent fibers. These afferent fibers are important for the regulation and adjustment of vegetative functions. The visceral reflexes are mediated through the spinal cord and brain stem. It is believed that visceral pain is carried by fibers in the sympathetic nerves, and that motor, vasomotor, and secretory reflexes are mediated over vagal fibers and do not reach consciousness. Taste is mediated over vagus, glossopharyngeal, and facial nerves. Impulses that give rise to hunger sensations are carried by the vagus. Sensations of bladder and colon distention are mediated over the afferent fibers of the pelvic nerve.

Interdependence of the Craniosacral and Thoracolumbar Systems. Marked stimulation of one system, or even part of one system, is likely to stimulate some part of the other system, thus checking excessive stimulation with the untoward results that might follow. For example, stimulation of the part of the vagus that supplies the bronchial tubes may cause such marked constriction of the tubes that interference with breathing, pain, and distress may result; this in turn stimulates the thoracolumbar system to lessen the contraction of the tubes. Or another example, the afferent branch of the vagus connected with the aorta is stimulated when the blood pressure within the vessel rises. These afferent impulses initiate efferent impulses which are (1) inhibitory to the heart, thus slowing its action, and (2) inhibitory to the vasoconstrictor center, thus lessening vasoconstriction.

A few examples of the antagonistic action of the craniosacral and thoracolumbar systems are listed so that the results following stimulation of these two systems may be compared.

The chief subcortical center for regulation of both parasympathetic and sympathetic activities lies in the hypothalamus. The anterior and medial areas of the hypothalamus control parasympathetic activities. When this region is stimulated, there are slowing of the heart rate, increased motility and tone of the alimentary muscle, and vasodilation of peripheral blood vessels. This area is also concerned with maintaining water balance. Diabetes insipidus results if this area is destroyed.

The posterior and lateral hypothalamic regions are concerned with control of sympathetic activities. When these areas are stimulated, the prompt sympathetic responses are dilation of the pupil, increased heart rate, vasoconstriction causing an elevation of blood pressure, and inhibition of the digestive organs and bladder. These centers complement each other in regulation of body processes. For instance, if the body temperature falls, the "heat conservation" center in the caudal hypothalamus initiates (1) shivering, which promptly increases heat production, and (2) marked vasoconstriction of cutaneous blood vessels, which reduces heat loss through the skin. If body temperature increases, a "heat loss" center in the anterior hypothalamus responds by initiating (1) sweating, (2) dilatation of cutaneous blood vessels, and (3) constriction of splanchnic blood vessels, which shunts blood to the skin's surface where heat is removed from the body by radiation and conduction. Sweating cools the skin if the external environmental conditions are conducive to rapid evaporation. If the posterior hypothalamus is destroyed, a state of almost total lethargy results. The hypothalamus sends fibers down to the preganglionic autonomic centers of the brain stem and to the lateral gray of the spinal cord. By these connections there are pathways through which impulses from receptors, responding to changes in the environment, are transmitted to the thalamus, to the cortex, to the hypothalamus, and finally to the viscera. It is through these and other pathways that "fleeting thoughts" or other emotional crises affect the heart rate, vascular beds, and other autonomic physiological processes.

Name of Part	Effect of Craniosacral (Parasympathetic) Stimulation	Effect of Thoracolumbar (Sympathetic) Stimulation
Eye—Iris	Constricts the pupil; miosis	Dilates the pupil; mydriosis
Ciliary muscle	Contracts ciliary muscle; accommodation of the lens for near vision	No effect
Lacrimal glands	Stimulates secretion	Little or no effect
Lungs—Bronchi	Constricts bronchial tubes	Dilates bronchial tubes
Heart—Muscle	Slows heart rate	Accelerates heart rate and strengthens ventricular contraction
Arteries in viscera		
Lungs	No effect	Very mildly constricts vessels
Coronary arteries	Constricts arteries	Vasodilation
Abdominal	No effect	Vasoconstriction
Arteries in somatic tissue		
Muscle	No effect	Vasoconstriction
Skin	No effect	Vasoconstriction
Glands—Sweat	No effect	Marked sweating
Salivary	Increased secretion; thin, watery, containing many enzymes	Vasoconstriction; decrease in amount of saliva; becomes viscid in character
Gastric	⎰ Increased secretion	Secretion inhibited
Intestinal	⎱ Increased tension in walls	Walls of gut relaxed
Liver	No effect	Glucose released
Gallbladder and ducts	Stimulates bile flow	Inhibits bile flow
Kidney	No effect	Vasoconstriction, which leads to decreased urine flow
Bladder	Muscle wall contracted; internal sphincter relaxed	Muscle wall relaxed; internal sphincter constricted
Intestinal Organs—		
Motility	Increased peristalsis and tone of wall increased	Decreased peristalsis and muscle tone; wall relaxed
Sphincters	Internal sphincter relaxed	Increase in tone; sphincter constricted
Adrenal gland		
Cortex	No effect	Increased secretion
Medulla	Little or no effect	Increased secretion
Basal metabolism	No effect	Metabolism markedly increased
Blood sugar	No effect	Increased; liver releases glycogen
Blood coagulation	No effect	Increased coagulation
Mental activity	No effect	Increased activity
Sex organs	Vasodilation and erection	Contraction of uterine musculature, ductus deferens, seminal vesicle, vasoconstriction
Piloerector muscles	No effect	Excited; hair stands on end

Cortical centers that regulate autonomic activity are located in prefrontal lobes and temporal regions. Stimulation of these areas during emotional states arouses autonomic areas of the hypothalamic centers. There are also regulating centers in the thalamus. Both conscious and unconscious areas of the cortex can cause autonomic response. The action of the sympathetic nervous system is augmented by the hormones of the adrenal medulla. See Chapter 17 (p. 503) for discussion.

QUESTIONS FOR DISCUSSION

1. Analyze the effect of emotional problems, scoldings, or discord of any kind on the digestive processes, heart action, and blood pressure.
2. An individual receives a penetrating wound of the back, right side, region of T_{11}, close to the vertebrae. The day is cold. Explain why the left leg and foot are very cold, but the right leg and foot are pink and warm.
3. An individual had been under stress and complained of increased peristalsis with severe cramps. The doctor ordered tincture of belladonna, 10 drops four times daily. Explain the *reason* for his symptoms and why belladonna was ordered.
4. Discuss the physiological reasons why stress raises blood pressure, and how it does so.

SUMMARY

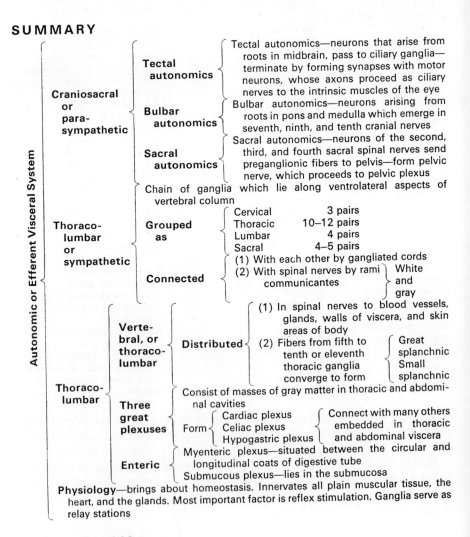

Autonomic or Efferent Visceral System

Craniosacral or parasympathetic

Tectal autonomics—Tectal autonomics—neurons that arise from roots in midbrain, pass to ciliary ganglia—terminate by forming synapses with motor neurons, whose axons proceed as ciliary nerves to the intrinsic muscles of the eye

Bulbar autonomics—Bulbar autonomics—neurons arising from roots in pons and medulla which emerge in seventh, ninth, and tenth cranial nerves

Sacral autonomics—Sacral autonomics—neurons of the second, third, and fourth sacral spinal nerves send preganglionic fibers to pelvis—form pelvic nerve, which proceeds to pelvic plexus

Thoraco-lumbar or sympathetic

Chain of ganglia which lie along ventrolateral aspects of vertebral column

Grouped as
- Cervical — 3 pairs
- Thoracic — 10–12 pairs
- Lumbar — 4 pairs
- Sacral — 4–5 pairs

Connected
(1) With each other by gangliated cords
(2) With spinal nerves by rami communicantes — White and gray

Thoraco-lumbar

Vertebral, or thoraco-lumbar

Distributed
(1) In spinal nerves to blood vessels, glands, walls of viscera, and skin areas of body
(2) Fibers from fifth to tenth or eleventh thoracic ganglia converge to form — Great splanchnic / Small splanchnic

Three great plexuses — Consist of masses of gray matter in thoracic and abdominal cavities

Form
- Cardiac plexus
- Celiac plexus
- Hypogastric plexus
Connect with many others embedded in thoracic and abdominal viscera

Enteric
Myenteric plexus—situated between the circular and longitudinal coats of digestive tube
Submucous plexus—lies in the submucosa

Physiology—brings about homeostasis. Innervates all plain muscular tissue, the heart, and the glands. Most important factor is reflex stimulation. Ganglia serve as relay stations

312

Craniosacral and Thoracolumbar Systems	Many of the viscera are supplied with nerves from both craniosacral and thoracolumbar systems—functions of these two sets are often antagonistic
	These two systems are interdependent, stimulation of one system or part of one system likely to stimulate some part of the other system
	Thoracolumbar system is stimulated by intense excitement; craniosacral system is not
	Nicotine paralyzes all autonomic ganglia. Most drugs affect either the craniosacral or the thoracolumbar, not both
	Norepinephrine is the chemical mediator for postganglionic sympathetic nerve endings, except fibers to sweat glands,
	Acetylcholine is the chemical mediator for all parasympathetic nerve endings and preganglionic sympathetic fibers
Subcortical Areas for Regulation of Parasympathetic Activities	Anterior and medial areas of hypothalamus—control parasympathetic activities
	This area also concerned with water balance and body temperature regulation
Regulation of Sympathetic Activities	Posterior and lateral hypothalamic areas—control sympathetic activities
	The parasympathetic and sympathetic nervous systems complement each other in regulation of body processes
	Augmented by hormones of adrenal medulla
Cortical Control	Located in prefrontal lobes and temporal regions

CHAPTER 11

Sensation: Pain,
The Tongue and Taste,
The Nasal Epithelium and
Smell, The Ear and
Hearing, The Eye and Sight

IT IS through the sense organs that man derives information about the world in which he lives and his relationship to it. Our receptors are insensitive to many forms of energy and their limitations restrict our knowledge. However, man has devised methods for converting some forms of physical energy into dimensions that fall within the sensitivities of the sense organs. Thus, knowledge of the microscopic forms of life depends upon the extension of sight by means of magnifying lenses.

All sensory impulses, except olfaction, feed into the thalamus. From the thalamus the impulses may go (1) to specific cortical areas to provide primary sensations, (2) to diffuse cortical areas to permit integration of sensory and motor activities, and (3) to hypothalamic regions to provoke appropriate autonomic responses. Hence, sensory impulses not only produce conscious sensation but also evoke visceral responses in the form of altered heart rate, modified digestive processes, blushing, and many other visceral changes.

Sensations are the conscious results of processes which take place within the brain in consequence of nervous impulses derived from receptors. Many sensations are not followed by motor reactions but are stored as memory concepts and may be called into play at any time. The sensitiveness of the numerous receptors to stimulation varies. In some parts of the body the slightest pressure will arouse a sensation, while a similar degree of pressure in another part may fail to produce any sensation at all.

Sensations are felt and *interpreted in the brain*. The habit of *projecting sensations* to the part that is stimulated tends to obscure this fact. In reality individuals see and hear in the brain, because the eye and ear serve only as end organs to receive the stimuli which must reach the brain before sight and hearing take place.

Classification. One classification of sensation is based on the part of the body to which the sensation is projected. On this basis, sensations may be classified as external and internal. The external are those in which the sensations are projected to the exterior of the body: namely, sight, hearing, taste, smell, touch, pressure, and temperature (warm and cold). The internal are those in which the sensations are projected to the interior of the body, and include pain, muscle sense, sensations from the semicircular canals and vestibule of the internal ear, hunger, thirst, fatigue, and other less definite sensations from the viscera.

The sensations of taste, smell, hearing, balance, and vision are termed "special senses" since their receptors are structurally more specialized and they are located in specific locations rather than generally throughout the body, as are cutaneous receptors.

The surface of the skin is a mosaic of tiny sensory "spots" separated by relatively wide intervals.

These various spots are placed either singly or in clusters. In some locations one variety predominates, in others another. It is a matter of common knowledge that the sensitiveness of these varieties of cutaneous sensation differs in different parts of the body; e.g., the tip of the finger is more sensitive to pressure or contact than to alterations of temperature. The warm and cold spots and the pressure points can be located by passing a metallic point slowly over the skin. At certain points a feeling of contact or pressure will be experienced, and at other points a feeling of cold or warmth, depending on whether the temperature of the instrument is higher or lower than that of the skin. The distal parts of the extremities are more sensitive to touch than are the proximal parts; the limbs are more sensitive than the trunk and the lips more sensitive than other parts of the face. At some, but not all, sites, these spots coincide with the location of morphologically specific receptors for that sensation. (See p. 229.)

Sensations derived from stimuli applied to receptors differ in intensity not only because of differences in the intensity of the applied stimulus and the rapidity with which it is applied, but also because of differences in the number of receptors stimulated. Then, too, different receptors in the region have different thresholds of sensitivity. This will make a difference in the sensation; e.g., a pencil point pressed on the skin causes a conical depression with different degrees of deformation at the base and sides of the depression.

A strong stimulus provokes an intense sensation because many receptors are strongly excited. Many afferent nerve fibers are carrying information to the nervous system. A weak stimulus provokes a faint sensation because only a few receptors are weakly excited. Few afferent nerve fibers are carrying minimal information to the nervous system.

Sensations are sometimes classified as *epicritic, protopathic, deep*, or *visceral*. In epicritic sensitivity the discriminative element predominates, i.e., the ability to discriminate accurately various degrees of intensity of stimuli and to locate the stimulus accurately; thus, when two points are simultaneously applied, they may be properly discerned, and small degrees of temperature are recognized. These sensations are often termed "vital" because they form the basis for cognitive and associative reactions which take place in the cerebral cortex. Protopathic sensation is less specific and more widespread and is of marked *affective* character. It gives little information as to the exact location or nature of the stimulus. It includes pain, temperature sensations aroused by extremes of heat and cold, visceral sensibility, and part of touch. Protopathic sensations are primarily related to reactions that most directly involve bodily welfare. The stimulus must be strong to arouse a sensation, but when aroused, the sensation is intense, poorly localized, diffuse, and of an unpleasant nature.

Deep sensations are those from deep structures, muscles, bones, joints, and tendons—proprioception, position, and vibratory sense. Visceral sensations are from the internal organs.

Sensations such as pain and temperature are rather general groupings of the many more specific interpretations of which the cerebral cortex is capable. Pain may be sharp, dull, aching; touch includes differentiation of satin from wool, soapy water from clear water, and so on. One learns by experience to critically evaluate the sensation when impulses arrive in the cerebral cortex. In addition, there may be transmission of the impulse to many other areas of the brain. For example, hearing the word *mother* requires stimulation of the *auditory* sensory area of the cortex. At the same time, the image of one's own mother may come to mind—a visual memory involving optic sensory areas.

PAIN

Pain perception is a physiological process which serves as a danger signal that something is wrong in a tissue or organ.

Receptors for pain are free nerve endings located in the skin and deep in muscles, tendons, joints, and fasciae.

The *viscera* are not sensitive to many mechanical and chemical stimuli; however, they are frequently the source of *intense pain*.

Fibers of pain receptors enter the spinal cord and ascend or descend for a segment or two before terminating in the medial gray. Fibers from this nucleus cross to the opposite side and ascend in the lateral spinothalamic pathway to terminate in the posterolateral and posteromedial nuclei of the thalamus from which the impulses may be relayed to the cortex. Awareness of pain takes place in the thalamus, but localization and recognition of the kind and intensity of pain take place in the postcentral convolution of the cerebral cortex. Pain impulses are also relayed to other thalamic nuclei and to the hypothalamus.

All individuals have about the same threshold for pain, but the reaction to pain varies widely between individuals, depending upon such factors as

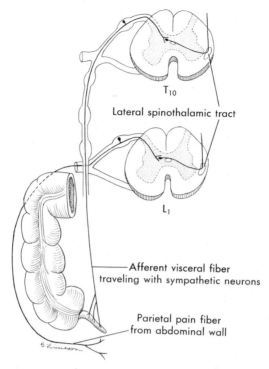

T$_{10}$

Lateral spinothalamic tract

L$_1$

Afferent visceral fiber
traveling with sympathetic neurons

Parietal pain fiber
from abdominal wall

B. Kinneson

Figure 11–1. Neural pathway for visceral pain.

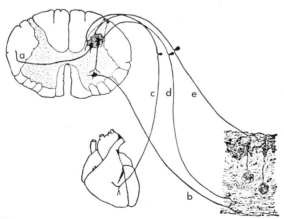

Figure 11–2. Diagram to show a possible neural path for referred pain of cardiac origin. Nerve impulses (*c*) from disturbed heart bring about an "irritable area" in gray matter of cord. Nerve fibers from skin and muscle (*d* and *e*) enter this same region. Nerve fibers from this region carry impulses over path *a* to the spinothalamic tract and the cerebral cortex, and over path *b* to the chest muscles, which contract in an exaggerated manner.

ethnocultural background, childhood experiences, and emotional status. Because of its emotional overlay, pain is very different from other sensations.

Pain may be described as sharp, dull, boring, piercing, pricking, aching, throbbing, stabbing, burning, constant, and intermittent. Aching pain is usually a deep pain with varying degrees of intensity and may be either diffuse or localized. Burning pain results from diffuse stimulation of all pain receptors in an area, e.g., burns or other types of tissue injury. As the intensity of the pain stimulus increases and more nerve fibers are involved, the intensity of the pain also increases. Deep pain is frequently associated with nausea and a fall in blood pressure, whereas superficial pain will quicken the pulse and raise blood pressure.

Visceral Pain. The meninges of the brain elicit pain in response to injury, but the brain itself is insensitive to pain. If the layers of the abdominal wall are anesthetized with local anesthesia, the visceral organs may be manipulated, cauterized, crushed, or incised without pain if there is no tugging or pulling on the mesentery. It is now believed that if the viscera are subjected to an *adequate stimulus*, pain will occur. For abdominal organs this includes ischemia, spasm, overdistention, or chemical irritation. In the abdominal cavity, but not the pelvic region, the sympathetic nerves conduct visceral pain, but the craniosacral rarely do.

Referred Pain. In some instances visceral pain is not localized specifically in the organ but is felt on the surface of the body. Pain of this kind is spoken of as *referred pain.* It has been shown that the different visceral organs have a more or less definite relation to certain areas of the skin. Pain arising from stimuli in the intestines is located in the skin of the back, loins, and abdomen, in the area supplied by the ninth, tenth, and eleventh thoracic nerves. Pain from irritations in the stomach are located in the skin over the ensiform cartilage, those from the heart in the scapular region. The explanation for this is that the pain is referred to the skin region that is supplied from the spinal segment from which the organ in question receives its sensory fibers. The misreference results from excitation of a secondary neuron in the spinal cord which also normally is excited by neurons that supply that particular skin area. Examples of referred pain are: in appendicitis, the abdominal pains are often remote from the usual position of the appendix; in some pneumonia cases, abdominal pain is the prominent symptom; in angina pectoris, the pain radiates to the left shoulder and down the left arm (Figs. 11-2 and 11-3). In this instance pain fibers from the heart are carried in the first, second, and third thoracic roots along with afferent fibers from the chest wall and arm.

Figure 11-3. Referred pain. Pain from cardiac region is referred to the left side of the chest and down the inside of the left arm.

Hunger. The feeling that is commonly designated as hunger occurs normally at a certain time before meals and is usually projected to the region of the stomach. It is presumably due to contractions of the empty stomach, which stimulate the receptors distributed to the mucous membrane. If food is not taken, hunger increases in intensity for a time and is likely to cause fatigue and headache. Professional fasters state that after a few days the pangs of hunger diminish and sometimes disappear. In illness hunger contractions may not occur at all, even when the food taken is not sufficient. Probably this results from a

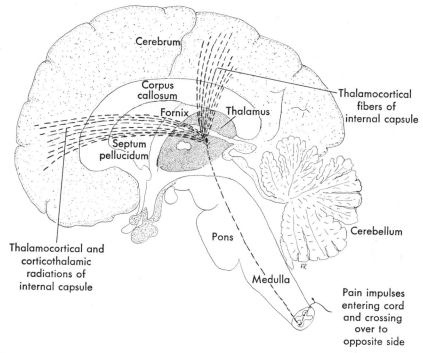

Figure 11–4. Medial aspects of brain, showing pathway for pain impulses in the brain.

lack of muscular tone in the stomach. On the other hand, hunger contractions may be frequent and severe even if an abundance of food is taken regularly, as in diabetes, or following a period of starvation.

Appetite is similar to hunger but is less related to physiological activity, such as stomach contractions. The desire for a specific food is related to appetite, whereas when one is hungry, any one of a variety of foods may satisfy. Cultural and social factors influence one's appetite so that certain foods satisfying and desirable to natives of the United States may be repulsive to natives of Africa.

Food intake is regulated by the hypothalamus (see p. 277), and many centers in the brain stem and spinal cord are involved in the actual process of eating, e.g., salivation, chewing, swallowing.

Thirst. This sensation is projected to the pharynx, particularly the tongue, and the known facts indicate that the sensory fibers of this region have an important function of mediating this sense. Normal thirst sensations are designated as pharyngeal thirst to indicate the probable origin of the sensory impulses. Local drying in this region, from dry or salty food or dry and dusty air, produces a sensation of thirst that may be appeased by moistening the membrane with a small amount of water not in itself sufficient to relieve a genuine water need of the body. Prolonged deprivation of water affects the water content of all the tissues and gives rise to sensations not of simple thirst alone but of actual pain and suffering. Under these conditions it is probable that sensory fibers are stimulated in many tissues, and in addition the metabolism of the nervous system is directly affected by loss of water.

Nausea. This sensation may be due to stimulation from the stomach, to substances in the blood, or to impulses coming from various parts of the body, e.g., the organs of sight, taste, and smell.

TASTE

The adequate stimulus for taste receptors is a substance in solution. In the case of dry substances saliva serves as the solvent. It is also necessary that the surface of the organs of taste be moist. The substances that excite the special sensation of *taste* act by producing a change in the taste buds, and this change initiates the nerve impulses.

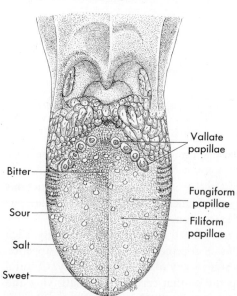

Vallate papillae

Bitter

Fungiform papillae

Sour

Filiform papillae

Salt

Sweet

Figure 11–5. The upper surface of the tongue, showing kinds of papillae and areas for taste.

Taste buds are ovoid bodies, with an external layer of supporting cells, and contain in the interior a number of elongated cells, which end in hairlike processes that project through the central taste pore. These cells are the sense cells, and the hairlike processes probably are the parts stimulated by the dissolved substances. The taste buds are found chiefly in the surface of the tongue, though some are scattered over the soft palate, fauces, and epiglottis.

The tongue is a freely movable muscular organ consisting of two distinct halves united in the center. The root of the tongue is directed backward and is attached to the hyoid bone by several muscles. It is connected with the epiglottis by three folds of mucous membrane, and with the soft palate by means of the glossopalatine arches.

Papillae of the Tongue. The tongue is covered with mucous membrane, and the upper surface is studded with papillae. The papillae are projections of connective tissue covered with stratified squamous epithelium and contain a loop of capillaries, among which nerve fibers are distributed. The papillae give the tongue its characteristic rough appearance. There are four varieties of these papillae:

Vallate (circumvallate) papillae are the largest, are circular in shape, and form a V-shaped row near the root of the tongue. They contain *taste buds*.

Fungiform papillae, so named because they resemble fungi in shape, are found principally on the tip and sides of the tongue.

Figure 11–6. (*A*) A vallate papilla cut lengthwise, (*c*) corium, (*e*) epidermis, (*n*) nerve fibers, (*t*) taste buds. (*B*) The two taste buds at *t* more highly magnified, the lower as seen from the outside showing (*c*) the outer or supporting cells; the upper as seen in section showing (*n*) four inner cells with processes (*m*) projecting at the mouth of the bud.

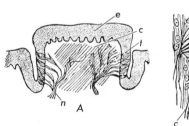
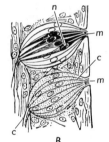

Filiform papillae cover the anterior two thirds of the tongue and bear delicate brushlike processes which seem to be specially connected with the sense of touch, which is very highly developed on the tip of the tongue.

Simple papillae similar to those of the skin cover the larger papillae and the whole of the mucous membrane of the dorsum of the tongue. All papillae contain taste buds.

Nerve Supply of the Tongue. The nerve fibers which terminate in the tongue are fibers of the lingual nerve, which is a sensory branch of the fifth, or trigeminal; fibers of the chorda tympani; a branch of the seventh, or facial; and fibers of the ninth, or glossopharyngeal, nerve. The twelfth, or hypoglossal, nerve is distributed to the tongue. It is a motor nerve.

The sense of touch is very highly developed in the tongue, and with it the sense of temperature and pain. Upon these tactile and muscular senses depends, to a great extent, the accuracy of the tongue in many of its important uses—speech, mastication, deglutition, sucking.

Physiology of Taste. Taste sensations are very numerous, but four fundamental, or primary, sensations are recognized, namely, salty, bitter, acid, and sweet. Quantitative appreciation of taste is not great. All other taste sensations are combinations of these or combinations of one or more of them with sensations of odor or with sensations derived from stimulation of other nerves in the tongue. The seemingly great variety of taste sensations is due to the fact that they are confused or combined with simultaneous odor sensations. Thus the flavors in fruits are designated as tastes because they are experienced at the time these objects are eaten. If the nasal cavities are closed, as by holding the nose, the so-called taste often disappears in large measure. Very disagreeable tastes are usually due to unpleasant odor sensations, hence the practice of holding the

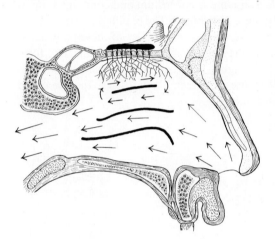

Figure 11–7. Diagram of lateral wall of left nasal cavity. The three black lines represent the region of the inferior, middle, and superior conchae. *Arrows* indicate the direction of air flow. The olfactory lobe is shown with nerve fibers extending through orifices in the cribriform plate of the ethmoid bone. Olfactory nerve fibers are distributed in the mucosa above the superior conchae, the cell bodies lying in the nasal mucosa.

nose when swallowing a nauseous dose. On the other hand, some volatile substances which enter the mouth through the nostrils and stimulate the taste buds are interpreted as odors. The odor of chloroform is largely due to stimulation of the sweet taste in the tongue.

Taste on the posterior third of the tongue is mediated by the glossopharyngeal nerve. Taste on the anterior two thirds of the tongue is mediated by the facial nerve. The vagus nerve mediates taste sensations from around the epiglottis. These fibers convey taste impulses to the medulla and pons where they terminate around cell bodies of the secondary fibers. These secondary fibers cross in the medulla and then ascend to the thalamus. Tertiary fibers are projected to the sensory cortex on the parietal lobe near the sylvian fissure.

SMELL

The sensory endings for the sense of smell are located in the olfactory membrane over the surface of the superior nasal conchae and the upper part of the septum. These sensory nerve endings are the least specialized of the special senses.

The Olfactory Nerves. The olfactory sensory endings are modified epithelial cells scattered freely among the columnar epithelium of the mucous membrane.

These sensory cells are called *olfactory cells*, and the other epithelial cells, supporting cells.

Olfactory cells are bipolar in form, and slender, peripheral, hairlike processes known as olfactory hairs extend beyond the surface of the epithelial membrane. The central or deep process passes through the basement membrane and joins adjacent processes to form bundles of unmyelinated fibers of the *olfactory nerve*. These bundles of nerves form a plexus in the submucosa and eventually form about 20 or more nerves which pierce the cribriform plate of the ethmoid bone and end in a mass of gray matter called the olfactory bulb. In the olfactory bulb these fibers form synapses with the dendrites of the mitral cells. Through the axons of the mitral cells impulses are conducted to their various terminations in the olfactory lobe, of either the same of the opposite side.

The cells of the bulb lie in synaptic relation to cells whose processes form the olfactory tract and finally terminate in the gray of the cortex in the parolfactory area and hippocampal gyrus of the temporal lobe. Some of the fibers terminate in other nuclei of the brain, and through the mammillary bodies impulses reach the thalamus.

The nerve fibers which ramify over the lower part of the lining membrane of the nasal cavity are branches of the fifth, or trigeminal, nerve. These fibers furnish the tactile sense and enable one to perceive, by the nose, the sensations of cold, heat, tickling, pain, and tension, or pressure. It is these nerve fibers which are affected by strong irritants, such as ammonia or pepper.

Odoriferous substances emit particles which usually are in gaseous form. These particles must penetrate into the upper part of the nasal chamber. In the olfactory area the cells are always bathed in fluid from *special glands*, so that the particles may be dissolved. The fluid acts chemically upon the sensitive hairs of the olfactory cells, which transmit impulses to the olfactory lobe and give rise to the sensation of smell. Few odors are detected in the dry, hot desert.

To smell anything particularly well, air is sniffed into the higher nasal chambers and thus brings the odoriferous particles in greater numbers into contact with the olfactory hairs. Odors can also reach the nose by way of the mouth. Many flavors of food are really odors rather than gustatory sensations, and one becomes aware of them just after swallowing. During swallowing the posterior nares are closed by the soft palate, which then opens, permitting odoriferous molecules to reach the sensory epithelium of the nose, through the wide posterior nares.

Each substance smelled causes its own particular sensation, and one is able not only to recognize a multitude of distinct odors but also to distinguish individual odors in a mixed smell. These odors are difficult to classify, i.e., it is not possible to pick out what might be called the fundamental odor sensations. One classification groups odors into pure odors, odors mixed with sensations from the mucous membrane of the nose, and odors mixed or confused with tastes. The pure odors are further subdivided into nine classes, namely, ethereal, aromatic, fragrant, ambrosial, garlic, burning odors, goat odors, repulsive odors, and nauseating or fetid odors. There is some evidence that the sense of odor is related to the radiant energy of the molecular vibrations of the substance giving the odor. This may lead to a more satisfactory classification.

The sensation of smell develops quickly after the contact of the odoriferous stimulus and may last a long time. When the stimulus is repeated, the sensation very soon dies out, and the end organs of the sensory cells quickly become adapted. This accounts for the fact that one may easily become accustomed to unpleasant odors, an advantage when these odors have to be endured. On the other hand, it emphasizes the importance of acting on the first sensation of a disagreeable odor, so as not to become accustomed to it.

The olfactory center in the uncus and the hippocampus of the brain is widely connected with other areas of the cerebrum. Olfactory memories may be vivid. The sense of smell is widely and closely connected with the other senses and with many psychical activities.

HEARING

The auditory apparatus consists of the external ear; the middle ear, or tympanic cavity; the internal ear, or labyrinth; and the acoustic nerve and acoustic center.

The external ear consists of an expanded portion, named the pinna or auricula, and the external acoustic meatus, or auditory canal.

The *pinna* projects from the side of the head. It consists of a framework of cartilage, containing some adipose tissue and muscles; in the lobe, the cartilage

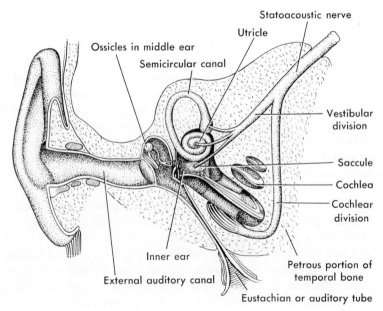

Figure 11–8.   Section of right ear showing middle and inner ear structures.

is replaced by soft connective tissues. The pinna is covered with skin and joined to the surrounding parts by ligaments and muscles. It is very irregular in shape. The pinna serves to some extent to collect sound waves and direct them toward the external acoustic meatus.

The external acoustic meatus (external auditory canal) is a tubular passage, about 2.5 cm (1 in.) in length, which leads from the concha to the tympanic membrane. It forms an S-shaped curve and is directed inward, forward, and upward, then inward and backward. Lifting the pinna upward and backward tends to straighten the canal; but in children it is best straightened by drawing the pinna downward and backward. The external portion of this canal consists of cartilage, which is continuous with that of the pinna; the internal portion is hollowed out of the temporal bone. It is lined by a prolongation of the skin, which in the outer half of the canal is very thick and not at all sensitive, and in the inner half is thin and highly sensitive. Near the orifice the skin is furnished with a few hairs and farther inward with modified sweat glands, and the ceruminous glands, which secrete the yellow, pasty cerumen, or earwax. The hairs and the cerumen protect the ear from the entrance of foreign substances.

The *tympanic membrane* (membrana tympani) separates the auditory canal from the tympanic cavity. It consists of a thin layer of fibrous tissue covered externally with skin and internally with mucous membrane. It is ovoid in form and extends obliquely downward and inward and forms an angle with the floor of the meatus. It is chiefly innervated by a branch of the mandibular nerve (branch of fifth trigeminal nerve).

The tympanic cavity, or the **middle ear,** is a small, irregular bony cavity, situated in the petrous portion of the temporal bone. This air cavity is so small that probably five or six drops of water would fill it. It is separated from the external auditory canal by the tympanic membrane, and from the internal ear by a very thin bony wall ($^1/_{24}$ in.) in which there are two small openings: the *fenestra vestibuli* (*ovalis*) and the *fenestra cochleae* (*rotunda*). In the posterior, or mastoid, wall there is an opening into the mastoid antrum and mastoid cells; and because of this, infection of the middle ear may extend into the mastoid cells and cause mastoiditis. The temporal bone at this point is very porous, and any suppurative process is exceedingly dangerous, for the infection may travel inward and invade the brain. In the anterior, or carotid, wall is an opening into the auditory tube, a small canal which leads to the nasopharynx. Thus, there are five openings in the middle ear; namely, the opening between it and the auditory canal; the fenestra vestibuli and the fenestra cochleae, which connect with the internal ear; the opening into the mastoid cells; and the opening into the auditory tube. The walls of the tympanic cavity are lined with mucous membrane, which is continuous anteriorly with the mucous membrane of the auditory tube and posteriorly with that of the mastoid antrum and mastoid cells.

Ossicles. Stretching across the cavity of the middle ear from the tympanic membrane to the fenestra vestibuli are three tiny, movable bones, named, because of their shapes, the *malleus*, or hammer, the *incus*, or anvil, and the *stapes*, or stirrup. The handle of the malleus is attached to the tympanic membrane, and the head is attached to the base of the incus. The long process of the incus is attached to the stapes, and the footpiece of the stapes occupies the fenestra vestibuli. These little bones are held in position, attached to each other, to the tympanic membrane, and to the edge of the fenestra vestibuli, by minute ligaments and muscles. They are set in motion with every movement of the tympanic membrane. Vibrations of the membrane are communicated to the malleus, received by the incus, and transmitted to the stapes, which rocks in the fenestra vestibuli and is therefore capable of transmitting to the fluid in the cavity of the labyrinth the impulses which it receives. These bones form a series of levers, the effect of which is to magnify the force of the vibrations received at the tympanum about 10 times that at the oval window.

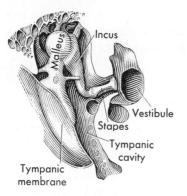

Figure 11–9. Chain of ossicles and their ligaments, seen from the front.

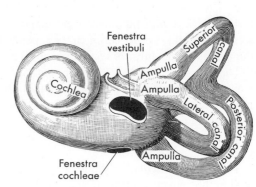

Figure 11–10. Left osseous labyrinth, viewed from lateral side. (Modified from Cunningham.)

The auditory, or *eustachian, tube* connects the cavity of the middle ear with the pharynx. It is about 36 mm (1½ in.) long and about 3 mm (⅛ in.) in diameter at its narrowest part and lined with mucous membrane. By means of this tube the pressure of the air on both sides of the tympanic membrane is equalized. In inflammatory conditions, the auditory tube may become occluded, and may prevent this equalization. Under such conditions, hearing is much impaired until the tube is opened. The pharyngeal opening of the tube is closed except when swallowing, yawning, and sneezing.

The internal ear, or **labyrinth,** receives the ultimate terminations of the statoacoustic nerve. It consists of an *osseous labyrinth*, which is composed of a series of peculiarly shaped cavities, hollowed out of the petrous portion of the temporal bone and named from their shape:

Osseous labyrinth $\begin{cases} \text{1. The vestibule} \\ \text{2. The cochlea (snail shell)} \\ \text{3. The semicircular canals} \end{cases}$

Within the osseous labyrinth is a *membranous labyrinth*, having the same general form as the cavities in which it is contained, though considerably smaller, being separated from the bony walls by a quantity of fluid called the *perilymph*. It does not float loosely in this liquid but is attached to the bone by fibrous bands. The cavity of the membranous labyrinth contains fluid—the *endolymph*—and on its walls the ramifications of the acoustic nerve are distributed.

The *vestibule* is the central cavity of the osseous labyrinth; it is situated behind the cochlea and in front of the semicircular canals. It communicates with the middle ear by means of the fenestra vestibuli in its lateral or tympanic wall. The membranous labyrinth of the vestibule does not conform to the shape of the bony cavity but consists of two small sacs, called respectively the *saccule* and the

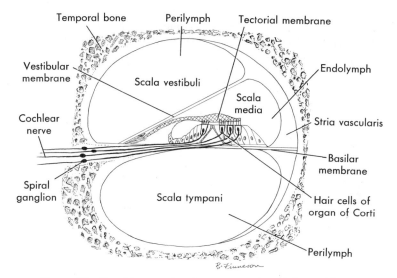

Figure 11–11. Diagram showing cross section of the cochlea.

utricle. The saccule is the smaller of the two and is situated near the opening of the scala vestibuli of the cochlea; the utricle is larger and occupies the upper and back part of the vestibule. These sacs are not directly connected with each other. From the posterior wall of the saccule, a canal, the *ductus endolymphaticus*, is given off. This duct is joined by a duct from the utricle and ends in a blind pouch on the posterior surface of the petrous portion of the temporal bone. The utricle, saccule, and ducts contain endolymph and are surrounded by perilymph. The inner wall of the saccule and utricle consists of two kinds of modified columnar cells on a basement membrane. One is a specialized nerve cell provided with stiff hairs, which project into the endolymph. Between the nerve cells are supporting cells, which are not ciliated and are not connected with nerve endings. The hair cells serve as end organs for fibers of the vestibular branch of the statoacoustic nerve, which arborize around the base of each hair cell. Small crystals of calcium carbonate, called *otoliths*, are located on the hair cells of the utricle. The otoliths give weight to the hair cells and make them more sensitive to change in position. Impulses are set up when the otoliths pull or push on the hairs.

The *cochlea* forms the anterior part of the bony labyrinth and is placed almost horizontally in front of the vestibule. It resembles a snail shell and consists of a spiral canal of 2¾ turns around a hollow, conical central pillar called the *modiolus*,

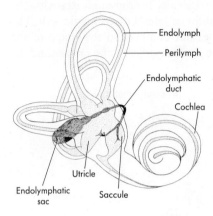

Figure 11–12. Diagram showing endolymphatic system of inner ear.

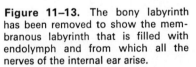

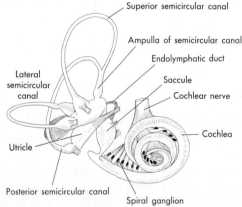

Figure 11–13. The bony labyrinth has been removed to show the membranous labyrinth that is filled with endolymph and from which all the nerves of the internal ear arise.

from which a thin *lamina* of bone projects like a spiral shelf about halfway toward the outer wall of the canal. Within the bony cochlea is a *membranous cochlea*, which begins at the fenestra ovalis and duplicates the bony structure.

The *basilar membrane* stretches from the free border of the lamina to the outer wall of the bony cochlea and completely divides its cavities into two passages, or *scalae*, which, however, communicate with each other at the apex of the modiolus by a small opening. The upper passage is the scala vestibuli, which terminates at the fenestra vestibuli; and the lower is the scala tympani, which terminates at the fenestra cochleae.

From the free border of the lamina, a second membrane, called the *vestibular membrane* (Reissner[1]), extends to the outer wall of the cochlea and is attached some distance above the basilar membrane. A triangular canal, called the *ductus cochlearis* or *scala media*, is thus formed between the scala vestibuli above and the scala tympani below.

On the basilar membrane the sound-sensitive epithelium of the *organ of Corti*[2] is located. This consists of a large number of *rod-shaped cells* and *hair cells*, extending into the endolymph of the scala media. The *tectorial membrane* projects from the spiral lamina over these cells of the organs of Corti. Some

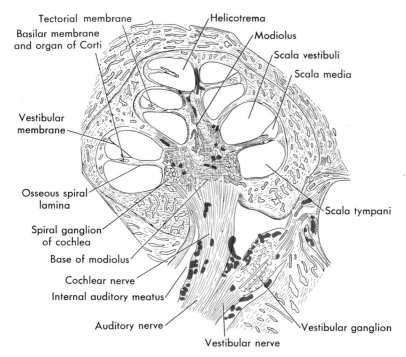

Tectorial membrane
Basilar membrane and organ of Corti
Vestibular membrane
Osseous spiral lamina
Spiral ganglion of cochlea
Base of modiolus
Cochlear nerve
Internal auditory meatus
Auditory nerve
Vestibular nerve
Helicotrema
Modiolus
Scala vestibuli
Scala media
Scala tympani
Vestibular ganglion

Figure 11–14. Section of the cochlea, showing the scalae. Red indicates blood supply. (Modified from Toldt.)

think the hairs of the hair cells are attached to the tectorial membrane so that as the basilar membrane vibrates, the hair cells are alternately stretched and relapsed. The fibers of the cochlear branch of the statoacoustic nerve arise in the nerve cells of the *spiral ganglion*, which is situated in the modiolus. These cells are bipolar and send fibers toward the brain in the statoacoustic nerve and the other fibers to end in terminal arborizations around the hair cells of the organ and the other fibers to end in terminal arborizations around the hair cells of the organ of Corti.

[1] Ernst Reissner, German anatomist (1824–1878).
[2] Alfonso Corti, Italian anatomist (1822–1888).

The *semicircular canals* are three bony canals lying above and behind the vestibule and communicating with it by five openings, in one of which two tubes join. They are known as the *superior, posterior,* and *lateral* canals, and their position is such that each one is at right angles to the other two. One end of each tube is enlarged and forms what is known as the *ampulla.*

The *semicircular ducts* (membranous semicircular canals) are similar to the bony canals in number, shape, and general form, but their diameter is less. They open by five orifices into the utricle, one opening being common to the medial end of the superior and the upper end of the posterior duct. In the ampullae the membranous canal is attached to the bony canal, and the epithelium is thrown into a ridge (the *crista ampullaris*) of cells with hairlike processes, which project into the endolymph. The hair cells are covered with a gelatinous substance which contains the otoliths. These are minute particles of calcium carbonate which pull

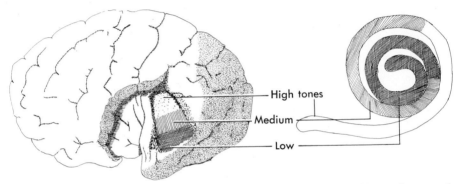

High tones

Medium

Low

Figure 11–15. Diagram showing relationship between cochlea and acoustic area of cortex and interpretations of sound in the brain. For more details, see Penfield and Rasmussen, *The Cerebral Cortex of Man*, The Macmillan Company, 1950.

and push on the hairs when the position of the head is changed. This forms the stimulus for initiation of reflexes that maintain balance against gravity. Some of the terminations of the vestibular branch of the acoustic nerve are distributed to these cells. Between the hair cells are supporting cells.

The Acoustic Center. The primary acoustic center is in the *temporal lobe* of the cerebrum. Removal of both temporal lobes is followed by complete deafness. Removal of one temporal lobe is followed by impairment of hearing. This suggests that some fibers from each ear cross at some point in their afferent pathways and terminate in the opposite cortex. This is similar to the partial decussation of visual fibers occurring in the optic chiasma (Fig. 11–24, p. 345).

The statoacoustic nerve (VIII) is sensory and contains at least two sets of fibers, which differ in their origin and destination and function. One set of fibers is known as the cochlear division and the other as the vestibular.

The cochlear nerve arises from bipolar cells in the spiral ganglion of the cochlea. The peripheral fibers pass to the cells of the organ of Corti, at which point the sound waves arouse the nerve impulses. The central fibers, forming part of the cochlear branch of VIII pass into the lateral border of the medulla, terminating in the dorsal and ventral cochlear nuclei. From these nuclei the path is continued by secondary neurons to the auditory centers in the medial geniculate bodies of the thalamus. Some of the fibers cross and some do not. The cell bodies of the thalamus form the third cell in the primary auditory pathway, the processes of which terminate in the temporal lobe of the cortex.

The vestibular nerve arises from bipolar cells in the *vestibular ganglion* (ganglion of Scarpa), situated in the internal acoustic meatus. The peripheral fibers divide into three branches, which are distributed around the hair cells of the saccule, the utricle, and the ampullae of the semicircular canals. The central fibers, forming part of the vestibular branch, terminate in the vestibular[3] nuclei in the

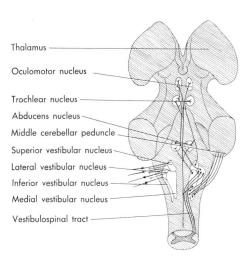

Figure 11–16. Diagram showing connections of vestibular nuclei with spinal cord, cerebellum, and centers controlling reflex eye movement.

Thalamus
Oculomotor nucleus
Trochlear nucleus
Abducens nucleus
Middle cerebellar peduncle
Superior vestibular nucleus
Lateral vestibular nucleus
Inferior vestibular nucleus
Medial vestibular nucleus
Vestibulospinal tract

medulla (Fig. 11–16). From these nuclei some fibers extend to the cerebellum, and others pass down the spinal cord as the vestibular spinal tract to form connections with motor centers of the spinal nerves.

The nuclei of the oculomotor, trochlear, and abducens nerves send motor fibers to the extrinsic eye muscles. These nuclei receive fibers from all the vestibular nuclei. These secondary vestibular fibers are essential for most conjugate eye movements. These connections between vestibular and ocular nuclei provide the neural circuitry for reflex eye movements which accompany changes in the position of the body in space.

Physiology of Hearing. All bodies that produce sound are in a state of vibration and communicate their vibrations to the air with which they are in contact. The range of air vibrations for sound is from 40 to 20,000 vibrations per second.

When these air waves, set in motion by sonorous bodies, enter the external

[3] Vestibular nucleus and Deiters' nucleus. Otto Friedrich Karl Deiters, German anatomist (1834–1863).

auditory canal, they set the tympanic membrane vibrating. The stretched tympanic membrane takes up these vibrations from the air with great readiness. The vibrations of the tympanic membrane are then communicated by means of the auditory ossicles stretched across the middle ear to the perilymph and then to the endolymph of the inner ear. The movements of the fluids, in the rhythm of the air, stimulate the nerve endings in the organ of Corti; and from these, impulses are conveyed to the center of hearing in the temporal cortex. Characteristics of the sensation of sound are *loudness*, which varies with the *amplitude* of vibrations; *pitch*, which varies with the frequency of vibrations; and *timbre*, which is due to the pattern which the complex of vibrations makes.

A unit for measuring the loudness of sound is the *bel* (which measures air pressure changes); for convenience a tenth of a bel, or a decibel, is used. Zero decibels is the threshold of hearing, and normal conversation is about 65 decibels. Various theories are held regarding the manner in which the organ of Corti is stimulated. Most recent work substantiates the *resonance* theory of Helmholtz. This theory postulates that the cochlea is the analyzer of sound. The theory makes use of the structure of the basilar membrane, which is said to have some 24,000 fibers running across it. These fibers vary gradually in length from around 130 μ at the base to about 275 μ at the apex of the cochlea. The short fibers vibrate in response to vibrations of the tympanic membrane brought about by high notes; the long fibers at the apex vibrate in response to low tone vibrations. It is said that man is able to distinguish more than 10,000 pitches of tone. There are also more than 15,000 hair cells on the basilar membrane and more than 15,000 fibers in the cochlear nerve. This almost constitutes an adequate physical mechanism for discrimination in auditory sensation. Abnormal conditions in any part of the auditory mechanism may excite the auditory nerve and give rise to noises that are described as rushing, roaring, humming, and ringing.

Since the cochlea is embedded in a bony cavity, vibrations from any or all skull bones can cause fluid vibrations of the cochlea itself. Thus, in deafness due to calcification and immobility of ossicles, it is possible to hear by bone conduction. Some hearing-aid devices amplify air waves into vibrations that will be readily transmitted through the mastoid bone. If disease has destroyed the receptor hair cells or the afferent nerve fibers, hearing aids will be of no use.

The Sense of Equilibrium.   Among the various means (such as sight, touch, and muscular sense) whereby one is enabled to maintain equilibrium, coordinate movements, and become aware of position in space, one of the most important is the *action of the vestibule and semicircular canals*. These structures are found in the inner ear and communicate with the cochlea. As a result of much experimental work, many facts regarding the effects of injury to the semicircular canals have been accumulated; but it is difficult to interpret these facts, and several theories have been proposed. One theory is that movements of the head set up movements in the endolymph of the canals and bend the receptor hair cells which in turn initiate nerve impulses that are then transmitted to the cerebellum.

The canals are so arranged (Fig. 11–17) that any movement of the head causes an increase in the pressure of the endolymph in one ampulla and a corresponding diminution in the ampulla of the parallel canal on the opposite side. Thus, a nodding of the head to the right would cause a flow of the endolymph from *a* to *b* in the right superior canal but from *b'* to *a'* in the left posterior canal. Hence, the pressure upon the hairs is decreased in *a* but increased in *a'*. Such stimulations of the sensory hairs are transmitted by fibers of the vestibular nerve, through the cell bodies of the vestibular ganglion and the axons of the statoacoustic nerve, to the cerebellum. Impulses from receptors in the semicircular canals and from the otoliths, due to change in position of the head, initiate the righting reflex. Balance against gravity is thus maintained by the coordinated or effective response of the antigravity muscles. The cerebellum links the impulses that arise from stimulation of the sensory nerves of the semicircular canals, joints, etc., and sends the nerve impulses on to the motor centers of the cerebrum and spinal cord.

Figure 11–17. Diagram showing relative position of the planes in which the semicircular canals lie. (*Rt.*) Right ear, (*Lt.*) left ear, (*S*) superior canal, (*P*) posterior canal, (*L*) lateral canal, (*a*) ampulla of right superior canal, (*a'*) ampulla of left posterior canal. The superior and posterior canals lie in nearly vertical planes. Each of the three canals lies in a plane practically at right angles to the other two. See text for explanation of fluid movement within the canals.

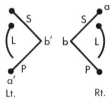

VISION

The visual apparatus consists of the bulb of the eye (eyeball), the optic nerve, and the visual center in the brain. In addition to these essential organs, there are accessory organs which are necessary for the protection and functioning of the eyeball.

Accessory Organs of the Eye. Under this heading are grouped eyebrows, eyelids, conjunctiva, lacrimal apparatus, muscles of the eyeball, and the fascia bulbi.

The eyebrow is a thickened ridge of skin, covered with short hairs. It is situated on the upper border of the orbit and protects the eye from too vivid light, perspiration, etc.

The eyelids (palpebrae) are two movable folds placed in front of the eye. They are covered externally with skin and internally with a mucous membrane, the conjunctiva, which is reflected from them over the bulb of the eye. They are composed of muscle fibers and dense fibrous tissue known as the *tarsal plates.* The upper lid is attached to a small muscle which is called the elevator of the upper lid (*levator palpebrae superioris*). Arranged as a sphincter around both lids is the *orbicularis oculi* muscle, which closes the eyelids.

The slit between the edges of the lids is called the palpebral fissure. It is the size of this fissure which causes the appearance of large and small eyes, as the size of the eyeball itself varies but little. The outer angle of this fissure is called the lateral palpebral commissure (*external canthus*); the inner angle, the medial palpebral commissure (*internal canthus*).

The eyelids provide protection for the eye—movable shades which cover the eye during sleep, protect the eye from bright light and foreign objects, and spread the lubricating secretions of the eye over the surface of the eyeball.

Eyelashes and Sebaceous Glands. From the margin of each eyelid, a row of short, thick hairs—the eyelashes—project. The follicles of the eyelashes receive a lubricating fluid from the sebaceous glands which open into them. If these glands become infected, a sty results. A *sty*, therefore, is comparable to a pimple or furuncle resulting from the infection of retained sebaceous fluid in other regions of the skin.

Lying between the conjunctiva and the tarsal cartilage of each eyelid is a row of elongated sebaceous glands—the tarsal, or meibomian, glands—the ducts of which open on the edge of the eyelid. The secretion of these glands lubricates their edges and prevents adhesion of the eyelids. Distention of the gland is termed a *chalazion*.

The Conjunctiva. The mucous membrane which lines the eyelids and is reflected over the forepart of the eyeball is called the conjunctiva. It is continuous with the lining membrane of the ducts of the tarsal glands, the lacrimal ducts, lacrimal sac, nasolacrimal duct, and nose.

Lacrimal Apparatus. This apparatus consists of the lacrimal gland, the lacrimal ducts, the lacrimal sac, and the nasolacrimal duct.

The *lacrimal gland* is a compound gland and is lodged in a depression of the frontal bone at the upper and outer angle of the orbit. It is about the size and shape of an almond and consists of two portions, a superior and inferior, which are partially separated by a fibrous septum.

Six to twelve minute *ducts* lead from the gland to the surface of the conjunctiva of the upper lid. The secretion (tears) is usually just enough to keep the eye moist and, after passing over the surface of the eyeball, flows through the *puncta* into two tiny *lacrimal ducts* and is conveyed into the *lacrimal sac* at the inner angle of the eye. The *lacrimal sac* is the expanded upper end of the *nasolacrimal* duct, a small canal that opens into the nose. It is oval in shape and measures from 12 to 15 mm in length. The *caruncula lacrimalis* (caruncle) is a small reddish body situated at the medial commissure. It contains sebaceous and sudoriferous glands and forms the whitish secretion which collects in this region.

The lacrimal gland secretes tears. This secretion is a dilute solution of various salts in water, which also contains small quantities of mucin. The ducts leading from the lacrimal gland carry tears to the eyeball, and the lids spread it over the surface. Ordinarily this secretion is evaporated, or carried away by the nasolacrimal duct, as fast as formed; but under certain circumstances, as when the conjunctiva is irritated or when painful emotions arise in the mind, the secretion of the lacrimal gland exceeds the drainage power of the nasolacrimal duct, and the fluid, accumulating between the lids, at length overflows and runs down the cheeks. The purpose of the lacrimal secretion is to keep the surface of the eyes

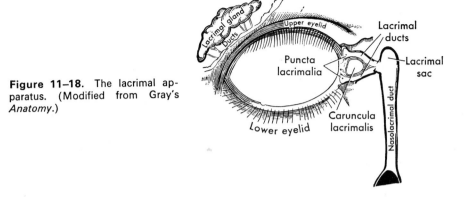

Figure 11–18. The lacrimal apparatus. (Modified from Gray's *Anatomy*.)

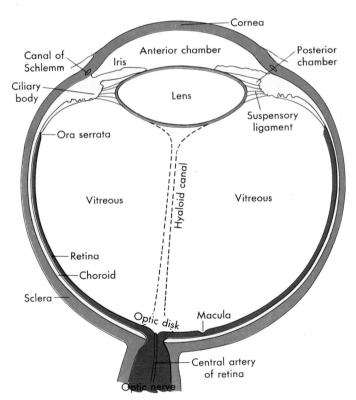

Figure 11–19. Horizontal section of the eyeball. Retina red, choroid yellow between red and blue. (Charles H. May, *Manual of the Diseases of the Eye*.)

moist and to help remove foreign bodies, microorganisms, and dust. It is slightly antiseptic. The secretion is increased by foreign bodies (molecules of volatile gases, liquids, dust, microorganisms) that come in contact with the eyeball or lids, irritation of the nasal mucous membrane, bright light, and emotional states. Inflammation from the nose may spread to the nasolacrimal ducts, blocking them and thus cause a slow dropping of tears from the inner angle of the eye. The lacrimal glands do not develop sufficiently to secrete tears until about the fourth month of life, hence, the need for protecting a baby's eyes from bright light and dust.

Muscles of the Eye. For purposes of description the muscles of the eye are divided into groups—intrinsic and extrinsic. The intrinsic muscles are the ciliary muscle and the muscles of the iris. The extrinsic muscles hold the eyeball in place and control its movements. They include the four straight, or recti, and the two oblique, already described. The rectus muscles are so arranged that the superior and inferior oppose each other; the medial and lateral do likewise. This action is comparable to the opposed action of the flexors and extensors of the arms and legs and ensures accuracy of movement. Sometimes these muscles (particularly the medial and lateral recti) are unequal in length or strength, the equilibrium of the opposed muscles is upset, and the eye is then turned in the direction of the stronger muscle, producing a squint, or strabismus. There are various kinds of strabismus.

Fascia Bulbi (Capsule of Tenon).[4] Between the pad of fat and the eyeball is a thin membrane—the fascia bulbi—which envelops the eyeball from the optic nerve to the ciliary region and forms a socket in which the eyeball rotates.

The Nerves of the Eye

Optic	{ Concerned with vision
Oculomotor (Nerve III)	{ Supplies medial, superior, and inferior recti and inferior oblique muscles
Autonomic Division of Nerve III (Craniosacral)	{ Ciliary muscle, circular muscle of iris (pupillary constriction)
Trochlear Nerve IV	{ Supplies superior oblique muscle
Abducens Nerve VI	{ Supplies lateral rectus muscle
Ophthalmic (a Branch of the Trigeminal)	{ General sensation to eye; branches to cornea, ciliary body, iris, conjunctiva, and lacrimal gland
Sympathetic Fibers (in Trigeminal)	{ From superior cervical ganglia—to radial muscle of iris (pupillary dilation)

The orbits are the bony cavities in which the eyeballs are contained. Seven bones assist in the formation of each orbit, namely, the frontal, malar, maxilla, palatine, ethmoid, sphenoid, and lacrimal. As three of these bones are mesial (frontal, ethmoid, and sphenoid), there are only 11 bones forming both orbits.

Each orbit is shaped like a funnel; the large end, directed outward and forward, forms a strong bony edge which protects the eyeball. The small end is directed backward and inward and is pierced by a large opening—the optic foramen—through which the optic nerve and the ophthalmic artery pass from

[4] Jacobus René Tenon, French anatomist and surgeon (1724–1816).

the cranial cavity to the eye. A larger opening to the outer side of the foramen—the superior orbital fissure—provides a passage for the orbital branches of the middle meningeal artery and the nerves which carry impulses to and from the muscles, i.e., the oculomotor, the trochlear, the abducent, and the ophthalmic. Each orbit contains the eyeball, muscles, nerves, vessels, lacrimal glands, fat, the fascia bulbi, and the fascia that holds these structures in place. The inner portion is lined with fibrous tissue and contains a pad of fat which serves as a cushion for the eyeball. During many forms of illness the body fat is oxidized at an unusual rate. Under such conditions the orbital fat becomes diminished, and the eyeballs sink in the orbits.

The bulb of the eye, or **eyeball,** is spherical; but its transverse diameter is less than the anteroposterior so that it projects anteriorly and looks as if a section of a smaller sphere had been engrafted on the front of it.

The bulb of the eye is composed of three coats, or tunics. From the outside of the eyeball inward toward its center these are:

Fibrous: (1) sclera, (2) cornea
Vascular: (1) choroid, (2) ciliary body, (3) iris
Nervous: retina

It contains four refracting media. These are:

Cornea
Aqueous humor
Crystalline lens and capsule
Vitreous body

The fibrous tunic is formed by the sclera and cornea.

1. *The sclera,* or *white of the eye,* covers the posterior five sixths of the eyeball. It is composed of a firm, unyielding, fibrous membrane, thicker behind than in front, and serves to maintain the shape of the eyeball and to protect the delicate structures contained within it. It is opaque, white, and smooth externally; behind, it is pierced by the optic nerve. Internally it is brown in color and is separated from the choroid by a fluid space. It is supplied with few blood vessels. A *venous sinus*—the canal of Schlemm[5]—encircles the cornea at the corneoscleral junction. Its nerves are derived from the ciliary nerve.

2. *The cornea* covers the anterior sixth of the eyeball. It is directly continuous with the sclera, which, however, overlaps it slightly above and below, as a watch crystal is overlapped by the case into which it is fitted. The cornea, like the sclera, is composed of fibrous tissue, which is firm and unyielding, but, unlike the sclera, it has no color and is perfectly transparent; it has been aptly termed the "window of the eye." The cornea is well supplied with nerves (derived from the ciliary) and lymph spaces which surround the nerves but is destitute of blood vessels, so that it is dependent on the lymph contained in the lymph spaces for nutriment.

[5] Friedrich Schlemm, German anatomist (1795–1858).

The vascular tunic (uvea, or uveal tract) consists, from behind forward, of the choroid, the ciliary body, and the iris.

1. *The choroid* is a thin, dark-brown membrane lining the inner surface of the posterior five sixths of the sclera. It is pierced behind by the optic nerve. The inner surface is attached to the pigmented layer of the retina and extends anteriorly to the ora serrata. It consists of a dense capillary plexus and small arteries and veins carrying blood to and from the plexus. Between these vessels are pigment cells which with other cells form a network, or stroma. The blood vessels and pigment cells render this membrane dark and opaque, so that it darkens the chamber of the eye by preventing the reflection of light. It extends to the ciliary body.

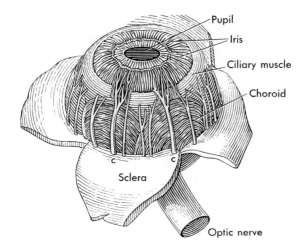

Figure 11–20. Diagram of the eyeball, sclera cut and turned back. Note pupil, iris, ciliary muscle, choroid; (*c*) ciliary nerves and optic nerve.

2. *The ciliary body* includes the orbicularis ciliaris, the ciliary processes, and the ciliaris muscle. The orbicularis ciliaris is a zone about 4 mm in width, which is directly continuous with the anterior part of the choroid.

Just behind the edge of the cornea, the choroid is folded inward and arranged in radiating folds, like a plaited ruffle, around the margin of the lens. There are from 60 to 80 of these folds, and they constitute the ciliary processes. They are well supplied with nerves and blood vessels and also support a muscle, the ciliaris (ciliary) muscle. The fibers of this muscle arise from the sclera near the cornea, and, extending backward, are inserted into the outer surface of the ciliary processes and the choroid. This muscle is the chief agent in accommodation. When it contracts, it draws forward the ciliary processes, relaxes the suspensory ligament of the lens, and allows the elastic lens to resume a more convex form.

3. *The iris* (*iris*, rainbow) is a circular, colored disk suspended in the aqueous humor in front of the lens and behind the cornea. It is attached at its circumference to the ciliary processes, with which it is practically continuous, and is also connected to the sclera and cornea at the point where they join one another.

Except for this attachment at its circumference, it hangs free in the interior of the eyeball. In the middle of the iris is a circular hole, the *pupil*, through which light is admitted into the eye chamber. The iris is composed of connective tissue containing branched cells, numerous blood vessels, and nerves. The color of the eye is related to the number and size of pigment-bearing cells in the iris. If there is no pigment or very little, the eye is blue; with increasing amounts of pigment the eye is gray, brown, or black. It also contains two sets of muscles. One set is arranged like a sphincter with its fibers encircling the pupil and is called the *sphincter pupillae* (constrictor of the pupil). The other set consists of fibers which radiate from the pupil to the outer circumference of the iris and is called the *dilator pupillae* (dilator of the pupil). The action of these muscles is antagonistic.

The posterior surface of the iris is covered by layers of pigmented epithelium of deep-purple tint, named *pars iridica retinae*. It is designed to prevent the entrance of light.

Physiology of the Iris. The function of the iris is to regulate the amount of light entering the eye and thus assist in obtaining clear images. This regulation is accomplished by the action of the muscles described above, as their contraction or relaxation determines the size of the pupil. When the eye is accommodated for a near object or stimulated by a bright light, the sphincter muscle contracts and diminishes the size of the pupil. When, on the other hand, the eye is accommodated for a distant object or the light is dim, the dilator muscle contracts and increases the size of the pupil.

The Retina, or Nervous Tunic. The *retina*, the innermost coat of the eyeball, is a delicate membrane of tissue which receives the images of external objects and transfers the impressions evoked by them to the center of sight in the cortex of the cerebrum. It occupies the space between the choroid coat and the hyaloid membrane of the vitreous body and extends forward almost to the posterior margin of the ciliary body, where it terminates in a jagged margin known as the *ora serrata*. It consists of three sets of neurons so arranged that the cell bodies and processes form seven layers. In addition there are two limiting membranes, one membrane (membrana limitans interna) in contact with the vitreous layer, and the second (membrana limitans externa) marking the internal limit of the rod-and-cone layer and a pigmented layer between the layer of rods and cones and the choroid coat.

The seventh layer, called the layer of rods and cones, is the light-sensitive layer where light energy is converted to nerve impulses which are transmitted to the brain by the optic nerve. To reach the light-sensitive receptors lying in this seventh retinal layer, light must pass through the cornea, aqueous humor, lens, vitreous humor, and each of the retinal layers before striking the rods and cones.

In the center of the receptor layer of the retina, there is a small special region, the fovea, in which there are only cones. Moving from the fovea to the periphery of the retina the concentration of cones diminishes and the concentration of rods increases until at the most peripheral edges of the retina one finds only rods.

The rods and cones are two different types of visual receptors. They differ both structurally and functionally, each subserving very important roles in vision.

The rods are particularly important for vision in dim illumination because it takes very little light to stimulate them. Although the rods are stimulated by most of the wave lengths in the visible spectrum, they cannot produce a color sensation. They permit light and dark discrimination and form and movement perception but provide poor visual acuity. Rhodopsin is the photosensitive pigment within the rods. This material is bleached by light, and it is slowly regenerated in the dark. It takes almost an hour in total darkness for complete resynthesis of rhodopsin. As the rhodopsin is regenerated, the sensitivity of the

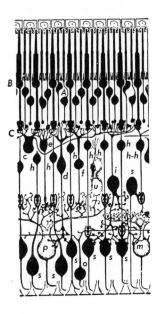

Figure 11–21. Scheme of the structure of the primate retina, as shown by Polyak. (*A*) Rod, (*B*) cone, (*C*) horizontal cell, (*d*) diffuse ganglionic cell. This diagram illustrates the very complex arrangement of retinal cells—a concept that the older diagrams do not give. (Courtesy of the University of Chicago Press.) For other identifications see S. R. Detwiler *Vertebrate Photoreceptors*, The Macmillan Company, 1943.

rods progressively increases. This gradual increase in retinal sensitivity is called dark adaptation. Vitamin A and nicotinamide are essential for resynthesis of rhodopsin and any vitamin A deficiency will delay or reduce rhodopsin regeneration. The resulting condition is known as night blindness (nyctalopia); the rods are less capable of increasing their sensitivity in dim illumination.

In contrast the cones are particularly important for color vision in bright illumination. The cones need more intense light to be excited than do the rods, and the cones maximally alter their sensitivity to decreased illumination within 10 to 15 minutes. Their range of sensitivity is small compared to the 100 million sensitivity range over which the rods can function. The cones are responsible for visual acuity. In the fovea, where only cones exist, there is only one cone per nerve fiber. It is as if each receptor has its own "private line" to the brain. The cones also contain a photosensitive pigment known as iodopsin. It must be assumed that there are three types of cone pigments with different spectral sensitivities if color vision is to be explained.

Blind Spot. The optic nerve pierces the eyeball not exactly at its most posterior point but a little to the inner side, called the blind spot. Because it contains no receptor cells, this point is insensitive to light. The central artery of the retina, a branch of the ophthalmic artery, and its vein pass into the retina along with the optic nerve.

Macula Lutea. One point of the retina is of great importance—the macula lutea, or yellow spot. It is situated about 2.08 mm ($1/_{12}$ in.) to the outer side of the exit of the optic nerve and is the exact center of the retina. In its center is a tiny pit—*fovea centralis*—which is the center of direct vision. At this point there is an absence of rods but a great increase in the number of cones. This is the region of greatest visual acuity. In reading, the eyes move so as to bring the rays of light from word after word into the center of the fovea.

Refracting Media. The cornea and the aqueous humor form the first refracting media. The *aqueous humor* fills the forward chamber; the latter is the space bounded by the cornea in front and by the lens, suspensory ligament, and ciliary body behind. This space is partially divided by the iris into an anterior and a posterior chamber. The aqueous humor is a clear, watery solution containing minute amounts of salts, mainly sodium chloride. It is derived mainly from the capillaries by diffusion and it drains away through the veins and through the spaces of Fontana [6] into the venous canal of Schlemm and then on into the larger veins of the eyeball.

The *crystalline lens* enclosed in its capsule is a transparent, refractive body, with convex anterior and posterior surfaces. It is placed directly behind the pupil, where it is retained in position by the counterbalancing pressure of the aqueous humor in front and the vitreous body behind, and by its own suspensory ligament, formed in part by the hyaloid membrane and in part by fibers derived from the ciliary processes. The posterior surface is considerably more curved than the anterior, and the curvature of each varies with the period of life. In infancy, the lens is almost spherical; in the adult, of medium convexity; and in the aged, considerably flattened. The capsule surrounding the lens is elastic, and with age it loses its original elasticity. Its refractive power is much greater than that of the aqueous or vitreous body. In cataract the lens or its capsule becomes less transparent and blurs or causes loss of vision. Cataracts are treated by removing the opaque lens and substituting an artificial lens, i.e., eyeglasses.

The *vitreous body*, a semifluid albuminous tissue enclosed in a thin membrane, the hyaloid membrane, fills the posterior four fifths of the bulb of the eye. The vitreous body distends the greater part of the sclera, supports the retina, which lies upon its surface, and preserves the spheroidal shape of the eyeball. Its refractive power, though slightly greater than that of the aqueous humor, does not differ much from that of water.

---

[6] Felice Fontana, Italian physiologist (1720–1805).

In glaucoma, intraocular pressure increases, cupping the optic disk and interfering with the proper distribution of blood to all the inner tissues of the eye. This increased pressure may be due to increased blood pressure in the larger blood vessels of the eye, to altered osmotic conditions of blood and eye fluids, to rigidity of the eyeball, or to improper functioning of intrinsic muscles of the eye. It may or may not cause pain. If the increased pressure persists, it can lead to irreversible damage to the visual cells.

Perception of Light and Color. Waves started by the motion of the molecules of bodies (especially hot bodies like the sun) cause ethereal vibrations, and these vibrations are of varying lengths. Vibrations from 400 mμ to 800 mμ long are called light and color waves. Those shorter than this are known as ultraviolet rays; those much longer are electrical waves. When vibrations varying between 400 mμ and 800 mμ enter the eye, they cause photochemical changes in the rods

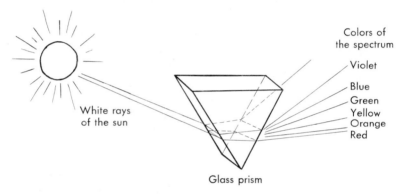

Figure 11–22. Colors of the spectrum. As sunlight strikes the glass prism, rays are not bent equally. The top indicates rays that are *most* bent; rays that are *least* bent are at the bottom. A beam of light through a windowpane is not bent; so only white light of the sun comes through.

and cones which give rise to impulses that are carried by the optic nerve to the brain and result in the visual sensation.

The millimicron (mμ) is a millionth part of a millimeter and is the unit of length usually used in measuring light waves.

Wave Lengths and Color
723 mμ–647 mμ = red
647 mμ–585 mμ = orange
585 mμ–575 mμ = yellow
575 mμ–492 mμ = green
492 mμ–455 mμ = blue
455 mμ–424 mμ = indigo
424 mμ–397 mμ = violet

(Figures from *Medical Physiology* by Philip Bard, 1961, p. 1294.)

Color blindness refers to the inability to discriminate colors properly. About 9 per cent of normal healthy males are color blind to some degree.

There are several kinds of color-blind individuals classifiable in relation to normal subjects who are called *trichromats*. Individuals lacking one type of cone pigment are called *dichromats*. The most usual type of dichromat is the *protanope* who lacks sensitivity to wave lengths in the red end of the spectrum. Another type of dichromat is the *deuteranope*, whose sensitivity is weak or lacking in the green region of the spectrum. Though the deuteranopes do not have a red deficiency, they confuse red and green. The *tritanope* is a rare type of dichromat who lacks blue-type cones. These individuals confuse blue and green. Some individuals have all three types of cone pigments, but one type may be deficient rather than absent, and they are called *anomalous trichromats*. These individuals rarely misname colors, but they confuse colors. These confusions provide the basis for some of the standard "hidden-figure" type of color tests.

Refraction. Light rays may be refracted, or bent from their course. This is due to the fact that they travel at different rates in media of different density. For instance, light travels less rapidly in water than in air. For this reason where a ray of light in air strikes a body of water obliquely, it will be bent out of a straight line. The bending is in proportion to the density of the medium. The cause of the refraction of oblique rays is that all the component rays do not reach the surface of the medium at the same time and those that enter first become retarded before those entering later. A ray of light which strikes a body of water perpendicularly will not be bent because all its component rays enter the water at the same time and hence are equally retarded.

The central components of a light wave enter the eyes perpendicularly, and the sides obliquely. For clear vision the oblique rays must converge and come to a focus with the central rays on the retina. The cornea, aqueous humor, the crystalline lens, and the vitreous humor form a system of refractory devices. Rays of light are bent, or undergo refraction, chiefly on entering the cornea from the air, on entering the lens from the aqueous humor, and on leaving the lens and entering the vitreous fluid.

Physiology of Vision. Visible objects reflect light rays which fall upon them. These reflected rays are brought to a focus on the rods and cones of the retina, and the resulting nerve impulses are transmitted to the optic nerve and thence through various relay stations to the centers of vision in the occipital lobes of the cerebrum. From here it is believed the impulses are transmitted to the association areas, where they awaken memories that enable one to interpret their meaning. The cones of the fovea centralis are the place of most acute vision and the part on which the light rays are focused when the eyes are accommodated for near objects. In a bright light the object is focused directly on the fovea, and the reflexes controlling accommodation help to bring this about. In a dim light the tendency is to diverge the eyes and thus bring the image into the peripheral and sensitive part of the retina. The visual field includes the entire expanse of space seen in a given instant without moving the eyes.

The temporal portion of the retina receives light waves from the nasal field of vision. The nasal portion of the retina receives light waves from the temporal field of vision. These fields may be tested to determine the specific areas of retinal (or optic tract) damage (Fig. 11–23).

Binocular Vision. The value of two eyes instead of one is that true binocular vision is possible. This is distinctive in that it is stereoscopic. A stereoscopic picture consists of two views taken from slightly different angles. In stereoscopic vision, two optical images are made from slightly different angles. This gives the impression of distance and depth and is equivalent to adding a third dimension to the visual field. The processes necessary for binocular vision are convergence, or turning the eyes inward; change in the size of the pupil; accommodation; and refraction.

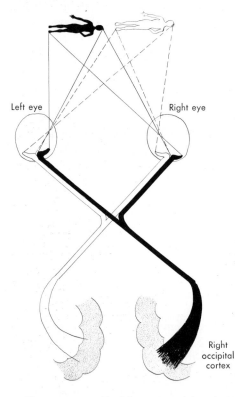

Left eye   Right eye

Figure 11–23. Diagram showing crossing of optic fibers. The fibers from the *nasal* half of the left retina and the fibers from the lateral half of the right retina are projected to the right occipital cortex and vice versa for the opposite side. See Figure 11–24 for optic pathway and synapsing of fibers.

Right occipital cortex

Convergence. In binocular vision it is necessary to turn the eyes inward, in order that the two images of a given object may lie upon what are called corresponding points of the two retinas. Excitation of two corresponding points causes only one sensation, which is the reason why binocular vision is not ordinarily double vision. Convergence of the eyes is brought about by innervation of the medial rectus muscles and is to some extent voluntary.

The Optic Chiasma. The correspondence of the two retinas and of the movements of the eyeballs is produced by a close connection of the nerve centers controlling the contraction of eye muscles and by the organization of the visual center. The optic fibers from each retina pass backward through the optic foramen; and shortly after leaving the orbit, the two nerves come together, and the fibers from the nasal portions of the retinas cross. This is called the optic chiasma and is an incomplete crossing of fibers because the fibers from the temporal retinas do not cross. (See Fig. 11–24.)

The optic nerve is formed by fibers of the ganglionic layer of the retina. They pass backward, forming the optic nerve and synapse in the *lateral geniculate body*. Cell bodies in the geniculate body form the optic radiation and terminate in the visual cortex of the occipital lobe. This means that there are two cells in the optic pathway. A branch of the optic nerve fibers passes to the superior colliculi. Cell bodies in the superior colliculi send collateral fibers to the nuclei of the oculomotor, trochlear, and abducens nucleus. The main fiber bundle from

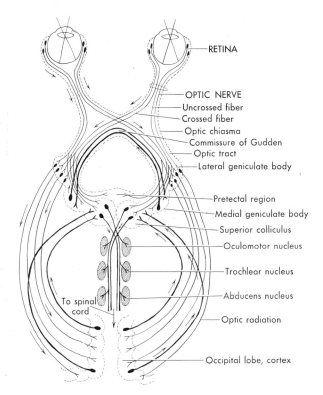

Figure 11–24. Diagram of visual pathway. Note the *arrows* as they indicate the direction in which impulses travel.

the superior colliculus descends into the upper part of the spinal cord (tecto-spinal tract) and terminates around the large motor cells of the ventral gray of cord.

Change in the Size of the Pupil. When one looks at a near object in a bright light, the pupil contracts, so that the entering rays are directed to the central part of the lens, i.e., the part where the convexity and the consequent refractive power are greatest and to the fovea centralis. In a dim light the pupil is dilated, causing a diffusion of the rays to the peripheral parts of the retina where the concentration of rhodopsin is high. The contraction of the pupil is brought about by the reflex contraction of the circular muscle of the iris by the oculo-motor nerve in response to strong light stimulating the retina; in dim light the stimulation of the retina is lessened and the pupil dilates. In excitement, fear, etc., its dilation is due to stimulation of autonomic nerve fibers that are distributed by the ophthalmic branch of the trigeminal nerve.

Accommodation. Accommodation is the adjustment of the eye to focus on objects at different distances, because a sharply focused image must fall upon the retina in order to produce clear vision. Accommodation involves three coordinated responses: (1) the convergence of the eyes, (2) pupillary constriction, and (3) alteration in the refractiveness of the lens. The first two reflexes were discussed in the preceding paragraphs. Alteration in lens refractiveness is also a reflex response. A blurred image on the retina initiates afferent impulses in the optic nerve which signal the motor center of the ciliary muscle, the chief effector in accommodation. When the eye is at rest or fixed upon distant objects, the suspensory ligament, which extends from the ciliary processes to the capsule of the lens, exerts a tension upon the capsule of the lens which keeps the lens flattened, particularly the anterior surface to which it is attached. When the eye fixates on near objects, as in reading or sewing, the ciliary muscle contracts and draws forward the choroid coat, which in turn releases the tension of the suspensory ligament upon the capsule of the elastic lens and allows the anterior surface to become more convex. The accommodation for near objects is an active process and is always more or less fatiguing. On the contrary, the accommodation for distant objects is a passive process; consequently the eye rests for an indefinite time upon remote objects without fatigue.

Refraction. Rays of light entering the eye are refracted, or bent, so that they come to a focus on the retina. Refraction occurs because of the varying densities of the successive refractive media.

Inversion of Images. Owing to refraction, light rays as they enter the eye cross each other and cause the image of external objects on the retina to be *inverted*. The question then arises, "Why is it that objects do not appear to be upside down?" This question is answered if it is remembered that actual visual sensations take place in the brain and that the projection of these sensations to the exterior is a secondary act that has been learned from experience.

Abnormal Conditions That Interfere with Refraction. The normal eye is one in which at a distance of about 20 ft parallel rays of light focus on the retina when the eye is at rest. Such an eye is designated as emmetropic, or normal. Any abnormality in the refractive surfaces or the shape of the eyeball prevents this focusing of parallel rays and makes the eye ametropic, or abnormal.

The most common refractive conditions are myopia, hypermetropia, presbyopia, and astigmatism.

Myopia. Myopia, or nearsightedness, is a condition in which rays of light converge too soon and are brought to a focus before reaching the retina. This is the opposite of hypermetropia and is caused by a cornea or lens that is too convex or an eyeball of too great depth. This condition is remedied by wearing concave lenses, which cause parallel rays of light to diverge before they converge and focus on the retina.

Hypermetropia. Hypermetropia, or farsightedness, is a condition in which rays of light from near objects do not converge soon enough and are brought to a focus behind the retina.

A hypermetropic eye must accommodate slightly for distant objects and over-accommodate for near objects. Hypermetropia is usually caused by a flattened condition of the lens or cornea, or an eyeball that is too shallow; and convex lenses are used to concentrate and focus the rays more quickly.

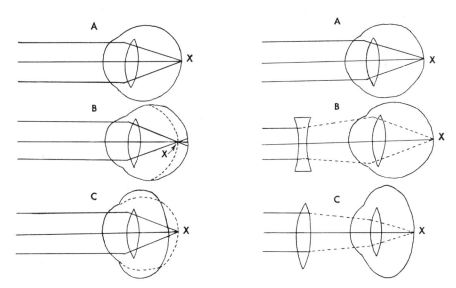

Figure 11–25. (*Left*) Diagrams illustrating rays of light converging in (*A*) normal eye, (*B*) myopic eye, and (*C*) hypermetropic eye. The parallel lines indicate light rays entering the eye; *X* is the point of convergence, or focus. In *A* the rays are brought to a focus (*X*) on the retina. In *B* they come to a focus in front of the retina. In *C* they would come to a focus behind the retina.
(*Right*) Diagrams illustrating the convergence of light rays in a normal eye (*A*), and the effects of concave lens (*B*) and convex lens (*C*) on rays of light.

Presbyopia. Presbyopia is a defective condition of accommodation in which distant objects are seen distinctly but near objects are indistinct. This is a physiological process which affects every eye sooner or later. It is said to be caused by a loss of the elasticity of the lens and lack of tone of the ciliary muscle.

Astigmatism. Astigmatism means that the curvature of the refracting surfaces is unequal; e.g., the cornea is more curved vertically than it is in a horizontal direction or vice versa.

The commonest form is that in which the vertical curvature is greater than the horizontal, and is described as regular astigmatism "according to rule." Regular astigmatism is remedied by the use of cylindrical lenses, the focal lengths of which are different in two meridians at right angles to one another.

QUESTIONS FOR DISCUSSION

1. An individual receives a third-degree burn of both lower extremities. The deep structures of the skin are destroyed.
   a. Which sensations are lost? Explain.
   b. Which receptors are involved?
   c. Where in the brain are these sensations interpreted?
2. Explain how receptors function as a protective mechanism.
3. Explain why injury to the right occipital lobe (visual area) causes partial loss of vision in both eyes.
4. When an individual has a severe "cold in the head," sense of taste for most foods is lost. Explain.
5. What sensation is disturbed by inflammation of the middle ear?
6. Explain the phenomenon of referred pain.
7. Trace the pathway for hearing from the external ear to the cerebral cortex.
8. Trace the nerve fibers forming the optic pathway from the retina to the visual area of the occipital lobe.
9. Explain how an individual perceives color.
10. Explain how the eye accommodates to near and to far vision.

SUMMARY

Sensation — The conscious result of processes which take place within the brain due to impulses derived from receptors

Cutaneous
 (1) Fibers for warm, cold, light pressure and tactile discrimination
 (2) Fibers for superficial pain
  Localization good
  Sensitivity good

Deep and visceral
 (1) Fibers for deep pain (not visceral)
 (2) Fibers for deep pressure
  Localization poor
  Sensitivity low

Pain
Excessive stimulation of any of the sense organs causes unpleasant sensations
Actual pain caused by stimulation of pain receptors, which are most abundant in the superficial parts of the body
Pain, and other receptors stimulated simultaneously, sensation modified, i.e., burning pain
Function—serves as danger signal

Visceral pain
 Pain from hollow organs carried over afferent fibers in sympathetic trunk
 Pain from other visceral structures probably carried over afferent fibers in vagus and sacral nerves

Referred pain
 Pain arising in visceral and referred to skin area supplied with sensory fibers from the same spinal segment

Hunger
Normal gastric hunger due to contractions of empty stomach, acting on nerves distributed to mucous membrane
Hunger contractions may be frequent and severe, even when food is taken regularly, as in diabetes

Appetite
Aroused in part through sensory nerves of taste and smell, associated with previous experiences
Thought of food associated with appetite induces flow of saliva and gastric fluid

Thirst
- Normal thirst sensations presumably due to stimulation of sensory nerves of pharynx
- Prolonged deprivation of water probably affects sensory nerves in many tissues and interferes with the metabolism of the nervous system

Nausea
- May be due to stimulation from the stomach, to substances in the blood, to impulses from organs of sight, taste, and smell

Taste
- Sensory apparatus
  - (1) Taste buds are end organs
  - (2) Nerve fibers of trigeminal, facial, and glossopharyngeal, vagus nerves
  - (3) Center in brain
- Solution of savory substances must come in contact with taste buds
- Taste buds are distributed over
  - Surface of tongue
  - Soft palate and fauces
  - Tonsils and pharynx

Tongue
- Freely movable muscular organ
- Attached to hyoid bone, epiglottis, and the glossopalatine arches
- Surface covered by papillae containing capillaries and nerves
  - Vallate
  - Fungiform
  - Filiform
  - Simple
- Nerves
  - Sensory
    - Lingual branch of trigeminal
    - Chorda tympani, branch of the facial
    - Glossopharyngeal
  - Motor—hypoglossal
- Sense of
  - (1) Taste
  - (2) Temperature
  - (3) Pressure
  - (4) Pain
  } are all well developed

Classification of Taste Sensations
- Four primary sensations
  - Salty, bitter, acid, sweet
- All others are
  - Combinations of primary sensations
  - Combinations of one or more plus odor

Smell
- Sensory apparatus
  - Olfactory nerve endings
  - Olfactory nerve fibers spread out in fine network over surface of superior nasal conchae and upper third of septum
  - Olfactory bulb and center in brain
- Odors
  - Minute particles usually in gaseous form
    - Must be capable of solution in mucus
  - Classify
    - Pure odors
      - Ethereal, aromatic, fragrant, ambrosial, garlic, burning, goat, repulsive, fetid
    - Odors mixed with sensations
    - Odors mixed or confused with taste
- Olfactory center in the brain is widely connected with other areas of the cerebrum
- Branches of trigeminal nerve found in lining of lower part of nose (pressure)

Hearing
- Auditory apparatus
  - External ear
  - Middle ear, or tympanic cavity
  - Internal ear, or labyrinth
  - Statoacoustic nerve
  - Acoustic center in brain
- Air waves enter meatus and cause vibrations of tympanic membrane. The vibrations are conveyed to nerve endings of organ of Corti and thence by the acoustic nerve to the brain

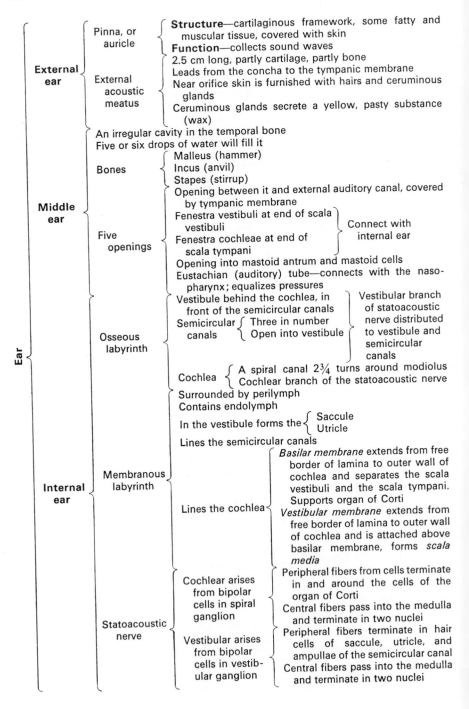

Ear

External ear
- Pinna, or auricle
  - **Structure**—cartilaginous framework, some fatty and muscular tissue, covered with skin
  - **Function**—collects sound waves
- External acoustic meatus
  - 2.5 cm long, partly cartilage, partly bone
  - Leads from the concha to the tympanic membrane
  - Near orifice skin is furnished with hairs and ceruminous glands
  - Ceruminous glands secrete a yellow, pasty substance (wax)

Middle ear
- An irregular cavity in the temporal bone
- Five or six drops of water will fill it
- Bones
  - Malleus (hammer)
  - Incus (anvil)
  - Stapes (stirrup)
- Five openings
  - Opening between it and external auditory canal, covered by tympanic membrane
  - Fenestra vestibuli at end of scala vestibuli ⎫
  - Fenestra cochleae at end of scala tympani ⎭ Connect with internal ear
  - Opening into mastoid antrum and mastoid cells
  - Eustachian (auditory) tube—connects with the naso-pharynx; equalizes pressures

Internal ear
- Osseous labyrinth
  - Vestibule behind the cochlea, in front of the semicircular canals ⎫
  - Semicircular canals { Three in number / Open into vestibule ⎬ Vestibular branch of statoacoustic nerve distributed to vestibule and semicircular canals
  - Cochlea { A spiral canal 2¾ turns around modiolus / Cochlear branch of the statoacoustic nerve
- Membranous labyrinth
  - Surrounded by perilymph
  - Contains endolymph
  - In the vestibule forms the { Saccule / Utricle
  - Lines the semicircular canals
  - Lines the cochlea {
    - *Basilar membrane* extends from free border of lamina to outer wall of cochlea and separates the scala vestibuli and the scala tympani. Supports organ of Corti
    - *Vestibular membrane* extends from free border of lamina to outer wall of cochlea and is attached above basilar membrane, forms *scala media*
- Statoacoustic nerve
  - Cochlear arises from bipolar cells in spiral ganglion
    - Peripheral fibers from cells terminate in and around the cells of the organ of Corti
    - Central fibers pass into the medulla and terminate in two nuclei
  - Vestibular arises from bipolar cells in vestibular ganglion
    - Peripheral fibers terminate in hair cells of saccule, utricle, and ampullae of the semicircular canal
    - Central fibers pass into the medulla and terminate in two nuclei

Physiology of Hearing
- Sonorous bodies produce air waves
- Air waves enter external auditory canal, set tympanic membrane vibrating, vibrations communicated to ossicles, transmitted through fenestra vestibuli to perilymph, stimulate nerve endings in organ of Corti, impulses carried to center of hearing in brain

Unit of measure of sound intensity is the *bel*. A tenth of a bel, or decibel, is used for measurement. Zero decibels is the threshold of hearing. Sixty-five decibels—normal conversations.

Sense of Equilibrium
- Function of the vestibule and semicircular canals
- Lining membrane supplied with sensory hairs and otoliths which connect with vestibular nerve
- Flowing of the endolymph stimulates the sensory hairs; this is transmitted to the vestibular branch of the acoustic nerve, thence to cerebellum

Visual Apparatus
- Bulb of the eye
- Optic nerve
- Center in brain

Accessory organs
- Eyebrows
- Eyelids
- Conjunctiva
- Lacrimal apparatus
- Muscles of the eyeball
- Fascia bulbi

Accessory Organs

Eyebrows
- Thickened ridges of skin furnished with short, thick hairs
- Protect eyes from vivid light, perspiration, etc.

Eyelids
- Folds of connective tissue covered with skin, lined with mucous membrane, conjunctiva, which is also reflected over the eyeball
- Provided with lashes
- Upper lid raised by levator palpebrae superioris
- Both lids closed by orbicularis oculi muscle
- Slit between lids called palpebral fissure
- Inner angle of slit called medial palpebral commissure (internal canthus)
- Outer angle of slit called lateral palpebral commissure (external canthus)
- Function
  - (1) Cover the eyes
  - (2) Protect eyes from bright light and foreign objects
  - (3) Spread lubricating secretions over surface of eyeball

Eyelashes and sebaceous glands
- Margin of each lid, a row of short hairs project
- Sebaceous glands connected with lashes
- Meibomian glands between conjunctiva and tarsal cartilage of each lid
- Secretion lubricates edges, prevents adhesion of lids

Conjunctiva
- Mucous membrane, lines eyelids and is reflected over eyeball. Continuous with mucous membrane of lacrimal ducts and nose

Lacrimal apparatus
- Lacrimal gland—in the upper and outer part of the orbit. Secretes tears
- Lacrimal ducts begin at puncta and open into lacrimal sac
- Lacrimal sac, expansion of upper end of nasolacrimal duct. Between lateral ducts is the lacrimal caruncle
- Nasolacrimal canal—extends from lacrimal sac to nose
- Tears
  - Secretion constant, carried off by nasal duct
  - Dilute solution of various salts in water, also mucin
  - Function
    - Keep surface of eyes moist
    - Help to remove foreign bodies, microorganisms, dust, etc.

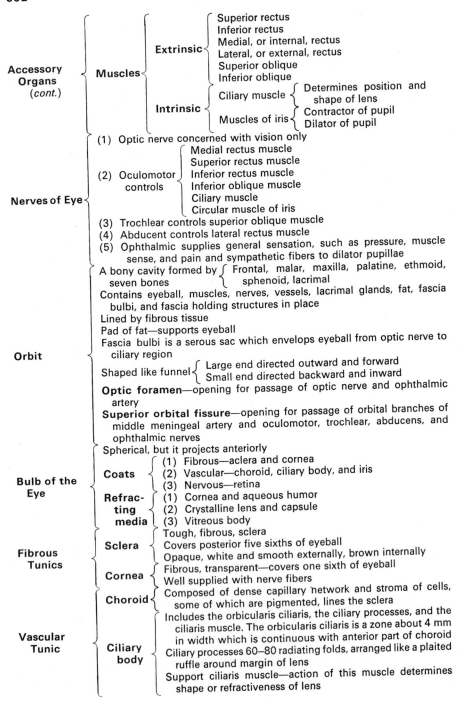

Accessory Organs (*cont.*)

Muscles

Extrinsic
- Superior rectus
- Inferior rectus
- Medial, or internal, rectus
- Lateral, or external, rectus
- Superior oblique
- Inferior oblique

Intrinsic
- Ciliary muscle — Determines position and shape of lens
- Muscles of iris — Contractor of pupil / Dilator of pupil

Nerves of Eye

(1) Optic nerve concerned with vision only

(2) Oculomotor controls
- Medial rectus muscle
- Superior rectus muscle
- Inferior rectus muscle
- Inferior oblique muscle
- Ciliary muscle
- Circular muscle of iris

(3) Trochlear controls superior oblique muscle

(4) Abducent controls lateral rectus muscle

(5) Ophthalmic supplies general sensation, such as pressure, muscle sense, and pain and sympathetic fibers to dilator pupillae

Orbit

A bony cavity formed by seven bones — Frontal, malar, maxilla, palatine, ethmoid, sphenoid, lacrimal

Contains eyeball, muscles, nerves, vessels, lacrimal glands, fat, fascia bulbi, and fascia holding structures in place

Lined by fibrous tissue

Pad of fat—supports eyeball

Fascia bulbi is a serous sac which envelops eyeball from optic nerve to ciliary region

Shaped like funnel — Large end directed outward and forward / Small end directed backward and inward

Optic foramen—opening for passage of optic nerve and ophthalmic artery

Superior orbital fissure—opening for passage of orbital branches of middle meningeal artery and oculomotor, trochlear, abducens, and ophthalmic nerves

Bulb of the Eye

Spherical, but it projects anteriorly

Coats
- (1) Fibrous—aclera and cornea
- (2) Vascular—choroid, ciliary body, and iris
- (3) Nervous—retina

Refracting media
- (1) Cornea and aqueous humor
- (2) Crystalline lens and capsule
- (3) Vitreous body

Fibrous Tunics

Sclera
- Tough, fibrous, sclera
- Covers posterior five sixths of eyeball
- Opaque, white and smooth externally, brown internally

Cornea
- Fibrous, transparent—covers one sixth of eyeball
- Well supplied with nerve fibers

Vascular Tunic

Choroid
- Composed of dense capillary network and stroma of cells, some of which are pigmented, lines the sclera

Ciliary body
- Includes the orbicularis ciliaris, the ciliary processes, and the ciliaris muscle. The orbicularis ciliaris is a zone about 4 mm in width which is continuous with anterior part of choroid
- Ciliary processes 60–80 radiating folds, arranged like a plaited ruffle around margin of lens
- Support ciliaris muscle—action of this muscle determines shape or refractiveness of lens

Vascular Tunic (*cont.*)	**Iris**	A circular colored disk suspended in front of lens and behind cornea. Hangs free except for attachment at circumference to the ciliary processes and choroid. Central perforation—pupil Pupil contracted by circular, or sphincter, muscle Pupil dilated by radial, or dilator, muscle Composed of connective tissue, containing numerous blood vessels and nerves. Contains pigment cells **Function**—regulates size of pupil and thereby amount of light entering eye

Nervous Tunic, or Retina

Nervous layer—contains elements essential for reception of rays of light. Situated between the choroid coat and hyaloid membrane of the vitreous humor, extends forward and terminates in the *ora serrata*

Has three sets of neurons so arranged that seven layers are formed. These are held in place by neuroglia and two membranes. Counting from the hyaloid membrane (membrana limitans interna) outward

(1) Nerve fibers, or stratum opticum
(2) Cell bodies of third-order neurons, or ganglionic layer
(3) Area of synapses of second and third neurons, or inner plexiform layer
(4) Cell bodies of second neurons, or inner nuclear layer
(5) Areas of synapses between first and second neurons, or outer plexiform layer
(6) Cell bodies of first neurons, or outer nuclear layer
   Membrana limitans externa, marking internal limit of rods and cones
(7) Rods and cones of first neurons are end organs, or receptors, for the optic nerve
   Pigmented layer between rods and cones and choroid

Blind spot	Entrance of optic nerve and central artery and vein of the retina There are no rods and cones Totally insensitive to light
Macula lutea	2 mm outer side of blind spot Central pit—fovea centralis—is the center of direct vision

Refracting Media

Cornea	Transparent, refractive structure covering the anterior one sixth of the eye bulb
Aqueous humor	Aqueous chamber is between cornea in front and lens, suspensory ligament, and ciliary body behind. Aqueous humor is a watery solution containing minute amounts of salts Dialyzed from capillaries, drains away through canal of Schlemm
Crystalline lens	Transparent, refractive body enclosed in an elastic capsule Double convex in shape. Situated behind the pupil Held in position by counterbalancing of aqueous humor, vitreous body, and suspensory ligament
Vitreous body	Semifluid, albuminous tissue enclosed in hyaloid membrane Fills posterior four fifths of bulb of the eye, distends sclera, and supports retina

Perception of Light and Color		Waves started by the motion of molecules of hot bodies cause vibrations in ether
	Waves vary in length	Waves between 400 and 800 mμ in length are called light and color waves—the visual spectrum

Refraction—bending or deviation in the course of rays of light, in passing obliquely from one transparent medium into another of different density

Vision
Visible objects reflect light waves which fall upon them
These reflected rays are brought to focus on receptors (rods and cones) of retina, where a chemical change in rhodopsin and iodopsin initiates nerve impulses, which are transmitted to optic nerve, and thence to centers of vision in occipital lobe of cerebrum, from here to association areas
Various theories are suggested to account for vision
Color blindness due to abnormal cones

Processes Necessary for Binocular Vision
(1) Convergence, or turning the eyes inward, in order to place the image on corresponding points of the two retinae
(2) Change in size of pupil—contracts in a bright light—dilates in a dim light
(3) Accommodation—ability of the eyes and lens to adjust so that objects at varying distances can be seen clearly
(4) Refraction—bending of light rays entering the pupil so they come to a focus on the retina

Abnormal Conditions

Myopia
Nearsightedness
Cause—rays of light converge too soon

Hypermetropia
Farsightedness
Cause—rays of light do not converge soon enough

Presbyopia
Defective condition of accommodation in which distant objects are seen distinctly but near objects are indistinct

Astigmatism
Condition in which the curvature of the refracting surfaces is defective

The Structural and
Functional
Relationships for
Correlation and
Coordination of
Internal Activities.
Metabolism

CHAPTER 12

The Blood: Characteristics, Volume, Composition, Physiology

EACH of the enormous number of living cells which make up the body is supplied with materials to enable it to carry on its activities, and at the same time materials resulting from its activities are removed. Most cells are far from the source of supplies and the organs of elimination, hence the need of a medium to distribute supplies and collect materials not needed by them. This need is met by the blood and tissue fluid, which consist of cells and an intercellular liquid.

CHARACTERISTICS OF BLOOD

The most striking external feature of the blood is its well-known color, which is bright red, approaching scarlet in the arteries, but a dark-red or crimson in the veins.

It is a somewhat viscous or sticky liquid. Its viscosity is about $4\frac{1}{2}$ to $5\frac{1}{2}$ times that of water, or it flows approximately $4\frac{1}{2}$ to $5\frac{1}{2}$ times more slowly than water under the same conditions. It is a little heavier than water; its specific gravity varies between 1.041 and 1.067.[1] The blood of men has a somewhat higher specific gravity than that of women. In general 1.058 is taken as a fair average. It has a characteristic odor, a salty taste, a temperature of about

[1] The specific gravity of a liquid is the ratio of the weight of the liquid (blood, urine, etc.) compared with the weight of an equal volume of distilled water at $15°C$ ($60°F$), the weight of the water being considered 1.000.

38°C (100.4°F), and a pH value of from approximately 7.35 to 7.45.[2] These ranges cover the values for both arterial and venous blood.

Blood Volume. In the adult, blood volume has been estimated to be about one thirteenth body weight and plasma volume about one twentieth of body weight. Normally there is little variation in quantity of blood. The ratio between blood quantity and tissue-fluid quantity, however, is not constant. Probably many factors cause this ratio to change. An example is body response to changes in environmental temperature. It is thought that as environmental temperature rises the quantity of blood increases in relation to the tissue fluid, whereas with decrease in environmental temperature there is increase in tissue fluid with a decrease in blood quantity.

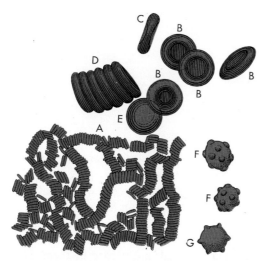

Figure 12–1. Erythrocytes of the blood, magnified. (*A*) Moderately magnified. The erythrocytes are seen lying in rouleaux. (*B*) Erythrocytes much more highly magnified, face view. (*C*) In profile. (*D*) In rouleau, more highly magnified. (*E*) An erythrocyte swollen into a sphere by imbibition of water. (*F*) Erythrocytes puckered or crenated all over. (*G*) Same at edge only.

The quantity of blood varies with age, sex, muscularity, adiposity, activity, state of hydration, condition of the heart and blood vessels, and many other factors. There are also wide and unpredictable individual variations. Plasma volume may be measured fairly accurately by laboratory methods. Prolonged bed rest results in a reduction in plasma volume. It has been estimated to be reduced from 300 to 500 ml. Peripheral venous pressure is also reduced, and fluid is lost from the blood to interstitial spaces.

Appearance of Blood. Seen with the naked eye, the blood appears opaque and homogeneous; but on microscopic examination, it is seen to consist of cells, or *corpuscles*, in an intercellular liquid, the *plasma*. The volume of cells and plasma is approximately equal. The percentage of the blood made up of *red blood* cells

---

[2] An alkaline solution is one in which the hydroxyl ions (OH⁻) are in excess of the hydrogen ions. An acid solution is one in which the hydrogen ions (H⁺) are in excess. A neutral solution is one in which the hydroxyl and hydrogen ions are in equal concentration. In physiology the concentration of hydrogen ions is expressed for convenience' sake as the hydrogen exponent (symbol pH). Substances having a pH of 7 are *neutral;* above, from 7 to 14, are increasingly *alkaline;* and below, from 7 to 1, are increasingly *acid.*

is called the hematocrit, the normal figure is $47\pm$ per cent. The ratio varies in relation to hydration and other clinical conditions. Averages for men are ±7; for women, ±5.

Erythrocytes. Under the microscope erythrocytes are seen to be homogeneous circular disks, without nuclei, and biconcave in profile. The average size is about 7.7 μ in diameter.[3] On microscopic examination, when viewed singly by transmitted light, they have a yellowish-red tinge. It is only when great numbers of them are gathered together that a distinctly red color is produced. Erythrocytes consist of a colorless, filmy, elastic framework, or stroma, in which hemoglobin is deposited, surrounded with a delicate membrane. The

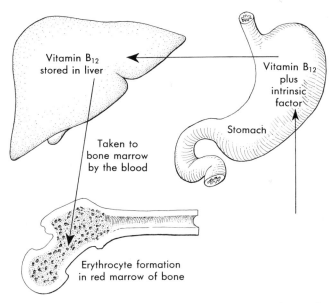

Vitamin B$_{12}$ stored in liver

Vitamin B$_{12}$ plus intrinsic factor

Stomach

Taken to bone marrow by the blood

Erythrocyte formation in red marrow of bone

Figure 12–2. Factors necessary for maturation of red blood cells.

stroma is composed of protein and lipid substances including cholesterol. The blood group substances A and B and the Rh antigen are located in the stroma. Erythrocytes are soft, flexible, and elastic, so that they readily squeeze through apertures and passages narrower than their own diameters and immediately resume their normal shape.

Origin of Erythrocytes—Hematopoiesis. In the embryo the first blood cells arise from mesenchymal cells in the yolk sac. The next phase of development is chiefly in the liver and to some extent the spleen. Hematopoiesis takes place in bone marrow at about the fifth month and decreases in the liver as it increases in red bone marrow. After birth red bone marrow is the only tissue concerned with red cell formation. (See p. 361 for stages in blood cell development.) Red

---

[3] The micron (symbol μ) equals $1/1000$ of a millimeter (0.001 mm).

cells arise from *endothelial cells* of the capillaries of the *red marrow* of bone called hemocytoblasts. The hemocytoblast loses its nucleus and cytoplasmic granules, becomes smaller, assumes the shape of the erythrocytes, and gradually develops hemoglobin before reaching the blood stream. Immature erythrocytes, reticulocytes, and normoblasts (nucleated) are sometimes found in blood.

The life-span of these cells is thought to be about 120 days. Sections of bone marrow show many stages of blood-cell formation. When and how the erythrocytes disintegrate are not known. One supposition is that as they age, they undergo hemolysis and fragmentation in the blood. Another is that they are destroyed in the spleen, lymph nodes, and liver. Most of the iron freed by the disintegration of erythrocytes is reused.

For complete maturation of the red cells vitamin B_{12} is necessary. The mucosa of the fundus of the stomach elaborates a substance called the *intrinsic factor.* The function of the intrinsic factor is to promote absorption of vitamin B_{12}, which is present in food. Absorbed vitamin B_{12} is the main antianemic principle in the liver. It is stored in the liver and liberated as needed, taken by circulation to the bone marrow where it functions enzymatically to complete the maturation of the red blood cell. Proteins, several vitamins, folic acid, copper, cobalt, and iron are essential for red cell formation.

Primary anemia, a pernicious anemia, results if the stomach fails to elaborate the intrinsic factor. Such anemias have been treated successfully by introducing purified vitamin B_{12} directly into the body by hypodermic injection.

Number of Erythrocytes.   The average number of erythrocytes in a cubic millimeter of normal blood is given as 5,500,000 to 7,000,000 for men and 4,500,000 to 6,000,000 for women. This would give about 20,000,000,000,000 as the total number in the blood of the body. Since the area of one cell is approximately 0.000128 sq m, the area of the total number of cells would be about 2,560 sq m. The figure frequently given is 25 trillion red blood cells with a total area of 3,200 sq m. Pathological conditions may cause a marked diminution in number, and differences have been observed in health. The number varies with altitude, temperature, nutrition, mode of life, and age, being greatest in the fetus and newborn child, and with the time of day, showing a diminution after meals.

Hemoglobin is comprised of a complex protein molecule named *globin* and a nonprotein portion named *heme* (hematin), which contains iron. One red cell contains several million molecules of hemoglobin. Since one molecule of hemoglobin contains four of iron, it can carry four molecules of oxygen. Hemoglobin combines with oxygen to form oxyhemoglobin. Under normal conditions the adult body produces about 6.25 gm of hemoglobin per day. The destruction of hemoglobin occurs coincidentally with that of the erythrocyte. The entire function of hemoglobin depends upon its capacity to combine with oxygen in the lungs and then release it readily in the capillaries of the tissues. In the tissues it picks up carbon dioxide.

Amount of Hemoglobin.   In adults 100 ml of normal blood contains on the average between 11.5 and 19 gm of hemoglobin—in males the average is 14 to

18 gm; in females, 11.5 to 16 gm. It has been suggested that 16.6 gm be taken as 100 per cent. In children (4 to 13 years old) the average is 12 gm; at birth it is about 17.2 gm of hemoglobin per 100 ml of blood. The *percentage of hemoglobin* can be obtained by comparing the color of blood with standard color comparators.

Hemolysis, or Laking. Disruption of the erythrocyte membrane leads to the cell's hemoglobin content going into solution in the plasma. This process is hemolysis, or laking. The resulting colorless erythrocytes are referred to as "ghosts." Substances that cause this action are called hemolytic agents. Hemolysis may be brought about (1) by hypotonic solutions, which diminish the concentration of substances in the plasma, (2) by the action of foreign blood serums, (3) by such agents as snake venom, the products of defective metabolism, the products of bacterial activity, or immunizing substances produced within the body, (4) by the addition of ether or chloroform, (5) by the addition of salts or fatty acids, (6) by the addition of bile salts, (7) by alternate freezing and thawing, (8) by amyl alcohol or saponin, and (9) by ammonia and other alkalis. Erythrocytes which have lost their hemoglobin are incapable of serving as oxygen carriers.

Genesis of the Red Cell

Hemocytoblast in red marrow
↓ forms the
Basophil erythroblast;
  | it then
↓ changes to
Polychromatophil
  erythroblast;
   | nucleus continues to shrink;
  ↓ more hemoglobin is formed;
Normoblast
  | nucleus disappears.
  ↓ Changes to
Reticulocyte;
  | continued
  ↓ maturation;
Erythrocyte

Synthesis of hemoglobin begins in this cell—
  nuclear changes begin

These cells have a mixture of basophilic material
  and red hemoglobin

Cytoplasm of normoblast becomes concentrated
  to about 35% hemoglobin

These cells have a delicate reticulum; a few enter
  the blood stream

Mature red cell

Substances needed for formation and maturation include amino acids, folic acid, iron, copper, zinc, vitamin B_{12}, and enzymes.

Color index is an expression which indicates the amount of hemoglobin in each erythrocyte compared with the amount considered normal for the cell. Color index is significant in the anemias, especially in pernicious anemia.

Functions of Erythrocytes. The erythrocytes have many functions, such as carrying oxygen to the tissues, carrying carbon dioxide from the tissues, and maintaining normal acid-base balance (pH value), viscosity, and specific gravity. In the capillaries of the lungs hemoglobin becomes fully saturated with oxygen, forming oxyhemoglobin. The erythrocytes carry this oxyhemoglobin to the capillaries of the tissues, where they give up the oxygen. Here part of the oxyhemoglobin becomes reduced hemoglobin and is ready to be carried to the lungs for a fresh supply of oxygen. The color of the blood is dependent upon the combination of the hemoglobin with oxygen; when the hemoglobin has its full complement of oxygen, the blood has a bright-red hue, and when the amount is decreased, it changes to a dark-crimson hue. The scarlet blood is usually found in the arteries and is called arterial; the dark-crimson is in the veins and is called venous blood.

Polycythemia. The condition in which there is an increase of erythrocytes above the normal is called polycythemia. Conditions associated with cyanosis and residence in high altitudes are usually followed by polycythemia. It is thought that low atmospheric pressure existing in high altitudes decreases the ability of hemoglobin to combine with oxygen, and this reduction of oxygen tends to stimulate the formation of new cells. This result represents the chief benefit anemic people derive from residence in high altitudes.

In shock due to diffusion of plasma to tissues, after profuse perspiration, diarrhea, and loss of body fluids from other causes, there is an apparent (not real) increase in erythrocytes, due to a decreased amount of plasma.

Anemia. This term is applied to conditions associated with a deficiency of erythrocytes or a deficiency of hemoglobin in the cells. A deficiency of erythrocytes results from (1) hemorrhage, (2) hemolysis, or (3) inability to produce new erythrocytes due to lack of nutritious food, diseases of the bone marrow, and various infections.

Insufficient iron in the diet may be one cause of anemia. Foods rich in iron include brain and visceral meats such as beef liver, heart, and gastric mucosa. Certain vegetables, such as kale, spinach, lentils, peas, and beans, and cereals, such as oatmeal and whole-grain wheat, contain a high percentage of utilizable iron.

White Blood Cells, or **Leukocytes.** White cells are minute ameboid cells, variable in size. They have been called the mobile units of the reticuloendothelial system. Some of them are formed in the red bone marrow and others are formed in lymphatic tissue.

The number of white cells in a cubic millimeter of blood is from 5,000 to 9,000 (about 1 white to 700 red). An increase in number is designated as *leukocytosis* and occurs in such infections as pneumonia, appendicitis, or other acute infection. A decrease in the number of leukocytes is designated as *leukopenia*.[4] It is a characteristic symptom of typhoid fever. Physiological leukocytosis up to 10,000 occurs under normal conditions, such as digestion, exercise, pregnancy, and cold baths. More than 10,000 per cubic millimeter usually indicates pathological leukocytosis.

Varieties of White Cells. White cells may be classified in many ways, depending upon structure, cytoplasmic granules, and their reaction to dyes.

	Number	Kind	Size
	Granulocytes 60–70%	Neutrophils	9–12µ
White		Eosinophils	10–14µ
Cells		Basophils	8–10µ
	Agranulocytes	Small	7–10µ
	Lymphocytes 20–30%	Large	Up to 20µ
	Monocytes 5–8%	Mononuclear	9–12µ
		Transitional	

[4] This should not be confused with *leukemia*, a disease characterized by an increase in the white cells of the blood. *Temporary* increases to 20,000 or more after exercise, etc., are thought to be due to changes in circulation.

GRANULOCYTES, or GRANULAR LEUKOCYTES, show marked pseudopodial movement. They are formed in red marrow from the myeloblast.

1. Neutrophils, or polymorphonuclear leukocytes, have a nucleus that is lobulated, and the granules of the cytoplasm stain with neutral dyes. They form from 55 to 65 per cent of the total number of leukocytes. They ingest bacteria (*phagocytosis*) and in the adult are formed in the marrow tissue.

2. Eosinophils are similar in size and structure to the neutrophils, but the granules of the cytoplasm are larger and stain with acid dyes such as eosin. Normally they are present in small numbers (2 to 4 per cent), but under certain pathological conditions they show a marked increase. It is thought they arise in the bone marrow, as do the neutrophils. After the administration of ACTH there is a decrease in the number of circulating eosinophils. Therefore, eosinophil counts are important, as they give evidence of adrenal function. Eosinophils are increased in certain allergic conditions.

3. Basophils are formed in bone marrow, have a polymorphic nucleus, and the granules of the cytoplasm stain with basic dyes. They are found in small numbers (½ per cent). Their function is unknown. However, their number increases during the healing process of inflammation and during chronic inflammatory processes. Basophils contain relatively large amounts of histamine (about one half of the histamine content of normal blood).

LYMPHOCYTES are formed in reticular tissue of lymph nodes and spleen and enter the blood stream from capillaries or via the thoracic duct. Their cytoplasm is nongranular, and the nucleus is large. Small lymphocytes are more numerous than large ones. The number of lymphocytes is high in early life, decreasing from about 50 per cent to about 35 per cent of the leukocytes at 10 years. The role of the lymphocytes in body defense is probably related to their ability to be transformed into macrophages at the site of tissue inflammation. Lymphocytes can also change into tissue histiocytes and into fibroblasts. The lymphocytes are also concerned with the formation of antibodies. The administration of the glucocorticoids causes atrophy of lymph nodes and depresses production of lymphocytes. In certain infectious diseases and local infections lymph node activity and resultant increase in circulating lymphocytes form a protective mechanism.

MONOCYTES include the large mononuclear and transitional types. They are large cells, each with an indented eccentric nucleus, and they can function effectively as phagocytes. Recent studies show that they have potentialities for tissue growth, development of enzyme systems, and ability to synthesize protein. The monocyte is formed chiefly in bone marrow.

Ameboid Movement. The neutrophils and monocytes possess the power of making ameboid movements, which has earned for them the name of "wandering" cells. White blood cells can squeeze through the walls of capillaries into surrounding tissues by the process called *diapedesis;* it occurs normally but is greatly stimulated and increased by pathological conditions. Diapedesis also refers to the migration of red blood cells through the walls of capillaries.

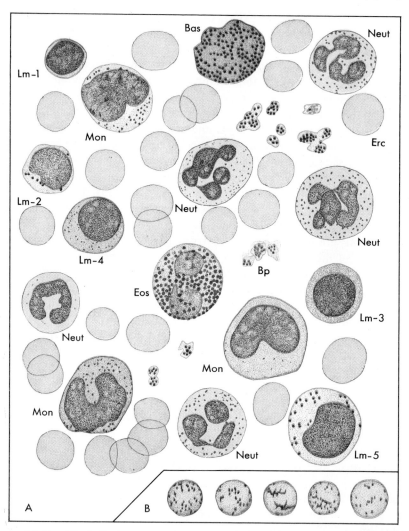

Figure 12–3. (*A*) Cells from normal human blood (Wright's stain). (*Bas*) Basophil leukocyte, (*Bp*) aggregations of blood platelets, (*Eos*) eosinophil leukocyte, (*Erc*) erythrocytes, (*LM 1–5*) lymphocytes (*1–3* are small and medium sizes and *4–5* are the less numerous larger forms), (*Mon*) monocytes, (*Neut*) neutrophil leukocytes. (*B*) Reticulocytes from normal human blood stained with dilute cresyl blue. (Modified from *Bailey's Textbook of Histology*, 13th ed., revised by P. E. Smith and W. M. Copenhaver. Courtesy of The Williams and Wilkins Company.)

Functions of the White Cells. The functions of the white blood cells are many and are incompletely understood. Important functions include: (1) They help to protect the body from pathogenic organisms. It is believed that they either ingest bacteria and thus destroy them directly, or that they form certain substances, called *bacteriolysins*, which have the power of dissolving them. Leukocytes which ingest bacteria are called *phagocytes*, and the process is *phagocytosis*. The neutrophils are thought to be most active in attacking bacteria; Metchnikoff[5] called them *microphages*. According to some authorities phagocytosis depends on certain substances in the blood known as opsonins which prepare bacteria for the ingestion by the leukocytes. (2) They cooperate in promoting tissue repair and regeneration. It is thought that the cells of connective and epithelial tissue cannot obtain material for growth directly from the blood. The leukocytes, however, can synthesize growth-promoting substances directly from the blood. It is proposed to call these substances *trephones*.

Genesis of Leukocytes

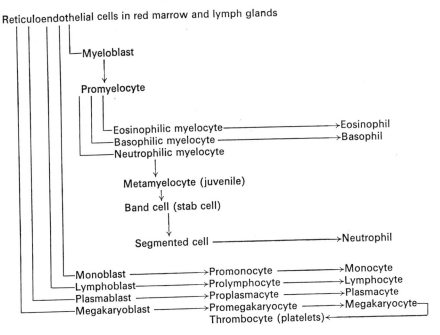

The proportion of the different classes of leukocytes in the blood varies during disease conditions, especially during infections. Differential counts have a great practical value in diagnosis.

The leukocytes do not swim, but "crawl"; hence they need surfaces such as capillary walls and connective tissue fibers to crawl on for their motion. In observation of blood flow through vessels in the frog they are seen to hug the vessel wall, whereas the red cells remain in the center of the stream.

Life Cycle of White Cells. Little is known of the life period of white cells, which is probably very short, but they are thought to be destroyed in the spleen, liver, and bone marrow. In the absence of infection neutrophils are believed to

[5] Elie Metchnikoff, Russian biologist (1845–1916).

Characteristics and Functions of the White Blood Cells

Name	Size	Number	Where Formed	Nucleus	Cytoplasm	Motility	Function
Lymphocytes 3 mo to 3 yr 3 yr to 5 yr 5 yr to 15 yr Adults	Small 7–10μ Large up to 20μ	52–64% 34–48% 28–42% 20–30%	Reticular tissue of lymph glands and nodes ; spleen ; bone marrow and other lymph tissue	Very large, single, generally spherical, may be indented. Sharply defined. Stains blue Paler nuclei	Stains pale blue. Occasional scattered reddish-violet granules. Cytoplasm abundant	Movement active in connective tissue. Leave blood stream in large numbers, especially in fasting	Form serum globulin, both beta and gamma. Form antibodies at site of inflammation. Can change into a macrophage or plasma cell
Monocytes	16–20μ	6–8%	Lymph glands, spleen	Single, lobulated or deeply indented, or horse-shoe shaped. Stains blue	Abundant—cytoplasm—stains a gray blue	Marked. Migrate readily through capillary walls into the connective tissues	Phagocytic for the bacilli of tuberculosis Phagocytic properties for cell debris and foreign material excellent Young cells most active

	Size	Percent	Origin	Nucleus	Cytoplasm/Granules	Motility/Migration	Function
Granular leukocytes, neutrophils Filamented types have 2 or more lobes in nucleus; nonfilamented types, 1 lobe	9–12μ	55–65%	In bone marrow from neutrophilic myelocytes	Lobulated—1 to 5 or more lobes. Stains deep blue. Number of lobes is significant in relation to the relative degree of maturity of cells	Fine neutrophilic granules in cytoplasm—pink cast	Marked. Migrate from blood stream. Believed to be removed from blood stream by reticuloendothelial system	Phagocytic properties extreme for many bacteria. Increased in infections and inflammatory conditions. Represents degree of toxic absorption. They make powerful proteolytic ferments. By disintegration and rupture of the cell itself become pus corpuscles. Lost in saliva, uterine secretions, as they destroy excess spermatozoa
Eosinophils	10–14μ	1–3%	In bone marrow from eosinophilic myelocytes	Shape irregular. Stains blue, but less deeply than neutrophils. Usually 2 lobes in nucleus	Sky-blue tinge with many coarse, uniform, round or oval bright-red granules	Less marked. Often extravascular, especially in fluids under the linings of respiratory and digestive tracts	No phagocytic action. Increased in infection by animal parasites, especially worms. Number decreased by glucocorticoids
Basophils	8–10μ	0.25–0.7%	In bone marrow from basophilic myelocytes	Light purple, indented or slightly lobulated, centrally located. Quite hidden by granules	Mauve color with many large deep-purple granules	Least motile Contain relatively large amounts of histamine	Function unknown

have a life-span of less than a day. The neutrophils may remain in the marrow reserve four or five days after development. It may take about four or five days to progress from a myeloblast to a segmented cell. It is possible that monocytes have a longer life-span and persist in areas of local infection considerably longer than neutrophils. Lymphocytes are believed to have a life-span of several months.

Characteristics and Functions of the White Blood Cells. Little is known of the functions of leukocytes while in the blood stream. However their function becomes apparent outside the vascular system. The movement of all leukocytes is identical with that of the ameba.

Inflammation. When tissues become inflamed either from injury or from infection, there is irritation, followed by an increased supply of blood to the part. If the irritation continues or is severe, the flow of blood slackens, and a condition of stasis, or engorgement, results. The leukocytes become active and migrate in large numbers through the walls of the blood vessels (diapedesis) into the infected tissues. Some of the blood plasma exudes, and a few erythrocytes are forced through the capillary walls. This constitutes inflammation; and the symptoms of redness, heat, swelling, pain, and loss of function are due to irritation caused by the toxins of the bacteria, to the increased supply of blood, to the engorgement of the blood vessels, and to the collection of fluid in the tissues (edema), which is spoken of as inflammatory exudate. Under these conditions a death struggle between the leukocytes and bacteria takes place. If the leukocytes win, they kill the bacteria, remove every vestige of the struggle, and find their way back to the blood. This process of recovery is described as *resolution* and is dependent upon the individual's resistance, i.e., the rapid formation of phagocytes, opsonins, etc. If the bacteria are victorious, large numbers of phagocytes and tissue cells will be destroyed, and *suppuration*, i.e., the formation of pus, ensues. *Pus* consists of dead and living bacteria, phagocytes, necrotic tissue, and material that has exuded from the blood vessels.

Also, in the case of a wound, the leukocytes accumulate in the region of the wound and act as barriers against infection. When inflammation is deep and the local symptoms cannot be observed, knowledge of the increase of the white cells is of assistance in determining the severity of the infection and the degree of resistance being offered by the body. This requires not only an absolute count, i.e., the total number of white cells in 1 cu mm of blood, but also the differential count, i.e., the relative number of each type of leukocytes, particularly the number of neutrophils. In making a *differential count*, the number of each kind of white cells in 100 is counted. A high absolute count with a high neutrophil percentage indicates severe infection and good body resistance. A high absolute count with a moderate neutrophil percentage indicates a moderate acute infection and good resistance. A low absolute count with a high neutrophil percentage indicates severe infection and weak resistance.

Blood platelets, or **thrombocytes,** are fragments of the cytoplasm of large megakaryocytes, a type of cell formed in red marrow. Thrombocytes are disk-shaped bodies about 2 to 4 μ in diameter. In edge view they appear as short rods; in face view, as round plates. The average number is about 400,000 per cubic millimeter of blood. Platelets can stick to foreign bodies in the circulation. Platelet agglutination is probably the first step in thrombus formation in arteries or veins. The sticking together of platelets seals small leaks in injured blood vessels and hence prevents further loss of blood.

Function. When exposed to air or rough surfaces (conditions accompanying a wound and hemorrhage), large numbers of blood platelets disintegrate and granules are released. These particles together with many other factors rapidly convert prothrombin to thrombin. When platelets disintegrate, histamine, nor-epinephrine, and serotonin are liberated. These substances have vasoconstrictor activity and hence play a role in control of bleeding.

Blood plasma is a complex fluid of a clear amber color. It contains a great variety of substances, as might be inferred from its double relation to the cells, serving as it does as a source of nutrition and as a means of removing products of metabolism.

Water. About nine tenths of the plasma is water. This proportion is kept fairly constant by water intake and water output by the kidneys. There is also the continual exchanges of fluid which take place between the blood, inter-cellular tissue fluid, and the cells. It has a specific gravity of 1.026, viscosity about five to six times greater than water, and pH of 7.4 with an average range of 7.32 to 7.41.

Blood Proteins. The hemoglobin of erythrocytes represents about two thirds of the blood proteins, and plasma proteins, about one third.

The Plasma Proteins. There are three major types of proteins in the plasma of circulating blood: serum albumin, serum globulin, and fibrinogen. Globulin and fibrinogen belong to a group of globulins and hence have many properties in common. Serum albumin belongs to a group of albumins.

Formation of Plasma Proteins. Practically all of the serum albumin and fibrinogen are formed in the liver. Plasma cells are the main (if not the sole) source of immune globulins.

The normal range of concentration of the plasma proteins is from 6.8 to 8.5 gm per 100 ml of plasma. These figures vary with age; in premature infants the concentration is low. There is a gradual increase with age. Normal levels are established at about 18 to 20 months.

Serum albumin forms about 53 per cent of the total plasma proteins. Globulins form about 43 per cent and fibrinogen about 4 per cent of the total plasma pro-teins.

It has also been found that in human plasma, serum albumin is the most mobile protein component. Next in line are alpha globulin, beta globulin, and fibrinogen. Gamma globulin is the least mobile (labile). The liver forms plasma proteins rapidly, as much as 100 gm in 24 hours. However, the synthesis of plasma proteins by the liver depends on the concentration of amino acids in the blood.

Function. The blood proteins serve to maintain colloidal (oncotic) charac-teristics of blood and give it viscosity. All of the plasma proteins, but especially serum albumin, are concerned with the regulation of blood volume. They are responsible for the colloidal osmotic pressure (oncotic) which provides the "pull pressure" of the plasma essential for holding and pulling water from the tissue fluid into the blood vessels. Plasma proteins serve as a source of nutrition for the tissues of the body, and contribute to the solution and transport of lipids, fat-soluble vitamins, bile salts, and hormones in the blood through the formation of complexes.

Immune substances are associated with serum globulin. Fibrinogen is essential for blood clotting. The plasma proteins aid in the regulation of acid-base balance.

Prothrombin is a plasma globulin, found in the blood in a concentration of about 15 mg per 100 ml. It is formed continually in the liver and is used by the body for the coagulation of blood. Vitamin K is essential for its synthesis.

Heparin is a conjugated polysaccharide that is secreted into the blood continuously by the *mast cells* found in the connective tissue surrounding capillary networks. It is a powerful anticoagulant. It prevents the change of prothrombin to thrombin and destroys thrombin.

Nutrients.   These are the end products resulting from the digestion of food —amino acids, glucose, and neutral fats. Under normal conditions amino acids are present in a small proportion; glucose concentration is from 80 to 120 mg per 100 ml of blood. Temporary increases in these amounts may follow the ingestion of a large quantity of food.

Cholesterol is found in all tissues and body fluids. Its source in the body is (1) from absorption in the intestinal tract from saturated fats (exogenous cholesterol) and (2) from formation in large quantities by the cells, especially liver cells (endogenous cholesterol). It is an essential component of all cells, especially nerve tissue.

Cholesterol is used by the liver to form cholic acid, which in turn helps to form bile salts; in the adrenal gland to form cortical hormones; by the ovaries to form progesterone and perhaps estrogen; and by the testes to form testosterone. Large quantities of cholesterol are precipitated in the corneum of the skin. Cholesterol and other lipids in the skin help prevent water evaporation.

The *electrolytes* found in the blood are derived from food and from the chemical reactions going on in the body. The most abundant is sodium chloride. (See Chap. 22.)

Gases.   Dissolved gases—oxygen, nitrogen, and carbon dioxide—are found in the blood. Carbonic acid is continually entering the blood from the tissues. However, the blood contains certain buffer substances, i.e., sodium bicarbonate, sodium phosphate, protein, hemoglobin, and others, which enter into combination with the carbon dioxide so that only a small percentage is present in simple solution.

Antibodies.   This term is applied to substances that are antagonistic to invading organisms. Antibodies are formed in all parts of the reticuloendothelial system, especially in the lymph nodes, the lymphoid tissue of the gastrointestinal tract, the liver, the spleen, and the bone marrow. The site of formation is related to the portal of entry of the invading organism (antigens). Lymphocytes can change into plasma cells and become active in antibody formation.

Recovery from many infections is due to an accumulation of these substances in the blood and to the effectiveness of the phagocytes in destroying the invading organisms. When bacteria enter the body, they stimulate the production of antibodies. Antibodies may be classified as (1) lysins, which act by dissolving organisms, (2) opsonins, which aid the white cells by sensitizing or preparing the organisms for ingestion, and (3) agglutinins, which clump the organisms in masses. Antitoxins are also classed as antibodies, because they neutralize the toxins formed by pathogenic organisms. The antibodies existing in the blood at any given time depend upon the condition of health, recovery from infection, etc.

Summary—Composition of Blood Plasma

Electrolytes

Cations	mEq/L	Proteins, gm per cent	
Sodium	138–142	Serum albumin	5–6
Potassium	4–5	Serum globulin	3
Calcium	4.5–5	Fibrinogen	0.4
Magnesium	2	Nonprotein Nitrogen, mg per cent	
Anions	mEq/L	Urea	26
Chloride	103	Uric acid	3
Phosphates	2	Creatinine	1.0
Sulfates	1	Creatine	0.4
Bicarbonates	27	Ammonium salts	0.2
Organic acid	6	Nutrients, gm per cent	
Protein	16	Glucose	80–120
Other Minerals		Lactic acid	7–8
Iron ⎤		Amino acids	5–6
Copper ⎬ Traces		Fatty acids	368–370
Iodine ⎦		Cholesterol	150–182
Enzymes ⎤ Variable		Phospholipids	200
Vitamins ⎬ concentrations		Cerebrosidin	15
Hormones ⎦		Lecithin	10–15
⎧ Variable in		Water	90% by volume
Antibodies ⎨ quantity and		*Gases*	
⎩ kind		Nitrogen	

Oxygen 2% (not very soluble)
Carbon dioxide 60–64% (soluble)

Functions of the Blood.   Blood is the transporting medium of the body. The functions as commonly listed are:

It carries oxygen from the lungs to the tissues and carbon dioxide from the tissues to the lungs.

It carries to the tissues nutritive materials absorbed from the intestine and transports them to the tissues for utilization.

It carries products formed in one tissue to other tissues where they are used. In other words, it transports hormones to the tissues requiring them.

It carries the products of metabolism to the organs of excretion—the lungs, kidneys, intestine, and skin.

It aids in maintaining the temperature of the body at the normal level.

It aids in maintaining the normal acid-base balance of the tissues.

It constitutes a defense mechanism against the invasion of harmful organisms.

It aids in maintaining fluid balance between blood and tissues.

It clots, preventing loss of blood after trauma (hemostasis).

The Clotting of Blood

Blood drawn from a living body is fluid. It soon becomes viscid and, if left undisturbed, forms a soft jelly. As the cells settle out of the plasma, a pale, straw-colored liquid begins to form on the surface, and finally the entire jelly separates into a firm mass, or *clot*, and a liquid called *blood serum*. If a portion of the clot is examined under the microscope, it is seen to consist of a network of fine needle-like fibers, in the meshes of which are entangled the red and some of the white cells. As the clot shrinks, the red cells are held more firmly by this network; but some of the white cells, owing to their power of ameboid movement, escape into the serum. The needlelike fibers are composed of fibrin. Many theories have been advanced to account for the formation of the insoluble fibrin from soluble fibrinogen. The exact process is not known, but it is thought to be comparable to the clotting of milk under the influence of rennin.

The Coagulation of Blood. The basic steps in the coagulation process include:

1. Thromboplastin and serotonin are released from injured tissues.

2. Thromboplastin initiates a series of chemical reactions which convert pro-thrombin into thrombin.

3. Thrombin functions as an enzyme to convert fibrinogen into fibrin threads that enmesh platelets, red cells, and plasma to form the clot.

Blood contains the substances antithromboplastin (antithrombin) and anti-prothrombin (heparin) concerned with *preventing* the clotting of blood in the blood vessels, and three substances concerned with the clotting of blood. These include (1) fibrinogen, (2) calcium ions, and (3) prothrombin (thrombogen). When blood clots, prothrombin and calcium ions form thrombin, and thrombin changes fibrinogen to fibrin, which is insoluble. The fibrin and the blood cells form the clot.

For the blood to clot, the two substances concerned with the prevention of clotting must be neutralized. These substances are neutralized by thromboplastin which is set free by the crushed tissue cells, the platelets, or thrombocytes, and the blood corpuscles. This accounts for the fact that blood clots only when tissues are wounded.

The following tables present the *factors* concerned with the clotting process and where they function.

The Factors Concerned with Blood Clotting

Probable Source	Factors	Synonyms and Description
Liver	I	Fibrinogen ; a globulin plasma protein
Liver	II	Prothrombin ; an albumin ; vitamin K essential for synthesis
Injured tissues and blood during coagulation process	III	Thromboplastin
Food	IV	Calcium
Liver	V	Proaccelerin ; a labile factor in plasma acceler-ator globulin (AcG)
	VI	(No six)
Liver	VII	Proconvertin; a stable factor; a globulin Serum prothrombin conversion accelerator (SPCA)

The Factors Concerned with Blood Clotting (*cont.*)

Probable Source	Factors	Synonyms and Description
Source unknown ; gene controlling production of VIII is on the X chromosome	VIII	Antihemophilic factor (AHF); a globulin, thromboplastinogen; plasma thromboplastic factor (PTF); platelet cofactor I
Liver	IX	Plasma thromboplastic component (PTC); a globulin ; Christmas factor (CF); platelet cofactor II
Liver	X	Stuart-Prower factor found in serum and plasma, not consumed during coagulation, is a globulin
Liver	XI	Plasma *thromboplastin* antecedent (PTA)
Liver	XII	Hageman factor ; when substance is absent, blood does not coagulate in a normal period of time on contact with a glass surface
	XIII	Fibrin-stabilizing factor

The genetic disorders related to blood coagulation include:

1. Antihemophilic factor (AHF) VIII deficiency causes 80 to 82 per cent of hemorrhagic disorders of the hemophilia type.

2. Plasma thromboplastin component (PTC) IX deficiency causes 11 to 15 per cent of hemorrhagic diseases.

3. Plasma thromboplastin antecedent (PTA) XI deficiency causes 5 to 7 per cent of hemorrhagic disorders.

Summary—Steps in the Coagulation of Blood

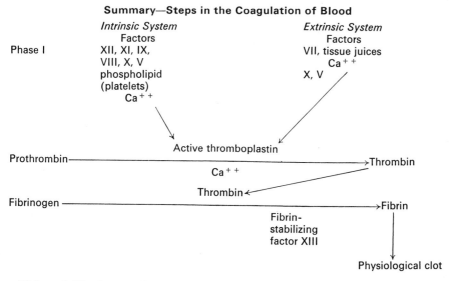

Value of Clotting. This property is of importance in arresting hemorrhage, the clot closing the openings of wounded vessels. The procedures used to check hemorrhage are directed toward hastening the formation of a clot and stimulating the blood vessels to contract so that a smaller-sized clot will be sufficient.

The time it takes for the blood of human beings to clot is usually about four to six minutes. Estimation of coagulation time is important as a preliminary to operation when there is any reason to expect dangerous capillary oozing, as in tonsillectomies or operations upon jaundiced persons. The normal time depends on type of test used. This time is known as *clotting time* and is used as a clinical index of the individual's blood-clotting properties. In rare individuals the blood does not clot readily or at all, so that any injury or operation involving hemorrhage is dangerous. This condition is called *hemophilia*. Only males suffer from this condition. Adult females are exempt from hemophilia, but they may transmit it to their offspring.

Conditions Affecting Clotting

1. *Clotting is hastened by:*

Injury to the walls of the blood vessels.

Contact with a rough surface or any foreign substance. Thus, clotting is hastened when gauze or a like substance is put into a wound.

The venom of certain snakes.

A temperature above 46°C (114.8°F) (e.g., the use of hot sponges or towels applied to a wound). This hastens clotting, probably by accelerating the formation of thrombin and the chemical changes of clotting.

Rest, which tends to prevent the dislodgment of clots forming at the opening of vessels. If blood is contained in a dish, agitation hastens the disintegration of the thrombocytes and thus favors the formation of tissue extract.

2. *Clotting is hindered by:*

Contact with the smooth lining of the heart and blood vessels.

A deficiency of the normal calcium salts.

The addition of citrates[6] or oxalates to the blood, because they interact with the calcium salts.

A very low temperature. Cold hinders the formation of a clot but is often used to check hemorrhage because it stimulates the blood vessels to contract.

A deficiency or abnormal condition of thrombocytes.

Concentrated solutions of such salts as magnesium sulfate, sodium sulfate, and sodium fluoride.

Leech extracts and the venom of certain snakes.

Low fibrinogen.

Deficiency of vitamin K. This vitamin is necessary for adequate production of prothrombin and proconvertin. Patients with obstructive jaundice may have prolonged clotting time because bile is necessary for the absorption of vitamin K from the intestine.

Removal of fibrin. If fresh blood, before it has time to clot, is whipped with a bundle of fine rods, fibrin will form on the rods. If the whipping of the blood is continued until all the fibrin has been removed, the blood will have lost the power of clotting. Such blood is called *defibrinated*.

Withdrawing the blood into a container lined with a coating of oil or paraffin.

---

[6] In transfusions the donor's blood is often rendered incoagulable as it is withdrawn by adding sodium citrate which reacts with the calcium of the blood to form calcium citrate, thus decreasing the amount of free calcium available for the clotting process.

Anticoagulants such as heparin and bishydroxycoumarin (Dicumarol). These are frequently given to retard the clotting process. Heparin is believed to retard conversion of prothrombin to thrombin. It does not affect bleeding time. Bishydroxycoumarin inhibits prothrombin synthesis in the liver.

Why Blood Does Not Clot Within the Blood Vessels. In accordance with the theory of clotting which has been considered, blood does not clot within the blood vessels because of: the absence of thrombloplastin and the presence of antiprothrombin and antithrombin.

Bleeding Time. If the ear lobe is punctured, blood will drip from the wound. In normal individuals the bleeding will stop spontaneously in a very few minutes. The time required for cessation of bleeding is called bleeding time. This process is controlled by vascular constriction and perhaps a platelet factor rather than by coagulation. Normal bleeding time is about 1 to 4 min.

Intravascular Clotting. It is well known that clots occasionally form within the blood vessels. The most frequent causes are:

1. Any foreign material, even air, that is introduced into the blood and not absorbed may stimulate the formation of thrombin and a clot.

2. When the internal coat of a blood vessel is injured, as for instance by a ligature or the bruising incidental to operations, the endothelial cells are altered and may act as foreign substances. If in addition there is a stasis of blood at this point, disintegration of the blood platelets and white cells may result in the formation of thrombin and a clot. The products of bacteria and other toxic substances may injure the lining of a blood vessel and produce the same result. Inflammation of the lining of a vein is called *phlebitis*.

Thrombus and Embolus. A clot which forms inside a blood vessel is called a thrombus, and the condition is called *thrombosis*. A thrombus may be broken up and disappear, but the danger is that it may lodge in the heart or certain parts of the brain, where it blocks circulation and causes instant death. A thrombus that becomes dislodged from its place of formation is called an embolus. Such a condition is called *embolism*.

Hemorrhage. During hemorrhage blood pressure falls and the heart rate is accelerated in an effort to maintain cardiac output. The liver and spleen give up all possible blood to increase venous return. If hemorrhage is not controlled, there is further reduction in arterial blood pressure. Vasoconstriction is marked, the pulse is thready and rapid, the skin clammy and cold, the individual is restless, anxious, and air hungry. Blood flow to the tissues is decreased and the cell needs in relation to oxygen are not met.

The ischemic kidney from any cause initiates the secretion of renin, a vasoexcitatory material (VEM). Renin in the presence of enzymes converts angiotensin I to angiotensin II which constricts arterioles and raises blood pressure. In this way blood supply to the kidney is increased. If hemorrhage has not been controlled and pressure continues to fall, the arterioles and precapillary sphincters relax and open and more blood moves into the capillaries. When this occurs, there is danger of irreversible shock due to hemorrhage.

Regeneration of the Blood after Hemorrhage. During hemorrhage it is probable that a healthy individual may recover from the loss of blood amounting to 3 per cent of the body weight. Experiments on animals show that the plasma of blood regains its normal volume within a few hours after a slight hemorrhage and within 24 to 48 hours if much blood has been lost. The number of red cells and hemoglobin are restored slowly, returning to normal after a number of days or even weeks.

When the need for increased volume is urgent, infusions of blood or other fluids are given.

Intravenous infusion is the injection of a solution directly into a vein. Physiological salt solution and various electrolyte solutions that approximate plasma concentration are used for this purpose. The solution is frequently introduced into the veins of the dorsal side of the hand or the cephalic or the median basilic vein. These veins are usually the largest, the most prominent, and nearest to the surface of the arm.

The disadvantage of intravenous infusion of normal saline is that the results effected are temporary, water being rapidly lost to the tissues, rendering them edematous. Infusion of blood plasma gives more permanent and satisfying results. In emergencies plasma expanders can be used as plasma substitutes.

Transfusion is the transfer of blood from one person (the donor) to another (the recipient). This may be accomplished by (1) the direct method, in which the blood flows through tubing from a needle inserted into the donor's vein to a needle inserted into the recipient's vein, or (2) the indirect method, more frequently used, in which donor's blood is withdrawn in a flask and prevented from clotting by the use of sodium citrate. It is then injected intravenously. Before blood is used, several laboratory tests are necessary: a blood-typing test, including Rh, for blood of recipient and donor should be of the same type; a test for isohemolysins in the serum, which would hemolyze red cells; a Wassermann test to exclude the possibility of transmitting syphilis; and other laboratory blood tests.

Blood Typing

Blood typing, or classification into groups, is dependent upon agglutination of blood cells. Figure 12–4 tabulates laboratory findings when blood of various types is added to serum of a known type. It also shows all combinations of agglutinogens and agglutinins possible in blood. To explain this phenomenon, blood cells are said to contain two substances called antigens or agglutinogens, designated by the capital letters A and B. Serum is said to have two antibodies called agglutinins, designated by a and b. Clumping occurs when an agglutinogen and an agglutinin of the same letter come into contact. These groups, or types, have been variously designated. Systems of nomenclature in current use are shown below with their relationship to the agglutinogens and agglutinins in each type. Landsteiner[7] named the groups in terms of the agglutinogens in the cells. He indicated the existence of other groups or subdivisions of these groups, for instance, the M, N, and S factors. The M, N, S system is of less importance.

The descriptive names O, A, B, AB are in terms of the agglutinogens in the cells.

Classification of Blood Groups, Landsteiner's Findings

Antigens in Red Cells (agglutinogens)	Antibodies in Serum (agglutinins)	Blood Group Name	Incidence in Caucasians
O	a and b	O	45
A	b (anti B)	A	41
B	a (anti A)	B	10
AB	None	AB	4

[7] Karl Landsteiner, Austrian physician and researcher in America (1868–1943).

Blood types are determined by adding whole blood to serum of a known type. If the cells are agglutinated by serum a, agglutinogen A must be present; similarly, agglutination with serum b indicates blood of type B. As indicated in Figure 12–4, in practice it is necessary only to use serum a and serum b to test for the four blood groups. These are the major blood groups; there are many subgroups. The most important are A_1 and A_2. The recognized subgroups are A_1, A_2, A_1B, and A_2B. About 80 per cent of individuals in group A belong to subgroup A_1; 20 per cent belong in subgroup A_2; about 60 per cent of individuals in group AB belong in subgroup A_1B and 40 per cent belong to A_2B.

Cross Matching. Before a blood transfusion is given, as a safety measure, cross matching is done to determine compatibilities. This means that a suspension of red cells from the donor and a small amount of defibrinated serum from the recipient are mixed together to determine whether or not agglutination occurs. A second test is done to cross-match the cells of the recipient to the serum of the donor. If no agglutination occurs, it can be assumed that the blood

AGGLUTININS IN SERUM

Figure 12–4. Blood typing. When agglutinogen A meets agglutinin a, or when agglutinogen B meets agglutinin b, agglutination takes place.

CELLS	ab	b	a	o
O	—	—	—	—
A	+	—	+	—
B	+	+	—	—
AB	+	+	+	—

(AGGLUTINOGENS)

+ agglutination
— absence of agglutination

of the donor and the blood of the recipient are of the same type.

The Rh Factor. Landsteiner and other researchers have discovered an agglutinogen in human blood which is also present in the rhesus monkey. For this reason it is called the Rh factor. In the United States, a study of the white population shows that about 85 per cent are Rh-positive and 15 per cent are Rh-negative. There are several subgroups of Rh-positive blood.

In giving a blood transfusion, if an Rh-negative person receives Rh-positive blood, the recipient will develop an anti-Rh agglutinin which may cause hemolytic reaction. Anti-Rh agglutinins are similar to the a and b agglutinins in their action, as they attach to Rh-positive red blood cells and cause them to agglutinate.

The major Rh types in blood include Rh_0, Rh', and Rh'' factors. The Rh_0 antigen is the one that is strongly antigenic. A person is considered to be Rh negative when his blood does *not* contain Rh factors.

According to the Fisher-Race concept, there are three sets of allelic genes, C and c, D and d, E and e; every person inherits a total of three genes from each parent, one gene from each pair. The resultant possible codes of genes gives cde, Cde, cdE, CdE, cDe, CDe, cDE, and CDE. Using all possible combinations, there are 36 different genotypes possible. Persons who have the D (Rh$_0$) antigen are considered as Rh positive and those who do not have the D (Rh$_0$) antigen are considered as Rh negative (Rh' = C; Rh″ = E).

The Hr Factor. When the Rh factor is absent, as in Rh-negative blood, another factor is present, designated as the Hr factor, to indicate relationship to Rh. There are three Hr factors, all of which are weakly antigenic. Rh antibodies are not normally found in blood plasma.

Inheritance of Rh factors

Mother Rh −   ×   Father Rh+
Rh − −   Rh+ +

— +
— +

Possibilities—all children will type for Rh positive but carry a recessive gene.

Mother Rh −   ×   Father Rh+, but carries a
                                                                recessive gene

+ −

— +
— −

Possibilities—there is a 50–50 chance that children will carry recessive genes and a 50–50 chance that the children will carry a dominant gene for Rh+.

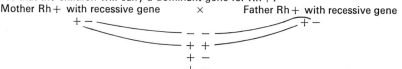

Mother Rh+ with recessive gene   ×   Father Rh+ with recessive gene
+ −   + −

— −

+ +
+ −
+ −

Possibilities—three children will type for Rh positive, but *two* will carry a recessive gene. One child will be Rh negative.

It is also believed that most cases (about 90 per cent) of *erythroblastosis fetalis* are caused by the production of anti-Rh agglutinins in the mother's blood (if the mother is Rh negative and the father is Rh positive, the child may be Rh positive). It is thought that leakage of agglutinogens through fetal circulation into mother's circulation causes formation of anti-Rh agglutinins which in turn destroy the red cells of the fetus. However, not all children born of such parents develop hemolytic reactions.

Blood groups are inherited, as mendelian dominants; therefore group O is recessive to groups A, B, and AB.

In the embryo agglutinogens are found in the red blood cells about the sixth week. At birth the concentration is about one fifth of the adult level. Normal concentrations are reached during adolescence. Agglutinins as a rule are not present in the blood of the newborn. Specific agglutinins are formed in blood plasma within two weeks and reach the highest concentration at about 10 years of age. Agglutinin concentration is variable in all individuals at all ages. Once established, blood groups do not change—that is, once a group B always a group B.

QUESTIONS FOR DISCUSSION

An individual has lost a considerable amount of blood and blood transfusions have been ordered.

1. Why is it important that whole blood be given?
2. Under what circumstances may plasma or a plasma expander be given?
3. How much blood may a donor give and what physiological responses occur in the donor to replace the blood lost?
4. Discuss the life cycle of the red blood cells.
5. What are the functions of:
   a. Red blood corpuscles?
   b. White blood cells?
   c. Platelets?
6. What are the functions of plasma proteins?
7. Why is it necessary to have a laboratory report on cross matching, blood groups, and Rh factors before a transfusion can be done?
8. What is cross matching?

SUMMARY

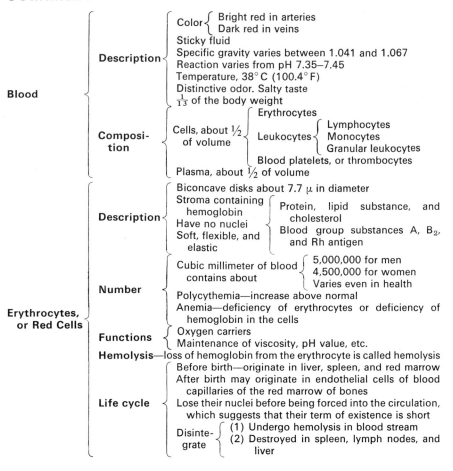

Blood

Description
Color { Bright red in arteries / Dark red in veins
Sticky fluid
Specific gravity varies between 1.041 and 1.067
Reaction varies from pH 7.35–7.45
Temperature, 38° C (100.4° F)
Distinctive odor. Salty taste
$\frac{1}{13}$ of the body weight

Composition
Cells, about ½ of volume {
Erythrocytes
Leukocytes { Lymphocytes / Monocytes / Granular leukocytes
Blood platelets, or thrombocytes
Plasma, about ½ of volume

Erythrocytes, or Red Cells

Description
Biconcave disks about 7.7 μ in diameter
Stroma containing hemoglobin { Protein, lipid substance, and cholesterol / Blood group substances A, B_2, and Rh antigen
Have no nuclei
Soft, flexible, and elastic

Number
Cubic millimeter of blood contains about { 5,000,000 for men / 4,500,000 for women / Varies even in health
Polycythemia—increase above normal
Anemia—deficiency of erythrocytes or deficiency of hemoglobin in the cells

Functions
Oxygen carriers
Maintenance of viscosity, pH value, etc.

Hemolysis—loss of hemoglobin from the erythrocyte is called hemolysis

Life cycle
Before birth—originate in liver, spleen, and red marrow
After birth may originate in endothelial cells of blood capillaries of the red marrow of bones
Lose their nuclei before being forced into the circulation, which suggests that their term of existence is short
Disintegrate { (1) Undergo hemolysis in blood stream / (2) Destroyed in spleen, lymph nodes, and liver

379

Erythrocytes, or Red Cells (*cont.*)

- **Hemoglobin**
  - Complex protein molecule
  - Combines with oxygen to form oxyhemoglobin
  - Body forms 6.25 gm per day
  - **Function**—transports oxygen to tissue cells and carbon dioxide from tissue cells

White Cells

- **Description**
  - Minute masses of nucleated protoplasm
  - Variable in size, sometimes smaller than red cells; majority are larger
  - Gray in color
- **Number**
  - Cubic millimeter of blood
    - 5,000 to 9,000
    - Increase = leukocytosis
    - Decrease = leukopenia
- **Varieties**
  - Lymphocytes
    - (*a*) Small
    - (*b*) Large
  - Monocytes
    - (*a*) Large mononuclear
    - (*b*) Transitional
  - Granular leukocytes
    - (*a*) Polymorphonuclear, or neutrophils
    - (*b*) Eosinophils, or acidophils
    - (*c*) Basophils
- **Functions**
  - Supposed to be different for different forms
  - (1) Protect the body from pathogenic bacteria
  - (2) Promote tissue repair
  - (3) Aid in absorption from intestine
- **Life cycle**
  - Lymphocytes arise from the reticular tissue of the lymph tissue of the body
  - Granular leukocytes arise from cells of bone marrow
  - Numbers lost in
    - (1) Battles against bacteria
    - (2) Hemorrhage
    - (3) Formation of granulation tissue or tissue regeneration

Inflammation

- (1) Irritation resulting from injury or infection
- (2) Increased supply of blood
- (3) Engorgement of blood vessels
- (4) Migration of white cells
- (5) Exudation of plasma
- **Symptoms**
  - Redness
  - Heat
  - Swelling
  - Pain
  - Loss of function
- **Result**
  - (*a*) Resolution—white cells destroy bacteria, clear up debris, and return to blood
  - (*b*) Suppuration—bacteria destroy white cells and form pus
  - (*c*) Pus consists of
    - Bacteria
      - Dead
      - Living
    - Phagocytes
    - Disintegrated tissue cells
    - Exudate from blood vessels

Blood Platelets, or Thrombocytes

- **Description**
  - Disk-shaped bodies. Always smaller than red or white cells
  - Formed from megakaryocytes in bone marrow by fragmentation of the cytoplasm
  - Assist in clotting of blood

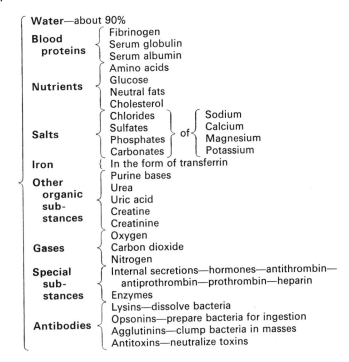

Plasma
- Water—about 90%
- **Blood proteins**
  - Fibrinogen
  - Serum globulin
  - Serum albumin
- **Nutrients**
  - Amino acids
  - Glucose
  - Neutral fats
  - Cholesterol
- **Salts**
  - Chlorides
  - Sulfates
  - Phosphates
  - Carbonates
  of
  - Sodium
  - Calcium
  - Magnesium
  - Potassium
- **Iron** — In the form of transferrin
- **Other organic substances**
  - Purine bases
  - Urea
  - Uric acid
  - Creatine
  - Creatinine
- **Gases**
  - Oxygen
  - Carbon dioxide
  - Nitrogen
- **Special substances**
  - Internal secretions—hormones—antithrombin—antiprothrombin—prothrombin—heparin
  - Enzymes
- **Antibodies**
  - Lysins—dissolve bacteria
  - Opsonins—prepare bacteria for ingestion
  - Agglutinins—clump bacteria in masses
  - Antitoxins—neutralize toxins

Functions of Blood
- Carries oxygen from lungs to tissues
- Carries carbon dioxide from tissues to lungs
- Carries food material to tissues
- Carries hormones and internal secretions
- Carries waste products to organs of excretion
- Aids in maintaining normal temperature
- Aids in maintaining acid-base balance of tissues
- White cells and globulins constitute defense mechanism against infection
- Aids in maintaining internal fluid pressure
- Clots, preventing loss of blood after trauma

Clotting
- Serum—blood minus fibrin and cells
- **Factors**
  - Contains 13 factors concerned with the clotting of blood
  - Intrinsic system—factors XII, XI, IX, VIII, X, V, IV
  - Extrinsic system—factors VII, IV, X, V
  - Thromboplastin activated
  - Prothrombin converted to thrombin
  - Active thrombin converts fibrinogen to fibrin
- **Process**
  - Cellular elements of blood and tissues → tissue extract
  - Thromboplastin neutralizes antithrombin and antiprothrombin
  - Prothrombin + calcium ions + thromboplastic substance + platelet accelerator → thrombin
  - Thrombin + serum activator → active thrombin
  - Active thrombin + fibrinogen + platelet factor → insoluble fibrin
  - Fibrin + cells of blood → clot
- Value—checks hemorrhage

Clotting (*cont.*)	**Hastened by**	Injury to the walls of the vessels Contact with a rough surface or any foreign material The venom of certain snakes A temperature above 46° C (114.8° F) Rest Agitation
	Hindered by	Contact with smooth lining of vessels A deficiency of the normal calcium ions The addition of citrates or oxalates to the blood A very low temperature A deficiency or abnormal condition of the thrombocytes Concentrated solutions of magnesium sulfate, sodium sulfate, and sodium fluoride Deficiency of vitamin K Leech extracts and the venom of certain snakes Low fibrinogen Removal of fibrin Reception in vessel coated with oil or paraffin

Bleeding Time
- **Definition** — Time required for cessation of bleeding after an injury (1 to 4 min)
- **Process** — Vasoconstriction and a platelet factor

Intravascular Clotting
- **Theory to account for absence of clotting**
  - Absence of tissue extracts
  - Presence of antithrombin and antiprothrombin
- **Causes**
  - Any foreign material introduced into blood and not absorbed will stimulate clotting
  - Injury to internal coat of blood vessels
- **Thrombus**—name given to clot which forms inside vessel
- **Embolus**—A thrombus that has become dislodged from place of formation

Regeneration of Blood After Hemorrhage — Plasma is regenerated rapidly, red cells within a few days or weeks

Treatments to Increase Volume of Blood
- **Hypodermoclysis**—injection of fluids into subcutaneous tissue
- **Intravenous infusion**—injection of solution into vein
- **Transfusion**—transfer of blood of one person to another

Blood Typing
- *Unknown blood* to be typed, after dilution, with citrated saline, is added to *known b* (anti B) *serum* and *a* (anti A) *serum*
- **Unknown belongs to**
  - Group O—no agglutination
  - Group A—agglutination in a serum only
  - Group B—agglutination in b serum only
  - Group AB—agglutination in b serum and a serum
- Group O—universal donor
- Group AB—universal recipient

Cross Matching — Suspension of cells from donor cross-matched with defibrinated serum of recipient and serum of donor cross-matched with cells of recipient

Rh Factor — **Population**
- 85% positive
- 15% negative

CHAPTER 13

The Cardiovascular System: Anatomy of the Heart, Arteries, Capillaries, Veins

THE BLOOD circulates continuously throughout the body in a network of blood vessels. It is driven along these blood vessels by the action of the heart, which is placed in the center of the vascular system. The arteries conduct the blood out from the heart and distribute it to the different parts of the body; the veins bring it back to the heart again. From the arteries the blood flows through a network of minute vessels, the capillaries, into the veins. The whole forms a closed system of tubes.

THE HEART

The heart is a hollow, muscular organ, situated in the thorax between the lungs and above the central depression of the diaphragm. It is about the size of the closed fist, shaped like a blunt cone, and so suspended by the great vessels that the broader end, or base, is directed upward, backward, and to the right. The pointed end, or apex, points downward, forward, and to the left. As placed in the body, it has an oblique position, and the right side is almost in front of the left. The impact of the heart during contraction is felt against the chest wall in the space between the fifth and sixth ribs, a little below the left nipple, and about 8 cm (3 in.) to the left of the median line.

The Heart Wall. The heart wall is composed of (1) an outer layer, the *epicardium*, (2) a middle layer, the *myocardium*, and (3) an inner layer, the *endocardium*. The epicardium is the serous membrane or visceral pericardium.

Pericardium. The heart is covered by a serous membrane called the pericardium. It consists of two parts: (1) an external fibrous portion and (2) an internal serous portion.

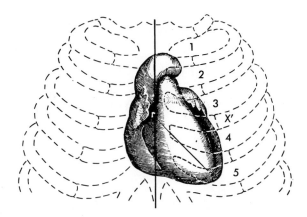

Figure 13–1. Heart in situ. (*1, 2, 3, 4, 5*) Intercostal spaces; vertical line represents median line. The space outlined by the triangle indicates the superficial cardiac region; *X'* shows the location of the nipple on the fourth rib. (Modified from Dalton.)

1. THE EXTERNAL FIBROUS pericardium is composed of fibrous tissue and is attached by its upper surface to the large blood vessels which emerge from the heart. It covers these vessels for about 3.8 cm (1½ in.) and blends with their sheaths. The lower border is adherent to the diaphragm, and the front surface is attached to the sternum.

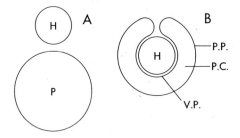

Figure 13–2. Diagram of the heart and serous pericardium. *A* shows the heart and pericardium lying separately. *B* shows the pericardium invaginated by the heart; (*P.C.*) pericardium cavity which actually is a very narrow space filled with pericardial fluid; (*P.P.*) parietal layer that lines the fibrous pericardium; (*V.P.*) visceral layer that clings close to the heart muscle.

2. THE INTERNAL, or SEROUS, PORTION of the pericardium is a completely closed sac; it envelops the heart and lines the *fibrous* pericardium. The heart, however, is not within the cavity of the closed sac (Fig. 13–2). The portion of the serous pericardium which lines it and is closely adherent to the heart is called the *visceral* portion (*viscus*, an organ); the remaining part of the serous pericardium, namely, that which lines the fibrous pericardium, is known as the *parietal* portion (*paries*, a wall). The visceral and parietal portions of this serous membrane are everywhere in contact. Between them is a small quantity of pericardial fluid preventing friction as their surfaces continually slide over each other with the

constant beating of the heart. The pericardial fluid may aid in cushioning the heart, which is especially important with rapid bodily movements.

Endocardium. The inner surface of the cavities of the heart is lined by a thin membrane called endocardium. It is composed of endothelial cells. It covers the valves, surrounds the chordae tendineae, and is continuous with the lining membrane of the large blood vessels. The endocardium contains many blood vessels, a few bundles of smooth muscle, and parts of the conducting system. Inflammation of the endocardium is called *endocarditis.*

Myocardium. The main substance of the heart is cardiac muscle, called myocardium. This tissue includes the muscle bundles of (1) the atria, (2) the ventricles, and (3) the atrioventricular bundle (of His).[1] Inflammation of the myocardium is known as myocarditis.

1. The principal muscle bundles of the atria radiate from the area which surrounds the orifice of the superior vena cava. One, the interatrial bundle, connects the anterior surfaces of the two atria. The other atrial muscle bundles are confined to their respective atria, though they merge more or less.

2. The muscle bundles of the ventricles begin in the atrioventricular fibrous rings. They form U-shaped bundles with the apex of the U toward the apex of the heart. There are many of these bundles, but for general description they may be divided into four groups. One group begins at the *left* atrioventricular ring, passes toward the right and the apex, where it forms whorls, and then ends either in the left ventricular wall, the papillary muscles, or the septum and the right ventricular wall (Fig. 13–3).

A second bundle repeats this path except that it starts at the *right* ventricular ring, passes to the left in the anterior wall of the heart, and ends in the same structures as above.

These two groups form an outer layer which winds around both ventricles. Under these is a third group of muscle bundles which again wind around both ventricles. There is a fourth group of muscle bundles which wind around the left ventricle. (See Fig. 13–3.) Thus the left ventricle has a much thicker wall than the right. During contraction the squeeze of the spirally arranged muscle bundles forces blood out of the ventricles.

3. The muscular tissue of the atria is not continuous with that of the ventricles. The walls are connected by fibrous tissue and the atrioventricular bundle of modified muscle cells. This bundle arises in connection with the atrioventricular (AV) node, which lies near the orifice of the coronary sinus in the right atrium. From this node the atrioventricular bundle passes forward to the membranous septum between the ventricles, where it divides into right and left bundles, one for each ventricle. In the muscular septum between the ventricles each bundle divides into numerous strands, which spread over the internal surface just under the endocardium. The greater part of the atrioventricular bundle consists of spindle-shaped muscle cells. The significance of the atrioventricular bundle is discussed on page 445.

---

[1] Wilhelm His, Jr., German physiologist (1863–1934).

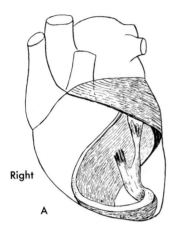

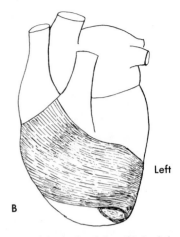

A, B. Note how the two groups of muscle fibers wind around both the right and the left ventricles on the outside.

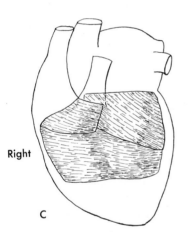

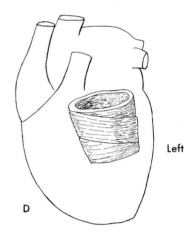

C. Note how the second layer of muscle fibers winds around both the right and left ventricles.
D. Note that the innermost layer winds around the left ventricle only.

Figure 13–3. Diagram showing arrangement of muscle fibers of the heart. When these muscles contract, what happens to blood in the ventricles? Position of heart more upright than normal. (Modified from Wiggers and Schaeffer.)

The Cavities of the Heart. The heart is divided into a right and a left half, frequently called the right heart and the left heart, by a muscular partition, the ventricular septum, which extends from the base of the ventricles to the apex of the heart. The atrial septum is inconspicuous. The two sides of the heart have no communication with each other after birth. The right side contains *venous* and the left side *arterial* blood. Each half is subdivided into two cavities: the upper, called the *atrium*, and the lower, the *ventricle*.

In keeping with the greater amount of work they must do in ejecting blood, the walls of the ventricles are thicker than those of the atria. The left ventricle ejects blood into the extensive systemic circulatory system under much higher pressure than is required of the right ventricle for ejecting blood into the relatively short pulmonary circulation. As may be expected, the left ventricle is much more muscular than is the right ventricle. (See Fig. 13–7.) Normally both the right and left sides of the heart contract and relax almost simultaneously.

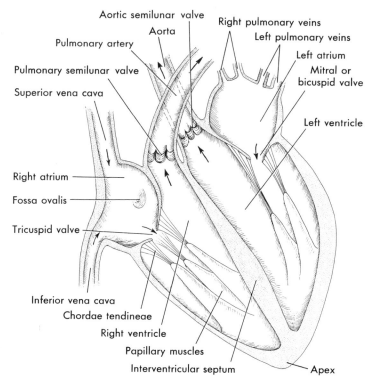

Figure 13–4. Longitudinal section of heart showing chambers and valves. *Arrows* indicate direction of blood flow.

Muscular columns, called the *trabeculae carneae (columnae carneae)*, project from the inner surface of the ventricles. They are of three kinds: The first are attached along their entire length and form ridges, or columns. The second is a rounded bundle; the moderator band (*trabecula septomarginalis*) projects from the base of the anterior papillary muscle to the ventricular septum. It is formed largely of specialized fibers concerned with the conducting mechanisms of the heart. It is prominent in the sheep's heart. The third are the *papillary muscles*, which are continuous with the wall of each ventricle at its base (Fig. 13–4). The apexes of the papillary muscles give rise to fibrous cords, called the *chordae tendineae*, which are attached to the cusps of the atrioventricular valves. These muscles contract when the ventricular walls contract.

Orifices of the Heart. The orifices comprise the left and right atrioventricular orifices and the orifices of eight large blood vessels connected with the heart.

On the right side of the heart, the superior and inferior venae cavae and coronary sinus empty into the atrium, and the pulmonary artery leaves the ventricle.

On the left side of the heart, four pulmonary veins empty into the atrium, and the aorta leaves the ventricle. There are some smaller openings to receive blood directly from the heart substance, and before birth there is an opening between the right and left atria called the *foramen ovale*. Normally this closes soon after birth. Its location is visible in Figure 25–15, page 753.

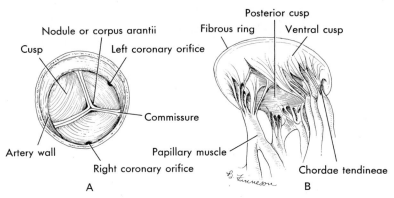

Figure 13–5. Valves of the left side of the heart. (*A*) Aortic valve closed, seen from above. (*B*) Mitral valve seen from below.

Valves of the Heart. Between each atrium and ventricle there is a somewhat constricted opening, the atrioventricular orifice, which is strengthened by fibrous rings and protected by valves. The openings into the aorta and pulmonary artery are also guarded by valves.

The Tricuspid Valve. The right atrioventricular valve is composed of three irregular-shaped flaps, or cusps, and hence is named *tricuspid*. The flaps are formed mainly of fibrous tissue covered by endocardium. At their bases they are continuous with one another and form a ring-shaped membrane around the margin of the atrial openings; their pointed ends project into the ventricle and are attached by the chordae tendineae to small muscular pillars, the papillary muscles, in the interior of the ventricles.

The Bicuspid Valve. The left atrioventricular valve consists of two flaps, or cusps, and is named the *bicuspid*, or *mitral*, valve. It is attached in the same manner as the tricuspid valve, which it closely resembles in structure except that it is much stronger and thicker in all its parts. Chordae tendineae are attached to the cusps and papillary muscles in the same way as on the right side; they are less numerous but thicker and stronger.

Physiology. The tricuspid and bicuspid valves freely permit the flow of blood from the atria into the ventricles because the free edges of the flaps are pointed in the direction of the blood current; but any flow forced backward gets between the flaps and the walls of the ventricles and drives the flaps upward until, meeting at their edges, they unite and form a complete transverse partition between the atria and ventricles. The valves remain open as long as the pressure of the blood is higher in the atria than in the ventricles. When the muscles of the ventricles

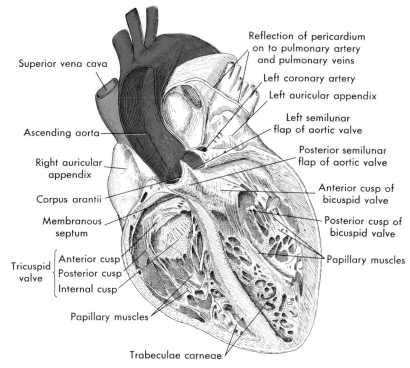

Figure 13–6. The heart, seen from the front. (Modified from Toldt.) What is the function of the right heart? The left heart? Why are valves needed?

begin to contract, the pressure in the ventricular chambers rises and the valves close. The valves are kept from everting into the atrial chambers by the chordae tendineae, which are kept taut by the papillary muscles.

Semilunar Valves. The orifice between the right ventricle and the pulmonary artery is guarded by the *pulmonary valve*, and the orifice between the left ventricle and the aorta is guarded by the *aortic valve*. These two valves are called *semilunar valves* and consist of three semilunar cusps, each cusp being attached by its convex margin to the inside of the artery where it joins the ventricle, while its free border projects into the lumen of the vessel. Small nodular bodies, called the *corpora Arantii*,[2] are attached to the center of the free edge of each pocket.

[2] Aranzio Arantius, Italian anatomist (1530–1589).

The aortic valve is larger and stronger, and the corpora Arantii are thicker and more evident. Between the cusps of the valve and the aortic wall are slight dilatations called the aortic sinuses or sinuses of Valsalva.[3] The coronary arteries have their origin from two of these sinuses.

PHYSIOLOGY. The semilunar valves offer no resistance to the passage of blood from the heart into the arteries, as the free borders project into the arteries, but they form a complete barrier to the passage of blood in the opposite direction. In this case each pocket becomes filled with blood, and the free borders are floated out and distended so that they meet in the center of the vessel. The corpora Arantii assist in the closure of the valves and help to make the barrier complete.

The orifices between the two caval veins and the right atrium and the orifices between the left atrium and the four pulmonary veins, are not guarded by valves. The opening from the inferior vena cava is partly covered by a membrane known as the caval (eustachian) valve.

Coronary Circulation. The blood vessels of the heart include the coronary arteries and coronary veins.

The *left coronary* artery has its origin in the left aortic sinus, runs under the left atrium, and divides into the anterior descending and circumflex branches. The anterior branch descends in the anterior interventricular sulcus to the apex, supplying branches to both ventricles. Occlusion of this artery is common. The circumflex runs in the left part of the coronary sulcus and curves around and nearly reaches the posterior sulcus. It supplies branches to the left atrium and ventricle.

The right coronary artery has its origin in the right aortic sinus and turns to the right under the right atrium to the coronary sulcus. There are two branches, the *posterior descending* and the *marginal branch.* Branches of the left and right coronaries anastomose and encircle the heart forming a crown, hence their name. They supply the heart muscle with blood. Blood within the cavities of the heart nourishes only the endocardium.

The Veins. The coronary sinus receives most veins of the heart and terminates in the right atrium.

The great cardiac veins begin at the apex and ascend to empty into the coronary sinus.

There are smaller veins: the small cardiac, middle cardiac, and posterior veins, which begin at the apex and ascend to enter the coronary sinus.

The mouths of the great and small cardiac veins have single cuspid valves, but are rarely efficient. Very small veins begin in the wall of the heart and open directly into the chambers of the heart (thebesian veins).

The Collateral Circulation. The channels of communication between the artery-capillary-vein system of the heart are complex and numerous. There are direct channels between the coronary arteries and the chambers of the heart. At the apex of the heart the descending branches of both coronaries form an im-

---

[3] Antonio Maria Valsalva, Italian anatomist (1666–1723).

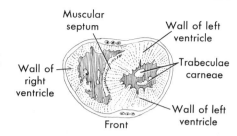

Figure 13–7. Cross section through ventricles, showing relative thickness of their walls and shape of cavities.

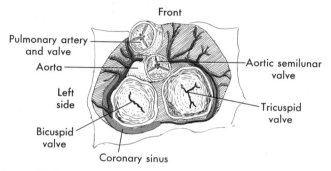

Figure 13–8. Valves of the heart as seen from above, atria removed.

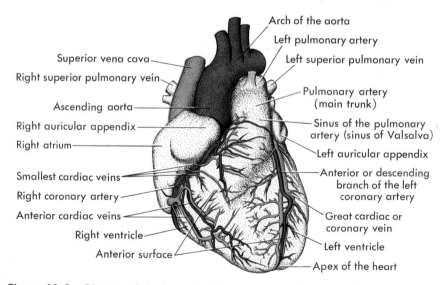

Figure 13–9. Diagram of the heart showing coronary arteries and veins. Anterior view. The great cardiac vein and artery indicate location of the septa. (Modified from Toldt.)

portant anastomosis. In the myocardium of the posterior wall of the heart, branches of the circumflex artery anastomose with branches of the right coronary. Thus two crowns are formed around the heart. Since adequate valves are not found in the coronary vessels, it is possible that blood may backflow into the myocardium and enter the chambers of the heart.

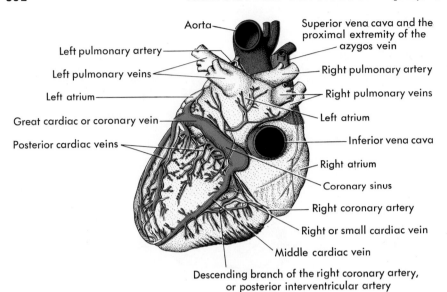

Figure 13–10.   Diagram of the heart showing the coronary sinus and large veins on the dorsal wall of the heart. Which ventricle is to the left in the diagram ? (Modified from Toldt.)

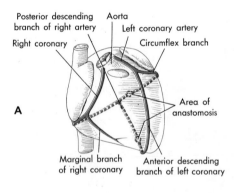

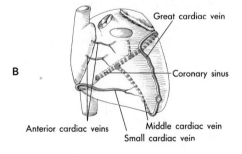

Figure 13–11.   Diagram showing coronary arteries (*A*) and veins (*B*) and their connections.

Nerve Supply. The heart is supplied with two sets of motor nerve fibers. One set reaches the heart through the vagus nerves of the craniosacral system. Nerve impulses over these fibers have a tendency to slow or stop the heartbeat and are called *inhibitory*. The other set is sympathetic, originating in the superior, middle,

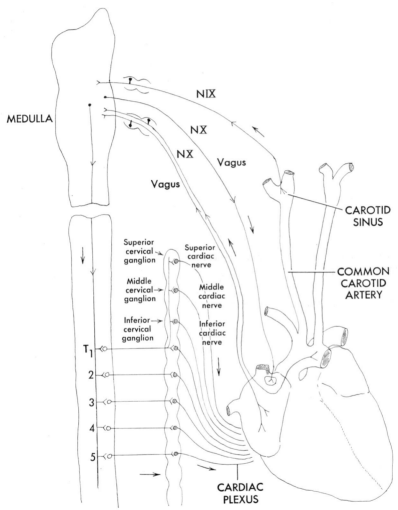

Figure 13–12. Diagram of the nerve supply to the heart. *Arrows* indicate the direction of nerve impulse travel.

and inferior cervical ganglia, forming the superior, middle, and inferior cardiac nerves. The visceral branches of the first five thoracic nerves have their cells of origin in the lateral column of gray of the spinal cord. These fibers terminate in the sympathetic ganglia. The postganglionic fibers pass to the heart where they quicken and augment the heartbeat and are called *accelerators*. The vagus nerve has its origin in a nucleus in the medulla. The accelerator nerves also have connections in the medulla and through these centers either set may be stimulated.

In addition, the heart is supplied with afferent nerve fibers: one set from the aortic arch, called *depressor* fibers; the other set from the right side of the heart, called *pressor* fibers. Both sets of afferent fibers run within the sheath of the vagi to the cardiac center in the medulla. Impulses over the depressor fibers bring about reflex inhibition of the heart—aortic reflex. Impulses over the pressor (sympathetic) fibers bring about reflex acceleration of the heart—right heart reflex.

Lymph Vessels. The heart is richly supplied with lymph capillaries, which form a continuous network from the endocardium, through the muscle layers to the epicardium. These capillaries form larger vessels which accompany the coronary blood vessels and finally enter the thoracic duct.

ARTERIES—STRUCTURE AND FUNCTION

The arteries carry blood from the heart to the capillaries. They are composed of three coats:

1. An inner coat (*tunica intima*) consists of three layers—a layer of endothelial cells, a layer of delicate connective tissue which is found only in vessels of considerable size, and an elastic layer consisting of a membrane or network of elastic fibers (Fig. 13–13).

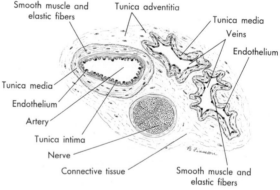

Smooth muscle and elastic fibers Tunica adventitia
Tunica media
Veins
Endothelium
Tunica media
Endothelium
Artery
Tunica intima
Nerve
Connective tissue
Smooth muscle and elastic fibers

Figure 13–13. Cross section through artery, veins, and nerve. Note differences in the structure of the walls of an artery and of a vein.

2. A middle coat (*tunica media*) consists mainly of smooth muscle fibers with various amounts of elastic and collagenous tissue. In the large arteries elastic fibers form layers which alternate with the layers of muscle fibers. In the largest arteries white connective-tissue fibers have been found in this coat.

3. The external coat (*tunica externa*, or *adventitia*) is composed of loose

connective tissue in which there are scattered smooth muscle cells or bundles of cells arranged longitudinally. In all but the smallest arteries this coat contains some elastic tissue. The structure and relative thickness vary with the size of the artery.

By virtue of the structure of the middle coat, the arteries are both extensile and elastic. The proper functioning of the arteries depends upon their extensibility and elasticity.

The great extensibility of the arteries enables them to receive the additional amount of blood forced into them at each contraction of the heart. Elasticity of arteries serves as a buffer to the large volume of blood forced into the system by the heartbeat. If these vessels were rigid (as is true in arteriosclerosis), the systolic blood pressure would be markedly increased.

The strength of an artery depends largely upon the outer coat; it is far less easily cut or torn than the other coats and serves to resist undue expansion of the vessel.

The arteries do not *collapse* when empty; and when an artery is severed, the orifice remains open. The muscular coat, however, contracts somewhat in the region of the opening; and the elastic fibers cause the artery to retract a little within its sheath, so as to diminish its caliber and permit a blood clot to plug the orifice. This property of a severed artery is an important factor in the arrest of hemorrhage.

Most of the arteries are accompanied by a nerve and one or two veins, all surrounded by a sheath of connective tissue, which helps to support and hold these structures in position.

Size of the Arteries. The largest arteries in the body, the aorta and pulmonary artery, measure more than 3 cm (1.2 in.) in diameter at their connection with the heart. These arteries give off branches which divide and subdivide into smaller branches. The smallest arteries are called *arterioles;* and at their distal ends, where only the internal coat remains, the capillaries begin. The arteriolar walls contain a great proportion of smooth muscle in relation to elastic tissue, and they are to be thought of as muscular rather than elastic.

The Elastic Arteries. These include the large arteries and are called *conducting* arteries because they conduct blood from the heart to the medium-sized arteries. The middle coat contains a large amount of elastic tissue, and the wall is comparatively thin for the size of the vessel.

The Muscular Arteries. These include the arteries of medium size, and their middle coat is chiefly muscular. Muscular arteries are also called *distributing* arteries because they distribute the blood to the various organs and by contraction or relaxation they aid in regulating the volume of blood passing to structures to meet varying functional demands.

Blood Supply of the Arteries. The blood which flows through the arteries nourishes only the inner coat. The external coat is supplied with arteries, capillaries, and veins, called *vasa vasorum,* or blood vessels of the blood vessels.

Vasomotor Nerves. The muscular tissue in the walls of the blood vessels is well supplied with nerve fibers, chiefly from the sympathetic portion of the autonomic system. These nerve fibers are called *vasomotor* and are divided into two sets: (1) vasoconstrictor and (2) vasodilator. They connect with the vasoconstrictor center in the medulla oblongata, which is constantly sending impulses to the vessels, thus keeping them in a state of tone. The vasoconstrictor center is a reflex center and is connected with afferent fibers coming from all parts of the body. Vasoconstrictor fibers are sympathetic and are widely distributed to arteries and arterioles. They mediate constriction of vessels, and by tonic action speed of blood flow is controlled. Vasodilator nerve fibers have several origins, and are found on the sympathetic, parasympathetic, and somatic sensory nerves. There is no direct evidence that they are tonically active, but they appear to "discharge selectively" when a local increase in blood flow is needed.

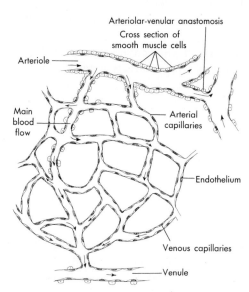

Figure 13–14. Diagram of capillary bed showing arteriole and venule. *Arrows* indicate direction of blood flow.

There is a diffuse network of sympathetic nerve fibers in the adventitia of all arteries, called the periarterial plexus. Nerve fibers are also present in the muscular coat. Arterioles are directly and completely under nervous control. By constriction of arterioles, blood flow is lessened. Pressure from increased volume, exerted on the blood stream in the muscular arteries, causes relaxation of the arterioles and more blood can move through to the capillary bed. The exact functioning of vasodilator nerve fibers is not well understood. Sudden, widespread relaxation of arterioles lowers blood pressure by decreasing peripheral resistance and shock may result.

Arterioles. As the arteries decrease in size and approach the capillary network, they are called arterioles. Proximal to the capillary channel there are modified arterioles called metarterioles. They have a wall which contains widely separated smooth muscle cells. A precapillary sphincter is located on the arteriole before it enters the capillary net. Arterioles are well supplied with vaso-constrictor fibers.

CAPILLARIES

The capillaries are exceedingly minute vessels which average about 7 to 9 μ in diameter. They connect the arterioles (smallest arteries) with the venules (smallest veins).

Structure. The walls of the capillaries consist of one layer of endothelial cells continuous with the layer which lines the arteries, the veins, and the heart. These cells are held together by cell cement. There is a substance called hyaluronic acid that forms a gelatinous material in the cell cement and tissue spaces. It holds cells together and binds water in the tissues.

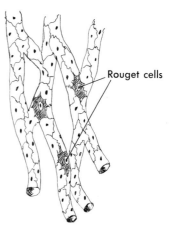

Rouget cells

Figure 13–15. Capillary networks form the means by which cells receive oxygen and nutrient materials. There are about 7000 sq m of capillaries in the adult.

Distribution. The capillaries communicate freely with one another and form interlacing networks of variable form and size in the different tissues. All the tissues, with the exception of the cartilages, hair, nails, cuticle, and cornea of the eye, are traversed by networks of capillary vessels. The capillary diameter is so small that the blood cells often must pass through them in single file, and very frequently the cell is larger than the caliber of the vessel and becomes distorted as it passes through. In many parts the capillaries lie so close together that a pin's point cannot be inserted between them. They are most abundant and form the finest networks in those organs where the blood is needed for purposes other than local nutrition, such as, for example, secretion or absorption. Electron micrographs show that the endothelial cells of capillaries have a variable number of pinocytic vesicles. These appear to be formed by invaginations of cell mem-branes during the process of "cell drinking," called pinocytosis.

Function. It is in the capillaries that the chief work of the blood is done; and the object of the vascular mechanism is to cause the blood to flow through these vessels in a steady stream. Krogh estimated that there are about 7,000 sq m of blood capillaries in the adult body. This gives a large area for exchange of substances between the blood and tissue fluid. In the glandular organs the capillaries supply the substances requisite for secretion; in the ductless glands they also take up the products of secretion; in the alimentary canal they take up some of the digested food; in the lungs they absorb oxygen and give up carbon dioxide; in the kidneys they discharge the waste products collected from other parts; all of the time, everywhere in the body, through their walls an interchange is going on which is essential to the life of the body. The greater the metabolic activity of the tissue, the denser the capillary nets.

VEINS—STRUCTURE AND FUNCTION

The veins carry blood to the heart and are formed by the confluence of the capillaries. The structure of the veins is similar to that of the arteries. They have three coats: (1) an inner endothelial lining, (2) a middle muscular layer, and (3) an external layer of areolar connective tissue. The main differences between the veins and arteries are: (1) the middle coat is not as well developed and not as

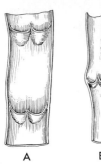

Figure 13–16. Diagram showing valves of veins. *(A)* Part of a vein, laid open, with two pairs of valves. *(B)* Longitudinal section of vein showing valves closed.

A   B

elastic in the veins; (2) many of the veins are provided with valves; (3) the walls of veins are much thinner than those of arteries and hence tend to collapse when not filled with blood.

Valves. The valves are semilunar folds of the internal coat of the veins and usually consist of two flaps, rarely one or three.

The convex border is attached to the side of the vein, and the free edge points toward the heart. Their function is to prevent reflux of the blood and keep it flowing in the right direction, i.e., toward the heart.

If for any reason the blood on its onward course toward the heart is driven backward, the refluent blood, getting between the wall of the vein and the flaps of the valve, will press them inward until their edges meet in the middle of the channel and close it. The valves are most numerous in the veins where reflux is most likely to occur, i.e., the veins of the extremities. For the same reason a greater number are found in the lower than in the upper limbs. They are absent in many of the small veins, in the large veins of the trunk, and in veins not subjected to muscular pressure. The veins, like the arteries, are supplied with blood vessels and sympathetic nerves.

It must be remembered that, although the arteries, capillaries, and veins each have the distinctive structure described, it is difficult to draw the line between the arteriole and the large capillary and between the large capillary and the venule. The veins, on leaving the capillary networks, only gradually assume their several coats, and the arteries dispense with their coats in the same imperceptible way as they approach the capillaries.

QUESTIONS FOR DISCUSSION

1. What is the normal circulation of blood through the heart and lungs? Where are the valves located and what is their function?
2. What might be the first indications or symptoms if the tricuspid valve fails to close completely? How would the symptoms differ if the mitral valve were involved? If the aortic valve failed to close completely?
3. What are the differences between arteries and veins? Compare in relation to structure, size, location, hydrostatic pressure, and blood flow.
4. How is heart rate controlled and what adjustments are necessary during muscular activity?

SUMMARY

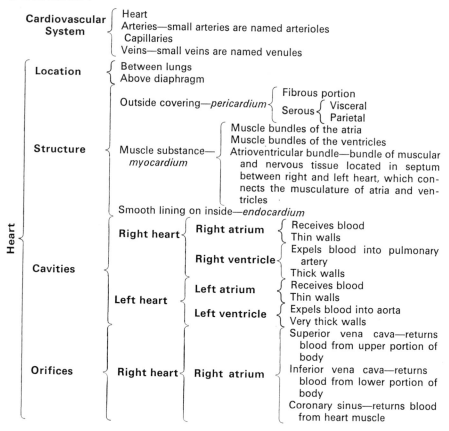

Cardiovascular System — Heart; Arteries—small arteries are named arterioles; Capillaries; Veins—small veins are named venules

Heart

Location — Between lungs; Above diaphragm

Structure —
Outside covering—*pericardium* — Fibrous portion; Serous — Visceral, Parietal

Muscle substance—*myocardium* — Muscle bundles of the atria; Muscle bundles of the ventricles; Atrioventricular bundle—bundle of muscular and nervous tissue located in septum between right and left heart, which connects the musculature of atria and ventricles

Smooth lining on inside—*endocardium*

Cavities —
Right heart —
Right atrium — Receives blood; Thin walls
Right ventricle — Expels blood into pulmonary artery; Thick walls

Left heart —
Left atrium — Receives blood; Thin walls
Left ventricle — Expels blood into aorta; Very thick walls

Orifices —
Right heart —
Right atrium — Superior vena cava—returns blood from upper portion of body; Inferior vena cava—returns blood from lower portion of body; Coronary sinus—returns blood from heart muscle

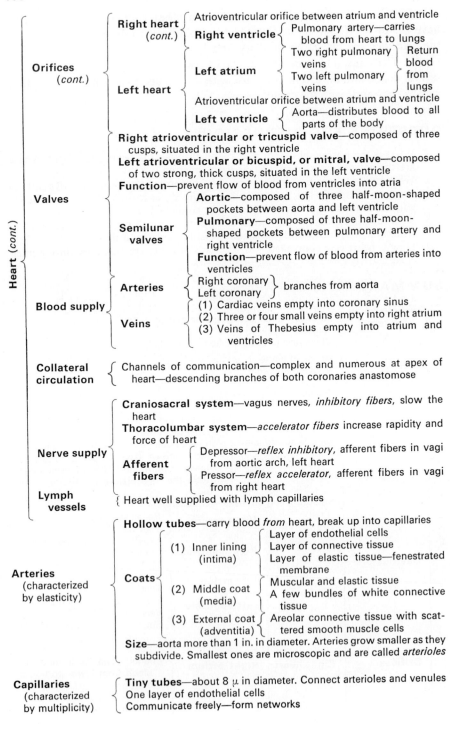

Heart (*cont.*)

Orifices (*cont.*)

Right heart (*cont.*)
- Atrioventricular orifice between atrium and ventricle
- **Right ventricle**
  - Pulmonary artery—carries blood from heart to lungs

Left heart
- **Left atrium**
  - Two right pulmonary veins } Return blood from lungs
  - Two left pulmonary veins
- Atrioventricular orifice between atrium and ventricle
- **Left ventricle**
  - Aorta—distributes blood to all parts of the body

Valves

Right atrioventricular or tricuspid valve—composed of three cusps, situated in the right ventricle

Left atrioventricular or bicuspid, or mitral, valve—composed of two strong, thick cusps, situated in the left ventricle

Function—prevent flow of blood from ventricles into atria

Semilunar valves
- **Aortic**—composed of three half-moon-shaped pockets between aorta and left ventricle
- **Pulmonary**—composed of three half-moon-shaped pockets between pulmonary artery and right ventricle
- **Function**—prevent flow of blood from arteries into ventricles

Blood supply

Arteries
- Right coronary } branches from aorta
- Left coronary

Veins
- (1) Cardiac veins empty into coronary sinus
- (2) Three or four small veins empty into right atrium
- (3) Veins of Thebesius empty into atrium and ventricles

Collateral circulation
- Channels of communication—complex and numerous at apex of heart—descending branches of both coronaries anastomose

Nerve supply
- **Craniosacral system**—vagus nerves, *inhibitory fibers*, slow the heart
- **Thoracolumbar system**—*accelerator fibers* increase rapidity and force of heart
- **Afferent fibers**
  - Depressor—*reflex inhibitory*, afferent fibers in vagi from aortic arch, left heart
  - Pressor—*reflex accelerator*, afferent fibers in vagi from right heart

Lymph vessels
- Heart well supplied with lymph capillaries

Arteries (characterized by elasticity)

Hollow tubes—carry blood *from* heart, break up into capillaries

Coats
- (1) Inner lining (intima)
  - Layer of endothelial cells
  - Layer of connective tissue
  - Layer of elastic tissue—fenestrated membrane
- (2) Middle coat (media)
  - Muscular and elastic tissue
  - A few bundles of white connective tissue
- (3) External coat (adventitia)
  - Areolar connective tissue with scattered smooth muscle cells

Size—aorta more than 1 in. in diameter. Arteries grow smaller as they subdivide. Smallest ones are microscopic and are called *arterioles*

Capillaries (characterized by multiplicity)
- **Tiny tubes**—about 8 μ in diameter. Connect arterioles and venules
- One layer of endothelial cells
- Communicate freely—form networks

Veins
(characterized
by valves)
{
Collapsible tubes—smallest ones, called *venules*, begin where
  capillaries end
Carry blood to heart
Three coats, same as arteries but thinner
Valves—semilunar pockets
}

Vasa vasorum—term applied to blood vessels that are supplied to coats of other blood
vessels

Vasomotor—term applied to *nerve fibers* supplied { Vasoconstrictor, well understood
to blood vessels   { Vasodilator, not as well understood

CHAPTER 14

Divisions of the Vascular System: Arteries, Veins, Portal System

THE ARCHITECTURAL ARRANGEMENT and structure of arteries and veins are important in the distribution of blood to and from the capillary beds where the real work of the vascular system is accomplished. The arteries deliver blood to the capillaries and the veins return it to the heart.

The arteries are distributed throughout the body in a systematic manner. The vessels leaving the heart are large but soon divide into branches. This division continues until minute branches are distributed to all parts of the body.

At each division the branches are smaller; but since they are numerous, the total of their diameters is much greater than that of the artery from which they sprang. This means that as the blood flows from the heart toward the capillaries it flows in an "ever-widening bed". The diameter of the aorta at the heart is usually given as 1 in.; the sum of the diameters of the systemic capillaries is about 600 to 800 in. The branches of the large arteries leave them at abrupt angles; the branches of the smaller arteries take progressively less abrupt changes of direction.

Division. The way in which the arteries divide varies. (1) An artery may give off several branches in succession and still continue as a main trunk, e.g., the thoracic or abdominal portion of the aorta. (2) A short trunk may subdivide into several branches at the same point, e.g., the celiac artery. (3) An artery may divide into two branches of nearly equal size, e.g., the division of the aorta into the two common iliacs.

402

Anastomosis.   The distal ends of arteries unite at frequent intervals, when they are said to anastomose. Such anastomoses permit free communication between the currents of the blood, tend to obviate the effects of local interruption,

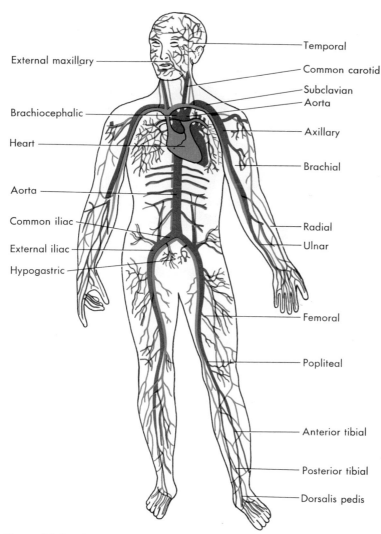

Figure 14–1.   A general diagram of the circulation. Many arteries are named.

and promote equality of distribution and of pressure. Anastomoses occur between the larger as well as the smaller arteries. Where great activity of the circulation is necessary, as in the brain, two branches of equal size unite; e.g., the two vertebral arteries unite to form the basilar (Fig. 14–12, p. 416). In the abdomen, the intestinal arteries have frequent anastomoses between their larger branches.

In the limbs, anastomoses are most numerous around the joints, the branches of the arteries above uniting with branches from the arteries below.

Anastomoses are of importance to the surgeon. By their enlargement, a collateral circulation is established after an artery is ligated. This means that subsidiary vascular channels, which are present in the circulatory network, form a secondary circulation through a part. The effectiveness with which these new channels transport blood varies.

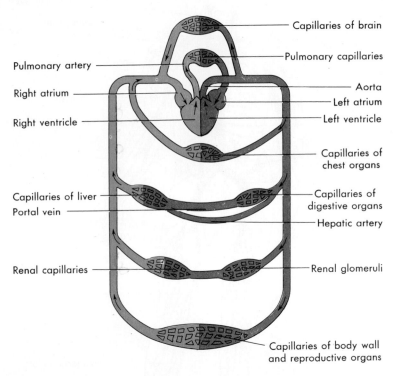

Pulmonary artery

Right atrium

Right ventricle

Capillaries of liver

Portal vein

Renal capillaries

Capillaries of brain

Pulmonary capillaries

Aorta

Left atrium

Left ventricle

Capillaries of chest organs

Capillaries of digestive organs

Hepatic artery

Renal glomeruli

Capillaries of body wall and reproductive organs

Figure 14–2. Diagram of circulation. In the portal circulation the two sets of capillaries are in different organs, the digestive organs and the liver, while in the renal circulation the two sets are in the same organ, the kidney.

The two sets of capillaries in the kidney are visible only on microscopic examination. The blood tubes connecting the renal glomeruli and renal capillaries are called efferent tubes or efferent arterioles. What work is accomplished in these capillaries?

A *plexus*, or network, is formed by the anastomosis of a number of arteries in a limited area. Arteries usually occupy situations *protected* against accidental injury or the effects of local pressure. Arteries usually pursue a fairly straight course, but in some parts of the body they are tortuous. The external maxillary (facial) artery, both in the neck and on the face, and the arteries of the lips (inferior and superior labial) are extremely tortuous and thereby accommodate themselves to the varied movements occurring in speaking, laughing, turning the head, and other movements.

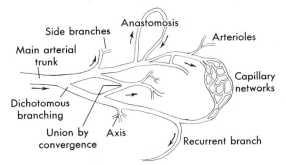

Figure 14–3. Diagram showing anastomosis, branching, and confluence of arteries. This arrangement permits free movement of blood.

DIVISIONS OF THE VASCULAR SYSTEM

The blood vessels of the body are arranged in two main systems: (1) The *pulmonary*, which is the shorter system, provides for the circulation of the blood from the right ventricle to the lungs and back to the left atrium. (2) The *systemic*,

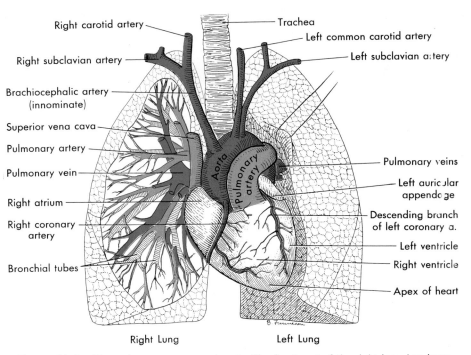

Figure 14–4. The pulmonary artery and aorta. The front part of the right lung has been removed, and the pulmonary vessels and the bronchial tubes are thus exposed.

which is the longer system, provides for the circulation of the blood from the left ventricle to all parts of the body by means of the aorta and its branches and the return to the right atrium by means of the venae cavae.

Blood Vessels of the Pulmonary System. The blood vessels of the pulmonary system are (1) the pulmonary artery and all its branches, (2) the capillaries which connect these branches with the veins, and (3) the pulmonary veins.

The pulmonary artery conveys venous blood from the right ventricle to the lungs. The main trunk is a short, wide vessel about 5 cm (2 in.) in length and a little more than 3 cm (1.2 in.) in width. It arises from the right ventricle and

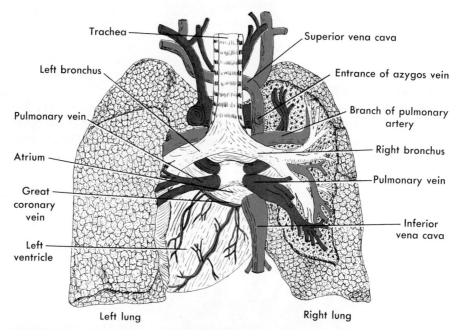

Figure 14–5. Pulmonary vessels, seen in a dorsal view of the heart and lungs. The left lung is pulled to the left; the right lung is partly cut away to show ramifications of the air tubes and blood vessels. *Red* indicates oxygenated blood.

passes upward, backward, and to the left. About the level of the intervertebral disk between the fifth and sixth thoracic vertebrae, it divides into two branches, the right and left pulmonary arteries, which pass to the right and left lungs. Before entering the lungs, each artery divides into two branches. The *right* pulmonary is longer and larger than the left. It runs horizontally to the right, *behind* the ascending aorta and superior vena cava to the root of the right lung, where it divides into two branches. The larger lower branch goes to the middle and lower lobes; the smaller upper branch goes to the upper lobe.

The *left* branch of the pulmonary artery is smaller and passes horizontally in *front* of the descending aorta and left bronchus to the root of the left lung, where it divides into two branches, one to each lobe. These branches divide and sub-divide, grow smaller in size, and finally merge into capillaries which form a network upon the walls of the air cells (alveoli). These capillaries unite, grow larger in size, and gradually assume the characteristics of veins. The veins unite to form the pulmonary veins.

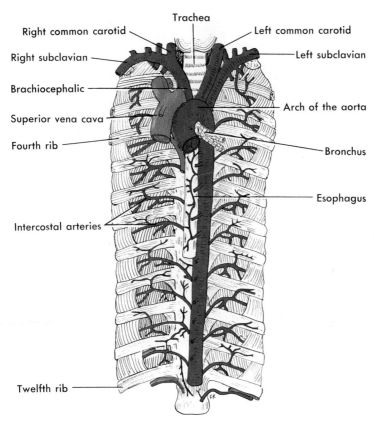

Trachea

Right common carotid

Left common carotid

Right subclavian

Left subclavian

Brachiocephalic

Superior vena cava

Arch of the aorta

Fourth rib

Bronchus

Esophagus

Intercostal arteries

Twelfth rib

Figure 14–6. Thoracic aorta. The thoracic aorta extends from the fourth to the twelfth thoracic vertebrae.

The pulmonary veins are four short veins, two from each lung, which convey the blood from the lungs to the left atrium. They carry oxygenated blood to be distributed by the systemic arteries. The pulmonary veins have no valves.

Blood vessels carrying blood away from the heart (aorta and coronary and pulmonary arteries) must be elastic to receive blood from the ventricles during systole. Blood enters the arteries under pressure during ventricular systole and against resistance in the arterial bed; hence blood vessels carrying blood to the lungs are elastic to adjust to the onward movement of blood. The pressure in the arteries of the pulmonary tree (while not as high as in the systemic vessels) keeps blood moving onward through the pulmonary capillaries and finally on into the veins. Blood enters the left atrium during diastole.

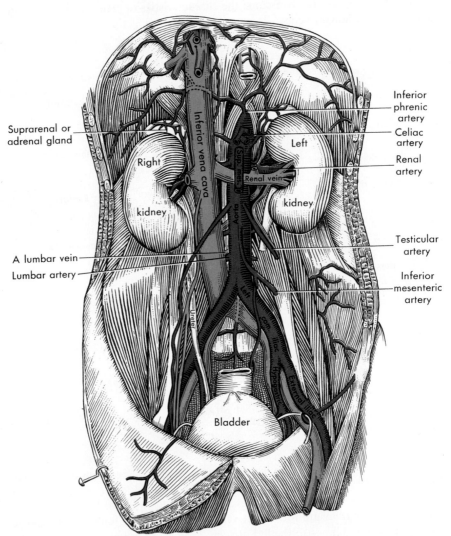

Labels on figure:
- Suprarenal or adrenal gland
- Right
- kidney
- A lumbar vein
- Lumbar artery
- Inferior vena cava
- Aorta
- Supra...
- Renal vein
- Ureter
- Left com. iliac
- Hypogastric
- External iliac
- Bladder
- Inferior phrenic artery
- Celiac artery
- Left
- Renal artery
- kidney
- Testicular artery
- Inferior mesenteric artery

Figure 14–7. The abdominal aorta and inferior vena cava. The abdominal aorta bifurcates into the right and left common iliac arteries opposite the fourth lumbar vertebra.

Blood vessels of the systemic system consist of (1) the *aorta* and all the arteries that originate from it, including the terminal branches called arterioles; (2) the capillaries which connect the arterioles and venules; and (3) all the venules and veins of the body which empty into the superior and inferior venae cavae and then into the heart, as well as those which empty directly into the heart (coronary veins).

The aorta is the main trunk of the arterial system. Arising from the left ventricle of the heart, it passes toward the right over the pulmonary artery, then arches toward the back over the root of the left lung, descends along the vertebral column, and, after passing through the diaphragm into the abdominal region, ends opposite the fourth lumbar vertebra by dividing into the right and left common iliac arteries. In this course the aorta forms a continuous trunk, which gradually diminishes in size from its commencement to its termination. It gives off large and small branches along its course.

The aorta is called by different names throughout its length: (1) the ascending aorta, (2) the arch of the aorta, and (3) the descending aorta, which (*a*) above the diaphragm is referred to as the thoracic aorta and (*b*) below the diaphragm is called the abdominal aorta.

1. THE ASCENDING AORTA is short, about 5 cm (2 in.) in length, and is contained within the pericardium. The only branches of the ascending aorta are the right and left *coronary arteries*, which have been described.

2. THE ARCH extends from the ascending aorta upward, backward, and to the left in front of the trachea, then backward and downward on the left side of the body of the fourth thoracic vertebra, where it becomes continuous with the descending aorta. Three branches are given off from the arch of the aorta—the *brachiocephalic*, the *left common carotid*, and the *left subclavian* arteries. Branches of these arteries supply the head and the upper extremities.

The *brachiocephalic* (innominate) artery arises from the right upper surface of the arch, and ascends obliquely toward the right until, reaching a level with the upper margin of the clavicle, it divides into the right common carotid and right subclavian arteries.

3. THE DESCENDING AORTA extends from the body of the fourth thoracic vertebra to the body of the fourth lumbar vertebra.

(*a*) *The thoracic aorta* is comparatively straight and extends from the fourth thoracic vertebra on the left side to the aortic opening in the diaphragm in front of the last thoracic vertebra. Branches from the thoracic aorta supply the body wall of the chest cavity and the viscera which it contains.

(*b*) *The abdominal aorta* commences at the aortic opening of the diaphragm in front of the lower border of the last thoracic vertebra, and terminates below by dividing into the two common iliac arteries. The bifurcation usually occurs opposite the body of the fourth lumbar vertebra, which corresponds to a spot on the front of the abdomen slightly below and to the left of the umbilicus. Branches from the abdominal aorta supply the body wall of the abdominal cavity and the viscera which it contains.

Arteries of the Trunk

Arteries of the Chest. The branches derived from the thoracic aorta are numerous but small, and the consequent decrease in the diameter of the aorta is not marked. These branches may be divided into two sets: (*a*) the visceral, or those which supply the viscera, and (*b*) the parietal, or those which supply the walls of the chest cavity.

Visceral Group	Parietal Group
Pericardial arteries	Intercostal arteries
Bronchial arteries	Subcostal arteries
Esophageal arteries	Superior phrenic
Mediastinal arteries	arteries

The pericardial arteries are small and are distributed to the pericardium.

The bronchial arteries extend to the lungs. They vary in number, size, and origin. As a rule, there are two left bronchial arteries, which arise from the thoracic aorta, and one right bronchial artery, which arises from the first aortic

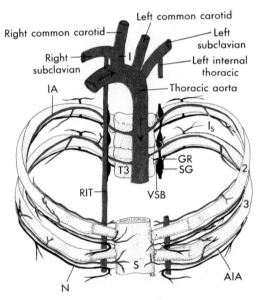

Figure 14–8. Internal thoracic artery and its branches to the intercostal muscles. (*2* and *3*) Second and third ribs, (*AIA*) anterior intercostal artery, (*GR*) gray ramus, (*I*) brachiocephalic artery, (*IA*) intercostal artery, (*IS*) intercostal space, (*N*) nerve, (*RIT*) right internal thoracic artery, (*S*) sternum, (*SG*) sympathetic ganglion, (*T3*) third thoracic vertebra, (*VSB*) ventral somatic branch of spinal nerve.

intercostal or from the upper left bronchial. Each vessel runs along the back part of the corresponding bronchus, dividing and subdividing along the bronchial tubes, supplying them and the cellular tissue of the lungs.

The esophageal arteries are four or five in number; they arise from the front of the aorta and form a chain of anastomoses along the esophagus. They anastomose with the esophageal branches of the thyroid arteries above and with ascending branches from the left gastric and the left inferior phrenic arteries below.

The mediastinal arteries are numerous small arteries which supply the nodes and areolar tissue in the posterior mediastinum.

The intercostal arteries are usually nine in number on each side; they arise from the back of the aorta and are distributed to the lower nine intercostal spaces. Each intercostal artery is accompanied by a vein and a nerve, and each one gives off numerous branches to the muscles and skin (Figs. 14–6 and 14–8) and to the vertebral column and its contents.

The subcostal arteries lie below the last ribs and are the lowest pair of branches derived from the thoracic aorta.

The superior phrenic arteries are small. They arise from the lower part of the thoracic aorta and are distributed to the posterior part of the upper surface of the diaphragm.

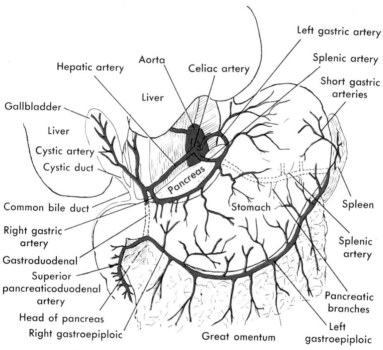

Figure 14–9. The celiac artery and its branches.

Arteries of the Abdomen. The branches derived from the abdominal aorta may be subdivided into two groups.

Visceral Branches	Parietal Branches
Celiac (celiac axis)	Inferior phrenics
Superior mesenteric	Lumbars
Middle suprarenals	Middle sacral
Renals	
Internal spermatics (male), ovarian (female)	
Inferior mesenteric	

The celiac artery is a short, wide vessel, usually not more than 1.25 cm (½ in.) in length, which arises from the front of the aorta just below the opening in the diaphragm. It divides into three branches: the *left gastric*, the *hepatic*, and the *splenic*, or *lienal* (Fig. 14–9).

THE LEFT GASTRIC courses along the lesser curvature of the stomach from left to right, distributing branches to both surfaces. It anastomoses with the esophageal arteries at one end of its course and with the right gastric artery at the other.

THE HEPATIC ARTERY supplies the liver with blood direct from the aorta via the celiac artery. It gives off three branches: (a) the *right gastric*, which courses from right to left along the lesser curvature of the stomach and anastomoses with the

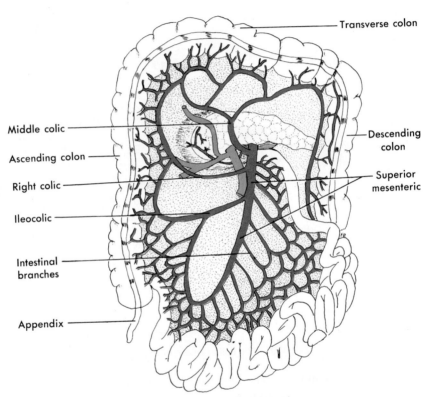

Figure 14–10. Superior mesenteric artery.

left gastric; (b) the *gastroduodenal*, which splits into two vessels: one (superior pancreaticoduodenal) supplies the duodenum and the head of the pancreas; the other (right gastroepiploic or gastro-omental) courses from right to left along the greater curvature of the stomach, distributes branches to it, and anastomoses with a branch of the splenic artery; (c) the *cystic artery*, which supplies the gallbladder. Before entering the liver, the hepatic artery divides into two branches, right and left, which supply the corresponding lobes of the liver.

THE LIENAL, OR SPLENIC, ARTERY is the largest of the three branches of the celiac. It distributes numerous vessels to the pancreas and several small and one large vessel—the left gastroepiploic—to the stomach. The left gastroepiploic (gastro-omental) runs along the greater curvature of the stomach from left to right and anastomoses with the right gastroepiploic.

The superior mesenteric artery arises from the front part of the aorta, a little below the celiac artery. It supplies all of the small intestine except the duodenum. It also supplies the cecum, the ascending colon, and half of the transverse colon (Fig. 14–10).

The middle suprarenal arteries are of small size. They arise from the side of the aorta and pass to the suprarenal, or adrenal, glands, where they anastomose with branches of the phrenic and renal arteries.

The renal arteries, right and left, arise from the sides of the aorta, below the superior mesenteric artery. The right is generally a little lower than the left. Each is directed outward, so as to form nearly a right angle with the aorta, and each divides into four or five branches before reaching the hilus of the kidney (Fig. 14–7).

The internal spermatic arteries arise from the front of the aorta, a little below the renal arteries. They supply the testes (Fig. 14–7).

The ovarian arteries in the female arise from the same portion of the aorta as the spermatic arteries in the male. They supply the ovaries and send small branches to the ureters and uterine tubes. One branch unites with the uterine artery (a branch of the hypogastric) and assists in supplying the uterus. During pregnancy the ovarian arteries become considerably enlarged.

The inferior mesenteric artery arises from in front of the aorta about 3.8 cm (1½ in.) above the division of the aorta into the common iliacs. It distributes branches to the left half of the transverse colon and to the descending and sigmoid colon; continued as the superior hemorrhoidal. It also takes part in the blood supply of the rectum. The middle and inferior hemorrhoidal arteries, branches of the internal iliac (hypogastric) artery, also supply the rectum, anal canal, sphincter muscles, and levatores ani. Branches of these arteries form a plexus, and, after circulating in the capillaries of the region, the blood via the rectal veins joins the hypogastric, either directly or via the internal pudendal vein. Blood is returned by tributaries to the inferior mesenteric vein, which flows into the portal vein and then into the vena cava.

The inferior phrenic arteries (two) may arise separately or by a common trunk from the aorta or celiac artery. They are distributed to the undersurface of the diaphragm.

The lumbar arteries, usually four in number on each side, are analogous to the intercostals. They arise from the back of the aorta opposite the bodies of the upper four lumbar vertebrae. Occasionally a fifth pair arises from the middle sacral artery. These arteries distribute branches to the muscles and skin of the back; a spinal branch enters the vertebral canal and is distributed to the spinal cord and its membranes, also to the lumbar vertebrae.

The middle sacral artery arises from the back part of the abdominal aorta and passes down in front of the fourth and fifth lumbar vertebrae, the sacrum, and the coccyx to the coccygeal gland. (The coccygeal gland consists of irregular masses of cells. It lies in front of, or just below, the coccyx.)

Arteries of the Pelvis.   When the descending aorta reaches the body of the fourth lumbar vertebra, it divides into the two *common iliac* arteries. These arteries pass downward and outward for about 5 cm (2 in.), and then each divides into the hypogastric, or internal, and external iliac artereis.

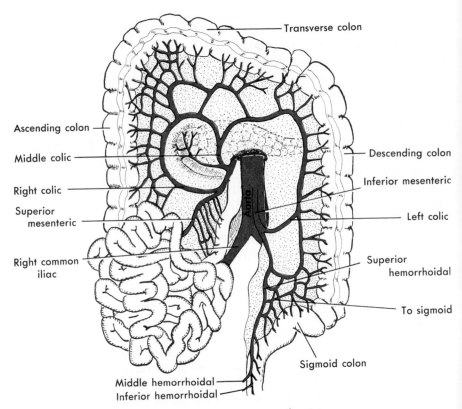

Figure 14–11.   Inferior mesenteric artery.

The internal iliac arteries send branches to the pelvic walls, pelvic viscera, the external genitals, the buttocks, and the medial side of each thigh. The uterine arteries in the female, which supply the tissues of the uterus with blood, are very important branches of the internal iliac arteries.

The external iliacs are larger than the internal iliacs and extend from the bifurcation of the common iliacs to a point halfway between the anterior superior spines of the ilia and the symphysis pubis. They enter the thigh and become the femoral arteries.

The external iliacs send small branches to the psoas major muscles and to the neighboring lymph nodes, and each gives off the *inferior epigastric* and the *deep iliac circumflex.* These arteries are of considerable size and distribute branches to the abdominal muscles and peritoneum, also to the region of the pubes.

Arteries of the Head and Neck

The principal arteries of the head and neck are the two common carotids (Figs. 14–12 and 14–13) and the vertebral.

The left common carotid arises from the middle of the upper surface of the arch of the aorta, and the *right common carotid* arises at the division of the brachiocephalic; consequently the left carotid is an inch or two longer than the right. They ascend obliquely on either side of the neck until, on a level with the upper border of the thyroid cartilage (Adam's apple), they divide into two great branches: (1) the external carotid, and (2) the internal carotid. At the root of the neck the common carotids are separated from each other by only a narrow interval, corresponding to the width of the trachea; but at the upper part, the thyroid gland, the larynx, and the pharynx project forward between them.

The external carotid is the more superficial and is placed nearer the middle line than the internal carotid. Each external carotid has nine branches, which in turn break up into smaller branches. These supply the thyroid gland, the tongue, throat, face, and ears; and the meningeal branches pass inside the cranium to the dura mater.

Each internal carotid has many branches, which are distributed to the brain, the eye and its appendages, the forehead, and the nose. Important branches are the cerebral, distributed to the brain, and the ophthalmic, which enters the orbital cavity through the optic foramen and distributes branches to the orbit, the muscles, and the bulb of the eye.

On the internal carotid, at the point where it diverges from the external carotid, is a slight enlargement known as the *carotid sinus* and an epithelial body, the *carotid body.* From receptors in their walls sensory fibers reach the cardiac center in the brain via the ninth and tenth cranial nerves. They play an important role in the control of blood pressure.

Vertebral Arteries. The vertebral arteries arise from the subclavian arteries and ascend on either side to the level of the sixth cervical vertebra, where they enter the foramina of the transverse processes and continue upward in the foramina of the upper six thoracic vertebrae. They wind behind the atlas, enter the skull through the foramen magnum, and unite to form the basilar artery.

Circle of Willis.[1] This is an arterial anastomosis at the base of the brain. It is formed by the union of the *anterior cerebral arteries*, which are branches of the internal carotid, and the *posterior cerebral arteries*, which are branches of the basilar. The *basilar* is formed by the union of the two *vertebrals*. It extends from the lower to the upper border of the pons, lying in the median groove. It ends by dividing into the two posterior cerebral arteries. These two arteries are connected on either side with the internal carotid by the posterior communicating

---

[1] Thomas Willis, English anatomist (1621–1675).

arteries. In front, the anterior cerebral arteries are connected by the anterior communicating arteries. These arteries form a complete circle (Fig. 14–12). This arrangement (1) equalizes the circulation of the blood in the brain and (2) in case of destruction of one of the arteries, provides for the blood reaching the brain through other vessels.

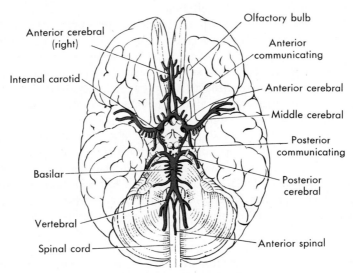

Figure 14–12. Diagram of the arterial circulation at the base of the brain, showing the arterial circle of Willis. From this circle the anterior, middle, and posterior cerebral arteries extend to each cerebral hemisphere. The anterior spinal artery supplies the cord.

Arteries of the Upper Extremities

The subclavian artery is the first portion of a long trunk which forms the main artery of each upper limb. Different portions are given different names, according to the regions through which they pass, viz., subclavian, axillary, brachial. At the elbow the brachial divides into the radial and ulnar arteries.

The *right subclavian* arises at the division of the brachiocephalic, and the *left subclavian* from the arch of the aorta. They pass a short way up into the neck and then turn downward to rest on the first ribs. At the outer border of the first ribs they cease to be called subclavian and are continued as the axillaries. While these arteries continue as the main arteries of the upper extremities, they distribute branches to (1) the base of the brain, (2) the shoulder regions, and (3) the chest.

1. *The vertebrals* have been described above.

2. *The thyrocervical* sends branches to the thyroid, trachea, esophagus, muscles of the neck, and scapula.

3. *The internal thoracic (mammary) artery* extends down just under the costal cartilages to the level of the sixth intercostal space, where it branches into the musculophrenic and superior epigastric arteries. It sends branches to the

mammary glands (these branches are of large size during lactation), the diaphragm, the areolar tissue and lymph nodes in the mediastinum, the intercostal muscles, the pericardium, and the abdominal muscles.

4. *The costocervical* sends branches to the upper part of the back, the neck, and the spinal cord and its membranes.

The axillary artery (continuation of the subclavian) extends from the outer border of the first rib to the lower border of the tendon of the teres major muscle, where it becomes the brachial. Its direction varies with the position of the upper limb. At the beginning it is deeply situated, but near its termination it is superficial. It gives off branches to the chest, shoulder, and arm.

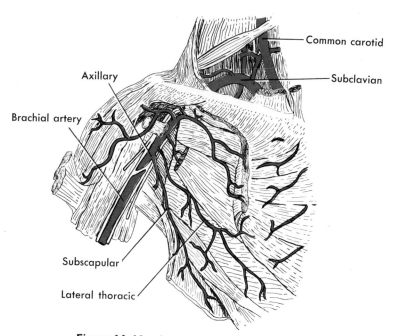

Common carotid

Axillary

Subclavian

Brachial artery

Subscapular

Lateral thoracic

Figure 14–13. Subclavian and axillary arteries.

The brachial artery (continuation of the axillary) extends from the lower margin of the tendon of the teres major muscle to a short distance (1 cm) below the elbow, where it divides into the radial and ulnar arteries. The upper part lies medial to the humerus; but as it passes down the arm it gradually lies in front of the bone, and at the bend of the elbow it lies midway between its epicondyles. It lies in the depression along the inner border of the biceps muscle. Pressure made at this point from within outward against the humerus will control the blood supply to the arm.

The ulnar, the larger of the two vessels into which the brachial divides, extends along the ulnar border of the forearm into the palm of the hand, where it divides into the branches which enter into the formation of the superficial and deep volar arches (palmar arches).

The radial artery appears by its direction to be a continuation of the brachial, although it does not equal the ulnar in size. It extends along the radial (thumb) side of the forearm as far as the lower end of the radius below which it turns around the lateral side of the wrist and passes forward into the palm of the hand, where it unites with the deep volar branch of the ulnar artery to form the deep volar arch. The superficial and deep volar arches anastomose and supply the hand with blood.

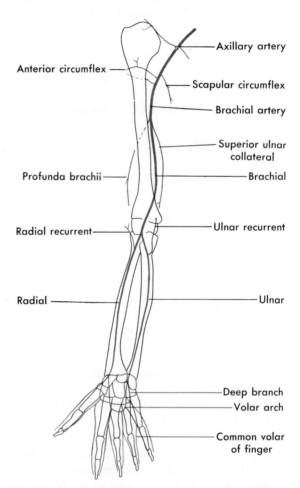

Figure 14–14.   Anterior view of the arteries of the arm, forearm, and hand.

SUMMARY

Blood Circulation in Upper Extremity

Blood leaves the left ventricle, traverses arteries, arterioles, capillaries, venules, and veins, and is returned to the right atrium via the superior vena cava

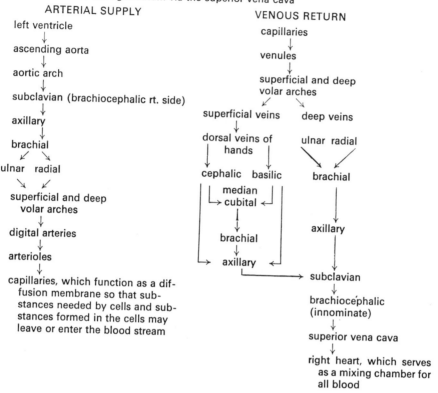

ARTERIAL SUPPLY

left ventricle
↓
ascending aorta
↓
aortic arch
↓
subclavian (brachiocephalic rt. side)
↓
axillary
↓
brachial
↙ ↘
ulnar radial
↘ ↙
superficial and deep
volar arches
↓
digital arteries
↓
arterioles
↓
capillaries, which function as a diffusion membrane so that substances needed by cells and substances formed in the cells may leave or enter the blood stream

VENOUS RETURN

capillaries
↓
venules
↓
superficial and deep
volar arches
↙ ↘
superficial veins   deep veins
↓   ulnar radial
dorsal veins of   ↘ ↙
hands   brachial
↓   ↓
cephalic basilic
median
→ cubital ←
↓
brachial   axillary
↓
axillary ←   ↓
subclavian
↓
brachiocephalic
(innominate)
↓
superior vena cava
↓
right heart, which serves as a mixing chamber for all blood

Arteries of the Lower Extremities

The external iliac forms a large, continuous trunk, which extends downward in the lower limb and is named, in successive parts of its course, femoral, popliteal, and posterior tibial.

The femoral artery lies in the upper three fourths of the thigh, its limits being marked above by the inguinal (Poupart's) ligament and below by the opening in the adductor magnus muscle. After passing through this opening, the artery receives the name of popliteal. In the first part of its course the artery lies along the middle of the depression on the inner aspect of the thigh, known as the femoral triangle (Scarpa's triangle).[2] Here the pulsation of the artery may be felt, and the circulation through the vessel may be most easily controlled by pressure. Branches from the femoral artery extend to the abdominal walls, the

[2] The femoral triangle (Scarpa's triangle) corresponds to the depression just below the fold of the groin. Its apex is directed downward. It is bounded above by the inguinal ligament, and the sides are formed laterally by the sartorius muscle and medially by the adductor longus. Antonio Scarpa, Italian anatomist (1752–1832).

419

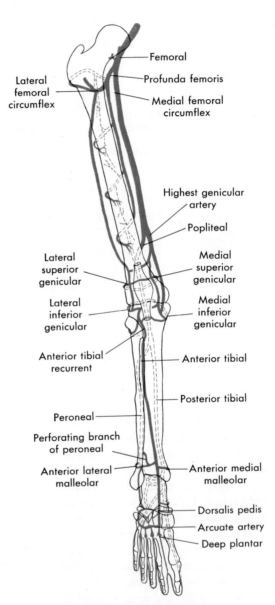

Figure 14–15. Diagram of arteries of the leg.

external genitalia, and the muscles and fasciae of the thigh; and a descending branch, the *lateral femoral circumflex*, anastomoses with branches of the popliteal to form the *circumpatellar anastomosis*, which surrounds the knee joints.

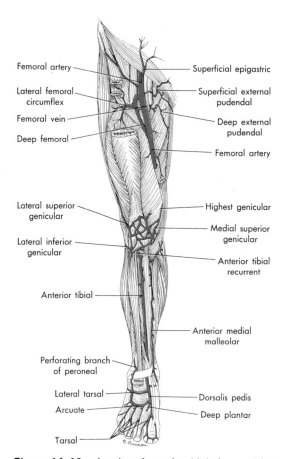

Figure 14–16. Arteries of anterior thigh, leg, and foot.

The popliteal artery, a continuation of the femoral, is placed at the back of the knee. It sends branches to the knee joint, the posterior femoral muscles (the biceps femoris, semitendinosus, and semimembranosus), the gastrocnemius and soleus muscles, and the skin of the back of the leg. Just below the knee joint it divides into the posterior tibial and anterior tibial arteries.

The posterior tibial artery lies along the back of the leg and extends from the bifurcation of the popliteal to the ankle. It distributes branches to the calf of the leg and nutrient vessels to the tibia and fibula. At the ankle it divides into the *medial* and *lateral plantar* arteries, which supply the structures on the sole of the foot, form the plantar arch, and anastomose with branches from the dorsalis pedis.

The peroneal artery is a large branch given off by the posterior tibial just about 2.5 cm (1 in.) below the bifurcation of the popliteal. The peroneal distributes blood to the structures on the medial side of the fibula and the calcaneus.

The anterior tibial artery, the smaller of the two divisions of the popliteal trunk, extends along the front of the leg to the front of the ankle joint and becomes the *dorsalis pedis artery.* The dorsalis pedis anastomoses with branches from the posterior tibial and supplies blood to the foot.

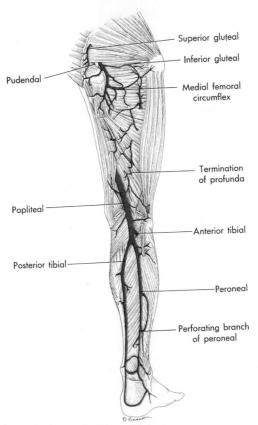

Figure 14–17. Arteries of posterior thigh, leg, and foot.

SUMMARY

Blood Circulation in Lower Extremity

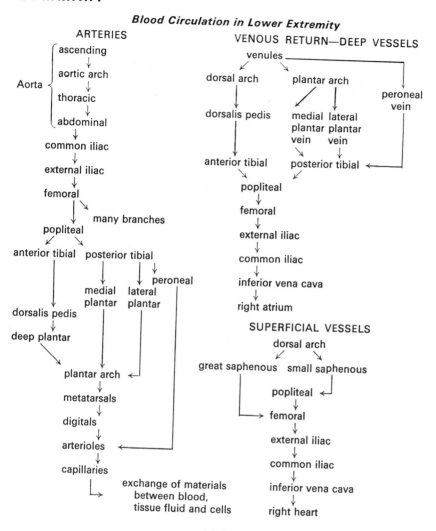

Veins

The arteries begin as large trunks, which gradually become smaller and smaller until they end in arterioles, which merge into capillaries, while the veins begin as small branches, called venules, which at first are scarcely distinguishable from the capillaries and which unite to form larger and larger vessels. They differ from the arteries in their larger size, greater number, thinner walls, and the presence of valves in many of them which prevent backward circulation. There are a greater number of veins carrying blood away from an organ than arteries carrying blood to it. Speaking generally, it can be said that the total diameter of the veins returning the blood from any organ is at least twice the

423

diameter of the arteries carrying blood to that organ. Hence, the total capacity of the venous system is much greater than that of the arterial system. In the lungs, the capacity of the pulmonary veins only slightly exceeds that of the pulmonary arteries.

The veins consist of two sets of vessels, the *pulmonary* and the *systemic veins*.

The pulmonary veins convey oxygenated blood from the lungs to the left atrium. These veins commence in the capillary network upon the air cells and unite to form one vein for each lobule. These further unite to form one vein for each lobe, two for the left lung and three for the right. The vein from the middle lobe of the right lung usually unites with that from the upper lobe, and finally two trunks from each lung are formed. They have no valves and open separately into the left atrium.

The systemic veins return the blood from all parts of the body to the right atrium of the heart. In other words, the blood distributed by the systemic arteries is returned by the systemic veins. The systemic veins are divided into three sets—superficial veins, deep veins, and venous sinuses.

The superficial veins are found just beneath the skin in the superficial fascia and return the blood from these structures. They are sometimes called cutaneous veins. The superficial and deep veins very frequently unite. The anastomoses of veins are more numerous than those of arteries.

The deep veins accompany the arteries and are usually enclosed in the same sheath. The deep veins accompanying the smaller arteries, such as the brachial, ulnar, radial, peroneal, and tibial, are found in pairs, one on each side of the vessel, and are called venae comitantes, or companion veins. Usually the larger arteries, such as the femoral, popliteal, axillary, and subclavian, have only one accompanying vein (vena comes).

In certain parts of the body the deep veins do not accompany the arteries. Examples are the veins in the skull and the vertebral canal, the hepatic veins in the liver, and the larger veins which return blood from the bones.

The venous sinuses are canals found only in the interior of the skull. They are formed by a separation of the layers of the dura mater, the fibrous membrane which covers the brain. Their outer wall consists of the dura mater, and their inner lining of endothelium is continuous with the lining membrane of the vessels that communicate with them (Fig. 14–18). Two important sinuses are located between the layers of the falx cerebri. The *superior sagittal sinus* is contained in the upper border, and the *inferior longitudinal* (inferior sagittal) *sinus*, in the lower border. Figure 14–18 shows these two sinuses, also the *straight sinus*, the *transverse*, or *lateral*, and the *superior petrosal sinuses* of one side of the head. Confluence of sinuses (torcular Herophili[3]) is the name applied to the dilated extremity of the superior sagittal sinus.

The systemic veins are divided into three groups: (1) veins that empty into the heart, (2) veins that empty into the superior vena cava, and (3) veins that empty into the inferior vena cava.

[3] Herophilus, Greek physician (335–280 B.C.).

Five of the veins of the heart empty into the right atrium by way of the coronary sinus. Some smaller veins empty directly into the atria and ventricles.

The veins of the head, neck, upper extremities, and thorax, and the azygos veins empty into the *superior vena cava*, which carries the blood to the right atrium.

The veins of the lower extremities and of the abdomen and pelvis empty into the *inferior vena cava*, which carries the blood to the right atrium. The azygos veins, however, deliver part of this blood to the superior vena cava.

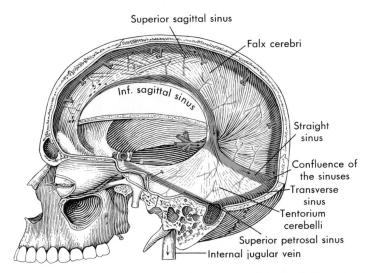

Figure 14–18. Diagram showing the great blood sinuses of the head. Other structures are also shown.

Veins of the Neck

The blood returning from the head and face flows on each side into two principal veins, the external and internal jugular.

The external jugular veins are the chief *superficial* veins of the neck. They are formed in the substance of the parotid glands by the union of the posterior facial and the posterior auricular veins of each side of the face. This union takes place on a level with the angle of the mandible, and each vein descends almost vertically down the neck to its termination in the subclavian vein. These two veins receive the blood from the deep parts of the face and the exterior of the cranium.

The internal jugular veins are continuous with the lateral sinuses and begin in the jugular foramen at the base of the skull. They descend on either side of the neck, first with the external carotid, then with the common carotid, and join the subclavian at a right angle to form the brachiocephalic (innominate) vein. They receive the blood from the veins and sinuses of the cranial cavity, from the superficial parts of the face, and from the neck. In a general way the tributaries of the internal jugular veins correspond to the branches of the external carotid arteries (Fig. 14–19).

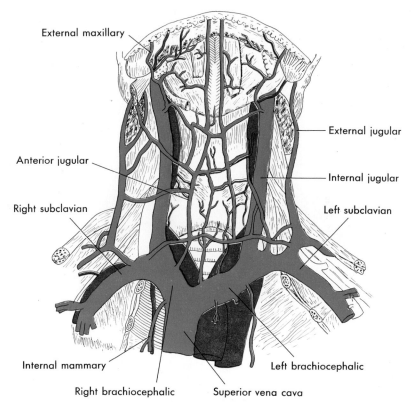

Figure 14–19. Veins of the neck and upper part of thorax, front view. Which hormones enter the circulation through these veins?

Veins of the Upper Extremities

The blood from the upper limbs is returned by a deep and a superficial set of veins. The deep veins are the venae comitantes of the forearm and arm and are called by the same names as the arteries, i.e., the deep volar venous arches, metacarpal veins, radial and ulnar veins, brachial veins, axillary veins, and subclavian veins. The deep veins have numerous anastomoses with one another and with the superficial veins.

The superficial veins are much larger than the deep veins and take a greater share in returning the blood, especially from the distal portion of the limb. They commence in two plexuses, one on the back of the hand, formed by the dorsal metacarpal veins—the dorsal venous network—and another plexus situated over the thenar and hypothenar eminences and across the front of the wrist. They include the following:

The cephalic vein begins in the dorsal network and winds upward around the radial border of the forearm to a little below the bend of the elbow, where it joins the accessory cephalic vein to form the cephalic of the upper arm.

The basilic vein begins in the ulnar part of the dorsal network and extends upward along the posterior surface of the ulnar side to a little below the elbow, where it is joined by the median basilic vein. It continues upward to the lower border of the teres major muscle.

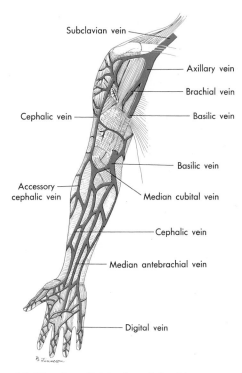

Figure 14–20. Superficial veins of shoulder, arm, and hand.

The axillary vein is a continuation of the basilic. It ends at the outer border of the first rib in the subclavian vein. It receives the brachial veins and, close to its termination, the cephalic vein. It also receives veins which correspond with the branches of the axillary artery.

The subclavian vein is a continuation of the axillary extending from the first rib to the joint between the sternum and clavicle, where it unites with the internal jugular to form the brachiocephalic vein. At the junction with the internal jugular the left subclavian vein receives the thoracic duct, and the right subclavian vein receives the right lymphatic duct.

Veins of the Thorax

On each side the **brachiocephalic (innominate) vein** formed by the union of the subclavian and internal jugular veins receives the blood returning from the head, neck, mammary gland, and the upper part of the thorax. These veins transmit this blood to the superior vena cava.

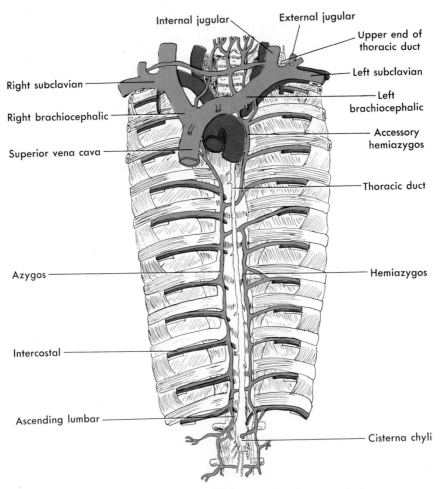

Figure 14–21.   Azygos and intercostal veins, also thoracic duct.

The right brachiocephalic is about 2·5 cm (1 in.) in length, and the left is about 6 cm (2½ in.) in length.

The internal thoracic veins receive tributaries corresponding to the branches of of the artery. They unite to form a single trunk and end in the brachiocephalic vein.

The superior vena cava is formed by the union of the right and left brachiocephalic veins, just behind the junction of the first right costal cartilage with the sternum. It is about 7.5 cm (3 in.) long and opens into the right atrium, opposite the third right costal cartilage.

A **supplementary channel** between the inferior and superior venae cavae is formed by the azygos veins. In case of obstruction, these veins form a channel by which blood can be conveyed from the lower part of the body to the superior vena cava. They are three in number and lie along the front of the vertebral column.

The azygos vein (right, or major, azygos) begins opposite the first or second lumbar vertebra as the *right ascending lumbar vein* or by a branch of the *right renal vein* or from the *inferior vena cava.* (The lumbar veins empty into the inferior vena cava. They correspond to the lumbar arteries given off by the abdominal aorta and return the blood from the muscles and skin of the loins and walls of the abdomen.)

The azygos vein ascends on the right side of the vertebral column to the level of the fourth thoracic vertebra, where it arches over the root of the right lung and empties into the superior vena cava.

The hemiazygos vein (left lower, or minor, azygos) begins in the left lumbar or renal vein. It ascends on the left side of the vertebral column, and at about the level of the ninth thoracic vertebra it connects with the right azygos vein. It receives the lower four or five intercostal veins of the left side and some esophageal and mediastinal veins.

The accessory hemiazygos vein (left upper azygos) connects above with the highest left intercostal vein and opens below into either the azygos or the hemiazygos. It varies considerably in size, position, and arrangement. It receives veins from the three or four intercostal spaces between the highest left intercostal vein and highest tributary of the hemiazygos; the left bronchial vein sometimes opens into it.

The azygos veins return blood from the intercostal muscles, etc., to the superior vena cava. The internal thoracic veins are venae comitantes for the internal thoracic arteries and are tributary to the right and left brachiocephalic veins respectively.

The Bronchial Veins. A bronchial vein is formed at the root of each lung and returns the blood from the larger bronchi and from the structures at the root of the lung; that of the right side opens into the azygos vein near its termination, that of the left side into the highest left intercostal or the accessory hemiazygos vein. A considerable quantity of the blood which is carried to the lungs through the bronchial arteries is returned to the left side of the heart through the pulmonary veins.

Veins of the Lower Extremities

The blood from the lower limbs is returned by a superficial and a deep set of veins. The superficial veins are beneath the skin between the layers of superficial fascia. The deep veins accompany the arteries. Both sets are provided with valves, which are more numerous in the deep than in the superficial veins.

The superficial veins of the lower extremities are the great saphenous veins, the small saphenous veins, and their tributaries. The superficial veins of the foot form venous arches on the dorsum and sole of the foot. These arches communicate with each other and receive branches from the deep veins. They drain the blood into a *medial* and *lateral* marginal vein.

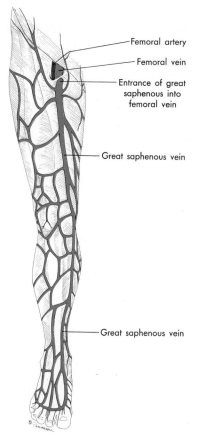

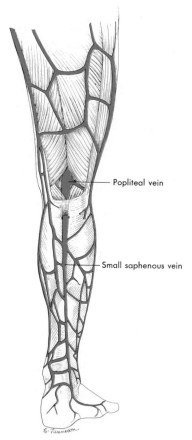

Figure 14–22. Superficial veins of lower extremity, anterior view.

Figure 14–23. Superficial veins of lower extremity, dorsal view.

The great saphenous vein begins in the medial marginal vein of the dorsum of the foot, extends upward on the medial side of the leg and thigh, and ends in the femoral vein a little more than 3 cm (1¼ in.) below the inguinal ligament. At the ankle it receives branches from the sole of the foot; in the leg it anastomoses with the small saphenous vein and receives many cutaneous veins. In the thigh it receives many branches. Those from the posterior and medial aspects of the thigh frequently unite to form an accessory saphenous vein which joins the great saphenous.

The small saphenous begins behind the lateral malleolus, as a continuation of the lateral marginal vein, and passes up the back of the leg to end in the deep popliteal vein. It receives many branches from the deep veins on the dorsum of the foot and from the back of the leg. Before it joins the popliteal, it gives off a branch that runs upward and forward and joins the great saphenous.

The deep veins accompany the arteries below the knee. They are in pairs and are called by the same names as the arteries. The veins from the foot empty into the *anterior tibial* and *posterior tibial veins*. They unite to form the single *popliteal vein*, which is continued as the *femoral* and becomes the *external iliac*.

The femoral veins are continuations of the popliteal veins and extend from the opening in the adductor magnus muscles to the level of the inguinal ligament. Each one receives numerous branches, and near its termination it is joined by the great saphenous vein.

Veins of the Abdomen and Pelvis

The external iliac veins are continuations of the femoral veins and extend from the level of the inguinal (Poupart's) ligaments on either side to the joint between the sacrum and the ilium.

The iliac veins are formed by the union of veins corresponding to the branches of the hypogastric arteries. They accompany the internal arteries and unite with the external iliac veins to form the common iliacs (Fig. 14–7, p. 408).

The common iliacs extend from the base of the sacrum to the fifth lumbar vertebra, and then the two common iliacs unite to form the inferior vena cava.

The inferior vena cava begins at the junction of the two common iliacs and thence ascends along the right side of the aorta, perforates the diaphragm, and terminates by entering the right atrium of the heart. The shape and position of the inferior vena cava are comparable to those of the abdominal aorta, and the vein returns blood from the parts below the diaphragm. It receives veins having the same names as the parietal and visceral branches of the abdominal aorta. These veins are (1) lumbar, (2) renal, (3) suprarenal, (4) inferior phrenic, (5) hepatic, and (6) right spermatic or ovarian. Most of these veins accompany the arteries of the same names.

There are a few exceptions:

1. The right suprarenal vein empties into the inferior vena cava; the left empties into the left renal or left inferior phrenic.

2. The right inferior phrenic empties into the inferior vena cava; the left often consists of two branches, one of which empties into the left renal or suprarenal vein and the other into the inferior vena cava.

3. The hepatic veins empty into the inferior vena cava, but they commence in the sinusoids of the liver.

4. The right spermatic vein empties into the inferior vena cava, but the left empties into the left renal vein. The ovarian veins end in the same way as the spermatic veins in the male.

The Portal System. The veins which bring back the blood from the spleen-stomach, pancreas, and intestines are included in the portal system. Blood is collected from the spleen by veins which unite to form the *splenic,* or *lienal, vein.* This vein passes back of the pancreas from left to right and ends by uniting with the *superior mesenteric* to form the *portal vein.* Before this union takes place, the splenic receives *gastric veins, pancreatic veins,* and usually the *inferior*

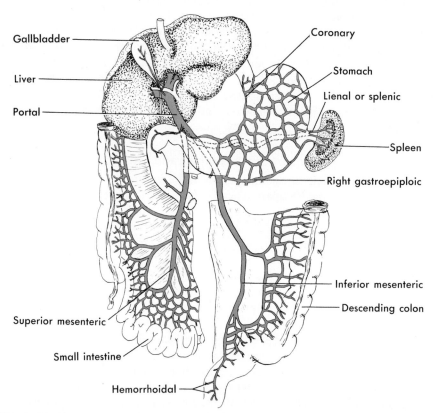

Figure 14–24. Portal system of veins. The liver is turned upward and backward, and the transverse colon and most of the small intestine are removed. The veins from the pancreas enter the lienal vein.

mesenteric vein, which returns the blood from the rectum, sigmoid, and descending colon. The *superior mesenteric vein* returns the blood from the small intestine, the cecum, and the ascending and transverse portions of the colon (Fig. 14–24).

The portal vein, formed at the level of the second lumbar vertebra by the union of the splenic or lienal and the superior mesenteric, passes upward and to the right to the transverse fissure of the liver. Here it divides into a right and a left branch, which accompany the right and left branches of the hepatic artery into the right and left lobes of the liver. Before entering the liver, the right branch usually receives the cystic vein, which returns blood from the gallbladder. The hepatic artery brings blood direct from the aorta, via the celiac artery to the liver. In the liver, blood from both sets of vessels enters into the interlobular vessels. These divide into smaller branches which finally form the capillarylike network of the liver. These are called sinusoids. Many of these capillaries follow the "chain of cells" from the edges to the centers of the lobules, where they form the intralobular veins. These unite to form the hepatic veins which finally enter the inferior vena cava. Thus, it will be seen that the liver receives blood from two sources. The hepatic artery carries blood relatively high in oxygen, since it comes directly from the left ventricle by way of the aorta and celiac artery. The portal

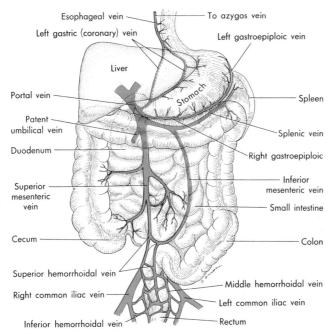

Figure 14–25. Accessory portal circulation. Note anastomosis with systemic circulation (esophageal, umbilical, and hemorrhoidal vessels).

vein carries blood relatively high in soluble materials such as simple sugars, amino acids, water, vitamins and other substances, and a small amount of digested fats which have been absorbed from the digestive tract.

The Accessory Portal System. Some of the veins which are tributaries to the portal vein have small branches whose blood reaches the heart via the superior and inferior venae cavae without going through the liver. For example, branches of the coronary vein of the stomach unite with the esophageal veins which enter the azygos, on its way to the heart, thus bypassing the liver. The inferior mesenteric communicates with the hemorrhoidal veins which empty into the hypogastric veins. There are also small communicating branches that unite the superior and inferior epigastric and internal thoracic veins and through the diaphragmatic veins with the azygos. These communications are called the accessory portal system and are important in returning blood to the superior vena cava when there is interference with portal circulation (Fig. 14–25).

QUESTIONS FOR DISCUSSION

1. Where are the most accessible places to take the pulse? Name the arteries in each instance.
2. What are the differences in blood flow in arteries, veins, and capillaries?
3. Where and how would you place pressure to stop bleeding from an artery?
4. Where would you place pressure to stop bleeding from a vein?
5. How would you know if it was a vein or artery bleeding?
6. Which veins are usually used for venipuncture? Why?
7. How do the end products of digestion reach the heart?
8. How do the cells of the body receive their nutrients from the arteries?

SUMMARY

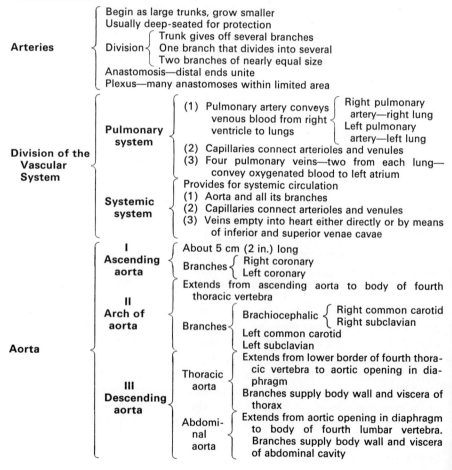

Arteries
- Begin as large trunks, grow smaller
- Usually deep-seated for protection
- Division
  - Trunk gives off several branches
  - One branch that divides into several
  - Two branches of nearly equal size
- Anastomosis—distal ends unite
- Plexus—many anastomoses within limited area

Division of the Vascular System

Pulmonary system
- (1) Pulmonary artery conveys venous blood from right ventricle to lungs
  - Right pulmonary artery—right lung
  - Left pulmonary artery—left lung
- (2) Capillaries connect arterioles and venules
- (3) Four pulmonary veins—two from each lung—convey oxygenated blood to left atrium

Systemic system
- Provides for systemic circulation
- (1) Aorta and all its branches
- (2) Capillaries connect arterioles and venules
- (3) Veins empty into heart either directly or by means of inferior and superior venae cavae

Aorta

I Ascending aorta
- About 5 cm (2 in.) long
- Branches
  - Right coronary
  - Left coronary

II Arch of aorta
- Extends from ascending aorta to body of fourth thoracic vertebra
- Branches
  - Brachiocephalic
    - Right common carotid
    - Right subclavian
  - Left common carotid
  - Left subclavian

III Descending aorta
- Thoracic aorta
  - Extends from lower border of fourth thoracic vertebra to aortic opening in diaphragm
  - Branches supply body wall and viscera of thorax
- Abdominal aorta
  - Extends from aortic opening in diaphragm to body of fourth lumbar vertebra. Branches supply body wall and viscera of abdominal cavity

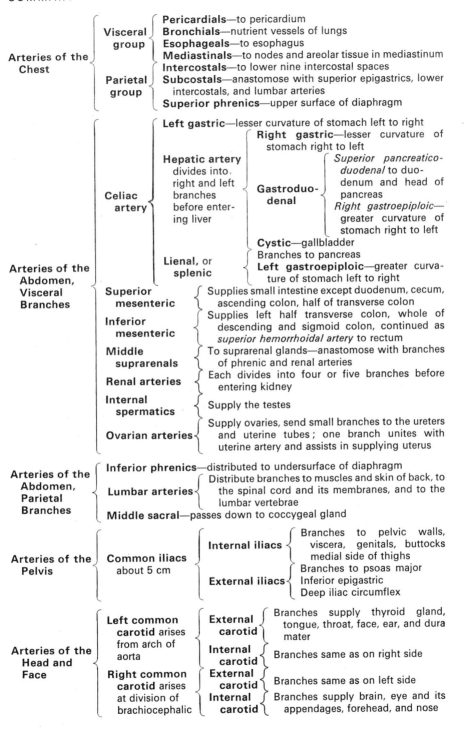

Arteries of the Chest
- **Visceral group**
  - **Pericardials**—to pericardium
  - **Bronchials**—nutrient vessels of lungs
  - **Esophageals**—to esophagus
  - **Mediastinals**—to nodes and areolar tissue in mediastinum
- **Parietal group**
  - **Intercostals**—to lower nine intercostal spaces
  - **Subcostals**—anastomose with superior epigastrics, lower intercostals, and lumbar arteries
  - **Superior phrenics**—upper surface of diaphragm

Arteries of the Abdomen, Visceral Branches
- **Celiac artery**
  - **Left gastric**—lesser curvature of stomach left to right
  - **Hepatic artery** divides into right and left branches before entering liver
    - **Right gastric**—lesser curvature of stomach right to left
    - **Gastroduodenal**
      - *Superior pancreaticoduodenal* to duodenum and head of pancreas
      - *Right gastroepiploic*—greater curvature of stomach right to left
    - **Cystic**—gallbladder
  - **Lienal, or splenic**
    - Branches to pancreas
    - **Left gastroepiploic**—greater curvature of stomach left to right
- **Superior mesenteric**—Supplies small intestine except duodenum, cecum, ascending colon, half of transverse colon
- **Inferior mesenteric**—Supplies left half transverse colon, whole of descending and sigmoid colon, continued as *superior hemorrhoidal artery* to rectum
- **Middle suprarenals**—To suprarenal glands—anastomose with branches of phrenic and renal arteries
- **Renal arteries**—Each divides into four or five branches before entering kidney
- **Internal spermatics**—Supply the testes
- **Ovarian arteries**—Supply ovaries, send small branches to the ureters and uterine tubes; one branch unites with uterine artery and assists in supplying uterus

Arteries of the Abdomen, Parietal Branches
- **Inferior phrenics**—distributed to undersurface of diaphragm
- **Lumbar arteries**—Distribute branches to muscles and skin of back, to the spinal cord and its membranes, and to the lumbar vertebrae
- **Middle sacral**—passes down to coccygeal gland

Arteries of the Pelvis
- **Common iliacs** about 5 cm
  - **Internal iliacs**—Branches to pelvic walls, viscera, genitals, buttocks medial side of thighs
  - **External iliacs**
    - Branches to psoas major
    - Inferior epigastric
    - Deep iliac circumflex

Arteries of the Head and Face
- **Left common carotid** arises from arch of aorta
  - **External carotid**—Branches supply thyroid gland, tongue, throat, face, ear, and dura mater
  - **Internal carotid**—Branches same as on right side
- **Right common carotid** arises at division of brachiocephalic
  - **External carotid**—Branches same as on left side
  - **Internal carotid**—Branches supply brain, eye and its appendages, forehead, and nose

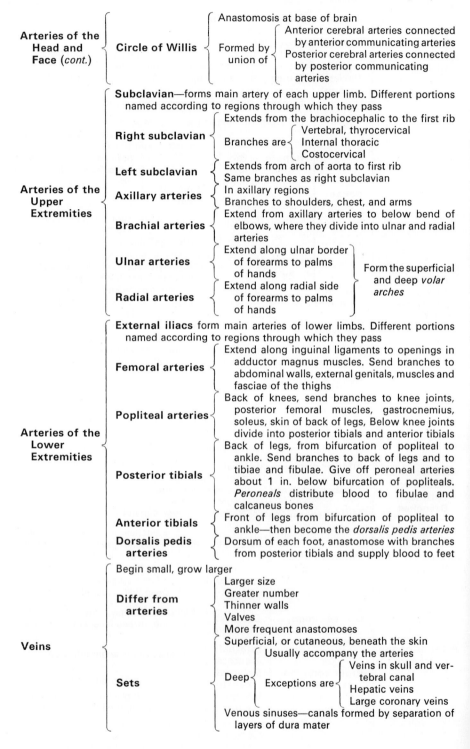

Arteries of the Head and Face (*cont.*)

Circle of Willis — Anastomosis at base of brain

Formed by union of — Anterior cerebral arteries connected by anterior communicating arteries

Posterior cerebral arteries connected by posterior communicating arteries

Arteries of the Upper Extremities

Subclavian—forms main artery of each upper limb. Different portions named according to regions through which they pass

Right subclavian — Extends from the brachiocephalic to the first rib

Branches are — Vertebral, thyrocervical / Internal thoracic / Costocervical

Left subclavian — Extends from arch of aorta to first rib / Same branches as right subclavian

Axillary arteries — In axillary regions / Branches to shoulders, chest, and arms

Brachial arteries — Extend from axillary arteries to below bend of elbows, where they divide into ulnar and radial arteries

Ulnar arteries — Extend along ulnar border of forearms to palms of hands

Radial arteries — Extend along radial side of forearms to palms of hands

Form the superficial and deep *volar arches*

Arteries of the Lower Extremities

External iliacs form main arteries of lower limbs. Different portions named according to regions through which they pass

Femoral arteries — Extend along inguinal ligaments to openings in adductor magnus muscles. Send branches to abdominal walls, external genitals, muscles and fasciae of the thighs

Popliteal arteries — Back of knees, send branches to knee joints, posterior femoral muscles, gastrocnemius, soleus, skin of back of legs, Below knee joints divide into posterior tibials and anterior tibials

Posterior tibials — Back of legs, from bifurcation of popliteal to ankle. Send branches to back of legs and to tibiae and fibulae. Give off peroneal arteries about 1 in. below bifurcation of popliteals. *Peroneals* distribute blood to fibulae and calcaneus bones

Anterior tibials — Front of legs from bifurcation of popliteal to ankle—then become the *dorsalis pedis arteries*

Dorsalis pedis arteries — Dorsum of each foot, anastomose with branches from posterior tibials and supply blood to feet

Veins

Begin small, grow larger

Differ from arteries — Larger size / Greater number / Thinner walls / Valves / More frequent anastomoses

Sets — Superficial, or cutaneous, beneath the skin

Deep — Usually accompany the arteries

Exceptions are — Veins in skull and vertebral canal / Hepatic veins / Large coronary veins

Venous sinuses—canals formed by separation of layers of dura mater

Veins (*cont.*)

Venae comitantes
: Deep veins accompanying smaller arteries, such as brachial, radial, ulnar, peroneal, tibial, are in pairs. A single deep vein accompanying a larger artery, such as femoral, popliteal, axillary, and subclavian artery, is called a *vena comes*

Three groups
: Coronary veins from heart
: **Superior vena cava** — Veins of head, neck, thorax, and upper extremities empty into this vein
: **Inferior vena cava** — Veins of abdomen, pelvis, and lower extremities empty into this vein

Veins of the Neck

External jugulars
: Formed in parotid glands, terminate in the subclavians. Receive blood from deep parts of the face and the exterior of the cranium

Internal jugulars
: Continuous with the lateral sinuses, unite with subclavians to form the innominates. Receive blood from the veins and sinuses of the cranial cavity, superficial parts of face and neck

Veins of the Upper Extremities

Superficial veins
: Are larger, take a greater share in returning blood
: **Cephalics** — Begin in dorsal venous network, join accessory cephalics of arms below elbows, empty into axillaries
: **Basilics** — Begin in dorsal venous network, are joined by median basilics below elbows, are continued as axillaries

Deep veins
: Accompany arteries, are called by same names, i.e., metacarpals, radials, ulnars, brachials, axillaries, and subclavians
: **Axillaries** — Are continuations of the basilics, end at outer border of first ribs, receive brachials, cephalics, and deep veins
: **Subclavians** — Are continuations of the axillaries, unite with internal jugulars to form brachiocephalics

Veins of the Thorax

Brachiocephalics
: Formed by union of internal jugular and subclavians. Receive internal thoracic veins
: One on each side of body

Superior vena cava
: Formed by union of right and left brachiocephalic veins. 7.5 cm (3 in.) long
: Opens into right atrium

Supplementary channel
: (1) **Azygos vein**
: (2) **Hemiazygos vein**
: (3) **Accessory hemiazygos vein**
: Connect inferior vena cava below with superior vena cava above

Bronchial veins
: Formed at the root of each lung
: Return blood from larger bronchi and structures at root of lungs
: Right bronchial vein empties into azygos
: Left bronchial vein empties into highest left intercostal or the accessory hemiazygos

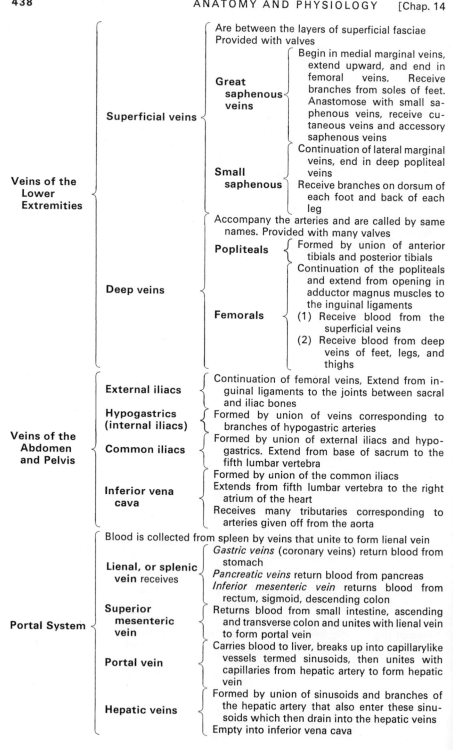

Veins of the Lower Extremities

- **Superficial veins**
  - Are between the layers of superficial fasciae
  - Provided with valves
  - **Great saphenous veins** — Begin in medial marginal veins, extend upward, and end in femoral veins. Receive branches from soles of feet. Anastomose with small saphenous veins, receive cutaneous veins and accessory saphenous veins
  - **Small saphenous** — Continuation of lateral marginal veins, end in deep popliteal veins. Receive branches on dorsum of each foot and back of each leg
- **Deep veins**
  - Accompany the arteries and are called by same names. Provided with many valves
  - **Popliteals** — Formed by union of anterior tibials and posterior tibials
  - **Femorals** — Continuation of the popliteals and extend from opening in adductor magnus muscles to the inguinal ligaments
    - (1) Receive blood from the superficial veins
    - (2) Receive blood from deep veins of feet, legs, and thighs

Veins of the Abdomen and Pelvis

- **External iliacs** — Continuation of femoral veins, Extend from inguinal ligaments to the joints between sacral and iliac bones
- **Hypogastrics (internal iliacs)** — Formed by union of veins corresponding to branches of hypogastric arteries
- **Common iliacs** — Formed by union of external iliacs and hypogastrics. Extend from base of sacrum to the fifth lumbar vertebra
- **Inferior vena cava**
  - Formed by union of the common iliacs
  - Extends from fifth lumbar vertebra to the right atrium of the heart
  - Receives many tributaries corresponding to arteries given off from the aorta

Portal System

- Blood is collected from spleen by veins that unite to form lienal vein
- **Lienal, or splenic vein receives**
  - *Gastric veins* (coronary veins) return blood from stomach
  - *Pancreatic veins* return blood from pancreas
  - *Inferior mesenteric vein* returns blood from rectum, sigmoid, descending colon
- **Superior mesenteric vein** — Returns blood from small intestine, ascending and transverse colon and unites with lienal vein to form portal vein
- **Portal vein** — Carries blood to liver, breaks up into capillarylike vessels termed sinusoids, then unites with capillaries from hepatic artery to form hepatic vein
- **Hepatic veins**
  - Formed by union of sinusoids and branches of the hepatic artery that also enter these sinusoids which then drain into the hepatic veins
  - Empty into inferior vena cava

Accessory
Portal
{
    **Azygos
    vein**
    {
        Small branches of superior and inferior epigastric
          and internal thoracic veins and through dia-
          phragmatic veins—unites with azygos
        Coronary unites with esophageal—branches also
          enter azygos
    }

    **Hypogastric
    vein
    (internal iliacs)**
    {
        Inferior mesenteric
        Unites with hemorrhoidal
        Enters hypogastric
    }
}

15

Physiology of Circulation

Circulation { *Pulmonary, Systemic, Coronary*

The Heart { *Function, Cardiac Cycle, Controls*

Factors Maintaining Circulation

Blood { *Arterial, Capillary,*

Pressure { *Venous*

EACH CELL of the body is dependent upon the blood for its very existence and it is the work of the heart, arteries, capillaries, and veins that makes possible the transporting of all substances to and from cells.

PHYSIOLOGY OF CIRCULATION

The function of the heart is to adjust circulation in relation to the metabolic rate of body cells. By chemical and nervous control, the needs of these cells are met promptly through adjustments of pulse rate and pulse volume, which increase and decrease the velocity and volume of blood in the tissue capillaries. Variable cellular needs are thus met by changes in the number, size, and area of the open capillaries and in the temperature and minute volume of the blood in these open capillaries.

The blood is contained in a closed set of vessels, which it completely fills. Interposed in this set of vessels is the heart, which fills with blood from the veins and then contracts, thereby forcing this blood into the capillaries of all parts of the body. The summaries on pages 442 and 443 give the details of circulation.

This is a description of the general circulation, but the student must understand that both sides of the heart contract almost simultaneously; i.e., the blood fills the atria and ventricles on both sides of the heart at the same time; both atria contract practically together,[1] forcing the blood over the open valves into the ventricles. After a brief pause both ventricles contract, and the blood is forced into the pulmonary artery and into the aorta. The ventricles pump out equal quantities of blood, but the blood from the left ventricle is sent on a longer circuit than the blood from the right.

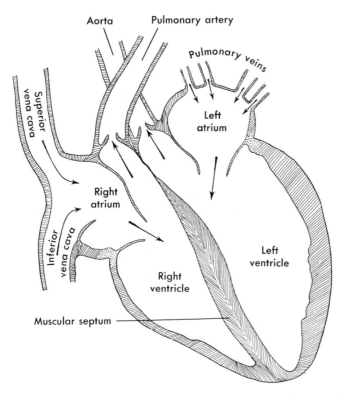

Figure 15–1. A diagram to show the four chambers of the heart and valves which guard their openings, seen from the front. *Arrows* indicate direction of blood flow.

The Pulmonary Circulation. The shorter circulation, from the right ventricle to the left atrium, is called the *pulmonary circulation*. The purpose of the pulmonary circulation is to carry the blood which has been through the body, giving up oxygen and collecting carbon dioxide, to the air sacs of the lungs, where the red cells are recharged with oxygen and the carbon dioxide is reduced to the normal amount.

The Systemic Circulation. The more extensive circulation, from the left ventricle to all parts of the body and the return to the right atrium, is known as the

---

[1] Careful measurements have shown that the contraction of the left atrium lags behind that of the right atrium from 0.01 to 0.03 second.

systemic circulation. The purpose of the systemic circulation is to carry oxygen and nutritive material to the tissues and remove products of metabolism from the tissues. After leaving the left ventricle, portions of the blood pursue different courses; some portions enter the coronary arteries, some go to the head, some to the upper and lower extremities, and some to the different internal organs. Some portions go on shorter circuits and arrive back at the heart sooner than other portions that travel farther away from the center.

An example of a long circuit in the systemic circulation is the circulation from the left heart to the toes and back to the right heart, then to the lungs and to the left heart.

An example of a short circuit in the systemic circulation is the circulation of blood through the walls of the heart itself.

Movement of Blood Through the Right Heart and Lungs

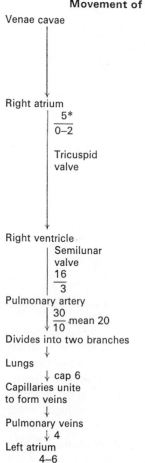

Venae cavae

Right atrium
$$\frac{5^*}{0-2}$$

Tricuspid
valve

Right ventricle
Semilunar
valve
$$\frac{16}{3}$$

Pulmonary artery
$$\frac{30}{10}$$ mean 20

Divides into two branches

Lungs
↓ cap 6
Capillaries unite
to form veins
↓
Pulmonary veins
↓ 4
Left atrium
$$\frac{4-6}{1-2}$$

During diastole of the atria, via the superior and the inferior venae cavae, coronary sinus, and other small vessels, blood enters and fills the right atrium and ventricle, which for the time may be thought of as a single chamber with the tricuspid valve open

The atrium contracts (atrial systole) and forces the blood over the open valve into the ventricle, which has been passively filled and now becomes well distended by the extra supply

After a brief pause (0.1 second), rising muscle tension causes rapid rise in the pressure of the ventricle; when this pressure exceeds that of the atrium, the cusps approximate each other to close the valve. Chordae tendineae become taut and prevent the cusps from everting

As soon as the rapidly rising pressure in the ventricle exceeds the pressure in the pulmonary artery, the pulmonary semilunar valve is forced open and blood moves on into the pulmonary artery. The valve closes rapidly

The pulmonary artery divides into the right and left branches and takes blood into the lungs

Here blood passes through innumerable capillaries that surround the alveoli of the lungs. Blood gives up carbon dioxide and the red cells are recharged with oxygen

The venules unite to form larger veins until finally two pulmonary veins from each lung are formed. These return the oxygenated blood to the heart and complete the pulmonary circulation

* Numbers indicate pressure, mm Hg.

Movement of Blood Through the Left Heart and to the Somatic Capillaries

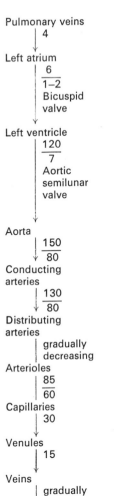

During diastole of the atria, oxygenated blood from the pulmonary veins enters the left atrium and fills it. The left ventricle relaxes and the pressure within it falls, the bicuspid valve opens and blood enters the ventricle and fills it. Systole of the atrium begins and ventricular filling is completed

Ventricular systole is initiated. Blood gets behind the cusps of the bicuspid valve and closes them. Intraventricular pressure rises, and when it exceeds the pressure in the aorta, the aortic semilunar valve opens and blood moves on into the aorta under high pressure. High pressure in the aorta causes the valve to close rapidly

Blood moves on into the conducting or elastic arteries (brachiocephalic, subclavian, common carotids, internal iliac, femoral, etc.)

Blood is forced onward through the elastic arteries into the distributing (muscular arteries) such as the axillary, radial, popliteal, tibial, and finally into the arterioles, where blood is moving in a steady stream, and then on into the capillaries, where the main work of the vascular bed is accomplished

The capillaries unite to form venules and these in turn unite to form veins, then larger veins, until blood finally reaches the right atrium and the circuit begins again

The Coronary Circulation. The purpose of the coronary circulation is to distribute blood, containing oxygen, nutrients, and other substances, to the cardiac muscle cells and return to general circulation the products of metabolism.

The coronary arteries leave the aorta close to the heart. These arteries fill during diastole and empty during systole of the heart. Under normal conditions the rate of blood flow through these vessels is from 50 to 75 ml of blood per 100 gm of heart muscle per minute, depending upon the heart rate and heart volume. In other words, if the heart weighs 300 gm, from 150 to 225 ml of blood will flow through coronary vessels per minute. Since the output of the heart has been estimated to be about 3 to 4 liters per minute, this means that about 10 per cent of the heart output flows through the coronary arteries. This blood is returned to the heart via the coronary sinus, which opens directly into the right atrium. The coronary vessels carry supplies to, and products of metabolism from, the tissues of the heart. If this circulation is interfered with (by occlusion of vessels), normal contractions of the heart are impossible.

The heart muscle receives 10 per cent of cardiac output; the brain, 15 per cent; the liver, stomach, and intestines, 25 per cent; the kidneys, 20 per cent; and the soma, 30 per cent of the cardiac output. Blood supply to the brain is the most constantly maintained. In other organs the supply varies directly with activity. During digestion the stomach and intestine receive far more blood than when at secretory rest.

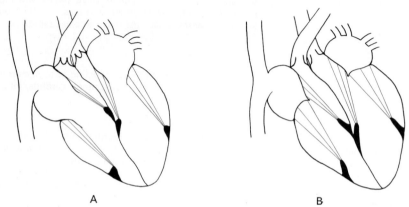

A   B

Figure 15–2. Diagrams to show position of heart valves in the cardiac cycle. No attempt has been made to show contraction.

In *A*, atrioventricular valves are open, and aortic and pulmonary valves are closed. In *B*, the atrioventricular valves are closed, and the aortic and pulmonary valves are open.

In man it takes about 23 seconds[2] to complete a circuit of medium length from the left ventricle to the right atrium (systemic circulation). The blood which enters the right atrium goes through the lungs (pulmonary circulation) before it gets back to the left atrium. This double circulation, pulmonary and systemic, is constantly going on, as each half of the heart is in a literal sense a force pump.

The Heart, the Cause of Circulation. The heart has four chambers, two thin-walled atria above and two thick-walled ventricles. It is divided by a septum into the right and left halves, commonly called the right and left heart. The right atrium has four main orifices, the superior and inferior venae cavae, the coronary sinus, and the atrioventricular orifice. This orifice is guarded by the right atrio-ventricular valve. The pulmonary artery leaves the right ventricle. It is guarded

[2] This shows how rapidly substances introduced into the blood stream can make their way through the body.

by the pulmonary semilunar valve. The left atrium has five orifices, the four pulmonary veins and the atrioventricular orifice. This orifice is guarded by the left atrioventricular valve. The aorta leaves the left ventricle. It is guarded by the aortic semilunar valve.

The Heart as a Pump. The muscles of the atria and ventricles are so arranged that when they contract they lessen the capacity of the chambers which they enclose. The contracting chambers drive the blood through the heart to the arteries.

The first visible sign of contraction is noted where the superior vena cava empties into the right atrium. The sinoatrial node (SA node) is the causal factor. It is therefore sometimes called the *pacemaker* of the heart. From this node the wave of contraction passes over the muscles of both atria. These contract almost simultaneously, driving the blood into the ventricles. The wave of contraction now spreads over the ventricles, causing them to contract simultaneously, driving the blood into the arteries.

The Sinoatrial Node (SA) and the Atrioventricular Node (AV). The SA and AV nodes are specialized cardiac cells found in the right atrium. The SA node is located beneath the opening of the superior vena cava. The specialized fibers are continuous over the atria. The AV node is located near the coronary sinus at the AV junction. The Purkinje system begins at the AV node, and forms the AV bundle which passes to the ventricular septum, where it divides into two large bundle branches which supply both ventricles. Each branch spreads along the endocardial surface of the septum to the apex of the heart and then turns upward over the lateral wall of each ventricle. Purkinje fibers enter the ventricular walls and finally fuse with heart muscle fibers. In this way each muscle fiber receives the impulse.

The SA node initiates the electrical impulse which spreads out over the atria (causing them to contract) to the AV node. From here the impulse spreads down the entire bundle and finally reaches each cardiac muscle fiber of the ventricles, causing them to contract (Fig. 15–3).

The Wave of Contraction. If a stimulus is applied to one end of a muscle, a wave of contraction sweeps over the entire tissue. It is therefore easy to conceive how a wave of contraction can sweep over the muscular tissue of the atria, which is practically continuous. The question is—how is this wave transmitted to the muscular tissue of the ventricles, which, in man, is *not* continuous with that of the atria? The connecting pathway is furnished by the atrioventricular node (AV node), which transmits the nerve impulses by means of the AV bundle and causes the wave of contraction to spread from the atrioventricular openings over the ventricles to the mouths of the pulmonary artery and the aorta.

The Electrocardiogram. During contraction, electrical changes constantly take place in heart muscle. Active cardiac muscle fibers are electrically negative to resting fibers. The electrical differences in various parts of the heart, which occur constantly, can be led off from the surface of the body by electrodes placed on the extremities and connected to a galvanometer. The standard leads used are: (1) from right and left arms; (2) from right arm and left leg; and (3) from left arm and left leg. Other leads are sometimes used.

Each lead shows the difference of electrical potentials in the heart as recorded at the body surface. The record made is called the electrocardiogram and shows

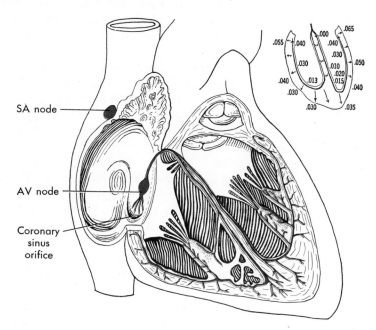

Figure 15–3. Diagram of the atrioventricular bundle of His. The atrioventricular (*AV*) node can be seen near the opening of the coronary sinus in the right atrium. At the upper end of the ventricular septum the bundle divides. The two branches run down in the ventricular septum and give off many smaller branches to the papillary muscles and to the muscular walls of the ventricles. Bundle indicated in *red*. Part of the sinoatrial node is seen in *red* between the base of the superior vena cava and the right auricular appendix. The tip of the left ventricular chamber is not shown. The figures in the small inset indicate the time in seconds taken for the nerve impulses to reach the areas indicated.

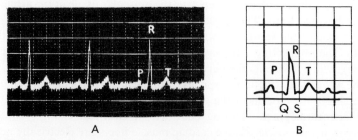

A   B

Figure 15–4. (*A*) Electrocardiogram. Lead II, showing contraction of different parts of the heart. (*B*) Diagram to show excitation during one cycle. Wave P occurs during atrial excitation or systole; waves QRS occur during ventricular systole; wave T occurs as ventricular excitation subsides.

the events of the cardiac cycle. Each electrical heart cycle begins with a peaked elevation, called the P wave, which is caused by the spread of excitation from the SA node out over the atria and to the AV node. The QRS deflections are recorded as the electrical impulse spreads down the AV bundle and out over the ventricles (ventricular systole). The T wave is recorded as ventricular excitation subsides. The electrocardiogram is of value in diagnosis of many types of heart disease.

Heart Block. Experimentally, the AV node and bundle may be damaged, with the result that they lose their power to conduct nerve impulses from the atria to the ventricles. The atria will continue to contract at the rate established by the nerve impulses, but the ventricles adopt a slower rate, usually about 30 to 40 a minute. Since the pulse is caused by ventricular contractions, the pulse drops to 30 or 40 per minute. This condition is known as heart block and may be caused by various diseases such as arteriosclerosis, chronic myocarditis, or syphilis, or by accumulative effects of digitalis.

Atrial Fibrillation. In the normal heartbeat, all groups of muscle fibers of the atria and the ventricles contract in almost simultaneous phase. This forces blood out of the atria and into the ventricles, followed by ventricular contraction, which forces blood into the pulmonary artery and the aorta. In atrial fibrillation the muscle fibers of the atria contract almost continuously and asynchronously. In consequence the muscles of the atria undergo irregular twitchy movements. More important, this means that the AV node is stimulated in an irregular fashion so that the ventricles contract normally but with a completely irregular rhythm. This results in an irregular and rapid pulse. The cause of atrial fibrillation is not known, but it is thought to be the abnormal initiation of numerous irregular impulses in many areas of the atrial muscle tissue. Ventricular contractions are so irregular that when a contraction occurs almost immediately after the preceding contraction, little blood is present in the ventricle, and therefore, the pulse is very feeble. This results in the peculiar finding that the pulse rate taken at the wrist may be 60 to 70, yet on listening to the heart, the rate may be 120 to 140. Thus, one can hear all the heartbeats, but some of the contractions may pump too little blood to be felt as a pulse in the wrist. The difference between the heart rate heard on listening to the heart and the pulse rate is called a *pulse deficit.* Normal people, of course, do not have a pulse deficit. Digitalis reduces the rate of ventricular contraction because of its effect upon the AV node in reducing the rate at which it can respond to the large number of impulses coming from the atria. This drug produces a slower, stronger, and more regular pulse, as well as reducing pulse deficit.

Ventricular Fibrillation is a separate disorder. In this case the ventricles are involved with the continuously asynchronous contraction of muscle fibers. Unless this disorder is interrupted within a few minutes after its onset, the patient will not survive because virtually no blood is pumped into the lungs or into the systemic circulation by ventricles that are fibrillating.

The cardiac cycle consists of three phases: (1) a period of contraction called the *systole,* (2) a period of relaxation called the *diastole,* and (3) a period of rest. The average heart rate of man at rest is 70 to 72 beats per minute. If we assume a pulse rate of 70 to 72, the time required for a cardiac cycle is 0.8$^+$ second, and half of this, or 0.4 second, represents the quiescent phase. When the heart beats more rapidly, it is the rest period that is shortened. See Figure 15–5.

Systole, starting at the venoatrial junction, moves over the atria and then, after a very brief pause at the fibrous rings surrounding the atrioventricular openings, continues over the ventricles in such a way as to lift the blood up into the great arteries.

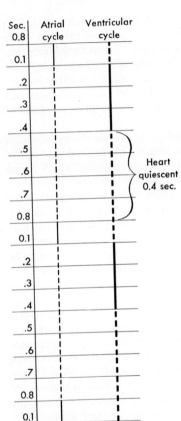

Figure 15–5. Atrial cycle and ventricular cycle, showing overlapping of diastole giving 0.4-second quiescent period of whole heart. (*Solid lines*) Systole, (*dotted lines*) diastole.

Cardiac Output.   At each systole a volume of blood variously estimated at around 80 ml (man at rest) is forced from the left ventricle into the aorta. This is known as the *stroke volume*. A similar amount is forced from the right ventricle into the pulmonary artery. The total cardiac output per beat is, therefore, 160 ml.

Taking a pulse rate of 70, 5.6 liters (70 × 80 ml) of blood leave the left ventricle per minute. This is known as the *minute volume*. A similar amount leaves the right ventricle. With an increase or decrease in stroke volume, in pulse rate, or in both, the total cardiac output per minute would be increased or decreased. During exercise the total cardiac output is greatly increased.

Heart Sounds and Murmurs. If the ear is applied over the heart, certain sounds are heard, which recur with great regularity. Two chief sounds can be heard during each cardiac cycle. The first sound is a comparatively long, booming sound; the second, a short, sharp one. The sounds resemble the syllables *lubb* ($\overline{oo}$) *dup* ($\breve{u}$). The first sound is thought to be due to the contracting muscle and to vibrations caused by the closure of the atrioventricular valves; the second, to the sudden closure of the semilunar valves. In certain diseases of the heart these sounds become changed and are called *murmurs.* These are often due to failure of the valves to close properly, thus allowing regurgitation.

Cause of the Heartbeat. The cause of the heartbeat is still unknown. General belief favors the *myogenic theory*, that is, the theory that the function of the nerve tissue in the heart is regulatory, that the contractions are due to the inherent power of contraction possessed by the muscle cells of the heart themselves. It is believed that inorganic ions, neurohumoral substances, and other factors still *unknown* are responsible for the innate myogenic rhythmicity, but the exact role of each remains to be determined. Three ions are especially important, namely, calcium, potassium, and sodium, which are always present in blood. An excised frog heart continues to beat if kept in a balanced solution of ions. If a mammalian heart is kept warm and supplied with oxygen by perfusing the coronary arteries with a balanced ionic solution that is oxygenated, it will beat for hours. There is a well-marked antagonism between the effects of calcium and the effects of potassium and sodium; calcium has a direct stimulating effect and promotes contraction; potassium and sodium promote relaxation. Heart muscle becomes flaccid and heart rate slows in the presence of excess potassium ions in extracellular fluids.

It is natural to question why the heart is not in a state of continuous contraction. In answer, the heart does not stay in a state of contraction because of the *long refractory phase* of the cardiac muscle. From the time just before the contraction process, in response to a stimulus, begins until some time after relaxation begins, the heart muscle is refractory to further stimulation. Once the heart muscle begins to contract, it must relax (partially or completely) before it will contract again.

Automaticity. The most remarkable power of cardiac muscle is its automaticity. By this is meant that the stimuli which excite it to activity arise within the tissue itself. The degree of automatic power possessed by different regions of the heart varies. Some parts beat faster than others. The most rapidly contracting part is the SA node. It is from this node that the wave of contraction radiates through the atrial muscle to the AV node. From here, it is transmitted over the atrioventricular bundle to the ventricles.

Nervous Control of the Heart. (See Fig. 13–12, p. 393.) Although the heart contracts automatically and rhythmically, the continuously changing frequency and volume of the heart are controlled by two sets of nerve fibers which enter the cardiac plexus. These consist of a craniosacral set of inhibitory fibers, extending from the inhibitory center in the medulla via the vagus nerves (afferent and efferent fibers) to the heart, and accelerator nerve fibers from the superior middle, and inferior cardiac accelerator nerves and from the visceral branches of the first five thoracic spinal nerves, of the thoracolumbar system. It is known that the cardioaccelerator center is also located in the medulla.

The sympathetic fibers follow along the coronary vessels and innervate all areas of both atria and ventricles. In general, stimulation of the sympathetic system increases the activity of the heart by *increasing* both force and rate of heartbeat, thereby increasing the effectiveness of the heart as a pump.

The vagus nerves chiefly innervate the atria and *decrease* the activity of the heart. At the SA node acetylcholine is secreted at the vagal endings, which decreases the rate and rhythm of the node. It also decreases excitability of the AV

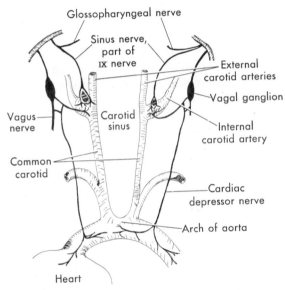

Figure 15–6. Diagram showing receptors on the arch of the aorta, cardiac depressor nerves, carotid sinus, and connections with nerve IX and nerve X.

junctional fibers between the muscles of the atria and the Purkinje system, thereby slowing transmission of impulses.

This means that the heartbeat is controlled by two antagonistic influences, one tending to slow the heart action and the other to quicken it. If the inhibitory center is stimulated to greater activity, the heart is slowed still further. If the activity of this center is depressed, the heart rate is increased, because the inhibitory action is removed. Stimulation of the accelerator nerves results in a quickened heartbeat.

Reflexes adjusting heart rate may be classified as those initiated by pressure receptors and those initiated by chemoreceptors.

Pressoreceptors or Baroreceptors

Right Heart Reflex. There are receptors in the large veins entering the right heart and right atrium that are sensitive to changes in venous pressure. Increased pressure will accelerate heart action. Venous return and cardiac output are increased which prevents pooling of blood in the venous system. Impulses are conveyed over afferent vagal fibers to the cardiac center in the medulla. This reflex is disclaimed by some researchers.

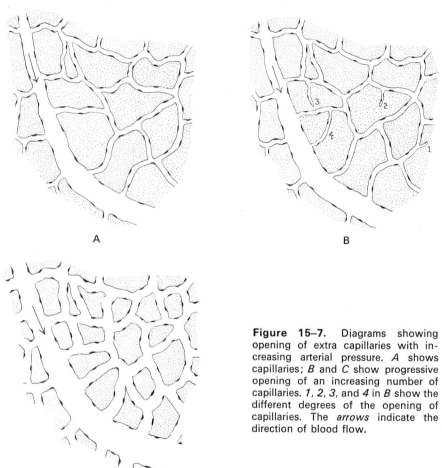

A

B

C

Figure 15–7. Diagrams showing opening of extra capillaries with increasing arterial pressure. *A* shows capillaries; *B* and *C* show progressive opening of an increasing number of capillaries. *1, 2, 3,* and *4* in *B* show the different degrees of the opening of capillaries. The *arrows* indicate the direction of blood flow.

Pressoreceptors or stretch receptors have been demonstrated on the pulmonary veins and in the wall of the left atrium. If pulmonary venous pressure increases, a reflex inhibition of the vasomotor center occurs which causes dilation of the vessels and reduction of pressure in the lungs. This reflex is important because it protects against pulmonary edema.

Pressoreceptors are also located in the arteries of the neck and thorax above the heart level. When pressure in these arteries falls, sympathetic response helps to maintain normal pressure.

The Aortic Reflex. There are pressoreceptors in the arch of the aorta (aortic sinus) that are sensitive to changes in blood pressure. Fluctuation in arterial pressure activates these receptors, and impulses are conveyed over afferent nerve fibers of cranial nerves IX and X to the cardiac centers and the heart is adjusted to meet body needs. A *rise* in pressure slows the heart rate.

The Carotid Sinus Reflex. The carotid sinus is a slightly dilated area of the internal carotid artery at the bifurcation of the carotid into the internal and external carotid arteries. Afferent nerve fibers in the cardiac branch of the glossopharyngeal nerve carry nerve impulses from pressure receptors in the carotid sinus to the cardiac center influencing heart action. These receptors respond to arterial pressure changes that initiate sympathetic reflexes which readjust or lower arterial pressure. Conversely, if pressure falls, these receptors respond and blood pressure is raised.

Chemoreceptors. These are chemoreceptors in the carotid bodies and aortic bodies that are sensitive to lack of oxygen. Impulses from these receptors are conveyed to the cardiac center and the heart rate is accelerated, thereby increasing cardiac output, and more blood is moved on to the tissue cells. Chemoreceptors are also stimulated by an increase in carbon dioxide.

Factors Affecting the Frequency and Strength of the Heart's Action. The frequency and strength of the heartbeat are affected by blood pressure; emotional excitement or keen interest; reflex influences which are of an unconscious character; the temperature of the blood; such characteristics of heart muscle as tone, irritability, contractility, and conductivity; physical factors such as size, sex, age, posture, and muscular exercise; changes in the condition of the blood vessels; and certain internal secretions.

Under normal conditions the pulse rate is inversely related to the arterial blood pressure; that is, a rise in the arterial blood pressure causes a decrease in pulse rate, and a decrease in arterial blood pressure causes an increase in pulse rate. On the other hand, the pulse rate is directly related to venous blood pressure (right heart reflex); that is, a rise in the pressure of blood entering the right atrium causes an increase in heart rate.

The pulse rate is very susceptible to changing sensations. Especially is this true in emotional excitement. The heart also responds to reflex influences which are of an unconscious character, such as activity of the visceral organs. After meals the heart increases in rate and strength of beat.

Experimentally it has been demonstrated that abnormally high or low temperatures of the blood affect the frequency of the beat. If the heart is perfused with hot liquid, the rate is increased in proportion to the temperature until the maximum point, about 44°C (111.2°F), is reached. If the temperature is raised above this, the heart soon ceases to beat. In fever the increased rate of the heart action is thought to be due partly to the effect of the higher temperature of the blood on the heart muscle. On the other hand, if cold liquid is perfused through an animal heart, the rate is decreased, and the heart ceases to beat at about 17°C (62.6°F). Slowing of the heart by carefully inducing a fall in body temperature (hypothermia) permits cardiac surgery which would not be possible with a rapidly moving heart at normal body temperature.

Conditions that affect the *irritability*, *contractility*, and *conductivity* of the heart muscle or reduce its normal *tone* are likely to change the frequency of the heartbeat, either accelerating or slowing the action. If the tone is decreased, the strength of the contractions is diminished.

In almost all warm-blooded animals the frequency of the heartbeat is in inverse proportion to the size of the body. An elephant's heart beats about 25 times per minute, a mouse's heart about 700 times per minute. Generally speaking, the smaller the animal, the more rapid is the consumption of oxygen in its tissues. The increased need for oxygen is met partly by a faster heart rate.

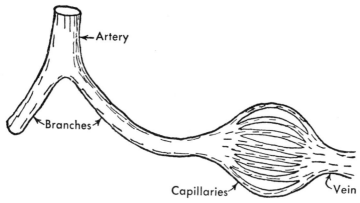

Figure 15–8. Diagram to illustrate variations in velocity of blood flow. A vessel divided into two branches; these are individually of smaller cross section than the main trunk, but united they exceed it. Linear velocity will be lower in the branches than in the parent artery. The sum of the cross-sectional areas of the capillaries is greater than that of the artery or vein.

The heartbeat is somewhat more rapid in women than in men. The heart rate of a female fetus is generally 140 to 145 per minute, that of the male, 130 to 135.

Age has a marked influence. At birth the rate is about 140 per minute, at three years about 100, in youth about 90, in adult life about 75, in old age about 70, and in extreme old age 75 to 80.

The *posture* of the body influences the rate of the heartbeat. Typical figures are: standing, 80; sitting, 70; and recumbent, 66. If an individual remains in a recumbent position and keeps quiet, the work of the heart may be decreased considerably. This is the reason why patients with *certain* types of heart disease are kept in a recumbent position. On other occasions the physician may suggest the sitting position for his heart patient, if the work of the heart is less in that position.

Muscular exercise increases the heart rate. It is due to (1) the activity of the cardioinhibitory center in the medulla being *depressed* by the motor impulses from the more anterior portions of the brain to the muscles, probably by means of collateral fibers to the cardiac center; (2) a stimulation of the cardioaccelerator center; (3) an increased secretion of epinephrine and other hormones which accelerate heart action; (4) increased temperature of the blood; and (5) the pressure of the contracting muscles (including respiratory movement) on the veins sending more blood to the heart, so that the right side is filled more rapidly. This increase of venous pressure reflexly accelerates the heartbeat.

In order to function effectively, the heart requires a certain amount of resistance, and normally this is offered by the blood vessels. The heart will beat more slowly and strongly in response to increased resistance, provided the resistance is not too great. In the latter case the heart is likely to dilate, and its action becomes frequent and weak. The most common causes of abnormally high resistance are lack of distensibility and hardening of the walls of the arteries (arteriosclerosis) and such interference with the venous circulation as occurs in some forms of heart and kidney diseases. When the resistance is below normal, the heartbeats are frequent and weak. Lessened resistance is due either to a relaxed condition of the blood vessels or to the loss of much blood or of much fluid from the blood.

Certain internal secretions affect the frequency and strength of the heartbeat. *Thyroxin* produces a faster pulse. The partial removal of excessively active thyroid glands results in a slower heart rate. *Epinephrine* from the adrenal glands increases the frequency and force of the heartbeat.

MODIFYING FACTORS OF CIRCULATION

Distribution of Blood to Different Parts of the Body. In health the distribution of blood varies, as determined by the needs of the different parts. When the digestive organs are active, they need an extra supply of blood, which may be furnished by redistribution of blood from less active organs. Other causes may result in an increased supply of blood to an organ. If the skin in exposed to high temperatures, the arterioles which bring blood to it are dilated, and the blood flow near the surface is increased. This aids in the radiation of heat and in the control of body temperature. On the other hand, slight chilling causes contraction of the skin arterioles and resulting paleness. The blood supply to the brain is relatively constant. According to recent studies, blood supply to the brain is not reduced during sleep and not increased by mental activity.

The table on page 455 summarizes and gives a general concept of the body's need for blood and the effect of activity on the needs in general.

During physical activity, the amount of blood passing through bones, skeletal muscles, heart, and lungs is increased proportionately to the activity. This means that other organs will receive less blood per unit of time.

Circulation time is the term used to denote the time needed for a substance injected into the antecubital vein to reach an artery or part (for example, the tongue) where it may be detected. This is a subjective means of testing and varies

Movement of Blood Through Organs

Name of Part	Resting Tissue (amount of blood per 100 gm of tissue per unit of time)	Effect of Activity and Needs in General
Skeletal muscle	5 ml	During exercise, the amount of blood needed is proportional to metabolic activity; strenuous exertion, about 35 ml per 100 gm of tissue per minute
Bone	Receives a rich blood supply	During physical activity, there is increased blood flow
Heart and coronary arteries	Receive 10 per cent of cardiac output	The amount then varies directly with heart rate. Flow is lowest during systole
Lungs	Blood passing through the lungs per minute is directly related to heart rate and stroke volume, i.e., if stroke volume is 70 ml and pulse rate is 72, about 5,040 ml of blood pass through the lungs in one minute	
Liver	200–300 ml per minute	Through the sluice mechanism located on the hepatic veins, the liver has the ability to either hold back or give blood to circulation as need arises
Stomach	25 ml per minute	When actively secreting digestive fluids and absorbing end products of digestion and fluids, the amount of blood through organs is tremendously increased
Intestines	65–70 ml per minute	
Kidneys	Receive about 1,300 ml of the total resting output of the heart	Normally, each minute, the glomeruli filter about 120 ml of protein-free-fluid, and at the tubule, about 119 ml are returned to the blood stream
Thyroid gland	560 ml per minute	Metabolic activity functions in relation to thyroxin; it is essential that blood flow and gland activity keep pace with metabolic needs
Spleen	40 ml per minute	The spleen serves as a reservoir for blood, and during excessive demands for blood by the body, the spleen releases blood
Human brain	Receives 15 per cent of cardiac output or about 200 ml per minute	Not affected by physical or mental activity

with the individual's ability to specify the instant the substance is tasted or recognized. Substances usually used in these instances are calcium gluconate, Decholin, saccharin, histamine, and others. Ether has been used; a small amount of ether is introduced into an antecubital vein and the time taken for the ether to be identified on the breath of the subject is measured. It has been found that circulation time from the antecubital vein to the tongue (using saccharin) is about 8 to 15 seconds. From arm to face (using histamine) it is from 14 to 25 seconds before the flush is noted.

Tonus of Blood Vessels. Normally the blood vessels maintain a state of tonus about halfway between contraction and dilatation. It is thought that adjustments in the blood supply to various parts are brought about by increasing or decreasing the tone of the local blood vessels. Two factors are important, (1) vasomotor nerve fibers and (2) chemical stimuli.

1. The vasomotor nerve fibers consist of two antagonistic sets. The vasoconstrictors cause the muscular coats of the blood vessels to contract, lessen the diameter of the vessels, and thereby increase resistance to blood flow. The vasodilator fibers increase the diameter of the blood vessels, probably by allowing the muscular coats to relax, and thereby decrease resistance to blood flow.

2. Chemical substances, such as the lactic acid and carbon dioxide produced during muscular activity, may lessen the tonus of the blood vessels in the part affected, resulting in local dilatation and an increased supply of blood to the part needing it. At the same time, chemoreceptors convey impulses to the vasoconstrictor center, stimulate it, and thereby increase the tonus of blood vessels in

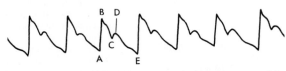

Figure 15–9. Sphygmogram from radial artery. Each pulse wave consists of an ascending portion, or *anacrotic* limb (*AB*), and a descending, or *catacrotic*, limb (*BE*). The ascending limb is smooth and steep and records the increasing distention or systolic pressure of the artery. The descending limb is more slanted and shows smaller waves, the most constant of which is the *dicrotic* wave (*D*) which is preceded by the dicrotic notch (*C*). The artery dilates rapidly and steadily, but its diameter decreases slowly and irregularly. The dicrotic wave is thought to be caused by the closure of the semilunar valve of the aorta.

other parts of the body. On the other hand, angiotensin and hormones, such as epinephrine and vasopressin, cause contraction of the blood vessels.

Epinephrine and ephedrine are used medicinally to cause vasoconstriction, and amyl nitrite is inhaled to bring about vasodilatation, particularly when a condition like angina pectoris[3] makes quick relief necessary. It was formerly thought that changes in the size of the blood vessels were limited to the arteries. It is now thought that not only the arteries but also the veins are capable of dilatation or constriction under the influence of nerve fibers or chemical stimuli.

In surgical shock there is marked interference with the circulation of the blood owing to dilatation of the arteriolar bed and consequent decrease in arterial pressure, which may fall below the level essential to the welfare of the tissues. The pulse becomes rapid and weak, and respiration increases. It is thought that dilatation of the arterioles may be brought about by substances such as histamine formed in injured tissues.

[3] Angina pectoris is a disease characterized by attacks of severe constricting pains in the chest, which radiate into the left arm. It is accompanied by a great sense of cardiac oppression and usually is caused by spasm of a coronary artery due to various pathological states.

Factors Maintaining Arterial Circulation. The most important factors maintaining *arterial* circulation are the pumping action of the heart, the extensibility and elasticity of the arterial walls, the peripheral resistance in the region of the small arteries, especially arterioles in the splanchnic areas, and the quantity of blood in the body.

The Extensibility and Elasticity of the Arterial Walls. During each systole the ventricles force blood into arteries that are already full (about 30 to 60 ml each). The extensibility of the arteries enables them to distend and receive this extra supply of blood. This period of distention corresponds to the systole of the heart. Just as soon as the force is removed, the elasticity of the arteries causes them to contract to their former diameter, and this exerts such a pressure on the contained blood that the blood is forced into the capillaries just rapidly enough to allow the arteries time to reach their usual size during diastole of the heart. The arteries thus not only serve as conducting vessels but exert a force that assists the heart in driving the blood into the capillaries.

The extensibility and elasticity of the arteries change with the health and age of the individual. Sometimes as the result of disease, and usually with age, the arterial walls become less elastic and less well adapted for the unceasing work they are called upon to perform.

Peripheral Resistance. Blood flow is opposed by frictional forces within the vessels. Friction results from the relationships between the layers of fluid wetting the vessel walls and the more central layers of the moving stream. Frictional resistance to flow varies therefore with the character of the fluid, that is, with its viscosity. This means that there is direct relationship between viscosity of the blood and peripheral resistance. The greater the viscosity, the greater the resistance to blood flow.

It is the function of the vasomotor fibers to "set" the diameters of the muscular arterioles in relation to constantly varying local needs for blood. The *elastic* arteries compensate for heart systole and diastole, thus maintaining a *steady flow* of blood in the capillaries, the arteries accommodating the extra blood forced into them during heart systole and by their recoil forcing this blood toward the capillaries during heart diastole. Inasmuch as local needs for blood vary constantly and through constantly varying limits, it is the function of the autonomic nervous system (and locally produced chemical substances such as carbon dioxide), reflecting these needs, to set the diameters of the arterioles so that the peripheral resistance meets these local needs (much blood needed, wide arterioles; less blood needed, narrower arterioles). *On the basis of peripheral resistance thus established,* it is the function of the arterioles, to expand and contract, changing an intermittent flow in the arteries to a steady flow in capillaries It is easily seen that this is a *fine* adjustment, the elastic arteries giving a *steady* flow in capillaries on *many bases of diameter* of arterioles set by local needs. This fine adjustment (associated with optimum activity of the heart) is the mechanism by means of which homeostasis, or state of constancy, of body fluids is maintained.

The kidneys play an important role in the regulation of arterial pressure. It is known that the kidneys can regulate arterial pressure by *increasing* urine output, which decreases volume and lowers pressure; or by *decreasing* urine output, thereby increasing blood volume, which raises arterial pressure. If the kidney is deprived of part of its blood supply from any cause, blood pressure rises. When the kidney is deprived of part of its blood supply, it secretes renin. Renin activates a globulin of a plasma protein which eventually becomes a substance called angiotensin II. This is the most active vasopressor substance known. It also acts on the adrenal cortex to increase aldosterone secretion, which stimulates the kidney to retain sodium and water. The net effect is an increase in blood pressure.

Quantity of Blood. It is evident that, other things being equal, the quantity of blood to be moved is an important factor. Except in cases of severe hemorrhage, loss of blood is compensated for by a transfer of liquid from the tissues into the blood vessels.

Factors Maintaining Venous Circulation. The effect of the pumping action of the heart is not entirely spent in forcing the blood through the arteries and capillaries. A little force still remains to propel the blood back to the heart again, and the presence of valves keeps it flowing in the right direction, i.e., toward the heart. The return flow is also favored by (1) the suction action of the heart caused by the negative pressure of the relaxing ventricle, (2) the heart and respiratory movements, which cause continual changes of pressure against the thin-walled veins in the thorax and abdomen, and (3) the contractions of the skeletal and visceral muscles, which exercise a massaging action upon the veins and, aided by the valves, propel the blood toward the heart.

Veins are capable of dilating, constricting, and storing large amounts of blood and giving blood to circulation when needed. The pressure in peripheral veins depends on the pressure maintained in the right atrium, so that if right atrial pressure is affected, all venous pressure is affected. Right atrial pressure is regulated by the ability of the heart to pump blood and the tendency of blood from the periphery to flow toward the heart.

A strong heartbeat is capable of pumping large quantities of blood with ease; this tends to *decrease* right atrial pressure; a weak heartbeat tends to *elevate* right atrial pressure. Factors that tend to *raise pressure* in the right atrium include increased blood volume, increase in venous tone, increased venous pressure, and dilatation of the small systemic blood vessels. Factors that tend to *reduce* right atrial pressure include reduced blood volume, decreased venous tone, and vasoconstriction of small systemic blood vessels.

These same factors also help to regulate cardiac output, as the amount of blood leaving the left heart depends on the flow of blood into the right heart. In a *standing* position venous pressure is lowest—10 mm Hg to 0 mm Hg above the level of the heart and about 90 mm Hg in the lower legs owing to the effect of gravity. This gravitational effect on the cardiovascular system may be markedly accentuated when the body undergoes angular acceleration, as when a plane rapidly accelerates upward. The centrifugal force pushes the pilot against the seat with many times the normal pull of gravity.

The physiological effect of *positive* gravity causes blood in the vascular system to be forced into vessels of the lower part of the body. Veins of the legs and abdominal cavity become distended with blood. The heart receives very little because blood does not return uphill to the heart. Cardiac output falls very low or may reach zero. Arterial pressure falls and unconsciousness results. A *small* positive acceleration can cause some dizziness, but on the whole, circulation is maintained so that cardiac output is sufficient to prevent blackouts. Pressure suits that cover the legs and place pressure over the abdomen prevent pooling of blood during positive acceleration. Tightening of the abdominal muscles also helps to prevent symptoms.

In negative acceleration, as when a plane dives, the reverse is true. Cardiac output increases and arterial pressure is increased. High pressure causes vessels in the head and brain to be overfilled with blood, and edema of the brain may occur.

The Velocity of the Blood Flow. In all the large arteries the blood moves rapidly; in the capillaries, very slowly; in the veins the velocity is augmented as they increase in size, but it never equals that in the aorta. The underlying principle is that in any stream the velocity is greatest where the cross section of the channel is least, and lowest where the cross section is greatest. When a vessel divides, the sum of the cross sections of the two branches is greater than that of the main trunk. Consequently the velocity will be reduced when arteries divide and increased when veins unite. One reason why the velocity in the veins never equals that in the aorta is that the cross section of the venae cavae is greater than the cross section of the aorta. The actual interchange of materials between the blood and the tissues takes place in the capillaries (since the walls of the arteries and veins are too thick to permit diffusion), hence the value of the slow, constant flow of blood in the capillaries.

The Pulse. The alternate dilatation and contraction of an artery constitute the pulse. When the finger is placed on an artery which approaches the surface of the body and is located over a bone, a sense of resistance is felt, which seems to be increased at intervals corresponding to the heartbeat. In certain arteries the pulse may be seen with the eye. When the finger is placed on a vein, very little resistance is felt; and under ordinary circumstances no pulse can be perceived by the touch or by the eye. The pulse *does not mark* the arrival of the ejected blood at the point felt, but represents the *pressure change* brought about by the ejection of blood from the heart into the already full aorta and propagated as a wave through the blood column and the arterial wall to the periphery.

As each expansion of an artery is produced by a contraction of the heart, the pulse as felt in any superficial artery is a convenient guide for ascertaining the character of the heart's action.

All arteries have a pulse, but it is more readily counted wherever an artery approaches the surface of the body. These locations are as follows: the *radial* artery, at the wrist—the radial artery is usually employed for this purpose on account of its accessible situation; the *temporal* artery, above and to the outer side of the eye; the *external maxillary* (*facial*) artery, where it passes over the lower jawbone, which is about on a line with the corners of the mouth; the *carotid* artery, on the side of the neck; the *brachial* artery, along the inner side of the biceps; the *femoral* artery, where it passes over the pelvic bone; the *popliteal* artery, behind the knee; the *dorsalis pedis*, over the instep of the foot.

Points to Note in Feeling a Pulse. In feeling a pulse, the following points should be noted:

1. The *frequency*, or *number of beats per minute*, should be normal for the individual concerned. The intervals between the beats should be of equal length. A pulse may be irregular in frequency and rhythm. When a pulsation is missed at regular or irregular intervals, the pulse is described as *intermittent*.

2. The *force*, or *strength*, of the heartbeat. Each beat should be of equal strength. Irregularity of strength is due to lack of tone of the cardiac muscle or of the arteries. Occasionally the heartbeat appears to be divided, and two pulsations are felt, the second being weaker than the first. This is known as a *dicrotic* pulse. The pulse is studied by the aid of a sphygmograph, which is an instrument that makes graphic tracings of the rise and fall of an artery. It consists of a tension spring to which a button is attached. The button is placed over the artery, and the pulsations are communicated to a lever, which records the tracings on paper.

3. The *tension*, or *resistance* offered by the artery to the finger, is an indication of the pressure of the blood within the vessels and the elasticity or inelasticity of the arterial walls. A pulse is described as *soft* when the tension is low and the wall of the artery is elastic. A pulse is described as *hard* when the tension is high and the wall of the artery is stiff, thick, and unyielding.

Average Frequency of the Pulse. The average frequency of the pulse in men is 65 to 70; in women, 70 to 80. A person in perfect health may have a much higher or a much lower rate. The relative frequency of the pulse and respirations is about four heartbeats to one respiration.

As a rule, the rapidity of the heart's action is in inverse ratio to its force. An infrequent pulse, within physiological limits, is usually a strong one, and a frequent pulse comparatively feeble, the pulse in fever or debilitating affections becoming weaker as it grows more rapid. As the pulse is an indication of the frequency of the heartbeat, it follows that the factors which influence the heartbeat will also influence the pulse.

Blood Pressure. Blood pressure is defined as the pressure the blood exerts against the walls of the vessels in which it is contained. The term includes arterial, capillary, and venous pressure; but it is commonly applied to pressure existing in the large arteries, usually the left brachial artery just above the elbow. A vein is easily flattened under the finger; an artery offers a stronger resistance. This is an indication of a great difference between arterial and venous pressure. This difference is also shown when an artery and a vein are cut; the blood springs from the artery in a pulsating spurt, indicating a high pressure, whereas the flow from the vein is continuous, and even when copious "wells up" rather than "spurts out," indicating a low pressure.

Blood pressure is highest in the arteries during the period of ventricular systole. This is systolic pressure. During ventricular diastole blood pressure tends to fall and reaches a minimum just before the beginning of the next systole. The minimum is called diastolic pressure. Diastolic pressure represents the pressure in the arteries when the heart is in diastole. Pressure in the arteries is high

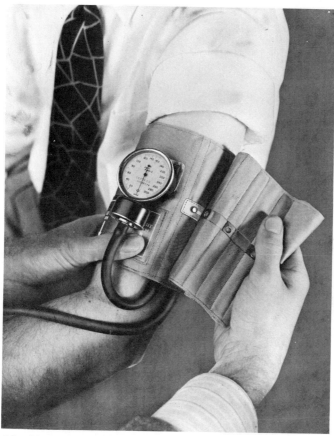

Figure 15–10. Method of using aneroid sphygmomanometer for measuring arterial blood pressure. (Courtesy of Taylor Instrument Company.)

and fluctuating, slightly higher in the large trunks than in their branches. When the blood reaches the capillaries, the surface is multiplied and the friction increased. This offers resistance to the flow, and the result is a *decided drop in the pressure*. Pressure in the veins is low and relatively constant. It must be higher in the small veins than in the large ones they unite to form, as the direction of the blood flow is from the smaller to the larger veins. Their chief effect on blood flow is their great relative ability to hold large volumes of blood under low pressure. When one rises from a recumbent or sitting position to standing, systolic pressure falls and diastolic pressure rises.

Method of Determining Blood Pressure. A rough estimate of systolic blood pressure may be determined at the radial artery. If the radial artery is hard and incompressible, it may indicate either that some change has occurred in the vessel or that the pressure is high. If, however, the pulse is easy to obliterate with the fingers, it is usual to find a low pressure.

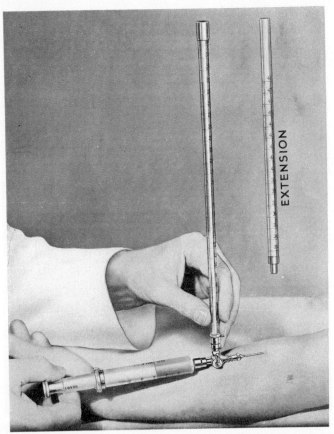

Figure 15–11. Use of water manometer for measuring venous blood pressure. (Courtesy of Taylor Instrument Company.)

Many forms of apparatus have been devised by which a more accurate knowledge of this phenomenon can be obtained (Fig. 15–10). The apparatus is called a sphygmomanometer and consists of a scaled column of mercury (mercury manometer) marked in millimeters, which is connected by rubber tubing with an elastic air bag contained in a fabric cuff. The air bag is in turn connected with a small hand pump. Some instruments are constructed with a spring scale (aneroid manometer), but the principle is the same. The air bag contained in the sleeve is wrapped snugly about the arm just above the elbow over the brachial artery. By placing of the finger upon the pulse at the wrist (as the bag is inflated), a point is finally reached where the pulse disappears; then the bag is very slowly deflated until the pulse can just be felt. The pressure in the bag, therefore, against the artery from the outside, as indicated by the reading on the instrument, is approximately equal to the pressure which the blood exerts against the wall of the artery from the inside. This is known as the *systolic pressure* and is the greatest pressure which cardiac systole causes in the brachial artery. In the auscultation method of reading blood pressure, a stethoscope is placed over the brachial artery in the bend of the elbow. Blood pressure is then indicated by sounds heard

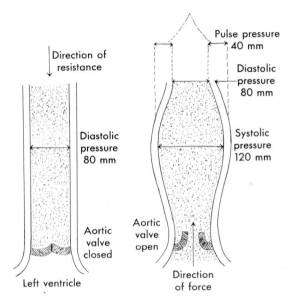

Figure 15–12. Diagram showing relationship between direction of resistance and direction of force in measuring arterial blood pressure.

through the stethoscope. The bag is inflated as before until all sounds cease. It is then slowly deflated until the pulse can just be heard. The reading on the manometer at this time indicates systolic pressure. The deflation of the bag is then continued, and the reading on the manometer just before the last sound of the disappearing pulse indicates *diastolic pressure*, which is the lowest pressure which cardiac diastole causes in the brachial artery.

As pressure falls in the sphygmomanometer, the sounds heard change. First a clear, sharp, tapping sound is heard that corresponds to systolic pressure. The next sounds become softer, and as pressure continues to fall the sound gets louder again, then becomes muffled—this corresponds to diastolic pressure. The sound lasts during the next 4 or 6 mm of Hg fall, and then all sounds cease to be heard. Diastolic pressure is usually recorded when the muffled sound is heard and when the sound is completely lost $\dfrac{120 \text{ (systolic)}}{80\text{–}75 \text{ (diastolic)}}$.

Pulse Pressure. In the normal adult, the height of a pulse, the systolic pressure, is about 120 mm Hg; its lowest point, the diastolic pressure, about 80 mm Hg. The difference between these two pressures is 40 mm Hg. This is called the *pulse pressure.* Factors that affect pulse pressure include stroke volume, output of the heart, and total distensibility of the arterial tree.

The greater the stroke volume, the greater the output and the greater the pressure rise during systole and the *greater* will it *fall* during diastole. This causes a greater pulse pressure. It is evident that pulse pressure varies and is dependent upon (1) the energy of the heart, (2) the elasticity of the blood vessels, (3) the peripheral resistance, and (4) the quantity of circulating blood.

Capillary pressure is the pressure of the blood within the capillaries. Capillary pressure in man when in a sitting position is on the average about 12 to 32 mm Hg. It is somewhat higher when standing and lower when lying down.

Venous pressure is the pressure blood exerts within the veins. Normal venous pressure is on the average 60 to 120 mm of water in a recumbent position. A needle is inserted into the antecubital vein with the needle connected to a water manometer. Venous pressure is expressed in relation to the level of the tricuspid valve. Increasing attention is being given to venous pressure, as it is a valuable index in determining the efficiency of heart muscle (Fig. 15–11).

Normal Degree of Blood Pressure. The average blood pressure of an adult male as recorded by the sphygmomanometer over the brachial artery is about 110 to 120 mm systolic and 65 to 80 mm diastolic. Some observers report that the systolic pressure is higher in men than in women. Individual variations are not uncommon, but 140 mm for men and 130 mm for women are considered the normal upper limits. A systolic pressure of 150 mm suggests hypertension. It varies during the mental and muscular work and shows a tendency to fall during fatigue. Cold, drugs, etc., which constrict the arterial pulse may raise the blood pressure. Heat and the drugs of the vasodilator group, like nitroglycerin, may lower it.

Blood pressure is dependent upon the force of the contraction of the ventricles, the elasticity of the arteries, and the tone of the muscular tissue in their walls, and the resistance offered to the flow of blood through the vessels. Minor factors are respiration and the accompanying pressure changes in the chest cavity, the amount of blood in the body, and gravity. Gravity tends to increase pressure in arteries below the level of the heart and to decrease pressure in arteries at levels above the heart.

Venous pressure is low; but when one is standing, the pressure in the veins of the legs and feet is high, owing to gravity—hence the frequency of varicose veins in the lower limbs. Walking relieves this pressure because the contraction of the muscles forces the blood upward in the veins and the valves of the veins favor this movement.

Variations in Blood Pressure Under Normal Conditions. Variation in arterial blood pressure is compatible with health and is affected by age, sex, muscular activity, digestion, emotions, position, and sleep.

At birth the average systolic pressure is 40 mm Hg. It increases rapidly during the first month to 80 mm. Then it increases slowly, and at the age of 12 years the average reaches 105 mm. At puberty a somewhat sudden increase occurs; the average is 120 mm. A steady, slow, but not marked increase in blood pressure occurs normally from adolescence throughout life.

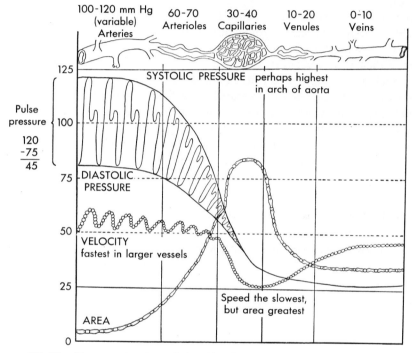

Figure 15–13. Diagram showing relationships between arterial, capillary, and venous blood pressures, relationship of area in various blood vessels, and speed with which blood moves through them.

Blood pressure is increased by muscular activity. The amount of increase depends upon the amount of energy required for the activity and upon individual differences. Systolic pressure is raised slightly after meals. Pain and emotional factors, such as fear or worry, raise systolic pressure considerably. Increased intracranial pressure also raises systolic blood pressure and slows the heart rate. During quiet, restful sleep systolic pressure falls; the lowest point is reached during the first few hours. It rises slowly until the time of waking. Excess weight causes an increase in the number of blood capillaries, raises blood pressure, and thereby places more work on the heart.

Systolic pressure is about 8 to 10 mm lower in women than in men. After menopause there is an increase, and the pressure remains a little above the male average.

Blood pressure is raised above normal when the distensibility of the arteries is reduced, as in arteriosclerosis; by various diseases of the heart, liver, and kidneys which interfere with the venous circulation; by stimulation from the vasoconstrictor center in the medulla; usually by fever and increased intra-cranial pressure, as in fracture of the skull. Blood pressure may also be abnormally high in persons who have increased peripheral resistance due to heredity.

Blood pressure is decreased below normal when the heartbeat is weak, when the blood vessels are relaxed, and when the total quantity of blood in the vessels is reduced. When blood volume is diminished, the mean circulatory filling pressure of the entire circulatory system falls. Venous pressure falls, venous return to the heart diminishes, and cardiac output and pressure in the capillaries fall. Since hydrostatic pressure is decreased, little fluid and oxygen move across the membrane at the arterial end of the capillary into the tissue spaces. However, fluid will move from the tissue spaces into the venous ends of the capillary, and absorption continues from all tissue spaces and the alimentary tract until volume is restored or until fluid in tissue spaces is exhausted. Blood loss causes thirst, and fluids given by mouth will aid in restoration of volume.

QUESTIONS FOR DISCUSSION

1. At rest, the normal *stroke volume* is 80 ml and the heart rate is 72. The normal blood volume is approximately 5.5 liters.
    a. Two patients run up two flights of stairs: At the top of the stairs, examination shows in Patient A that her stroke volume is 100 ml and pulse rate is 130. The stroke volume of Patient B is found to be 86 ml and heart rate 150. Compute the cardiac output of each patient at this time.
    b. In Patient A the heart rate increased from 72 to 130 and in Patient B the rate increase was from 72 to 150. If the increase in the stroke volumes of each had been the same, which patient would be expected to endure moderate exercise and still have a good reserve for further strenuous exercise?
2. Lucy, aged 10, did not participate in physical activity because she said her heart beat too fast and she felt weak. The doctor said she was anemic owing to inadequate nutrition.
    a. Why would anemia affect the heart rate?
    b. Why would weakness be associated with anemia?
    c. What preventive measures would avoid this problem?
    d. What nerves control heart rate and what adjustments are essential during muscular activity?
3. Assume that each time the heart beats, 80 ml of blood moves into the lungs and the heart rate is 72 beats per minute. How much blood moves through the heart to the lungs in one minute, one hour, one day, one week, one month, one year, 10 years, 80 years?
4. How would exercise, rest, and sleep each affect the above findings?

5. What factors maintain and modify circulation?
6. What is the relationship between blood pressure, heart rate, speed of blood flow, and size of blood vessels?
7. Does the heart ever rest? Explain.

SUMMARY

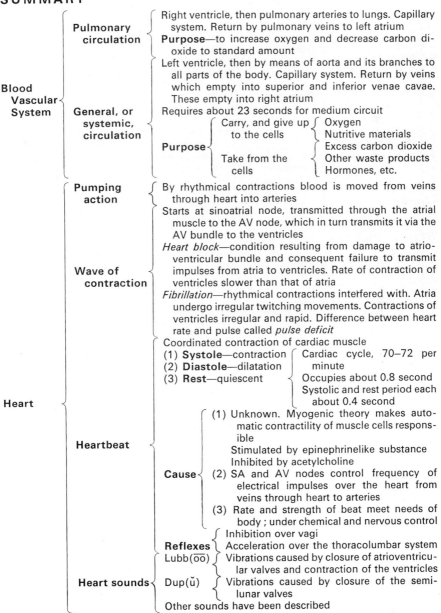

Blood Vascular System

Pulmonary circulation — Right ventricle, then pulmonary arteries to lungs. Capillary system. Return by pulmonary veins to left atrium
Purpose—to increase oxygen and decrease carbon dioxide to standard amount

General, or systemic, circulation — Left ventricle, then by means of aorta and its branches to all parts of the body. Capillary system. Return by veins which empty into superior and inferior venae cavae. These empty into right atrium
Requires about 23 seconds for medium circuit
Purpose
Carry, and give up to the cells — Oxygen / Nutritive materials
Take from the cells — Excess carbon dioxide / Other waste products / Hormones, etc.

Heart

Pumping action — By rhythmical contractions blood is moved from veins through heart into arteries

Wave of contraction — Starts at sinoatrial node, transmitted through the atrial muscle to the AV node, which in turn transmits it via the AV bundle to the ventricles
Heart block—condition resulting from damage to atrioventricular bundle and consequent failure to transmit impulses from atria to ventricles. Rate of contraction of ventricles slower than that of atria
Fibrillation—rhythmical contractions interfered with. Atria undergo irregular twitching movements. Contractions of ventricles irregular and rapid. Difference between heart rate and pulse called *pulse deficit*
Coordinated contraction of cardiac muscle
(1) **Systole**—contraction
(2) **Diastole**—dilatation
(3) **Rest**—quiescent
Cardiac cycle, 70–72 per minute
Occupies about 0.8 second
Systolic and rest period each about 0.4 second

Heartbeat
Cause
(1) Unknown. Myogenic theory makes automatic contractility of muscle cells responsible
Stimulated by epinephrinelike substance
Inhibited by acetylcholine
(2) SA and AV nodes control frequency of electrical impulses over the heart from veins through heart to arteries
(3) Rate and strength of beat meet needs of body; under chemical and nervous control
Reflexes — Inhibition over vagi / Acceleration over the thoracolumbar system

Heart sounds
Lubb($\overline{oo}$) — Vibrations caused by closure of atrioventricular valves and contraction of the ventricles
Dup($\breve{u}$) — Vibrations caused by closure of the semilunar valves
Other sounds have been described

Factors Affecting the Frequency and Strength of the Heart's Action

Characteristics of the Heart's Action

- **Temperature of blood**—Elevated temperature increases rate, and low temperature decreases rate of heartbeat

- **Characteristics of heart muscle**
  - Tonus
  - Irritability
  - Conductivity
  - Contractility

  Anything affecting these factors likely to affect frequency and force of heart's action. Cardiac muscle specially dependent on property of conductivity

- **Physical**
  - **Size**—frequency of heartbeat is in inverse proportion to size of animal. Elephant, 25 per minute. Mouse, 700 per minute
  - **Sex**—frequency of heartbeat higher in women than in men
  - **Age**
    - At birth about 140 per minute
    - At three years about 100 per minute
    - In youth about 90 per minute
    - Adult life about 75
    - Old age 75–80 per minute
  - **Posture**
    - (1) Standing—about 80 per minute
    - (2) Sitting position—about 70
    - (3) Recumbent—about 66
  - **Muscular exercise**
    - Increases frequency of heartbeat
    - (1) Activity of the cardiac inhibitory center in the medulla depressed by motor impulses from brain to muscles
    - (2) Stimulation of cardiac accelerator center
    - (3) Heart action accelerated by epinephrine and other hormones
    - (4) Increased temperature of the blood
    - (5) Pressure of contracting muscles sends more blood to the heart
  - **Resistance**
    - Normally heart requires certain amount of resistance—offered by blood vessels
    - Normal amount—heart action slow and strong
    - Increased amount—heart action frequent and weak
  - **Condition of blood vessels**
    - Arteriosclerosis—loss of elasticity of arteries
    - Relaxation due to loss of blood volume

- **Internal secretions**
  - The thyroid—thyroxin stimulates
  - The adrenals—epinephrine stimulates

Distribution of Blood to Different Parts of the Body
- Quantity of blood in body usually about the same, but quantity in any given part adjusted to needs
- Adjustments dependent on
  - (1) Vasomotor nerves
  - (2) Chemical stimuli

Factors Maintaining Arterial Circulation
- (1) Pumping action of the heart
- (2) The extensibility and elasticity of the arterial walls
- (3) Peripheral resistance
- (4) The quantity of blood in the body
- (5) Kidneys—secretion of renin

Factors Maintaining Venous Circulation
- (1) Some force due to pumping action of the heart
- (2) Suction action of the heart
- (3) Changes of pressure in thorax and abdomen due to heart and respiratory movements
- (4) Contractions of the skeletal muscles
- (5) Veins store and give blood to circulation

Velocity of Blood Flow
- Arteries—blood moves rapidly in large arteries, more slowly in smaller ones
- Capillaries—blood moves very slowly
- Veins—blood moves slowly in small veins, more rapidly in larger veins, but never as rapidly as in arteries

Pulse
- Alternate dilatation and contraction of artery, corresponding to heartbeat
- **Locations where pulse may be counted** — Radial artery, temporal artery, external maxillary artery, carotid artery, brachial artery, femoral artery, popliteal artery, dorsalis pedis artery
- **Points to note**
  - Frequency
  - Force, or strength
  - Tension, or resistance — Hard / Soft
- **Pulse rate**
  - Factors which influence heartbeat also influence pulse
  - Average — 65–70 in men / 70–80 in women
  - Ratio of pulse to respiration is about 4 to 1

Blood Pressure
- Pressure blood exerts against walls of vessels
- **Arterial** — High and fluctuating
  - Not uniform
    - (1) Highest during ventricular contraction = systolic pressure
    - (2) Lowest before beginning of next systole = diastolic pressure
    - (3) Increases with age
    - (4) Decreases if heart or arteries lose their tone
- **Venous**—low and constant
- **Systolic**—greatest pressure which contractions of heart cause. Average systolic pressure in brachial artery of adult, 110–120 mm
- **Diastolic**—lowest point to which blood pressure drops between beats. Average diastolic pressure in brachial artery of adult, 65–80 mm
- **Varies**
  - During mental and muscular work and shows a tendency to fall during fatigue
  - Cold, drugs, etc., which constrict arterioles may raise it
  - Heat, drugs of the vasodilator group may lower it
- **Dependent upon**
  - Strength of the heartbeat
  - Elasticity of the arteries and tone of muscular tissue in walls
  - Resistance offered
  - Other factors
    - Respiration and resulting changes in chest cavity
    - Amount of blood in body
    - Gravity
- **Increased by**
  - Arteriosclerosis
  - Heart, liver, and kidney diseases which interfere with venous circulation
  - Stimulus from vasoconstrictor center in the medulla which constricts arteries and veins
  - Fever
- **Reduced**
  - When the heartbeat is weak
  - When the blood vessels are relaxed
  - When the total quantity of blood in the vessels is reduced
- **Determined by use of sphygmomanometer**
  - (1) Two types — mercury / aneroid
  - (2) Types similar in principle; each consists of an air bag for attachment to arm, a hand pump for inflating the bag and a scaled device for measurement of pressure in bag, which is equal to pressure of blood against wall of artery

Pulse Pressure
- Difference between systolic and diastolic pressure
- **Indicates**
  - How well the heart is overcoming resistance offered
  - How successfully it is driving blood to the periphery
  - Condition of arteries
- **Dependent upon**
  - Energy of heart
  - Elasticity of blood vessels
  - Peripheral resistance
  - Quantity of blood circulating

16

Lymph: Lymph Vascular System, Physiology. The Reticuloendothelial System

THE LYMPHATIC SYSTEM has been called the "middle man" between blood and tissue fluid. Colloidal material cannot re-enter the blood capillaries; hence, the lymph capillaries are ever present to receive colloids as well as electrolytes, water, and other substances and return them to the blood stream. Lymph nodes function in the protective mechanism of the body.

LYMPH

Composition of Lymph. Lymph, tissue fluid, and plasma are similar in composition. Lymph consists of a fluid plasma containing a variable number of lymphocytes, a few granulocytes, no blood platelets (hence clots slowly), carbon dioxide, and *very* small quantities of oxygen. Other contained substances vary in kinds and amounts in relation to the location of lymphatic vessels. In the lymphatics of the intestine, fat content is high during digestion. Water, glucose, and salts are in about the same concentration as in blood plasma. Protein concentration is lower. Enzymes and antibodies are also present. Lymph has a specific gravity between 1.015 and 1.023.

Sources of Lymph. Lymph is formed from tissue fluid by the physical process of filtration. Colloidal substances from tissue fluid are returned to lymph capillaries rather than to the blood. Water, crystalloids, and other substances also enter the lymph capillaries. Since the process of tissue-fluid formation is continuous, lymph formation is also continuous. The lymph system supplements the capillaries and veins in the return of the tissue fluid to the blood. This drainage system is called the lymph vascular system. Even with this system, fluid may accumulate in the tissue spaces, although it does not do so normally. Other factors influencing movement through the cell membrane (as discussed in Chap. 3) affect capillary diffusion.

Physiology. Filtration pressure will under normal conditions be highest in blood capillaries (as compared with tissue-fluid pressure and lymph pressure) because of beating heart and elastic arteries. Substances like the colloids, therefore, which are filtered out of the blood capillaries cannot enter them again but

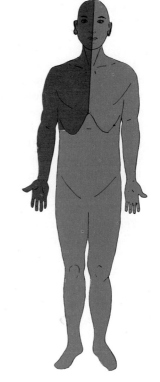

Figure 16–1. The regions from which lymph flows into the right lymphatic duct are suggested by the *red* area, those which are tributary to the thoracic duct by the *blue* area.

can enter the lymph capillaries. Hence, it is frequently said that one function of the lymph capillaries is to return blood proteins from tissue fluids to the blood stream.

Another function of the lymph capillaries is to maintain volume and pressure conditions in the spaces occupied by the tissue fluids. Hydrostatic pressure maintained by the heart and elastic arteries is sufficient to supply fluids via the tissue spaces to the cells; but lacking this hydrostatic pressure to remove the fluids, the extra lymph capillaries are needed. Some authors speak of the great ability of the endothelial cells of capillary walls to make cell cement, which is constantly destroyed by the hydrostatic pressure of the blood escaping into the tissue spaces.

The amount of blood plasma filtering from capillaries into tissue spaces will be directly related to the *difference* in hydrostatic pressure against capillary walls from inside and from outside and will be *selective* only in relation to the size of particles passing through the meshwork of the filter.

Some of the substances pass through the tissues by diffusion rather than by filtration.

Lymph Vascular System

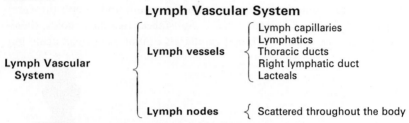

Lymph Vessels. The plan upon which the lymphatic system is constructed is similar to that of the blood vascular system, if the heart and the arteries are omitted. In the tissues are located the closed *ends of minute microscopic vessels, called lymph capillaries*, which are comparable to, and often larger and more permeable than, the blood capillaries. The lymph capillaries are distributed in the same manner as the blood capillaries. Just as the blood capillaries unite to form veins, the lymph capillaries unite to form larger vessels called *lymphatics*. The lymphatics continue to unite and form larger and larger vessels until finally they converge into two main channels, (1) the thoracic duct, and (2) the right lymphatic duct.

The thoracic duct, or *left lymphatic*, begins in the dilatation called the *cisterna chyli* (chyle cistern), located on the front of the body of the second lumbar vertebra. It ascends upward in front of the bodies of the vertebrae and enters the brachiocephalic vein at the angle of junction of the left internal jugular and left subclavian veins. It is from 38 to 45 cm (15.2 to 18 in.) long, about 4 to 6 mm in diameter, and has several valves. At its termination a pair of valves prevent the passage of venous blood into the duct. It receives the lymph from the left side of the head, neck, and chest, all of the abdomen, and both lower limbs, and also the chyle from the lacteals. Its dilatation, the cisterna chyli, receives the lymph from the lower extremities and from the walls and viscera of the pelvis and abdomen.

The right lymphatic duct is a short vessel, usually about 1.25 cm (½ in.) in length. It pours its contents into the brachiocephalic vein at the junction of the right internal jugular and subclavian veins. Its orifice is guarded by two semilunar valves.

The lymphatics from the right side of the head, neck, the right arm, and the upper part of the trunk enter the right lymphatic duct. The parts drained by each are suggested by Figure 16–1.

Structure of the Lymph Vessels. The lymphatics resemble the veins in their structure as well as in their arrangement. The smallest consists of a single layer of endothelial cells which have a peculiar dentated outline. The larger vessels have three coats similar to those of the veins, except that they are thinner and more transparent. Their valves are like those of the veins but are so close together that when distended they give the vessel a beaded or jointed appearance. They are usually absent in the smaller networks. The valves allow the passage of material from the smaller to the larger lymphatics and from these into the veins.

Distribution and Classification of Lymph Vessels. In general the lymph vessels accompany and are closely parallel to the veins. Lymph vessels have been found in nearly every tissue and organ which contain blood vessels. The nails, cuticle, and hair are without them, but they permeate most other organs. No lymphatic *capillaries* have been found in the central nervous system, the *internal* ear, cartilage, epidermis, spleen, or eyeball. Lymphatic vessels have not yet been demonstrated in the cornea, but lymph spaces are represented by the channels in which nerve fibers run. These channels are lined by an endothelium. The lymph, like the blood in the veins, is returned from the limbs and viscera by a superficial and a deep set of vessels. The superficial lymph vessels are placed immediately beneath the skin and accompany the superficial veins. In certain regions they join the deep lymphatics by penetrating the deep fasciae. In the interior of the body they lie in the submucous tissue throughout the whole length of the gastropulmonary and genitourinary tracts and in the subserous tissue of the thoracic and abdominal walls. The deep lymphatics accompany the deep veins. They are fewer in number and are larger than the superficial lymphatics.

The Lacteals. The lymphatics that have their origin in the villi of the small intestine are called *lacteals*. During the process of digestion they are filled with chyle, white in color from the fat particles suspended in it. The lacteals enter the lymphatic vessels that run between the layers of the mesentery, pass through the mesenteric nodes, and finally terminate in the cisterna chyli.

Physiology. The function of the lymphatics is to carry tissue fluid from the tissues to the veins. Functionally, they may be considered supplementary to the capillaries and the veins, as they gather up a part of the fluid which exudes through the thin capillary walls and return it to the brachiocephalic veins. Here it becomes mixed with the blood and enters the superior vena cava and then the right atrium of the heart. The function of the lacteals is to help in the absorption of digested food, especially fats.

Lymph nodes are small, oval or bean-shaped bodies, varying in size from that of a pinhead to that of an almond, and are located in the course of the lymphatics. They generally present a slight depression, called the *hilus*, on one side. The blood vessels enter and leave through the hilus. The outer covering is a capsule of connective tissue containing a few smooth muscle fibers. The capsule sends fibrous bands called *trabeculae* into the substance of the node, dividing it into irregular spaces, which communicate freely with each other. The irregular spaces are occupied by a mass of lymphoid tissue, which, however, does not quite fill them as it never touches the capsule or trabeculae but leaves a narrow interval between itself and them. The spaces thus left form channels for the passage of the lymph, which enters by several afferent vessels. After circulating through the node, the lymph is carried out by efferent vessels which emerge from the hilus. The trabeculae support a free supply of blood vessels. It is said that no lymph on its way from the lymph capillaries ever reaches the blood stream without passing through at least one node.

Location of Nodes.   There are a superficial and a deep set of nodes just as

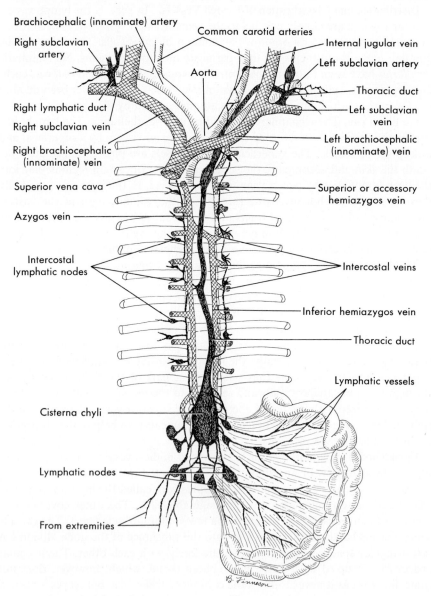

Figure 16–2.   Lymphatic drainage to cisterna chyli and thoracic duct.

there are a superficial and a deep set of lymphatics and veins. Occasionally, a node exists alone, but they are usually in groups or chains at the sides of the great blood vessels. Lymph nodes are found on the back of the head and neck, draining the scalp; around the sternomastoid muscle, draining the back of the tongue, the pharynx, nasal cavities, roof of the mouth, and face; and under the rami of the mandible, draining the floor of the mouth.

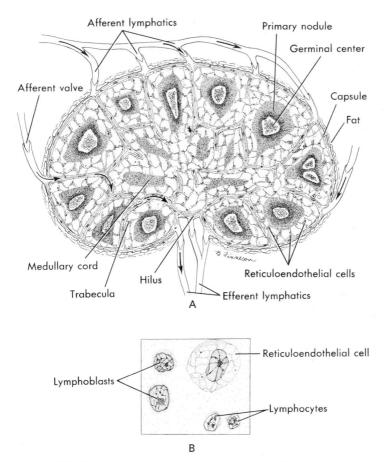

Figure 16–3. (*A*) Diagram of a lymph node, highly magnified. (*B*) Cells found in lymph nodes.

In the upper extremities there are three groups—a small one at the bend of the elbow, which drains the hand and forearm; a larger group in the axillary space, into which the first group drains; and a still larger group under the pectoral muscles. The last-named drains the mammary gland and the skin and muscles of the chest.

In the lower extremities there is usually a small node at the upper part of the anterior tibial vessels, and in the popliteal space back of the knee there are several; but the greater number are massed in the groin. These nodes drain the lower extremities and the lower part of the abdominal wall. The lymph nodes of the abdomen and pelvis are divided into a parietal and a visceral group. The parietal nodes are behind the peritoneum and in close association with the larger blood vessels. The visceral nodes are associated with the visceral arteries. The lymph nodes of the thorax are similarly divided into a parietal set, situated in the thoracic wall, and a visceral set associated with the heart, pericardium, trachea, lungs, pleura, thymus, and esophagus.

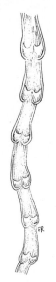

Figure 16–4. Diagram illustrating valves of lymphatics.

Physiology of the Lymph Nodes. The lymph nodes are credited with two important functions.

1. They produce lymphocytes and antibodies. As lymph passes through the nodes, fresh lymphocytes are added to the fluid. The lymphocytes are formed in the nodes by cell division. Serum globulin and antibodies are also added to lymph in the nodes.

2. The nodes are located in the course of the lymph vessels, and the lymph takes a tortuous course among the cells of the node. This suggests that they serve as filters and are a defense against the spread of infection. The lymph draining from an infected area carries the products of suppuration, and perhaps the infecting organisms themselves, to the first nodes in its pathway. Unless the infection is severe, the odds are against the organisms, and the lymph is more or less "disinfected" before it passes on. Nodes engaged in such a struggle are usually enlarged and tender, and if they are overpowered, they themselves may become the foci of infection.

Factors Controlling the Flow of Lymph. The flow of tissue fluid from the tissue spaces to the lymph capillaries and on to the veins is maintained chiefly by three factors.

1. Differences in Pressure. The tissue fluid is under greater pressure than the lymph in the lymph capillaries, and the pressure in the larger lymphatics near the ducts is much less than in the smaller vessels. Consequently the lymphatics form a system of vessels leading from a region of high pressure, the tissues, to a region of low pressure, the interior of the large veins of the neck.

2. Muscular Movements and Valves. Contractions of the skeletal muscles compress the lymph vessels and force the lymph on toward the larger ducts. The numerous valves prevent a return flow in the backward direction. The flow of lymph from resting muscles is small in quantity, but during muscular exercise and massage it is increased. The flow of chyle is greatly assisted by the peristaltic and rhythmical contractions of the muscular coats of the intestines. Pulsation waves moving over the enormous number of minute arteries existing everywhere act to "push ahead" the lymph from valve to valve, on to the larger lymphatics.

3. Respiratory Movements. During each inspiration the pressure on the thoracic duct is less than on the lymphatics outside the thorax, and lymph is accordingly sucked into the duct. During the succeeding expiration the pressure on the thoracic duct is increased, and some of its contents, prevented by the valve from escaping below, are pressed out into the brachiocephalic veins.

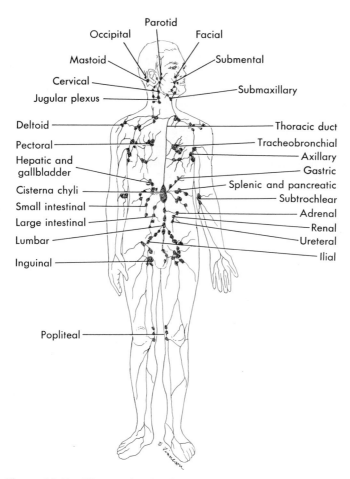

Figure 16–5. Diagram showing location of lymph nodes of the body.

Edema. The fluid in the various tissues of the body varies in amount from time to time, but under normal circumstances remains fairly constant. Under abnormal conditions, these limits may be exceeded, and the result is known as edema. Similar excessive accumulations may also occur in the larger fluid spaces, the serous cavities.

Among the possible causes of edema are:

Any obstruction to the flow of lymph from the tissues, such as an infection in the lymph nodes.

An excessive formation, the fluid gathering in the tissues faster than it can be carried away by a normal flow.

General or local changes in capillary blood pressure.

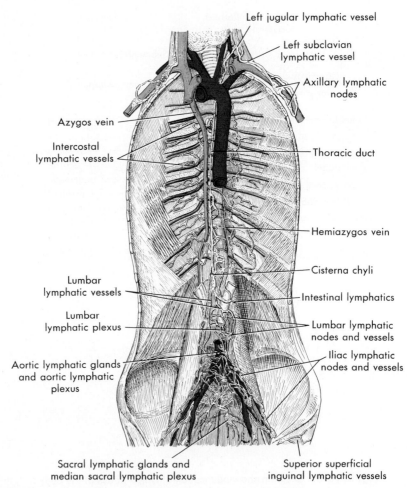

Figure 16–6. The lymph nodes and vessels on the dorsal body wall. (Modified from Toldt.)

Increased permeability of capillary membrane.

Edema may also be a symptom of some other primary conditions, such as certain types of cardiac, liver, and renal diseases, or mechanical obstruction of veins.

The spleen (lien) is a highly vascular, bean-shaped organ situated directly

beneath the diaphragm, behind and to the left of the stomach. It is covered
by peritoneum and held in position by folds of this membrane. Beneath the
serous coat is a connective-tissue capsule from which trabeculae run inward,

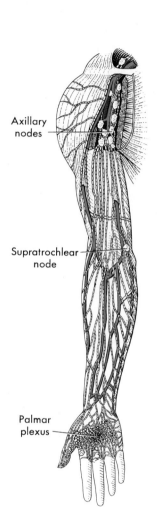

Axillary
nodes

Supratrochlear
node

Palmar
plexus

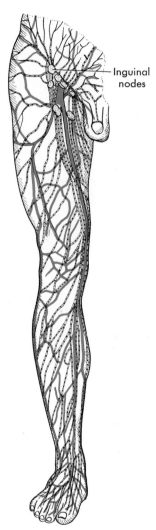

Inguinal
nodes

Figure 16–7. The lymph nodes and vessels of the upper limb.

Figure 16–8. The lymph nodes and vessels of the lower limb.

forming a framework, in the interstices of which is found the *splenic pulp*, made
up of a network of fibrillae and blood cells—red corpuscles, the various forms
of white cells, and large, rounded phagocytic cells (the macrophages of the reticuloendothelial system), which engulf fragmentary red corpuscles and invading
organisms such as the *Salmonella typhosa*. Scattered throughout the pulp are

masses of lymphoid tissue called malpighian follicles.[1] Smooth muscle fibers are found in both the outer capsule and the trabeculae.

The blood supply is brought by the splenic artery, a branch of the celiac artery; the splenic artery divides into six or more branches, which enter the concave side of the spleen at a depression called the hilum. The arrangement of the blood vessels is peculiar to this organ. After entering, the arteries divide into many branches and terminate in tufts of arterioles, which open freely into the splenic pulp. Each follicle lies in close relation to a small artery. The blood is collected by thin-walled veins, which unite to form the splenic vein. The splenic vein unites with the superior mesenteric to form the portal vein, which carries the blood to the liver.

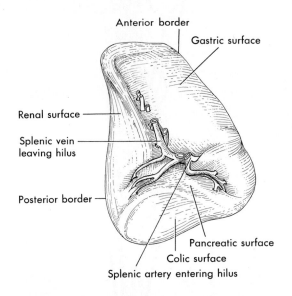

Anterior border

Gastric surface

Renal surface

Splenic vein leaving hilus

Posterior border

Pancreatic surface

Colic surface

Splenic artery entering hilus

Figure 16–9. The spleen, dorsal surface, showing large number of arteries and veins supplying this small organ.

Physiology. The spleen serves as a major place of destruction of aged red blood cells or a place of preparation for their destruction by the liver and as a reservoir of blood cells to be liberated under such conditions as exercise or emotional stress. The malpighian follicles are a place of origin for lymphocytes.

The sinusoids of the spleen are incompletely lined with RE cells. It is thought that the spleen produces both erythrocytes and leukocytes during fetal life and also in the adult after certain types of anemia. The spleen undergoes rhythmical variations in size; and by means of this activity, which may be increased under certain physiological demands, it controls mechanically both the quality and volume of the blood by undergoing greater periodic contractions during severe exercise, decrease in barometric pressure, carbon monoxide poisoning, asphyxia, or hemorrhage, in which an "emergency call" is made by the tissues for oxygen.

[1] Marcello Malpighi (1628–1694), a physician and professor of comparative anatomy at Bologna.

Its structure is well adapted to this function as the circulation is, in part, an open one and is sluggish. Also, the distribution of smooth muscle fibers within the trabeculae makes possible these rhythmical contractions which occur about once a minute, less frequently during digestion, and more vigorously during emergency demands. It is estimated that the spleen can release about 150 ml of blood (almost entirely erythrocytes) to circulation.

Enlargement of the spleen occurs in certain pathological conditions (Banti's disease, Gaucher's disease, certain anemias), and splenectomy gives favorable results. Enlargement also accompanies malaria, leukemia, Hodgkin's disease; but removal in these cases is medically contraindicated.

The thymus, as part of the lymphatic system, usually consists of two lobes, but they may unite to form a single lobe or may have an intermediate lobe between

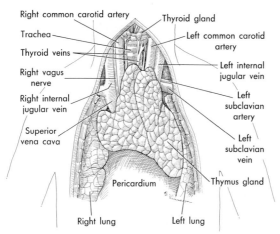

Right common carotid artery
Thyroid gland
Trachea
Thyroid veins
Right vagus nerve
Right internal jugular vein
Superior vena cava
Left common carotid artery
Left internal jugular vein
Left subclavian artery
Left subclavian vein
Pericardium
Thymus gland
Right lung
Left lung

Figure 16–10.   Thymus gland of newborn infant.

them. It is situated in the upper chest cavity along the trachea, overlapping the great blood vessels as they leave the heart. Each lobe has several lobules, each of which is composed of an outer *cortex* and *medulla*. The cortex is composed of closely arranged lymphocytes which obscure the fewer number of reticular cells. In the medulla the reticulum is coarser and the lymphoid cells are fewer in number. There are many reticular cells. In the medulla are rounded nests of cells, 30 to 100 μ in diameter, called the corpuscles of Hassall.[2] The arteries are derived from the internal thoracic and the superior and inferior thyroids. The nerves are derived from the vagi of the craniosacral system and from the thoracolumbar system. At birth the thymus is large, and it gradually decreases in size after puberty, the corpuscles of Hassall disappearing more slowly than other portions.

Experiments with animals have shown that stress situations reduce the size of the thymus markedly. Recent research clearly demonstrates that the thymus is

[2] Arthur Hill Hassall, English physician (1817–1894).

essential for the normal development of immunological functioning in the mouse. In the mouse, if the thymus is removed at birth, it fails to produce circulating antibodies against foreign substances. For example, a thymectomized mouse will accept a skin graft from an unrelated animal. Normally the skin graft is rejected.

It is believed that the thymus sends a messenger substance or factor to the spleen and to all lymph glands that prompts these organs to form lymphocytes themselves which function from then on in the production of a substance capable of reacting with antigens. This messenger substance is believed to be a hormone, which to date is unnamed.

Tonsillar tissue is composed of a mass of lymphoid tissue embedded in mucous membrane. The epithelial lining dips between the lymphoid tissue forming crypts or glandlike pits. Many reticuloendothelial cells are found in the tonsils.

THE RETICULOENDOTHELIAL SYSTEM

The reticuloendothelial system (RES) is composed of cells and tissue that function in phagocytizing microorganisms or foreign particles or are capable of forming antibodies (immune bodies) against them. The RE cells also have the ability (1) to develop into lymphocytes in the lymph nodes, (2) to develop into tissue histocytes which wander through tissues and function as phagocytes, and (3) to form plasma cells which are the primary producers of immune bodies.

Reticular connective tissue is characterized by fibers which form an interlacing network or reticulum, in which are formed reticular cells. The cells are usually stellate in shape with many processes and centrally placed nuclei.

RE cells are mainly aggregated in the spleen, bone marrow, lymph nodes, tonsils, and thymus. Large numbers of stellate RE cells (Küpffer cells) are located along the liver sinusoids. RE cells also lie along the sinusoids of the

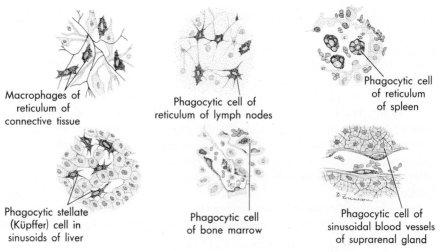

Macrophages of reticulum of connective tissue

Phagocytic cell of reticulum of lymph nodes

Phagocytic cell of reticulum of spleen

Phagocytic stellate (Küpffer) cell in sinusoids of liver

Phagocytic cell of bone marrow

Phagocytic cell of sinusoidal blood vessels of suprarenal gland

Figure 16–11. Cells of the reticuloendothelial system.

pituitary and adrenals and along all blood vessels. The microglia cells of the nervous system and macrophages and plasma cells of loose connective tissue are components of the RE system.

It is believed that RE cells are probably derived from primitive mesenchymal cells which form the hemopoietic cells.

The functions of this system cannot be overemphasized in the normal individual, and in pathological conditions it is the active agent in the removal of broken-down tissue cells and microorganisms and in the formation of antibodies.

QUESTIONS FOR DISCUSSION

Mr. Green was admitted to the hospital with an infected toe. There was a red streak up the leg, associated with large painful masses in the groin. His foot and leg were edematous. He was taken to surgery for drainage of the toe infection and given antibiotics, and the leg was placed at rest.

1. What was the cause of the red streak in the leg?
2. The masses in the groin were enlarged lymph nodes. Explain why they were so large and painful.
3. Where else in the body are lymph nodes found and what is their function?
4. What were some of the probable causes of the edema in Mr. Green's leg and why was it placed at rest?
5. Explain why lymph capillaries, vessels, and nodes are important in everyday living.
6. What is believed to be the function of the thymus gland?
7. What are antibodies? Are they helpful or harmful? In what ways?

SUMMARY

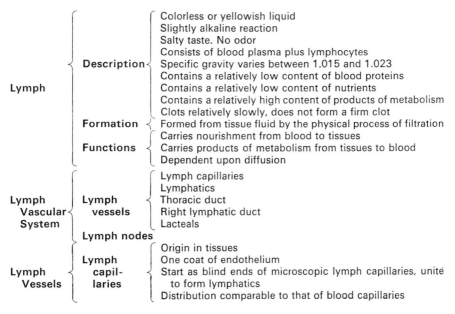

Lymph	Description	Colorless or yellowish liquid Slightly alkaline reaction Salty taste. No odor Consists of blood plasma plus lymphocytes Specific gravity varies between 1.015 and 1.023 Contains a relatively low content of blood proteins Contains a relatively low content of nutrients Contains a relatively high content of products of metabolism Clots relatively slowly, does not form a firm clot
	Formation	Formed from tissue fluid by the physical process of filtration
	Functions	Carries nourishment from blood to tissues Carries products of metabolism from tissues to blood Dependent upon diffusion
Lymph Vascular System	Lymph vessels	Lymph capillaries Lymphatics Thoracic duct Right lymphatic duct Lacteals
	Lymph nodes	
Lymph Vessels	Lymph capillaries	Origin in tissues One coat of endothelium Start as blind ends of microscopic lymph capillaries, unite to form lymphatics Distribution comparable to that of blood capillaries

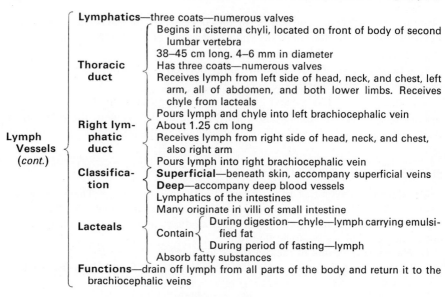

Lymph Vessels *(cont.)*

Lymphatics—three coats—numerous valves

Thoracic duct
- Begins in cisterna chyli, located on front of body of second lumbar vertebra
- 38–45 cm long. 4–6 mm in diameter
- Has three coats—numerous valves
- Receives lymph from left side of head, neck, and chest, left arm, all of abdomen, and both lower limbs. Receives chyle from lacteals
- Pours lymph and chyle into left brachiocephalic vein

Right lymphatic duct
- About 1.25 cm long
- Receives lymph from right side of head, neck, and chest, also right arm
- Pours lymph into right brachiocephalic vein

Classification
- **Superficial**—beneath skin, accompany superficial veins
- **Deep**—accompany deep blood vessels

Lacteals
- Lymphatics of the intestines
- Many originate in villi of small intestine
- Contain
  - During digestion—chyle—lymph carrying emulsified fat
  - During period of fasting—lymph
- Absorb fatty substances

Functions—drain off lymph from all parts of the body and return it to the brachiocephalic veins

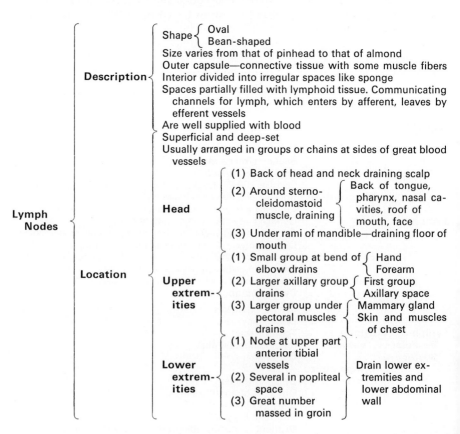

Lymph Nodes

Description
- Shape
  - Oval
  - Bean-shaped
- Size varies from that of pinhead to that of almond
- Outer capsule—connective tissue with some muscle fibers
- Interior divided into irregular spaces like sponge
- Spaces partially filled with lymphoid tissue. Communicating channels for lymph, which enters by afferent, leaves by efferent vessels
- Are well supplied with blood

Location
- Superficial and deep-set
- Usually arranged in groups or chains at sides of great blood vessels

Head
- (1) Back of head and neck draining scalp
- (2) Around sternocleidomastoid muscle, draining
  - Back of tongue, pharynx, nasal cavities, roof of mouth, face
- (3) Under rami of mandible—draining floor of mouth

Upper extremities
- (1) Small group at bend of elbow drains
  - Hand
  - Forearm
- (2) Larger axillary group drains
  - First group
  - Axillary space
- (3) Larger group under pectoral muscles drains
  - Mammary gland
  - Skin and muscles of chest

Lower extremities
- (1) Node at upper part anterior tibial vessels
- (2) Several in popliteal space
- (3) Great number massed in groin

Drain lower extremities and lower abdominal wall

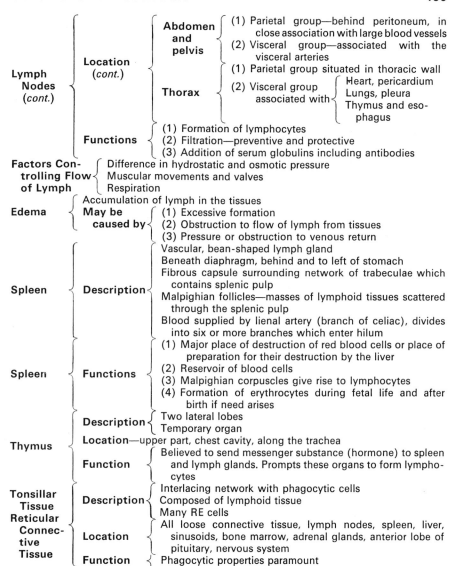

Lymph Nodes (cont.)

Location (cont.)

Abdomen and pelvis
(1) Parietal group—behind peritoneum, in close association with large blood vessels
(2) Visceral group—associated with the visceral arteries

Thorax
(1) Parietal group situated in thoracic wall
(2) Visceral group associated with
- Heart, pericardium
- Lungs, pleura
- Thymus and esophagus

Functions
(1) Formation of lymphocytes
(2) Filtration—preventive and protective
(3) Addition of serum globulins including antibodies

Factors Controlling Flow of Lymph
Difference in hydrostatic and osmotic pressure
Muscular movements and valves
Respiration

Edema
Accumulation of lymph in the tissues
May be caused by
(1) Excessive formation
(2) Obstruction to flow of lymph from tissues
(3) Pressure or obstruction to venous return

Spleen

Description
Vascular, bean-shaped lymph gland
Beneath diaphragm, behind and to left of stomach
Fibrous capsule surrounding network of trabeculae which contains splenic pulp
Malpighian follicles—masses of lymphoid tissues scattered through the splenic pulp
Blood supplied by lienal artery (branch of celiac), divides into six or more branches which enter hilum

Spleen

Functions
(1) Major place of destruction of red blood cells or place of preparation for their destruction by the liver
(2) Reservoir of blood cells
(3) Malpighian corpuscles give rise to lymphocytes
(4) Formation of erythrocytes during fetal life and after birth if need arises

Thymus

Description
Two lateral lobes
Temporary organ

Location—upper part, chest cavity, along the trachea

Function
Believed to send messenger substance (hormone) to spleen and lymph glands. Prompts these organs to form lymphocytes

Tonsillar Tissue Reticular Connective Tissue

Description
Interlacing network with phagocytic cells
Composed of lymphoid tissue
Many RE cells

Location
All loose connective tissue, lymph nodes, spleen, liver, sinusoids, bone marrow, adrenal glands, anterior lobe of pituitary, nervous system

Function
Phagocytic properties paramount

17

Glands, Secretions, Hormones: Classification, Structure, and Physiology

PHYSIOLOGICAL ORGANIZATION is brought about by the higher centers (hypothalamus) of the nervous system and by chemical substances in the circulatory fluids which are carried everywhere in the body, bringing about local changes in equilibrium of physical and chemical conditions and effecting correlations of these changes in a body-wide way.

Glands are groups of cells which take certain materials from tissue fluid and make new substances of them. All cells in the body take, from the surrounding fluid, substances essential for their nutrition and give off products of their metabolism. Certain cells of the body also manufacture specific substances, not for their own use, but to be extruded from the cell and used elsewhere in the body, such as, for example, *secretions* of the gastrointestinal tract. Other cells form substances that are called excretions, such as sweat. These cells are known as *gland cells*, or glandular epithelium. A group of such cells that have definite structure for the specific purpose of either secretion or excretion is called a *gland*.

Classification. Glands may be classified into groups: (1) *exocrine*, or *duct*, *glands*, which secrete into a cavity or on the body surface, and (2) *endocrine* (from the Greek, *to separate within*), *incretory*, or *ductless*, *glands*, which secrete into the tissue fluid and blood. Many glands have both exocrine and endocrine secretions, such as for instance the pancreas, and may therefore be called *heterocrine glands*. On this basis all exocrine glands may be classed as heterocrine, since they all also "secrete within." From another point of view glands may be classed as *mucous* if their secretions contain *mucin,* or as *serous* if their secretions contain *serum.* Some glands are of a mixed type, containing both serous cells and mucous cells, as in the submaxillary salivary gland. Again, glands may be grouped according to their structure into *lymphoid* glands and *epithelial* glands. Also, every cell may be thought of as a gland, its excretions (as far as the cell itself is concerned) being considered as secretions or excretions to the body as a whole, depending on whether they have further value to the body or are useless.

Glands of External Secretions

These glands may consist of a single cell, or may be a simple pocketlike depression of a membrane, or may consist of a vast number of such secreting membranous depressions. The pancreas and liver are examples of the last. The glandular epithelium is supported by loose connective tissue carrying a dense network of capillaries close to the secreting cells. Cells from surface epithelium grow down into the underlying tissue forming epithelial cords, called tubules. The cords separate and form a duct. The deepest cells become secretory. It is the arrangement of cells in the secretory portion that determines the type of exocrine gland. The secretory cells become highly specialized.

These glands may be classed according to structure:

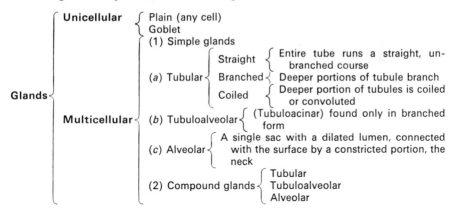

The Simple Glands. The simple tubular glands are divided in relation to the structure of the fundus into straight, branched, and coiled. The *straight* tubular glands are found in the large intestine; the branched glands may have several branches and are found in the gastric and uterine mucosa; the coiled tubular glands are found in the skin (the sweat glands).

The simple tubuloalveolar glands are of the branched form. This group includes the smaller glands of the respiratory tract. The mucous glands of the esophagus and Brunner's glands of the duodenum are included in this group by some histologists, since they are frequently enlarged toward their ends.

The simple branched alveolar glands which have a common duct that gives rise to a number of saccules are seen in the meibomian[1] glands of the eyelid and the large sebaceous glands.

The Compound Glands. The compound glands may be tubular, tubulo-alveolar, or alveolar. The *compound tubular* glands have a large number of distinct duct systems, which eventually open into a main or common excretory duct. The liver, kidneys, and testes are good examples of these glands.

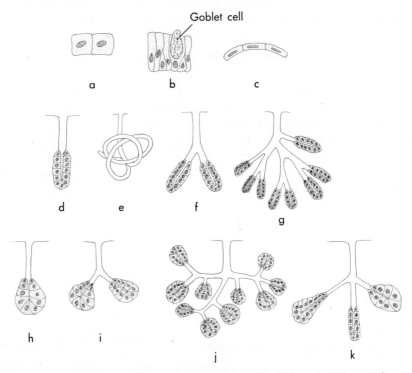

Figure 17–1. Diagram showing types of glands. (*a*) Plain cuboidal secreting cells, (*b*) plain columnar secreting cells, one of which is a "goblet gland," (*c*) plain flat secreting cells, (*d, e, f, g*) tubular glands: simple, twisted, branched, and several times branched. (*h, i, j*) Saccular or alveolar glands: (*h*) simple, (*i*) branched, (*j*) much-branched. (*k*) Compound tubuloalveolar gland.

The Compound Tubuloalveolar Glands. These glands are numerous, and while the general principle of structure is about the same in all of them, there is considerable variation in their minute structure. These glands also have many distinct duct systems which eventually open into a common duct. All of the salivary glands, the pancreas and some of the larger mucous glands of the esophagus, the seromucous gland of the respiratory pathway, and many of the duodenal glands belong in this group.

The Compound Alveolar Glands. These glands are very much like the other

---

[1] Heinrich Meibom, German anatomist (1638–1700).

compound glands in general structure; however, the terminal ducts end in alveoli with a dilated saclike form. The mammary glands are good examples of this kind of gland.

The Activities of Glands

A **secretion** is a fluid made by cells from substances brought to them by the blood and tissue fluid. Examples of external secretions are the digestive fluids (secreted by salivary, gastric, and intestinal glands, the pancreas, and the liver) and the secretions of the lacrimal, meibomian, ceruminous, sebaceous, sweat, and mammary glands.

Secretion Formation. The work of the secretory cells consists of two phases: (1) active secretion, including a considerable flow of water, and (2) a period of recovery, during which special substances are produced in the cells. During the second period the protoplasm of the gland cells becomes filled and in some cases distended with granules. During active secretion the granules are lost, the protoplasm clears, and the cells shrink in size.

Tissue fluid forms the only source of materials for the formation of secretions. The basic materials for the secretions are brought to the tissue fluid by the blood. Energy, together with the necessary nutrients, is used by the cell for the synthesis of organic substances, the secretions. The secretory materials accumulate around the Golgi apparatus and are then extruded through the surface of the cell into the lumen of the gland. At the same time the by-products of glandular cell activity enter the tissue fluid and enter either the blood or lymph capillary.

Regulation of Glandular Secretion. Glandular cells are well supplied with nerve fibers from the autonomic nervous system. The stimuli for varying the amount of secretory product may be chemical, nervous, or hormonal.

THE ENDOCRINE GLANDS

The functions of the body are regulated by the nervous system and by hormones. In general, the nervous system regulates the rapidly changing activities such as skeletal movements, smooth muscle contraction, and many glandular secretions. The hormonal system regulates the many *metabolic functions* of the body and the varying rates of chemical reactions. Hormones influence transport of substances through cell membranes and various aspects of cell metabolism. In some instances there are specific interrelationships between nervous stimuli and hormonal secretion. There are also many interactions between hormones, so that a disturbance in one endocrine gland can interfere with activities of other hormones. Hormones are specific in action.

Local Hormones. Some physiologically active substances are released from specific sites in tissue. These function at the point of origin and are normally destroyed rapidly. These substances have been termed local hormones. See page 510.

Hormones are varied in composition. Some are of protein origin; for example, thyroxin and epinephrine are of simple structure and are derived from a single amino acid; others, such as vasopressin, are relatively simple peptides formed by eight different amino acids, whereas insulin, whose structure has now been determined in considerable detail, proves to be composed of many different amino acids. The steroid hormones, secreted by the adrenal cortex, the ovaries, and the testes, are lipids of complex structure and are derived from cholesterol. Some of the hormones have been synthesized in the laboratory, notably thyroxin, epinephrine, vasopressin, insulin, and ACTH; this is not the case with any enzyme to date. The secretion of hormones is controlled by "feedback" mechanisms. Each gland has a tendency to oversecrete its specific hormone, but when physiological effects are achieved, the *feedback* mechanisms in some way check secre-

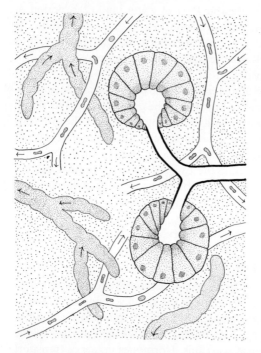

Figure 17–2. Diagram of a thin section of two alveoli of a gland lying in areolar connective tissue (*stippled*). In the near neighborhood are blood capillaries (containing red blood cells), *which have been cut in making the section*, and lymph capillaries, wider and thinner walled than the blood capillaries and closed (blind) at the end. The areolar tissue is filled with tissue fluid.

tion. If there is undersecretion, the blood level falls and the gland is stimulated to active secretion. In this way the levels of concentration of each hormone in the blood stream are controlled in relation to body needs.

The methods of study of hormones are (1) observation of conditions caused by disease or removal of the glands, (2) administration of glands, extracts, synthetic preparations, or active principles, and (3) injection of glandular extracts into normal animals and animals from which the glands have been removed.

The Hypophysis. The hypophyseal gland weighs about 0.5 to 0.7 gm and is located in the sella turcica of the sphenoid bone. The infundibular stem attaches the gland below and the hypothalamus above. The hypophysis is highly vascular and receives its blood supply from the superior and inferior hypophyseal arteries. These are branches of the internal carotid artery and from the posterior communicating artery.

The superior hypophyseal artery extends medially to the upper part of the hypophyseal stalk and divides into the anterior and posterior branches. These

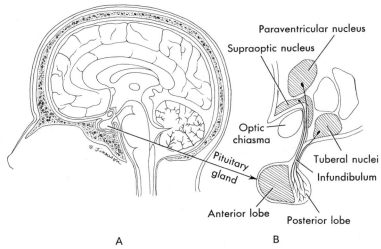

A   B

Figure 17–3. (*A*) Diagram showing brain, brain case, and location of pituitary gland. (*B*) Diagram to show fibers from hypothalamus to the neurohypophysis.

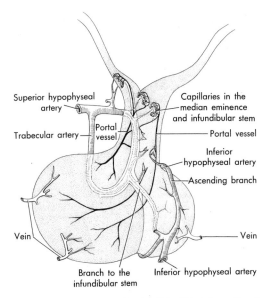

Figure 17–4. Blood supply to the hypophysis. (Modified from Crosby, Humphrey, and Lauer.)

FUNCTIONS (briefly)

TSH (thyroid-stimulating hormone) influences structure and secretory activity of the thyroid. The thyroid influences metabolic rate.

STH (somatotropic hormone) influences growth of bones, muscles, and viscera. In some way it is related to protein metabolism.

The adrenal *cortex* influences Na^+, Cl^-, K^+ reabsorption in the kidney. Influences carbohydrate, protein, and fat metabolism. The adrenal *medulla* functions in relation to "fight and flight" and other reactions. Increases blood glucose levels which, in turn, promote secretion of insulin.

FSH (follicle-stimulating hormone) is concerned with the ripening of follicles, production of estrogen, and activity of the seminiferous tubules.
LH (luteinizing hormone) influences secreting cells of the ovaries and testes and maintains their normal activity. In the male, stimulates secretion of testosterone.
Lactogenic hormone maintains secretion of corpus luteum and initiates lactation. LTH stimulates corpus luteum to form progesterone and the mammary glands to produce milk.

ADH (antidiuretic hormone) controls water reabsorption in the kidney tubules and in this way helps to regulate water and electrolyte balance of body fluids.
Oxytocin is secreted during parturition—causes uterine contraction and active ejection of milk.

HORMONE   GLAND

TSH ——— Thyroid

STH ——— Long bone

ACTH ——— Adrenal gland

FSH + LH + LTH ——— Testis / Ovary

ADH ——— Kidney

HYPOTHALAMUS

Influence through blood "Portal system"

Nerve fibers

Posterior lobe

Anterior lobe

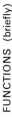

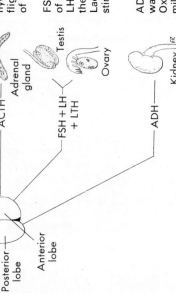

Figure 17–5. Diagram showing some of the functions of the pituitary hormones on physiological activities.

branches anastomose and supply the upper part of the infundibular stem. Another branch supplies the superior surface and connective tissue of the pars distalis. This artery does not supply the glandular tissue. Branches of the inferior hypophyseal artery divide into the medial and lateral branches and supply the *posterior lobe*. The blood supply to the *anterior lobe* is mainly through a portal system of veins. Branches of the internal carotid arteries break up into capillaries in the median eminences of the hypothalamus and in the lower infundibular stalk. These capillaries form portal vessels which then terminate in blood capillaries and sinusoids in the pars distalis (anterior lobe) of the pituitary gland. The capillaries and sinusoids finally empty into the hypophyseal veins, which enter the circular and cavernous sinus (see Figs. 17–4 and 17–6).

The neurohypophysis is well supplied with nerve fibers which descend in the hypophyseal tract; there is no nerve supply to the pars distalis. The nerve supply from the sympathetic plexus terminates around the internal carotid artery and is vasomotor in its function.

The hypophysis consists of two main lobes; the larger anterior lobe is derived embryologically from the primitive pharyngeal epithelium; the posterior lobe is derived from neural ectoderm.

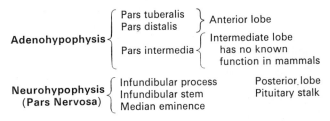

The adenohypophysis (pars distalis) consists of glandular tissue, the cells of which give characteristic staining (chromophobic, indifferent to dyes; acidophilic, taking red stain called alpha cells; and basophilic cells [beta cells], taking blue stain). The tissue is composed of irregular branching cords of epithelial cells, supported by fine reticular fibers. Between the cords of cells are many blood sinuses which form a plexus. The pars distalis, influenced by hypothalamic releasing factors (p. 277), forms hormones which have their primary site of action on other endocrine glands, "target glands." These are known as tropic hormones and exert specific influence on the activity of the target gland.

1. ADRENOCORTICOTROPIC HORMONE (ACTH) is believed to be secreted by the chromophobic cells and has influence on the integrity of adrenal cortex. Its greatest effect is to stimulate the secretion of the glucocorticoid hormones.

2. SOMATOTROPIC HORMONE (STH) or growth hormone (GH) is secreted by the acidophils of the pars distalis. It has specific effect on the growth of tissues, especially of bone, muscle, and viscera. It is essential for growth and development, and promotes both increased mitosis and increased sizes of cells. STH has effect on metabolic processes; these include increased rate of protein synthesis (Chap. 3), decreased rate of carbohydrate utilization in muscle and adipose

tissue, mobilization of stored fat, and increased use of fats for energy. Thyroxin and insulin are also necessary for growth. Selye believes that STH has a pro-inflammatory effect upon tissues.

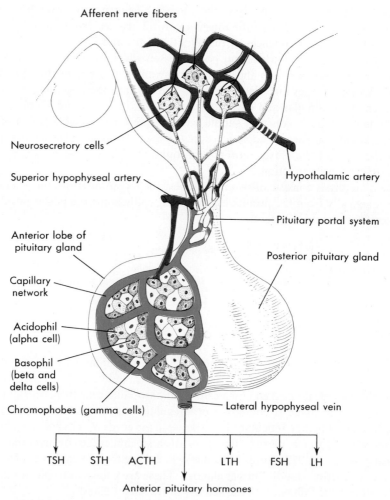

Figure 17–6. Pituitary portal system. Note the relationship of capillaries in the hypothalamus and adenohypophysis.

Excess of the growth hormone in early life results in giantism; the result of hyperactivity of the gland in later life is acromegaly, in which the jaws, bones, hands, and feet show overdevelopment and the features become enlarged and coarse. Hypoproduction of the growth hormone results in dwarfism. Growth of the body and sexual development are arrested. In the adult, the result is called Simmonds' disease, in which emaciation, muscular debility, loss of sexual function, and general apathy occur.

3. THE THYROTROPIC HORMONE. It is believed that the thyrotropin-releasing factor (TFR), secreted by cells in the hypothalamus, stimulates the secretion of TSH. TSH influences both the *structure* and all *secretory activity* of the thyroid gland. An increase in concentration of thyroxin in body fluids has an inhibitory effect on the rate of secretion of thyrotropin and this feedback mechanism prevents overactivity or underactivity of the thyroid gland. A decrease in thyroxin stimulates its secretion.

4. GONADOTROPIC HORMONES (FSH, LTH, LH, and ICSH). These hormones influence the activity of the gonads, the development of the mammary gland during pregnancy and the subsequent secretion of milk.

Follicle-stimulating hormone (FSH) causes proliferation and maturation of the ovarian follicle cells of the ovary. It also has a stimulating effect on these cells to secrete estrogens. FSH is essential for ovulation.

In the male, FSH influences spermatogenesis by its action on the seminiferous tubules.

Luteotropin (LTH, prolactin) stimulates the corpus luteum to produce progesterone and estrogens. It also has a stimulating effect on the mammary glands, influencing the final development of glandular tissue and promoting secretion of milk.

Luteinizing hormone (LH) functions along with FSH and influences maturation of the ovarian follicles, initiates rupture of the ripe follicle, and stimulates formation of corpus luteum and production of progesterone. LH also functions in the male and influences the interstitial cells of the testis to secrete testosterone. Hence this hormone is frequently called the interstitial-cell-stimulating hormone (ICSH). In turn testosterone causes masculinizing effects in the male and is necessary for spermatogenesis.

The reciprocal relationship between these hormones and the hormones of the gonads are discussed in detail in Chapter 24.

The neurohypophysis consists of the infundibular process and stem and the median eminence. The infundibular process (posterior pituitary) is composed of numerous nerve fibers and glial-like cells known as pituicytes. Nerve fibers arise from cells located in the paraventricular and supraoptic nuclei of the hypothalamus and descend in the hypothalamohypophyseal tract and terminate on capillaries in the posterior pituitary (Fig. 17–3). The hormones of the posterior pituitary are formed in these hypothalamic nuclei and trickle down the nerve fibers into the infundibular process (posterior pituitary), where they are stored in the pituicytes or enter the blood stream directly.

Two hormones are stored in the infundibular process (posterior lobe): the *antidiuretic hormone* and *oxytocin*. Both hormones are polypeptides and have been synthesized in the laboratory.

ANTIDIURETIC HORMONE (ADH) increases the permeability of the cells of the distal tubule and collecting ducts in the kidney, hence decreases urine formation. In the absence of ADH large amounts of urine with a very low specific gravity are eliminated (polyuria); at the same time fluid intake is markedly increased (polydipsia).

Secretion of ADH is regulated by the osmolarity of the blood. It is believed that cells in the supraoptic nuclei function as osmoreceptors which are sensitive to the concentration of solutes in plasma. A rise in osmotic pressure increases the secretion of ADH and inhibits water reabsorption. (See Chap. 23.) In other words, concentrated body fluids stimulate the osmoreceptors and increase secretion of ADH, whereas dilute concentrations of body fluids inhibit ADH secretion.

Diabetes insipidus, a disease in which the urinary output is greatly increased, was formerly thought to result from hyposecretion of the posterior lobe; but it has been shown that a similar polyuria results from injury to the hypothalamic region (supraoptic nuclei) of the brain. It is therefore probable that involvement of either the posterior lobe of the pituitary or the hypothalamus will cause the disease.

ADH is also known as vasopressin. It was so named because, when large quantities of ADH are injected into an animal, it stimulates smooth muscle of arterioles, vasoconstriction occurs, and arterial pressure rises. This pressor action is not of physiological importance.

OXYTOCIN has a stimulating effect upon smooth muscles of the pregnant uterus; physiological concentrations have no effect upon the nonpregnant uterus. Oxytocin is secreted in increased amounts during parturition, thereby increasing the contraction of the uterus. Oxytocin is also secreted during the process of lactation and causes ejection of milk from the alveoli into the ducts so that the infant can obtain it by suckling. The suckling stimuli increases the secretion of oxytocin.

The Thyroid Gland.   The thyroid gland consists of two lobes, situated at the sides of the trachea and thyroid cartilage. These lobes are connected by strands of thyroid tissue called the isthmus, ventral to the trachea. The external layer of the thyroid is connective tissue which extends inward as trabeculae and divides the gland into closed follicles of irregular size. Centrally, each of these follicles contains a colloid or jellylike substance which is secreted by the columnar epithelial cells which line the follicle. Thyroxin combines with this colloidal substance and is stored here. The thyroid gland contains numerous lymphatics.

An abundant blood supply is derived from the external carotids and the subclavian arteries and is returned via the superior, middle, and inferior thyroid veins to the jugular and left brachiocephalic veins. It has been estimated that about 4 to 5 liters of blood pour through the gland per hour.

The nerves are derived from the second to fifth thoracic spinal nerves through the superior and middle cervical ganglia of the thoracolumbar system and from the vagus and glossopharyngeal nerves of the craniosacral system.

The hormones of the thyroid are thyroxin and triiodothyronine. The latter is more active than thyroxin, but its action is not as sustained. The thyrotropic hormone of the pituitary stimulates the growth and activity of the follicular cells of the thyroid, and in this way the formation of thyroxin is controlled.

Iodine is taken up by the cells of the thyroid gland and soon appears in diiodotyrosine, thyroxin, and triiodothyronine, all of which are stored in the center of the follicle in a protein combination known as thyroglobulin. When the hormones thyroxin and triiodothyronine are released into the blood, they combine with plasma protein, to form protein-bound iodine (PBI). The measurement of the protein-bound iodine in blood provides a reliable means for determining the activity of the thyroid gland. This value is closely related to the rate of the basal metabolism. The normal range for PBI is between 4 and 7.5 μg per 100 ml of blood serum.

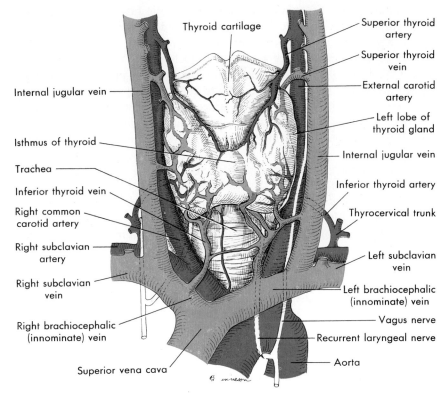

Figure 17–7. The thyroid gland and related blood vessels. (Modified from Pansky and House.)

The functions of thyroxin include the following:

1. It regulates the metabolic and oxidative rates in tissue cells of the body, including the liver. It is believed not to influence oxidative rates in the brain, testes, and spleen. It increases the rate of glucose absorption from the intestine and increases the rate of glucose utilization by cells. These effects are believed to be through enzyme systems.

2. It stimulates the growth and differentiation of tissues.

3. In the liver it influences conversion of glycogen from noncarbohydrate sources, and conversion of glycogen to glucose, thus raising blood sugar.

4. It increases osteoclastic and osteoblastic activity of bone.

5. It influences the rate of metabolism of lipids, proteins, carbohydrates, water, vitamins, and minerals.

6. In the child it influences both physical and mental development. In the adult as well as in the child it stimulates the mental processes.

7. It has action on enzyme systems and influences the quantity of enzymes, hence increases the need for vitamins. Since the rate of metabolism directly affects cardiac output, this hormone increases the heart rate.

One milligram of thyroxin increases the metabolic rate about 2.5 per cent. Carbohydrates, proteins, and fats are all oxidized in increased amounts. The thyroid hormones regulate cell metabolism primarily by controlling the activities of oxidizing enzymes within the mitochondria. This in turn increases the activity of carbohydrases, amidases, transferases, and proteolytic enzymes.

When thyroxin is given experimentally to animals or human beings, nitrogen loss exceeds intake. Glucose tolerance is decreased and stored glycogen is also decreased, although blood glucose may be normal or below. The thyroid gland is believed to be related in some way to the metabolism of calcium and phosphorus, since, when the hormone is given experimentally, an increased amount of calcium and phosphates is eliminated in the feces and urine. Blood levels remain constant, which indicates that calcium is being lost from bone. Cases of hypoactivity of the gland may show as much as 50 per cent decrease in the metabolic rate; cases of hyperactivity may show an increase up to 60 to 100 per cent and more. Injection or feeding of thyroid tissue results in increased basal metabolism, loss of weight, increase in elimination of nitrogen, increased heartbeat—which results at times in an abnormality called tachycardia—and nervous excitability.

The size of the thyroid varies with age, sex, and general nutrition. It is relatively larger in the young, in women, and in the well-nourished. Removal of the gland does not cause death but, unless the hormone is replaced, brings about marked changes, such as lowered basal metabolism and general malnutrition. Disturbances in the secretion of thyroxin are classed under two headings: (1) hypothyroidism, or decreased secretion, and (2) hyperthyroidism, or excess secretion. The liver removes excess thyroxin from the blood stream.

Goiter is an enlargement of the gland. It may result from increased functional activity due to a decrease in the iodine content of the gland. This in turn is usually due to a decrease or lack of iodine in water and food. Goiter occurs frequently in adolescent girls, but its incidence is greatly reduced if iodine is given. A goiter may be due to the presence of a tumor or increased thyroxin secretion.

Hypothyroidism. In man certain pathological conditions are caused by hypothyroidism, i.e., cretinism and myxedema.

Cretinism is caused by congenital defects of the thyroid or by atrophy in early life. The growth of the skeleton ceases, although the bones may become thicker than normal and there is marked arrest of mental development. Children so afflicted are called cretins. They are not only dwarfed but ill-proportioned, having large heads, protruding abdomens, weak muscles, and slow speech.

Myxedema is a condition that results from atrophy or removal of the thyroid in adult life. The most marked symptoms of this condition are slowness of both body and mind, usually associated with tremors and twitchings. The skin becomes rough and dry, owing to lack of cutaneous secretions, and assumes a yellow, waxlike appearance. There is an overgrowth of the subcutaneous tissues, which in time is replaced by fat; the hair grows coarse and falls out; the face and hands are swollen and puffy; the metabolic rate is low and the mental activities apathetic. Cretinism and myxedema are both caused by insufficient secretion of thyroxin, which may be supplied by feeding the thyroid of other animals. The treatment must be kept up throughout the patient's life.

Hyperthyroidism. Overactivity of the thyroid gland, i.e., increase in the amount of the internal secretion, produces a condition called Graves' disease or exophthalmic goiter. It is characterized by protruding eyeballs, quickened and sometimes irregular heart action, elevated temperature, nervousness, and insomnia. The appetite may be excessive, but this is accompanied by loss of weight due to increased metabolism and digestive disturbances. This condition is sometimes remedied by removing part of the gland.

The Parathyroid Glands. The parathyroids, usually four in number and arranged in pairs, are independent of the thyroid both in origin and in function but are usually located on its dorsal surface. These small reddish glands are about 6 to 7 mm long and 2 to 3 mm thick. Accessory nodules are sometimes found surrounding the glands or embedded in connective tissue. The glands consist of closely packed epithelial cells richly supplied with capillaries from branches of the inferior and superior thyroid arteries. The nerve supply is from the vagus and glossopharyngeal nerves of the central nervous system and from the cervical autonomics of the thoracolumbar system.

Physiology. The parathyroids secrete a hormone, parathyroid hormone, or parathormone, protein in nature, which plays an important part in the maintenance of the normal calcium level of the blood. It also regulates phosphorus metabolism. The action of the hormone is on the renal tubule to increase the excretion of inorganic phosphate. Parathormone in the presence of vitamin D influences the absorption of calcium in the intestine. Parathormone exerts action on bone and stimulates osteoclastic activity. This may be a phagocytic action whereby bony particles are digested with a final release of calcium and phosphate into the body fluids.

Acute symptoms of hypoparathyroidism, known clinically as tetany, may result from removal of the parathyroids or may possibly occur spontaneously; the concentration of blood calcium falls and increased nerve irritability causes muscle spasms that may result in death if untreated. Symptoms are relieved by giving solutions of calcium.

In hyperparathyroidism there are muscular weakness, pain in the bones, and an increase in the calcium in blood and urine. The bones show decalcification and deformity, and spontaneous fractures may occur. These symptoms are sometimes accompanied by a parathyroid tumor, the removal of which brings about a reduction in the blood calcium; and considerable resolidification of the bones occurs. Deposits of calcium may occur, especially in the kidney, and nitrogenous wastes may become excessive in blood and lymph.

The Thymus.   Although the thymus is considered to be part of the lymphatic system (p. 481), recent research clearly demonstrates that it has hormonal function. To date the hormone is unnamed.

The substance functions as a messenger between the thymus gland and the spleen, all lymph glands and lymphatic tissue, Kupffer cells of the liver, the microglia cells of the nervous system, and the macrophages of loose connective tissue in the infant and child. The messenger prompts the lymphocytes in the various tissues to produce a substance that functions as an antibody.

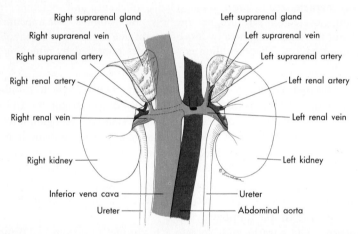

Right suprarenal gland	Left suprarenal gland
Right suprarenal vein	Left suprarenal vein
Right suprarenal artery	Left suprarenal artery
Right renal artery	Left renal artery
Right renal vein	Left renal vein
Right kidney	Left kidney
Inferior vena cava	Ureter
Ureter	Abdominal aorta

Figure 17–8.   Diagram showing position of adrenal glands and kidneys. Note blood vessel arrangement.

Adrenal Glands.   The adrenal glands are two small bodies which lie at the superior pole of each kidney. The right adrenal gland is somewhat triangular in shape and the left one more semilunar. They vary in size, and the average weight of each is about 5 to 9 gm. Each gland is surrounded by a thin capsule and consists of two parts known as the cortex, or external tissue, and the medulla, or chromophil tissue. These parts differ in origin and function.

Embryologically the adrenal cortex develops from mesoderm; the medulla has the same embryological origin as the thoracolumbar division of the autonomic nervous system, namely, from an outgrowth from the neural ectoderm. It is also functionally related to the sympathetic nervous system.

At birth the adrenal glands weigh about 8 gm, which is proportionately 20 times greater than in the adult. They gradually decrease in size, and by one year of age the two adrenals weigh 4.5 gm. The more mature the infant, the more adequately the adrenal cortex responds to stress.

Blood Supply. The arteries supplying this highly vascular gland are derived from the aorta, the inferior phrenics, and the renal arteries. Blood is returned via the suprarenal veins. It has been estimated that a quantity of blood equal to about six times each gland's weight passes through it per minute.

Nerves. The nerve fibers are derived from the celiac and renal plexuses (splanchnic nerves). Removal of the gland has long been known to be followed by prostration, muscular weakness, and lowered vascular tone, with subsequent death in a few days. These symptoms are caused by the removal of the adrenal cortex. Removal of the medulla causes no serious disturbance.

Hormones of the Adrenal Cortex. The adrenal cortex secretes a group of hormones called corticosteroids. These include the *mineralocorticoids* and the *glucocorticoids*. It also secretes small amounts of androgenic hormones and minute quantities of estrogenic hormones.

The structure of the cortex is as follows:

1. The outer zone, or zona glomerulosa. The cords of cells are arranged in ovoid groups with capillaries between them. Mineralocorticoids, mainly aldosterone, are secreted in this area.

2. The middle zone, or zona fasciculata. The cords of cells run parallel to each other in a straight line with capillaries between them. The glucocorticoids are believed to be secreted in greatest amounts in this area.

3. The inner zone, or zona reticularis. The cords of cells are arranged in a regular course, but obliquely toward the medulla. Capillary networks are arranged between the cords. The gonadal hormones are believed to be secreted in this area.

The hormones of the adrenal cortex include *cortisol, corticosterone, aldosterone, androgens, estrogens,* and *gestagens*. Cortisol and corticosterone are called glucocorticoids because they have a specific effect on glucose metabolism. Aldosterone has been called a mineralocorticoid because its chief action is to promote sodium retention and potassium excretion. The chief functions of these hormones are as follows:

THE MINERALOCORTICOIDS. The salt or mineral hormone aldosterone functions at the renal tubule and stimulates the reabsorption of Na^+ which then attract Cl^- and cause their reabsorption into the blood. In this way the Na^+ and Cl^- content of the extracellular fluids is maintained. Water is reabsorbed with the salt as the result of increased osmotic pressure. The reabsorption of K^+ is depressed and hence the $Na^+ - K^+$ ratio is controlled in body fluids. Fluid balance is also controlled through regulation of these electrolytes. Aldosterone secretion is increased by—

1. A decrease in extracellular volume
2. An increase in extracellular potassium
3. A decrease in extracellular sodium
4. Angiotensin formation

Any of these conditions excites the adrenal cortex to activity. Conversely, high extracellular volume, low extracellular potassium, and high extracellular sodium decrease aldosterone secretion.

THE GLUCOCORTICOIDS.   The actions of the glucocorticoids are chiefly from cortisol (hydrocortisone or compound F). The glucocorticoids are hormones whose predominant action is the regulation of metabolism of carbohydrate, protein, and fat.

A. *Effect on Carbohydrate Metabolism.*   These hormones stimulate gluconeogenesis by the liver. The liver forms glycogen from amino acids supplied by the peripheral tissues.

B. *Effect on Protein Metabolism.*   The glucocorticoids reduce protein stores by increased catabolism of protein and by a decreased rate of protein synthesis. Liver protein is increased and in turn plasma proteins are released into the blood. Glucocorticoids increase permeability of the liver cells to amino acids and decrease the permeability of muscle cells and lymphocytes to amino acids. These effects could perhaps be explained in terms of alterations in cellular enzyme systems.

C. *Effects on Fat Metabolism.*   As need arises, the glucocorticoids either promote fat mobilization from fat depots (adipokinesis) or increase the rate of storage of fat deposition as adipose tissue (lipogenesis).

D. *Effect on Lymph and Blood.*   The corticosteroids influence the activity of lymphoid tissue and the number of eosinophils in circulating blood. Administration of adrenal cortical hormones decreases the number of circulating eosinophils and the size of lymphoid tissue. Large doses of the glucocortoids reduce or may completely block antibody formation in lymphoid tissue. Cortisone and hydrocortisone are the two widely known hormones in this group.

E. *Stress Situations.*   The adrenal cortex in some way aids the body to cope more effectively with adverse environmental situations, or what is commonly known as stress situations. See discussion and diagram, pages 504 and 505.

F. *Gonadal Hormones.*   Several hormones have been isolated from the adrenal cortex that have influence on the sex organs, for example, androgen, estrogen, and progestins.

When the adrenal cortex, ovaries, or testes are removed, certain physiological changes take place. Removal of the ovaries or testes results in an enlargement of the adrenal cortex.

If the adrenal glands fail to function, corticotropin, secreted by the pituitary gland, is greatly increased. This is believed to explain why there is decreased production of the gonadal hormones. On the other hand, sex hormones can affect adrenocortical function. Estrogens from the ovary inhibit the formation of FSH and LH by the pituitary; however, at the same time corticotropin is increased.

The adrenal cortex activity, specifically that of the zona fasciculata, is regulated by the anterior pituitary hormone, adrenocorticotropin, ACTH. Aldosterone secretion is not increased to any great extent by ACTH.

Cortical hypofunction is recognized as the cause of Addison's disease, which, if untreated, is fatal within from one to three years.

Symptoms of Addison's disease are muscular weakness and general apathy, gastrointestinal disturbances, pigmentation of the skin and mucous membranes, loss of weight, and depressed sexual function. The pigmentation is the outstanding symptom and is due to excessive deposition of the normal cutaneous pigment, melanin. Treatment with cortical extract gives favorable results.

Cortical hyperfunction appears to be associated with cortical tumors. It results in the young in precocious sexual development with profuse growth of hair, and in the case of adult females, in the development of secondary male characteristics.

Hormones of the Adrenal Medulla. The adrenal medulla consists of large, granular cells arranged in a network. It secretes two hormones, amine in nature, called epinephrine (Adrenalin) and norepinephrine (noradrenalin). The chromaffin cells, which compose the larger portion of the medulla, give a characteristic reaction when treated with chromic acid (stain a brownish-yellow). Similar cells are located along the abdominal aorta and other parts of the body. All cells showing this reaction are assumed to have a similar function.

Epinephrine affects all structures of the body innervated by the sympathetic nervous system and thereby reinforces its action.

The hormones, *epinephrine* and *norepinephrine*, belong to a group of chemicals known as *catecholamines* and are frequently referred to as *sympathomimetic amines* because they have the same physiological effect as the sympathetic nervous system. Through the glycogenolytic effect of *catecholamines*, these hormones provide the body with a means of sparing carbohydrates for the brain during periods of hypoglycemia. They also have ability to stimulate the release of free fatty acids from adipose tissue. These, in turn, are used by muscle tissue of the body in place of glucose, thereby providing another physiological means of conserving circulating glucose. On the whole, norepinephrine is more effective in vasoconstriction and epinephrine has a more pronounced effect on carbohydrate metabolism.

Comparison of Effects of

Epinephrine (Adrenalin)	Norepinephrine (Noradrenalin)
1. Slight constriction of blood vessels. Systolic pressure raised	1. Pressor effects marked raises in both systolic and diastolic pressures
2. Increases cardiac output and venous return	2. Slight effect
3. Hyperglycemic effects marked	3. Much less effect
4. Marked increased basal metabolic rate	4. Much less effect
5. Lipolytic effect—liberates nonesterified fatty acids from fat depots	5. Slightly greater effect
6. Excitation of central nervous system marked	6. No effect
7. Eosinophils decreased in number	7. Slight effect

Examples of the use of epinephrine in medicine are to bring about vasoconstriction, which prolongs the action of local anesthetics and reduces the absorption of the substance producing the anesthesia; to relax the bronchioles in asthma; to constrict arterioles of the mucous membranes and of the skin, thus reducing the loss of blood in minor operations.

Cannon and his associates noted that the supply of epinephrine to the blood by the adrenal medulla is increased under emotional stress. This increase results in a more rapid and forceful heartbeat; a greater flow of blood to the muscles, central nervous system, and heart; an increased output of glucose from the liver; inhibition of the intestinal muscle coat; and closure of the sphincters. The muscle coat of the bronchi is relaxed and there is contraction of the splenic capsule, which gives more blood to circulation. By means of these reactions the stable environment of cells is maintained during periods of great functional demands. Whether these reactions are in direct response to the increased secretion of the medulla or are brought about by the action of the sympathetic nervous system alone is undetermined. Nevertheless, it may be said that the medulla in normal physiological activities carries on certain emergency functions such as constriction of skin and splanchnic blood vessels, vasodilation in skeletal and cardiac muscle, a rise in general blood pressure and increased output of the heart, the liberation of glucose supplies from the liver, the contraction of both smooth and striated muscles, decrease in the coagulation time of the blood, discharge of red blood cells from the spleen, and an increase in the depth and rate of respiration. These and other accompanying reactions, such as emotional responses, result in equipping the individual to meet the emergency at hand.

Stress

The anterior pituitary and adrenal glands play an important role in aiding the body to deal effectively with stress. In recent years much has been clarified in relation to how the body fights back.

In *any type of injury* to tissues or cells, exposure to intense cold or heat, hemorrhage, excessive exercise, deprivations such as starvation, or infections or in emotional stress, there is a definite pattern of physiological response. Selye found that no matter what the stressor was, including physical restraint, certain changes always occurred in the animal. These were atrophy of the thymus gland, marked enlargement of the adrenal cortex, and hemorrhage into the gastric mucosa. The reasons for all these changes have not been clarified. It is known that the stress situation calls out ACTH and the response is an increased production of adrenal cortical hormones. There is also increased sympathetic nervous system activity with a calling out of epinephrine, which in turn stimulates production of ACTH as well as bringing about the usual body adjustments for emergency physiology. The following chart indicates many of the physiological adjustments necessary for survival of the individual.

The term "general adaptation syndrome" is used to explain the three stages of physiological changes to stress according to Selye.

1. The Alarm Stage. Sodium and chloride levels in extracellular fluids fall, while potassium rises. Blood glucose falls, but later rises.

2. Stage of Resistance. The body fights back. Blood levels return to normal. More ACTH is released, and the body tries to combat factors causing stress. The adrenal cortex increases in size.

3. Stage of Exhaustion. If the original stress is not removed, the adrenal gland becomes depleted of cholesterol, there is hemorrhage into the cortex, and ACTH fails

Response of Body to Stress

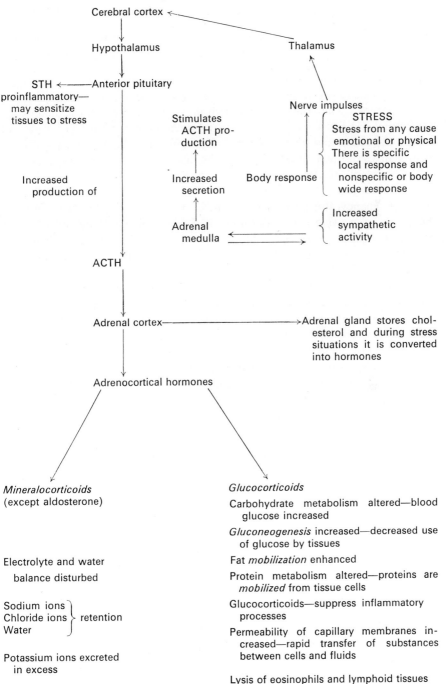

Cerebral cortex

Hypothalamus   Thalamus

STH ←————Anterior pituitary
proinflammatory—
may sensitize   Nerve impulses
tissues to stress
                     Stimulates   STRESS
                     ACTH pro-   Stress from any cause
                     duction   emotional or physical
                                         There is specific
Increased   Increased   Body response   local response and
production of   secretion   nonspecific or body
                                                 wide response

                     Adrenal   Increased
                     medulla   sympathetic
                                            activity

ACTH

Adrenal cortex————————————→Adrenal gland stores chol-
                                            esterol and during stress
                                            situations it is converted
                                            into hormones

Adrenocortical hormones

Mineralocorticoids   *Glucocorticoids*
(except aldosterone)
                                        Carbohydrate metabolism altered—blood
                                            glucose increased

                                        Gluconeogenesis increased—decreased use
                                            of glucose by tissues

Electrolyte and water   Fat *mobilization* enhanced
   balance disturbed
                                        Protein metabolism altered—proteins are
                                            mobilized from tissue cells
Sodium ions ⎫
Chloride ions ⎬ retention   Glucocorticoids—suppress inflammatory
Water ⎭   processes

                                        Permeability of capillary membranes in-
Potassium ions excreted   creased—rapid transfer of substances
   in excess   between cells and fluids

                                        Lysis of eosinophils and lymphoid tissues

to be formed. Sodium and chloride and glucose levels in blood fall, potassium and phosphate levels rise, and death results from exhaustion. It is evident that prompt, skilled care is necessary if the individual is to survive severe stress.

On the other hand, the helpful properties of stress should be remembered. For instance, normal bone needs the stress of weight bearing if it is to retain its mineral content. In fact, all tissues of the body need moderate stress to maintain normal functioning. The aim should not be to eliminate stress from life situations, but effort should be made to understand and moderate stress before it becomes excessive.

The Gonads. The *ovary* produces two internal secretions whose actions are understood. (1) Follicular hormone, or estrogen, is secreted by the ovary and acts on the uterus and fallopian tubes, the vagina, and the mammary glands in their changes throughout the phases of the menstrual cycle. Estrogen is present in the blood of females from puberty to the menopause, reaching its highest concentration just before ovulation. It is present in large amounts in the blood during pregnancy. It is also present in the urine of males and has been found in the tissues of growing plants and animals. Several different kinds of estrogens have been isolated from human blood plasma. Three are present in significant amounts: β-estradiol, estrone, and estriol. β-estradiol is the most important and most potent. The liver plays an important role in estrogen excretion. (2) The corpus luteum hormone, or progesterone, supplements the action of estrogen, promoting further development of the uterine mucosa in preparation for implantation of the developing ovum. It suppresses estrus and ovulation and is essential for the growth of the mammary glands. It is essential to the complete development of the maternal portion of the placenta and to the development of the mammary glands during pregnancy.

In the nonpregnant female most of the progesterone is secreted during the latter half of each ovarian cycle. It is secreted in larger quantities than is estrogen. It is rapidly changed to other steroids that have no progesteronic effect. The liver is important for these metabolic changes. The end product is pregnanediol.

The following chart summarizes the effects of estrogens and progesterone:

Name	Where Function	Effect
Estrogens	Fallopian tubes and endometrium	Cause glandular cells to proliferate Increase number of ciliated epithelial cells. Activity of cilia enhanced
	Breasts	Initiates growth of breast Cause fat deposition and development of stromal tissues. Lobules and alveoli develop to slight extent
	Skeleton	Cause osteoclastic activity at puberty. There is a rapid growth rate which causes early uniting of the epiphyses with the shafts of long bone
	Pelvis	Broaden pelvis
	Calcium and phosphate in blood stream	Cause retention to promote bone growth

Name	Where Function	Effect
Estrogens	Metabolism	Apparently have no effect on metabolic rate but do cause greater deposition of fat
	Skin	Cause skin to develop a soft, smooth texture and increase its vascularity
	Electrolyte balance	Cause Na^+ and Cl^- and H_2O retention by the kidney
Progesterone	Uterus	Promotes secretory changes and storage of nutrients in the endometrium, thus prepares it for implantation of the fertilized ovum Inhibits contractibility of the myometrium
	Fallopian tubes	Promotes secretions of mucosa
	Breasts	Promotes final development of lobules and alveoli ; causes proliferation of cells and causes cells to become secretory. Enlarges breasts
	Electrolyte balance	Enhances Na^+, Cl^-, and H_2O reabsorption from distal tubules of kidney
	Protein	Has a mild catabolic effect

There is a feedback mechanism of both these hormones on the adenohypophyseal secretion of the gonadotropic hormones (see Chap. 24).

Recent texts refer to the possibility of there being one or more substances referred to as *relaxin* present in the blood of pregnant mammals. It is believed to bring about relaxation of the pelvic ligaments in preparation for parturition.

Two male hormones have been isolated—the androgens: *androsterone* from male and also female urine, and *testosterone* and *androstenedione* from the testicle. Testosterone promotes the development of the male sex organs, the development of masculine characteristics, and retention of nitrogen, leading to increase in growth of tissues and muscular vigor.

Attention is called to the fact that both the male and female sex hormones are produced in both sexes. The sex of the animal determines whether male or female hormones will be secreted in preponderance.

The adrenal cortex is also a source of androgens, estrogens, and progestational substances found in normal urine and is the only source of the substances in urine after ovariectomy or castration.

The Placenta. The placenta is a source of many hormones, including estrogen and progesterone, and of chorionic gonadotropin which has similar action to the gonadotropic principles of the anterior pituitary hormones (LH). The placenta is also a source of a rich supply of immune bodies and of a blood coagulant. See Chapter 24 for complete discussion.

Internal Secretions of the Gastric and Intestinal Mucous Membranes. *Gastrin* is a hormone secreted into the blood by the parietal cells of the mucous membrane lining the stomach. This hormone is carried by the blood to the peptic and pyloric glands, which it stimulates. Some investigators believe that the mucous membrane of the intestine, particularly the duodenum, contains cells which secrete a substance known as *prosecretin,* which is inactive until the medium is acid. When the acid chyme from the stomach enters the duodenum, prosecretin is liberated, changed to *secretin,* absorbed by the blood, and carried to the pancreas, stimulating it to secretory activity. There are other hormones produced in the intestinal mucosa. See Chapter 20.

It should be recognized that hormones are but one factor in the complex chemical system of the body fluids controlling physiological integration, health, development, and behavior. It is evident that if experimental studies were made that cause disturbances in the kinds and concentrations and physical states of the other constituents of these heterogeneous body fluids, the results would be as striking as those described in relation to experiments with hormones.

Islet of Langerhans   Islet of Langerhans

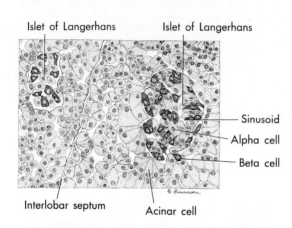

Sinusoid

Alpha cell

Beta cell

Interlobar septum   Acinar cell

Figure 17–9. Diagram of microscopic view of a thin section of pancreas showing islet of Langerhans. Alpha cells light, beta cells dark.

The Pancreas. Deep within the pancreas are special groups of cells, the *islets of Langerhans.* These cells form an internal secretion, protein in nature, called *insulin,* which is essential for normal glucose metabolism. Several types of cells are in the islet group. The beta cells secrete insulin, and the alpha cells secrete *glucagon.* It is now believed that insulin increases cell permeability to glucose and in some way influences phosphorylation. Glucose transport through cell membranes does *not* occur against a concentration gradient in tissue cells.

Insulin promotes the utilization of glucose in tissue cells and thereby decreases blood glucose concentration. In the liver it inhibits glycogen formation from noncarbohydrate sources; it promotes glycogen storage. *Glucagon functions* in the liver and aids in the conversion of glycogen to glucose.

Insulin is essential for the maintenance of normal levels of blood glucose. Hypoglycemia results from increased insulin secretion (hyperinsulinism) or from the injection of insulin. Marked decrease in the blood sugar level leads to coma, convulsions, and death. Hyperglycemia and glycosuria may result from insufficient secretion of insulin. Marked increased levels of blood sugar, if untreated,

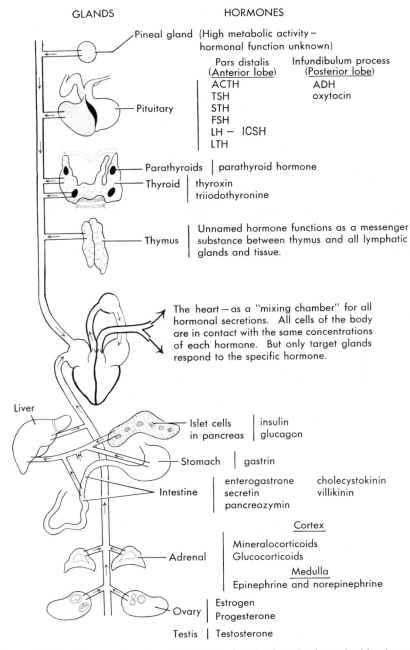

GLANDS   HORMONES

Pineal gland (High metabolic activity –
hormonal function unknown)

	Pars distalis (Anterior lobe)	Infundibulum process (Posterior lobe)
Pituitary	ACTH TSH STH FSH LH – ICSH LTH	ADH oxytocin

Parathyroids | parathyroid hormone

Thyroid | thyroxin
triiodothyronine

Thymus | Unnamed hormone functions as a messenger substance between thymus and all lymphatic glands and tissue.

The heart – as a "mixing chamber" for all hormonal secretions. All cells of the body are in contact with the same concentrations of each hormone. But only target glands respond to the specific hormone.

Liver

Islet cells
in pancreas | insulin
glucagon

Stomach | gastrin

Intestine | enterogastrone   cholecystokinin
secretin   villikinin
pancreozymin

<u>Cortex</u>
Adrenal | Mineralocorticoids
Glucocorticoids
<u>Medulla</u>
Epinephrine and norepinephrine

Ovary | Estrogen
Progesterone

Testis | Testosterone

Figure 17–10. Diagram showing relationship of endocrine glands to the blood stream. The blood stream is always moving, so that small quantities of hormones enter the blood continuously.

lead to coma and death. This condition is known as diabetes mellitus (see Chap. 21).

Local or tissue substances should be recognized as a factor in the complex chemical system of the body fluids. These substances act in the area of their release. They function at point of origin and are normally destroyed rapidly. Some of the more important ones are:

1. Acetylcholine is secreted at the parasympathetic and skeletal nerve endings. It is a chemical transmitter and also may be necessary for rhythmical activities in the heart.

2. Norepinephrine is secreted at most endings of postganglionic sympathetic nerve fibers. Important exceptions are the sympathetic fibers to sweat glands and certain of the fibers to striated muscle arterioles.

3. Histamine and heparin are present in mast cells. Histamine is believed to play a role in some allergic states. Histamine causes arteriolar and capillary dilatation, a rise in skin temperature, a fall in diastolic blood pressure, and an increase in heart rate. It is a powerful stimulant to hydrochloric acid in the stomach. Heparin is important in the manufacturing of the mucopolysaccharides of connective tissue.

4. Serotonin is found in the mucosa of the alimentary tract, in blood platelets, and in the brain. Serotonin constricts blood vessels.

5. Angiotensin stimulates smooth muscle of blood vessels and raises blood pressure.

The pineal gland, or epiphysis is part of the epithalamus and is located in the brain between the superior quadrigeminate bodies. It has been the subject of active investigation for many years. In boys, tumors of the gland are frequently associated with sexual precocity. Studies in rats indicate that removal of the gland before sexual development produces gonadal precocity.

Studies with radioactive substances show that the gland has high metabolic activity. Recent studies show that the gland produces many active physiological agents, but to date there is no evidence of hormonal secretion.

QUESTIONS FOR DISCUSSION

1. Name the hormones of the anterior pituitary and explain the function of each.
2. Explain the anatomical relationship between the hypothalamus and the hypophysis.
3. What is the "hypothalamic-portal system"?
4. List the hormones of the pars distalis and explain their function.
5. Explain the "feedback mechanism" for control of the secretion of one hormone.
6. Which of the adrenal hormones are essential for life? Explain.
7. Differentiate between diabetes mellitus and diabetes insipidus.

8. Differentiate between the actions of epinephrine and norepinephrine.
9. Explain briefly the physiological response to stress.
10. If it becomes necessary to remove an individual's pituitary gland, which hormone(s) must be given? Explain.

SUMMARY

Physiological integration of different systems of body brought about in part by secretions of glands

A **gland** is a cell or a group of cells which forms new substances

Glands

- **Classification**
  - According to place of secretion
    - Exocrine, or duct glands
    - Endocrine, or ductless glands
    - Heterocrine, both exocrine and endocrine
  - According to kind of secretion
    - Mucous (mucin)
    - Serous (serum)
  - According to structure
    - Lymphoid
    - Epithelial

  Glands of external secretion—see p. 487 for classification

  Secretion, a new substance made by cells from substances obtained from blood or tissue fluid

- **Endocrine glands**
  - Hormones stimulate activities
  - Methods of study
    - (1) Observation of pathological conditions or removal
    - (2) Feeding of glands, extracts, or synthetic principles of glands
    - (3) Observation of results of injections of extracts
  - Hypophysis, pineal body, thyroid, parathyroids, suprarenal, gonads, placenta, pancreas, intestinal mucosa

Regulation of Secretion

Stimuli may be either chemical, nervous, or hormonal. Secretion of hormones is controlled by "feedback" mechanisms

Local Substances or Mediators

- Physiologically active substances that are released from specific sites in tissue
- They function at point of origin
- Acetylcholine
- Norepinephrine
- Histamine
- Serotonin
- Angiotensin

Name of Gland	Location	Secretion	Probable Function	Diseases Associated with It
Pituitary, or Hypophysis Cerebri Mass of reddish-gray tissue about 1 cm in diameter. Consists of an anterior and posterior lobe and a tuberal part containing colloid	Lodged in the sella turcica of the sphenoid bone	Hypothalamus—stored in posterior lobe ADH	Antidiuretic—controls water reabsorption in the distal kidney tubule Pressor effects unimportant physiologically	**Hypofunction** (or hypothalamic lesion) results in *diabetes insipidus*
		Oxytocin	Oxytocic effect—muscles of pregnant uterus contract	
		Pars distalis (anterior lobe) Several hormones	ACTH influences adrenal cortex secretion STH influences growth of tissues TSH influences structure and secretory activity of thyroid gland Gonadotropic hormones FSH, LTH, LH, ISCH influence gonadal functions	**Hypofunction** may result in Simmonds' disease, dwarfism, polyuria, depressed sexual function, and scanty growth of hair **Hyperfunction** may result in gigantism (early life), acromegaly (adult life), and glycosuria
Thyroid Weighs about 1 oz Consists of two lobes connected by an isthmus	In front of trachea and beside thyroid cartilage	*Thyroxin*—contains 65% of the body iodine *Triiodothyronine*	Influence the general rate of oxidation in the body, also growth and development in the young Influence through enzyme systems	**Hypothyroidism** may result in cretinism (early life) and myxedema (adult life) **Hyperthyroidism** may result in Graves's disease (exophthalmic goiter)
Parathyroids Four small glands	Between the posterior borders of the lobes of the thyroid gland and its capsule	*Parathyroid hormone (parathormone)*	Regulates the blood-calcium level and the irritability of the nervous system and muscles Increases excretion of inorganic phosphate in the renal tubule	When the parathyroids are removed, **tetany** develops **Hyperparathyroidism**— Muscular weakness High blood calcium
The Thymus has two lobes (see p. 481)	Upper chest cavity	*Unnamed hormone* in youth	Functions as a messenger between thymus gland and spleen and all lymphatic tissue. Prompts lymphocytes to produce a substance which functions as an antibody	Unknown except for failure to produce antibodies

Gland	Location	Hormones	Function	Effects of Removal/Dysfunction
Adrenal Glands Two small glands, each surrounded by a fibrous capsule and consisting of two parts { cortex, medulla	Placed above and in front of the upper end of each kidney			Removal causes death. **Hypofunction** results in Addison's disease and poor response to stress. **Hyperfunction** may cause precocious sexual development (Cushing's syndrome) and virilism in the adult female. Removal of the medulla causes no serious physiological disturbance
Cortex consists of epithelial cells arranged in columns. These cells are derived from the part of the mesoderm that gives rise to the kidneys		*Several hormones* (glucocorticoids, mineralocorticoids)	Regulate electrolyte and water balance. Influences fat, carbohydrate, and protein metabolism; activity of lymphoid tissue and sexual organs. Aids body to cope more effectively with stress situations	
Medulla consists of a network of large granular cells which when treated with chromic acid give a yellow or brown reaction. Derived from neural crest of ectoderm		Medulla— Epinephrine	Constitutes a reserve mechanism that comes into action at times of stress. Epinephrine augments the response of sympathetic nerves, increases the heartbeat, increases blood supply to muscles, nervous system, and heart, and increases output of glucose from liver. Raises B.P.	
		Norepinephrine	Vasoconstriction, elevates blood pressure	
Gonads *Ovaries* Two almond-shaped bodies which weigh 2–3.5 gm	One on each side of the uterus, attached to the broad ligament and below the uterine tubes	*Estrogen*	Seems to act by maintaining nutrition and mature size of female reproductive organs	Excessive ovarian function produces precocious puberty. Diminished ovarian function characterized by late onset of menstruation, faulty development of genital organs, delayed menstruation
		Progesterone	Sensitizes the mucous membrane of the uterus so that it responds to the contact of the developing ovum and assists in implantation	

Name of Gland	Location	Secretion	Probable Function	Diseases Associated with It
Testes Two glandular organs which weigh 10.5–14 gm	In the scrotum	*Testosterone*	Influences the development of secondary sex characteristics in the male	The tendency to become obese after castration
Placenta	Pregnant uterus	Estrogen, progesterone, chorionic gonadotropin	Similar action to the anterior pituitary gonadal hormones	See Chapter 24 for details of gonadal hormones
Pancreas A compound gland which weighs between 2 and 3 oz	In front of the first and second lumbar vertebrae behind the stomach	Islets of Langerhans furnish two hormones *Insulin* and *Glucagon*	(1) Restores the power to utilize the glucose of the blood (2) Accelerates the synthesis of sugar to glycogen and the storage of glycogen (3) Restricts production of glucose in liver from protein and fat Aids in the conversion of glycogen to glucose in the liver	**Diabetes mellitus**—results from insufficient secretion of insulin
Gastric Mucosa	Stomach	*Gastrin* is hormone of internal secretion	Carried by blood to fundic and pyloric glands and stimulates secretion of pepsin and HCl	
Intestinal Mucosa	Intestine-duodenum	Cells of duodenum produce *prosecretin*, changed by acid to *secretin*	Secretin stimulates the pancreas to activity	

18

The Respiratory System

Anatomy, $\left\{ \begin{array}{ll} \textit{Nasal Cavity} & \textit{Trachea} \\ \textit{Nasopharynx} & \textit{Bronchi} \end{array} \right.$

Histology $\quad\left\lfloor \begin{array}{ll} \textit{Larynx} & \textit{Lungs} \end{array} \right.$

Physiology $\left\{ \begin{array}{l} \textit{Oxygen} \\ \textit{Carbon Dioxide} \\ \textit{Nervous Controls} \end{array} \right.$

THE NORMAL SEQUENCE of chemical changes in tissue cells depends on oxygen, hence the need of a continuous supply. One of the chief end products of these chemical changes is carbon dioxide, hence the need for continuous elimination of carbon dioxide. In unicellular animals the intake of oxygen and the output of carbon dioxide occur at the surface of the one-celled animal. As organisms increase in size and complexity, specialized structure is developed which functions to bring oxygen to the cells of the organism.

NEED FOR OXYGEN

In man the circulating blood in the alveolar capillaries takes up oxygen and gives up carbon dioxide, and later in the capillaries of the tissues it gives up oxygen and takes up carbon dioxide.

This exchange of gases is known as respiration and is dependent upon the proper functioning of certain organs, the *respiratory system*. The essentials of a respiratory system consist of a moist and permeable membrane, with a moving stream of blood containing a relatively high percentage of carbon dioxide on one side and air or fluid containing a relatively high percentage of oxygen on the other. In most aquatic animals the respiratory organs are external in the form of gills; in mammals the respiratory organs are situated internally in the form of lungs. The lungs are placed in communication with the nose and mouth by means of the bronchi, trachea, and larynx.

515

Nose

The nose is the special organ of the sense of smell, but it also serves as a passageway for air going to and from the lungs. It filters, warms, and moistens the entering air and also helps in phonation. It consists of two parts—the external feature, the nose, and the internal cavities, the nasal fossae.

The external nose is composed of a triangular framework of bone and cartilage, covered by skin and lined by mucous membrane. On its undersurface are two oval openings, the nostrils (*anterior nares*), which are the external openings of the nasal cavities.

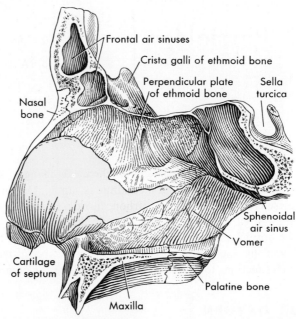

Figure 18–1. Bones and cartilage of septum of nose, left side. (Modified from Gray's *Anatomy.*)

The nasal cavities are two wedge-shaped cavities, separated from each other by a partition, or septum. The septum is formed in front by the crest of the nasal bones and the frontal spine; in the middle, by the perpendicular plate of the ethmoid; behind, by the vomer and sphenoid; below, by the crest of the maxillae and palatine bones. The septum is usually bent more to one side than the other, a condition to be remembered in giving nasal treatments.

The conchae (Fig. 18–2) and processes of the ethmoid, which are exceedingly light and spongy, project into the nasal cavities and divide them into three incomplete passages from before backward—the superior, middle and inferior meatus. The palate and maxillae separate the nasal cavities from the mouth, and the horizontal plate of the ethmoid forms the partition between the cranial and nasal cavities.

The nasal cavities[1] communicate with the air in front by the anterior nares, and behind they open into the nasopharynx by the two *posterior nares*. The cavities are lined with mucous membrane. At the entrance each cavity or vestibule is lined with thick, stratified, squamous epithelium containing sebaceous glands and numerous coarse hairs. The middle, or respiratory, portion of the cavity is lined with pseudostratified epithelium with many ciliated and goblet

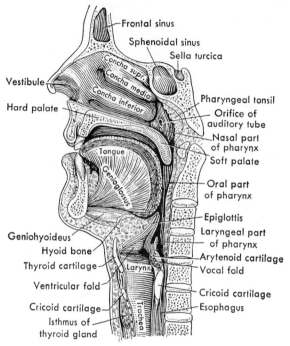

Figure 18–2. Sagittal section of the nose, mouth, pharynx, and larynx. (Modified from Gray's *Anatomy*.)

cells. The upper, or olfactory, portion is lined with neuroepithelium which contains olfactory cells which are the receptors for smell. This membrane, which is highly vascular, is continuous externally with the skin and internally with the mucous membrane lining the sinuses and other structures connected with the nasal passages. Inflammatory conditions of the nasal mucous membrane may extend into the sinuses.

[1] Eleven bones enter into the formation of the nasal cavities: the floor is formed by the palatine (2) and part of the maxillae bones (2); the roof is formed chiefly by the horizontal plate of the ethmoid bone (1), the sphenoid (1), and the small nasal bones (2); in the outer walls we find, in addition to processes from other bones, the two conchae (2). The vomer (1) forms part of the septum.

One reason for the emphasis on the prevention or early cure of head colds is due to this possibility. The infection may spread upward into the nasolacrimal duct, lacrimal sac, and conjunctiva; into the head sinuses, such as the frontal, ethmoidal, sphenoidal, or the antrum of Highmore; through the pharynx into the larynx, trachea, and bronchi; or through the eustachian tube to the middle ear and the mastoid portion of the temporal bones. Perhaps the most serious possibility is the extension of the infection to the meninges by way of the olfactory nerve.

Advantage of Nasal Breathing.   Under normal conditions breathing should take place through the nose. The arrangement of the conchae makes the upper part of the nasal passages very narrow; these passages are thickly lined and freely supplied with blood, which keeps the temperature relatively high and makes it possible to moisten and warm the air before it reaches the lungs. The hairs at the entrance to the nostrils and the cilia of the epithelium serve as filters to remove particles which may be carried in with the inspired air.

Nerves and Blood Vessels.   The mucous membrane of the superior conchae and upper third of the septum contains the endings of the olfactory nerve fibers. The nerve fibers for the muscles of the nose are fibers of the facial (seventh cranial), and the skin receives fibers from the ophthalmic and maxillary nerves, which are branches of the trigeminal (fifth cranial). Blood is supplied to the external nose by branches from the external and internal maxillary arteries, which are derived from the external carotid. The lateral walls and the septum of the nasal cavities are supplied with nasal branches of the ethmoidal arteries, which are derived from the internal carotid.

The mouth serves as a passageway for the entrance of air, and the pharynx transmits the air from the nose or mouth to the larynx, but both are closely associated with digestion and will be described with the digestive organs.

Respiratory Tract

The respiratory tract is composed of the following organs in addition to the nose and nasopharynx already described: (1) larynx, (2) trachea, (3) bronchi, and (4) lungs.

The larynx, or organ of voice, is placed in the upper and front part of the neck between the root of the tongue and the trachea. Above and behind it lies the pharynx, which opens into the esophagus, or gullet; and on either side of it lie the great vessels of the neck. The larynx is broad above and shaped somewhat like a triangular box, with flat sides and prominent ridge in front. Below, it is narrow and rounded where it blends with the trachea. It is made up of nine fibrocartilages, united by extrinsic and intrinsic ligaments and moved by numerous muscles.

Cartilages of the Larynx

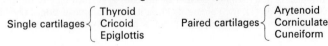

Single cartilages { Thyroid Cricoid Epiglottis   Paired cartilages { Arytenoid Corniculate Cuneiform

The thyroid cartilage resembles a shield and is the largest. It rests upon the cricoid and consists of two square plates, or laminae (right and left), which are joined at an acute angle in the middle line in front and form by their union the laryngeal prominence (Adam's apple).

The cricoid cartilage resembles a seal ring with the hoop part in front and the signet part in the back.

The epiglottis is shaped like a leaf. The stem is inserted in the notch between the two plates of the thyroid cartilage.

The arytenoid cartilages resemble a pyramid in form and rest on either side of the upper border of the lamina of the cricoid cartilage.

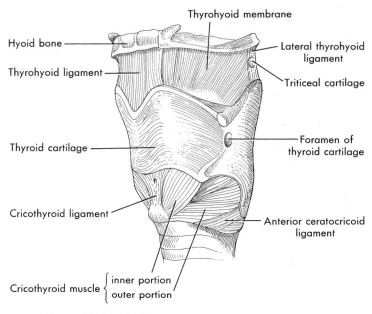

Figure 18–3. The larynx seen from the left side and front.

The corniculate cartilages are small, conical nodules of elastic cartilage articulating with the upper inner surface of the arytenoid cartilage. They prolong the arytenoid cartilages backward and medialward.

The cuneiform cartilages are small, elongated pieces of elastic cartilage placed on each side in the aryepiglottic fold.

The larynx is lined throughout with mucous membrane, which is continuous above with that lining the pharynx and below with that lining the trachea.

The cavity of the larynx is divided into two parts by two folds of mucous membrane stretching from front to back but not quite meeting in the middle line. They thus leave an elongated fissure called the *glottis*, which is the narrowest segment of the air passages. The glottis is protected by a lid of fibrocartilage called the *epiglottis*.

THE VOCAL FOLDS. Embedded in the mucous membrane at the edges of the slit are fibrous and elastic ligaments, which strengthen the edges of the glottis and give them elasticity. These ligaments, covered with mucous membrane, are firmly attached at both ends to the cartilages of the larynx and are called the inferior or *true vocal folds*, because they function in the production of the voice. Above the vocal folds are two ventricular folds, which do not function in the production of the voice but serve to keep the true vocal folds moist, in holding the breath, and in protecting the larynx during the swallowing of food.

The glottis varies in shape and size according to the action of muscles upon the laryngeal walls. When the larynx is at rest during quiet breathing, the glottis is V-shaped; during a deep inspiration it becomes almost round, while during the production of a high note the edges of the folds approximate so closely as to leave scarcely any opening at all.

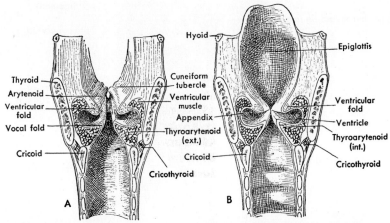

Figure 18–4. Larynx, frontal section. (*A*) Posterior segment, (*B*) anterior segment. (J. P. Schaeffer, *Morris' Human Anatomy.* Courtesy of The Blakiston Company.)

MUSCLES OF THE LARYNX. Many of the muscles of the neck, face, lips, and tongue are concerned with speech. The muscles of the larynx are extrinsic and intrinsic.

The extrinsic muscles include the:

1. Infrahyoid Muscles	2. Suprahyoid Muscles (some of)
Omohyoid	Stylopharyngeus
Sternohyoid	Palatopharyngeus
Thyrohyoid	Inferior and middle constrictors of
Sternothyroid	the pharynx

Physiology. (1) In prolonged inspiratory efforts, such as in singing, these muscles produce tension on the lower part of the cervical fascia and hence prevent the apices of the lungs and the large blood vessels from being compressed. (2) In the act of swallowing, the larynx and hyoid bone are drawn up with the pharynx—these muscles depress them. (3) They elevate and depress the thyroid cartilage.

The intrinsic muscles are confined entirely to the larynx and are shown in Figure 18–4.

Physiology. The posterior cricoarytenoid muscles rotate the arytenoid cartilages outward, thereby separating the vocal cords. The lateral cricoarytenoid muscles rotate the arytenoid cartilages inward, thereby approximating the vocal cords. The arytenoid muscles approximate the arytenoid cartilages, especially in the back. These muscles also open and close the glottis.

The cricothyroid muscles elevate the arch of the cricoid cartilage in front, causing the lamina to be depressed and thereby increasing the distance between the vocal processes and thyroid cartilages.

The thyroarytenoid muscles draw the arytenoid cartilages forward toward the thyroid, and in this way they shorten and relax the vocal cords. Working together, these muscles regulate the degree of tension on the vocal cords.

NERVES AND BLOOD VESSELS. The laryngeal nerves are derived from the internal and external branches of the superior laryngeal, branches of the vagi. Blood is supplied to the larynx by branches of the superior thyroid artery which arises from the external carotid, and from the inferior thyroid, a branch of the thyroid axis, which arises from the subclavian artery.

Phonation. This term is applied to the production of vocal sounds. All of the respiratory organs function in the production of vocal sounds, but the vocal folds, the larynx, and the parts above are specially concerned. The speech centers and parts of the brain which control all of the movements of the tongue and jaw are of special importance. The organs of phonation in man are similar to those of many animals much lower in the scale of life; the association areas of the brain account for the greater variety of sounds that man can produce.

Voice. The vocal folds produce the voice. Air driven by an expiratory movement out of the lungs throws the two elastic folds into vibrations. These impart their vibrations to the column of air above them and so give rise to the sound which we call the voice. The pharynx, mouth, and nasal cavities above the glottis act as resonating cavities. The volume and force of the expired air and the amplitude of the vibrations of the vocal folds determine the loudness or intensity of the voice. The pitch of the voice depends upon the number of vibrations occurring in a given unit of time. This in turn is dependent on the length, thickness, and degree of elasticity of the vocal folds and the tension by which they are held. When the folds are tightly stretched and the glottis almost closed, the highest sounds are emitted.

Differences Between the Male and Female Voice. The size of the larynx varies in different individuals, and this is one reason for differences in pitch. At the time of puberty, the growth of the larynx and the vocal folds is much more rapid and accentuated in the male than in the female. In the male the increase in the size of the larynx causes an increase in the length of the vocal folds and also gives rise to the laryngeal prominence. These changes in structure are accompanied by changes in the voice, which becomes deeper and lower. Before the characteristic adult voice is attained, there occurs what is described as a break in the voice, due to the inability of the individual to control the longer vocal folds.

The trachea, or **windpipe,** is a membranous and cartilaginous tube, cylindrical, in shape, about 11.2 cm (4½ in.) in length and about 2 to 2.5 cm (1 in.) from side to side. It lies in front of the esophagus and extends from the larynx on the level of the sixth cervical vertebra to the level of the upper border of the fifth thoracic vertebra, where it divides into the two bronchi, one for each lung.

The walls are strengthened and rendered more rigid by rings of hyaline cartilage embedded in the fibrous tissue. These rings are C-shaped and incomplete behind, the cartilaginous rings being completed by bands of smooth muscle

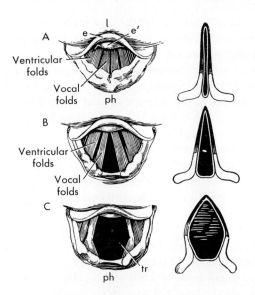

Figure 18–5. The larynx as seen by means of the laryngoscope in different conditions of the glottis. *A.* While singing a high note. *B.* In quiet breathing. *C.* During a deep inspiration. (*l*) Base of tongue, (*e*) upper free edge of epiglottis, (*e'*) cushion of epiglottis, (*ph*) part of anterior wall of pharynx, (*tr*) trachea.

tissue where the trachea is flattened and comes in contact with the esophagus. Like the larynx, it is lined with mucous membrane and has a ciliated epithelium on its inner surface; goblet cells are numerous. The mucous membrane, which extends into the bronchial tubes, keeps the internal surface of the air passages free from dust particles, the mucus entangles particles inhaled, and the movements of the cilia continually sweep this dust-laden mucus upward into the pharynx. The submucosa consists of loose connective tissue and contains mixed glands and fat.

The Bronchi. The two bronchi into which the trachea divides differ slightly, the right bronchus being shorter, wider, and more vertical in direction than the left. They enter the right and left lung, respectively, and then break up into a great number of smaller branches, which are called the bronchial tubes and bronchioles. The two bronchi resemble the trachea in structure, but as the bronchial tubes divide and subdivide into the smaller bronchi, the incomplete rings of cartilage are replaced by cartilaginous plates, and as they further divide their walls become thinner, the small plates of cartilage cease, the fibrous tissue disappears, and the smallest tubes are composed of only a thin layer of muscular and elastic tissue lined by ciliated epithelium. Each bronchiole terminates in an elongated saccule called the atrium. Each atrium bears, on all parts of its surface,

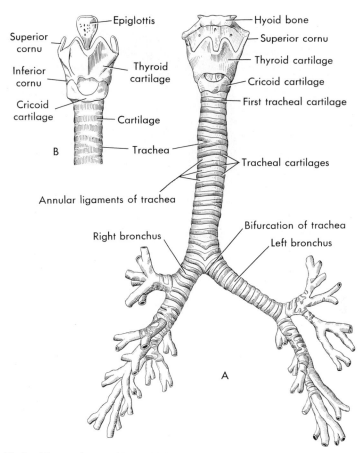

Figure 18–6. The trachea and bronchial ramification, front view. (*A*) Showing ramifications. (*B*) Showing details of glottis and epiglottis. (Modified from Toldt.)

small, irregular projections known as *alveoli*, or air cells. The lining of the walls of the alveoli consists of very thin epithelial cells. Underlying it is a thin homogeneous basement membrane. There is close approximation between this membrane and the capillary.

Nerves and Blood Vessels of the Trachea and Bronchi. The nerves are composed of fibers derived from the vagi, the recurrent nerves, and from the thoracolumbar system. Blood is supplied to the trachea by the inferior thyroid arteries.

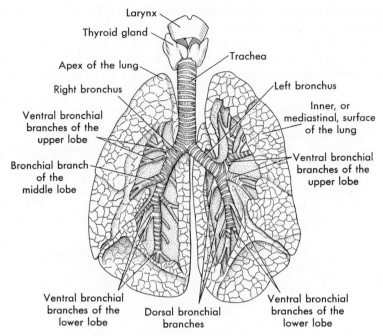

Larynx

Thyroid gland

Apex of the lung

Right bronchus

Ventral bronchial branches of the upper lobe

Bronchial branch of the middle lobe

Trachea

Left bronchus

Inner, or mediastinal, surface of the lung

Ventral bronchial branches of the upper lobe

Ventral bronchial branches of the lower lobe

Dorsal bronchial branches

Ventral bronchial branches of the lower lobe

Figure 18–7. The trachea, bronchi, and bronchial tubes. The tissues have been removed to show the air tubes.

Lungs

Anatomy. The lungs (pulmones) are cone-shaped organs which fill the two lateral chambers of the thoracic cavity and are separated from each other by the heart and other contents of the mediastinum. Each lung presents an outer surface which is convex, a base which is concave to fit over the convex portion of the diaphragm, and an apex which extends about 2.5 to 4 cm (1 to 1½ in.) above the level of the sternal end of the first rib. Each lung is connected to the heart and trachea by the pulmonary artery, pulmonary vein, bronchial arteries and veins, the bronchus, plexuses of nerves, lymphatics, lymph nodes, and areolar tissue, which are covered by the pleura and constitute the *root* of the lung. On the inner surface is a vertical notch called the *hilum*, which gives passage to the structures which form the root of the lung. Below and in front of the hilum there is a deep concavity, called the cardiac impression, where the heart lies; it is larger and deeper on the left than on the right lung, because the heart projects farther to the left side.

The right lung is larger and broader than the left, due to the inclination of the heart to the left side; it is also shorter by 2.5 cm (1 in.), as a result of the diaphragm's rising higher on the right side to accommodate the liver. It is divided by fissures into three lobes—superior, middle, and inferior.

The left lung is smaller, narrower, and longer than the right. It is divided into two lobes—superior and inferior.

The substance of the lungs is porous and spongy; owing to the presence of air it crepitates when handled and floats in water. It consists of bronchial tubes and their terminal dilatations, numerous blood vessels, lymphatics, and nerves, and an abundance of elastic connective tissue. Each *lobe* of the lung is composed of many *lobules*, and into each lobule a *bronchiole* enters and terminates in an *atrium*. Each atrium presents a series of air cells, or *alveoli*, 700,000,000 or more in number. Each alveolus is somewhat globular in form with a diameter of about 100 μ. The amount of surface exposed to the air and covered by the capillaries

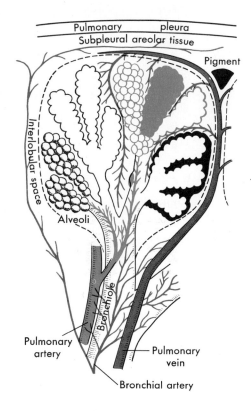

Figure 18–8. Diagram of a lobule of the lung. A bronchiole is seen dividing into two branches, one of which runs upward and ends in the lobule. At the left, two atria are seen from the outside. Next are three atria in vertical section, the alveoli of each opening into the common passageway. In the next group the first atrium shows a pulmonary arteriole surrounding the opening of each alveolus, and the second gives the same with the addition of the close capillary network in the wall of each alveolus. Around the fourth group is a deep deposit of pigment, such as occurs in old age and in the lungs of those who inhale coal dust, etc. On the bronchiole lies a branch of the pulmonary artery (*blue*), bringing blood to the atria for aeration. Beginning between the atria are the radicles of the pulmonary vein (*red*). The bronchial artery is shown as a small vessel bringing nutrient blood to the bronchiole. (Modified from Gerrish.)

is enormous. It is estimated that the entire inner surface of the lungs amounts to about 90 sq m, more than 100 times the skin surface of the adult body. Of this lung area about 70 sq m are respiratory.

Nerves of the Lungs. The craniosacral nerve supply is made up of fibers in the vagus nerves.

The thoracolumbar nerve supply is made up of fibers in the visceral branches of the first four thoracic spinal nerves.

Blood Vessels of the Lungs. Two sets of vessels are distributed to the lungs: (1) branches of the pulmonary artery which bring blood from the right ventricle, and (2) branches of the bronchial arteries, which bring blood from the aorta.

1. The branches of the pulmonary artery accompany the bronchial tubes and form a plexus of capillaries around the alveoli. The walls of the alveoli are thin; they consist of a single layer of modified squamous epithelium surrounded by a fine, elastic connective tissue. The capillary plexus lies in the elastic connective tissue, and the air in the alveoli is separated from the blood in the capillaries only by the thin membranes forming their respective walls. The air sacs are surrounded

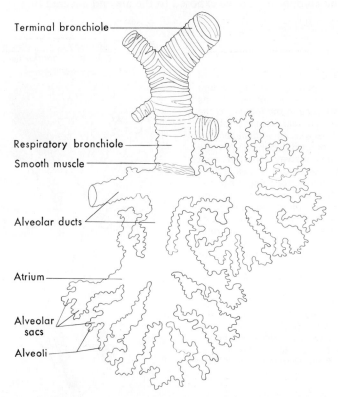

Terminal bronchiole

Respiratory bronchiole

Smooth muscle

Alveolar ducts

Atrium

Alveolar sacs

Alveoli

Figure 18–9. A pulmonary, or lung, unit. There is cartilage in the wall of the terminal bronchiole, and the lining is ciliated epithelium. There is no cartilage in the wall of the respiratory bronchiole, and the lining changes from ciliated epithelium to simple squamous epithelium.

by capillaries which form a surface area of about 150 sq m for the exchange of oxygen and carbon dioxide. Blood pressure in the pulmonary arteries is about 20 to 22 mm Hg. In the soma the capillaries are surrounded by tissue fluid, which exerts pressure against the capillaries; but the capillaries in the lungs are not opposed by such pressures. This means that pressures must be lower to prevent disturbances of hydrostatic and osmotic forces of the blood in the lungs. The pulmonary veins begin in the pulmonary capillaries, which coalesce to form larger branches. These run through the substance of the lung, communicate with other branches, and form larger vessels, which accompany the arteries and bronchial tubes to the hilum. Finally the pulmonary veins open into the left atrium.

2. The branches of the bronchial arteries supply blood to the lung substance— the bronchial tubes, coats of the blood vessels, the lymph nodes, and the pleura. The bronchial veins formed at the root of each lung receive veins which correspond to the branches of the bronchial arteries. Some of the blood supplied by the bronchial arteries passes into the pulmonary veins, but the greater amount is returned to the bronchial veins. The right bronchial vein ends in the azygos vein, the left in the highest intercostal or hemiazygos vein.

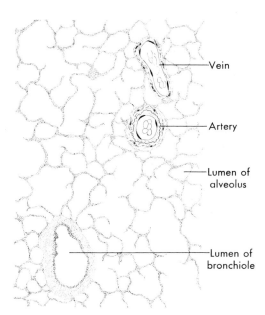

Figure 18–10. Diagram of lung section. There are about 700 to 800 million alveoli in the lungs. These are surrounded by a network of capillaries for the exchange of oxygen and carbon dioxide.

Pleura. Each lung is enclosed in a serous sac, the pleura, one layer of which is closely adherent to the walls of the chest and diaphragm (parietal); the other closely covers the lung (visceral, or pulmonary).

Named Areas of the Pleura		
Visceral—pulmonary (outer layer of wall of lungs)		
Parietal— (inner layer of chest wall)	Cervical—neck region of chest wall	
	Costal—rib region of chest wall	
	Diaphragmatic—upper layer of diaphragm	
	Mediastinal—outer aspect of mediastinum	

The pleura is a thin, transparent, moist, serous membrane which forms two closed sacs, the right and the left, each invaginated by the lung. The visceral portion is closely adherent to the lung, the parietal portion more loosely attached to the underlying tissues of the chest walls and diaphragm. Both layers meet around the root of the lung.

The two layers of the pleural sacs, moistened by serum, are normally in close contact, and the so-called pleural cavity is a potential rather than an actual

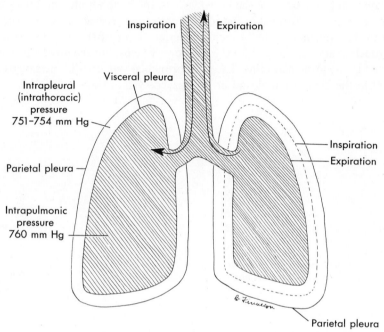

Figure 18–11. Diagram showing parietal and visceral pleura and pressure changes during respiration.

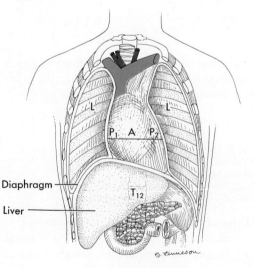

Figure 18–12. Diagram showing thoracic cavity. Line *A* indicates the mediastinum; P_1 and P_2, the mediastinal pleura; *L*, lung space surrounded by pleura.

cavity; they move easily upon one another with each respiration. If the surface of the pleura becomes inflamed (pleurisy), friction results; and the sounds produced by this friction can be heard if the ear is applied to the chest.

Normally only a small amount of fluid is secreted, and its absorption by the lymphatics keeps pace with its secretion, so that the amount of serum is very small. In pleurisy the amount may be considerably increased, owing to the extra activity of the irritated secretory cells and excessive transudation from the congested blood vessels. The amount may be sufficient to separate the two layers of the pleura, thus changing the potential pleural cavity into an actual one. This is known as pleurisy with effusion. If the effusion becomes purulent, the condition is called empyema and requires surgical treatment to provide free drainage.

If a puncture occurs through the chest walls so that air enters between the two layers of the pleura (pneumothorax), the lung will collapse. If the puncture is closed, the air will be gradually absorbed, and the lung will resume its normal position. Certain types of tuberculosis are treated by artificial pneumothorax. This is accomplished by surgical removal of part of the chest wall or by injections of air into the chest cavity.

The mediastinum, or interpleural space, lies between the right and left pleurae in the median plane of the chest. It extends from the sternum to the spinal column and is entirely filled with the thoracic viscera, namely, the thymus, heart, aorta and its branches, pulmonary artery and veins, venae cavae, azygos vein, various veins, trachea, esophagus, thoracic duct, lymph nodes, and lymph vessels, all lying in connective tissue.

Physiology of Respiration

The main purposes of respiration are to supply the cells of the body with oxygen and eliminate the excess carbon dioxide which results from oxidation. Respiration also helps to maintain the normal temperature of the body and eliminate about 350 ml of water, each 24 hours.

It is common to discuss respiration under three headings:

1. The process of *ventilation* (*breathing*) may be subdivided into inspiration, or breathing in, and expiration, or breathing out.

2. *External respiration* includes external oxygen supply, or the passage of oxygen from the alveoli of the lungs to the blood, and external carbon dioxide elimination, or the passage of carbon dioxide from the blood to the lungs.

3. *Internal respiration* includes internal oxygen supply, or the passage of oxygen from the blood to the tissue cells, and internal carbon dioxide elimination, or the passage of carbon dioxide from the tissue cells to the blood.

It is evident that external respiration is a process which takes place in the lungs and internal respiration is a process which takes place in the cells that make up the tissues.

Ventilation (Breathing). The thorax is a closed cavity which contains the lungs. The lungs may be thought of as elastic sacs, the interiors of which remain permanently open to the outside air by way of the bronchi, trachea, glottis, and nasopharynx; alveolar pressure, or the pressure against the lungs from inside, is therefore atmospheric pressure and is usually given as 760 mm Hg at sea level. The lungs are protected externally from atmospheric pressure by the walls of the chest. Intrathoracic (intrapleural) pressure, or pressure against the lungs from the thoracic cavity, varies with thoracic conditions.

During life the size of the thoracic cavity is constantly changing with the respiratory movements. When all the muscles of respiration are at rest, that is, at the end of a normal expiration, the size and position of the chest may be regarded as normal. Any enlargement constitutes active inspiration, the result of which is to bring more air into the lungs. In quiet breathing, following this active inspiration the thoracic cavity returns to its normal position, giving an expiration. Normal quiet respiratory movements are of this type, an *active inspiration* followed by a *passive expiration*. In deeper or more rapid breathing expiration may also be active.

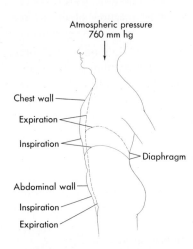

Figure 18–13. Changes in position of diaphragm and abdominal wall, and in size of thoracic cavity during respiration.

Mechanism of Inspiration and Expiration. Active *inspiration* is the result of the contraction of the muscles of inspiration; passive expiration is due mainly to the elastic recoil of the parts previously stretched. In inspiration the thoracic cavity is enlarged in all directions—vertical, dorsoventral, and lateral. The increase in the vertical diameter is brought about by the downward movement of the diaphragm. The dorsoventral and lateral diameters are increased by the contraction of the intercostal and other muscles which cause the sternum and ribs to move upward and outward. The lungs are expanded in proportion to the increase in the size of the thorax.

Muscles of Inspiration. The number of muscles used in inspiration varies greatly. The diaphragm and all the muscles that contract simultaneously with it are classed as inspiratory. Those that contract alternately are classed as expiratory. The following are the inspiratory muscles: muscles of diaphragm, external intercostals, the scaleni, the sternocleidomastoid, the pectoralis minor, and the serratus posticus superior. In forced inspirations the action of these muscles is supplemented by additional muscles of the trunk, larynx, pharynx, and face.

The Scaleni (*Scalenus*, singular). There are three: scalenus anterior, scalenus medius, and scalenus posterior. They arise from the transverse processes of the cervical vertebrae and are inserted in the first and second ribs.

The serratus posticus superior extends from the spinous processes of the seventh cervical and upper two or three thoracic vertebrae to the upper borders of the second, third, fourth, and fifth ribs.

Muscles of Expiration. Normal expiration is considered a passive act due to gravity and the elastic recoil of the lungs. But in forced expirations diminution in the size of the thorax may be accomplished in two ways: (1) by forcing the diaphragm farther up into the thoracic cavity, a result obtained *not* by direct action of the diaphragm but by contraction of the muscular walls of the abdomen, the external and internal oblique, the rectus, and the transversalis; and (2) by depressing the ribs. The muscles which depress the ribs are the internal intercostals and the triangularis sterni. Some authorities add the iliocostalis, serratus posticus inferior, and the quadratus lumborum, but it has not been definitely determined whether they act simultaneously with the diaphragm or alternately.

Transversus thoracis, or triangularis sterni, is found on the front and inner side of the thoracic wall. Its fibers pass from the sternum running upward and outward to be inserted in the costal cartilages from the second to the sixth rib.

The iliocostalis is one of the divisions of the sacrospinalis and is inserted into the inferior borders of the lower six or seven ribs.

The serratus posticus inferior arises from the spinous processes of the lower two thoracic and upper second or third lumbar vertebra, and the insertion is in the inferior borders of the lower four ribs.

Types of Respiration. Two types of respiration are noted. The sequence of movements is the distinguishing factor. In the costal type the upper ribs move first and the abdomen second. The elevation of the ribs is the more noticeable movement. In the diaphragmatic type, the abdomen bulges outward first, and this is followed by a movement of the thorax. Diaphragmatic respirations are deeper. Restriction of the action of the diaphragm by tight clothing is thought to be the cause of costal respiration.

The respiratory center is located in the medulla oblongata, and this center has connections in the pons. Both centers share in the control of respiration. The medulla is the center for the nervous control of the depth and frequency of respiration, that is, the quantity of air moved through the lungs per minute (lung ventilation). This center has been found to be sensitive to changes in the acidity, per cent of carbon dioxide, per cent of oxygen, the temperature of the blood, and also to the blood pressure in the blood vessels around it. Nerve impulses from all the sense organs reach this center, as do all nerve impulses from the cerebral cortex and from the hypothalamus. From the respiratory center, nerve impulses pass via the spinal cord and spinal nerve to the intercostal muscles of the diaphragm, and the abdominal muscles, adjusting respiratory depth and rhythm to body needs. The respiratory rhythm is regulated also reflexly from the lungs themselves. This is called the lung reflex or the Hering-Breuer reflex. These reflexes are elicited by inflation or deflation of the lungs. Inflation of the lung inhibits respiration, whereas deflation of the lung has a stimulating effect on respiration. The receptors are located in the lungs, and impulses reach the respiratory center over afferent fibers in the vagus nerve. This reflex is perhaps the most powerful in regulating respirations. Chemoreceptors in the carotid and aortic bodies are sensitive to carbon dioxide excess and oxygen lack. The carotid sinus and aortic arch also respond to changes in pressure; as

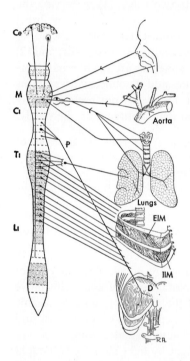

Figure 18–14. Diagram to show nervous control of respiration. (*Ce*) Cerebral cortex, (*C₁*) spinal cord at first cervical level, (*D*) diaphragm, (*EIM* and *IIM*) external and internal intercostal muscles, (*L₁*) spinal cord at first lumbar level, (*M*) medulla, (*P*) phrenic nerve, (*T₁*) spinal cord at first thoracic level. Nerves to abdominal muscles not shown.

arterial pressure rises, the pressoreceptors are stimulated and respiration is inhibited. Stimulation of the chemoreceptors increases the depth and rate of respiration.

Control of Respiratory Rate. It is possible to increase or decrease the respiratory rate within certain limits, by voluntary effort, for a short time. If respirations are arrested or their frequency is diminished, the carbon dioxide concentration in the blood increases, and eventually the stimulus becomes too strong to be controlled. According to some observers, the "breaking point" is reached in 23 to 27 seconds. If, before the breath is held, several breaths of pure oxygen are taken, the breaking point may be postponed; or, if the lungs are thoroughly aerated by forced breathing, so that the carbon dioxide is forced out and more oxygen breathed in, the breaking point may be postponed as long as eight minutes.

Cause of the First Respiration. The human fetus makes respiratory movements while in the uterus, possibly moving amniotic fluid in and out of the lungs. This may play a part in dilation of the future air passages. After birth and the

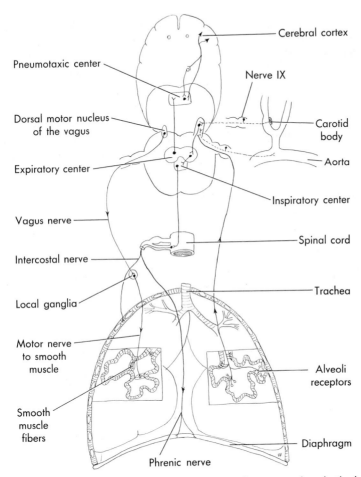

Figure 18–15. Nervous control of respiration, showing connections in the brain.

interruption of the placental circulation, the first breath is taken. The immediate cause of this activity on the part of the respiratory center must be connected, if not identical, with the cause of the automatic activity of the center during life. Three views are held regarding the immediate cause: that it is due to the increased amount of carbon dioxide in the blood, brought about by cutting the umbilical cord; that it is due to stimulation of the sensory nerves of the skin, due to cooler air, handling, drying, etc.; and that it is due tó a combination of these causes.

If stimulation through the blood and stimulation through the nerves normally coincide, it may be that the essential cause is the increased tension of the carbon dioxide, and therefore the increased concentration in acidity, following the cutting of the cord.

During intrauterine life, the fetal blood is aerated so well by exchange with the maternal blood that there is not adequate carbon dioxide to act as a stimulus to the fetal respiratory center.

Depth of Respiration. This is usually given as about 500 cc for quiet breathing. Necessity for increased oxygen supply and need of eliminating carbon dioxide are met by increased depth of respiration before increased rate is brought into play.

In the following table it will be noted that the minute ventilation of lungs is multiplied more than three and a half times, and mainly by increasing the completeness of contraction of the respiratory muscles rather than by causing them to contract a greater number of times.

Increase in Respiratory Depth and Rate on Increasing CO_2 in Inspired Air

% CO_2 in Inspired Air	Average Depth of Respiration, cc	Average Respiratory Rate	Minute Lung Volume, liters
Normal (0.04)	673	14	9.4
3.07	1216	15	18.2
5.14	1771	19	33.6

Frequency of Respiration. The average rate of respiration for an adult is about 14 to 20 per minute. In health this rate may be increased by muscular exercise or emotion. Anything that affects the heartbeat will have a similar effect on the respirations. Age has a marked influence. The average rate during the first year of life is about 44 per minute, and at the age of five years, 26 per minute. It is reduced between the ages of 15 and 25 to the normal standard.

External Respiration. This term is applied to the interchange of gases that takes place in the lungs. There is a continuous flow of blood through the capillaries, so that at least once or twice each minute all the blood in the body passes through the capillaries of the lungs. This means that the time during which any portion of blood is in a position for respiratory exchange is only a second or two. Yet during this time, the following changes take place: the blood loses carbon dioxide and moisture; it gains oxygen, which combines with the reduced hemoglobin of the red cells, or erythrocytes, forming oxyhemoglobin, and as a result of this the crimson color shifts to scarlet; and its temperature is slightly reduced.

It is helpful to compare the average amounts of oxygen and carbon dioxide found in venous and in arterial blood. The actual amounts of oxygen and carbon dioxide in venous blood vary with the metabolic activity of the tissues and differ, therefore, in the various organs according to the state of activity of each organ and the volume of its blood supply per unit of time. The main result of the respiratory exchange is to keep the gas content of the arterial blood nearly constant at the figures given. Under normal conditions it is not possible to increase appreciably the amount of oxygen absorbed by the blood flowing through the lungs.

Capacity of the Lungs. After the lungs are once filled with air they are never completely emptied. In other words, no expiration ever completely empties the alveoli; neither are they completely filled. The quantity of air which a person can expel by a forcible expiration, after the deepest inspiration possible, is called the *vital capacity* and averages about 4,000 to 4,800 cc for an adult man. It is the sum of tidal, complemental, and supplemental air. Figure 18–16 illustrates lung capacity.

Tidal air designates the amount of air that flows in and out of the lungs with each quiet respiratory movement. The average figure for an adult male is 500 cc.

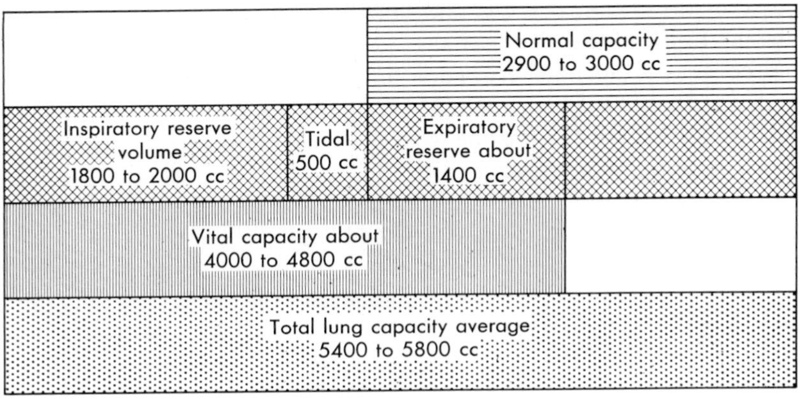

Figure 18–16.

Inspiratory reserve volume designates the amount of air that can be breathed in over and above the tidal air by the deepest possible inspiration. It is estimated at about 1,800 to 2,000 cc.

Expiratory reserve volume is the amount of air that can be breathed out after a quiet expiration by the most forcible expiration. It is equal to about 1,400 cc.

Residual air is the amount of air remaining in the lungs after the most powerful expiration. This has been estimated to be about 1,200 to 1,500 cc.

Reserve air is the residual air plus the supplemental air in the lungs under conditions of normal breathing, that is, about 3,000 cc.

Minimal Air. When the thorax is opened, the lungs collapse, driving out the supplemental and residual air; but before the alveoli are entirely emptied, the small bronchi leading to them collapse and entrap a little air in the alveoli. The small amount of air caught in this way is designated as minimal air.

Before birth the lungs contain no air. If, after birth, respirations are made, the lungs do not collapse completely on account of the capture of minimal air. Whether or not the lungs will float has constituted one of the facts used in medicolegal cases to determine if a child was stillborn.

However dry the external air may be, the expired air is nearly, or quite, saturated with moisture. An average of about 500 ml of water is eliminated daily in the breath. Whatever the temperature of the external air, the expired air is nearly as warm as the blood, having a temperature between 36.7° and 37.8°C (98° and 100°F). In man, breathing is one of the subsidiary means by which the temperature and the water content of the body are regulated. The heat required to warm the expired air and vaporize the moisture is taken from the body and represents a daily loss of heat. It requires about 0.5 Cal to vaporize 1 gm of water.

Taking the respiratory rate as 18 per minute and respiratory depth at 500 cc, one breathes in and out 12,000 liters of air per day. Since inspired air contains about 20 per cent oxygen and expired air about 16 per cent, this difference of 4 per cent represents the oxygen retained by the body—some 480 liters per day—and used by the tissues. This amount is often stated as about 350 cc per minute.

Internal Respiration. The exchange of oxygen and carbon dioxide in the tissues constitutes internal respiration and consists of the passage of oxygen from the blood into the tissue fluid and from the tissue fluid into the tissue cells and the passage of carbon dioxide from the cells into the tissue fluid and from the tissue fluid into the blood.

After the exchange of oxygen and carbon dioxide in the lungs, the aerated blood is returned to the heart and distributed to all parts of the body. In passing through the tissue capillaries, the blood is brought into exchange with tissue fluid in which the oxygen pressure is low. Consequently the blood in passing through the capillaries gives up much of its oxygen, which passes to the tissue fluid and from the latter to the tissue cells. On the contrary, the concentration of carbon dioxide is higher in the cells than in the blood, and this facilitates the passage of carbon dioxide from the cells to the tissue fluid and from the latter to the blood.

It is important to remember that the blood does not give up all its oxygen to the tissues.

Factors Influencing Respiration

Pressures. INTRA-ALVEOLAR PRESSURE. The respiratory muscles cause respiration by *compressing* or distending the lungs, which, in turn, will cause pressures in the alveoli to rise or fall. On *inspiration* pressures become slightly negative in relation to atmospheric pressure, about −3 mm Hg. Air is pulled inward through the respiratory airways. On *expiration* intra-alveolar pressure rises to about +3 mm Hg, which causes air to move *outward* through the respiratory airway. During expiratory effort intra-alveolar pressure can increase markedly. Inspiratory effort can reduce the pressure markedly.

INTRAPLEURAL PRESSURE. The intrapleural space is a potential space between the lung and the chest wall. The lungs fill the chest cavity, because the moist membranes constantly absorb any gas or fluids that may enter the space. However, the lungs have a continual tendency to collapse and to pull away from the chest wall. The reason for this is that the lung tissue contains numerous elastic fibers that are constantly stretched and are attempting to shorten. In addition, the *surface tension of fluids* lining the alveoli gives a continuous tendency for the lung to collapse. For this reason the lungs tend to pull away from the chest wall. After the lungs have been *stretched on inspiration*, the tendency to collapse is increased to about −5 or −6, and on *expiration*, the collapse tendency is about −4 mm Hg in relation to atmospheric pressure of 760 mm.

Oxygen and Carbon Dioxide Exchange in the Lung.. Two gas laws can be applied to the exchange of gases:

1. Boyle's Law. This law states that "volume varies inversely with the pressure at constant temperature." If pressure is applied to a gas, the molecules are forced closer together and volume decreases.

On inspiration as the diaphragm descends, the thoracic cavity enlarges and pressure in the pleural space decreases to about 751 mm Hg. Since the atmospheric pressure is 760 mm Hg, air rushes into the expanded lungs against the lower pressure.

On *expiration* the diaphragm relaxes and rises. As a result the volume of the thoracic cavity *decreases*. This *decrease* in volume is associated with an *increase* in pressure in the lung tissue. Since lung tissue is elastic, the lung is expanded, and pressure within the lung tissue is increased about 7 mm Hg. Thus the elasticity of the expanded lung increases pressure slightly above 760 mm Hg and air is forced out of the lung.

2. Charles's (Gay-Lussac's) Law. If pressure of a given quantity of gas remains constant, but the temperature *varies*, the volume of gas *increases* directly in proportion to the increase in temperature. Therefore, there are more molecules of oxygen, for example, in cold air than in warm air of equal volume.

Oxygen and Carbon Dioxide Volumes Per Cent in Blood

Gas	Arterial Blood		Venous Blood	
	Total %	In Solution	Total %	In Solution
Oxygen	19–21	0.240	12–14	0.1
Carbon dioxide	48–50	2–2.5	56–58	3.0

As blood is poured into the right heart, all substances (nutrients, water, hormones) are mixed well and equalized so that as blood moves into the pulmonary artery, it contains its full quota of each substance, with the exception of oxygen and carbon dioxide. From the pulmonary artery blood moves into the lung capillary networks, where the exchange of oxygen and carbon dioxide takes place. This is called *gas exchange* in the lungs. The blood contains a carbon dioxide concentration of about 56 to 58 per cent by volume and an oxygen concentration of about 12 to 14 per cent by volume, with some of each gas in solution. The rates of gaseous exchange are controlled by the following factors: (1) area of contact for the exchange, (2) length of time blood and air are in contact, (3) volume of blood passing through the alveolar network, (4) permeability of cells forming the capillary and alveolar membranes, (5) differences in concentrations of gases in alveolar air and the blood, and (6) rate at which chemical reaction takes place between the gases and the blood. Respiratory efficiency is also related to the number of red cells, hemoglobin content of the red cells, and area of the red cell.

In the alveoli the total area for exchange of gases has been estimated to be 25 to 50 times the total surface area of the body. The respiratory mechanism is delicately balanced, so that alveolar air remains constant at about 14 to 15 per cent by volume of oxygen and 5.5 per cent by volume of carbon dioxide. It is with this air that the blood is in contact for gaseous exchange. Research has shown that in health the amount of blood in the alveolar capillaries is proportionate to the amount of physical activity. At rest, the amount of blood in alveolar capillaries is about half the amount present during hard work.

Translating the concepts of concentrations of oxygen and carbon dioxide expressed in volumes per cent into terms of partial pressures, they may be stated simply as follows:

Atmospheric pressure at sea level exerts about 1 ton pressure per square foot, usually expressed in millimeters or inches. The total pressure of gases in the atmosphere is 760 mm Hg or 30 inches. Because oxygen forms 20.96 or about 21 per cent by volume of the atmosphere, its partial pressure is 21 per cent of 760, or 160 mm Hg (159.6). Carbon dioxide forms about 0.04 per cent by volume of the atmosphere, and its partial pressure is 0.04 per cent of 760, or 0.30 mm Hg. The other gases exert partial pressures in direct proportion to their volumes. Nitrogen exerts the highest partial pressure since its volume per cent is 79.

The tension of a gas in solution equals the partial pressure of that particular gas in the gas mixture with which the solution has established equilibrium. For example, in atmospheric air the partial pressure and tension of oxygen remain constant at 160 mm Hg and will change only if the relative concentrations of oxygen in the total mixture are changed. The absolute amount or quantity of a gas in solution varies, even if the partial pressure and tension remain constant. In applying the law of partial pressures, if the temperature remains constant the quantity of gas which goes into solution in any given liquid, e.g., plasma, is proportional to the partial pressure of the gas.

The following table illustrates the partial pressure of gas in inspired, expired, and alveolar air.

Gas	Inspired Air	Expired Air	Alveolar Air
Oxygen	160	116	103
Carbon dioxide	0.30	28	40
Nitrogen	594.70	569	570
Water vapor	5.00	47	47
	760.00 mm Hg	760 mm Hg	760 mm Hg

Analyzing the figures for oxygen in this table, it will be seen that oxygen pressure from inspired air (atmospheric air) to alveolar air falls and for carbon dioxide the decrease in pressure is in the reverse direction. That is, carbon dioxide pressure in the alveolar air is high, and in the inspired or atmospheric air the pressure is low. These inverse relationships between the pressures for oxygen and carbon dioxide in alveolar air promote the interchange of these gases in the lungs. The tensions of oxygen and carbon dioxide in alveolar air vary with depth and frequency of respiration. For example, in voluntary hyperventilation carbon dioxide tension falls and oxygen tension rises. If respiration is suspended for any reason, carbon dioxide tension rises and oxygen tension falls.

Nitrogen is an inert gas in relation to respiration; however, about 0.83 per cent by volume of the gas is dissolved in the plasma. This is neither used nor produced in the body.

Partial pressure or tension of oxygen in blood varies in relation to venous and arterial blood. The tension of oxygen in arterial blood is about 100 mm Hg, and in venous blood, about 36 to 38 mm. The tension of carbon dioxide in arterial blood is about 40 to 45 mm, and in venous blood the tension varies directly in relation to muscular activity, but for mixed venous blood the average tension is about 48 to 50 mm.

In the lung the alveoli are separated from the capillaries by thin membranes which are permeable to the gases. Since the pressure gradient for oxygen in alveolar air is high and in the capillary tension low, there is rapid diffusion of oxygen from the alveolar air to the blood. The reverse is true for carbon dioxide: the pressure gradient is high in blood and low in the alveoli—hence equilibrium is rapidly and progressively established between oxygen and carbon dioxide in the blood and alveolar air as blood moves along in the capillary network. Many factors may interfere with gaseous exchange in the lung capillaries.

As blood moves into the somatic and visceral capillaries, oxygen tension is high and carbon dioxide tension is low in the capillary network, and tension of oxygen in tissue fluid and cells is relatively low. Carbon dioxide tension is relatively high in the tissue fluid and cells and relatively low in the capillary. This means that the pressure gradients of the gases favor exchange between tissue fluid and blood. Changes in the pressure gradients cause a disequilibrium between blood plasma and oxyhemoglobin, favor the chemical changes taking place in blood between oxygen and carbon dioxide, and promote a steady, constant flow of oxygen from the blood to tissue fluid and cells and a constant flow of carbon dioxide from the cells and tissue fluid to blood.

From the viewpoint of the kinetic theory of *gases*, this means that the pressure against any membrane is determined by the number of molecules striking the membrane at any moment times the average kinetic energy of these molecules.

Carriage of Oxygen and Carbon Dioxide. As shown in Figure 18-17, oxygen reaches the cells in three steps: (1) environment to lungs, (2) lungs to blood, and (3) blood to cells. In each step the method of oxygen transfer is diffusion, and each step is continuous inasmuch as there is a constant source of oxygen on one side of the diffusion membrane, which keeps the concentration of diffusible oxygen relatively high, and a place of disappearance of diffusible oxygen on the other side of the diffusion membrane, which keeps the concentration of oxygen relatively low. Then, too, the place of disappearance of oxygen in step 1 becomes the source of oxygen in step 2, and the place of disappearance of oxygen in step

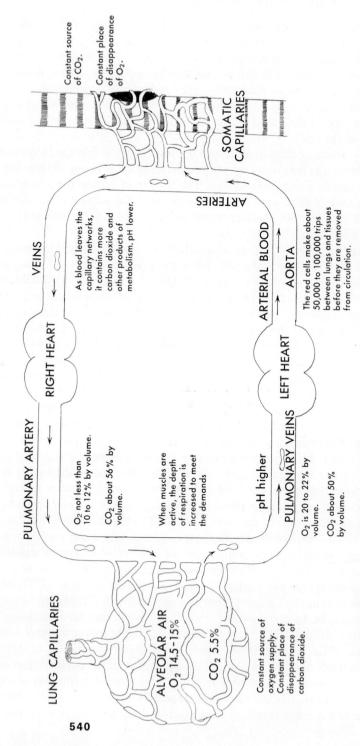

540

Figure 18–17. Oxygen and carbon dioxide levels of the alveolus and blood as it moves through the circulatory system.

LUNG CAPILLARIES

ALVEOLAR AIR
O₂ 14.5–15%

CO₂ 5.5%

Constant source of oxygen supply.
Constant place of disappearance of carbon dioxide.

PULMONARY ARTERY

RIGHT HEART

VEINS

O₂ not less than 10 to 12% by volume.

CO₂ about 56% by volume.

When muscles are active, the depth of respiration is increased to meet the demands

As blood leaves the capillary networks, it contains more carbon dioxide and other products of metabolism, pH lower.

SOMATIC CAPILLARIES

Constant source of CO₂.

Constant place of disappearance of O₂.

ARTERIES

ARTERIAL BLOOD

AORTA

The red cells make about 50,000 to 100,000 trips between lungs and tissues before they are removed from circulation.

LEFT HEART

PULMONARY VEINS

pH higher

O₂ is 20 to 22% by volume.

CO₂ about 50% by volume.

2 becomes the source for step 3. In this way the periodic intake of oxygen (respiratory rate 14 to 18) is changed to a steady flow to the cells for normally variable activities.

As the blood flows through the lung capillaries, oxygen diffuses from the alveoli into the plasma and then into the red blood corpuscles and combines with the hemoglobin to form oxyhemoglobin. On leaving the lungs, practically all the hemoglobin exists as oxyhemoglobin, and the plasma is saturated with oxygen in solution. When the blood reaches the tissue capillaries, there is a continuous diffusion of oxygen from erythrocytes to plasma, plasma to tissue fluid, tissue fluid to cells. The rate of this diffusion of oxygen depends upon the rate of use of oxygen by the cells. These diffusions are started by the use of oxygen in the cell.

The blood carries *from the lungs* about 20 volumes of oxygen per 100 volumes of blood, more than 19 per cent as oxyhemoglobin (stored as oxyhemoglobin) in the erythrocytes and less than 1 per cent (diffusible) in solution in the water of the blood, hence mainly in plasma. While the blood is flowing through the alveolar capillaries, oxygen diffuses from a place kept relatively high in diffusible oxygen (by breathing) to a place kept relatively low in diffusible oxygen (circulating blood).

The blood leaves in the tissues about 10 volumes of oxygen per 100 volumes of blood. While the blood is flowing through the tissue capillaries, oxygen diffuses from a place kept relatively high in diffusible oxygen (flowing blood) to a place kept relatively low in diffusible oxygen (used in cells).

Carbon dioxide is produced in living cells at varying rates, depending upon activity.

Carbon dioxide is believed to enter the blood from the tissue cells by diffusion. Some of it remains in solution in the plasma, but most of it diffuses from plasma into the erythrocytes where the enzyme *carbonic anhydrase* catalyzes the formation of carbonic acid ($H_2O + CO_2 \rightarrow H_2CO_3$). This results in an increase in hydrogen ions and favors the decomposition of oxyhemoglobin ($HHbO_2 \rightarrow HHb + O_2$) and the escape of oxygen to tissue cells. Inasmuch as reduced hemoglobin is a weaker acid than is oxyhemoglobin, this reaction decreases the hydrogen ion concentration within the erythrocyte. A further decrease results from the reaction of carbonic acid with the potassium salts of hemoglobin ($KHb + H_2CO_3 \rightarrow HHb + KHCO_3$). During these reactions the concentration of bicarbonate ions (HCO_3^-) within the red blood cells has increased; consequently these ions diffuse from erythrocytes into the plasma thus building up the sodium bicarbonate concentration in plasma. In compensation for the entrance of these anions, chloride ions (Cl^-) diffuse from plasma into the erythrocytes; this adjustment is known as the *chloride shift*. Part of the carbon dioxide which enters the erythrocytes combines directly with hemoglobin to form carbamino hemoglobin; this combination is limited, however, to the availability of free amino groups on the hemoglobin. Thus, various means are provided in erythrocytes and plasma for transportation of a relatively large quantity of carbon dioxide with remarkably little change in the pH of blood. When the blood reaches the lungs, oxygen is available and carbon dioxide can escape. With the entrance of oxygen, the sequence of reactions which took place at the tissue cells is reversed. The *concentration gradients* of the two substances concerned—oxygen and carbon dioxide—are reversed in the blood in the tissue capillaries and in the blood in the alveolar capillaries.

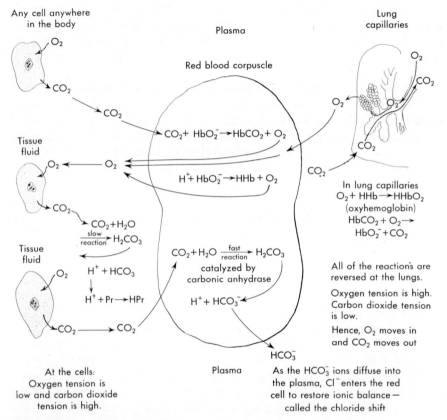

Figure 18–18. Diagram illustrating some of the chemical changes taking place with oxygen and carbon dioxide exchange at the cells and lungs.

In summary, carbon dioxide is carried in venous blood:

1. As bicarbonate (HCO_3^-), about 90 per cent, one third in the red cell and two thirds in the plasma.
2. As carbamino hemoglobin.
3. As a small per cent dissolved physically in plasma.
4. In other chemical combinations.

Each intake of air is accompanied by a low rustling sound, which can be heard if the ear is applied to the chest wall. It is thought that the dilation of the alveoli produces this sound, and absence of it indicates that the air is not entering the alveoli over which no sound is heard or that the lung is separated from the chest wall by effused fluid. The air passing in and out of the larynx, trachea, and bronchial tubes produces a louder sound, which is called a bronchial murmur. Normally this murmur is heard directly above or behind the tubes; but when the lung is consolidated as in pneumonia, it conducts sound more readily than usual, and the murmur is heard in other parts of the chest. In diseased conditions the normal sounds are modified in various ways and are then spoken of under the name of *rales*.

Eupnea. This term is applied to ordinary quiet respiration made without obvious effort.

Dyspnea. In its widest sense, *dyspnea* means any increase in the force or rate of the respiratory movements. These movements show many degrees of intensity, corresponding with the strength of the stimulus. Usually the term *dyspnea* is reserved for the more labored breathing, in which the expirations are active and forced. Dyspnea may be caused by (1) stimulation of the sensory nerves, particularly the pain

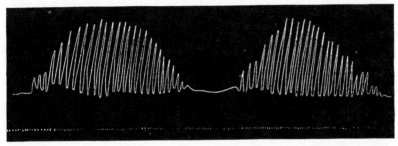

Figure 18–19. Stethograph tracing of Cheyne-Stokes respirations. The time is marked in seconds. (Halliburton.)

nerves, (2) an increase in the hydrogen ion concentration of the blood, and (3) any condition that interferes with the normal rate of the respirations or of the heart action or prevents the passage of air in or out of the lungs.

Hyperpnea. The word *hyperpnea* is applied to the initial stages of dyspnea, when the respirations are simply increased.

Apnea. The word means a lack of breathing. In physiological literature, it is used to describe the cessation of breathing movements due to lack of stimulation of the respiratory center, brought about by rapid and prolonged ventilation of the lungs. In medical literature, the term is sometimes used as a synonym for asphyxia, or suffocation.

Cheyne-Stokes Respirations. This is a type of respiration which was first described by the two physicians [2] whose names it bears. It is an exaggeration of the type of respiration which is often seen during sleep in normal people. The respirations increase in force and frequency up to a certain point and then gradually decrease until they cease altogether; there is a short period of apnea, then the respirations recommence, and the cycle is repeated. Cheyne-Stokes respirations are associated with

[2] John Cheyne, Scottish physician (1777–1836). William Stokes, Irish physician (1804–1878).

conditions that depress the respiratory center, especially in brain, heart, and kidney diseases.

Edematous Respiration. When the air cells become infiltrated with fluid from the blood, the breathing becomes edematous and is recognized by the moist, rattling sounds, or rales, caused by the passage of the air through the fluid. It is a serious condition because it interferes with aeration of the blood and often results in asphyxia.

Asphyxia. Asphyxia is produced by any condition that causes prolonged interference with the aeration of the blood, viz., obstruction to the entrance of air to the lungs, depression of the respiratory center, an insufficient supply of oxygen, or a lack of hemoglobin in the blood. The first stages are associated with dyspnea and convulsive movements; then the respirations become slow and shallow and are finally reduced to mere twitches. The skin is cyanosed, the pupils of the eyes dilate, the reflexes are abolished, and respirations cease. If the heart continues to beat, resuscitation is often accomplished by artificial respiration, even after breathing has ceased.

Hypoxia is a general term that should be used for oxygen deficiency when arterial oxygen saturation is *not less* than 80 per cent. **Anoxia** is a marked deficiency or absence of oxygen reaching the tissue cells. It may be due to:

1. Decreased oxygen-carrying capacity of hemoglobin, due to presence of methemoglobin, or carbon monoxide hemoglobin, or low hemoglobin content of blood. This is called *anemic anoxia*.

2. *Anoxic anoxia*—the volume of oxygen in arterial blood is low due to low oxygen tension or inadequate pulmonary ventilation or pulmonary disease.

3. *Stagnant anoxia*—due to disturbances in circulation that slow down circulation in the capillaries, e.g., cardiac disease.

4. *Histotoxic anoxia*—due to interference with cellular respiration, as in cyanide poisoning.

Oxygen Therapy

A continuous supply of oxygen is essential for all cells throughout the body. Any shortage of oxygen interferes with production of energy. Hypoxia, frequently referred to as anoxia, reduces cell activities and, if severe, endangers the life of cells. The causes of oxygen deficiency are many and varied; but the conditions most frequently requiring oxygen therapy are the acute shortages which result in lowered oxygen tension of blood plasma and a consequent decrease in the rate of oxidation of hemoglobin.

Such conditions may develop during prolonged anesthesia, especially when the respiratory center has been depressed by drugs. With normal lung tissue, such conditions are quickly corrected. The increased need for oxygen is also associated with abnormalities of lung tissue, as in inflammations or destruction of lung tissue from disease. These conditions limit the amount of oxygen crossing the thin membrane which separates the alveoli of the lung from the blood capillaries. Carbon monoxide poisoning interferes with oxygen transportation because hemoglobin combines with carbon monoxide and hence cannot carry oxygen.

The signs of oxygen need are not always clearly defined. Cyanosis may occur. It results from an increase in reduced hemoglobin in the blood and consequently decreased oxyhemoglobin. Various studies indicate that even experienced observers may not detect this sign before the proportion of oxyhemoglobin has dropped from the normal 96 per cent to as low as 85 per cent. A person who is anemic and has a low hemoglobin level will not appear cyanotic although he may lack oxygen. In carbon monoxide poisoning, the skin becomes a cherry red rather than the blue of cyanosis. The earliest symptoms are frequently vague and related to decrease of oxygen to brain cells, which are very sensitive to oxygen shortage.

The purpose of oxygen therapy is to increase the oxygen tension of blood plasma and restore the oxyhemoglobin in the red blood cells to normal proportion, thus supplying oxygen to meet the needs of the tissue cells. This is done by providing oxygen in higher concentration than in air: by enriching the atmosphere in an oxygen tent, by introducing oxygen into the trachea through a nasal tube, or by using an oxygen mask. The concentration of oxygen is adjusted by regulating the rate of flow of the gas from a tank where it is stored under pressure. Concentrations of 40 to 60 per cent are usually used although even 100 per cent oxygen can be supplied through the mask technique. Ordinarily the gas is supplied at atmospheric pressure; the increased proportion of oxygen in the mixture increases the tension of oxygen in the alveoli and more oxygen will be absorbed across the alveolar-capillary membrane. Once the hemoglobin has been saturated with oxygen, little or no further advantage is obtained by increasing the oxygen concentration. In carbon monoxide poisoning, increased oxygen concentration in the blood favors release of carbon monoxide from its combination with hemoglogin and the hemoglobin thus released can combine with oxygen. When oxygen therapy is successful, the symptoms associated with hypoxia disappear.

Oxygen leaves the tank as a dry gas, free from water vapor, and as such would be very irritating to the membranes of the trachea, bronchi, and alveoli. Consequently the oxygen must be moistened by bubbling it through water; this is the function of the humidifier. It is also important that the air entering the lungs should be cool and, therefore, the temperature of the tent should be about 20° C (68° F). Increased oxygen concentration in air always increases the danger of fire. The temperature at which burning occurs becomes progressively lower as the oxygen concentration increases. Consequently, it is of utmost importance to safeguard the area where oxygen is in use against possible sources of ignition.

Oxygen Intoxication. Increased oxygen pressure in the blood does not significantly increase the amount of oxygen combined with hemoglobin, because the hemoglobin is already saturated; but it does continue to increase the amount of oxygen dissolved in the water of the blood. When this occurs, there is a change in the rates of many chemical reactions within tissue cells (metabolic rates).

The tissue most sensitive is the nervous system. Convulsions may occur or there may be actual brain cell destruction.

In the lungs, since the pulmonary membranes are directly exposed to high oxygen pressure, pulmonary edema may result. Oxygen intoxication will also interfere with the hemoglobin oxygen buffer system.

The alarming incidence of blindness in infants born prematurely has led to a better understanding of the relationship between oxygen and the development of blood vessels of the retina. In the human fetus, these vessels are developing during the fifth, sixth, and seventh months. Hence, they are in a sensitive developmental stage when the baby is born prematurely. Observations indicate that high concentrations of oxygen irritate and destroy the capillary network supplying blood to the retinal cells.

The resulting lack of blood supply causes retrolental fibroplasia and blindness. For this reason, oxygen therapy is used very conservatively for the premature infant.

RESPIRATION AND ATMOSPHERIC CHANGES

Low Barometric Pressure. Several changes that take place in the atmosphere as altitude increases affect man's reactions in high-altitude flying. These may be briefly stated as follows:

Oxygen concentration in air at 40,000 ft is about the same as at sea level, but barometric pressure is lower.

Oxygen begins to decrease at 80,000 ft, and above this height oxygen and nitrogen amounts decrease and the amounts of helium and hydrogen increase. Barometric pressure is also an important factor in high altitudes. At sea level the pressure is 760 mm Hg, while at 18,000 ft pressure is about half, or 380 mm Hg; and as altitude increases, barometric pressure continues to decrease. Another factor is temperature; the higher the altitude the lower the temperature. With every 500 ft of rise in altitude there is about $1°C$ drop in temperature.

These atmospheric changes affect man considerably as ascent in an airplane is made. Oxygen lack causes anoxia, the barometric pressure changes and extremes of cold also directly affect and modify man's reactions. Above 15,000 ft symptoms of oxygen lack are present. The individual becomes quiet, and the lips, ear lobes, and nail beds become slightly bluish. As a higher altitude is reached the blue color deepens, and weakness and dizziness occur. Since the brain cells are dependent upon oxygen, deprivation causes specific symptoms to become evident. The power of attention is diminished, muscular coordination is lessened, mental confusion is present, and there is interference with perception of objects. Breathing is embarrassed. At still higher altitudes these symptoms become more apparent; the individual may become irritable, the mental confusion increases, and speech is interfered with. Muscular coordination may be so lost that writing is impossible. There is difficulty in understanding written words. There may be drowsiness, headache, apathy, and loss of self-control. Vision and memory are impaired, judgments are unsound, pain sensations are dulled, and appreciation of passage of time is altered. Cyanosis becomes more apparent, dyspnea and vomiting may occur. Each sense is finally lost.

In airplane travel oxygen tension, pressures, and temperature are regulated by artificial means, thus preventing any physiological changes that occur at high altitudes.

High Barometric Pressure. High barometric pressure increases the amount of gases that diffuse from the alveoli into the blood and eventually are dissolved in all body fluids. Increased oxygen absorption will damage tissues. Hemoglobin releases oxygen more rapidly, which results in cellular damage due to deranged cellular metabolism. The brain usually shows early effects which result in twitching, convulsions, and coma. Such an increase in barometric pressure occurs in deep-sea exploration or, less severely, in scuba diving.

Carbon Dioxide. If, for example, a diver's helmet collects high concentrations of carbon dioxide, respiratory acidosis and coma can result.

Nitrogen. It is well known that high concentrations exert an anesthetic effect on the central nervous system. To avoid the problem, nitrogen is frequently substituted with helium, as it does not cause anesthetic effects and also leaves the body fluids rapidly. Nitrogen not only has anesthetic effects, but the gas bubbles in the body fluids when the diver surfaces. This condition is known as decompression sickness, the bends, caisson disease, and diver's paralysis. The most damage is done when bubbles develop in the brain and cord. Serious mental damage or paralysis may occur due to ruptured nerve fibers. Sudden gastrointestinal distention due to gas in the stomach and intestine may also occur. The condition can be prevented by slow ascent or by placing the diver or other worker in a decompression chamber.

QUESTIONS FOR DISCUSSION

1. Discuss the relationship between lung capacity and speech or singing.
2. Discuss Boyle's law and relate it to respiration.
3. Compare the pressure gradients of oxygen and carbon dioxide in the lungs and in the tissues.
4. List and discuss four factors that influence respiratory rate and depth.
5. Discuss the nervous control of respiration.
6. Describe the effects of hyperventilation upon the respiratory center.

SUMMARY

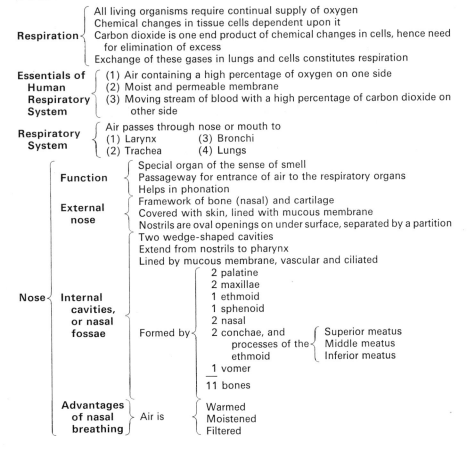

Respiration
- All living organisms require continual supply of oxygen
- Chemical changes in tissue cells dependent upon it
- Carbon dioxide is one end product of chemical changes in cells, hence need for elimination of excess
- Exchange of these gases in lungs and cells constitutes respiration

Essentials of Human Respiratory System
- (1) Air containing a high percentage of oxygen on one side
- (2) Moist and permeable membrane
- (3) Moving stream of blood with a high percentage of carbon dioxide on other side

Respiratory System
- Air passes through nose or mouth to
- (1) Larynx (3) Bronchi
- (2) Trachea (4) Lungs

Nose

Function
- Special organ of the sense of smell
- Passageway for entrance of air to the respiratory organs
- Helps in phonation

External nose
- Framework of bone (nasal) and cartilage
- Covered with skin, lined with mucous membrane
- Nostrils are oval openings on under surface, separated by a partition

Internal cavities, or nasal fossae
- Two wedge-shaped cavities
- Extend from nostrils to pharynx
- Lined by mucous membrane, vascular and ciliated
- Formed by
  - 2 palatine
  - 2 maxillae
  - 1 ethmoid
  - 1 sphenoid
  - 2 nasal
  - 2 conchae, and processes of the ethmoid
    - Superior meatus
    - Middle meatus
    - Inferior meatus
  - 1 vomer
  - ⎯⎯⎯
  - 11 bones

Advantages of nasal breathing
- Air is
  - Warmed
  - Moistened
  - Filtered

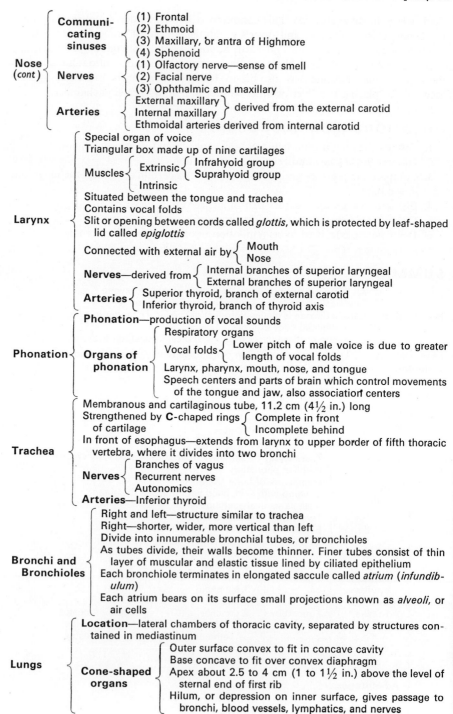

Nose (cont)
- Communicating sinuses
  - (1) Frontal
  - (2) Ethmoid
  - (3) Maxillary, or antra of Highmore
  - (4) Sphenoid
- Nerves
  - (1) Olfactory nerve—sense of smell
  - (2) Facial nerve
  - (3) Ophthalmic and maxillary
- Arteries
  - External maxillary ⎱ derived from the external carotid
  - Internal maxillary ⎰
  - Ethmoidal arteries derived from internal carotid

Larynx
- Special organ of voice
- Triangular box made up of nine cartilages
- Muscles
  - Extrinsic
    - Infrahyoid group
    - Suprahyoid group
  - Intrinsic
- Situated between the tongue and trachea
- Contains vocal folds
- Slit or opening between cords called *glottis*, which is protected by leaf-shaped lid called *epiglottis*
- Connected with external air by
  - Mouth
  - Nose
- Nerves—derived from
  - Internal branches of superior laryngeal
  - External branches of superior laryngeal
- Arteries
  - Superior thyroid, branch of external carotid
  - Inferior thyroid, branch of thyroid axis

Phonation
- Phonation—production of vocal sounds
- Organs of phonation
  - Respiratory organs
  - Vocal folds
    - Lower pitch of male voice is due to greater length of vocal folds
  - Larynx, pharynx, mouth, nose, and tongue
  - Speech centers and parts of brain which control movements of the tongue and jaw, also association centers

Trachea
- Membranous and cartilaginous tube, 11.2 cm (4½ in.) long
- Strengthened by **C**-chaped rings of cartilage
  - Complete in front
  - Incomplete behind
- In front of esophagus—extends from larynx to upper border of fifth thoracic vertebra, where it divides into two bronchi
- Nerves
  - Branches of vagus
  - Recurrent nerves
  - Autonomics
- Arteries—Inferior thyroid

Bronchi and Bronchioles
- Right and left—structure similar to trachea
- Right—shorter, wider, more vertical than left
- Divide into innumerable bronchial tubes, or bronchioles
- As tubes divide, their walls become thinner. Finer tubes consist of thin layer of muscular and elastic tissue lined by ciliated epithelium
- Each bronchiole terminates in elongated saccule called *atrium* (*infundibulum*)
- Each atrium bears on its surface small projections known as *alveoli*, or air cells

Lungs
- Location—lateral chambers of thoracic cavity, separated by structures contained in mediastinum
- Cone-shaped organs
  - Outer surface convex to fit in concave cavity
  - Base concave to fit over convex diaphragm
  - Apex about 2.5 to 4 cm (1 to 1½ in.) above the level of sternal end of first rib
  - Hilum, or depression on inner surface, gives passage to bronchi, blood vessels, lymphatics, and nerves

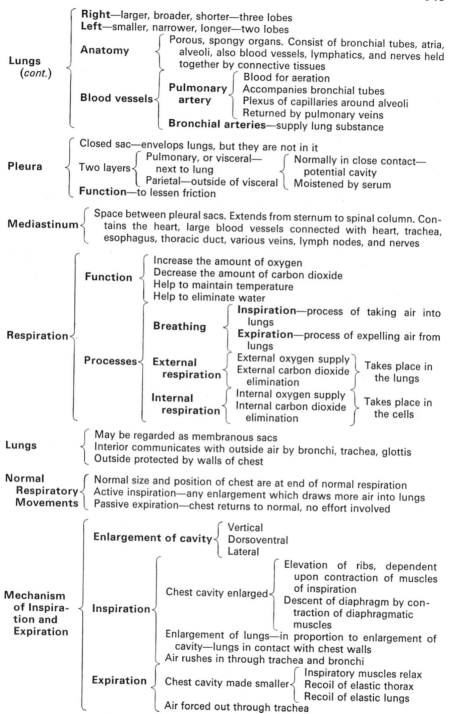

Lungs
(cont.)

- **Anatomy**
  - Right—larger, broader, shorter—three lobes
  - Left—smaller, narrower, longer—two lobes
  - Porous, spongy organs. Consist of bronchial tubes, atria, alveoli, also blood vessels, lymphatics, and nerves held together by connective tissues
- **Blood vessels**
  - **Pulmonary artery**
    - Blood for aeration
    - Accompanies bronchial tubes
    - Plexus of capillaries around alveoli
    - Returned by pulmonary veins
  - **Bronchial arteries**—supply lung substance

Pleura
- Closed sac—envelops lungs, but they are not in it
- Two layers
  - Pulmonary, or visceral—next to lung — Normally in close contact—potential cavity
  - Parietal—outside of visceral — Moistened by serum
- Function—to lessen friction

Mediastinum
- Space between pleural sacs. Extends from sternum to spinal column. Contains the heart, large blood vessels connected with heart, trachea, esophagus, thoracic duct, various veins, lymph nodes, and nerves

Respiration
- **Function**
  - Increase the amount of oxygen
  - Decrease the amount of carbon dioxide
  - Help to maintain temperature
  - Help to eliminate water
- **Processes**
  - **Breathing**
    - Inspiration—process of taking air into lungs
    - Expiration—process of expelling air from lungs
  - **External respiration**
    - External oxygen supply
    - External carbon dioxide elimination — Takes place in the lungs
  - **Internal respiration**
    - Internal oxygen supply
    - Internal carbon dioxide elimination — Takes place in the cells

Lungs
- May be regarded as membranous sacs
- Interior communicates with outside air by bronchi, trachea, glottis
- Outside protected by walls of chest

Normal Respiratory Movements
- Normal size and position of chest are at end of normal respiration
- Active inspiration—any enlargement which draws more air into lungs
- Passive expiration—chest returns to normal, no effort involved

Mechanism of Inspiration and Expiration
- **Enlargement of cavity**
  - Vertical
  - Dorsoventral
  - Lateral
- **Inspiration**
  - Chest cavity enlarged
    - Elevation of ribs, dependent upon contraction of muscles of inspiration
    - Descent of diaphragm by contraction of diaphragmatic muscles
  - Enlargement of lungs—in proportion to enlargement of cavity—lungs in contact with chest walls
  - Air rushes in through trachea and bronchi
- **Expiration**
  - Chest cavity made smaller
    - Inspiratory muscles relax
    - Recoil of elastic thorax
    - Recoil of elastic lungs
  - Air forced out through trachea

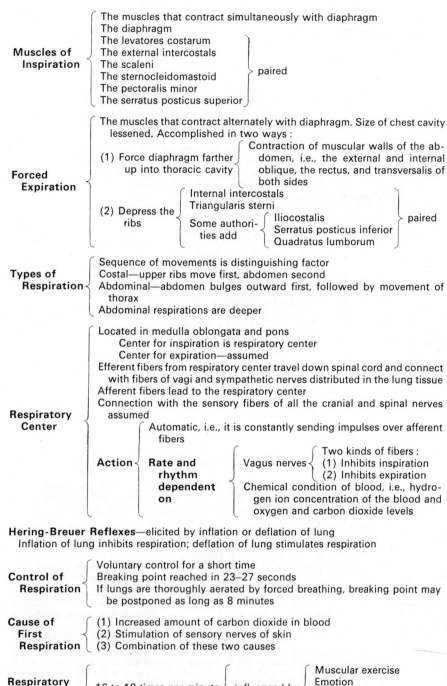

Muscles of Inspiration
{
The muscles that contract simultaneously with diaphragm
The diaphragm
The levatores costarum
The external intercostals
The scaleni   } paired
The sternocleidomastoid
The pectoralis minor
The serratus posticus superior
}

Forced Expiration
{
The muscles that contract alternately with diaphragm. Size of chest cavity lessened. Accomplished in two ways :

(1) Force diaphragm farther up into thoracic cavity {
Contraction of muscular walls of the abdomen, i.e., the external and internal oblique, the rectus, and transversalis of both sides
}

(2) Depress the ribs {
Internal intercostals
Triangularis sterni
Some authorities add { Iliocostalis
Serratus posticus inferior
Quadratus lumborum } paired
}
}

Types of Respiration
{
Sequence of movements is distinguishing factor
Costal—upper ribs move first, abdomen second
Abdominal—abdomen bulges outward first, followed by movement of thorax
Abdominal respirations are deeper
}

Respiratory Center
{
Located in medulla oblongata and pons
    Center for inspiration is respiratory center
    Center for expiration—assumed
Efferent fibers from respiratory center travel down spinal cord and connect with fibers of vagi and sympathetic nerves distributed in the lung tissue
Afferent fibers lead to the respiratory center
Connection with the sensory fibers of all the cranial and spinal nerves assumed

Action {
Rate and rhythm dependent on {
Automatic, i.e., it is constantly sending impulses over afferent fibers

Vagus nerves {
Two kinds of fibers :
(1) Inhibits inspiration
(2) Inhibits expiration
}
Chemical condition of blood, i.e., hydrogen ion concentration of the blood and oxygen and carbon dioxide levels
}
}
}

Hering-Breuer Reflexes—elicited by inflation or deflation of lung
Inflation of lung inhibits respiration; deflation of lung stimulates respiration

Control of Respiration
{
Voluntary control for a short time
Breaking point reached in 23–27 seconds
If lungs are thoroughly aerated by forced breathing, breaking point may be postponed as long as 8 minutes
}

Cause of First Respiration
{
(1) Increased amount of carbon dioxide in blood
(2) Stimulation of sensory nerves of skin
(3) Combination of these two causes
}

Respiratory Rate
{
16 to 18 times per minute { influenced by {
Muscular exercise
Emotion
Heartbeat
Age
}
}
}

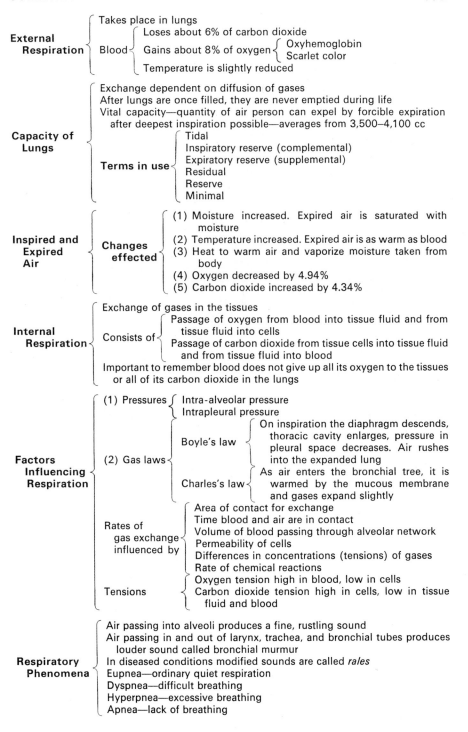

External Respiration
- Takes place in lungs
- Blood
  - Loses about 6% of carbon dioxide
  - Gains about 8% of oxygen
    - Oxyhemoglobin
    - Scarlet color
  - Temperature is slightly reduced

Capacity of Lungs
- Exchange dependent on diffusion of gases
- After lungs are once filled, they are never emptied during life
- Vital capacity—quantity of air person can expel by forcible expiration after deepest inspiration possible—averages from 3,500–4,100 cc
- Terms in use
  - Tidal
  - Inspiratory reserve (complemental)
  - Expiratory reserve (supplemental)
  - Residual
  - Reserve
  - Minimal

Inspired and Expired Air
- Changes effected
  - (1) Moisture increased. Expired air is saturated with moisture
  - (2) Temperature increased. Expired air is as warm as blood
  - (3) Heat to warm air and vaporize moisture taken from body
  - (4) Oxygen decreased by 4.94%
  - (5) Carbon dioxide increased by 4.34%

Internal Respiration
- Exchange of gases in the tissues
- Consists of
  - Passage of oxygen from blood into tissue fluid and from tissue fluid into cells
  - Passage of carbon dioxide from tissue cells into tissue fluid and from tissue fluid into blood
- Important to remember blood does not give up all its oxygen to the tissues or all of its carbon dioxide in the lungs

Factors Influencing Respiration
- (1) Pressures
  - Intra-alveolar pressure
  - Intrapleural pressure
- (2) Gas laws
  - Boyle's law
    - On inspiration the diaphragm descends, thoracic cavity enlarges, pressure in pleural space decreases. Air rushes into the expanded lung
  - Charles's law
    - As air enters the bronchial tree, it is warmed by the mucous membrane and gases expand slightly
- Rates of gas exchange influenced by
  - Area of contact for exchange
  - Time blood and air are in contact
  - Volume of blood passing through alveolar network
  - Permeability of cells
  - Differences in concentrations (tensions) of gases
  - Rate of chemical reactions
- Tensions
  - Oxygen tension high in blood, low in cells
  - Carbon dioxide tension high in cells, low in tissue fluid and blood

Respiratory Phenomena
- Air passing into alveoli produces a fine, rustling sound
- Air passing in and out of larynx, trachea, and bronchial tubes produces louder sound called bronchial murmur
- In diseased conditions modified sounds are called *rales*
- Eupnea—ordinary quiet respiration
- Dyspnea—difficult breathing
- Hyperpnea—excessive breathing
- Apnea—lack of breathing

Respiratory Phenomena (*cont.*)
- Cheyne-Stokes — Respirations increase in force and frequency, then gradually decrease and stop. Cycle repeated
- Edematous—air cells filled with fluid, hence moist, rattling sounds
- Asphyxia—oxygen starvation

Oxygen Therapy
- Hypoxia—oxygen lack, not lower than 80%
- Anoxia—oxygen deficiency or absence
- Cyanosis—bluish color due to oxygen need
- General purpose—to increase oxygen tension in blood plasma

Oxygen Intoxication
- Nervous tissue most sensitive
- Pulmonary edema may occur
- High oxygen concentration irritates and destroys capillary networks in the retina of premature infants

Oxygen Lack
- Causes tissue anoxia
- Disturbances of perception
- Diminished power of attention
- Individual becomes irritable
- Mental confusion
- Speech disturbed

High Barometric Pressure
- Increases the amount of gases that diffuse from alveoli into the blood
- Oxygen released rapidly
- Deranged cellular metabolism

CHAPTER 19

The Digestive System: Anatomy and Histology

WITHIN THE DIGESTIVE TRACT is carried on the necessary transformation of ingested complex food substances into the simpler substances which may pass into the blood stream and be distributed to the cells of the body.

The means by which foods are transformed into simple substances are both physical and chemical, and constitute the digestive processes; the organs which take part in them form the digestive system.

Processes concerned with such changes can be classified into two groups:

1. Those concerned with moving foods along through the alimentary tract with optimum speed. This means slowly enough for all the necessary changes in each organ to be accomplished in preparation for those in the next organ and yet fast enough so that proper absorption shall take place and bacterial decomposition or deleterious changes shall not occur.

2. Those concerned with the comminution of the food to particles small enough to pass through the wall of the alimentary tract into the body fluids. This is a physical comminution brought about by mastication and by the various types of muscular activity that are described on pages 605 and 612, and a subsequent chemical comminution of large molecules to molecules sufficiently small to pass into the blood. Normal motility of the alimentary tract and the proper functioning of the neuromuscular mechanisms by which it is carried on are essential to health.

The parts of the digestive system are the *alimentary canal,* and the *accessory organs:* tongue, teeth, salivary glands, pancreas, and liver.

The alimentary canal, or **digestive tube,** is a continuous tube and as measured on the cadaver is about 9 m (30 ft) long, which extends from the mouth to the anus. *In the living subject the length of the alimentary canal is much shorter, due probably to shortening of its longitudinal coats.* The greater part is coiled up in the cavity of the abdomen.

The peritoneum, the largest serous membrane in the body, in the male consists of a closed sac (in the female the uterine tubes open into the peritoneal cavity); the *parietal* layer lines the walls of the abdominal cavity, and the *visceral* layer

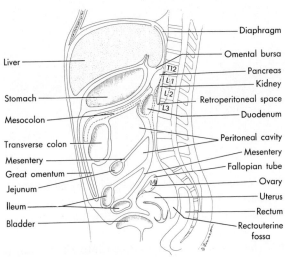

Figure 19–1. Diagram of a side view of the body, showing abdominal cavity, peritoneum, mesentery, and omentum. The *continuous lines* indicate the free surfaces of the peritoneum; the *dotted lines* indicate those parts of the peritoneum in which the free surfaces have disappeared.

is reflected over the abdominal organs and the upper surface of some of the pelvic organs. The space between the layers, the peritoneal cavity, is under normal conditions a potential cavity only, since the parietal and visceral layers are in lubricated contact. The arrangement of the peritoneum is very complex, for elongated sacs and double folds extend from it, to pass in between and either wholly or partially surround the viscera of the abdomen and pelvis. One important fold is the *greater omentum,* which hangs in front of the stomach and the intestines; another is the *mesentery,* which is a continuation of serous coat and attaches the small and much of the large intestine to the posterior abdominal wall.

When the abdominal cavity is opened, the intestines appear to lie loosely coiled within it. If a coil is lifted, a clear, glistening sheet of tissue is found attached to it. This is the mesentery, the dorsal portion of which is gathered into folds which are attached to the dorsal abdominal wall along a short line of insertion, giving the mesentery the appearance of a ruffle or flounce. The mesentery acts as an important bridge supporting the blood vessels and lymph vessels supplying the intestine.

Functions of the Peritoneum. The peritoneum serves to prevent friction between contiguous organs by secreting a serous fluid, which acts as a lubricant. It aids in holding the abdominal and pelvic organs in position. The omentum usually contains fat, sometimes in considerable amounts.

The Omentum. The lesser and greater omentum are peritoneal sheets which attach the stomach to the *body wall.* The *lesser* omentum extends from the lesser curvature of the stomach and upper duodenum to the liver. It is continuous with both layers of the peritoneum. The *greater* omentum consists of a thin double layer of peritoneum folded on itself so that four layers are formed, two anterior and two posterior layers, separated by the potential cavity of the omental bursa or lesser peritoneal sac (Fig. 19–1). The greater omentum lies between the greater curvature of the stomach and the spleen. From the stomach body wall it hangs as a fat-laden apron down and in front of the small intestine.

There are numerous lymph nodes in the omentum and other parts of the abdominal cavity, and many lymphatic vessels lead from the abdominal cavity into the blood stream, so there is great rapidity with which fluids can leave the cavity. This may aid in protecting the peritoneal cavity against infections. (See Figs. 16–2, p. 474, and 16–6, p. 478.)

Divisions of the Alimentary Canal. The alimentary canal has been given different names in different parts of its course. These names are:

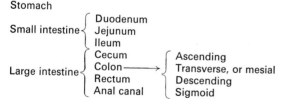

Mouth cavity, containing tongue, orifices of ducts of salivary glands, and teeth
Pharynx
Esophagus
Stomach

Small intestine
{ Duodenum
  Jejunum
  Ileum

Large intestine
{ Cecum
  Colon ——→ { Ascending
  Rectum   Transverse, or mesial
  Anal canal   Descending
                Sigmoid

Mouth Cavity, Pharynx, Esophagus

The mouth, oral or **buccal cavity,** is a cavity bounded laterally and in front by the cheeks and lips; behind, it communicates with the pharynx. The roof is formed by the hard and soft palate, and the greater part of the floor is formed by the tongue and sublingual region and lower jaw. The space bounded externally by the lips and cheeks and internally by the gums and teeth is called the *vestibule.* The cavity behind this is the *mouth cavity proper. The lips,* two musculomembranous folds, surround the orifice of the mouth and are important in speech.

The *cheek* walls of the mouth cavity proper are distensible and permit holding large mouthfuls of food during chewing.

The palate consists of a hard portion in front, formed by processes of the maxillae and palatine bones, which are covered by mucous membrane. Suspended from the posterior border is the soft palate, a movable fold of mucous membrane, enclosing muscle fibers, blood vessels, nerves, adenoid tissue, and mucous glands. Hanging from the middle of its lower border is a conical process called the palatine *uvula*.

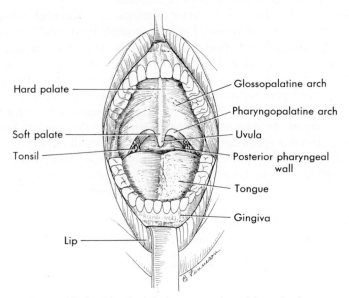

Hard palate

Soft palate

Tonsil

Lip

Glossopalatine arch

Pharyngopalatine arch

Uvula

Posterior pharyngeal wall

Tongue

Gingiva

Figure 19–2.   Mouth and pharynx as viewed from the front.

The fauces is the name given to the aperture leading from the mouth into the pharynx, or throat cavity. At the base of the uvula on either side is a curved fold of muscular tissue covered by mucous membrane, which shortly after leaving the uvula divides into two pillars; one runs downward, lateralward, and forward to the side of the base of the tongue; the other, downward, lateralward, and backward to the side of the pharynx. These arches are known respectively as the *glossopalatine arch* (anterior pillars of the fauces) and the *pharyngopalatine arch* (posterior pillars of the fauces).

The palatine tonsils are two masses of lymphoid tissue situated, one on either side, in the triangular space between the glossopalatine and the pharyngopalatine arches. The surface of the tonsils is marked by openings called crypts, which communicate with channels that course through the substance of the tissue. They are supplied with blood from the lingual and internal maxillary arteries, which are derived from the external carotid arteries. They receive nerve fibers from both divisions of the autonomic nervous system. Situated below the tongue are masses of lymphoid tissue called the *lingual tonsils;* however, the term tonsil as commonly used refers to the palatine tonsils.

The function of the tonsils is similar to that of other lymph nodes. They aid in the formation of white blood cells and help to protect the body from infection by acting as filters and preventing the entrance of microorganisms. If they are abnormal, their protective function is reduced, and they may serve as foci of infection, which passes directly into the lymph and so into the blood. If they are much enlarged, they tend to fill the throat cavity and interfere with the passage of air to the lungs. Inflammation of the palatine tonsils is called tonsillitis.

The palate, uvula, palatine arches, and tonsils are plainly seen if the mouth is widely opened and the tongue depressed.

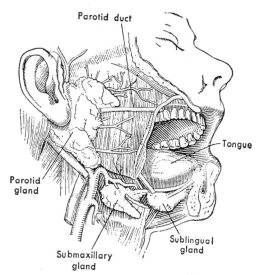

Figure 19–3. The salivary glands and their ducts. These glands manufacture about 1500 ml of saliva in 24 hours.

The tongue is the special organ of the sense of taste. It assists in mastication, deglutition, and digestion by movements which help to move the food and keep it between the teeth; the glands of the tongue secrete mucus, which lubricates the food and makes swallowing easier; and stimulation of the end organs (taste buds) of the nerves of the sense of taste increases the secretion of saliva and starts the first flow of gastric juices. The sense of taste is mediated over the sensory fibers of cranial nerve VII (anterior two thirds of the tongue) and cranial nerve IX (posterior third of the tongue). Probably more than half of the so-called tastes are due to stimulation of olfactory receptors rather than taste receptors. The reason for loss of taste perception when an individual has a "head cold" is congestion of the nasopharynx, so that fewer odors can reach the olfactory receptors. The tongue is essential for speech.

The Salivary Glands. The mucous membrane lining the mouth contains many minute glands called *buccal glands*, which pass their secretion into the mouth. The chief secretion, however, is supplied by three pairs of compound saccular glands, the salivary glands, named parotid, submaxillary, and sublingual glands. Each *parotid* gland is placed just under and in front of the ear; its duct, the parotid (Stensen's),[1] opens upon the inner surface of the cheek opposite the second molar of the upper jaw. The *submaxillary* (submandibular) and *sublingual* glands lie below the jaw and under the tongue, the submaxillary being placed farther back than the sublingual. One duct (Wharton's[2]) from each submaxillary (submandibular) and a number of small ducts from each sublingual open in the floor of the mouth beneath the tongue. The secretion of the salivary glands, mixed with that of the small glands of the mouth, the buccal secretion, is called *saliva*.

Nerves and Blood Vessels.   The facial (VII) and glossopharyngeal (IX) nerves supply these glands. The fibers are both secretory and vasomotor and are derived from the craniosacral and thoracolumbar systems. Blood is supplied to the salivary glands by branches of the external carotid artery and is returned, after traveling through many branch arteries and capillaries, via the jugular veins.

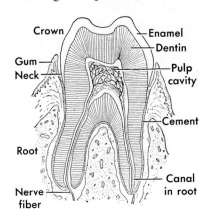

Figure 19–4.   Section of human molar tooth. In the pulp cavity are located blood vessels and nerves.

The Teeth (Dentes).   The alveolar processes of the maxillae and mandible contain *alveoli*, or sockets, for the teeth. Dense connective tissue covered by smooth mucous membrane—the gums, or gingivae—covers these processes and extends a little way into each socket. The sockets are lined with periosteum, which connects with the gums and serves to attach the teeth to their sockets and as a source of nourishment.

Each tooth consists of three portions: the *root*, consisting of one to three fangs contained in the socket; the *crown*, which projects beyond the level of the gums; and the *neck*, or constricted portion between the root and the crown.

Each tooth is composed principally of ivory, or *dentin*, which gives it shape and encloses a cavity, the pulp cavity. The dentin of the crown is capped by a dense layer of *enamel*. The dentin of the root is covered by *cement*. These three substances—enamel, dentin, and cement—are all harder than bone, enamel being the hardest substance found in the body. They are developed from epithelial

---

[1] Nicolaus Stensen, Danish anatomist (1638–1686).
[2] Thomas Wharton, English anatomist (1610–1673).

tissue. The pulp cavity is just under the crown and is continuous with a canal that traverses the center of each root and opens by a small aperture at its extremity. It is filled with dental pulp, which consists of connective tissue holding a number of blood vessels and nerves, which enter by means of the canal from the root.

There are two sets of teeth developed during life: the first, deciduous, or milk, teeth; and the second, permanent.

Deciduous Teeth. In the first set are 20 teeth, 10 in each jaw: 4 incisors, 2 canines, and 4 molars. The cutting of these teeth usually begins at six months and ends at about the age of two years. In nearly all cases the teeth of the lower jaw appear before the corresponding ones of the upper jaw.

Deciduous Teeth

	Molars	Canine	Incisors	Canine	Molars
Upper	2	1	4	1	2
Lower	2	1	4	1	2

The deciduous teeth are usually cut in the following order:

Lower central incisors	6–9 months
Upper incisors	8–10 months
Lower lateral incisors and first molars	15–21 months
Canines	16–20 months
Second molars	20–24 months

Another way of expressing the number of teeth is referred to as the "dentition formula." In such cases the formula is written as:

$$\frac{2:1:4:1:2}{2:1:4:1:2}$$

Permanent Teeth. During childhood the temporary teeth are replaced by the permanent. In the second set are 32 permanent teeth, 16 in each jaw. The first molar usually appears between five and seven years of age.

Permanent Teeth

	Molars	Premolars	Canine	Incisors	Canine	Premolars	Molars
Upper	3	2	1	4	1	2	3
Lower	3	2	1	4	1	2	3

The permanent teeth appear at about the following periods:

First molars	6 years
Two central incisors	7 years
Two lateral incisors	8 years
First premolars	9 years
Second premolars	10 years
Canine	11–12 years
Second molars	12–13 years
Third molars	17–25 years

The "dentition formula" for permanent teeth would be:

$$\frac{3:2:1:4:1:2:3}{3:2:1:4:1:2:3}$$

According to their shape and use the teeth are divided into incisors, canines, premolars, or bicuspids, and molars. *Incisors*, eight in number, form the four front teeth of each jaw. They have a sharp cutting edge and are especially adapted for biting food. *Canines* are four in number, two in each jaw. They have sharp, pointed edges, are longer than the incisors, and serve the same purpose in biting and tearing. *Premolars*, or *bicuspids*, are eight in number in the permanent set (none in the temporary set). There are four in each jaw, two placed just behind each of the canine teeth. They are broad, with two points or cusps on each crown, and have only one root, which is more or less completely divided into two. Their function is to grind food. *Molars* are 12 in number in the permanent set (eight in the deciduous set). They have broad crowns with small, pointed projections, which makes them well fitted for crushing food. Each upper molar has three roots, and each lower molar has two roots, which are grooved and indicate a tendency to division. The 12 molars do not all replace temporary teeth but are gradually added with the growth of the jaws. The hindmost molars are the last teeth to be added. They may not appear until 25 years of age, hence are called *late teeth* or "wisdom teeth."

Long before the teeth appear through the gums their formation and growth are in progress. The deciduous set begins to develop about the sixth week of intra-uterine life; and the permanent set, with the exception of the second and third molars, begins to develop about the sixteenth week. About the third month after birth, the second molars begin to grow, and about the third year, the third molars, or wisdom teeth, do likewise. Diseases such as rickets retard the eruption of the temporary teeth, and severe illness during childhood may interfere with the normal development of the permanent teeth so that they are marked with notches and ridges. Moreover, cavities form in them readily. The diet of the mother during pregnancy and the diet of the child during the first years of life are important factors in determining the quality of the teeth and the development of caries. When the central incisors are notched along their cutting edges and the lateral incisors are pegged, they are named Hutchinson's[3] teeth and are a diagnostic sign of congenital syphilis.

Physiology. The principal functions of the teeth are those of *biting* with the incisors and *chewing* or *mastication* with the molars. A third function, that of *grasping* and *tearing* the food with the canines, is frequently employed by children. Mastication of the more solid foods is good for the teeth because they are made to sink and rise in their sockets with a massaging effect upon the gums, which tends to promote circulation in the pulp.

The pharynx, or throat cavity, is a musculomembranous tube shaped somewhat like a cone, with its broad end turned upward and its constricted end downward to end in the esophagus. It may be divided from above downward into three parts, nasal, oral, and laryngeal. The upper, or *nasopharynx*, lies behind the posterior nares and above the soft palate. The middle, or *oral*, part of the pharynx reaches from the soft palate to the level of the hyoid bone. The *laryngeal* part reaches from the hyoid bone to the esophagus. The pharynx communicates with the nose, ears, mouth, and larynx by seven apertures: two in front above, leading into the back of the nose, the *posterior nares*; two on the lateral walls of the nasopharynx, leading into the auditory tubes, which communicate with the ears; one midway in front, the *fauces* connecting with the mouth in front; two

---

[3] Sir Jonathan Hutchinson, English surgeon (1828–1913).

below—one, the well-defined glottis, opening into the larynx, and the other, the poorly defined, opening into the esophagus.

The mucous membrane lining the pharynx is continuous with that lining the nasal cavities, the mouth, the auditory tubes, and the larynx. It is well supplied with mucous glands. The walls of the pharynx are provided with sensory receptors, which are sensitive to mechanical stimulation and are important in the mechanisms of swallowing. When food or liquid stimulates these touch receptors, the complicated reflex of swallowing is initiated. If these sensory areas are anesthetized, as by swabbing the throat with procaine, swallowing becomes difficult. About the center of the posterior wall of the nasopharynx is a mass of lymphoid tissue, the pharyngeal tonsil. When abnormally large it is called *adenoids.*

Usually lymphoid tissue is larger in children than in adults and tends to grow smaller with age. Owing to their position, adenoids may become infected or enlarged, block the auditory tubes, and interfere with the passage of air through the nose.

Nerves and Blood Vessels. Both divisions of the autonomic system supply nerve fibers to the pharynx. There are both sensory and motor fibers within the glossopharyngeal and vagus nerves. Blood is supplied by branches from the external carotid artery.

Functions. The pharynx transmits the air from the nose or mouth to the larynx and serves as a resonating cavity in the production of the voice. It also serves as a channel to transmit food from the mouth to the esophagus. Closure of the mouth and nasopharynx during deglutition or swallowing effectively shuts off the pharynx from the outside atmosphere. Dilatation of the closed pharynx by contraction of pharyngeal muscles results in development of a slight negative pressure. This aspiration effect, combined with the thrust caused by other contracting muscles, pushes the food downward and onward into the esophagus.

The esophagus, or **gullet,** is a muscular tube, about 23 to 25 cm (9 to 10 in.) long and 25 to 30 mm wide, which begins at the lower end of the pharynx, behind the trachea. It descends in the mediastinum in front of the vertebral column, passes through the diaphragm at the level of the tenth thoracic vertebra, and terminates in the upper, or cardiac, end of the stomach, about the level of the xiphoid process.

Structure. The walls of the esophagus are composed of four coats: (1) an external, or fibrous, (2) a muscular, (3) a submucous, or areolar, and (4) an internal, or mucous, coat. The muscular coat consists of an external longitudinal and an internal circular layer. The muscles in the upper part of the esophagus are striated. These are gradually replaced by nonstriated muscle tissues. The lower third of the esophagus is completely nonstriated tissue. Contractions of these layers produce peristaltic waves which propel food to the stomach. Striated muscle contracts more rapidly than nonstriated; hence food travels most rapidly through the upper esophagus. The areolar coat serves to connect the muscular and mucous coats and to carry the larger blood and lymph vessels.

The mucous membrane is arranged in longitudinal folds which disappear when the esophagus is distended by the passage of food. It is studded with minute papillae and small glands, which secrete mucus to lubricate the canal.

Nerves and Blood Vessels. The nerve fibers are from the vagus and the thoracolumbar nervous system. They form a plexus between the layers of the muscular coat and another in the submucous coat. Blood is supplied to the esophagus by arteries from the inferior thyroid branch of the thyrocervical trunk, which arises from the subclavian; from the thoracic aorta; from the left gastric branch of the celiac artery; and from the left inferior phrenic of the abdominal aorta. Blood is returned via the azygos, thyroid, and left gastric veins of the stomach.

Functions. The esophagus receives food from the pharynx and by a series of peristaltic contractions passes it on to the stomach.

The Stomach

In the abdominal cavity the esophagus ends in the stomach (gaster), which is a collapsible, saclike dilatation of the alimentary canal serving as a temporary receptacle for food. It lies obliquely in the epigastric, umbilical, and left hypo-

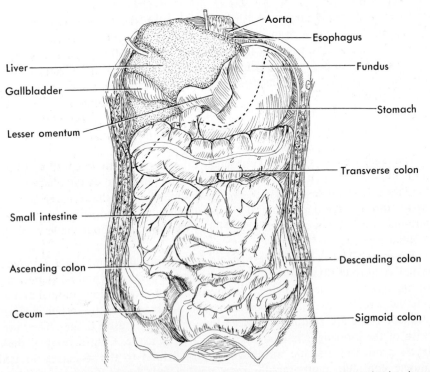

Figure 19–5. The stomach and intestines, front view, the great omentum having been removed and the liver turned up and to the right. The *dotted line* shows the normal position of the anterior border of the liver.

chondriac regions of the abdomen, directly under the diaphragm. The shape and position of the stomach are modified by changes within itself and in the surrounding organs. These modifications are determined by the amount of the stomach contents, the stage of digestion which has been reached, the degree of development and power of the muscular walls, and the condition of the adjacent intestines. It is never entirely empty, but always contains a little gastric fluid and mucin. When the stomach is contracted, its shape as seen from the front is comparable to that of a sickle. At an early stage of gastric digestion, the stomach usually consists of two segments, a large globular portion on the left and a narrow tubular portion on the right. When distended with food, it has the shape shown in Figure 19-6. The stomach presents two openings and two borders, or curvatures.

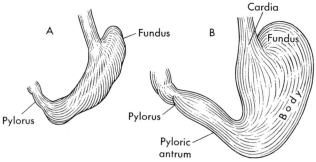

Figure 19–6. Form and outline of the stomach at different stages of digestion when seen from the front. *(A)* Contracted. *(B)* Early stage of digestion.

Openings. The opening by which the esophagus communicates with the stomach is known as the *cardiac*, or esophageal, orifice; the orifice which communicates with the duodenum is known as the *pyloric*. The pyloric aperture is guarded by a ringlike muscle, or sphincteric mechanism, which when contracted keeps the orifice closed. Although a distinct muscle is absent from the cardiac aperture, it is kept closed by the manner in which the muscles are arranged and the diaphragm is attached. Research shows that the pyloric antrum, pyloric sphincteric mechanism, and duodenal bulb function as a unit. The circular fibers of the pyloric sphincter serve to guard against backflow of intestinal contents into the stomach: normally the pyloric sphincter does *not* regulate stomach emptying. The movement of stomach contents into the small intestine is dependent upon the maintenance of a relatively small pressure gradient from the antrum to the pylorus. The food is kept in the stomach until such a pressure gradient is present. The relaxation of this aperture may be related to the consistency of the stomach contents and to the regular peristaltic waves moving over the stomach on to the duodenum.

Curvatures. In all positions the stomach is more or less curved upon itself. A line drawn from the cardiac orifice along the concave border to the pyloric orifice follows the lesser curvature. A line connecting the same points, but following the convex border, follows the greater curvature.

Component Parts. The *cardia* is the portion surrounding the esophageal opening. The upward turn of the stomach forms a J position. There are great differences in the position of the stomach. Much depends upon body stature, position, respiratory movement, and content of the stomach. The *fundus* is the rounded end of the stomach, above the entrance of the esophagus. The opposite, or smaller, end is the *pyloric portion*. The central portion, between the fundus and the pyloric portion, is called the *body*, or corpus. The part of the stomach adjacent to the pyloric portion is the *antrum*.

Structure. The wall of the stomach consists of four coats: serous, muscular, submucous (or areolar), and mucous.

1. *The serous coat* is part of the peritoneum and covers the organ. At the lesser curvature the two layers come together and are continued upward to the liver as the *lesser omentum*. At the greater curvature the two layers are continued downward as the apronlike *greater omentum*, which is suspended in front of the intestines.

2. *The muscular coat* of the stomach is beneath the serous coat and closely connected with it. It consists of three layers of unstriated muscular tissue: an outer, longitudinal layer; a middle, or circular layer; and an inner, less well-developed, oblique layer limited chiefly to the cardiac end of the stomach. This arrangement facilitates the muscular actions of the stomach by which it presses upon food and moves it back and forth.

3. *The submucous coat* consists of loose areolar connective tissue connecting the muscular and mucous coats.

4. *The mucous coat* is thick, the thickness being mainly due to the fact that it is densely packed with small glands embedded in areolar connective tissue. It is covered with columnar epithelium and in its undistended condition is thrown into folds, or *rugae*. The surface is honeycombed by tiny, shallow pits, into which the ducts or mouths of the glands open. Figure 19–7 and its legend describe the coats and the tissues which compose them.

The gastric glands are of three varieties: cardiac, fundic, and pyloric.

Cardiac glands occur close to the cardiac orifice. They are of two kinds—simple tubular glands with short ducts, and compound racemose glands. *Fundic glands* are simple tubular glands which are found in the body and fundus of the stomach. These glands are lined with epithelial cells, of which there are two varieties. (1) One variety of cells is found lining the lumen of the tube. These are called chief cells and secrete pepsinogen. (2) A second variety, called parietal cells, is found behind the chief cells. These cells secrete hydrochloric acid into the lumen of the tube through minute ducts. Pepsinogen, in the presence of acid, is converted into pepsin. *Pyloric glands* are branched tubular glands found most plentifully about the pylorus. They secrete pepsinogen and mucin.

The combined secretion of these glands forms the gastric fluid. There is a high concentration of ribonucleoprotein in the enzyme-producing cells. Numerous mitochondria and a Golgi complex have been readily demonstrated in these cells.

Gastrin, a hormone, is formed by some of the cells of the pyloric mucosa. It is not secreted into the stomach lumen, but is carried by the blood to the fundus and body of the stomach. Gastrin is a potent stimulus for secretion of acid by the parietal cells.

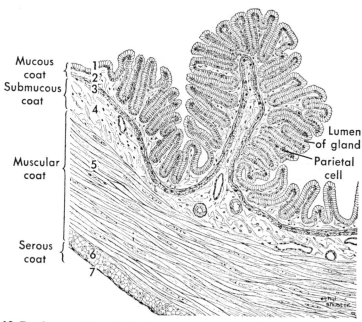

Figure 19–7. Cross section of a bit of the wall of the stomach, highly magnified to show coats. One ruga covered with glands is shown. Parietal cells are shown communicating with the lumen of the glands by clefts between the chief cells which line the lumen. (*1*) Columnar epithelium, (*2*) areolar connective tissues, (*3*) muscularis mucosae, (*4*) areolar connective tissue, (*5*) circular layer of smooth muscle, (*6*) longitudinal layer of smooth muscle, (*7*) areolar connective tissue and mesothelium.

Nerves and Blood Vessels. The stomach is supplied with thoracolumbar nerve fibers from the celiac plexus. Terminal branches of the right vagus are distributed to the posterior part of the organ; branches from the left vagus are distributed to the anterior part. Stimulation of the vagus fibers increases secretion and peristalsis. Stimulation of the thoracolumbar autonomic fibers has just the opposite effect, i.e., inhibits secretion and peristalsis. The blood vessels are derived from the three divisions of the celiac artery, i.e., the left gastric, hepatic, and splenic. Blood is returned via the right gastroepiploic, which joins the superior mesenteric, the left gastroepiploic and several short gastric veins which join the splenic and the left gastric. All of these eventually join the portal vein.

A small quantity of blood is returned to the azygos and hemorrhoidal veins instead of entering the portal vessel.

Physiology. Probably the most important function of the stomach is to store food. Without a food reservoir it would be necessary to eat small amounts at frequent intervals. The digestive functions consist of chemical changes of the proteins of food under the action of the enzyme *pepsin* in an acid medium, and of maceration of the food bolus by the mechanics of contractions of the stomach musculature. The mucosa of the fundus of the stomach elaborates a substance called the *intrinsic factor*, which is essential for absorption of vitamin B_{12}. (See pp. 359 and 360.)

The Small Intestine

The small, or thin, intestine extends from the pylorus to the colic valve. It is a folded tube, which in the cadaver is about 7 m (23 ft) in length, and is contained in the central and lower part of the abdominal cavity.

At the beginning the diameter is about 3.8 cm (1½ in.), but it gradually diminishes and is hardly 1 in. at the lower end. For descriptive purposes the small intestine is divided into three portions: the duodenum, jejunum, and ileum are continuous and show only slight variations.

The duodenum is 25 cm (10 in.) long, and is the shortest and broadest part of the small intestine. It extends from the pyloric end of the stomach to the jejunum. Beginning at the pylorus, the duodenum at first passes upward, backward, and to the right, beneath the liver. It then makes a sharp bend and passes downward in front of the right kidney; it makes a second bend, toward the left, and passes horizontally across the front of the vertebral column. On the left side, it ascends for about 2.5 cm (1 in.) and then ends in the jejunum opposite the second lumbar vertebra.

The jejunum, or empty intestine, so called because it is always found empty after death, constitutes about two fifths of the remainder, or 2.2 m (7½ ft), of the small intestine and extends from the duodenum to the ileum.

The ileum, or twisted intestine, so called from its numerous coils, constitutes the remainder of the small intestine and extends from the jejunum to the large intestine, which it joins at a right angle. The orifice is guarded by a sphincter muscle, which functions as a valve and prevents the return of material that has been discharged into the large intestine. This is known as the colic, or ileocecal, valve. There is no definite point at which the jejunum ceases and the ileum begins, although the mucous membranes of the two divisions differ somewhat.

The coats of the small intestine are four in number and correspond in character and arrangement to those of the stomach. (1) The *serous* coat furnished by the peritoneum forms an almost complete covering for the whole tube except for part of the duodenum. (2) The *muscular* coat of the small intestine has two layers: an outer, thinner layer with longitudinally arranged fibers and an inner, thicker layer with circularly arranged fibers. This arrangement aids the peristaltic action of the intestine. (3) The *submucous* or loose connective tissue coat connects the muscular and mucous coats. (4) The *mucous* coat is thick, glandular, and very vascular.

Circular Folds. About 3 or 4 cm (1 or 2 in.) beyond the pylorus the mucous and submucous coats of the small intestine are arranged in circular folds (valvulae conniventes, or plicae circulares) which project into the lumen of the tube (Fig. 19–8). Some of these folds extend all the way around the circumference of the intestine; others extend part of the way. Unlike the rugae of the stomach, the circular folds do not disappear when the intestine is distended. About the

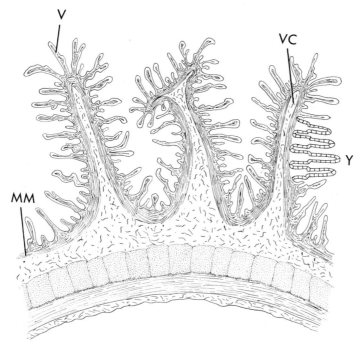

Figure 19–8. Longitudinal section of small intestine. Three valvulae conniventes (*VC*) are shown. Many villi (*V*) are shown on the valvulae and between them. At *Y* four villi with glands between them have been diagramed; (*MM*) muscularis mucosae.

middle of the jejunum they begin to decrease in size, and in the lower part of the ileum they almost entirely disappear. The major function of these folds is to present a greater surface area for secretion of digestive juices and absorption of digested food.

Villi. Throughout the whole length of the small intestine the mucous membrane presents a velvety appearance due to minute, fingerlike projections called *villi*, which number between 4,000,000 and 5,000,000 in man. Each villus consists of a central lymph channel called a *lacteal*, surrounded by a network of blood capillaries held together by lymphoid tissue. This in turn is surrounded by a layer of columnar cells. After the food has been digested, it passes into the capillaries and lacteals of the villi.

Glands and Nodes of the Small Intestine. In addition to these projections, the mucous membrane is thickly studded with secretory glands and nodes. These are known as:

Intestinal glands or crypts of Lieberkühn [4]

Duodenal or Brunner's glands [5]

Lymph nodules—(1) solitary lymph nodules, (2) aggregated lymph nodules

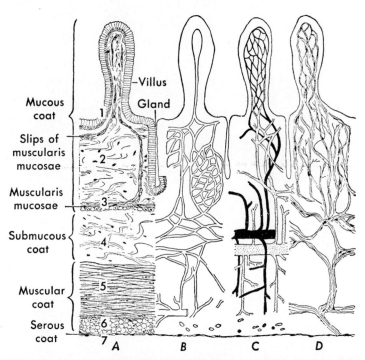

Figure 19-9. Diagram of a cross section of small intestine. *A* shows coats of intestinal wall and tissues of coats, (*1*) columnar epithelium, (*2*) areolar connective tissue, (*3*) muscularis mucosae, (*4*) areolar connective tissue, (*5*) circular layer of smooth muscle, (*6*) longitudinal layer of smooth muscle, (*7*) areolar connective tissue and endothelium. *B* shows arrangement of central lacteal, lymph nodes, and lymph tubes. *C* shows blood supply; arteries and capillaries *black*, veins *stippled*. *D* shows nerve fibers, the submucous plexus lying in the submucosa, the myenteric plexus lying between the circular and longitudinal layers of the muscular coat. (*A* and *C* drawn from microscopic slide of injected specimen; *B* and *D* modified from Mall.)

Intestinal glands are found over every part of the surface of the small intestine. They are simple tubular depressions in the mucous membrane, lined with columnar epithelium and opening upon the surface by circular apertures.

[4] Johann Nathanael Lieberkühn, German anatomist (1711–1756).
[5] Johann Conrad Brunner, Swiss anatomist (1653–1727).

Brunner's glands are located chiefly in the submucosa, and pass their secretions by long ducts to the intestinal surface. These glands secrete mucus while the cells of other glands in the duodenum secrete an alkaline fluid, mucus, and enzymes. Collectively the intestinal secretions are called *succus entericus*.

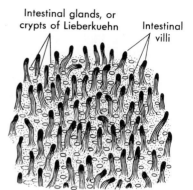

Intestinal glands, or crypts of Lieberkuehn   Intestinal villi

Figure 19-10. Mucous membrane of the ileum, showing villi and the mouths of the intestinal glands.

1. Lymph Nodules. Closely connected with the lymphatic vessels in the walls of the intestine are small, rounded bodies of the size of a pinhead, called *solitary lymph nodules.* They are most numerous in the lower part of the ileum and consist of a rounded mass of fine lymphoid tissue, the meshes of which are crowded with leukocytes. Into this mass of tissue one or more small arteries enter and

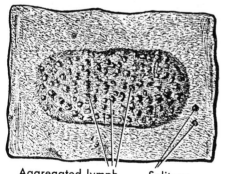

Figure 19-11. Aggregated lymph nodules in wall of ileum (Peyer's patch). (Modified from Toldt.)

Aggregated lymph nodules, or Peyer's patch   Solitary lymph nodule

form a capillary network, from which the blood is carried away by one or more small veins. Surrounding the mass are lymph channels which are continuous with the lymphatic vessels in the tissue below.

2. Aggregated lymph nodules are collections of lymph nodules, commonly called Peyer's[6] patches. These patches are circular or oval in shape, from 10 to 30 in number, and vary in length from about 2.5 to 10 cm (1 to 4 in.). They are

[6] Johann Conrad Peyer, Swiss anatomist (1653–1712).

largest and most numerous in the ileum. In the lower part of the jejunum they are small and few in number. They are occasionally seen in the duodenum. Peyer's patches may be the seat of local inflammation and ulceration in typhoid fever and intestinal infections, particularly tuberculosis of the intestine.

Figure 19–9 describes the coats of the small intestine and the tissues which compose them and the relationship of blood vessels, lymph tubes, and nerve fibers.

Nerves and Blood Vessels. The vagus nerves supply secretory and motor fibers to the small intestine. Thoracolumbar nerve fibers are derived from the plexuses around the superior mesenteric artery. From this source they run to the myenteric plexus (Auerbach's plexus) of nerves and ganglia situated between the circular and longitudinal muscular fibers. Branches from this plexus are distributed to the muscular coats; and from these branches another plexus, the submucous (Meissner's) plexus, is derived (Fig. 10–6, p. 305). It sends fibers to the mucous membrane. The sensory fibers in the vagus nerve are concerned with intestinal reflexes, while the sensory fibers of the thoracolumbar nerves carry pain sensations. Thus, the pain from an ulcer in the duodenum is abolished after cutting of the thoracolumbar fibers, even though the ulcer is still active.

Blood Supply. The arteries supplying the small intestine are branches of the superior mesenteric. These vessels distribute branches, which lie between the serous and muscular coats and form frequent anastomoses. Blood is returned by the superior mesenteric vein, which unites with the splenic to form the portal tube.

Physiology. It is in the small intestine that the greatest amount of digestion and absorption takes place. It receives bile and pancreatic juice from the liver and the pancreas. The glands of the small intestine secrete succus entericus. The intestinal mucosa, containing glands and covered with villi, is arranged in folds, so that the surface areas for action of digestive juice and absorption are greatly increased. Some of the cells of the mucous membrane (particularly in the duodenum) secrete *secretin*. Secretin is carried by the blood to the liver and pancreas, stimulating them to secretory activity.

The Large Intestine

The large, or thick, intestine is about 1.5 m (5 ft) long but is wider than the small intestine, being about 6.3 cm (2½ in.) at the cecum. It extends from the ileum to the anus. It is divided into four parts: the cecum with the vermiform appendix, colon, rectum, and anal canal.

The Cecum. The small intestine opens into the side wall of the large intestine about 6 cm (2½ in.) above the commencement of the large intestine. This 6 cm of large intestine forms a blind pouch called the cecum. The opening from the ileum into the large intestine is provided with two large projecting lips of mucous membrane forming the colic, or ileocecal, valve, which allows the passage of material into the large intestine but effectually prevents the passage of material in the opposite direction.

The vermiform appendix is a narrow tube attached to the end of the cecum. The length, diameter, direction, and relations of the appendix are very variable. The average length is about 7.5 cm (3 in.).

The functions of the appendix are not known. It is most fully developed in the young adult and at this time is subject to inflammatory and gangrenous conditions commonly called appendicitis.

The reasons for this are that its structure does not allow for ready drainage, its blood supply is limited, and its circulation is easily interfered with because the vessels anastomose to a very limited extent.

The colon, although one continuous tube, is subdivided into the *ascending, transverse* or *mesial, descending,* and *sigmoid colon.* The ascending portion ascends on the right side of the abdomen until it reaches the undersurface of the liver, where it turns abruptly to the left (right colic or hepatic flexure) and is

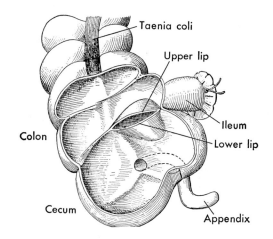

Figure 19–12. Cavity of the cecum, its front wall having been cut away. The valve of the colon (colic) and the opening of the appendix are shown. One of the three muscular bands (taenia coli) shows on the outside, and the location of another is shown on the inside.

continued across the abdomen as the transverse colon until, reaching the left side, it curves beneath the lower end of the spleen (left colic or splenic flexure) and passes downward as the descending colon. Reaching the left iliac region on a level with the margin of the crest of the ileum, it makes a curve like the letter S—hence its name of sigmoid—and finally ends in the rectum (Fig. 19–5).

The rectum is about 12 cm (5 in.) long and is continuous with the sigmoid colon and anal canal. From its origin at the third sacral vertebra it descends downward and forward along the curve of the sacrum and coccyx and finally turns sharply backward into the anal canal. In small children the rectum is much straighter than in adults.

The anal canal is the terminal portion of the large intestine and is about 2.5 to 3.8 cm (1 to 1½ in.) in length. The external aperture, called the *anus,* is guarded by an internal and external sphincter. It is kept closed except during defecation.

The condition known as *piles* or *hemorrhoids* is brought about by enlargement of the veins of the anal canal. They may be *external,* wherein enlargement is of the veins just outside the anal orifice, or *internal*, wherein the enlargement is of veins within the canal.

The coats of the large intestine are the usual four, except in some parts where the *serous* coat only partially covers it and in the anal canal, where the serous coat is lacking. The *muscular* coat consists of two layers of fibers, the external

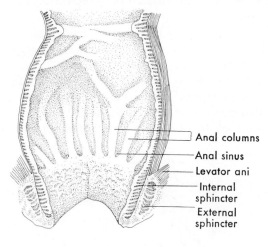

Anal columns

Anal sinus

Levator ani

Internal
sphincter

External
sphincter

Figure 19–13. Longitudinal section of the anal canal. Shows anal columns, anal sinuses, and sphincter muscles.

The three bands of longitudinal
muscular fibers

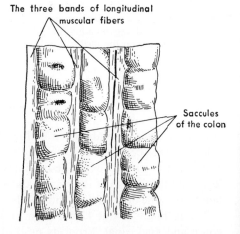

Saccules
of the colon

Figure 19–14. The muscular coat of the opened large intestine, showing the longitudinal fibers.

arranged longitudinally and the internal circularly. The longitudinal fibers form a thicker layer in some regions than in others. The thick areas form three separate bands, the *taeniae coli*, which extend from the cecum to the beginning of the rectum, where they spread out and form a longitudinal layer which encircles this portion. Because these bands (about 5 to 7 mm wide) are about one sixth shorter than the rest of the colon, their walls are puckered into numerous *sacculations*. The third coat consists of *submucous areolar tissue* and the fourth, or inner, coat consists of *mucous membrane*. The mucous coat possesses no villi and no circular folds. It contains intestinal glands and solitary lymph nodules which closely resemble those of the small intestine.

Nerves and Blood Vessels. Fibers from both divisions of the autonomic system reach the large intestine, nerves from the mesenteric and hypogastric plexuses being distributed in a way similar to that found in the small intestine.

The arteries are derived mainly from the superior and inferior mesenteric arteries. Branches of the superior mesenteric artery supply the cecum, appendix, and ascending and transverse colon. Branches of the inferior mesenteric artery supply the descending colon and the rectum. The rectum also receives branches from the hypogastric arteries. Blood from the large intestine is returned via the superior and inferior mesenteric veins; and blood from the rectum is returned via the superior rectal, which joins the left colic vein, and the middle and inferior rectal, which join the internal iliac vein.

Physiology. Nearly all the processes of food digestion and absorption are completed in the small intestine. Only the indigestible components remain to reach the colon. Perhaps the most important function of the colon is the re-absorption of water and electrolytes. By this process the liquid contents of the colon are dehydrated to form *feces.*

The Cranial Nerves Related to Digestive Processes

Through the olfactory, optic, and cochlear nerves impulses reach the brain and cause reflex stimulation of digestive juices.

The oculomotor, trochlear, and abducens nerves supply the motor fibers to extrinsic and intrinsic muscles of eye so that adjustment may be made to vision.

The trigeminal and facial nerves are sensory to teeth and mouth and motor to muscles; they are necessary for movement of jaw in mastication, secretion of saliva (submaxillary and sublingual glands), taste on the anterior part of the tongue, and swallowing.

The glossopharyngeal nerve is concerned with secretion of saliva (parotid gland), taste on the posterior part of the tongue, and general sensation of pharynx and tongue.

The vagus nerve is concerned with taste in the region of the epiglottis; motor to the pharyngeal muscles, sensory to the pharynx; motor to the esophagus, stomach, small intestine, and part of large intestine; secretory to glands of the esophagus, stomach, small and large intestine, liver and pancreas.

The accessory nerve is motor to muscles of pharynx and is concerned with the act of swallowing.

The hypoglossal nerve is motor to muscles of the tongue for mastication and swallowing.

Accessory Organs of Digestion

The accessory organs of digestion are: (1) the tongue, (2) the teeth, (3) the salivary glands, (4) the pancreas, (5) the liver, and (6) the gallbladder. The first three have been described.

The pancreas is a soft, reddish- or yellowish-gray gland which lies in front of the first and second lumbar vertebrae and behind the stomach. In shape it somewhat resembles a hammer and is divided into head, body, and tail. The right end, or head, is thicker and fills the curve of the duodenum, to which it is firmly attached. The left, free end is the tail and reaches to the spleen. The intervening portion is the body. Its average weight is between 60 and 90 gm (2 to 3 oz); it is about 12.5 cm (5 in.) long and about 5 cm (2 in.) wide.

Structure. The pancreas is a compound gland composed of lobules. Each lobule consists of one of the branches of the main duct, which terminates in a cluster of pouches, or alveoli. The lobules are joined together by areolar tissue to form lobes; and the lobes, united in the same manner, form the gland. The

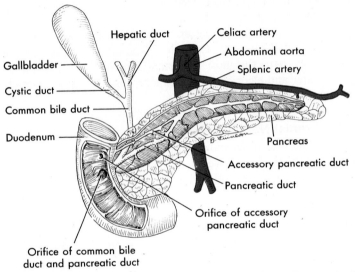

Figure 19–15.   Diagram of pancreas showing its relation to aorta, celiac artery, gallbladder, and hepatic and common bile ducts.

small ducts from each lobule open into one main duct about 3 mm in diameter, which runs transversely from the tail to the head through the substance of the gland. This is known as the pancreatic duct or duct of Wirsung.[7] The pancreatic and common bile ducts usually unite and pass obliquely through the wall of the duodenum about 7.5 cm (3 in.) below the pylorus. The short tube formed by the union of the two ducts is dilated into an ampulla, called the *ampulla of Vater.*[8] Sometimes the pancreatic duct and the common bile duct open separately into the duodenum, and there is frequently an accessory duct (duct of Santorini)[9] which opens into the duodenum about 1 in. above the orifice of the main duct.

Islets of Langerhans. Between the alveoli small groups of cells are found,

[7] Johann Georg Wirsung, Bavarian anatomist (died 1643).
[8] Abraham Vater, German anatomist (1684–1751).
[9] Giovanni Domenico Santorini, Italian anatomist (1681–1739).

which are termed the islets of Langerhans[10] (interalveolar cell islets). They are surrounded by a rich capillary network and furnish the internal secretion of the pancreas (insulin and glucagon).

Physiology. Two secretions are formed in the pancreas. (1) The pancreatic fluid is an external secretion and is poured into the duodenum during intestinal digestion. (2) The secretions formed by the islets of Langerhans are the internal secretions of insulin and glucagon, which are absorbed by the blood, carried to the tissues, and aid in regulating glucose metabolism. (See p. 508.)

The liver (hepar) is the largest organ in the body, weighing ordinarily from 1.2 to 1.6 kg (42 to 56 oz). It is located in the right hypochondriac and epigastric regions and frequently extends into the left hypochondriac region. The upper convex surface fits closely into the undersurface of the diaphragm. The under concave surface of the organ fits over the right kidney, the upper portion of the ascending colon, and the pyloric end of the stomach.

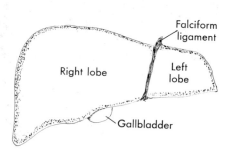

Figure 19–16. Superior surface of liver. The liver measures 20 to 22.5 cm (8 to 9 in.) from side to side, 10 to 12.5 cm (4 to 5 in.) from front to back, and 15 to 17.5 cm (6 to 7 in.) from above downward in its thickest part. It has many diverse functions.

Ligaments. The liver is connected to the undersurface of the diaphragm and the anterior walls of the abdomen by five ligaments, four of which—the falciform, the coronary, and the two lateral—are formed by folds of peritoneum. The fifth, or round, ligament is a fibrous cord resulting from the atrophy of the umbilical vein of intrauterine life.

Fossae. The liver is divided by four fossae, or fissures, into four lobes.

The important fossae are the left sagittal; the portal, or transverse, which transmits the portal blood vessel, hepatic artery, nerves, hepatic duct, and lymphatics; the fossa for the gallbladder; and the fossa for the inferior vena cava.

Lobes. The liver is divided into four lobes:

1. Right (largest lobe)
2. Left (smaller and wedge-shaped)
3. Quadrate (square)
4. Caudate (tail-like)

Vessels. The liver has five sets of vessels:

1. Branches of portal vein
2. Bile ducts
3. Branches of hepatic artery
4. Hepatic veins
5. Lymphatics

Nerves and Blood Vessels. The nerve fibers are derived from the left vagus and the thoracolumbar system. They enter at the transverse fossa and accompany

[10] Paul Langerhans, German anatomist (1847–1888).

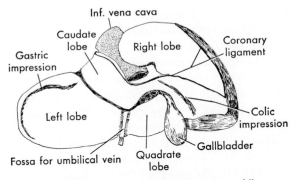

Figure 19–17. Diagram of undersurface of liver.

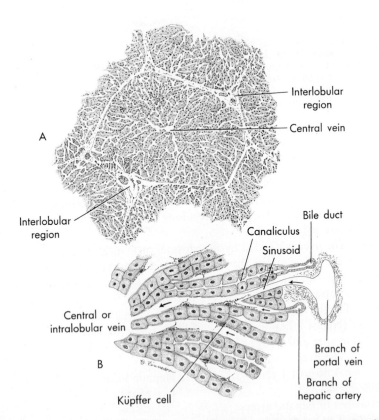

Figure 19–18. Diagram of microscopic views of pig liver. (*A*) Low power, showing one complete lobule in cross section and relation to other lobules. (*B*) High power, cords of liver cells, bile canaliculi, and blood sinusoids. *Arrows* show direction of blood flow and bile flow.

the vessels and ducts to the interlobular spaces. From here fibers are distributed to the coats of the blood vessels and ramify between and within the cells. The blood vessels connected with the liver are the hepatic artery, the portal vein, and the hepatic veins.

Histology of Liver. The liver is made up of many minute units called lobules. The lobule is the *unit of microscopic structure.* Each *lobule* is an irregular body composed of *chains* or *cords of hepatic cells* held together by connective tissue. Between the cords of hepatic cells are capillaries, called sinusoids, which are formed from the portal vein and hepatic artery. Kupffer[11] cells are located along the sinusoids. Nerve fibers are also present. The cords of cells are formed by two cells with a bile canaliculi between them, which empties into a bile duct. The cords of cells with their blood and lymph supply are the units of minute structure. Together they give an enormous area of contact between liver cells and capillaries for the volume of tissue concerned. Thus each lobule has all the following: (1) blood vessels in close connection with secretory cells, (2) cells which are capable of forming a secretion, and (3) ducts by which the secretion is carried away.

The portal blood vessel brings to the liver blood from the stomach, spleen, pancreas, and intestine. After entering the liver, it divides into a vast number of branches which form a plexus, the interlobular plexus in the spaces between the lobules. From this plexus the blood is carried into the lobule by fine branches which converge toward the center. The walls of these small vessels are incomplete, so that the blood is brought in direct contact with each cell. These channels are termed *sinusoids,* and at the center of the lobule they empty the blood into the intralobular vein. The intralobular veins from a number of lobules empty into a much larger vein, upon whose surface a vast number of lobules rest; and therefore the name *sublobular* (under the lobule) is given to these veins. They empty into still larger veins, the *hepatic,* which converge to form three large trunks and empty into the *inferior vena cava,* which is embedded in the posterior surface of the gland.

The Hepatic Artery. The blood brought to the liver by the portal vein is venous blood; arterial blood is brought by the *hepatic artery.* It enters the liver with the portal vein, divides and subdivides in the same manner as the portal vein, thus forming another network between the lobules, and in the lobules between the cells. The capillaries from the portal vein and the hepatic artery empty into the intralobular vein near the center of each lobule. From here the blood from the hepatic artery and from the portal vein is returned by the hepatic veins, which empty into the inferior vena cava. Blood flow through the liver has been estimated to be about 800 to 1,000 ml per minute, the greater proportion coming from the portal vein.

Lymphatics. There are a superficial and a deep set of lymphatic vessels. They begin in irregular spaces in the lobules, form networks around the lobules, and run always from the center outward.

[11] Karl William Von Kupffer, German anatomist (1829–1902).

The Bile Ducts. The surfaces of the hepatic cells are grooved, and the grooves on two adjacent cells fit together and form a passage into which the bile is poured as soon as it is formed by the cells. These passages form a network between and around the cells as intricate as the network of blood vessels. They are called *intercellular biliary channels* and radiate to the circumference of the lobule, where they empty into the interlobular bile ducts. These unite and form larger and larger ducts until two main ducts, one from the right and one from the left side of the liver, unite in the portal fossa and form the *hepatic duct.*

The hepatic duct passes downward and to the right for about 5 cm (2 in.) and then joins (at an acute angle) the duct from the gallbladder, termed the *cystic duct.* The hepatic and cystic ducts together form the *common bile duct* (*ductus choledochus*), which passes downward for about 7.5 cm (3 in.) and enters the

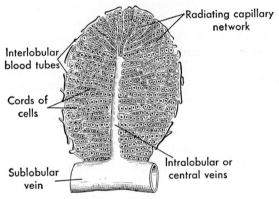

Figure 19–19. Diagram of a hepatic lobule as seen in longitudinal section.

Interlobular vessels bring blood in   { Branches of hepatic artery / Branches of portal vein

Intralobular vessels take blood out   { Tributaries to hepatic vein

duodenum about 7.5 cm below the pylorus. This orifice usually serves as a common opening for both the common bile duct and the pancreatic duct. It is very small and is guarded by a sphincter muscle, which keeps it closed except during digestion.

The liver is invested in an outer capsule of fibrous tissue called *Glisson's*[12] *capsule.* This capsule is reflected inward at the transverse fossa and envelops the vessels and ducts which pass into the liver. With the exception of a few small areas, the liver is enclosed in a serous tunic derived from the peritoneum.

Physiology of the Liver. The liver has many functions of a complex nature, some of which are carried on independently of one another. It is possible that one function may be interfered with while other functions proceed normally. The liver functions in a variety of ways to maintain and regulate homeostasis of body fluids and control of body processes.

[12] Francis Glisson, English anatomist (1597–1677).

1. Secretory Functions. The liver forms and secretes daily about 800 to 1,200 ml of bile consisting of bile salts, bile pigments, and cholesterol. The bile salts are important in the intestinal phases of digestion. The bile pigments are formed from blood pigment (hemoglobin) of disintegrated red blood cells. About 80 per cent of the bile salts secreted by the liver are reabsorbed again from the small intestine; this *enterohepatic* circulation serves to conserve essential fractions of the bile acids. There is little or no enterohepatic circulation of the other bile constituents.

2. In Relation to Blood. The liver helps to regulate the blood volume by means of a sluice mechanism, which adjusts the volume of blood leaving the liver, via the hepatic vein. Since the liver is an expandable and contractible organ, it has the ability to store large quantities of blood in its vessels.

At birth the ductus venosus gradually becomes completely occluded, more blood flows through the liver, and it gradually assumes the functions characteristic of the normal adult organ. The liver forms red blood cells in the embryo and stores vitamin B_{12}, which is essential for the development of the red blood cells.

It forms prothrombin and fibrinogen, which are concerned with the clotting of blood, and heparin, an anticoagulant of the blood. (Heparin is also found in the spleen, heart, lung, thymus, and muscle. The lung is probably the richest source of heparin.)

The liver also plays a part, along with the spleen, in disposing of the products resulting from disintegration of erythrocytes which are no longer able to function in oxygen transport. A vasodepressor substance (VDM) is formed in the liver during late stages of shock due to hemorrhage.

3. In Relation to Storage. The liver forms vitamin A from carotene. Vitamins A and D are stored in the liver. Iron, copper, and perhaps other minerals are stored in the liver also. It utilizes vitamin K to form prothrombin.

4. In Relation to Metabolism:

(*a*) CARBOHYDRATE. The liver stores glycogen which is synthesized primarily from glucose, fructose, and galactose (glycogenesis). It synthesizes glycogen from noncarbohydrates (gluconeogenesis) and converts glycogen to glucose (glycogenolysis) to maintain blood sugar constancy.

(*b*) FAT. The liver is a great center for fat metabolism; it oxidizes fatty acids, synthesizes phospholipids and ketones, and synthesizes fats from glucose; it forms lipoproteins. Cholesterol is esterified and is formed and excreted in bile.

(*c*) PROTEIN. The liver deaminizes amino acids and synthesizes urea. It converts amino acids into glucose and synthesizes amino acids from other amino acids. It also synthesizes plasma proteins, fibrinogen, and prothrombin. It forms essential nonprotein nitrogen compounds.

5. Detoxification Functions. The importance of the "protective" role of the liver cannot be overemphasized. It not only controls the concentration of various substances, but by a variety of chemical reactions such as oxidation, reduction, conjugation, and by other means, the liver detoxifies certain end products of digestion, for example, phenol, skatole, and indole. These are aromatic substances which give odor to fecal material. Through bile the liver eliminates certain drugs and heavy metals such as mercury; morphine and strychnine can be absorbed and stored by the liver and freed slowly so that by dilution their toxicity is diminished. By virtue of the Kupffer cells, which are located in the liver sinusoids, the liver has the ability to detoxify substances. These cells have phagocytic action and hence have an important role in the defense mechanism of the body.

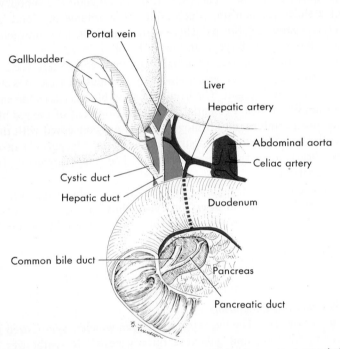

Figure 19–20. Diagram of gallbladder, pancreas, and duodenum to show relationships of bile and pancreatic ducts. Note also circular folds of duodenum.

Hippuric acid is synthesized from benzoic acid through conjugation with glycine and is eliminated in the urine. As a result of its many chemical activities the liver provides a great deal of heat for the body. The liver plays an important role in estrogen inactivation and thus helps to maintain the estrogen level in the blood by excreting it into the bile.

The gallbladder is a pear-shaped (when full) sac lodged in the gallbladder fossa on the undersurface of the liver, where it is held in place by connective tissue. It is about 7 to 10 cm (3 to 4 in.) long, 2.5 cm (1 in.) wide, holds about 36 ml, and is composed of three coats: (1) the inner one is mucous membrane; (2) the middle one is muscular and fibrous tissue; and (3) the outer one is serous membrane derived from the peritoneum. It is only occasionally that the peritoneum covers more than the undersurface of the organ.

Most of the bile secreted continuously by the liver enters the gallbladder, where it is concentrated; thus it serves as a reservoir for bile. When required, the

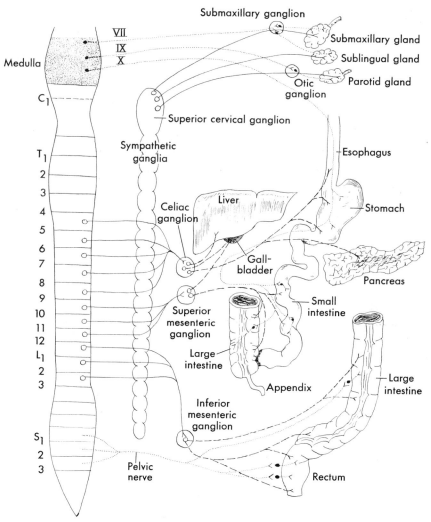

Figure 19–21. Innervation of the digestive pathway. Parasympathetic fibers are *dotted.* The ganglia of the vagus and the pelvic nerves lie in or near the organs.

gallbladder contracts and expels its bile content into the duodenum. The most potent stimuli for evacuation are the acid gastric juice and fatty foods in the small intestine. A hormone, cholecystokinin, is elaborated by cells of the small intestine in the presence of fat. This hormone causes the gallbladder to contract, thereby emptying its contents of bile into the intestine. Although bile contains no digestive enzymes, its bile salts are important for digestion of fats. The bile salts emulsify the fat into globules which can be acted on by an enzyme from the pancreas (see p. 614), and they also render the end products of digestion soluble so that they can be absorbed into the villi.

The sphincter of Oddi is relaxed much of the time. However, when pressure in the intestine increases, the sphincter contracts to prevent ascent of intestinal contents into the biliary tract. The sphincteric mechanism must be relaxed when the gall-bladder contracts; if not, the contents will not be evacuated, and the resulting distention of the bile duct will cause sharp, unbearable pain called biliary colic. This pain is also produced when the duct is obstructed by so-called "stones."

QUESTIONS FOR DISCUSSION

1. Mr. X had his entire stomach removed (i.e., total gastrectomy). Continuity of his digestive tract was established by anastomosis between the esophagus and small intestine.
    a. Mr. X learned early that if he were to keep in good nutritional state, but not have overdistention, he had to eat small meals at frequent intervals. Discuss why.
    b. His physician frequently administered vitamin B_{12} by intramuscular injection. Discuss.
    c. Although Mr. X obviously no longer had gastric pepsin for digestion of proteins, he nevertheless had only little impairment in protein digestion. Why?
2. List all the anatomical structures necessary for rendering food soluble and explain the structure in terms of its function.
3. About how long will it take for the food to reach the large intestine?
4. Discuss the functions of the liver.

SUMMARY

Digestion. Digestion is dependent on the proper functioning of certain organs that are grouped together and called the digestive system

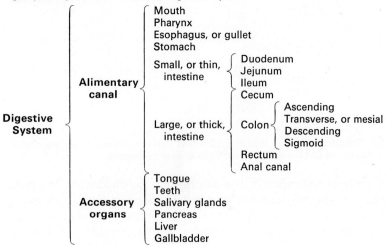

Alimentary Canal
- Continuous tube from mouth to anus
- About 9 m (30 ft) long in cadaver
- Esophagus—four coats
  - Internal, or mucous
  - Submucous, or areolar
  - Muscular
  - Fibrous
- From stomach to rectum—four coats
  - Mucous
  - Submucous, or areolar
  - Muscular
  - Peritoneum

Mouth, or Buccal, Cavity
- Roof—palate
  - (1) Hard palate
    - Maxillae
    - Palatine } processes
  - (2) Soft palate—uvula, palatine arches, and tonsils
- Floor—tongue
- Bounded laterally and in front by cheeks and lips
- Behind it communicates with pharynx
- Contains
  - Tonsils. Orifices of ducts of salivary glands
  - Tongue. Teeth

Tonsils
- Masses of lymphoid tissue occupy triangular space between palatine arches on either side of throat
- Function
  - Similar to that of other lymph nodes
  - (1) Aid in formation of white cells
  - (2) Act as filters and protect body from infection

Tongue
- Special organ of sense of taste
- Assists in
  - Mastication
  - Deglutition
  - Digestion

Salivary Glands
- Parotid—just under and in front of ear
- Submaxillary
- Sublingual } Below jaw and under tongue
- Function—form a secretion which, mixed with the secretion of the glandular cells of the mouth, is called saliva
- Nerves—fibers from both divisions of autonomic system
- Blood vessels—branches of external carotid artery

Teeth
- Contained in sockets of alveolar processes of maxillae and mandible
- Gums—cover processes and extend into sockets, or alveoli
- Sockets—lined with periosteum
  - Attach teeth to sockets
  - Source of nourishment
- Three portions
  - Root—one or more fangs contained in alveolus
  - Crown—projects beyond level of gums
  - Neck—portion between root and crown
- Composed of three substances developed from epithelium
  - Dentin
    - Gives shape. Encloses pulp cavity, which contains nerves and blood vessels that enter by canal from root
  - Enamel—caps crown
  - Cement—covers root
- Two sets
  - (1) Deciduous—6 months–2 years
    - Incisors 8
    - Canines 4 } 20
    - Molars 8
  - Begin to develop about the sixth week of intrauterine life
  - (2) Permanent—6½ years–25 years of age
    - Incisors 8
    - Canines 4
    - Premolars 8 } 32
    - Molars 12
  - With the exception of the second and third molars the permanent teeth begin to develop about the sixteenth week of intrauterine life
- Function—to assist in the process of mastication

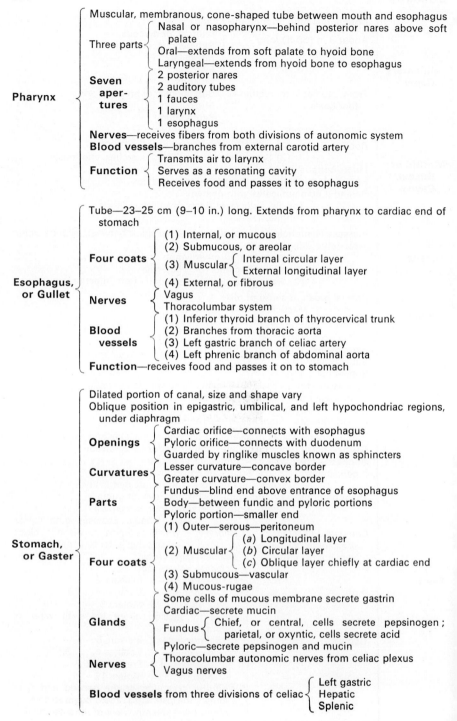

Pharynx

Muscular, membranous, cone-shaped tube between mouth and esophagus

Three parts
- Nasal or nasopharynx—behind posterior nares above soft palate
- Oral—extends from soft palate to hyoid bone
- Laryngeal—extends from hyoid bone to esophagus

Seven apertures
- 2 posterior nares
- 2 auditory tubes
- 1 fauces
- 1 larynx
- 1 esophagus

Nerves—receives fibers from both divisions of autonomic system

Blood vessels—branches from external carotid artery

Function
- Transmits air to larynx
- Serves as a resonating cavity
- Receives food and passes it to esophagus

Esophagus, or Gullet

Tube—23–25 cm (9–10 in.) long. Extends from pharynx to cardiac end of stomach

Four coats
- (1) Internal, or mucous
- (2) Submucous, or areolar
- (3) Muscular
  - Internal circular layer
  - External longitudinal layer
- (4) External, or fibrous

Nerves
- Vagus
- Thoracolumbar system

Blood vessels
- (1) Inferior thyroid branch of thyrocervical trunk
- (2) Branches from thoracic aorta
- (3) Left gastric branch of celiac artery
- (4) Left phrenic branch of abdominal aorta

Function—receives food and passes it on to stomach

Stomach, or Gaster

Dilated portion of canal, size and shape vary

Oblique position in epigastric, umbilical, and left hypochondriac regions, under diaphragm

Openings
- Cardiac orifice—connects with esophagus
- Pyloric orifice—connects with duodenum
- Guarded by ringlike muscles known as sphincters

Curvatures
- Lesser curvature—concave border
- Greater curvature—convex border

Parts
- Fundus—blind end above entrance of esophagus
- Body—between fundic and pyloric portions
- Pyloric portion—smaller end

Four coats
- (1) Outer—serous—peritoneum
- (2) Muscular
  - (a) Longitudinal layer
  - (b) Circular layer
  - (c) Oblique layer chiefly at cardiac end
- (3) Submucous—vascular
- (4) Mucous-rugae

Glands
- Some cells of mucous membrane secrete gastrin
- Cardiac—secrete mucin
- Fundus
  - Chief, or central, cells secrete pepsinogen; parietal, or oxyntic, cells secrete acid
- Pyloric—secrete pepsinogen and mucin

Nerves
- Thoracolumbar autonomic nerves from celiac plexus
- Vagus nerves

Blood vessels from three divisions of celiac
- Left gastric
- Hepatic
- Splenic

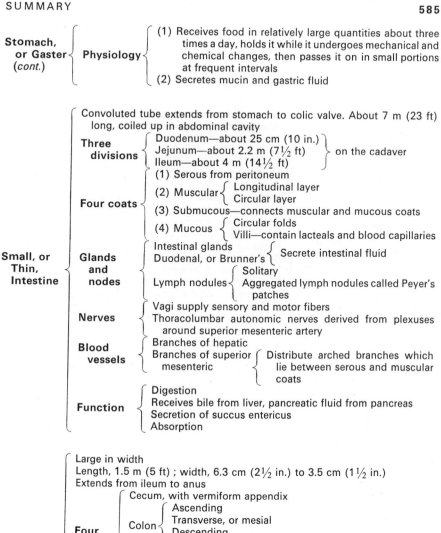

Stomach, or Gaster *(cont.)*

Physiology
(1) Receives food in relatively large quantities about three times a day, holds it while it undergoes mechanical and chemical changes, then passes it on in small portions at frequent intervals
(2) Secretes mucin and gastric fluid

Small, or Thin, Intestine

Convoluted tube extends from stomach to colic valve. About 7 m (23 ft) long, coiled up in abdominal cavity

Three divisions
Duodenum—about 25 cm (10 in.)
Jejunum—about 2.2 m (7½ ft)
Ileum—about 4 m (14½ ft)
} on the cadaver

Four coats
(1) Serous from peritoneum
(2) Muscular { Longitudinal layer / Circular layer
(3) Submucous—connects muscular and mucous coats
(4) Mucous { Circular folds / Villi—contain lacteals and blood capillaries

Glands and nodes
Intestinal glands
Duodenal, or Brunner's } Secrete intestinal fluid
Lymph nodules { Solitary / Aggregated lymph nodules called Peyer's patches

Nerves
Vagi supply sensory and motor fibers
Thoracolumbar autonomic nerves derived from plexuses around superior mesenteric artery

Blood vessels
Branches of hepatic
Branches of superior mesenteric { Distribute arched branches which lie between serous and muscular coats

Function
Digestion
Receives bile from liver, pancreatic fluid from pancreas
Secretion of succus entericus
Absorption

Large, or Thick, Intestine

Large in width
Length, 1.5 m (5 ft) ; width, 6.3 cm (2½ in.) to 3.5 cm (1½ in.)
Extends from ileum to anus

Four parts
Cecum, with vermiform appendix
Colon { Ascending / Transverse, or mesial / Descending / Sigmoid
Rectum—about 12 cm (5 in.)
Anal canal—3.5 cm (1–1½ in.) { Internal sphincter
Anus { External sphincter

Four coats
(1) Serous, except that in some parts it is only a partial covering, and at rectum it is lacking
(2) Muscular { Longitudinal layer { Arranged in three ribbonlike bands that begin at appendix and extend to rectum / Circular layer
(3) Submucous
(4) Mucous { No villi / No circular folds / Numerous { Intestinal glands / Solitary lymph nodules

Nerves—fibers from both divisions of autonomic nervous system

Large, or Thick, Intestine (*cont.*)

- **Blood vessels**
  - Superior mesenteric supplies cecum, ascending and transverse colon
  - Inferior mesenteric supplies descending colon and rectum. Rectum also receives branches from hypogastric arteries
- **Function**
  - Continuance of digestion and absorption
  - Elimination of waste

Pancreas

In front of first and second lumbar vertebrae, behind stomach

- **Hammer shape**
  - Head attached to duodenum
  - Body in front of vertebrae
  - Tail reaches to spleen
- **Size**
  - About 12.5 cm (5 in.) long
  - About 5 cm (2 in.) wide
- **Average weight**—60–90 gm (2–3 oz)
- **Structure**
  - Compound gland—each lobule consists of one of the branches of main duct, which terminates in cluster of pouches, or alveoli
  - Lobules held together by connective tissue form lobes
  - Lobes form gland
  - Duct from each lobule empties into pancreatic duct, also called duct of Wirsung
  - Scattered throughout pancreas are islets of Langerhans
- **Physiology**
  - (1) Secretes pancreatic fluid—digestive fluid
  - (2) Forms internal secretions—aids in metabolism of glucose (insulin and glucagon)

Liver

Largest gland in body

- **Location**
  - Right hypochondriac region
  - Epigastric region
  - Left hypochondriac region
- Convex above—fits under diaphragm
- Concave below—fits over right kidney, ascending colon, and pyloric end of stomach
- **Five ligaments**
  - (1) Falciform
  - (2) Coronary
  - (3) Right lateral } Formed by folds of peritoneum
  - (4) Left lateral
  - (5) Round ligament } Results from atrophy of umbilical vein
- **Four fossae**
  - (1) Left sagittal fossa
  - (2) Portal, or transverse, fossa transmits
    - Portal vein
    - Hepatic artery
    - Hepatic duct
    - Lymphatics
    - Nerves
  - (3) Gallbladder fossa
  - (4) Fossa for inferior vena cava
- **Four lobes**
  - (1) Right (largest lobe)
  - (2) Left (smaller and wedge-shaped)
  - (3) Quadrate (square)
  - (4) Caudate (tail-like)
- **Five sets of vessels**
  - (1) Branches of portal vein
  - (2) Branches of hepatic artery
  - (3) Hepatic veins
  - (4) Lymphatics
  - (5) Bile ducts
- Nerves—derived from left vagus and thoracolumbar autonomic system
- **Blood vessels**
  - Hepatic artery
  - Portal vein
  - Hepatic veins

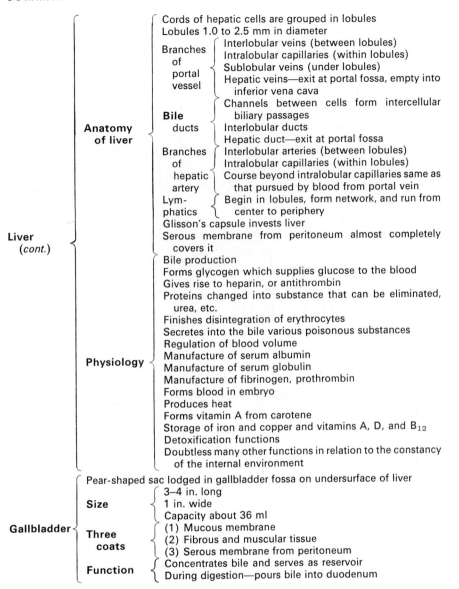

Liver (*cont.*)

Anatomy of liver

Cords of hepatic cells are grouped in lobules
Lobules 1.0 to 2.5 mm in diameter

Branches of portal vessel
- Interlobular veins (between lobules)
- Intralobular capillaries (within lobules)
- Sublobular veins (under lobules)
- Hepatic veins—exit at portal fossa, empty into inferior vena cava

Bile ducts
- Channels between cells form intercellular biliary passages
- Interlobular ducts
- Hepatic duct—exit at portal fossa

Branches of hepatic artery
- Interlobular arteries (between lobules)
- Intralobular capillaries (within lobules)
- Course beyond intralobular capillaries same as that pursued by blood from portal vein

Lymphatics
- Begin in lobules, form network, and run from center to periphery

Glisson's capsule invests liver
Serous membrane from peritoneum almost completely covers it

Physiology

Bile production
Forms glycogen which supplies glucose to the blood
Gives rise to heparin, or antithrombin
Proteins changed into substance that can be eliminated, urea, etc.
Finishes disintegration of erythrocytes
Secretes into the bile various poisonous substances
Regulation of blood volume
Manufacture of serum albumin
Manufacture of serum globulin
Manufacture of fibrinogen, prothrombin
Forms blood in embryo
Produces heat
Forms vitamin A from carotene
Storage of iron and copper and vitamins A, D, and B_{12}
Detoxification functions
Doubtless many other functions in relation to the constancy of the internal environment

Gallbladder

Pear-shaped sac lodged in gallbladder fossa on undersurface of liver

Size
- 3–4 in. long
- 1 in. wide
- Capacity about 36 ml

Three coats
- (1) Mucous membrane
- (2) Fibrous and muscular tissue
- (3) Serous membrane from peritoneum

Function
- Concentrates bile and serves as reservoir
- During digestion—pours bile into duodenum

20

Foods $\left\{\begin{array}{l} \textit{Protein} \\ \textit{Carbohydrate} \\ \textit{Fat} \end{array}\right.$

Mineral Metabolism

Vitamins $\left\{\begin{array}{l} \textit{Fat-Soluble} \\ \textit{Water-Soluble} \end{array}\right.$

Physiology of $\left\{\begin{array}{l} \textit{Mechanical} \\ \textit{Chemical} \end{array}\right.$
Digestion

NATURAL NUTRIENTS are in general nondiffusible and held in cells. The cells of plants and animals constitute a natural food supply for man. These foods are taken periodically, digested, absorbed, stored, in general, in nondiffusible form in cells, redigested by endoenzymes, and delivered to the cells by the circulatory fluids for use. Food is any substance taken into the body to yield energy, to build tissue, and to regulate body processes.

All the body activities require a certain amount of energy; this energy is supplied by food. The energy released in cells during the interaction of oxygen and food is present in the form of potential, or latent, energy, binding the atoms into molecules and the molecules into larger masses. The splitting of these complex molecules into smaller and simpler ones releases this energy as kinetic energy. Food material, over and above what is needed for this purpose, is stored in the body in the form of glycogen or as fat. This may be regarded as reserve fuel which, when needed, is oxidized to release energy.

Food supplies material for the manufacture of protoplasm, for either growth (increase in the bulk of protoplasm) or repair (replacing the protoplasm incidentally oxidized day by day).

Nutrition and growth are dependent upon certain essential substances called vitamins. Water and inorganic salts are necessary to maintain the normal composition of the tissues.

Classification of Food. Chemical analysis shows that the chemical elements found in the body are also found in food. Various combinations of these elements give a great variety of substances which are grouped as follows:

$$
\text{Nutrients} \begin{cases} \text{Water} & \text{Mineral salts} \\ \text{Carbohydrates} & \text{Vitamins} \\ \text{Lipids} \\ \text{Proteins} \end{cases}
$$

Water constitutes more than two thirds of the material ingested daily.

The water content of the body comes from three sources: beverages or other liquids; foods, especially vegetables and fruits; and the water formed in the tissues as the result of metabolic activities. (See Chap. 21.)

Carbohydrates are the most abundant and most economical sources of energy. All simple sugars and all substances which can be converted into simple sugars by hydrolysis are carbohydrates. The names of these compounds suggest the number of simple sugar groups they will yield on hydrolysis: monosaccharides, disaccharides, and polysaccharides.

1. Monosaccharides, or simple sugars, contain one sugar group, $C_6H_{12}O_6$. They are soluble and can be absorbed into the body fluids without further change. They are the units from which the more complex carbohydrates are formed.

$$
\text{Monosaccharides} \begin{cases} \text{Glucose, or dextrose, found in fruits, especially the grape,} \\ \quad \text{and in body fluids} & C_6H_{12}O_6 \\ \text{Fructose, or levulose, found with glucose in fruits} & C_6H_{12}O_6 \\ \text{Galactose, obtained by hydrolysis of lactose and certain} \\ \quad \text{gums} & C_6H_{12}O_6 \end{cases}
$$

2. Disaccharides. The formula, $C_{12}H_{22}O_{11}$, shows that disaccharides consist of two monosaccharide groups. During the process of digestion, they are split into their component monosaccharides, e.g., sucrose into glucose and fructose; lactose into glucose and galactose, and maltose into two molecules of glucose. Only one splitting is necessary, and it utilizes one molecule of water as seen in the following equation.

Sucrose   Water   Glucose   Fructose
$$
C_{12}H_{22}O_{11} + H_2O \rightarrow C_6H_{12}O_6 + C_6H_{12}O_6
$$

$$
\text{Disaccharides} \begin{cases} \text{Sucrose, or cane sugar, found in vegetables, fruits, and} \\ \quad \text{juices of plants} & C_{12}H_{22}O_{11} \\ \text{Lactose, or milk sugar, found in the milk of all mammals} & C_{12}H_{22}O_{11} \\ \text{Maltose is an intermediate product in the digestion of} \\ \quad \text{starch, found in the body, in germinating cereals, malts,} \\ \quad \text{and malt products} & C_{12}H_{22}O_{11} \end{cases}
$$

3. Polysaccharides are represented by the molecular formula $(C_6H_{10}O_5)_n$. The elements are present in the same proportion, but the value of n may be large and is probably different for the different polysaccharides. For instance, the value of n for the starch molecule is said to be 300 or more, representing as many sugar groups, whereas for the dextrin molecule it is smaller, so that a single molecule of starch when hydrolyzed produces several molecules of dextrin of the same relative composition. Since the polysaccharides are complex, they must pass through several hydrolyses before they are changed to simple sugars. Each splitting of the molecule gives substances with simpler composition, though with the same relative proportion of the constituents, and to each is given a special name. The number of molecules of simple sugar resulting from the hydrolysis of any polysaccharide would depend upon the value of the n.

A summary of the hydrolysis of starch to glucose may be expressed as follows.

$$
\begin{array}{cc}
\text{Starch} & \text{Glucose} \\
(C_6H_{10}O_5)_n + nH_2O & \rightarrow nC_6H_{12}O_6
\end{array}
$$

Polysaccharides
$$
\left\{
\begin{array}{ll}
\text{Starch—found in grain, tubers, roots, etc.} & (C_6H_{10}O_5)_n \\
\text{Cellulose—outside covering of starch grains and basis} & \\
\quad \text{of all woody fibers} & (C_6H_{10}O_5)_n \\
\text{Glycogen—form in which carbohydrate is stored in the} & \\
\quad \text{liver and muscles, etc.} & (C_6H_{10}O_5)_n \\
\text{Dextrin—formed from starch by partial hydrolysis} & (C_6H_{10}O_5)_n
\end{array}
\right.
$$

Starch is the principal form in which carbohydrate is stored in plants. During the ripening process in some plants (e.g., apple and banana) starch is changed to glucose; in other plants (e.g., corn and peas) the opposite process occurs.

Cellulose constitutes the supporting tissue of plant cells. When derived from mature plants, cellulose is quite resistant to the action of dilute acids or digestive enzymes and passes through the digestive tract unchanged. The chief value of cellulose in human nutrition is to give bulk to the intestinal contents and thereby facilitate peristalsis.

Glycogen is the form in which reserve carbohydrate is stored in the animal body, in greatest quantity in the liver and muscles.

Dextrins are formed from starch by the action of enzymes, acids, or heat.

Lipids.   Lipids are a heterogeneous group of organic compounds which contain fatty acids, usually combined with an alcohol as an ester. They may be divided into two groups—*simple lipids* (fats, oils, and waxes) and *compound lipids* (phospholipids, glycolipids, and sterols). The word *fat* is sometimes used in an anatomical sense and sometimes in a chemical sense. In an anatomical sense, fat denotes adipose tissue. In a chemical sense, fats are glyceryl esters of fatty acids. In other words, fats are hydrolyzed to yield three molecules of fatty acid and one molecule of glycerol. The ordinary fats of animal and vegetable food are not simple substances but are mixtures of simple fats named palmitin, stearin, olein, etc., which are derived from the fatty acids—palmitic, stearic, and oleic acid, and the alcohol glycerol. Oils are chemically similar to fats but are usually liquid at room temperature, whereas fats are usually solid. Oils also contain more unsaturated[1] bonds than fats do. Vegetable oils in particular tend to be highly unsaturated—a fact which may be of medical significance in regard to metabolic utilization of the fat, although the details to date have not been

---

[1] Carbon compounds having a single bond between the carbon atoms are called *saturated* compounds; those with one or more double or triple bonds between carbon atoms are termed *unsaturated* compounds.

clarified. Experimental evidence indicates the necessity of including some of the unsaturated fatty acids such as linoleic acid and linolenic acid, which are found in most fatty foods.

Fats are compounds of carbon, hydrogen, and oxygen, the same elements found in carbohydrates; but these elements are present in different combinations and proportions. The fats contain proportionately less oxygen and more carbon and hydrogen than the carbohydrates; consequently they make a more concentrated source of energy. Under the influence of lipases, secreted principally by the pancreas, fats and oils are split to glycerol and fatty acids by hydrolysis.

$$\underset{\text{(Stearin)}}{C_3H_5(C_{18}H_{35}O_2)_3} + \underset{\text{(Water)}}{3H_2O} \rightarrow \underset{\text{(Glycerol)}}{C_3H_5(OH)_3} + \underset{\text{(Stearic Acid)}}{3H \cdot C_{18}H_{35}O_2}$$

Waxes are esters of fatty acids with high-molecular-weight alcohols. They are not found in the human body and have no nutritional value for humans. They are not hydrolyzed by lipases and are therefore indigestible.

Compound Lipids. These contain other groups in addition to fatty acids and an alcohol in the lipid molecule. These may be phosphate, carbohydrate, or nitrogen-containing radicals.

1. *Phospholipids,* or *phosphatides,* contain both phosphorus and nitrogen. The best known are the lecithins, which are abundant in egg yolk and occur in brain and nerve tissue and in all the cells of the body. Cephalins and sphingomyelin are other examples.

2. *Glycolipids,* or *cerebrosides,* are compounds of fatty acids with a carbohydrate and contain nitrogen but no phosphoric acid. Cerebrosides are found in the myelin sheaths of nerve fibers in connection with, possibly in combination with, lecithin.

3. *Sterols* are complex monohydroxyalcohols of high molecular weight, which are found in nature combined with fatty acids. They contain carbon, hydrogen, and oxygen. The best known is cholesterol, which is very widely distributed in the body, being found in the medullary coverings of nerve fibers, in the blood, in all the cells and liquids of the body, in the sebum secreted by the sebaceous glands of the skin, and in the bile. In the blood cholesterol protects the erythrocytes against the action of hemolytic substances, and in the sebum it protects the skin. Cholesterol serves as the precursor of the female sex hormone, pregnanediol; of cholic acid in the bile salts; and of the steroid hormones of the adrenal gland. Under the influence of ultraviolet rays (direct sunlight or from a mercury-vapor quartz lamp) other sterols closely related to cholesterol may be so changed as to acquire the property of an antirachitic vitamin. These are called "provitamin D" sterols.

Proteins are more complex than either carbohydrates or fats and differ from them in containing *nitrogen.* Proteins always contain carbon, hydrogen, oxygen, and nitrogen; sometimes sulfur, phosphorus, or iron is present. Proteins are built up of simpler substances called *amino acids.* Amino acids are acids that contain an amino group (NH_2) instead of a hydrogen atom. In acetic acid, which is one of the simplest organic acids, the formula is CH_3COOH. If one of the three hydrogen atoms in the CH_3 group is replaced by NH_2, a substance results which has the formula $CH_2(NH_2)COOH$ and is called aminoacetic acid or *glycine* or glycocoll. Another organic acid is propionic acid, which has the formula C_2H_5COOH; if an atom of hydrogen is replaced by the amino group, $C_2H_4(NH_2)COOH$, aminopropionic acid, or *alanine*, results.

Some 40 or more amino acids have been described as occurring in nature and many more have been synthesized. However, only 23 amino acids have been unequivocally accepted as common "building stones" of the proteins. No one protein contains all of them, but caseinogen of milk yields 17 or more. The proteins of one animal differ from those of another; even the proteins of different tissues are not identical. This is also true of the proteins of plants. The proteins of milk, fish, egg, cereal, and vegetables represent different combinations of amino acids and are therefore different compounds. This means that proteins differ in relation to the numbers of amino acids present, the ratio of one amino acid to another, and the order in which they are linked (see p. 593). Among vegetables the legumes—peas, beans, lentils, and peanuts—are especially rich in proteins.

Examples of Protein Constituents of Food

Albumin, the white substance seen when egg is heated, the scum that forms on the top of milk when its temperature is raised above 76° C (170° F), the white coating that forms on meat when it has been in a hot oven for a short time

Casein, the substance that forms a curd when acid or rennin is added to milk or when milk sours

Glutenin, the gummy substance in wheat

Legumin, a protein substance contained in the legumes

Gelatin, from intercellular substance of connective tissues, including bones and tendons

Organic extracts, protein substances formed in animals and plants as a result of their metabolism. The flavor of meats and some plant foods is due to extractives

Amino Acids That Have Been Found in the Food Proteins of Man

Indispensable	Dispensable
Valine	Glycine
Leucine	Alanine
Isoleucine	Norleucine
Phenylalanine	Tyrosine
Threonine	Serine
Methionine	Cystine
Arginine	Aspartic acid
Lysine	Glutamic acid
Histidine	Hydroxyglutamic acid
Tryptophan	Proline
	Hydroxyproline

The body can synthesize arginine, but not rapidly enough to meet the demands of normal growth. Histidine may be synthesized in adult tissues or by intestinal microorganisms.

The following show a few of the many possible combinations of carbon, hydrogen, oxygen, and nitrogen to form amino acids.

Glycine $CH_2(NH_2) \cdot COOH$
Lysine $CH_2(NH_2) \cdot CH_2 \cdot CH_2 \cdot CH_2 \cdot CH(NH_2) \cdot COOH$
Aspartic acid $COOH \cdot CH_2 \cdot CH(NH_2) \cdot COOH$
Tyrosine $CH_2 \cdot CH(NH_2) \cdot COOH$

Proline

Tryptophan

Methionine $CH_3 \cdot S \cdot CH_2 \cdot CH_2 \cdot CH(NH_2) \cdot COOH$

Classification. Proteins are classified in two main groups:

1. Simple proteins when hydrolyzed yield only amino acids or their derivatives. Examples are serum albumin, globulin, scleroproteins.

2. Conjugated proteins are substances which contain a simple protein molecule united to some other nonprotein molecule known as the prosthetic group. On hydrolysis they yield amino acids and another molecule. This molecule is nucleic acid in the nucleoproteins, a carbohydrate in the glycoproteins, a phosphate in the phosphoproteins, pigment in the chromoproteins and hemoglobins, and a fatty substance in lipoproteins. Proteins are hydrolyzed to polypeptides and finally to amino acids.

Specific catalysts are pepsin, trypsin, and peptidases.

Nutritive Value of Different Proteins. Proteins vary in their constituents and in their nutritive value, depending on their amino acid composition. Because of this they are classed as *adequate* proteins, or those containing all the amino acids for the growth and maintenance of the body, and *inadequate* proteins, which furnish material for energy needs but not for growth and the repair of tissue. In general, the protein of animal origin most nearly meets the essential needs of the human for synthesis of tissue. Gelatin is an example of an inadequate protein; on the other hand, the casein of milk and the glutenin of wheat contain all essential amino acids and can furnish energy and build tissue. Combinations of incomplete proteins provided at the same meal can supplement each other. However, amino acids as such are not stored, and an inadequate provision of amino acids by the proteins of one meal cannot be supplemented by the proteins of a later meal. If adequate protein is provided but the caloric demands of the body are not being met, amino acids will be used for the production of energy.

Nitrogen Equilibrium. Nitrogen continues to be excreted in the urine even though the diet is devoid of nitrogen. This represents a condition in which the body is oxidizing its own tissues to supply its needs. The nitrogenous portion of the protein molecule of ingested proteins is not stored in the body but is eliminated chiefly in the urine and to a limited extent in the feces. It is therefore important that the body receive daily an amount of protein nitrogen equal to the amount eliminated in the excreta. When this condition exists, the body is said to be in nitrogen equilibrium. If there is a positive balance in favor of the food, it means that protein is being made into body protoplasm; and this is an ideal condition during the period of growth or convalescence from wasting illness. If the balance is negative, it means that the body is oxidizing its own protein. Minimum nitrogen equilibrium can be maintained on about 40 gm of protein or less per day, but it is thought that higher protein intake results in greater resistance to disease and a higher state of physiological efficiency. It is customary to add 50 per cent to the average indicated as the actual requirement based on laboratory experiments, thus bringing the amount up to 60 to 100 gm of protein per day, which is somewhat more than 1 gm per kilogram of body weight.

Mineral Metabolism

The mineral elements which enter into the composition of the body are listed on page 18. Mineral constituents form about 4 per cent of the body weight and are primarily located in the skeleton. Since each element enters into the metabolism of body cells, a constant supply of each is necessary to meet the daily loss. These elements are supplied in food. On analysis many of them are classified as ash constituents, since they remain after incineration of the food. These "ash constituents" may function in the body in several ways: as constituents of bone, giving rigidity to the skeleton; as essential elements of all protoplasm associated with enzyme activity; as soluble constituents of the fluids of the body influencing the elasticity and irritability of the muscles and nerves, supplying material for the acidity or alkalinity of all body fluids, helping to maintain the acid-base equilibrium of the body fluids as well as their osmotic characteristics and solvent power; and probably in many other ways. Not only must the body be supplied with certain minerals which are important for its functions, but these must be supplied in readily absorbable form. Thus, only a small fraction, several milligrams, of the ion which is ingested is absorbed daily.

The importance of the optimum concentrations of each of these mineral salts in the tissues and fluids of the body is so great that any considerable change from the normal endangers life.

Calcium is a constituent of all protoplasm and of body fluids, and is present in large proportions in bone and teeth. There is more calcium than any other cation in the body. Ninety-nine per cent of body calcium is in bones and teeth. Calcium is essential for all cellular activities. It is related to normal permeability of cellular membranes, excitability of muscle, normal heart action, and nerve activity, and must be present in ionic form for normal blood clotting. Children as well as pregnant and lactating animals require large amounts. Milk is the best source of calcium, but calcium is also present in leafy vegetables. The body cannot readily adapt itself to calcium shortage; therefore, a liberal amount is needed daily. It is estimated that an intake of 1 gm of calcium would maintain the body fluids at optimum concentration. Calcium deficiency is a definite problem in the diet of Americans.

A growing child requires at least 1 to 1.4 gm each of calcium and phosphorus per day. A pregnant woman requires at least 2 gm of calcium per day during the latter half of pregnancy and during lactation.

Phosphorus is essential to the normal development of bones and teeth. It is a necessary constituent of all cells, particularly nerve and muscle tissue. About 80 per cent of the total is combined with calcium in the bones and teeth. It is in organic combination such as phospholipids, phosphocreatine, and phosphorylated intermediates of carbohydrate metabolism. Blood plasma and body fluids are relatively low in phosphates. The phosphate ester is of great importance in energy transfer. (See p. 633.) Phosphorylation is also important in the absorption of carbohydrate from the intestine and in the reabsorption of glucose by the renal tubule. It is also concerned with maintaining acid-base balance and enzyme systems and their functioning.

Good sources are milk, cheese, meat, liver, kidney, fish, and eggs. The intake of phosphorus is considered sufficient if the diet is adequate in calcium. Vitamin D apparently is needed for reabsorption of phosphates in the renal tubules.

Iron in the adult body amounts to about 4.5 gm, distributed in the hemoglobin of red cells (2.5 gm), myoglobin of skeletal muscle, intracellular enzyme systems (particularly the cytochrome system), and in the tissues as ferritin. This latter is the storage form of iron—bound to protein—and is found primarily in the liver, as well as the spleen, bone marrow, and lymph nodes. In hemoglobin it is the iron-containing part of the molecule to which the oxygen is attached and which carries oxygen to the cells. Traces of copper are essential for utilization of iron in the formation of hemoglobin. Requirements for iron are: infants, 1 mg per kilogram of body weight per day; adults, 10 to 12 mg of iron and 2 mg of copper per day; adolescents, pregnant and lactating women, 15 mg of iron and 2 mg of copper per day. Iron absorption occurs only if the iron is in a readily ionizable form. The acid of the stomach ionizes dietary iron. In gastric disease when acid production is reduced, iron absorption is usually impaired.

Storage of iron in the body is limited; therefore, foods containing it should be included in the daily diet. These foods are whole grains, egg yolk, beef (especially beef liver), fruits, green vegetables, fish, oysters, dates, figs, and beans.

At birth, a baby has a special store of iron in its body, which serves during the period of lactation. During the latter half of the first year, egg yolk and iron-bearing vegetables should be added gradually to the diet, so that as the reserve iron is depleted, fresh supplies will be available. In premature infants this special store of iron is absent; preparations of iron and copper are added to the milk.

Copper is a factor in hemoglobin formation, though it is not a part of the molecule. It must be present for the utilization of iron in hemoglobin synthesis. Since it is not a part of the hemoglobin molecule, it is believed to function as part of an enzyme-catalyzing system necessary for hemoglobin formation. It is considered an essential element in nutrition, and has a wide distribution in foods; good sources are liver, nuts, legumes, fruits, and leafy vegetables. Requirements are a daily allowance of 2 mg.

Magnesium is found in the intracellular fluid of the body and in the extracellular space of skeletal tissue, in about equal amounts in each space. Total magnesium content of the body is approximately 21 to 28 gm. Magnesium is a vital element in cell physiology because it serves as a cofactor in the metabolism of glucose, of pyruvic acid, and of adenosine triphosphate. In excessive amounts it has a depressing action on nerve impulse transmission and nerve tissue functioning in general. The daily requirement is 220 mg, readily available since cells of meat and vegetables contain large amounts.

Potassium content of the body is about 125 gm, found primarily inside the cells where it functions in association with various enzymes. It is intimately concerned with transmission of the nerve impulse, with skeletal muscle contraction, and with cardiac contraction. Excess or lack of the normal amount of potassium causes immediate malfunctioning of the heart. Daily requirements are estimated at 2 to 4 gm per day. The average diet will readily supply this amount since potassium is widespread in vegetables, fruit, and meat.

Iodine is utilized by the thyroid gland in the synthesis of thyroxin. To maintain the body store of iodine and meet the loss in metabolism, it is estimated that a normal adult requires 0.15 to 0.30 mg of iodine daily. Regions in which the supply of iodine is insufficient in water report good results in reducing the incidence of goiter by administration of iodine. Milk, leafy vegetables, and fruits grown in nongoitrous regions, fresh and canned salmon, cod, halibut, haddock, lobsters, and oysters are sources of iodine.

Cobalt is a constituent of vitamin B_{12} and is concerned with red-cell formation.

Manganese is an essential element widely distributed in plant and animal tissues. Rich sources are liver, kidney, lean meat, spinach, lettuce, and whole-grain cereals. Its specific function in the body is not clear, but it is known that it activates several important enzymes.

Zinc is essential in plant nutrition and it is evident that it is necessary in animal nutrition for it functions in enzyme systems, including carbonic anhydrase. It is universally distributed in plant and animal tissue.

Fluorine is found in bones and teeth and other tissues. In very small amounts it apparently improves tooth structure. Animal research has not provided evidence of its essentiality in the diet.

"Trace element" is the name given to a number of other elements, such as cesium and strontium, which are found in the body in minute quantities or traces. It is believed that they have important metabolic functions, as in nerve tissue, and may also be involved in some disease processes.

A diet which furnishes sufficient carbohydrate, fat, and protein may be lacking in calcium, phosphorus, iron, iodine, and copper unless vegetables and fruits are added in sufficient quantities to prevent this deficiency. The amount of calcium and phosphorus needed is relatively large, and definite provision must be made for it. The amount of iron needed is minute; but since the quantities in food materials are also minute, the sources of supply must be considered in planning the diet. If the requirements for calcium and iron are met, it is probable that all other minerals will also be supplied in the same foods.

Another aspect of mineral metabolism is its relationship to water and electrolyte balance, which involves sodium, potassium, and hydrogen in particular. This will be discussed in Chapter 22.

The Vitamins

Vitamins are organic substances present in small amounts in natural food-stuffs, which are essential for growth and normal metabolism. They are considered to be essential to all cells and are needed in the diet in minute amounts. Several members of the vitamin-B group are known to be components of respiratory enzymes and of other enzymes which act as catalysts for cell processes. Recent experiments emphasize the determination of optimum (as distinguished from merely adequate) amounts of the vitamins and their physiological effects. The vitamins constitute a *nutritional factor*, which has been defined as a single substance or any group of substances performing a specific vital function in nutrition.

The Fat-Soluble Vitamins

The fat-soluble vitamins require the presence of bile in the intestinal tract for absorption. Hence any defect in fat absorption may lead to deficiencies of the fat-soluble vitamins.

Vitamin A and its provitamins, or precursory substances, called alpha, beta, and gamma carotenes and cryptoxanthin, constitute a nutritional factor essential to growth and to the efficiency of the general nutritional processes at all ages. The precursory substances occur in yellow pigments of plants such as paprika, carrots, pumpkins, and sweet potatoes, and in the green parts of plants. These plants contain no vitamin A but do contain the precursory substances which the body can make into vitamin A, chiefly in the liver and in the wall of the small intestine. They add to the vitamin-A value of the food but not to its vitamin content. Fish-liver oils contain vitamin A as well as the precursory substances; hence, they add to the vitamin content of the foods as well as to their vitamin value.

Two forms of vitamin A are detectable—as an acid and as an aldehyde. Vitamin-A acid is responsible for the maintenance of epithelial tissues; vitamin-A aldehyde functions in the adaptational changes of the retina to light and darkness. It makes up part of the molecule of rhodopsin, the retinal pigment.

Deficiency results in disturbances associated with nervous and epithelial tissues: (1) retarded growth, (2) susceptibility to xerophthalmia, an eye condition conducive to subsequent infection and resulting blindness, (3) a dermatosis or dry skin, (4) generally impaired epithelial tissues and resulting increased susceptibility to infections of the lungs, skin, bladder, sinuses, ears, and alimentary tract, and (5) night blindness, which results from failure of the normal regeneration of visual purple after its light-induced change. (See p. 340.)

Important sources of the vitamin are milk, butter, eggs, cream cheese, green and yellow vegetables, liver oils of halibut, cod, and other fish, and liver and glandular organs in general. Carotenes can be changed to vitamin A in the liver and stored as vitamin A. This is of importance in adult nutrition. Recent studies indicate that excessively large doses of vitamin A may be harmful if taken over a long period of time; liver enlargement seen in Eskimos is attributed to high vitamin-A content of their fish diets.

Vitamin D. All of the vitamins D have antirachitic properties, but there is a difference in potency. Irradiated ergosterol (D_2) and irradiated cholesterol (D_3) are powerful antirachitic vitamins. The crystalline form which has been isolated is calciferol.

Role in Physiology. There is a close relationship of action between vitamin D and the hormone of the parathyroid gland in calcium metabolism. Vitamin D is needed for absorption of calcium from the intestine and apparently for reabsorption of phosphates in the renal tubules. It is needed for normal bone growth, and is considered a factor in the maintenance of the normal functioning of the respiratory system, in the formation of normal teeth, and in protection against dental caries. Deficiency in vitamin D has long been known to result in rickets, which may be cured by administration of vitamin D, by direct sunlight, by ultraviolet irradiation of the body, or by administration of ergosterol or similar substances produced by irradiation. The effect of ultraviolet irradiation of the skin is through its transformation of provitamin D of skin-gland secretions into vitamin D, which is absorbed by the skin. The effective rays are those that cause tanning.

Excellent sources of vitamin D are cod- (and other fish) liver oil, egg yolk, whole milk, and butter fats. It is relatively stable in ordinary cooking and also at autoclave temperatures. Since an ordinary diet is commonly somewhat deficient in this vitamin, children should be given it in concentrated form. Ingestion of excessive amounts of vitamin D results in elevated calcium levels in blood and tissue fluids and in abnormal calcification of soft tissues.

The Tocopherols. Vitamin E (antisterility) prevents sterility in both male and female rats. It is fat soluble, and its wide distribution in foods leads research workers to believe that it has no significant relationship to human sterility.

Vitamin K possesses antihemorrhagic properties. For this reason, inadequate fat absorption due to lack of bile salts is particularly significant in regard to vitamin K. It is considered a factor essential to normal clotting of blood, as it promotes the synthesis of prothrombin and proconvertin by the liver. The blood of animals having a deficiency of this vitamin shows a lowered content of prothrombin and a delayed clotting time.

Vitamin K is fat soluble and appears to be found in a great variety of foods, but knowledge regarding quantitative requirements of this vitamin is still limited. The newborn infant may have an alimentary deficiency, since the vitamin is not readily passed from mother to fetus, hence the need for giving vitamin K to the newborn and to mothers before delivery. It is also used medically to counteract undesirable effects of drugs which block its formation in the liver.

The Water-Soluble Vitamins

Vitamin B is of multiple nature and is usually referred to as "the vitamin-B complex." In general, this group of vitamins is necessary for formation of many enzymes, particularly those involved in (1) oxidation-reduction reactions and energy transformation; and (2) formation of red blood cells.

Thiamine (Vitamin B_1). ROLE IN PHYSIOLOGY. Thiamine combines with phosphate to form cocarboxylase, which plays an essential role in carbohydrate metabolism. It is essential for oxidation reactions within the cell and for transformation of the amino acid tryptophan to niacin. An adequate supply of it is necessary for normal appetite and normal motility of the digestive tract.

Good sources include wheat germ and bran; but milling, polishing, refining, etc., usually eliminate it from such foods as rice, white flour, hominy, and corn meal. Other important sources of it are tomatoes, eggs, green vegetables, and yeast. Deficiency in vitamin B_1 is known to cause symptoms of beriberi or polyneuritis, impaired gastric function, and imperfect growth. It is believed that an adequate supply of vitamin B_1—and of many other important nutritional factors as well—will be provided if half of the needed food calories are taken as milk, eggs, fruit, and vegetables and half of the breadstuffs and cereals used are wholegrain or "dark" forms.

Beriberi occurs chiefly among Oriental nations that make great use of rice as food. The disease takes a variety of forms, but the symptoms are gastrointestinal disturbances, paralysis, and atrophy of the limbs. This condition is caused by limiting the diet to polished rice. If the polishings are restored to the diet, the condition disappears; or if meat or barley is used with the polished rice, the condition is avoided.

Riboflavin (Vitamin B_2) is somewhat more heat-stable than is B_1. Phosphorylation of riboflavin is essential for its absorption in the intestine. It was first isolated from milk and named *lactoflavin* and is frequently referred to as the "flavin factor." Riboflavin is the essential component of the flavoprotein coenzymes. These coenzymes catalyze hydrogen transfer in various cell reactions leading to the oxidation of hydrogen to water. Riboflavin is thus an important factor in tissue respiration and is considered essential to normal growth and nutrition at all ages.

SOURCES. Riboflavin has a wide distribution; the best sources are milk, yeast, liver, eggs, and green, leafy vegetables.

Niacin and Niacinamide (nicotinic acid and nicotinic acid amide) are constituents of two coenzymes which play vital roles in metabolism. These coenzymes function as hydrogen and electron transfer agents in oxidation-reduction reactions.

SOURCES. Good sources of niacin include liver, poultry, and milk.

Deficiency may result in dermatitis, diarrhea, stomatitis, or glossitis. Niacin is specific for the treatment of acute pellagra.

Pyridoxine (B_6). Vitamin B_6, as pyridoxine, pyridoxal, or pyridoxamine, is important for normal growth and nutrition, and in its active form is essential for the functioning of several enzyme systems. These are the enzymes which catalyze the removal of carboxyl (–COOH) groups from amino acids and those which aid in transfer of amino (NH_2) groups from one substance to another. Pyridoxine also functions in the metabolic reactions involving fatty acids, and in the conversion of tryptophan to niacin. Deficiency produces dermatitis. It shows a distribution in foods somewhat similar to that of niacin. Meat, cereals, fish, and legumes are potent sources.

Pantothenic Acid. The vitamin pantothenic acid is a constituent of coenzyme A which combines with acetate to form acetyl coezyme A. It is essential for the intermediate metabolism of fats, carbohydrates and certain amino acids (see p. 644). Acetyl coenzyme A is involved in the formation of cholesterol and the steroid hormones, also of acetylcholine, which is essential to the transmission of nerve impulses. Excellent food sources include egg yolk, kidney, liver, broccoli, lean beef, heart. Deficiencies rarely occur in man. In animals the symptoms include growth failure, dermatitis, and nerve involvement.

Cyanocobalamin (Vitamin B_{12}), so called because of the presence of cobalt in its complex molecule, is also named the antipernicious anemia factor. The absorption of this vitamin in the gastrointestinal tract is dependent upon the presence of a gastric factor, "intrinsic factor." The intrinsic factor is a constituent of gastric mucoprotein. It is found mostly in the cardiac and fundic portions of the stomach. Hence patients who have had a total gastrectomy will also develop vitamin B_{12} deficiency and anemia, as absence of the intrinsic factor prevents absorption of vitamin B_{12} from the intestine. It is required for normal metabolism and is essential in the formation of the red blood cell. It is possibly a growth factor for children, but this is uncertain.

Good sources are liver, kidney, lean meat, milk, and cheese.

Folic Acid (Pteroylglutamic Acid). This vitamin is believed to be concerned chiefly with enzyme systems involved in red-cell formation. Its relationship metabolically to B_{12} is close, though as yet unclear. They both stimulate hematopoiesis. It is believed that folic acid can be synthesized in the intestine, and that it is concerned with the use of proteins for growth and development. Good sources are fresh green leafy vegetables, legumes, and liver.

Other B-Complex Factors. *Biotin.* It is thought to function in metabolic processes, but its specific role in the human is not clear. It probably is not a vitamin.

Inositol, like biotin, is found in the vitamin-B complex, but its role as a vitamin is not clear. It can be synthesized in the intestine of most animals and possibly also in man. It may act in the utilization of carbon dioxide in certain chemical reactions within the cell. Good sources are liver, heart, yeast, and peanuts.

Choline is not a true vitamin; however, its role in nutrition is essential. Choline is a constituent of the lecithins and is also importantly concerned in the metabolism of fats. In the form of acetylcholine, it is essential as the chemical mediator of nerve activity. Nerve tissue (brain), egg yolk, and the germ layer of the kernel of grains are good sources of choline. Deficiencies in experimental animals show tissue damage and abnormal accumulation of fat in the liver particularly, and also in the heart and blood vessels.

Ascorbic acid (vitamin C) has long been known to be essential in the prevention of scurvy. Early records of sea voyages reveal many epidemics of scurvy, and it was reported from Austria and Russia during World War I. The cause is lack of fresh fruit and vegetables; the prevention is the use of these. Early cures were through the use of citrus fruit juices. Laboratory experiments on animals and men prove conclusively that scurvy is due to lack of vitamin C in the diet.

Role in Physiology. More recently vitamin C has been shown to be of importance in tissue respiration, which is decreased in scurvy. Shortage of vitamin C is shown to impair general nutrition, to prevent healing of bone wounds, and to be a contributory factor in capillary fragility and the general resistance of the body. Vitamin C is essential for the formation and maintenance of the intercellular cement and collagen. It is necessary for the integrity of capillary membranes and plays an important part in the formation of blood cells in bone marrow. It is also an important factor in the healing of wounds. The adrenal cortex contains a large quantity of vitamin C, which suggests its use in the metabolic synthesis of the steroid hormones. A liberal daily intake of vitamin C throughout life is recommended. The relationship of deficiency to dental caries is undetermined, but the soundness of teeth and their supporting bones and gums is believed to be dependent upon the amount of vitamin C supplied by the food.

Sources. The citrus fruits (oranges, lemons, grapefruit), tomatoes (raw or canned), and broccoli are rich sources. All fresh vegetables are sources. It is the least resistant of the vitamins; heating and drying usually destroy it. Ascorbic acid is sensitive to oxidation, particularly in alkaline solutions; this destruction is hastened by contact with metals such as iron and copper. There is considerable loss during storage, canning, or drying, and in cooking.

Symptoms of scurvy are loss of weight, pallor, weakness, breathlessness, palpitation of the heart, swelling of the gums, loosening of the teeth, pains in the bones and joints, edema, nervousness, and slight hemorrhages appearing as red spots under the skin and forming hidden bleeding places in the muscles and internal organs. The heart hypertrophies and shows degenerative changes, which often cause sudden death.

Fat-Soluble

Vitamins	Sources	Effects of Cooking	General Effects of Optimum Intake	Evidences of Deficiency
A	Milk, butter, eggs, fish-liver oils, green vegetables, yellow vegetables. (provitamins)	Resists heat in absence of air; readily destroyed by oxidation	A factor in— Decreasing susceptibility to skin infections Preserving general health and vigor Effecting chemistry necessary for vision Promoting growth	Failure to gain weight, susceptibility to xerophthalmia, night blindness, dry skin, impaired epithelial tissues, increased incidence of respiratory diseases and of skin (toad skin), ear and sinus infections, inflammations and infections of alimentary and urinary tracts, degenerative changes in nervous tissues
D	Egg yolk, whole milk, butter, fish-liver oils	Slight; relatively stable	A factor in well-developed bone and teeth, calcium and phosphorus metabolism	Rickets (in children) Osteomalacia (in adults), bone demineralization
E	Seeds of plants, eggs, lettuce, spinach, meat, wide distribution	Unusually heat resistant	A factor in normal gestation in rats	Sterility in rats
K	Wide distribution, especially green leaves	Destroyed by prolonged heating, by temperatures higher than boiling	A factor in normal functioning of liver and normal clotting time	Delayed clotting time
B₁ Thiamine	Whole-grain cereals, legumes, eggs, pork	Destroyed by prolonged heating, by temperatures higher than boiling	A factor in— Normal carbohydrate metabolism Maintenance of normal appetite, digestion, absorption	Beriberi, polyneuritis Stunted growth of children, lowered appetite, reduced intestinal motility
B₂ Riblofavin	Milk, eggs, green vegetables, liver, heart	Relatively heat stable	A factor in— Tissue respiration Normal growth and nutrition and vitality at all ages	Dermatitis, pellagra (in part) Well-defined eye lesions

	Liver, milk, poultry	Destroyed by high heat	Essential in metabolic processes which release energy	Low nutritional level
Niacin	Liver, milk, poultry	Destroyed by high heat	Essential in metabolic processes which release energy	Florid type of dermatitis (experimental pellagra in rats)
B$_{6}$ Pyridoxine Pyridoxal Pyridoxamine	Whole-grain cereals, yeast, milk, eggs, pork, liver, legumes	Unusually heat resistant	A factor in normal metabolism of fats, amino acids	Nervousness, irritability, and insomnia
B$_{12}$ Cyanocobalamin	Liver, kidney, lean meat, milk, cheese	Relatively heat stable	A factor in red cell formation	Pernicious anemia
Pantothenic acid	Egg yolk, kidney, liver, yeast, broccoli, lean meat, heart	Destroyed by high heat	Essential for synthesis of acetyl coenzyme A, metabolism of fats, carbohydrates, and certain amino acids; A factor in— Functioning of enzyme systems	Rarely occurs in man
Folic acid	Fresh green leafy vegetables, liver, legumes		Essential in metabolic processes—growth and development; A factor in—	Anemia
C Ascorbic acid	Citrus fruits (raw or canned), tomatoes (raw or canned), broccoli	Readily destroyed by heat, especially slow cooking	Red cell formation; Normal integrity of capillaries; Normal development of teeth and maintenance of health of gums; Healing of wounds and protection against infections; Normal cellular chemistry of all tissues	Low nutritional level; Fragility of capillary networks; Scurvy and possibly predisposition to dental caries and systemic type of pyorrhea

Water-Soluble

It is obvious that the major function of the vitamins is in relation to enzyme functioning. In the case of the B vitamins, it is known that they make up part of the molecular structure of coenzymes, or cofactors, which accept atoms or groups of atoms which are removed from a substrate. These are listed in the accompanying coenzyme table:

	Coenzyme	*Function*	*Vitamin*
(DPN)	Diphosphopyridine nucleotide ⎫	As hydrogen acceptors	Niacinamide
(TPN)	Triphosphopyridine nucleotide ⎭	in dehydrogenases	
(FMN)	Flavin mononucleotide ⎫	As hydrogen acceptors	Riboflavin
(FAD)	Flavin adenine dinucleotide ⎭	in aerobic dehydrogenases	
	Pyridoxal phosphate	As transaminases, amino acid decarboxylases	Pyridoxine
	Thiamine pyrophosphate	As cocarboxylase	Thiamine
(CoA)	Coenzyme A	In condensing enzymes, fatty acid utilization, acetate transfer	Pantothenic acid

ACCESSORY DIET FACTORS

In addition to the foodstuffs proper, foods contain numerous substances which add to their attractiveness, stimulate appetite, and increase secretion of digestive fluids. These may be classified as flavors and condiments, and stimulants. The first group includes the various oils and esters that give odor and taste to food, and the condiments such as salt, pepper, and mustard. Stimulants include tea, coffee, meat extracts, and alcohol. Tea and coffee owe their stimulating effect to caffeine. It prevents sleepiness, probably because of its action in raising blood pressure. Cocoa and chocolate with the addition of sugar contain nourishment in the form of carbohydrate, fat, and protein. Their stimulating effects are due to theobromine. Meat extracts contain secretagogues which stimulate the gastric glands. Alcohol is psychologically stimulating to the appetite of many individuals. It stimulates the flow of acid gastric juice by its action on the brain centers regulating gastric secretion. Alcohol is metabolized therefore as a source of energy similar to fats and carbohydrates. Chronic excessive alcohol ingestion causes atrophic changes in the gastric and intestinal mucosa thus interfering with digestion and absorption.

All fruits and vegetables, to varying degrees, contain cellulose, which is a nondigestible but necessary part of the diet, for it creates bulk and facilitates movement of material through the intestinal tract and from the body.

DIGESTIVE PROCESSES

Digestion includes all the changes, physical and chemical, which food undergoes in the body, making it absorbable. In some instances no change is necessary; water, minerals, and certain carbohydrates in fruits are ready to be absorbed. In other instances cooking processes initiate chemical changes in food before it enters the body, for example, changing starch to dextrin, partially splitting fats into glycerol and fatty acids, and changing some proteins to the first stages of their hydrolytic products. Cooking in many instances improves the appearance, odor, and taste of food, and these changes stimulate the end organs of the optic and olfactory nerves and the taste buds, causing a reflex stimulation of the digestive mechanisms. Cooking also tends to destroy microorganisms which would be harmful to the body.

The digestive processes are controlled by the nervous and hormonal mechanisms. Any strong emotion which affects the nervous system unpleasantly inhibits the secretion of the digestive fluids and interferes with digestion, often checking the appetite and even preventing the taking of food. On the other hand, pleasurable sensations aid digestion, hence the value of attractively served food, pleasant surroundings, and cheerful conversation.

Mechanical digestion includes the various physical processes that occur in the alimentary canal. It serves the following purposes: taking food in and moving it along through the alimentary canal just rapidly enough to allow the required chemical changes to take place in each part; lubricating the food by adding the mucin and water secreted by the glands of the alimentary canal; liquefying the food by mixing it with the various digestive juices; and grinding the food into small particles, thereby increasing the amount of surface to come in contact with the digestive fluids.

Chemical digestion is essentially a process of hydrolysis which is dependent upon the presence of enzymes. An example of hydrolysis (hydrolytic cleavage) is the splitting of maltose into glucose (also called dextrose) under the influence of maltase.

$$C_{12}H_{22}O_{11} + H_2O \rightarrow C_6H_{12}O_6 + C_6H_{12}O_6$$

Necessity for Chemical Digestion. Chemical digestion is necessary because foods in general cannot pass through animal membranes, and the tissues cannot use them; hence, they must be reduced to smaller molecules and to such substances as the tissues can use, i.e. (1) simple sugars, resulting from the hydrolysis of all carbohydrate foods; (2) glycerol and fatty acids, resulting from the hydrolysis of fats; and (3) amino acids, resulting from the hydrolysis of proteins.

Agents of Chemical Digestion. Hydrolytic cleavages similar to those of digestion can be brought about in several ways. Boiling foodstuffs with acids, treating them with alkali, or subjecting them to superheated steam will accomplish these changes. The *remarkable* fact is that strong acids and high temperatures, or both, are necessary to produce these changes in the laboratory, whereas in the digestive tract they take place at body temperature and are due to the enzymes present in the digestive juices.

Enzymes Functioning in the Digestive Pathway

The enzymes that bring about chemical digestion in the alimentary tract are exoenzymes—organic catalysts which are produced by cells, secreted into the digestive tract where they act. They may be classified as follows:

1. The Sugar-Splitting Enzymes. The glucosidases, which hydrolyze disaccharides to monosaccharides. Examples: maltase splits maltose to glucose; sucrase splits cane sugar to glucose and fructose; and lactase splits milk sugar (lactose) to glucose and galactose.

2. The Amylolytic, or Starch-Splitting, Enzymes. Examples: salivary amylase and pancreatic amylase cause hydrolysis of starch.

3. The Lipolytic, or Fat-Splitting, Enzymes. Example: lipase found in the pancreatic secretion causes hydrolysis of fat.

4. The Proteolytic, or Protein-Splitting, Enzymes. Examples: pepsin of gastric juice and trypsin and chymotrypsin of pancreatic juice, which cause hydrolysis of the proteins.

Changes the Food Undergoes in the Mouth

Mastication. When solid food is taken into the mouth, its comminution is immediately begun. It is cut and ground by the teeth, being pushed between them again and again by the muscular contractions of the cheeks and the movements of the tongue, until the whole is thoroughly crushed.

Insalivation. During the process of mastication saliva is poured in large quantities into the mouth and, mixing with the food, lubricates, moistens, and reduces it to a softened mass known as a *bolus*, which can be readily swallowed.

Secretion of Saliva. The nerve supply of the salivary glands is derived in part from the craniosacral and in part from the thoracolumbar divisions of the autonomic system. Both sets of nerves carry secretory and vasomotor fibers. The cranial nerves carry vasodilator fibers and, when stimulated by the sight or smell of food, (1) dilate the blood vessels, increasing the volume of the gland, and (2) cause the glands to produce a secretion that is copious in amount and watery in consistency.

The consistency of saliva depends in part on the relative number of serous and mucous cells which are secreting. Serous cells produce a thin watery secretion while the mucous cells produce a thick secretion. The thoracolumbar nerves carry vasoconstrictor fibers, and perhaps are relatively unimportant for controlling normal function of the salivary glands. However, if the sympathetic fibers are stimulated, vasoconstriction occurs and a scanty, viscid saliva is produced. Under normal conditions, the secretion of saliva is the result of stimulation of the secretory nerves by the smell, taste, or sight of food. Obviously, the taste buds of the tongue, fauces, and cheeks are the sense organs which are stimulated by the presence of food in the mouth.

Saliva. Saliva is secreted by the salivary glands—parotid, submaxillary, and sublingual—and by the numerous minute buccal glands of the mucosa of the mouth.

It consists of a large amount of water (some 99.5 per cent) containing some protein material, mucin, inorganic salts, and *salivary amylase*. It has a specific gravity of about 1.005 and is nearly neutral in reaction (pH about 6.4 to 7.0).

Although the amount of saliva secreted per day varies considerably, an average amount is from 1 to 1.5 liters. Substances in saliva include inorganic salts in solution, chlorides, carbonates, and phosphates of sodium, calcium, and potassium.

The other substances are organic, mainly mucin, salivary amylases, serum albumin and globulin and urea. The calcium carbonate and phosphate in combination with organic material may be deposited on the teeth as tartar, especially if the saliva is alkaline and contains considerable mucin. Occasionally these salts may be also deposited in the ducts of the salivary glands.

The functions of saliva are to soften and moisten the food, assisting in mastication and deglutition; to coat the food with mucin, lubricating it and ensuring a smooth passage along the esophagus; to moisten or liquefy dry and solid food, providing a necessary step in the process of stimulating the taste buds, as taste sensations play a part in the secretion of gastric juice; to digest starch by means of salivary amylase.

Salivary Amylase. Salivary amylase changes starch to dextrins and maltose. The process of reducing starch to maltose is a gradual one, consisting of a series of hydrolytic changes which take place in successive stages and result in a number of intermediate compounds. The change is best effected at the temperature of the body, in a neutral solution. Boiled starch is changed more rapidly and completely than raw, but food is rarely retained in the mouth long enough for the saliva to do more than begin the digestion of starch.

Deglutition, or **swallowing,** is divided into three stages which correspond to the three regions—mouth, pharynx, and esophagus—through which the food passes. The *first stage* consists of the passage of the bolus of food through the fauces. Contractions of the constrictor muscles of the pharynx force the bolus along. The *second stage* consists of the passage of the bolus through the laryngeal pharynx. During this stage, the respiratory opening into the larynx is closed by the approximation of the vocal folds which close the glottis, by the elevation of the larynx, and by contraction of the muscles of deglutition. The parts are crowded together by the descent of the base of the tongue, the lifting of the larynx, and the coming together of the vocal folds.

The *third stage* consists in the passage of the bolus through the esophagus. Apparently the consistency of the food affects this stage of the process. Solid or semisolid food is forced down the esophagus by a peristaltic movement and requires from four to eight seconds for passage from mouth to stomach. About half of this time is taken up in the passage through the esophagus, and the remainder is spent in transit through the cardiac orifice of the stomach. Liquid or very soft food is shot through the esophagus, which is reflexly inhibited, and arrives at the lower end in about 0.1 second. It may pass into the stomach at once or may be held in the esophagus for moments, depending on the condition of the cardiac sphincter. Repeated deglutition causes the tension of the muscles which function as a cardiac sphincter to diminish progressively, until they become completely relaxed, and food passes into the stomach. Following this, relaxation finally disappears and the sphincter becomes more contracted than usual and remains so for considerable time.

Summary. During the process of mastication, insalivation, and deglutition the food is reduced to a soft, pulpy condition, and any starch it contains may begin to be changed into sugar.

Vomiting is controlled by a nerve center in the medulla which can be stimulated by chemical and physical qualities of the tissue fluid in the center and by nerve impulses which reach it. Under ordinary circumstances the contractions of the cardiac "sphincter" prevent the regurgitation of food. During vomiting the stomach, esophagus, and esophagogastric junction (so-called cardiac sphincter) are all relaxed. Spasmodic contractions of the abdominal muscles synchronously with contraction of the diaphragm cause phasic increases in intragastric pressure, which results literally in squeezing out the stomach contents in spurts. It is wrong to think that the stomach muscles contract or show reverse peristalsis; the stomach behaves passively like a water-filled rubber bulb which spurts when it is compressed. After the stomach contents have been evacuated, the pyloric sphincter may also relax and permit the duodenal contents to be evacuated. This is usually preceded by a sensation of nausea and excessive salivation. Vomiting is a reflex act brought about by mechanical irritation of the throat or by irritating substances in the stomach and duodenum, and by pain, motion sickness, and certain emotions such as fear and repulsion.

Changes the Food Undergoes in the Stomach

The food which enters the stomach is delayed there by the contraction of the sphincter muscles at the cardiac and pyloric openings. The cavity of the stomach is always the size of its contents, which means that when there is no food in it,

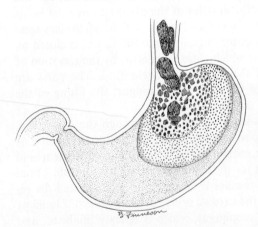

Figure 20–1. Diagram of stomach showing in fine stippling the food which first entered the stomach and has undergone digestive processes. Size of dots indicates progressive physical and chemical breakdown of food particles.

it is contracted, but when food enters, it expands just enough to hold it. Within a few minutes after the entrance of food small contractions start in the middle region of the stomach and run toward the pylorus. These contractions are regular and in the pyloric region become more forcible as digestion progresses.

Weak rippling peristaltic movements, called *mixing waves*, pass over the stomach about every 15 to 25 seconds. As a result of these movements the food in the prepyloric and pyloric portions is macerated, mixed with the acid gastric fluid, and reduced to a thin liquid mass called *chyme*. At certain intervals the pyloric sphincter relaxes, and the wave of contraction forces some of the chyme into the duodenum. The fundic end of the stomach is less actively concerned with these movements but serves as a reservoir for food. The food at the fundic end may remain undisturbed for an hour or more and thus escape rapid mixture with the gastric fluid, which, therefore, penetrates slowly to the interior of the mass; hence salivary digestion may continue for a time. As the chyme is gradually forced into the duodenum, the pressure of the fundus forces the food into the pyloric end.

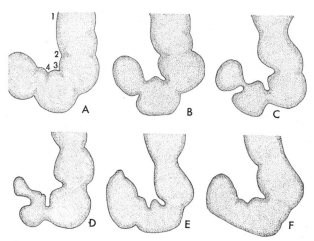

Figure 20–2. Diagrams to show peristalsis in the stomach. Locate *1, 2, 3, 4* in succeeding figures to trace a peristaltic wave over the stomach.

The time required for gastric digestion depends upon the nature of the food eaten. Liquids taken on an empty stomach pass through the pylorus promptly. Small test meals may remain from one to two hours, but average meals probably stay in the stomach from three to four and one-half hours. The shape of the stomach ("fishhook," "steerhorn") is an important factor in determing evacuation time. It has been demonstrated that emptying time was about 50 per cent faster in individuals with a "steerhorn" stomach than those with a "fishhook" (or J-shaped) stomach.

Shortly after ingestion of a meal, peristaltic waves begin to traverse the lower stomach. These waves begin about the middle of the stomach, and sweep downward, usually passing over the pyloric sphincter and often into the duodenum. The fundic part of the stomach contains the meal and functions as a storage chamber. While it shows no peristaltic waves, it does show progressive increase in muscle tension. The increasing tension forces food toward the lower end of the stomach where it comes in contact with the peristaltic waves.

Emptying of the stomach depends *almost entirely* on a pressure gradient between the stomach and duodenum. For material to leave the stomach, the *intragastric* pressure must be greater than the *intraduodenal*. The intragastric pressure is due to (1) gastric tonus changes and (2) head pressure of the peristaltic wave. The pyloric sphincter *does not* control evacuation. The sphincter may actually be relaxed during most of the digestion period *without* emptying occurring. When the intragastric pressure is adequately greater than the intraduodenal, about 2 to 5 ml of gastric content is passed into the duodenum with each peristaltic wave.

When the intraduodenal pressure exceeds the intragastric pressure, reflex constriction of the pyloric sphincter prevents the duodenal content from entering the stomach. *The major role of the pyloric sphincter is to prevent regurgitation.* With the exception of the rectal sphincter, the major role of all sphincters of the digestive tract is to prevent retrograde movement of digestive contents.

The secretion of gastric juice is constant. Even in the period of fasting there is a small continuous secretion, but during the act of eating and throughout the period of digestion the rate of secretion is greatly increased.

Gastric juice is produced by the mucous membrane of the stomach. The complete cycle of the activities of the gastric glands is frequently divided into three phases: the *cephalic*, the *gastric*, and the *intestinal*. The *cephalic phase* of gastric secretion refers to reflex stimulation of the gastric glands through the central nervous system by the sight, smell, or taste of food. The *gastric phase* refers to all of the activities of the gastric glands, which are brought about by conditions within the stomach itself. It includes the gastric mechanisms as well as local chemical stimulation by secretagogues (any substance which stimulates secretion by a gland), which occur as a result of the contact of the gastric mucosa with the products of digestion and the stimulation caused by distention of the stomach. The *intestinal phase* of gastric secretion is believed to be due to the presence of food in the small intestine, which may stimulate the gastric glands through a hormone or secretagogue. Fats inhibit gastric secretion, by stimulating the production of intestinal hormones, e.g., *enterogastrone*.

Gastric juice is secreted by the gastric glands lining the mucous membrane of the stomach. It is a thin, colorless, or nearly colorless liquid with an acid reaction and a specific gravity of about 1.003 to 1.008. The acid which is secreted by the parietal cell has a pH of about 0.9. However, after reaching the lumen of the stomach, the acid is partially neutralized by the gastric mucus, the more alkaline saliva, and the alkaline intestinal content which may be regurgitated into the stomach. This reduction in acidity results in a gastric content of about pH 2.5. The quantity secreted depends upon the amount and kind of food to be digested, possibly an average of 1.5 to 2.5 liters per day. Upon analysis it is found to be a watery secretion containing some protein, some mucin, and inorganic salts; but the essential constituents are hydrochloric acid and one or possibly two enzymes—pepsin and gastric lipase.

Hydrochloric Acid. It is believed that the parietal (acid, or oxyntic) cells of the gastric glands secrete the hydrochloric acid from chlorides found in the blood. The chloride ion combines with the hydrogen ion and is then secreted upon the free surface of the stomach as hydrochloric acid. In normal gastric juice it is found in the proportion of about 0.5 per cent. It serves to activate pepsinogen and convert it to pepsin; to provide an acid medium, which is necessary for the pepsin to carry on its work; to swell the protein fibers, thus giving easier access to pepsin; to help in the inversion of cane sugar, which is the easiest of the disaccharides to hydrolyze; and to destroy many organisms that enter the stomach.

Excessive secretion of hydrochloric acid, or gastric hyperacidity, is often found associated with peptic ulceration of the duodenum, and with some forms of gastritis, but there is little evidence that there is a cause-effect relationship between hypersecretion and ulcer disease. Secretion of hydrochloric acid below normal, or hyposecretion, is associated with other forms of gastritis and frequently with carcinoma of the stomach. Acid secretion is totally absent in pernicious anemia.

Pepsin is formed in the pyloric glands and the chief cells of the gastric glands. It is present in these cells in the form of a zymogen, an antecedent inactive substance called propepsin or pepsinogen, which is quickly changed to active pepsin by the action of hydrochloric acid.

Pepsin (gastric protease) is a proteolytic enzyme requiring an acid medium in which to function. It has the property of hydrolyzing proteins through several stages into polypeptides. This action is preparatory to the more complete hydrolysis that takes place in the intestine under the influence of trypsin (pancreatic protease) and various peptidases, for polypeptides are not absorbed but undergo a further hydrolysis to amino acids.

Various observers have described other enzymes in addition to the gastric protease, but the evidence regarding these is inconclusive. It is probable that the salivary amylase swallowed with the food continues the digestion of starchy material in the fundus for some time. Regarding the fats, it is believed that they undergo no digestion in the stomach. They are set free from their mixture with other foods by the digestive action of the gastric fluid; they are liquified by the heat of the body and are scattered through the chyme as a coarse emulsion by the movements of the stomach, all of which prepare them for digestion. Emulsified fats such as cream may be acted upon to a limited extent by a third enzyme called *gastric lipase*, but the acid condition of the stomach contents prevents any considerable change of this sort. This enzyme is more important in the child than in the adult.

Summary. The stomach serves as a place for temporary storage and maintains a gradual delivery to the intestine; it also serves as a place for the continuation of the salivary digestion of starch, the beginning of the digestion of proteins and perhaps fats, and germicidal activity. While the food is in the pyloric region it is subjected to the acidity of the gastric fluid.

Inhibition of Gastric Digestion. The secretion of gastric fluid is inhibited by stimulation of the thoracolumbar system, so that various emotions and also a distaste for food may delay digestion. Secretion is also inhibited by active exercise soon after a meal, because active exercise increases the amount of blood in the skeletal muscles and decreases the supply to the stomach. When gastric digestion is much delayed, organisms are likely to cause fermentation of the sugars, producing gas which may cause distress.

Changes the Food Undergoes in the Small Intestine

The chyme entering the duodenum after an ordinary meal is normally free from coarse particles of food and is acid in reaction; both the hydrochloric acid and the lactic acid produced by fermentation contribute to this condition. Much of the food is undigested. The proteins are partly digested; some progress has been made in hydrolyzing starch; fats have been liquefied and mixed with other food but probably have not been hydrolyzed themselves. If milk is part of the diet, it will have been curdled and redissolved. It is in the small intestine that this mixture undergoes the greatest digestive changes. These changes, which constitute intestinal digestion, are effected by the movements of the intestine, the pancreatic fluid, the succus entericus, or secretion of the intestinal glands, and the bile.

It is convenient to describe the secretion and digestive action of these three fluids separately, but it must be remembered that they act simultaneously. The pancreatic fluid and the bile enter the intestine about 7 to 10 cm beyond the pylorus, and therefore, the foods in the small intestine throughout its length are subjected to a mixture of pancreatic fluid, bile, and small intestinal fluid.

Movements of the small intestine are described as peristaltic, rhythmical, and pendular.

Peristalsis may be defined as a wave of dilation brought about by the contraction of longitudinal muscles, followed by a wave of constriction caused by the contraction of circular muscles. The purpose is to pass the food slowly forward. *Peristaltic waves* pass very slowly along short distances of the small intestine, with an occasional rapid wave known as the *peristaltic rush*, which moves the food along greater distances. The stimulus seems to be partly mechanical, since experimental swallowing of a tube to which a small balloon is attached initiates peristalsis and propulsion of the balloon through the intestine.

The rhythmical movements consist of a series of local constrictions of the intestinal wall which occur rhythmically at points where masses of food lie. These constrictions divide the food into segments. Within a few seconds each of these segments is halved, and the corresponding halves of adjoining segments unite. Again constrictions occur, and these newly formed segments are divided, and the halves re-form. In this way every particle of food is brought into intimate contact with the intestinal mucosa and is thoroughly mixed with the digestive fluids.

Pendular movements are constrictions which move onward or backward for short distances, gradually moving the chyme forward and backward over short distances in the small intestine. These may be seen in the rabbit and other small mammals, but their presence is doubted in the human.

The varied muscular movements of the small intestine increase the blood supply, bringing materials for secretion and removing absorbed materials faster. They assist the minute glands in emptying their secretion, mix the digestive fluids and food intimately, and bring fresh absorbable material constantly to the mucosa, thereby increasing absorption.

Secretion of Pancreatic Juice. Pancreatic secretion, like gastric secretion, consists of two parts: a neurally induced secretion, caused by the secretory fibers in the vagus and splanchnic nerves, and a chemically induced secretion, caused by the action of the hormones *secretin* and *pancreozynin*. The acid gastric fluid and the products of partially digested proteins upon reaching the duodenum

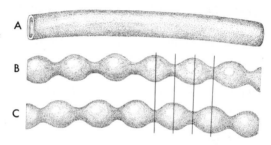

Figure 20–3. Three diagrams of a portion of the small intestine to show rhythmical movements. The small straight lines indicate the same area of the intestine at different intervals.

and jejunum stimulate the production of these hormones. They are taken by way of the blood to the pancreas where they cause secretion of large quantities of fluid rich in enzymes. It is thought that the neurally induced secretion provides pancreatic fluid in the early stages of intestinal digestion and that the chemical secretion maintains the flow until all the stomach contents reach the duodenum.

Pancreatic Juice. The *nervous secretion* of pancreatic juice is thick, and rich in enzymes and proteins. The *chemical secretion* is thin, watery, and is also rich in enzymes. Pancreatic juice is alkaline and becomes more so with increasing rates of secretion. This is due to an increase in bicarbonates and at the same time a decrease in chloride concentration. These two ions vary in a reciprocal manner, so that the *sum* of the concentrations of these two ions is practically constant.

Pancreatic juice contains three groups of enzymes, pancreatic protease or trypsin, amylase, and lipase. The amount of pancreatic juice secreted each day varies between 600 and 800 ml.

The proteolytic enzyme, trypsin, under favorable conditions may hydrolyze the protein molecule to its constituent amino acids. Trypsin is secreted in an inactive form called *trypsinogen* and is activated by *enterokinase*, an enzyme that is secreted by glands of the small intestine.

Trypsin hydrolyzes proteins into polypeptides and some amino acids.

Another proteolytic enzyme, *chymotrypsin*, also is present in pancreatic juice. It is secreted in an inactive form, *chymotrypsinogen*, which is activated by the enzyme, trypsin.

Nuclease is a nucleic acid-splitting enzyme which results in the production of nucleotides—the subunits which form nucleic acids. There has been some question about its presence in pancreatic juice.

The amylolytic enzyme (amylase) is similar to salivary amylase in action. It causes hydrolysis of starch with the production of maltose. The starchy food that escapes digestion in the mouth and stomach becomes mixed with this enzyme and continues under its action until the colic valve is reached. Maltose is further acted upon by the maltase of the intestinal secretion and is hydrolyzed to glucose.

The lipolytic enzyme (lipase) is capable of hydrolyzing fats to glycerol and fatty acids. The process of hydrolysis is preceded by emulsification, in which bile salts play a leading role. The lipase splits some of the fats to fatty acids and glycerol; emulsification increases the surface of fat exposed to the chemical action of the lipase and is a mechanical preparation for the further action of lipase. The glycerol and fatty acids produced by the action of the lipase are absorbed by the epithelium of the intestine. It is thought that the fatty acids form soluble and diffusible compounds with the bile salts and are absorbed in this form. After absorption the fatty acids and glycerol again combine to form fat, but is it probable that they combine in such proportions as to make fat which is characteristic of man. The action of lipase is said to be reversible; i.e., it causes both the splitting of the fats and the synthesis of the split products, not only in the intestine but in the various tissues, during the metabolism or the storage of fat. Lipases are found in blood and in many of the tissues. Although lipases are also secreted by the small intestine, that secreted by the pancreas accounts for about 80 per cent of all fat digestion. For this reason impaired fat digestion is an important result of pancreatic dysfunction.

The intestinal secretion (succus entericus) is a clear, yellowish fluid, and amounts to about 2 to 3 liters per day. Its composition varies; in the duodenum and jejunum it is slightly acid. The acidity is greatest in the duodenum and in the ileum the secretion is practically neutral. In the duodenal bulb and the region down to the ampulla of Vater it is almost entirely mucous. Extracts of the walls of the small intestine have been found to contain four or five enzymes which influence intestinal digestion to a marked extent. The enzymes are to be found in the secretion, and their actions are as follows.

Enterokinase is an enzyme which activates the trypsin of the pancreatic fluid; aminopeptidase, carboxypeptidase, and dipeptidase are enzymes which hydrolyze peptides to amino acids, thus completing the work begun by pepsin and trypsin.

Maltase acts upon the products formed in the digestion of starches, i.e., maltose, and hydrolyzes them to glucose. *Sucrase* acts upon sucrose and hydrolyzes it to glucose and fructose. *Lactase* acts upon lactose and hydrolyzes it to glucose and galactose. This hydrolysis is necessary because disaccharides cannot be used by the tissues, but in the form of simple sugars they are readily utilized.

Nucleases act upon the nucleic acid component of nucleoproteins.

Bile is formed in the liver and is an alkaline fluid, pH about 6.8 to 7.7, the specific gravity of which varies from about 1.010 to 1.050. Approximately 800 to 1,000 ml are secreted daily. It is usually yellow, brownish yellow, or olive green in color. The color of bile is determined by the respective amounts of the bile pigments, (1) biliverdin and (2) bilirubin, that are present. Bile consists of water, bile pigments, bile acids, bile salts, cholesterol, lecithin, and neutral fats.

The bile acids are glycocholic and taurocholic, occurring as sodium glyco- cholate and sodium taurocholate. These salts are alternately poured into the duodenum, then reabsorbed, and reappear in the bile. Thus, by continued cir- culation, the bile salts repeat their function many times. This enterohepatic circulation helps to conserve bile salts, as each circuit is accomplished with only about 10 to 15 per cent loss. Synthesis of new bile salts from materials in the diet makes up the deficit. The mucous membranes of the bile ducts and gallbladder add a mucinlike protein called nucleoalbumin, which, together with some mucin, gives bile its mucilaginous consistency.

Secretion of bile is continuous, but the amount varies, increasing when the blood flow is increased and vice versa. It is thought that the presence of bile in the intestine stimulates secretion in the liver and that this is due to the bile salts, which act as a choleretic. Bile enters the duodenum only during the period of digestion. Between these periods, resistance to the entrance of bile in to the duo- denum is high, so that the bile is diverted into the gallbladder, where it becomes concentrated by loss of water. Apparently the ejection of chyme into the duodenum causes the contraction of the gallbladder and ejection of bile. The hormone cholecystokinin, formed by cells of the duodenal mucosa, mediates this response.

1. DIGESTIVE SECRETION. Bile salts are essential for the action of lipase. Mixtures of bile and pancreatic fluid split the fats more rapidly than pancreatic fluid alone. Bile salts lower surface tension, which aids in the emulsification of fats with concurrent production of a greater surface area which enables lipase and other enzymes to act more effectively. Bile salts are also important for ab- sorption of fat.

Bile is essential for the absorption of vitamin K and other fat-soluble vitamins. It also stimulates intestinal motility and neutralizes the acid chyme, creating a favorable hydrogen ion concentration for pancreatic and intestinal enzyme ac- tivity; bile salts help to keep cholesterol in solution.

2. EXCRETION. The bile is an excretory medium for toxins, metals, and cholesterol. The liver cells excrete the bile pigments that are brought to them by the blood, just as the kidney cells remove the urea from the blood. The choles- terol of bile is probably a waste product of cellular disintegration.

3. ANTISEPTIC. It was formerly believed to have an antiputrefactive action, but it is now thought that the greater amount of putrefaction in the absence of

bile is brought about by the action of bacteria on proteins and carbohydrates which have remained undigested because of the protective covering of insoluble fat which is found on them in the absence of bile.

GALLSTONES. Cholesterol may become so concentrated in the gallbladder that it tends to crystallize out, and these crystals form gallstones. Inflammatory conditions, which are often due to the typhoid and colon bacilli or to a change in the character of the bile, may cause this crystallization. Gallstones are usually formed in the gallbladder. Their passage through the cystic and common bile ducts often causes severe pain, called gallbladder colic. They may plug the duct and cause obstructive jaundice.

JAUNDICE. When the flow of bile through the bile duct is interfered with, bilirubin is not removed from the blood but is carried to all parts of the body, producing a condition of jaundice, which is characterized by a yellow discoloration of the skin and of the whites of the eyes. The urine is of a greenish hue because of the extra quantity of pigment eliminated by the kidneys, and the stools are grayish in hue, owing to the lack of bile. Jaundice may also be due to the incapacity of the liver cells to eliminate pigments, or to the presence of excessive amounts of bilirubin as in the case of too rapid destruction (hemolysis) of erythrocytes.

Action of organisms in the small intestine hydrolyzes carbohydrates and proteins constantly. Fermentation of the carbohydrates gives rise to organic acids, such as lactic and acetic, but none of the products of this fermentation is considered toxic. On the other hand, the putrefaction of proteins gives rise to a number of end products that are toxic when present in large amounts. Under normal conditions and on a mixed diet, carbohydrate fermentation is the characteristic action of the organisms in the small intestine, whereas protein putrefaction occurs in the large intestine. These microorganisms are in many ways beneficial to the body. They synthesize vitamins which may be absorbed; their presence in the intestinal tract is not irritating and at the same time it prevents other, potentially harmful organisms which might be ingested or present in small amounts from multiplying and causing infection.

The time required for digestion in the small intestine is influenced by many factors. It depends largely on the varying proportions of the different foods included in a meal. Twenty to thirty-six hours are required for the passage of ingested food material through the gastrointestinal tract of adults who are on a mixed diet. There is considerable variation among individuals, and usually not all of the residue from a single meal is evacuated at the same time. In diarrheal conditions the time is much shortened.

According to observations made upon a patient with a fistula at the end of the small intestine, food begins to pass into the large intestine from two to five hours after eating, and it requires nine hours or more after eating before the last of a meal has passed the colic valve.

Hormones of the Intestinal Pathway

Gastrin is secreted by the pyloric mucosa and excites the fundic glands of the stomach to active secretion of acid.

Enterogastrone is secreted by the duodenal mucosa and inhibits gastric secretion and gastric motility.

Secretin is secreted by the upper intestinal mucosa and excites the pancreas to secrete bicarbonate and water, poor in enzymes.

Pancreozymin is secreted by the jejunal mucosa and stimulates the pancreas to secrete fluid rich in enzymes.

Cholecystokinin is secreted by cells in the upper small intestine and causes contraction of the smooth muscle of the gallbladder, causing it to empty.

Enterocrinin is secreted by cells in the upper small intestine; it stimulates secretion by glands of the small intestine.

It must be remembered that these hormones, like others, are secreted into the blood stream and reach all cells through the circulatory system. However, only *certain* cells respond to each hormone.

Changes the Food Undergoes in the Large Intestine

Movements of the Large Intestine. The opening from the small intestine into the large is controlled by the colic valve and the colic sphincter, which is normally in a state of tone. Food begins to pass into the large intestine within two to five hours after eating. Transit of the meal through the small intestine apparently occurs at a steady rate, so that the total time for the whole meal to pass the colic valve will be determined principally by the gastric evacuation time. As food passes the colic valve, the cecum becomes filled, and gradually the accumulation reaches higher and higher levels in the ascending colon. The contents of the ascending colon are soft and semisolid, but in the distal end of the transverse colon they attain the consistency of feces.

A type of movement characteristic of the large intestine is called *haustral churning*. The pouches, or sacculations, that are present in the large intestine become distended and from time to time contract and empty themselves. Another type of movement is designated as *mass peristalsis*. It consists of the vigorous contraction of the entire ascending colon, which transfers its contents to the transverse colon. Such movements occur only three or four times a day, last only a short time, and are usually connected with eating. When food enters the stomach and duodenum, peristalsis is initiated in the colon through the autonomic nerves of the areas involved. These reflex actions are termed the gastrocolic and duodenocolic reflexes. They are most noticeable after the first meal of the day and cause increased excitability of the colon, which initiates the defecation reflexes.

The secretion of the large intestine contains much mucin, shows an alkaline reaction, and is said not to contain enzymes. When the contents of the small intestine pass the colic valve, they still contain a certain amount of unabsorbed food material. This remains a long time in the intestine; and since it contains the digestive enzymes received in the duodenum, the process of digestion and absorption continues.

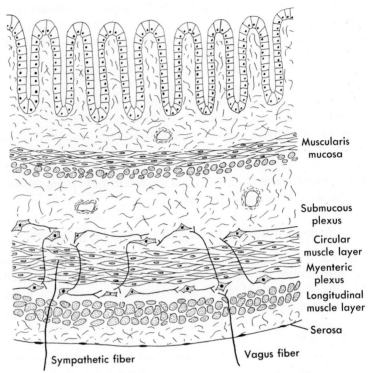

Muscularis mucosa

Submucous plexus

Circular muscle layer

Myenteric plexus

Longitudinal muscle layer

Serosa

Sympathetic fiber

Vagus fiber

Figure 20–4. Cross section of large intestine, showing muscle layers and autonomic plexuses.

Action of organisms in the large intestine brings about, in an alkaline reaction, constant putrefaction of whatever proteins are present as the result of not having been digested and absorbed in the small intestine. The splitting of the protein molecules by this process is very complete; not only are they hydrolyzed to amino acids, but these amino acids are deaminized and changed to simpler groups. The list of simple substances resulting from putrefaction is long and includes various peptides, ammonia, and amino acids, and also indole, skatole, phenol, fatty acids, carbon dioxide, and hydrogen sulfide. Some of these are given off in the feces; others are absorbed and carried to the liver, where they are changed to less toxic compounds, e.g., ethereal sulfates, such as indoxyl sulfate and skatoxyl sulfate, and ultimately excreted in the urine. Therefore, the amount of these sulfates in the urine is indicative of the degree of intestinal putrefaction. The ethereal sulfates are produced during putrefaction when oxidation follows deamination. When oxidation precedes deamination, more toxic substances, such as tyramine, tryptamine, and histamine, are thought to be formed. Even though these sulfates and allied compounds are less toxic than those from which they are derived, some investigators believe that bacterial putrefaction is harmful. A conservative view is that some intestinal organisms are not beneficial, but under normal conditions the body is able to neutralize their effects. Some organisms of the large intestine are useful in that they are capable of synthesizing several of the vitamins needed for normal metabolism. These vitamins include several of the B group and vitamin K.

The Feces. Two classes of material may be mingled in the content of the colon: (1) the residues of the diet with microorganisms and their products, and (2) the excretions of the digestive tube and its glands. The proportion existing between these two is variable. The feces consist of water; the undigested and indigestible parts of the food; pigment due to undigested food or to metallic elements contained in it and to the bile pigments; great quantities of microorganisms of different kinds; the products of bacterial decomposition, i.e., indole, skatole, etc.; the products of the secretions; mucous and epithelial cells from the walls of the alimentary tract; cholesterol or a derivative, which is probably derived from the bile; some of the purine bases; inorganic salts of sodium, potassium, calcium, magnesium, and iron.

Defecation. The anal canal is guarded by an internal sphincter and an external sphincter muscle, which are normally in a state of tonic contraction and protect the anal opening. Normally the rectum is empty until just before defecation. Various stimuli (depending on one's habits) will produce peristaltic action of the colon, so that a small quantity of feces enters the rectum. This irritates the sensory nerve endings and causes a desire to defecate. The voluntary contraction of the abdominal muscles, the descent of the diaphragm, and powerful peristalsis of the colon all combine to empty the colon and rectum.

One of the commonest causes of constipation is the retention of feces in the rectum because of failure to act on the desire for defecation. After feces once enter the rectum there is no retroperistalsis to carry them back to the colon, and the sense of irritation becomes blunted. The desire may not recur for 24 hours, during which time the feces continue to lose water and become harder and more difficult to expel. The best means to prevent and overcome constipation are: Act upon the desire for defecation, and have a regular time for doing so. Use a liberal amount of fruit and vegetables and a liberal intake of water. Some authorities teach that a certain amount of indigestible materials in the diet is wholesome. It stimulates the lining of the intestines, promotes peristalsis, and as it is pushed along the tube takes with it the less bulky but more toxic wastes. Daily exercise which uses all the muscles, especially the abdominal muscles, aids regularity. Constipation may be due to increased tonicity of the distal part of the colon, which causes a decrease in the lumen of the colon. Onward peristalsis is impaired, haustration is extreme, and hyperirritability and motility with delayed evacuation result. This is called *spastic* constipation. Constipation also may be due to a relaxed state of the muscle layers of the colon. The muscles fail to produce sufficient peristaltic action. The colon becomes relaxed, distended with fecal accumulation. This is called *atonic* constipation. It may follow excessive use of cathartics.

QUESTIONS FOR DISCUSSION

1. What are the chemical digestive processes necessary for rendering the food soluble and absorbable?

2. What are the functions of each hormone in the digestive process?

3. If a person has had a total gastrectomy. What physiological process will be interfered with and what medication will the person need? Why?

4. Explain the role of vitamins and electrolytes in enzyme systems.

5. Distinguish between a proenzyme and an enzyme. Name three proenzymes and state their function.

SUMMARY

Food
- Any substance taken into the body
  - (1) To yield energy
  - (2) To provide material for growth of tissues
  - (3) To regulate body processes

Classification
- Chemical analysis shows that elements found in body are found in food
  - Nutrients, or food principles
    - Water
    - Carbohydrates
    - Fats
    - Proteins
    - Mineral Salts
    - Vitamins

Water
- Enters into composition of all tissues; most tissues contain from 75 to 90%
- Greater proportion in young animals and active tissues
- Constitutes about two thirds of daily intake
  - Sources of water content of body
    - Beverages
    - Water contained in food
    - Water formed in the tissues
  - Supplies fluid for
    - Secretions
    - Chemical reactions
    - Transfer of food material
    - Elimination of waste
- Important in heat regulation
- Under normal conditions amount in body remains about the same

Carbohydrates
- Most abundant and most economical source of energy
- Include sugars and starches
  - Monosaccharides
    - Contain one sugar group
    - Glucose, or dextrose
    - Fructose, or levulose
    - Galactose
  - Disaccharides
    - Contain two sugar groups
    - Sucrose, or cane sugar
    - Lactose, or milk sugar
    - Maltose, or malt sugar
  - Polysaccharides
    - Contain many sugar groups
    - Starch
    - Cellulose
    - Glycogen
    - Dextrin

620

Lipids
- Used in anatomical sense = adipose tissue
- Used in chemical sense = esters of fatty acids and glycerol
- Under influence of body enzymes, split into substances out of which they are built

Compound Lipids
- Esters of fatty acids containing groups in addition
- *Phospholipids*—contain phosphorus and nitrogen, e.g., lecithin
- *Glycolipids*—compounds of fatty acids with a carbohydrate unit
- *Sterols*—solid alcohols of complex structure—e.g., cholesterol

Proteins

Contain C, H, O, N; usually S, sometimes P and Fe may be present

Built up of simpler substances called amino acids

Amino acids are derivatives of ammonia, as indicated by the amino group (NH_2), and of organic acids, as indicated by carboxyl group (COOH). The NH_2 replaces one hydrogen atom

Acetic acid—CH_3COOH—for H substitute

$(NH_2) \rightarrow CH_2(NH_2)COOH$ = aminoacetic acid

Propionic acid—C_2H_5COOH—for H substitute

$(NH_2) \rightarrow C_2H_4(NH_2)COOH$ = aminopropionic acid

About 40 amino acids have been derived from proteins, and various combinations result in many different kinds of proteins, i.e., milk, meats, fish, egg, peas, beans, lentils, and peanuts

Amino acids classed as dispensable, indispensable

Examples of protein constituents of food
- Albumin—found in egg, milk, meat
- Caseinogen—found in milk
- Glutenin—gummy substance in wheat
- Legumin—found in legumes
- Gelatin—derived from connective tissues, including bone and tendon
- Organic extracts—flavor of meats and some plant foods due to these

Classification

Simple
- Consist only of amino acids
- Yield only amino acids or derivatives

Conjugated
- Contain protein molecule united to some other molecule otherwise than as a salt—yield amino acids and some other molecule
- Nucleoproteins—yield amino acids and nuclein
- Glycoproteins—yield amino acids and a carbohydrate
- Phosphoproteins—yield amino acids and phosphates
- Hemoglobins—yield amino acids and hematin
- Lecithoproteins—yield amino acids and a fatty substance

Derived
- Primary—involve only slight alterations of the protein molecule
- Secondary—products of further hydrolytic cleavage, such as proteoses, peptones, and peptides

Chemical Elements
- Fifteen or more elements enter into composition of body
- Five may be furnished by carbohydrates, fats, proteins, and water
- Others to be provided include :
  - Iron, calcium, sodium, potassium, magnesium, phosphorus, chlorine, iodine, fluorine, silicon

Chemical Elements (*cont.*)
- **Function**
  - As constituents of bone
  - As essential elements of soft tissues
  - As soluble salts held in solution in fluids of body
- **Standard daily allowance of elements which should be stressed in daily diet**
  - Calcium   0.8 gm
  - Phosphorus   1.5 gm
  - Iron   0.020 gm
  - Iodine   0.000014 gm

Vitamins
- Essential for growth and nutrition
- Influence the metabolism of foodstuffs
- Current research stresses determination of optimal amounts
  - **Vitamin A**
    - Vitamin A and the related carotenes essential to growth, and to nutrition and health at all ages
    - Recent clinical observation indicates desirability of securing optimal quantity
  - **Vitamin D**
    - Gives protection in childhood against rickets
    - Ergosterol transformed into vitamin D by ultraviolet light
  - **Vitamin E**
    - Deficiency results in sterility in both male and female rats
    - Its value in treatment of human sterility not yet proved
  - **Vitamin K**
    - Essential to normal clotting of blood
  - **Vitamin-B Group**
    - Of multiple nature
    - Essential to health, related to composition and activity of many enzyme systems
    - Liberal use of leafy green vegetables, unprocessed flours, and whole-grain cereals provides optimal amount
  - **Vitamin C**
    - *Ascorbic acid* (commercial product, *cevitamic acid*)
    - Essential to normal development of bones and teeth, integrity of capillary walls, and wound healing
    - Subclinical shortage frequent; attention should be given to optimal intake

Accessory Articles of Food
- **Flavors and condiments**
  - Have no nutritive value, but increase the secretion of gastric fluid
- **Stimulants**
  - Tea and coffee—stimulating action due to caffeine
  - Cocoa
    - Contains carbohydrate, fat, and protein
    - Stimulating effects due to theobromine
  - Meat extracts
    - Contain secretagogues which stimulate the gastric glands to secretion
- **Alcohol**
  - Oxidized rapidly, yields energy
  - End products
    - Carbon dioxide
    - Water
  - Favors obesity
    - Moderate drinking creates keen appetite and thus favors overeating
    - Lessens need for oxidation of fat or carbohydrates; hence these accumulate in the body

Digestive Processes
- Include various physical processes that are preliminary to the more important chemical digestion
- **Mechanical**
  - Mastication—comminution and mixing
  - Deglutition, or swallowing
  - Peristaltic action of esophagus
  - Movements of stomach
  - Movements of intestines
  - Defecation

Digestive Processes (cont.) — **Chemical**
- Splitting of complex substances into simpler ones
- Process of hydrolysis that is dependent on enzymes
- Rendered necessary by variety and complexity of foods, which must be reduced to standard and simple substances that the tissues can use, i.e.,
  - End products
    - Simple sugars
    - Glycerol and fatty acids
    - Amino acids

Enzymes
- Substances produced by living cells which act by catalysis, i.e., vary speed of reactions
- It is suggested that each hydrolytic enzyme be designated by the name of the substance on which it acts, together with the suffix, *ase*
- **Classification according to action**
  - (1) Sugar-splitting
    - (a) Hydrolytic
    - (b) To yield simple sugars
  - (2) Amylolytic, or starch-splitting
  - (3) Lipolytic, or fat-splitting
  - (4) Proteolytic, or protein-splitting

Changes Food Undergoes in the Mouth
- Mastication (chewing)—comminution and mixing
- Insalivation (mixing with saliva)
- **Saliva**
  - Secreted by salivary glands
    - Parotid
    - Submaxillary
    - Sublingual
    - and mucous glands of mouth
  - Craniosacral autonomic fibers
    - Carry secretory and vasodilator fibers
    - Stimulated by sight or smell of food
    - Causes a production of a copious amount of watery secretion
  - Thoracolumbar autonomic fibers
    - Carry secretory and vasoconstrictor fibers
    - Stimulated by food in mouth
    - Produce a smaller amount of thicker secretion
  - Consists of water, some protein material, mucin, inorganic salts, and the enzyme salivary amylase
  - Specific gravity 1.004–1.008. Neutral in reaction—pH 6.6–7.1
  - Amount—1 to 1.5 liters per day
  - **Physiology**
    - (1) Assists in mastication and deglutition
    - (2) Serves as lubricant
    - (3) Dissolves or liquifies the food, thus stimulating the taste buds and indirectly the secretion of gastric fluid
    - (4) Amylase hydrolyzes starch to dextrin and maltose; maltase changes maltose to glucose
- Deglutition (swallowing). Passage of food through (1) fauces, (2) pharynx, and (3) esophagus. Consistency of food affects third stage

Changes Food Undergoes in the Stomach
- Time required—depends on nature of food eaten; average meal of mixed food requires 3–4½ hr
- Food held in stomach by cardiac and pyloric sphincters
- Cavity size of contents—never empty—always few milliliters of gastric fluid in stomach
- When food enters, expands just enough to receive it; contractions start in middle region and run towards pylorus; food in prepyloric and pyloric regions macerated, mixed with gastric fluid, and reduced to **chyme**
- Salivary digestion continues until gastric fluid penetrates bolus of food

Changes Food Undergoes in the Stomach (*cont.*)

Gastric juice

- Periods of fasting—secreted in small amount
- While eating and during period of digestion—amount increased
- Secretion
  - Psychic or appetite, secretion
    - Sensations of eating
    - Taste and odor of food
  - Chemical
    - Secretagogues contained (1) in food and (2) in products of digestion
    - Gastric secretin
- Secreted by glands of stomach
  - Cardiac
  - Fundus, or oxyntic
  - Pyloric
- Acid reaction due to free hydrochloric acid
- Enzymes
  - Pepsin
  - Gastric lipase
- Inhibited by
  - Stimulation of sympathetic system, anger, pain, fear, worry, distaste for food
  - Secretion dependent on blood, hence checked if blood supply is diverted

Hydrochloric Acid

- Secreted by parietal cells of gastric glands from chlorides found in blood
- Chloride ions combine with hydrogen ions to form hydrochloric acid
- Normal amount about 0.5%
- Physiology
  - Activates pepsinogen and converts it to pepsin
  - Provides acid medium for pepsin to carry on its work
  - Swells protein fibers
  - Helps in inversion of cane sugar, easiest disaccharide to hydrolyze
  - Germicidal in action

Pepsin

- Formed in pyloric glands and chief cells of gastric glands
- Pepsinogen—zymogen, changed by HCl to active pepsin
- Weak proteolytic enzyme—requires acid medium
- Hydrolyzes proteins through several stages to peptides, which action is preparatory to more complete hydrolysis in intestine

Gastric Lipase—limited action on emulsified fats like cream

Functions of Stomach

- Serves as temporary storage reservoir
- Contractions promote mechanical reduction of food
- Salivary digestion continues until acidity is established
- Gastric digestion
  - Pepsin hydrolyzes proteins
  - Gastric lipase may hydrolyze emulsified fats
- HCl has germicidal action

Digestion in the Intestine

Small intestine

- Movements
  - Peristaltic—pushes food forward slowly
  - Rhythmic—facilitates mixing with secretions
- Secretions
  - Pancreatic fluid
  - Succus entericus
  - Bile
- Bacteria
  - Decompose carbohydrates
  - Little or no effect on protein
- Time required
  - Depends on proportions of different foodstuffs
  - Food begins to pass into large intestine 2–5¼ hr after eating, requires 9 hr or more before last of meal has passed

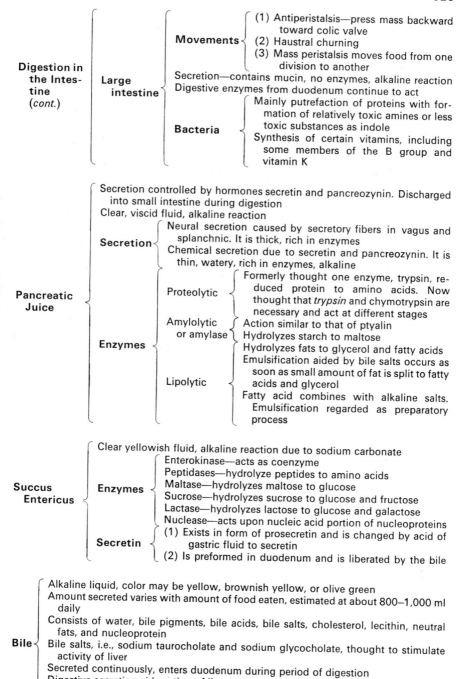

Digestion in the Intestine (cont.)

Large intestine

Movements
(1) Antiperistalsis—press mass backward toward colic valve
(2) Haustral churning
(3) Mass peristalsis moves food from one division to another

Secretion—contains mucin, no enzymes, alkaline reaction
Digestive enzymes from duodenum continue to act

Bacteria
Mainly putrefaction of proteins with formation of relatively toxic amines or less toxic substances as indole
Synthesis of certain vitamins, including some members of the B group and vitamin K

Pancreatic Juice

Secretion controlled by hormones secretin and pancreozynin. Discharged into small intestine during digestion
Clear, viscid fluid, alkaline reaction

Secretion
Neural secretion caused by secretory fibers in vagus and splanchnic. It is thick, rich in enzymes
Chemical secretion due to secretin and pancreozynin. It is thin, watery, rich in enzymes, alkaline

Enzymes

Proteolytic
Formerly thought one enzyme, trypsin, reduced protein to amino acids. Now thought that *trypsin* and chymotrypsin are necessary and act at different stages

Amylolytic or amylase
Action similar to that of ptyalin
Hydrolyzes starch to maltose

Lipolytic
Hydrolyzes fats to glycerol and fatty acids
Emulsification aided by bile salts occurs as soon as small amount of fat is split to fatty acids and glycerol
Fatty acid combines with alkaline salts. Emulsification regarded as preparatory process

Succus Entericus

Clear yellowish fluid, alkaline reaction due to sodium carbonate

Enzymes
Enterokinase—acts as coenzyme
Peptidases—hydrolyze peptides to amino acids
Maltase—hydrolyzes maltose to glucose
Sucrose—hydrolyzes sucrose to glucose and fructose
Lactase—hydrolyzes lactose to glucose and galactose
Nuclease—acts upon nucleic acid portion of nucleoproteins

Secretin
(1) Exists in form of prosecretin and is changed by acid of gastric fluid to secretin
(2) Is preformed in duodenum and is liberated by the bile

Bile
Alkaline liquid, color may be yellow, brownish yellow, or olive green
Amount secreted varies with amount of food eaten, estimated at about 800–1,000 ml daily
Consists of water, bile pigments, bile acids, bile salts, cholesterol, lecithin, neutral fats, and nucleoprotein
Bile salts, i.e., sodium taurocholate and sodium glycocholate, thought to stimulate activity of liver
Secreted continuously, enters duodenum during period of digestion
Digestive secretion aids action of lipase
Excretion—eliminates toxins, metals, and cholesterol
Antiseptic—thought to limit putrefaction

Abnormal Conditions
{
Gallstones—concentrated cholesterol or bile salts which crystallizes out and forms gallstones

Jaundice—due to absorption of bile by blood; bile carried throughout body; pigments deposited in skin and whites of eyes
}

Feces
{
Consist of {
Residues of diet, microorganisms and their products
Excretions of digestive tube and its glands
}

Contain (1) water, (2) the residues of food, (3) pigment, (4) microorganisms, (5) products of bacterial decomposition, indole, skatole, etc., (6) products of secretions, (7) mucous and epithelial cells, (8) cholesterol, (9) purine bases, and (10) inorganic salts
}

Defecation—term applied to the act of expelling feces from rectum

Summary of Digestive Secretions

Secretion	pH / Volume per Day	Proenzyme/ Substance Which Activates	Enzyme/ Substance Which Activates	Substrate	End Products
Saliva	6.8 / 1–1½ liters		1. Salivary amylase chloride	Starch	Maltose
Gastric juice	2–4 / 1.5–2.5	Pepsinogen/HCl	1. Rennin (infants)	Casein	Paracasein
			2. Pepsin	Proteins, paracasein	Proteoses, peptones, polypeptides
			3. Gastric lipase	Emulsified fats	Fatty acids, glycerol
Pancreatic juice	8–8.4 / 600–800 ml	1. Trypsinogen/ enterokinase	1. Trypsin	Chymotrypsinogen	Chymotrypsin
				Proteins, paracasein, peptones, proteoses, polypeptides	Polypeptides, dipeptides
		2. Chymotrypsinogen/ trypsin	2. Chymotrypsin	Proteins, paracasein, peptones, proteoses, polypeptides	Polypeptides, dipeptides
			3. Pancreatic amylase	Starch, glycogen	Disaccharides
			4. Pancreatic lipase	Emulsified fats	Fatty acids, glycerol
				Unemulsified fats	Emulsified fats
Bile	7.5 / 800–1000 ml	Bile salts (not an enzyme—action is physical)			
Intestinal juice	7–9 / 2–3 liters		1. Peptidase	Polypeptides, dipeptides	Amino acids
			2. Enteric lipase	Emulsified fats	Fatty acid, glycerol
			3. Sucrase	Sucrose	Glucose, fructose
			4. Maltase	Maltose	Glucose
			5. Lactase	Lactose	Glucose, galactose
			6. Enterokinase	Trypsinogen	Trypsin

Absorption, Metabolism of Carbohydrates, Fats, and Proteins. Basal Metabolism, Temperature Regulation

THE SECRETORY and motor activities of the gastrointestinal tract are all directed toward changing ingested food into substances appropriate for absorption from the alimentary canal into the blood stream.

Each individual has specific needs in relation to food requirements, and all metabolic processes must be regulated and controlled.

ABSORPTION

Absorption from the gastrointestinal tract consists of transfer of materials across the cell membrane boundary and involves processes previously discussed (Chap. 3), namely, diffusion, hydrostatic pressure, osmosis, and active transport. Particle size and concentration of the materials are among the important physical factors which influence these processes.

Conditions which determine the amount of absorption which takes place from any part of the alimentary canal are the area of surface for absorption, the length of time food remains in contact with the absorbing surface, the concentration of fully digested material present, and the rapidity with which absorbed food is carried away by the blood.

Absorption in the Small Intestine. It is in the small intestine that these conditions are most favorable for absorption; therefore, it is here that the greatest amount of absorption takes place.

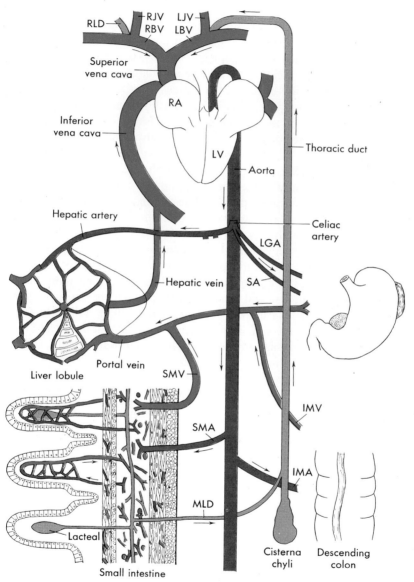

Figure 21–1. Diagram to show absorption. (*IMA*) Inferior mesenteric artery, (*IMV*) inferior mesenteric vein, (*LGA*) left gastric artery, (*LBV*) left brachiocephalic vein, (*LJV*) left jugular vein, (*LV*) left ventricle, (*MLD*) mesenteric lymph duct, (*RA*) right atrium, (*RBV*) right brachiocephalic vein, (*RJV*) right jugular vein, (*RLD*) right lymph duct, (*SA*) splenic artery, (*SMA*) superior mesenteric artery, (*SMV*) superior mesenteric vein.

The circular folds and villi of the small intestine increase the internal surface enormously. It is estimated to be more than 10 sq m.

Food remains in the small intestine for several hours; during this time the most complete digestive changes occur.

The blood flows steadily within the wall of the small intestine. The blood in the capillaries is separated from the digested nutrients in the small intestine by the walls of the capillaries and the intestinal mucosa. On the intestinal side of the wall are the products of digestion and the digestive fluids. Sugars, glycerol, fatty acids, and amino acids are relatively abundant and pass into the blood. The continuous digestion of foods, the muscular activity of the intestinal wall, and the lashing and pumping activities of the villi stir up the intestinal contents and keep relatively high the concentration of absorbable materials in contact with the absorbing membrane. These motions also increase the circulation in the villi, and therefore the absorbed materials are moved on, keeping the concentration in the blood relatively low. Absorption takes place through the membrane from a constantly higher concentration of absorbable particles to a constantly lower concentration until all digested material is absorbed. The more nearly normal the muscular activity of the gastrointestinal tract, the greater will be the blood flow through its walls, and hence the more prompt will be the absorption of the digested nutrients. It is probably in relation to gastrointestinal motility that thiamine, or vitamin B_1, plays its part in absorption. (See p. 599.) In addition to the activity of the muscular wall itself, bringing about peristalsis, rhythmical segmentations, and pendular action, there is the activity of the muscularis mucosa, giving marked motility of the villi as well as of the other superficial parts of the mucosa. This all means not only that the area of the food in contact with the absorbing surface is vastly greater in the small intestine, but that this area of food is constantly renewed.

Absorption in the Stomach. There is no active transport mechanism in the stomach, so that absorption is limited to water and alcohol. In general "foodstuffs" require chemical digestion by the pancreatic and intestinal enzymes, hence are not absorbed from the stomach. However, many drugs and chemicals such as metallic salts and mercurial compounds are rapidly absorbed.

The Paths of Absorption. Absorption in the intestine is an active process by which the products of digestion enter the blood capillaries of the villi and intestinal mucosa and the lacteals of the villi and lymph ducts.

Fats are absorbed into the central lymph channel of each villus and forced into the larger lymphatics. After reaching the large lymph vessels, the absorbed material flows to the thoracic duct and enters the brachiocephalic vein at the junction of the left internal jugular and left subclavian veins.

The products of carbohydrate and protein digestion and probably some of the glycerol and fatty acids are absorbed by the capillaries of the villi and carried to the portal vein, which in turn carries them to the liver.

Absorption in the Large Intestine. When the contents of the small intestine pass the colic valve, they still contain a certain amount of unabsorbed food material. Enzymes are present, and digestion and absorption continue, but to a greatly reduced degree. The consistency is about that of chyme, because the absorption of water from the small intestine is counterbalanced by diffusion or secretion of water into it. In the large intestine the absorption of water continues, so that under usual conditions the formation of semisolid or hard feces occurs.

Absorption of water is not appreciable in the stomach. Most of the water of the intestinal contents is absorbed in the small intestine, but the most conspicuous change in the fluidity of the intestinal contents takes place in the large intestine, mainly in the ascending colon and proximal end of the transverse colon.

Absorption of mineral salts from any part of the intestines depends upon the nature of the salt and the concentration of the solution. Certain salts are readily absorbed, e.g., chlorides, and most of the ammonium salts; on the other hand,

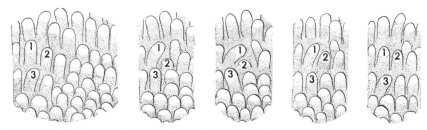

Figure 21–2. Diagram of surface view of the lining of the small intestine as it would be seen if the intestine were opened and stretched under a microscope. Several villi "stand" with tips toward observer. Villus *1* bends to right and then straightens up. Villus *2* telescopes itself and then stretches out. Villus *3*, bent to right, swings to left and over to right again.

tartrates, citrates, and some of the sulfates are very slowly absorbed. To be absorbed, salts must be in higher concentration in the intestine than in the blood.

Cathartic Action of Salts in Solution in Water. The cathartic salts are very slowly absorbed from the gastrointestinal tract. For example, the cation magnesium and the anions citrate, tartrate, sulfate, and phosphate are slowly absorbed. When taken as salts they remain in the intestine for a comparatively long period of time. The tissues between the salts in solution and the blood stream form a semipermeable membrane which is readily permeable to water. Consequently fluid moves from the blood stream to the intestinal cavity, thereby increasing the bulk of the intestinal content. The increased bulk acts as a distention stimulus to promote increased peristalsis and bowel evacuation.

The end products of digestion are simple sugars, derived from the various carbohydrates; fatty acids and glycerol, derived from the various fats; and amino acids, derived from the various proteins.

These substances are diffusible although the foodstuffs from which they are derived are not. Starch, even when boiled for a long time, does not make its way through ordinary membranes; the simple sugars do. Fats are not absorbed; fatty acids and glycerol are. Amino acids pass freely through membranes.

The simple sugars pass into the capillaries and thence by way of the portal vein to the liver. In this way simple sugars are absorbed even though the blood sugar is higher in concentration.

The fatty acids and glycerol are absorbed in the small intestine. The bile furnishes bile salts (sodium glycocholate and sodium taurocholate) which aid in the absorption of fatty acids. During their passage through the intestinal walls most of the fatty acids and glycerol recombine to form fats or triglycerides. The

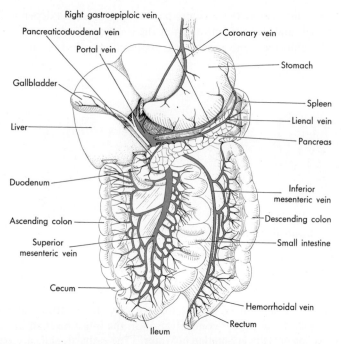

Figure 21-3. Organs of digestion and blood vessels that transport absorbed nutrients to the liver. Which digestive organs are not shown in this diagram?

greater part of the fat is absorbed by the lacteals in the villi and carried to the thoracic duct, which empties into the left brachiocephalic vein. In addition it is considered probable that some of the fat is absorbed directly as fatty acid and glycerol by the capillaries of the villi and carried by way of the portal vein to the liver, before reaching the general circulation. Fat is present in the blood stream as tiny droplets called chylomicrons, collections of fat molecules.

The amino acids pass into the capillaries of the villi, although there is experimental evidence that, after excessive feeding of protein, a portion may enter the lymphatics. Amino acids are found in the blood, which distributes them to the tissues.

METABOLISM

General metabolism includes the changes that occur in digested foodstuffs from the time of their absorption until their elimination in the excretions. In actuality, *metabolism refers to the sum total of the chemical changes which take place within cells*. **Metabolic changes** may be classified under two heads: *anabolism*, or constructive process or synthesis; and *catabolism*, which implies the breakdown of large molecules, the products of which are of smaller molecular size.

The changes classified as anabolic include the processes by which cells take food substances from the blood and make them a part of their own protoplasm. This involves the conversion of nonliving material into living material and is a building-up, or synthetic, process. The synthesis of glycogen and of fats within the cells is also anabolism. Anabolism is accompanied by the storage of chemical energy.

The changes classified as catabolic consist of the processes by which cells resolve into simpler substances (1) part of their own protoplasm or (2) substances which have been stored in them. This disintegration yields simpler substances, some of which may be used by other cells, though most of them are excreted. Release of chemical energy accompanies this process.

In the tissues, the participation of oxygen in the chemical changes of the body forms an integral part of the processes of metabolism.

The chemical reactions occurring within the cell have two over-all purposes:

1. Forming molecules which make up the cell itself, e.g., cell membrane, endoenzymes, and cytoplasm, as the cell increases in size or divides; and forming molecules to be secreted from the cell, e.g., hormones, exoenzymes, and serum albumin and globulin.

2. Supplying energy for the synthetic processes listed above and for such specialized cell activities as muscle contraction, transmission of nerve impulse, ciliary movement, and sperm motility.

Fats and carbohydrates are primarily used for energy supply, although they are also necessary for synthesis of such materials as glycoproteins and cholesterol. Amino acids are primarily utilized in synthesis but may be utilized as energy sources, if fat and carbohydrate supply is inadequate. Energy supply seems to have priority over anabolism.

The chemical reactions within the cell which release energy occur in the mitochondria and are primarily oxidative reactions, that is, transfer of electrons or hydrogen from one substance to oxygen or to another substance. Oxidation may then occur aerobically (utilizing oxygen) or anaerobically. The aerobic oxidative processes yield the largest amount of energy.

Strictly speaking, with the exception of heat produced, energy is not "freed" from a substance but rather transferred. One of the most important substances in the cell in regard to energy transfer is adenosine triphosphate. To synthesize this substance, present in all cells, energy is used to form adenosine from ribose and adenine, and then to attach one, two, or three phosphate groups, adenosine monophosphate (AMP), adenosine diphosphate (ADP), and adenosine triphosphate (ATP). Large amounts of energy are required to attach the second and third phosphate groups; this same amount of energy is released when the phosphate groups, through enzymatic action, are broken off during cell activity. Oxidation in the cell is thus a step-by-step reaction, producing small amounts of energy for storage in ATP molecules which are held in reserve for utilization as needed. At the same time, utilization of ATP is a safety factor, for the release of excessive amounts of energy at one time might destroy the cell.

Muscle cells, in addition to ATP, synthesize another compound with a high-energy phosphate bond, creatine phosphate, which acts as an energy storehouse like ATP until the muscle contracts as energy is needed.

Needless to say, none of the chemical reactions within the cell, energy-transferring, or of a synthetic nature could occur rapidly enough in the absence of the appropriate enzyme. Reference to the enzyme chart on page 38 and the coenzyme chart of page 604 will be helpful in the discussions to follow.

Metabolism of Carbohydrates

Metabolism of carbohydrates may be considered under three headings—supply, storage, and use by cells.

Supply is regulated by the diet.

Storage is temporarily provided for by the liver, the muscles, and the cells of the tissues. During the process of digestion the carbohydrates are changed to simple sugars. Absorption of glucose takes place mainly into the capillaries of the small intestine. These capillaries pour their contents into the portal vein, which carries the blood, rich with glucose, to the liver. The liver cells take this glucose from the blood and convert it to glycogen, which is stored in the liver cells. By the storing up of glycogen and doling out of glucose as needed, the liver helps to maintain the normal quantity of glucose—80 to 120 mg per 100 ml of blood. From the blood stream glucose is taken up by the skeletal muscles and stored as glycogen until needed; or it is utilized by any and all cells as a source of energy or for synthesis of appropriate cell constituents and secretions. Hence the liver functions to help maintain a constant supply of blood glucose to meet the demands of active cells. The percentage of glycogen in a muscle is small, though the total content of all the muscle cells may equal that of the liver. The maximum storage of glycogen in the body is about 400 gm, or nearly 1 lb. The need of the blood for glucose is constant, because it is constantly giving up glucose to the tissues.

The amount of glucose oxidized is controlled by the energy needs of the tissues, particularly muscle tissue, for their activity is the principal factor determining the rate of oxidation; naturally the amount of glucose required will be in proportion to the rate at which it is used.

Physiology of Carbohydrate Metabolism.   In all cells, the first step in carbohydrate metabolism is the formation of glucose phosphate by transferring a phosphate radical from ATP to glucose, a reaction catalyzed by hexokinase. (In the liver fructose and galactose are transformed to glucose.) Glucose phosphate then may be transformed to glycogen (*glycogenesis*) in the case of liver or skeletal muscle cells; or *glycolysis* may occur—breakdown of glucose for energy release. Glycolysis is anaerobic, producing pyruvic acid (and lactic acid in skeletal muscle cells). Further oxidation of lactic acid and pyruvic acid is aerobic, resulting in eventual formation of carbon dioxide and water via the citric acid cycle—a pathway utilized in oxidation of fats and amino acids as well.

Hormones Concerned with Carbohydrate Metabolism. The complex processes by which glucose is utilized, glycolysis, glycogenesis, glycogenolysis (breakdown of glycogen to glucose), and gluconeogenesis (formation of glucose from amino acids and fat), require regulation. Many aspects of the regulatory processes are poorly understood. However, certain hormones are known to be important.

Pancreas. Insulin, secreted by the beta cells of the islets of Langerhans, is believed to be concerned with the diffusion of glucose across tissue cell membranes from the extracellular fluids, or with phosphorylation of glucose by ATP. Hexokinase functions as the catalyst. Phosphorylation must occur before glucose can be oxidized by tissue cells or converted to either glycogen or fat. In the liver insulin inhibits glycogen formation from noncarbohydrate sources (glyconeogenesis). The alpha cells secrete *glucagon*, a hyperglycemic factor, which promotes the conversion of glycogen to glucose in the liver.

Insulin is ineffective when taken by mouth, because it is destroyed in the alimentary canal and because the size of the molecule is too large for intestinal absorption; consequently, it is injected under the skin. The reduction of blood sugar by insulin does not necessarily stop at the normal level; if it proceeds further, prostration may occur. Such reaction is avoided by taking orange juice or sugar when the sensation of weakness is first felt. The incidence of hypoglycemic reaction with protamine zinc insulin is much less than with regular insulin, and from 30 to 40 per cent of the total insulin used in the United States and Canada is now in this form. The improvement of patients receiving insulin is marked, but insulin does not cure diabetes. It is palliative in character, and usually dependence on the insulin continues.

The anterior pituitary secretes somatotropin, which is insulin antagonizing, and ACTH. They act both directly and indirectly and through the adrenal cortex exert effects that are opposed to the action of insulin; i.e., they inhibit glucose phosphorylations by inhibiting hexokinase and glucose utilization in the tissues.

Adrenal Cortex. The glucocorticoids decrease the use of tissue glucose, increase blood sugar, increase gluconeogenesis from amino acids, and increase the production of glucose from glycogen.

Adrenal Medulla. Epinephrine causes a rapid conversion of liver glycogen to glucose and increases the rate of use of glycogen in muscle tissue.

Thyroid Gland. Thyroxin influences glucose metabolism by increasing the rate of oxidation in tissue cells. In the liver it increases the rate of glycogen formation from noncarbohydrate sources.

Oxidation of Glycogen—A Summary

Glycogenolysis

Glycogen + Phosphate

↓

Glucose-1-phosphate*

↓

Glucose-6-phosphate

↓

ATP + Fructose-6-phosphate

↓

Fructose-1,6-diphosphate + ADP

|

↓   ↓

Dihydroxyacetone phosphate ⇌ Glyceraldehyde-3-phosphate

| + DPN + phosphate

Glycogenolysis does not   1,3-Diphosphoglyceric acid + DPNH$_2$
require oxygen; the end product
is *lactic acid*. The energy yield is | + ADP
relatively small

3-Phosphoglyceric acid + ATP

| + ADP

↓

Lactic acid + DPN ⇌ DPNH$_2$ + Pyruvic acid + ATP

+

DPN

DPNH$_2$

+

↓

Carbon dioxide + acetyl coenzyme A
enters the
Citric acid cycle
for oxidation to

↓

Carbon dioxide + water

Terminal oxidation to carbon dioxide   DPN = Diphosphopyridine nucleotide
and water, via the *citric acid cycle*,   DPNH$_2$ = Diphosphopyridine nucleotide
requires oxygen. The energy yield   (reduced)
is relatively large

* In all instances, numbers refer to the carbon atoms which carry the phosphate groups. Thus glucose has 6
carbons :

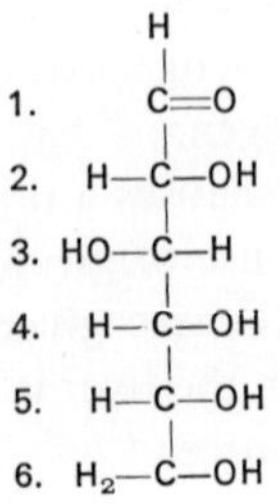

$$
\begin{array}{ll}
 & H \\
 & | \\
1. & C=O \\
 & | \\
2. & H-C-OH \\
 & | \\
3. & HO-C-H \\
 & | \\
4. & H-C-OH \\
 & | \\
5. & H-C-OH \\
 & | \\
6. & H_2-C-OH
\end{array}
$$

Factors That Influence Blood Glucose Levels

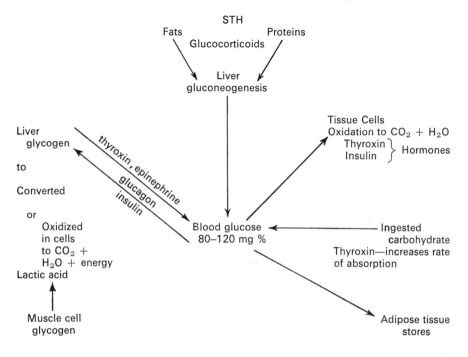

Note that the direction of the arrows (inward and outward) indicates raising and lowering of blood glucose. What organ is the primary regulator of the blood glucose level?

Functions of Carbohydrates. The oxidation of glucose serves the following purposes: It furnishes the main source of energy for muscular work. The glycogen of a muscle disappears in proportion to the work done by the muscle, and it is thought the oxidation of the glucose furnishes the energy which is utilized by the muscles. It furnishes an important part of the heat needed to maintain the body temperature. The oxidation of each gram of glucose yields 4 Cal of heat; and since the carbohydrates form the largest part of our diet and are easily oxidized, they must be regarded as specially available material for keeping up body heat. Glucose prevents oxidation of the body tissues, because it constitutes a reserve fund that is the first to be drawn upon in time of need. As carbohydrate food is increased, protein food may be diminished to a certain irreducible minimum, which is probably the amount necessary for the reconstruction of new tissue. Carbohydrates, in excess of the amount that can be stored as glycogen in the liver and muscles, are converted into depot or stored fat. Nutritional experiments show that the fat of the body may be formed from carbohydrate food.

End Products of Carbohydrate Metabolism. Eventually the glucose derived from the glucose of the blood or from the glycogen of the cell is oxidized by the cell, via the citric acid cycle, to *carbon dioxide* and *water*.

Summary—Some Important Steps in Carbohydrate Metabolism

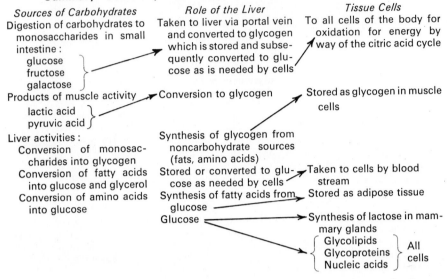

Sources of Carbohydrates

Digestion of carbohydrates to monosaccharides in small intestine :
- glucose
- fructose
- galactose

Products of muscle activity
- lactic acid
- pyruvic acid

Liver activities :
  Conversion of monosaccharides into glycogen
  Conversion of fatty acids into glucose and glycerol
  Conversion of amino acids into glucose

Role of the Liver

Taken to liver via portal vein and converted to glycogen which is stored and subsequently converted to glucose as is needed by cells

Conversion to glycogen

Synthesis of glycogen from noncarbohydrate sources (fats, amino acids)
Stored or converted to glucose as needed by cells
Synthesis of fatty acids from glucose
Glucose

Tissue Cells

To all cells of the body for oxidation for energy by way of the citric acid cycle

Stored as glycogen in muscle cells

Taken to cells by blood stream
Stored as adipose tissue
Synthesis of lactose in mammary glands
{ Glycolipids Glycoproteins Nucleic acids } All cells

Derangements of Carbohydrate Metabolism. The sugar-regulating mechanism of the body may prove inadequate.

Ingestion of a larger amount of sugar than the liver and muscles can store results in an increased amount in the blood (hyperglycemia). A higher percentage of glucose than normal in the blood is irritating to the tissues, and it is excreted in the urine. This is designated as temporary glycosuria.

The mechanism of consumption of glucose in the tissues for energy purposes breaks down in diabetes mellitus. Removal of the pancreas of an animal is followed by the appearance of glucose in the urine in large amounts. If the extirpation is complete, glycosuria is followed by emaciation and muscular weakness, which finally end in death in two or three weeks. On the other hand, if a portion of the pancreas is left, even though its connection with the duodenum is interrupted, it may prevent glycosuria partly or completely. This indicates that the internal secretion is the important factor in the metabolism of glucose.

Diabetes Mellitus. In mankind derangements of carbohydrate metabolism manifest themselves chiefly in the disease known as diabetes mellitus, the early symptoms of which are excessive secretion of urine (polyuria) containing abnormal amounts of glucose and electrolytes, especially sodium, potassium, and chlorides; an abnormal thirst (polydipsia); and excessive eating (polyphagia). In this disease the daily loss of glucose in the urine may be very large. In severe cases all the carbohydrate of the food may be excreted in the form of glucose; and even when no carbohydrate food is eaten, glucose continues to be excreted in considerable amounts. In the latter case the sugar is supposed to have its source in the proteins of the food or of the tissues. The opinion of experts in this field is that a lesion in the islets of Langerhans in the pancreas results in a reduction of the supply of insulin to the body, and in consequence the tissues cannot use the glucose brought to them by the blood. In addition to the glucose found in the urine in diabetes, this secretion may contain considerable amounts of the acetone bodies. These acetone bodies are intermediary products in the metabolism of fats, and their presence in excess is due to increased utilization of fat. The accumulation of acetone bodies in the blood and tissues of the diabetic is responsible for the condition called *diabetic acidosis*.

Metabolism of Fats

The results of experimental work confirm the view that after fat is split into glycerol and fatty acids by the lipase of the pancreatic fluid, it is absorbed by the epithelial cells and in the act of passing through them combines to form fat, termed triglycerides, or "neutral fat." This combination is brought about by a lipase. The greater portion of the fat passes into the central lymph channel of each villus (Fig. 21–1). From these small lacteals it finds its way through the larger lymphatics in the mesentery to the thoracic duct and then through the thoracic duct to the blood. It seems probable that some of the fatty acid and glycerol is absorbed by the capillaries in the villi, enters the portal vein, and passes through the liver before reaching the general circulation. Fat is carried by the blood to all parts of the body, and the tissues slowly take it out as they need it in their metabolic processes. Within tissues other than nerve tissue, it is oxidized to supply the energy needs of the cells. Nerve cells oxidize glucose only, whereas heart muscle uses a high proportion of fat.

Physiology of Fat Metabolism. Much of the fat absorbed from the intestine is deposited in fat-storage cells which are widely distributed throughout the body. From these cells fat is constantly being withdrawn to meet the demands of active cells. Some is oxidized to provide energy, some is used for synthesis of lipids for cell use. When the food eaten is in excess of the energy requirements of the individual, fat accumulates in the storage cells, thus increasing the amount of adipose tissue. It is a valuable reserve of nutrient and also provides protection and support for organs and insulation for the animal. Adipose tissue stores are composed largely of neutral fat, whereas the lipids in the active tissue cells are largely phospholipids, cholesterol, and cholesterol esters of fatty acids.

Oxidation of Fat in the Body. It is thought that the first step in the splitting of fat is brought about by the lipase found in the tissues. The fat stored in adipose tissue in various parts of the body (e.g., under the skin, in the peritoneum) does not undergo oxidation in these places. In time of need it is reabsorbed by the blood and redistributed to the more active tissues. It is thought that lipases control the output of fat to the blood, just as the liver enzymes control the supply of glucose in the blood. After the action of the lipase, oxidation takes place in a series of steps which reduces the higher fatty acids two carbons at a time until a four-carbon fragment then splits in half. The two-carbon or acetyl fractions enter the citric acid cycle with eventual formation of carbon dioxide and water.

The glycerol portion of fats is transformed to glucose and metabolized as such.

Origin of Body Fat. The modern view is that the fat of the body is formed from the fats, carbohydrates, and proteins of the food. Proteins are usually a small part of the daily diet, and it is thought that body fat is formed from fat and carbohydrate foodstuffs first. If the amino acids resulting from the digestion of protein food are not built into body protein, they are deaminized, and the organic acid radical left may be converted to glucose, glycogen, or fat.

When carbohydrate is removed from the diet and the glycogen of the body has been depleted, as in fasting or underfeeding and in severe diabetes, the body lives on its fats and proteins.

The Role of the Liver in Fat Metabolism. The liver has many functions in relation to fat metabolism. (1) It synthesizes fatty acids from carbohydrate intermediates; (2) rebuilds fatty acids through lengthening and shortening chains, with saturation or desaturation to provide the lipids characteristic of the human; and (3) oxidizes fatty acids to acetyl fragments, which may be used for synthesis of other substances, such as cholesterol, and phospholipids, or oxidized to carbon dioxide and water.

The liver initiates the first steps in the oxidation of fatty acids. During beta oxidation, two carbon units are split off at a time, and in the liver they are condensed to form acetoacetic acid. Acetoacetic acid and beta-hydroxybutyric acid and acetone, the ketone bodies, leave the liver via the hepatic vein and are taken to muscle cells, where they are oxidized by way of the citric acid cycle to carbon dioxide and water with release of energy. Oxaloacetic acid is essential for the oxidation of ketone bodies in the citric acid cycle.

It is evident then that in diabetes mellitus or starvation, when carbohydrate is not available for oxidation, an excess of ketone bodies is produced in the liver. Normally the blood contains 1 mEq per liter of keto acids, but may contain 20 to 30 mEq per liter. This condition is called ketosis. The liver stores lipids chiefly as phospholipids and neutral fat and cholesterol. A condition known as fatty liver occurs in individuals on high-fat diets and also in diabetes mellitus that is untreated.

Because of their tendency to form ketone bodies under certain conditions, fatty acids are said to have ketogenic properties. A few amino acids are also ketogenic. On the other hand, carbohydrates, the sugar-forming amino acids, and glycerol are antiketogenic.

Obesity is said to be of two kinds. One is caused by eating more food than the body needs, lack of exercise, or both. A diet that is rather bulky but not highly nutritious, including fruit and the coarser vegetables, is recommended for this type of obesity. The second kind is less frequent and is associated with endocrine disturbances. Castration, the menopause, disease of the hypophysis, myxedema, and other physiological and pathological disturbances are usually, though not always, accompanied by deposits of abnormal amounts of fat.

Factors Affecting Fat Metabolism. Certain substances, termed *lipotropic factors*, are necessary for synthesis of phospholipids in the liver. Choline and methionine, an amino acid, are the most important of these substances. Without them, fat accumulates in liver cells and phospholipid formation is impaired.

Summary—Some Important Steps in Fat Metabolism

Sources of Fat	Blood Stream	Role of the Liver	Tissue Cells
Foods Digestion of fats to fatty acids and glycerol in the intestine	Found as neutral fats in form of chylomicrons (fat droplets visible under the microscope)	Stores phospholipids and glycerides	Good source of energy by way of citric acid cycle to CO_2 and H_2O —9 Cal per gm of fat
		Oxidation of fatty acids to acetyl fragments	Necessary constituent of all cells, especially muscle cells for use in the citric acid cycle
		Formation of unsaturated fatty acids	Phospholipids and cholesterol essential constituent of all cells
	Phospholipids (lecithin)	Phospholipids formed at a higher rate than in any other organ, except intestinal mucosa during absorption	Lecithin—essential for formation of myelin sheaths
	Cholesterol	Formation of cholesterol	Cholesterol found in all living cells. It is essential for the formation of steroid hormones in the adrenal cortex and gonads
Cells Mobilization of fat from adipose tissue cells	Cholesterol esters	Cholesterol esters formed and distributed to the cells or excreted in the bile	Cholesterol enters into basic structure of the cell and is essential for the normal permeability of cell membranes
Liver Synthesis of lipids from: Glucose, Acetic acid, Amino acid, Pyruvic acid	Ketone bodies	Ketone bodies formed in the liver in the course of oxidation of fatty acids	Ketone bodies oxidized in muscle and other cells. Excess excreted by kidney
		Acetate converted to fatty acids for neutral fats and phospholipids	

Heparin has been shown experimentally to reduce the blood level of lipids; i.e., it "clears" the plasma of lipids. How this action functions physiologically is not entirely known.

Hormones also affect fat metabolism. Epinephrine, norepinephrine, adrenocorticotropin, and glucagon stimulate the release of fatty acids from depot fats.

Metabolism of fat is not so clearly understood as that of carbohydrate. Much experimental work has recently been devoted to the subject owing to the relationship of heart attacks and deposits of lipids, including cholesterol, in the walls of arteries (atherosclerosis). It is known that high levels of serum lipids lead to increased deposits of lipids in the arterial wall. How to decrease these high levels has not been reliably established, although fatty acids containing many "unsaturated" or double bonds between carbon atoms seem more effective than fatty acids that are "saturated" (no double bonds). The essential fatty acids (those that must be present in the diet) are all unsaturated—linoleic, linolenic, and arachidonic acids. Although heart attacks do appear to be related to the deposits of lipids in arterial walls, there still is no concrete evidence that changing from a diet high in "saturated" fatty acids to one high in "unsaturated" fatty acids is beneficial.

Metabolism of Proteins

As a result of digestion, proteins are hydrolyzed to amino acids, which are absorbed by the blood capillaries of the villi, pass into the portal vein, are carried through the liver into the blood of the general circulation, and are distributed to the tissues. The tissues select and store certain of these substances; and in each organ they are either synthesized into new tissue or used to maintain and repair tissue. Amino acids not used in synthesis of protoplasm are broken down or deaminized in the liver. In deaminization, the amino groups are removed from amino acid molecules; transamination involves the transfer of the amino group from an amino acid to another organic acid. These NH_2 groups may be used for synthesis of other amino acids or for formation of urea by the liver. In the kidney, ammonia is formed from certain amino acids and is used for the production of ammonium salts, thus sparing the sodium ions of the blood in maintaining acid-base balance (p. 672).

In skeletal muscle amino acids are utilized to form creatine and creatine phosphate substances which have an active role in muscle contraction.

The nonnitrogenous portion of the amino acid molecule which is left after deaminization is oxidized to furnish energy (see citric acid cycle, p. 644), or is synthesized into glycogen or into fat. Therefore, this portion of the amino acid molecule may be regarded as a source of energy. It is obvious that some of the amino acids are used to synthesize tissue protein under the influence of RNA (see p. 26) and other substances in the body, and the balance not needed for this purpose serves to supply energy.

The blood contains amino acids at all times. Fasting does not free the tissues from them nor does a high-protein diet result in any great increase in the blood or tissues. Amino acids are considered intermediary products in the building up and breaking down of body protein. Both the building up and breaking down are thought to occur in all the tissues.

Certain amino acids have physiological roles that are distinctive. *Glycine* is used by the liver in detoxification of benzoic acid, a food preservative, and in formation of hemoglobin, one of the bile acids, purines, and fatty acids. *Methionine* reacts with niacin and participates in formation of phospholipids, ergosterol, and histamine and in the detoxification of certain poisons such as chloroform and carbon tetrachloride. *Tryptophan* is a precursor of niacin and of serotonin, a vasoconstrictor.

Nucleoproteins. These conjugated proteins are found in the nuclei of cells, as well as in the cytoplasm, and are abundant in the nucleated cells of the glandular organs, such as the liver, pancreas, and thymus. Foods rich in nucleoproteins are sweetbreads, kidney, roe, liver, and sardines. Foods with a fairly high nucleoprotein content are beef, veal, mutton, pork, chicken, turkey, goose, and other game, fish (cod excepted), spinach, asparagus, and beans. In the course of digestion the protein is separated from the nucleic acid and is eventually reduced to amino acids. The nucleic acid gives rise to substances known as purines. Uric acid is the end product of the metabolism of purines from which it arises as a result of oxidation; it is excreted in the urine.

Summary—Some of the Important Steps in Protein Metabolism

Sources of Protein	*Role of the Liver*	*Tissue Cells*
Digestive processes Digestion of protein foods to amino acids	Taken to liver via portal vein Amino acids	To all cells of body for maintenance, growth, and repair of tissues
	Synthesis of: Serum albumin Serum globulin Fibrinogen Prothrombin	Nucleoproteins in cytoplasm and in nucleus of all cells
	Synthesis of essential nitrogen containing nonproteins: Choline Purines Creatine Pyrimidines	Synthesis of certain hormones and enzymes
	Deaminization of amino acids, conversion of amino acids into glucose and fats	
	Synthesis of amino acids from other amino acids	Excess amino acids oxidized by way of citric acid cycle to carbon dioxide and water
	Formation of keto acids ⟶	Oxidized by way of citric acid cycle to carbon dioxide and water

Citric Acid Cycle. The final stage in oxidation of glucose, fatty acids, and amino acids is by way of the citric acid cycle—a complex series of chemical reactions in which acetyl fragments are first activated by combination with coenzyme A. The acetyl coenzyme A then reacts with oxaloacetic acid to form citric acid, releasing coenzyme A. By a series of steps hydrogen and carbon dioxide contained in the original acetyl radical are released with eventual formation of oxaloacetic acid. Hydrogen is combined with oxygen in the presence of cytochrome enzymes.

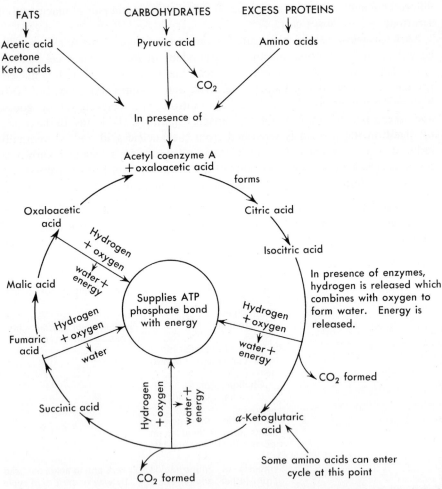

Figure 21–4. Citric acid cycle. Using fats, carbohydrates, and excess amino acids as fuel, the citric acid cycle supplies energy-rich bonds to adenosine triphosphate. A series of acids are converted one to another by enzymes with release of carbon dioxide and transfer of hydrogen to oxygen, forming water. The energy released is used to form ATP and to provide body heat. ATP is essential for all muscle contraction and is also found in all cells of the body.

Ketogenic amino acids (which form ketone bodies on oxidation) and gluco-
genic amino acids (forming pyruvic acid) enter the cycle as acetyl fragments, as
do fatty acids and their ketone bodies. Lactic acid is transformed to pyruvic
acid before entering the cycle. Thus pyruvic acid and the acetyl radical in particular are crucial intermediary products in oxidation and provide the means by
which carbohydrates can be synthesized from noncarbohydrate sources, since
much of the pathway is reversible.

The citric acid cycle, however, is not merely a cycle which eventually forms
carbon dioxide and water. Its purpose is the release of energy in the acetyl
radical; formation of carbon dioxide and water is incidental. The large amount
of energy is transferred to adenosine as phosphate radicals are attached to it,
with eventual formation of ATP.

Basal Metabolism

Sources of the Body's Energy. The body is able to oxidize any or all of the
foods to produce energy. Consequently, the most convenient way to compare
food values is in terms of their energy value.

The energy of food is not used directly as heat, but it is customary to measure
it in heat units. To determine the amount of energy produced by the oxidation of
food, the amount of heat produced on oxidation is measured by a calorimeter
in terms of calories. A large calorie is the amount of heat required to raise the
temperature of 1 kg (2.2 lb) of water 1°C. The large calorie (Cal) is the one
referred to in physiology. When undergoing complete oxidation in the bomb
calorimeter, the foodstuffs yield the following:

Carbohydrate	1 gm—4.10 Cal
Fat	1 gm—9.45 Cal
Protein	1 gm—5.65 Cal

The oxidation of protein in the body is never quite complete, for the urea,
creatinine, uric acid, etc., eliminated in urine still contain about 113 Cal per
gram of protein catabolized by the cells. Hence, protein yields to body cells only
4.35 Cal (5.65 less 1.3 calories) per gram of protein received by them. The cells
oxidize the carbon and the hydrogen completely but only partially oxidize the
nitrogen of the proteins which they receive. It is said that on the average about
98 per cent of the carbohydrates, about 95 per cent of the fats, and about 92
per cent of the proteins ingested are absorbed and reach the body cells. Some
deductions are made for what are called *losses in digestion*. The practical figures
used in estimating the fuel value of food are therefore:

Carbohydrate	1 gm—4 cal (98% of 4.10 Cal)
Fat	1 gm—9 cal (95% of 9.45 Cal)
Protein	1 gm—4 cal (92% of 4.35 Cal)

Basal metabolism is the rate of energy metabolism required to keep the body
alive. The term *basal metabolism* is used clinically to indicate the rate of energy
metabolism of the body when the subject is lying quiet and relaxed in a room of
comfortable temperature in what is called "postabsorptive" state, i.e., 12 to 18

hours after the last meal. The digestion and absorption of the meal should be completed, and only such expenditure of energy should occur during the test as is required to maintain body warmth, minimal cell activity, respiration, and circulation; or, briefly, conditions should represent *functional activity at a minimum.* The basal rate of energy metabolism is used as a starting point for the calculation of total energy requirements in food under varying conditions and as a basis for diagnosis.

Basal metabolism may be determined by *the direct method,* in which the subject is placed in a respiratory chamber and the amount of heat evolved is measured, or *the indirect method,* in which the heat given off is computed from the respiratory exchange. Metabolism rates determined by the indirect method are based on the respiratory quotient, which is the ratio between the volume of carbon dioxide excreted and the volume of oxygen consumed. It is found by dividing the former by the latter. It has been demonstrated that energy calculated from the amount of carbon dioxide excreted and oxygen absorbed by a subject is equivalent to the heat given off by the body.

The amount of oxygen required to oxidize a given amount of carbohydrate, fat, or protein is not the same. In the oxidation of carbohydrate, the volume of carbon dioxide produced is equal to the volume of oxygen absorbed. The respiratory quotient (or RQ) is, therefore,

$$\frac{\text{Volume } CO_2 \text{ produced}}{\text{Volume } O_2 \text{ consumed}}, \text{ or } RQ = 1$$

There are slight variations in the respiratory quotients for different fats, owing to differences in molecular weight. For human fat, the quotient is 0.703. For protein, the quotient is 0.8 to 0.82. These figures show that the carbon dioxide produced is generally less than the oxygen which has disappeared in the exchange.

If the combustion of carbohydrate alone were possible, the respiratory quotient would be 1; if only protein were burned, it would be 0.80 to 0.82; if fat, about 0.7.

Under ordinary conditions, the respiratory quotient is about 0.85, but it may vary within rather wide limits, depending on the diet.

Basal metabolism in terms of body weight is not often determined, but it is sometimes convenient to use this method of estimation. If the basal rate is 1 Cal per kilogram per hour, the adult standing 5 ft 8 in. tall and weighing 70 kg would have a basal metabolism of 1,680 Cal for 24 hours ($1 \times 70 \times 24$).

Basal metabolism calculated on the basis of surface area of the body is more nearly accurate than that determined in terms of body weight, because heat loss increases in proportion to surface rather than weight. A table for this purpose has been worked out. According to this table, a woman standing 5 ft 4 in. tall and weighing 56 kg with 1.6 sq m of body surface will have a basal metabolism of about 36.9 Cal per square meter per hour with a total basal metabolism of 1,400 Cal per day ($1.6 \times 24 \times 36.9$). Likewise, a man of 50 years of age, weighing 70 kg and measuring 5 ft 8 in. in height, will have a body surface of 1.83 sq m, and his basal metabolism will be about 1,700 Cal per day ($1.83 \times 24 \times 39.7$).

Variations in Basal Metabolism. It has been found that a number of factors, such as age, sex, sleep, and thyroid hormone, influence the basal metabolic rate. In women the rate is a little lower than in men; it gradually decreases with age; it may be increased by systematic exercise over a long period; prolonged under-nourishment reduces it; all the preceding relate in great degree to the amount of muscle tissue in the individual, which has a higher metabolic rate than adipose tissue; certain races appear to have a slightly higher rate than others.

Emotional tension increases it, but the individual then is not basal—i.e., not completely relaxed. Temperature has a marked effect on the metabolic rate. Fever causes an increase—often beyond the energy supplied in the diet, and body tissues are utilized for energy. Similarly, a decrease in body temperature decreases metabolic rate and therefore decreases the amount of oxygen required.

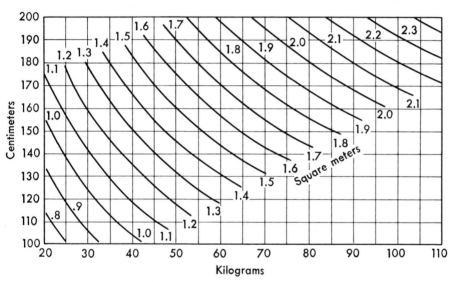

Figure 21–5. Chart for determining surface area of adults from weight and height. Height in inches divided by 0.393 gives height in centimeters. Weight in pounds divided by 2.2. gives weight in kilograms. (Courtesy of Dr. Eugene Du Bois and the *Archives of Internal Medicine*.)

Daily Calorie Requirement

If constant weight is to be maintained showing neither gain nor loss, the daily output of calories (as determined by calorimeter tests) must be balanced by calories taken in. On such data the daily food requirement in terms of calories is based. Since basal metabolism represents the heat given off when physio-logical work is at a minimum (in the morning after a comfortable night's rest, relaxed in bed, before breakfast), it is obvious that any increase in physiological activity, even the slightest (sitting up under the same conditions), increases the metabolic rate over the minimum. Comparison of the basal metabolic rate with the metabolic rates during various types of work shows that work results in an increment in the amount of heat eliminated. Muscular activity, even the slightest, increases the metabolic rate. Such increases have been estimated and graded for the average individual according to the calories required as follows:

	Calories Per Hour
Very light work, or sitting at rest	100
Light work	120
Moderate work	175
Severe work	350

Total Calorie Requirement. The metabolic rate is reduced about 10 per cent beyond the basal level during sleep. Allowance is made for this in estimating the total daily calorie requirement of an individual. On the other hand, the process of digestion of food itself brings about a need for an increase of 6 to 10 per cent of the calorie intake. This is called the *specific dynamic action of food* (S.D.A.), and allowance must be made for it. After consideration of all these factors the total calorie requirement of the average man will be found to be about as follows:

	Calories
8 hours of sleep at 65 Cal	520
2 hours of light exercise at 120 Cal	240
8 hours of moderate work at 175 Cal	1,400
6 hours sitting at rest at 100 Cal	600
	2,760
6–10 per cent for S.D.A.	250
Total requirement for 24 hours	3,010

It will be seen that increase in weight or loss of weight is to be determined largely by control of the caloric intake of food. The three types of food should be considered from the standpoint of their relative nutritional values and of the amount of energy the oxidation of each releases.

In a diet of 3,000-Cal energy value, the proportions of the main constituents should be approximately as shown below.

	Calories	Approximate % of Total Calories	Grams
Carbohydrate	1,440	48	380
Fat	1,200	40	133
Protein	360	12	90

It is obvious that increased calorie need occurs in the growing child and in pregnancy.

Physiology of Body Temperature

From the standpoint of heat control, animals may be divided into two great classes:

Constant-temperature (homeothermic) animals, or those whose temperature remains practically constant whether the surrounding air is hotter or cooler than the body. Birds and mammals (including human beings) are in this class.

Variable-temperature (poikilothermic) animals, or those whose temperature varies with that of the surrounding medium, e.g., reptiles, frogs, fishes. In winter their temperature is low, and in summer their temperature approximates that of their surroundings. The human fetus is in this class.

At birth the heat-regulating mechanism is not "in working order," and infants are not able to regulate their body temperature, hence the importance of keeping them warm. Premature infants are even less able to regulate their body temperature, hence the need of special means to keep them warm, but they should not be kept at the temperature of the adult.

Between the two groups are various classes of hibernating animals.

The great difference between these two classes of animals is in their reactions to external temperature. A cold environment reduces the temperature of the cold-blooded creature, reduces the metabolism of all its tissues, and thus reduces its heat production. The warm-blooded animal reacts in the opposite way. In a cold environment its temperature remains fairly constant. When shivering occurs metabolism increases and thus heat production increases.

Production of Heat. The heat produced within the body represents the difference between the energy used in the anabolic processes and the energy provided by the catabolic processes. Some heat is produced directly. Some comes from energy used to do work in the cells, such as contraction of muscle or secretion, and then is transformed into heat. Thus, every cell produces heat. But the more active tissues, such as skeletal muscle, the liver, and actively secreting glands, provide more heat in relation to their weight than do less active tissues. The heat lost from the body represents the caloric value of the food which must be supplied to the healthy individual who is maintaining constant weight.

Distribution of Heat. The blood permeates all the tissues and serves as an absorbing medium for the heat. Wherever oxidation takes place and heat is generated, the temperature of the blood circulating in these tissues is raised. Wherever, on the other hand, the blood vessels are exposed to conditions which are cool because of heat lost by evaporation, etc., as in the moist membranes in the lungs or the more or less moist skin, the temperature of the blood is lowered. But these changes are not effected instantaneously, and consequently the temperature of some internal parts must always be higher than that of others. This is particularly true of the liver because its blood vessels are well protected against loss of heat. Because of this the temperature of the blood in different parts of the body varies slightly; but the circulation, moving through warmer and then through cooler parts tends to keep the average temperature of the blood at about 38°C.

Loss of Heat. Heat is continually being produced in the body and continually leaving the body by the skin and the lungs, and by the urine and feces, which are at the temperature of the body when eliminated.

If weight is being neither lost nor gained, the calories lost per day match the calories taken in per day. One record of heat lost during a 24-hour day follows:

Lost from skin	2,156 Cal, or　87.5%
1,792 Cal, or 73.0%, by radiation and conduction	
364 Cal, or 14.5%, by evaporation of perspiration	
Lost in expired air	266 Cal, or　10.7%
182 Cal, or 7.2%, vaporization of water	
84 Cal, or 3.5%, warming air	
Lost in urine or feces	48 Cal, or　　1.8%
Total heat loss per 24-hour day	2,470 Cal, or 100.0%

From these figures it is evident that the skin is the important factor in eliminating body heat. This is due to the large surface offered for radiation, conduction, and evaporation and to the large amount of blood which constantly flows through the skin.

The temperature and humidity of the atmosphere may cause considerable difference in the percentages given above. A low temperature will increase the loss of heat by radiation, conduction, and convection and decrease that by evaporation. A high temperature will increase the relative amount of heat lost by evaporation, owing to the greater production of perspiration. Heat is lost by the evaporation of perspiration, by the warming of air taken into the lungs, and by the evaporation of the water which leaves the body by the lungs. It requires about 0.5 Cal for the evaporation of 1 gm of water, or about 250 Cal for the evaporation of 500 gm (1 pt) of water. It is estimated that under ordinary circumstances it requires about 250 Cal daily for the evaporation of the perspiration and about 250 Cal for the evaporation of the water (about 500 ml) lost through the lungs. In hot weather the perspiration may be greatly increased, and more heat than usual may be lost by evaporation of this water from the skin, particularly if the humidity is not excessive. Under these conditions there is less water lost as urine. High humidity interferes with the evaporation of perspiration, because air can take up only a certain amount of moisture. For this reason heat is more acutely felt when the humidity is high, even though the temperature is low, than when the humidity is low and the temperature high. Heat prostration and sunstroke are more likely to occur on hot days when the humidity is high than when it is low. Moving air favors evaporation because it tends to drive away evaporated moisture, hence the comfort derived from an electric fan, which keeps the air in motion.

The Regulation of Body Temperature

The constant temperature of the body is maintained by means of a balance between heat production (thermogenesis) and heat loss (thermolysis). The body must control the production and the loss of heat (thermotaxis). It is important to remember that although heat production may be increased by increasing the rate of metabolism, it is not possible to decrease metabolic rate as a means of producing less heat. The part the nervous system plays in this relationship is not completely understood. The fact that infants cannot perform this function until some time after birth indicates that heat regulation follows a course parallel to

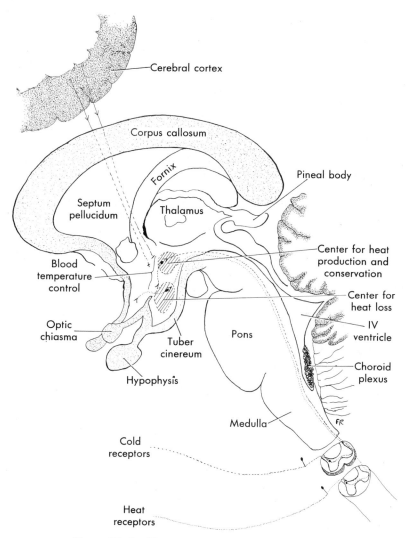

Figure 21–6. Nervous control of body temperature.

the development of the nervous system. Experimental work indicates that the accurate *balance* between heat production and heat loss is controlled by nerve fibers connected with a temperature-regulating center in the hypothalamus.

Heat production (chemical regulation) in the body is varied by increasing or decreasing the physiological oxidations. This end is effected in part by *taking*

Heat Production (thermogenic center in hypothalamus)

- Amount and frequency food intake (available calorific value) — Appetite, psychological states, and hunger, which relate to the tone of the smooth muscle cells of the stomach
- Metabolic rate (rate of use of foods) — Related to activity of all cells of the body, but especially to striated muscle cells and cells of large glands (great bulk of living human tissue)

Heat Loss (heat-loss center in hypothalamus)

- *Radiation and conduction* related to quantity of blood through skin capillaries per unit of time — Concerned with tone of smooth muscle cells of arterioles
- *Evaporation of perspiration* related to quantity of blood through skin capillaries per unit of time and, therefore, to temperature of skin and availability of raw materials for manufacture of perspiration — Concerned with tone of smooth muscle cells of arterioles and venules and with activity of cells of sweat glands

food and by *muscular exercise*. In this connection the action of enzymes and some of the internal secretions (e.g., thyroxin—and possibly epinephrine) is important. *Thyroxin* increases the metabolism of the body and stimulates all of the metabolic processes. During digestion heat is produced partly by the peristaltic action of the intestines and partly by the activity of the various digestive glands, particularly the liver. *Cold weather* stimulates the appetite; and an increased amount of food, usually accompanied by an increase of fats, increases heat production. Cold causes the muscles to contract and speeds up the processes of oxidation. Muscular contractions give rise to heat; therefore, muscular activity counteracts the effects of external cold. On the other hand, muscular activity does not increase the body temperature in warm weather to any marked extent. This is accounted for by the fact that when muscular exertion speeds up circulation, the blood vessels in the skin dilate, the sweat glands pour out more abundant secretion, and the heated blood passes in larger quantities through the cutaneous vessels, which are kept well cooled by the evaporation of the perspiration; the general average temperature of the body is thus maintained. Study Figure 21–5 for centers that regulate body temperature.

Heat Loss (Physical Regulation). To a small extent heat loss is controlled through an increase in the respiratory rate. The increased respirations associated with muscular activity aid somewhat in eliminating the excess heat produced, although this factor is not as important as sweating and flushing of the skin. In man respiration plays only a small part in temperature regulation; but in animals that do not perspire, respiration is an important means of regulating the temperature.

During muscular activity or when the external temperature is high, receptors for heat are stimulated, and impulses are transmitted over sensory fibers to the nerve centers controlling the motor fibers of the sweat glands. The motor fibers stimulate the activity of the sweat glands, and an increased amount of perspiration occurs. An increased amount of heat is required to vaporize this perspiration, and thus heat is lost. Excessive humidity interferes with the evaporation of water and thus interferes with the loss of heat, hence the discomfort experienced on hot, humid days.

The receptors for heat not only transmit impulses that stimulate the sweat glands to activity but at the same time transmit impulses that result in the depression of the vasoconstrictor center leading to the arterioles of the skin. In consequence the arterioles dilate, and more blood is sent to the surface to be cooled. This tends to increase the temperature of the skin and hence increases the heat lost by conduction and radiation. When the external temperature is low, the receptors for cold transmit impulses which result in stimulation of the vasoconstrictors and consequent contraction of the arterioles of the skin. This lessens the amount of blood in the skin arterioles, reduces the temperature of the skin, and so lessens the amount of heat loss.

The flow of blood through the skin tends to raise skin temperature, while the loss of heat to the environment tends to lower it. The nervous system adjusts the flow of blood in the skin in relation to environmental temperature at the skin surface in such a way that the body maintains a constant temperature. Temperature and heat-dissipating capacities of the environment at the skin surface are modified by clothing (amount, texture, style, color, etc.) and by ventilation of rooms.

Thermal comfort seems to be closely related to skin temperature, and optimal average skin temperature seems to be about 33°C (91.4°F). If skin temperature rises or falls, physiological adjustments of heat production and heat loss can be made in order to maintain the normal body temperature, but they will not be made at the optimum physiological level. A sitting-resting person in thermal comfort is said to produce about 50 Cal per hour per square meter of surface area and, in a well-ventilated room (temperature 70°F, air movement at about 20 ft per minute, and humidity somewhat under 50 per cent), would lose less than 25 per cent (12 Cal) by evaporation of insensible perspiration and about 38 Cal per hour per square meter of surface area by radiation and conduction through the clothing to the environment. This gives a way of gauging (by means of heat-insulation value) the clothing needed in relation to activity, and room temperature, in order to keep skin temperature at approximately 33°C, or the temperature needed in relation to activity and clothing.

It has been suggested that the concentration of the blood is a factor to be considered. The water of the body holds heat; and when the external temperature is low, water is withdrawn from the blood to the tissues, leaving the blood more concentrated. When the external temperature is high, water is withdrawn from the tissues to the blood. When the blood is dilute, an increased amount of water is brought to the surface, and an increased loss of heat results; but when the water is withheld in the interior of the body, less heat is lost. Other factors to be considered are size, age, and constitution.

Size. The quantity of heat produced by well-nourished animals, including man, is relatively constant; but the larger the surface of the body exposed to a cooler medium, the greater must be the loss of heat, since the heat lost is related to the *area of surface*. Small animals present a proportionately larger surface to the surrounding medium than larger animals; hence, the loss per unit of weight is greater, and this must be compensated for by a greater heat production. Skin secretions of different animals have varied effects in relation to heat insulation, and account must be taken of this also.

Age.   In children the heat production is relatively large, because they are active and growing. Moreover, young children have not the constancy of temperature which is an evolved characteristic of adult life. On the contrary, they are subject to changes of body temperature which would be of grave import in an adult.

Constitution.   Individuals differ greatly in their power of heat loss. Apart from differences in size and in the faculty of perspiration, there exist differences in compactness of shape, in the amount of adipose tissue protecting the viscera, etc.

Clothing aids in the maintenance of heat, though, of course, clothes are not in themselves usually sources of heat. The kind of clothing to be worn should be determined by the necessity for diminishing the loss of heat, as in cold weather, or facilitating this loss, as in warm weather. Clothing of any kind captures a layer of warm and moist air between it and the skin and thus diminishes greatly the loss by evaporation, conduction, and radiation. In considering the heat value of clothing, the important properties are amount, quality, texture, style, and color.

Materials that are loosely woven are warmer than those that are tightly woven, because the meshes in a loosely woven material are capable of holding air, which is a poor conductor of heat. Two layers of thinner material are usually warmer than one layer of thicker material, because a layer of air is held between the two.

Thick material does not allow the warm air next to the body to penetrate to the outside.

Light-colored or white materials reflect heat, while dark-colored materials absorb heat to some extent; hence, they are warmer than light-colored textiles.

Thick, porous materials keep the body warm. Wool has an additional advantage, as evaporation takes place more slowly from it than from linen, cotton, or silk; and it has a greater capacity for absorbing moisture, so that the layer of air next to the skin does not become saturated with moisture. Thin and very porous materials help to keep the body cool, because they allow the air to penetrate to the skin, and thus assist the evaporation of sweat. Loose clothing facilitates heat loss.

Hot Baths.   The primary effect of a hot bath is to prevent loss of heat from the surface of the body, and some increase in temperature may result. If the bath is not continued for too long a time, this effect is counteracted by the increased perspiration that follows.

Cold, or Tonic, Baths.   The primary effect of a cold bath is similar to the prolonged effect of cold air. The cold bath contracts the arterioles of the skin, drives the blood to the interior, and increases oxidation. If the bath is a short one and is followed by friction (contrast condition, cold followed by heat), the reaction is dilatation of arterioles. The heated blood is sent to the surface, the circulation is quickened, and there is a consequent loss of heat. In health the gain in heat is usually balanced by the loss of heat, and the purpose of a cold bath is to exercise the arterioles and stimulate the circulation. If the bath is continued for some time, the temperature of the skin and of the muscles lying beneath is reduced, and either the heat-producing processes may be checked and a loss of temperature result, or shivering may intervene. In this case the muscular contractions and constriction of the blood vessels increase metabolism and heat production. When cold baths are given for the purpose of increasing heat elimination, friction is used during the bath to prevent shivering. Friction stimulates the sensory fibers of the skin, causes dilation of the arterioles, and favors the flow of warm blood to the surface, thus decreasing the sensation of cold and increasing heat elimination. If properly given, cold baths stimulate the nervous system, improve the tone of the muscles, including the muscles of the heart and blood vessels, stimulate the circulation, and favor the elimination of heat.

Variations in Temperature

The temperature of the human body is usually measured by a thermometer placed in the mouth, axilla, or rectum. Such measurements show slight variations. The normal temperature by mouth is about 37°C (98.6°F), by axilla the temperature is lower, and by rectum it is usually 1° higher.

Normal variations depend upon such factors as time of day, exercise, meals, age, sex, season, climate, and clothing. The temperature is usually lowest between 3 and 5 A.M. It rises slowly during the day, reaches its maximum at about 4 P.M., and falls again during the night. This corresponds to the usual temperature ranges in fever, when the minimum is in the early morning and the maximum is in the evening. Muscular activity and food cause a slight increase in temperature. This probably accounts for the increase in temperature during the day. In the case of nightworkers who sleep during the day, the increase in temperature occurs during the night, which is the period when food is eaten and work performed. Age has some influence. Infants and young children have a slightly higher temperature (about 1°) than adults. Their heat-regulating mechanism is more easily disturbed, and rise of temperature is caused by slight disturbances of digestion or metabolism and usually is less significant than the same increase in adults. Aged people show a tendency to revert to infantile conditions, and their temperature is usually slightly higher than in middle life. It is said that women have a slightly higher temperature than men. The effects of climate and clothing have been discussed.

Subnormal Temperature. In order to carry on the activities essential to life, the body must maintain a normal temperature. If the temperature falls much below normal, to about 35°C (95°F), life may be threatened. Subnormal temperature may be due to excessive loss of heat, profuse sweating, hemorrhage, and lessened heat production, as in starvation. In cases of starvation the fall of temperature is very marked, especially during the last days of life. The diminished activity of the tissues first affects the central nervous system; the patient becomes languid and drowsy, and finally unconscious; the heart beats more and more feebly, the breath comes more and more slowly, and the sleep of unconsciousness passes insensibly into the sleep of death.

Hypothermia. It is possible to decrease body temperature by giving sedatives to depress the hypothalamic thermostat and then using ice packs or other measures of cooling. Temperature can be maintained considerably below 32.2°C (90°F). Artificial cooling of the body is used during heart surgery so that the heart can be stopped for several minutes at a time without apparent untoward physiological results, since the metabolic rate decreases and oxygen need is less.

Abnormal Variations. *Fever.* The term *fever* is applied to an abnormal condition characterized by increased temperature, increased rate of heart action, increased respirations, increased tissue waste, faulty secretion, and various other symptoms such as thirst, weakness, and apathy. Some of the symptoms accompanying fever may be due to the substances or conditions causing the fever, some to the high temperature, and some to both.

CAUSE. The exact cause of fever is unknown. It may be due to diminished heat loss, increased heat production, or both. Fever is usually accompanied by increased catabolism of body tissue, as shown in the increased urea content of the urine, even though the dietary protein is not increased; in explanation of this it is suggested that the toxins which cause the fever produce some change in the cells which makes them susceptible to the action of oxidizing enzymes, so that oxidation and heat production are abnormally increased. Fever is accompanied also by retention of water in the tissues, resulting in a concentration of the blood. Usually the superficial blood vessels are contracted, and this is thought to be caused by the toxins acting on the vasoconstrictor centers. It is believed that fever and the conditions that accompany it are protective reactions to overcome the effect of toxins on the body. The reasons for this are based on various laboratory experiments. Animals have been inoculated with bacteria or bacterial toxins and then kept for a time at a temperature of about 40°C (104°F), with the result that they resisted the infection better than animals who were not subjected to this higher temperature. In connection with this, bacteriologists remind us that many organisms are killed at a temperature slightly above that of the body, and it may be that a high body temperature favors the formation of immune bodies. The contraction of the superficial blood vessels sends more blood to the interior of the body, thus providing an increased number of phagocytes and antibodies to fight the infection.

In fever therapy an artificial hyperpyrexia is brought about by the use of a hypertherm, or heating cabinet, in which the body temperature may be raised and held at some specific temperature, say 41.1 to 41.7°C (106 to 107°F), for a varying period of hours in order to render certain pathogenic organisms in the body nonviable. With such strenuous treatment care is taken to combat the decreased oxygen saturation in the body fluids by the use of oxygen and carbon dioxide mixture and to prevent excess alkalosis by the use of saline fluids.

QUESTIONS FOR DISCUSSION

1. Assuming that the foods are normally digested, what are the end products and how do they reach the blood stream?

2. If the quantity of food from a meal is in excess of immediate energy needs, what will become of the excess? Through what metabolic processes might this be accomplished?

3. Since the body does not use the food per se for energy, what is the function of the citric acid cycle?

4. Which hormones influence the level of blood glucose? What other factors are involved?

5. What is the role of the liver in relation to metabolism of carbohydrates, fats, and proteins?

6. Differentiate between metabolism and basal metabolism and explain three factors that will affect each one.

7. How can you determine your metabolic needs? Why is "calorie counting" important (a) for growing children, (b) for energy production, (c) for individuals who have a tendency to put on weight, and (d) for "senior" individuals with a "heart condition"?

SUMMARY

Absorption

Passage of digested food material from the cavity of the alimentary canal to the blood

Determining conditions
(1) Area of surface for absorption
(2) Length of time food is in contact with absorbing surface
(3) Concentration of digested material present
Above conditions are realized in small intestine

Small intestine
(1) Circular folds and villi increase internal surface
(2) Food remains for several hours
(3) Products of digestion higher in intestine, lower in blood

Paths of absorption
(1) Capillaries of villi absorb sugars, amino acids, and some of the glycerol and fatty acids, carry them to portal vein, then to liver
(2) Central lymph channel of villus absorbs glycerol and fat, empties into larger lymph vessels, then into thoracic duct, superior vena cava, and right atrium of heart

Stomach
Alcohol and alcoholic solutions absorbed
Small amounts of sugar, amino acids may be absorbed
Water not absorbed

Large intestine
Limited absorption of digested foodstuffs, marked absorption of water

Place of Absorption of Digested Foodstuffs

Water—absorbed in small intestine but loss made good by secretion, marked absorption in large intestine
Salts—absorption may take place from any part of intestines, depends upon concentration of solution and nature of salt
Simple sugars—pass into capillaries and then by way of portal vein to liver
Fatty acids and glycerol—absorbed by lacteals in villi, synthesized to form fat. Fat carried to thoracic duct, which empties into left subclavian vein
Amino acids—pass into capillaries of villi

Metabolism

May include all processes involved from time food enters the body until waste is excreted
In this chapter metabolism is limited to include only changes that occur in cells

Metabolism (cont.)

Consists of

Anabolism—processes by which living cells take food substances from the blood and make them into protoplasm and stored products

Catabolism—processes by which living cells change into simpler substances (1) part of their own protoplasm, or (2) stored products

Catabolic processes
- (1) Simple splitting of complex molecules into simpler ones
- (2) Hydrolysis, or the splitting of complex molecules into simpler ones through reaction with water
- (3) Oxidation, with the production of carbon dioxide and water

Physiology

Growth and repair of tissue

Release of chemical energy in the form of heat, nervous activity, muscular activity, etc.

Factors
- (1) Oxygen absorbed from lungs
- (2) Enzymes secreted by tissue cells
- (3) Hormones secreted by ductless glands
- (4) Vitamins furnished by food
- (5) The nervous system

Metabolism of Carbohydrates

Supply regulated by diet

Storage provided temporarily, by liver, muscles, and cells of tissues. Carbohydrate stored as glycogen

Consumption controlled by energy needs of tissues

Processes

Glycogenesis, or the production of glycogen in the liver

Glycogenolysis, or the conversion of glycogen to glucose according to body needs

Glycolysis, or the anaerobic oxidation in the tissues

Glyconeogenesis formation of glycogen or glucose from noncarbohydrate sources

Glycosuria, or loss of glucose in the urine

Citric acid cycle—process by which intermediate products of carbohydrate, fat and amino acids are metabolized to carbon dioxide and water, with production of energy for use in formation of ATP

Regulation of blood glucose

(1) Hormonal:

Pancreas—produces *insulin* for metabolism of glucose
- (a) Concerned with phosphorylation of glucose
- (b) Inhibits glycogen formation in liver from noncarbohydrate sources
- (c) Decreases plasma glucose level

Glucagon—favors glycogenolysis

Anterior pituitary—opposes action of insulin in glucose phosphorylation, increases glucose formation from noncarbohydrate sources

Adrenal cortex—glucocorticoids decrease tissue utilization of glucose, increase blood glucose and gluconeogenesis, promote formation of glycogen

Adrenal medulla—epinephrine stimulates glycogenolysis in liver and muscle

Thyroid—thyroxin increases oxidative rate, therefore, utilization of glucose, increases glyconeogenesis

(2) Nervous:

Center in hypothalamus which regulates carbohydrate metabolism

Emotional excitement influences through sympathetic system and hormones

Metabolism of Carbohydrates (cont.)

Physiology
- Furnish main source of energy for muscular work and all the nutritive processes
- Help to maintain body temperature
- Protect body tissues by forming reserve fund for time of need (glycogen)
- Excess carbohydrates are converted into depot fat
- May be used in constructive processes

End products
- When completely oxidized, the waste products are carbon dioxide and water

Derangements of
- (1) Glycogenesis breaks down, giving rise to alimentary glycosuria
- (2) Glycogenolysis impaired
- (3) Glycolysis breaks down
- (4) Plasma glucose level rises and renal threshold is exceeded

Metabolism of Fats

Reconstruction—in act of passing through epithelial cells of villi, glycerol and fatty acids combine to form fat

Dependent upon lipase

Physiology
- Yield heat and other forms of energy
- Stored as adipose tissue
- Synthesized to form compound fats and fatlike substances; lecithin, cholesterol
- Glycerol may be converted to glucose

Oxidation
- First step brought about by lipase
- Lipase controls output of fat to blood
- Oxidation takes place after lipase has acted
- Fatty acids split; 2-carbon units enter citric acid cycle; eventually oxidized to carbon dioxide and water

Body fat
- Formed from fats, carbohydrates, and proteins of food in order named

Obesity
- May be caused by eating more food than body needs, by lack of exercise, or both
- May be due to endocrine disturbances

Factors affecting
- Choline and methionine essential for synthesis of phospholipids in the liver
- Heparin in some way 'clears' the plasma of lipids
- Hormones—epinephrine and norepinephrine, ACTH, and glucagon stimulate release of fatty acids from depot fats

Metabolism of Proteins

Absorbed as amino acids. From villi pass to portal vein, thence to liver, and general circulation

Tissues select amino acids
- (1) To build new tissue and serum proteins
- (2) To maintain cell activity

Amino acids not used in synthesis of protoplasm are deaminized and split into nonnitrogenous and nitrogenous portions

Nonnitrogenous portion oxidized to carbon dioxide and water, or converted into glycogen

Nitrogenous portion passes through a series of changes—end product, urea, or ammonium salts

Classification
- Endogenous, includes building up of amino acids to tissue protoplasm and final disintegration to creatinine and urea
- Exogenous, includes reactions affecting uncombined amino acids, formation of urea from nitrogenous portion, and glucose from nonnitrogenous portion, also secondary production of glycogen

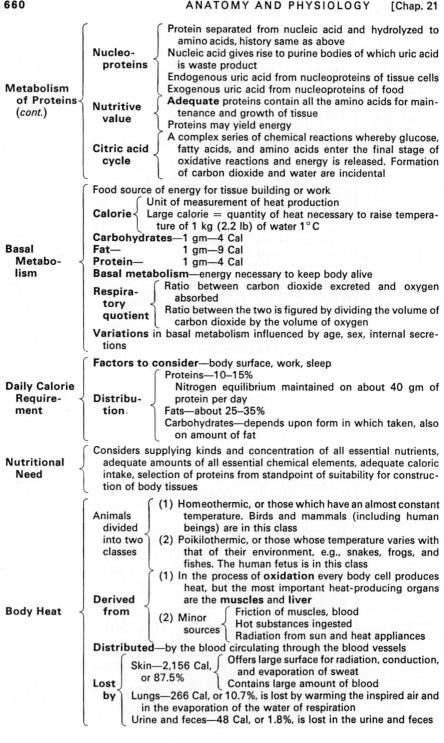

Metabolism of Proteins *(cont.)*

Nucleo-proteins
- Protein separated from nucleic acid and hydrolyzed to amino acids, history same as above
- Nucleic acid gives rise to purine bodies of which uric acid is waste product
- Endogenous uric acid from nucleoproteins of tissue cells
- Exogenous uric acid from nucleoproteins of food

Nutritive value
- **Adequate** proteins contain all the amino acids for maintenance and growth of tissue
- Proteins may yield energy

Citric acid cycle
- A complex series of chemical reactions whereby glucose, fatty acids, and amino acids enter the final stage of oxidative reactions and energy is released. Formation of carbon dioxide and water are incidental

Basal Metabolism
- Food source of energy for tissue building or work
- **Calorie**
  - Unit of measurement of heat production
  - Large calorie = quantity of heat necessary to raise temperature of 1 kg (2.2 lb) of water 1°C
- Carbohydrates—1 gm—4 Cal
- Fat— 1 gm—9 Cal
- Protein— 1 gm—4 Cal
- **Basal metabolism**—energy necessary to keep body alive
- **Respiratory quotient**
  - Ratio between carbon dioxide excreted and oxygen absorbed
  - Ratio between the two is figured by dividing the volume of carbon dioxide by the volume of oxygen
- **Variations** in basal metabolism influenced by age, sex, internal secretions

Daily Calorie Requirement
- **Factors to consider**—body surface, work, sleep
- **Distribution.**
  - Proteins—10–15%
    Nitrogen equilibrium maintained on about 40 gm of protein per day
  - Fats—about 25–35%
  - Carbohydrates—depends upon form in which taken, also on amount of fat

Nutritional Need
- Considers supplying kinds and concentration of all essential nutrients, adequate amounts of all essential chemical elements, adequate caloric intake, selection of proteins from standpoint of suitability for construction of body tissues

Body Heat
- **Animals divided into two classes**
  - (1) Homeothermic, or those which have an almost constant temperature. Birds and mammals (including human beings) are in this class
  - (2) Poikilothermic, or those whose temperature varies with that of their environment, e.g., snakes, frogs, and fishes. The human fetus is in this class
- **Derived from**
  - (1) In the process of **oxidation** every body cell produces heat, but the most important heat-producing organs are the **muscles** and **liver**
  - (2) Minor sources
    - Friction of muscles, blood
    - Hot substances ingested
    - Radiation from sun and heat appliances
- **Distributed**—by the blood circulating through the blood vessels
- **Lost by**
  - Skin—2,156 Cal, or 87.5%
    - Offers large surface for radiation, conduction, and evaporation of sweat
    - Contains large amount of blood
  - Lungs—266 Cal, or 10.7%, is lost by warming the inspired air and in the evaporation of the water of respiration
  - Urine and feces—48 Cal, or 1.8%, is lost in the urine and feces

Regulation of Body Heat

Due to maintenance of *balance* between heat production and heat dissipation

Heat production { By physiological oxidations, due to { Food intake and utilization / Muscular exercise

Heat loss
(1) The respiratory center
(2) The sweat center and sweat nerves
(3) The vasomotor center and nerves
(4) The water content of the blood

Coordinated by heat-regulating centers in the hypothalamus

Other factors
(1) Size
(2) Age
(3) Constitution

Aided by
(*a*) Use of suitable clothing
(*b*) Use of hot and cold baths

Variations in Temperature

The normal temperature by mouth is about 37°C (98.6°F)

Normal

(1) Depends on where temperature is taken { Mouth / Axilla / Rectum

(2) Depends on time of day { Lowest in early morning, between 3 and 5 A.M. / Highest in late afternoon, about 4 P.M.

(3) Slightly increased by muscular activity and the digestive processes

(4) Age. Higher and more variable in { Infants, children, and the aged

(5) Sex   (7) Climate
(6) Season   (8) Clothing

Subnormal due to
Excessive loss of heat
Profuse sweating and hemorrhage
Lessened heat production, as in starvation

Abnormal

Fever

Physiological effects
Increased temperature
Increased pulse
Increased respirations
Increased tissue waste
Faulty secretion
Various other effects such as thirst, weakness, and apathy

Cause—mainly unknown
Value—may be a protective reaction

CHAPTER 22

The Physiology of Water and Electrolyte Balance. Buffers

WATER is the universal medium in which all of the complex metabolic processes of life take place. Water is the largest single constituent of living cells; life itself depends upon a constant source of and utilization of water in the body. Enzyme activity and electrolyte balance are closely related to water balance—each being dependent upon and influencing the other.

WATER

Water constitutes more than two thirds of the material ingested daily.

The water content of the body comes from three sources: beverages or other liquids; foods, especially vegetables and fruits; and the water formed in the tissues as the result of metabolic activities.

Water enters into the composition of all the tissues within the cell as well as in tissue fluid, most tissues containing between 75 and 90 per cent water by weight, although there are exceptions. Bone, which makes up a large percentage of the body weight, contains little water (less than 20 per cent). Thus the total body water is less than 70 per cent in most individuals. Adipose tissue water content is also low and, as this tissue increases in the body, the over-all body water decreases; this accounts for the sex differences in adults. Women characteristically are less muscular than men and have a thicker layer of subcutaneous fat; body water content is about 50 per cent for women and 60 per cent for men. Age is another variable. Seventy to seventy-five per cent of infant body weight is water (extracellular water content is higher); after the first few months of life this gradually decreases. As tissues continue to age, they become relatively dehydrated, so that the total body water may be around 40 or 50 per cent in those over 65 years. However, the greatest change is in childhood. Water supplies fluid for the secretions and serves as a medium for the chemical changes occurring in digestion. Its most obvious functions are in connection with the absorption of

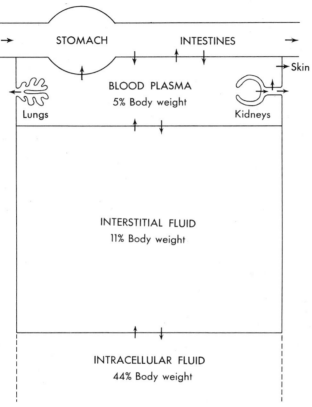

Figure 22–1. Diagram illustrating distribution of water in the body and exchange of water between compartments, normal sources of body fluid, and fluid loss. Figures are average for lean muscular adult. (Reprinted by permission of the publishers from James Lawder Gamble, *Chemical Anatomy, Physiology and Pathology of Extracellular Fluid : A Lecture Syllabus.* Cambridge, Mass. : Harvard University Press, Copyright, 1942, 1947, 1954, by The President and Fellows of Harvard College.)

food in solution and the removal of dissolved products of metabolism. By its evaporation from the skin and the respiratory passages, it helps to keep the body temperature from rising above normal.

Under normal conditions the amount of water in the body remains about the same, even though the intake may vary considerably. If the intake of water is increased, the excretion of urine is increased. If the intake of water is decreased, the resulting sensation of thirst is such that steps are taken to relieve it.

Distribution of Water in the Body. Water is distributed in the body in three main compartments (figures are in terms of adult male):

1. Blood plasma   5% of body weight
2. Interstitial fluid   11% of body weight
3. Intracellular fluid   44% of body weight

This means that if an individual weighs about 70 kg there are about 3.5 liters of water in the plasma compartment, 7.7 liters of water in the interstitial compartment, and 30.8 liters of water within the cells. This makes a total of 42 liters of water. The amount of fluid in each compartment may be measured with relative accuracy, and the measurement of plasma volume is done frequently.

Plasma volume may be measured by giving a known quantity of the blue dye T 1824 (Evans blue). It is nontoxic, soluble in water, but not in fat, it does not readily pass through the capillaries, it leaves the blood stream very slowly; hence, it can be used to measure plasma volume. The dye is given intravenously and after it has had opportunity to be mixed well in the blood stream, samples of blood are taken. Plasma is separated from the cells and matched against samples of similar known dye dilutions. These values are considered along with hematocrit readings, i.e., the ratio of cells to plasma.

Movement of water between compartments takes place freely. At the blood capillaries, which is the functional boundary between plasma and interstitial fluid, all solutes in these two fluids except protein are almost freely diffusible across the capillary membrane. The cell membrane, however, regulates the movement of electrolytes into and out of the cell so that sodium and chloride remain in high concentration outside the cell and potassium is high inside. This membrane is very permeable to the solutes—glucose, amino acids, urea, carbon dioxide, bicarbonate ions, but not to proteins.

Figure 22–1 illustrates the distribution of water; by means of arrows, movement of water from one compartment to the other is also shown. Under normal conditions fluid enters the body via the mouth. In the stomach, fluid moves from the blood plasma to the cells of the gastric glands for the manufacture of about 1,500 ml of gastric juice in 24 hours. This fluid moves, along with ingested foods and fluids, to the intestine. Here again large quantities of water move from the blood plasma to gland cells for the manufacture of large quantities of digestive fluids, and finally the fluids and end products of digestion are returned to the blood stream. Small amounts of fluid (about 150 to 200 ml) are lost in feces daily. This describes the tremendous exchange of fluids between plasma and secreting cells and back to the plasma again.

The fluid in the plasma compartment also loses water via the lungs, the skin, and the kidneys. During respiration, as blood circulates through the lungs, plasma loses about 350 ml of fluid in 24 hours. Water loss via the skin in the form of perspiration varies; but, under ordinary circumstances, there are about 600 ml or more lost as insensible perspiration in 24 hours. Increased amounts are caused by increased temperature or humidity, exercise, nervousness, pain, diaphoretic drugs, nausea, and certain diseases. Sodium chloride is also lost from the body in perspiration. The skin prevents water loss from tissues and capillaries by the protective covering formed by stratified squamous epithelium. Excessive loss of water through perspiration from any cause may deplete the body fluids.

Through the kidney, plasma normally loses about 1,500 ml of water in 24 hours. Since water loss through the kidney is rigorously controlled, urine output varies with fluid intake. The kidney also rigorously regulates the kinds and amounts of substances in solution in the water lost in the form of urine.

In reality interstitial fluid functions as the "middleman" between plasma and cells. Plasma volume and cell volume are kept relatively constant by temporary reduction or increase in the amount of fluid in the interstitial compartment. Movement of fluid in the *extra*cellular compartments takes place mainly through the cardiovascular system and the lymph channels.

The total forces that hold fluid in the various compartments are not completely understood. However, in the plasma compartment the blood proteins, especially serum albumin, play a large part in the control; and the large percentage of protein within the cell forms an osmotic relationship which holds water within the cells. The electrolytes also function in regulating water movement across membranes.

Fluid Intake. In Figure 22–2 fluid balance is illustrated. Fluid intake is in the form of water, other liquids or beverages, and foods. Normally water furnishes about a third or so of the required need, and the rest is furnished by other liquids and foods. Some foods have a much higher water content than do others. Another source of water to the body fluids is the water of metabolism. An ordinary mixed diet yields about 250 ml in 24 hours. On the whole, 100 gm of starch yields 55 gm of water, 100 gm of fat yields 107 gm of water, and 100 gm of protein yields 41 gm of water.

The amount of fluid needed is related to size, weight, and activities of an individual. This means that fluid intake may vary from 1,800 to 3,000 ml in 24 hours.

Fluid Output. Normally fluid output is directly related to fluid intake. Water loss via the kidneys is rigorously controlled and varies from 1,000 to 1,500 ml in 24 hours. As a rule water loss through feces is about 100 to 150 ml. Through insensible perspiration about 450 to 800 or so ml of water is lost in 24 hours and via the lungs about 250 to 350 ml. There is a relationship between water loss through kidneys and through the skin. Usually when large quantities of water are lost via the skin, urine volume is decreased.

It is readily understandable that excessive loss of fluid by diarrhea, vomiting, or perspiration, excess loss by the kidneys, loss due to burns, or loss of fluid through hemorrhage causes fluid loss from the plasma and interstitial compartments. Failure to ingest sufficient quantities of fluid may also deplete the fluid in the interstitial compartment, and eventually the plasma compartment may be disturbed.

When excess amounts of fluids are taken by mouth, water is rapidly absorbed into the plasma compartment. If large quantities are taken with no food, absorption is complete in about 30 to 40 minutes. Blood volume may be temporarily increased, as well as cardiac output. However, there is rapid adjustment to the increased water load by the opening of capillary networks to increase the vascular bed; the sinusoids of the liver and spleen open to hold more blood, and fluid is rapidly transferred to the interstitial compartment. The kidneys eliminate excess water and balance is restored within two or three hours.

Bases for Understanding Fluid Loss and Importance of Replacement of Water and Electrolytes

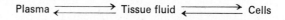

Arrows indicate the movement of fluid between compartments

Fluid Exchange During a 24-Hour Period

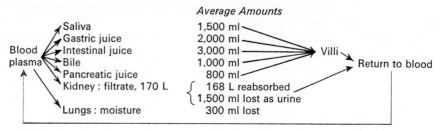

From the above figures it can be seen that the kidney has an important function in maintaining water and electrolyte balance. What is the composition of each of the above fluids?

The antidiuretic hormone (ADH) (also known as vasopressin) is formed by the cells in the supraoptic and paraventricular nuclei of the hypothalamus. ADH travels through the supraopticohypophyseal tract to the posterior pituitary, where it is stored. ADH augments water reabsorption in the kidney tubule. The mineralocorticoid aldosterone promotes excretion of potassium and retention of sodium chloride.

In severe stress situations, such as in burns, shock, and hemorrhage, electrolytes, especially sodium chloride and the body fluids, must be conserved. In some way ACTH of the pituitary and the adrenal-cortex hormones respond to the stress situation and play a large role in maintaining homeostasis of the body fluids.

"Reserve" Body Water.   It is useful in considering water balance to think in terms of the individual's water "reserve"—his ability to withstand water loss. That is, should he be faced with a stress such as lack of water for drinking, or unusual loss as in vomiting and diarrhea, or excessive perspiration, how good is his reserve? Obviously the person with the greatest percentage of body water, other things being equal, has the best reserve. Obesity is the commonest cause of decreased body water. The very obese person's body water content may be as little as 25 to 30 per cent of his body weight.

Infants also have poor reserve. Although they have more body water in terms of percentage than most adults, they also lose relatively more in urinary output each 24 hours; thus their reserve is poor. Under normal conditions this large water loss is matched by a large water intake. Stressful situations such as those mentioned above easily cause severe dehydration in infants.

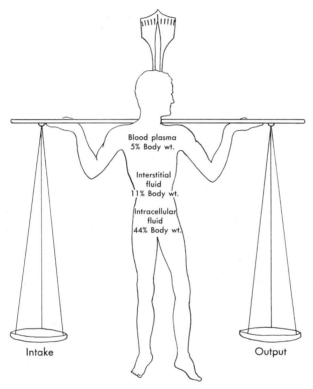

Blood plasma
5% Body wt.

Interstitial
fluid
11% Body wt.

Intracellular
fluid
44% Body wt.

Intake

Output

Figure 22–2. Diagram illustrating a balance between fluid intake and output. During periods of rapid growth, intake must exceed output. If output exceeds intake, dehydration results.

The Electrolytes

Acids, bases, and salts are known as electrolytes because, when in water solution, they conduct an electric current. Such solutions owe their chemical activity to the presence of dissolved ions. In general, the higher the concentration of the ions, the more active the solution. Some electrolytes ionize freely and provide a high concentration of ions; these are known as strong electrolytes. Some electrolytes maintain a reserve of neutral molecules in the solution, consequently, a low ion concentration; these are known as weak electrolytes. Both weak and strong electrolytes are important physiologically.

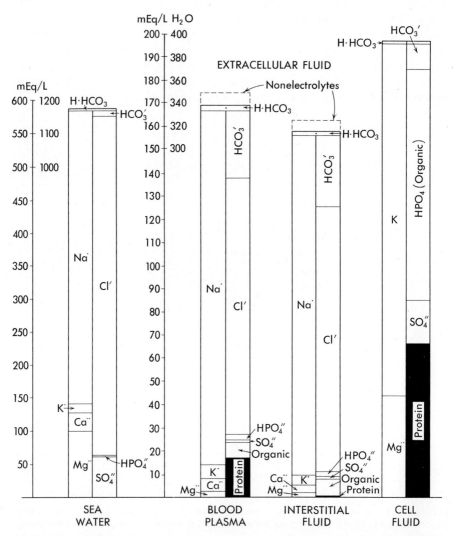

Figure 22–3. Chart illustrating the distribution of electrolytes and nonelectrolytes in the body. It will be noted that blood plasma and interstitial fluid are almost identical. Comparison with sea water is very interesting. (Reprinted by permission of the publishers from James Lawder Gamble, *Chemical Anatomy, Physiology and Pathology of Extracellular Fluid : A Lecture Syllabus.* Cambridge, Mass. : Harvard University Press, Copyright, 1942, 1947, 1954, by The President and Fellows of Harvard College.)

Within the body, electrolytes (especially sodium, potassium, chloride, and bicarbonate ions) function in various ways to hold fluid within compartments, and to maintain the acid-base relationship essential for enzyme activities. A study of Figure 22–3 illustrates the distribution of various ions within the blood plasma, interstitial fluid, and cells. The concentrations of the various ions are expressed in milliequivalents per liter, the measuring unit which provides a basis for comparing relative concentrations of ions.

To transpose values recorded in milligrams per 100 ml of blood to milliequivalents per liter, it is necessary to know the equivalent weight of the ion. This is obtained by dividing the atomic weight of the element or formula weight by its valence. Thus, for sodium with an atomic weight of 23 and a valence of one, the equivalent weight of the sodium ion is $\frac{23}{1}$ = 23. To transpose from milligrams per 100 ml to milliequivalents per liter:

$$Na^+ \quad \begin{array}{ll} 330 \text{ mg per} & 100 \text{ ml blood plasma} \\ 3,300 \text{ mg per} & 1,000 \text{ ml blood plasma} \quad (1 \text{ liter}) \end{array}$$

Therefore $\frac{3,300}{23}$ = 143 milliequivalents of Na^+ per liter, expressed 143 mEq/L.

Study of the chart (Fig. 22–3) shows that sodium and chloride ions are in higher concentration in plasma and interstitial fluid than in intracellular fluid. Sodium ion concentration, to a large degree, controls the movement of water between cells and the interstitial fluids. Potassium ions are in much higher concentration within cells than in the extracellular fluids. The distribution of negatively charged ions is also of significance. Phosphates, sulfates, and proteinates predominate within cells where their presence is attributed to metabolic activities in the cells. The electrolytes function in the control of osmotic pressures in the various compartments and thereby help to regulate water balance. They also help to maintain the acid-base balance essential for normal cell activities.

The Acid-Base Balance. Within the body as a whole, the balance between acid and alkaline components is maintained within a remarkably constant range. This is strikingly illustrated by the range within blood plasma which normally varies only between pH 7.35 and 7.45, with an average value of pH 7.4. (See Fig. 22–4.)

The sources of acids and bases in the body are (1) the cells and (2) the ingestion of food.

The Cells. The cells continuously form carbon dioxide through the metabolism of carbohydrates, fats, and proteins. This forms carbonic acid by combination with water. Lactic acid is a product of carbohydrate metabolism; acetoacetic acid is formed in the liver from fatty acids; sulfuric acid is formed from certain amino acids. These substances escape from the cells and, when ionized, tend to increase the hydrogen ion concentration of blood and tissue fluids.

The Foods. Various organic acids enter with the food, for instance, acetic, citric, and tartaric acids. Fatty acids are also absorbed from the intestine as end products of fat digestion. These tend to increase the hydrogen ion concentration of blood. Plant cells contain salts, chiefly potassium salts of weak acids. Sodium salts, such as sodium chloride and sodium bicarbonate, are frequently added to foods during preparation.

The constancy with which the hydrogen ion concentration of blood is regulated is due to three well-integrated mechanisms. These are the presence of buffer systems in extracellular fluids and within cells, the elimination of carbon dioxide at the lungs, and selective elimination of various ions by the kidney.

The buffer systems of the body consist of weak acids accompanied by their sodium or potassium salts. The three important buffer systems are:

In Plasma:

$$\frac{\text{Carbonic acid}}{\text{Sodium bicarbonate}} \qquad \frac{\text{H}_2\text{CO}_3}{\text{NaHCO}_3}$$

$$\frac{\text{Sodium dihydrogen phosphate}}{\text{Sodium monohydrogen phosphate}} \qquad \frac{\text{NaH}_2\text{PO}_4}{\text{Na}_2\text{HPO}_4}$$

$$\frac{\text{Hydrogen proteinate}}{\text{Sodium proteinate}}$$

The efficiency of the buffers is determined largely by the ratio of acid to salt.

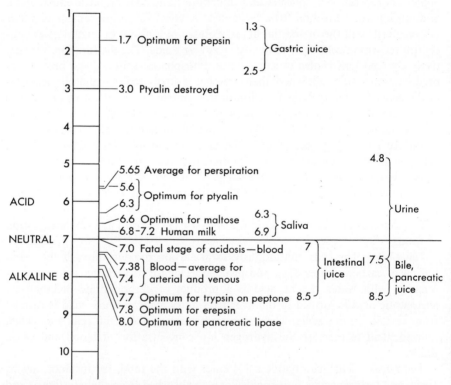

Figure 22–4. The pH scale runs from 1 to 14. In physiology the pH range is comparatively narrow; in tissue fluids it is more restricted. Buffer systems maintain the range optimum for cellular enzyme activity. Figures represent average values.

In Cells. The same buffers occur but the salts are potassium salts.

A buffer system acts through an exchange of ions which results in reduction of ion concentration through the formation of molecules of a weaker electrolyte. This may be illustrated by reference to the functioning of the carbonic acid–sodium bicarbonate buffer system.

When any acid stronger than carbonic acid enters the blood, it will be buffered by the reaction with the sodium bicarbonate salt. Hydrogen ions will be removed to form molecules of carbonic acid and a sodium salt of the stronger acid. For example:

Lactic acid + Sodium bicarbonate → Sodium lactate + Carbonic acid

The carbonic acid thus formed can be buffered by both the phosphate salt buffers or the protein. In fact, the most important buffer for carbonic acid is the potassium salt of hemoglobin within the erythrocytes. Most of the carbon dioxide which enters the plasma goes into the red blood cells. Part of it then combines with water and forms carbonic acid (p. 541), which in turn reacts with the hemoglobin salts to make the hemoglobin acid, a much weaker acid than is carbonic acid. In this way, respiration plays an important role in buffer systems.

Strong bases such as sodium hydroxide and potassium hydroxide are not usual components of food, nor are they products of cell metabolism. Nevertheless, intake of substances that tend to increase the salt of the buffer pair will influence the pH because the relative amounts of each salt determines the degree of ionization of its appropriate acid. For example, as the sodium bicarbonate increases, there is less ionization of the carbonic acid and vice versa. The various buffering mechanisms of cells, tissue fluids, and plasma thus serve to maintain the pH within rather narrow limits whether metabolic end products tend to lower or raise the pH.

The critical aspect of acid-base balance, however, is the removal of excessive hydrogen ions from the body, or their conservation when necessary. This involves regulation of the carbonic acid–sodium bicarbonate buffer pair primarily and concerns the respiratory system as well as the kidneys. Carbonic acid is lost via respirations as carbon dioxide and water (see p. 540). As respiratory rate and depth increase, more is lost; shallow, slow respirations conserve carbonic acid. The kidneys control excretion of carbonic acid and of sodium bicarbonate as well as their conservation.

The urine, which is formed from the blood, may be either more acid or more alkaline than the blood, depending upon the adjustments needed to maintain the buffer systems of the body. With the usual meat-containing diet, the urine excreted is somewhat more acid than the blood. This means that hydrogen ions are being excreted. There are two common mechanisms of adjustment. There is an increase in the proportion of dihydrogen phosphate salts, presumably at the expense of monohydrogen phosphate salts and carbonic acid. This favors return of more sodium bicarbonate to the blood, as is suggested in the following equation.

$$Na_2HPO_4 + H_2CO_3 \rightarrow NaH_2PO_4 + NaHCO_3$$

Excreted   Reabsorbed
in urine   into the blood

The second method is the production of ammonia in the kidney cells as a result of the deamination of certain amino acids, particularly glutamine. The kidney cells form ammonia, which moves into the lumen of the tubule where it combines with hydrogen ions to form ammonium ions and ammonium salts. These are eliminated in the urine. This permits sodium ions to be conserved in the plasma in exchange for the hydrogen ions which are thus excreted in the ammonium salts.

On a diet rich in fruits and vegetables or after the ingestion of alkaline-forming salts, the urine tends to be less acid, even slightly alkaline. Under these conditions, the concentration of dihydrogen phosphate ions in the urine diminishes. The kidney forms fewer ammonium ions, but eliminates more potassium, sodium, and bicarbonate ions.

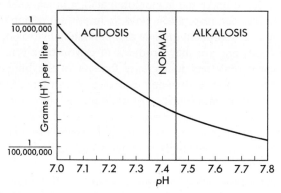

Figure 22–5. Diagram illustrating the range of hydrogen ion concentration compatible with life. It will be noted that the physiological range lies on the alkaline side of neutrality. In health the hydrogen ion range is between pH 7.35 and 7.45. (Reprinted by permission of the publishers from James Lawder Gamble, *Chemical Anatomy, Physiology and Pathology of Extracellular Fluid: A Lecture Syllabus.* Cambridge, Mass.: Harvard University Press, Copyright, 1942, 1947, 1954, by The President and Fellows of Harvard College.)

In spite of the remarkable adjustments thus made among the electrolytes, if abnormal demands are made on the system, disturbance of the acid-base balance does occur and acidosis or an alkalosis may result.

Acidosis is a condition caused by the entrance into the blood of acids in excessive amounts and the accompanying reduction of alkaline components or by accumulation of acid components.

This condition may be the result of:

1. The loss of sodium and potassium ions (as in diarrhea). In diarrhea, bicarbonate ions and to some extent chloride ions are lost together with sodium and potassium ions. This condition may be further complicated by ketosis if the diarrhea is accompanied by vomiting and the inability to take food; the diacetic acid which is thus produced in increased quantity makes a further drain on the buffer salts of the blood.

2. The retention of hydrogen ions by the kidneys.

3. Metabolic disturbances such as ketosis, which accompanies acute starvation.

4. The interference with carbohydrate metabolism as in the diabetic.

5. Respiratory disorders with reduced elimination of carbon dioxide thus increasing carbonic acid level in the plasma.

Alkalosis is an abnormal condition caused by either excessive ingestion of base-forming salts, such as large doses of sodium bicarbonate, or excessive loss of acid, such as loss of hydrochloric acid during acute vomiting or in gastric drainage. Less frequently, it may develop through respiratory disturbances accompanied by abnormal loss of carbon dioxide, such as in hyperventilation.

The body's response to these pathological disturbances will be observed in adjustments in respiration to favor discharge of carbon dioxide in acidosis, or to retain carbon dioxide in alkalosis. At the kidneys, the elimination of ions will be adjusted with conservation of the ions essential for maintaining the acid-base balance within the body. The extent of the disturbance can be determined in the laboratory (1) by measurement of the pH of the blood or (2) by quantitative determination of the alkaline reserve of the blood (i.e., the concentration of bicarbonate salts in the blood plasma).

QUESTIONS FOR DISCUSSION

1. An adult female was admitted to the hospital with a history of vomiting for two days. Urine output was scant. The doctor's orders included: nothing by mouth and 3,000 ml of physiological saline with 5 per cent glucose, to be given within the first 18 hours. Measure and record intake and output of all fluids.
   a. What electrolytes were being lost by vomiting?
   b. What is the usual amount of gastric juice formed each 24 hours?
   c. Would there be a tendency for this patient to develop acidosis or alkalosis? Explain.
   d. Why was urine output decreased in amount? Explain in detail.
   e. Discuss why sodium chloride and glucose solution was ordered.
   f. What is meant by acid-base balance?
   g. What are the fluid compartments of the body? What factors hold fluid in each compartment?

2. When an individual perspires profusely (e.g., during a baseball game on a hot day), how is total body fluid kept within normal limits?

3. Which organs and hormones are essential for maintaining the constancy of body fluids in relation to electrolytes?

4. When faced with acute lack of water, which would suffer most: the mother, the father, or a six-month-old infant? Which least? Explain.

5. When an individual takes one large teaspoonful of bicarbonate of soda in water for indigestion, what happens to the blood pH?

SUMMARY

Water Balance

Distribution of water in the body
- (1) Blood plasma 5% of body weight
- (2) Interstitial fluid 11% of body weight
- (3) Intracellular fluid 44% of body weight

Movement of water
- Water and solutes move freely between compartments

Water intake, 1,800 to 3,000 ml to 24 hours
- Water
- Other fluids
- Foods
- Water metabolism 300–350 ml in 24 hours

Water output

Feces	100 to	150 ml
Skin	450 to	800 ml
Lungs	250 to	350 ml
Urine	1,000 to	1,500 ml

Adjustment to excess fluid intake
- Fluid rapidly absorbed into blood stream
- Blood volume may be temporarily increased
- Cardiac output may be increased
- Capillary networks open, vascular bed increased
- Sinusoids of liver and spleen hold more blood
- Fluid rapidly transferred to interstitial compartment
- Kidney eliminates excess water and balance is restored in several hours

Regulation by hormones
- ADH regulates water reabsorption in the kidney tubule
- Aldosterone of the adrenal cortex regulates Na^+-K^+ ratio in plasma and their elimination by the kidney, thus aiding in the regulation of water balance

Stress situations
- ACTH and the adrenal-cortex hormones respond to stress situations and play a large role in maintaining homeostasis of the body fluids

Reserve body water
- Ability of individual to withstand water loss from any cause
- Person with greatest percentage of body water has best reserve
- Obesity reduces water reserve
- Infants have poor reserve

Electrolyte Balance

An electrolyte may be an acid, base, or salt which, in solution, has the power to conduct an electric current. Some are chemically more active than others

Distribution
- In extracellular fluids: Chiefly Na^+, Cl^-, HCO_3^-; small quantities of K^+, Ca^{++}, HPO_4^{--}, SO_4^{--}, Mg^+
- Intracellular fluids: Chiefly K^+, Mg^{++}, HPO_4^{--}; small quantities of SO_4^{--}, HCO_3^-, Na^+

Milliequivalents
- Concentrations expressed in terms of milliequivalents: Shows relative magnitudes and interrelationships

To transpose milligrams per 100 ml to milliequivalents

Must know:
- Number of milligrams per 100 ml
- Formula weight and valence of the ion

Plasma concentrations	Na^+	330 mg per 100 ml $\times 10 \div 23 \times 1$
	Cl^-	365 mg per 100 ml $\times 10 \div 35 \times 1$
	Ca^{++}	10 mg per 100 ml $\times 10 \div 40 \times 2$
	Mg^{++}	2.7 mg per 100 ml $\times 10 \div 24 \times 2$
	K^+	20 mg per 100 ml $\times 10 \div 39 \times 1$
Whole blood	HPO_4^{--}	mg per 100 ml $\times 10 \div 31 \times 1.8$
	SO_4^{--}	mg per 100 ml $\times 10 \div 32 \times 2$

674

Acid-Base Balance

Ions functioning in acid-base balance:

Important cations—		Important anions—	
Na^+	142 mEq/L	Cl^-	103 mEq/L
Ca^{++}	5 mEq/L	HCO_3^-	27 mEq/L
Mg^{++}	3 mEq/L	HPO_4^{--}	2 mEq/L
K^+	5 mEq/L	SO_4^{--}	1 mEq/L
		Organic acids	6 mEq/L
		Protein	16 mEq/L

Regulation

Normal pH range 7.35–7.45, average 7.4

Acid-base regulated by
(1) Secretion of acid urine, removing hydrogen ions
(2) Production of ammonia in kidney cells with conservation of sodium ions in blood
(3) Elimination of carbonic acid in lungs

Sources of Acid and Base

(1) The cell. Products of metabolism of: Carbohydrates, Fats, Proteins — Carbon dioxide and water, lactic acid, acetoacetic acid, and from protein, sulfuric, and phosphoric acids

(2) From foods. The average diet provides various acids and salts of organic acids:
Citric, Lactic, Acetic, Fatty — Acids
Potassium salts
Sodium bicarbonate

Buffering

Potassium salts buffer within the cells
Sodium salts buffer in the extracellular fluids
Cell proteins, especially hemoglobin, are effective buffers
Buffering is accomplished through exchange of ions
Acids react with buffer salts to form weaker acids
Bases react with buffer acids to form water and salts

Electrolyte Regulation

Electrolyte concentrations controlled most effectively by the kidneys and by elimination of carbon dioxide in the lungs

CHAPTER **23**

The Urinary
System
$\left.\begin{array}{l}\end{array}\right\{$
Anatomy

Histology

Physiology

*Physiology of Urine
Formation and
Elimination*

The Role of the Kidneys
in Maintaining Homeostasis
of Body Fluids

NUTRIENTS added to the blood stream by the digestive organs and oxygen from the lungs are utilized by cells of the body for growth and repair, for synthesis of hormones or other secretions, and as a source of energy for these and other cell activities. As a result of the complex chemical reactions taking place within the cell, certain products are formed which tend to alter the normal internal and external environment of the cell. Unless these are kept within the normal range, cell functioning will deteriorate, causing eventual death of the cell and possibly of the individual.

MATERIALS FOR ELIMINATION

1. Liquid—water
2. Gas—carbon dioxide
3. Metabolic end products of protein metabolism—e.g., urea, creatinine, uric acid, sulfates
4. Heat

To these may be added the dead and living microorganisms constantly excreted in large numbers in the feces.

Substances eliminated are classed as excreta and the process by which they are removed from the body as excretion, or elimination.

EXCRETORY ORGANS

The organs that function as excretory organs and the products which they eliminate may be tabulated as follows:

	Essential	*Incidental*
Lungs	Carbon dioxide	Water, heat
Kidneys	Water and soluble salts, resulting from metabolism of proteins, neutralization of acids, etc.	Carbon dioxide, heat
Alimentary canal	Solids, secretions, etc.	Water, carbon dioxide, salts, heat
Skin	Heat	Water, carbon dioxide, salts

Since the function of the lungs, the alimentary system, and the skin in the elimination of waste products has been discussed in previous chapters, attention is now turned to the urinary system.

	2 kidneys	Form urine from materials taken from the blood
	2 ureters	Ducts which convey urine from kidney to bladder
Urinary System	1 bladder	Reservoir for the reception of urine
	1 urethra	Tube which conveys urine from bladder to external environment

Anatomy of the Kidneys

The kidneys are compound tubular glands, placed at the back of the abdominal cavity, one on each side of the spinal column and behind the peritoneal cavity. They correspond in position to the space included between the upper border of the twelfth thoracic and the third lumbar vertebrae. The right kidney is a little lower than the left, because of the large space occupied by the liver.

Each kidney with its vessels is embedded in a mass of fatty tissue termed an *adipose capsule*. The kidney and the adipose capsule are surrounded by a sheath of fibrous tissue called the *renal fascia*. The renal fascia is connected to the fibrous tunic of the kidney by many trabeculae, which are strongest at the lower end. The kidney is held in place partly by the renal fascia, which blends with the fasciae on the quadratus lumborum and psoas major muscles and also with the fascia of the diaphragm, and partly by the pressure of neighboring organs.

The kidneys are bean-shaped, with the medial or concave border directed toward the medial line of the body. Near the center of the concave border is a fissure called the *hilum* (hilus), which serves as a passageway for the ureter, and for the blood vessels, lymph vessels, and nerves going to and from the kidney. Each kidney is covered by a thin but rather tough envelope of fibrous tissue. At the hilum of the kidney the capsule becomes continuous with the outer coat of the ureter. If a kidney is cut in two lengthwise, it is seen that the upper end of the ureter expands into a basinlike cavity, called the *pelvis* of the kidney. The substance of the kidney consists of an outer portion called the cortical substance (cortex) and an inner portion called the medullary substance (medulla). Between

677

the cortical and medullary substances are the arterial and venous arches. (See Fig. 23–3.)

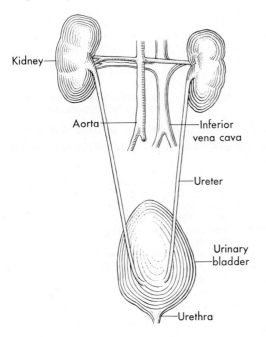

Kidney

Aorta

Inferior vena cava

Ureter

Urinary bladder

Urethra

Figure 23–1. The urinary system, viewed from behind.

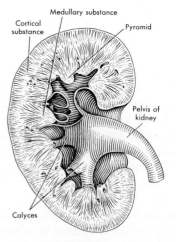

Medullary substance

Cortical substance

Pyramid

Pelvis of kidney

Calyces

Figure 23–2. Diagrammatic longitudinal section of the human kidney. Each kidney is about 11.25 cm long, 5.0 to 7.5 cm broad, and 2.5 cm thick, and weighs about 135 gm. (Modified from Henle.)

The medullary substance is red in color. It consists of from 8 to 18 radially striated cones, the renal pyramids, which have their bases toward the circumference of the kidney, while their apices converge into projections called papillae which are received by the cuplike cavities, or calyces, of the pelvis of the kidney.

The cortical substance is reddish brown, and contains the renal corpuscles, the convoluted tubules, and blood vessels. It penetrates for a variable distance between the pyramids, separating and supporting them. These interpyramidal extensions are called the *renal columns* (Bertin)[1] and support the blood vessels. A glance across the shiny surface of a freshly cut kidney discloses both a granular

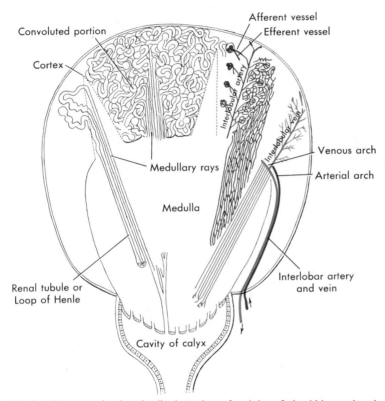

Figure 23–3. Diagram of a longitudinal section of a lobe of the kidney showing the arrangement of tubules and blood vessels in the lobe. The calyx embraces the apex of the pyramid. It is lined with epithelium, which continues from it over the apex, the latter being perforated with the many apertures of collecting tubules. Note the arrangement that leads to the granular and radial striations in the cortex. Nephron, arteriole, and venous units are diagrammed separately; in actuality they all occur in each pyramid and cortex section. (Modified from Gerrish.)

structure and also areas showing radial striations. In general these alternate with each other. The granular areas contain the renal capsules, glomeruli, and convoluted areas of the tubule. The radially striated areas contain other parts of the tubule. (See Fig. 23–2.)

The bulk of the kidney substance, in both cortex and medulla, is composed of minute tubes, or tubules, closely packed together, having only enough connective tissue to carry a large supply of blood vessels and a number of lymphatics

[1] Exupère Joseph Bertin, French anatomist (1712–1781).

and nerve fibers. The appearance of the cortex and medulla is due to the arrangement of these tubules, the *nephrons*, or functional units.

The nephron, or unit pattern of the kidney, consists of a renal tubule with its blood supply. The renal tubules vary in length, and the glomeruli vary in size. The largest ones are found nearest the medulla.

The *renal tubule* begins as a closed, invaginated layer of epithelium, the *renal capsule*, or capsule of Bowman.[2] The inner layer of this globelike expansion closely invests a capillary tuft called a renal *glomerulus*. The glomerulus consists of a few capillary loops which do not anastomose and which are completely

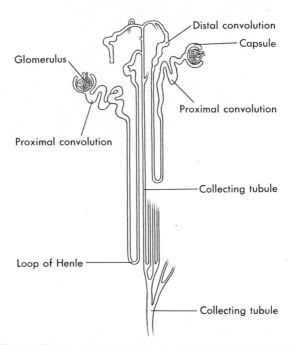

Figure 23–4.   Diagram of the course of two renal tubules.

encapsulated by the expansion of the tubule except at the point where an *afferent vessel* enters and an *efferent vessel* leaves the capillary tuft. The glomerulus, a basement membrane, and the enveloping capsule make up a renal corpuscle, or malpighian[3] body. More than 1,000,000 of these corpuscles are said to be in the cortex of each kidney.

There is bulging of the nuclei of the endothelial cells into the lumen of the glomerular capillaries. Around each bulged area the cytoplasm of each endothelial cell spreads out into a very thin film, so that the capillary walls are formed by a thin film of cytoplasm. In this thin wall are actual pores varying in size which are believed to play an important role in the filtration process.

[2] Sir William Bowman, English anatomist and ophthalmologist (1816–1892).
[3] Marcello Malpighi, Italian anatomist (1628–1694).

The cells in the visceral layer of Bowman's (glomerular) capsule have numerous large arms of cytoplasm, called major processes, extending from its cell body which terminates as "feet" on the membrane of the glomerular capillary wall. These cells are called *podocytes* (Fig. 23-6). Smaller processes and "feet" inter-digitate with the major processes around the glomerular capillaries, leaving tiny spaces between them. It has been suggested that these podocytes may have contractile or elastic power. The renal capsule joins the rest of the tubule by a constricted *neck*; the tubules, after running a very irregular course, open into

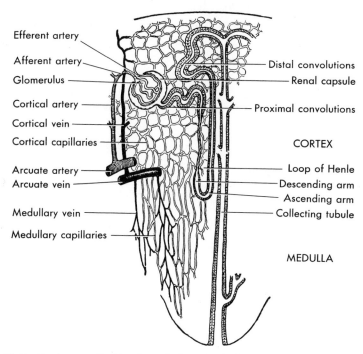

Figure 23-5. Nephron and its blood supply. Length of tubule is approximately 35 to 40 mm ; diameter, about 0.02 mm; diameter of capsule, about 0.2 mm.

collecting ducts which pour their contents through their openings on the pointed ends, or papillae, of the pyramids into the calyces of the kidney. About 20 of these collecting ducts empty into the calyces from each papilla.

The epithelial lining of the renal tubule varies in different parts of the tubule. In the convoluted tubules and ascending limb of Henle's[4] loop the cells are columnar, while in the glomerular capsule and descending limb of Henle's loop they are thin, squamous cells. The collecting tubules have well-defined columnar cells, definitely resembling those of excretory ducts. These and other differences in tubular structure are important in consideration of the physiology of urine formation and conduction (Fig. 23-5).

[4] Friedrich Gustav Jakob Henle, German anatomist (1809–1885).

The Blood Supply of the Kidney.   The kidney is abundantly supplied with blood by the *renal artery*, which is a branch of the abdominal aorta. Before or immediately after entering the kidney at the hilum, each artery divides into several branches, which follow the wall of the ureter into the kidney. They are sometimes called *interlobar arteries.*

When these arteries reach the boundary zone between the cortex and medulla, they divide laterally and form the *arch*, or *arcuate arteries*. From the convexity of these arches, the *interlobular arteries* (cortical) enter the cortex, giving off at intervals minute *afferent arterioles*, each of which branches out as the *capillaries of a glomerulus*. These capillaries reunite to form an *efferent arteriole* much

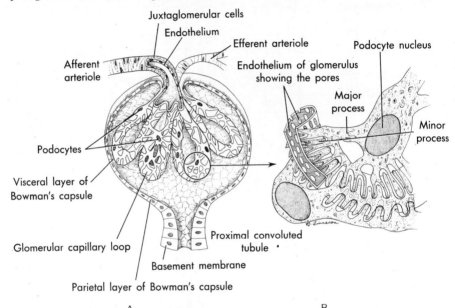

Juxtaglomerular cells
Endothelium
Efferent arteriole
Podocyte nucleus
Afferent arteriole
Endothelium of glomerulus showing the pores
Major process
Minor process
Podocytes
Visceral layer of Bowman's capsule
Proximal convoluted tubule
Glomerular capillary loop
Basement membrane
Parietal layer of Bowman's capsule

A   B

Figure 23–6.   Schematic diagram from an electron micrograph of the glomerulus. (*A*) Renal malpighian corpuscle. Parietal and visceral layers of endothelium of Bowman's capsule are continuous. Note that the afferent artery is wider than the efferent artery. Is there capillary anastomosis in the glomerulus? (Modified from Bailey.) (*B*) Enlarged microscopic section of *A*. Note the many processes of podocytes and their relation to the glomerular capillary pores. (Modified from Harris.)

smaller than the afferent arteriole. The efferent arteriole breaks up into a close meshwork, or *plexus*, of capillaries, which are in close approximation with both the convoluted tubule in the cortex and the loop of Henle in the medulla. These capillaries unite to form the *interlobular veins* (cortical) and *medullary veins*, which pour their contents into the *arcuate veins* lying between the cortex and the medulla. The arcuate veins converge to form the *interlobar veins*. These merge into the *renal vein*, which emerges from the kidney at the hilum and opens into the inferior vena cava.

The nerves of the kidneys are derived from the *renal plexus*, which is formed by branches from the celiac plexus, the aortic plexus, and the lesser and lowest splanchnic nerves. They accompany the renal arteries and their branches and are distributed to the blood vessels. They are vasomotor nerves, and by regulating the diameters of the small blood vessels, they control the circulation of the blood in the kidney.

Physiology of the Kidneys. The functions of the kidneys include:

1. Regulation of osmotic pressure of extracellular fluids is accomplished by the relative amounts of water and sodium chloride excreted. If large quantities of fluids are ingested, more water will be eliminated, and the ratio between water and electrolytes will change. This is evidenced by change in specific gravity (s.g.) of urine. Conversely, ingestion of excess sodium chloride without an increase of fluid intake will raise the s.g. of urine.

2. Regulation of the Electrolytic Pattern of Extracellular Fluids. The kidneys not only regulate the total concentration of water and electrolytes, but also regulate the concentration of each electrolyte. The regulation is complex and is accomplished by tubular reabsorption and tubular secretion. The processes are

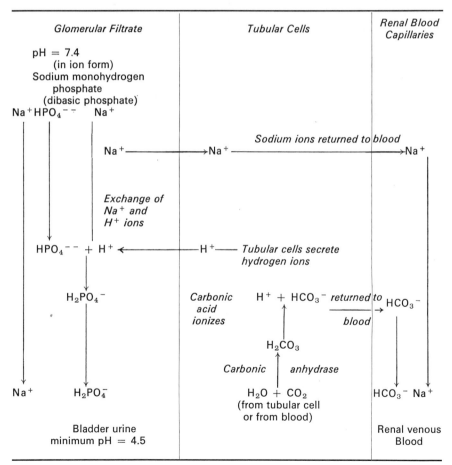

Modified from Davenport.

under the influence of hormones produced in the hypothalamus and adrenal cortex.

3. Excretion of metabolic wastes, particularly those arising in protein metabolism, such as urea, uric acid, creatinine, and ammonia.

4. Regulation of Acid-Base Ratio. By regulating the rate of excretion of hydrogen ions and electrolytes, the kidney helps to keep the pH of the plasma within normal limits. The kidney secretes hydrogen ions from the tubular cells in exchange for Na^+ ions present in the filtrate. These hydrogen ions result from the ionization of carbonic acid, which was formed by union of carbon dioxide and water under the influence of the enzyme carbonic anhydrase. Carbon dioxide and water appear in the tubular cell as a result of metabolic activity as well as by diffusion from the capillaries in contact with the cell. The reabsorption of sodium from the filtrate and diffusion of the bicarbonate ions into the blood stream are favorable mechanisms for keeping plasma acidity low. On the other hand, when it is necessary to conserve hydrogen ions, potassium ions are secreted by tubular cells in exchange for sodium. Ammonia is formed from glutamine chiefly, secreted from the tubular cells and excreted in urine as ammonia salts. (See chart, below) By this mechanism the urine pH is kept from being excessively acid. Urine pH is usually acid, with a pH range of 5.5 to 7.5; the average is about pH 6.

Formation of Ammonia by the Kidney

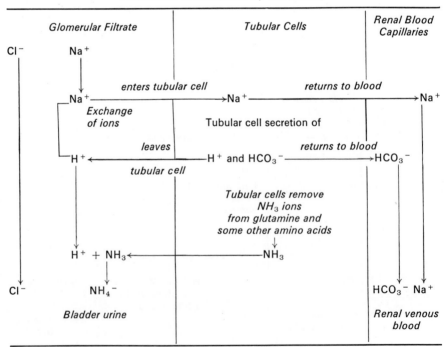

Modified from Davenport.

5. The kidneys aid in the *regulation of the volume of extracellular fluid* by elimination of water.

6. Certain cells located in the juxtaglomerular apparatus (JGA) of the afferent arterioles respond to pressure changes and secrete an enzyme substance called *renin*. Renin enters the blood and functions as a proteolytic enzyme which activates a plasma globulin known as angiotensinogen to form angiotensin I. Under the influence of another plasma enzyme, two amino acid units are split off from angiotensin I to form angiotensin II, an extremely potent vasopressor substance. In addition, angiotensin II stimulates the release of aldosterone from the adrenal cortex.

How the Kidney Does Its Work. The glomeruli function as an ultrafilter, permitting particles smaller than the size of the endothelial pores to escape, thus filtering colloidal and cell-free ultrafiltrates of the plasma into the tubule. The average rate of filtration is about 120 ml per minute. This means that about 170 to 180 liters are filtered in 24 hours into the tubules. Urine output is about 1 ml per minute, or about 1½ liters in 24 hours. As the protein-free filtrate passes through the tubule, it is changed in both volume and composition by the reabsorption of about 168 or 169 liters of water and certain of its constituents. The tubule cells also add substances to urine. Reabsorption takes place in:

1. Proximal tubule and descending limb	Glucose, bicarbonate, and sodium (largely under influence of aldosterone) are actively reabsorbed; chloride, sulfate, phosphate ions and urea are passively reabsorbed; water is reabsorbed with these substances, leaving the filtrate osmotic pressure unchanged. Eighty to ninety per cent of the water is reabsorbed in this way and is known as obligatory water reabsorption (a must)
2. Loop of Henle	Sodium is actively transported from the filtrate in the ascending limb into the medullary interstitial fluid, thus raising its osmotic pressure. This causes more water to be reabsorbed from the descending limb and the collecting duct and results in the concentration of the urine
3. Distal tubule and collecting ducts	Active reabsorption of sodium (in exchange for secreted potassium or hydrogen) and reabsorption of water. Filtrate is progressively more concentrated and volume greatly reduced as water continues to be reabsorbed, under the influence of ADH, depending on body needs. This is known as facultative reabsorption (optional). About 10 to 15 per cent of the water may be absorbed in this way

The filtering process in the glomerulus is directly related to blood pressure. Hydrostatic pressure in the glomerulus is about 75 to 80 mm Hg and the protein osmotic (oncotic) pressure is about 25 mm Hg. This means that the effective hydrostatic pressure, or filtration pressure, is about 50 or more mm Hg. This pressure is essential for the filtration of 170 to 180 liters of the protein-free filtrate. The pressure must also be adequate to overcome resistance to movement of fluid within the tubule. This back pressure has been estimated to be about 7 mm Hg. The total filtration pressure is therefore equal to the glomerular hydrostatic pressure, minus the oncotic pressure and the back pressure within the tubules. Back pressure in the tubules is increased by intraureteral pressure, which may be affected by interference with the onward movement of filtrate in the tubule or pelvis of the kidney from any cause. It is evident that filtration at the glomerulus is directly related to blood pressure. Although systemic blood pressure may vary, the pressure in the glomerulus is maintained by alterations in the lumen of the efferent arteriole as compared with the afferent arteriole. Thus filtration continues until blood pressure falls to very low levels; and when hypertension is present, filtration continues at the normal rate.

Hormonal Control of Kidney Function.   The reabsorption of water in the distal tubules of the kidney is promoted primarily by the antidiuretic hormone ADH, also called vasopressin. The regulation and production of the ADH are under the influence of the hypothalamus. There are receptor cells in the hypothalamus called *osmoreceptors* that are sensitive to the osmotic pressure of the plasma. A rise causes an increased secretion of ADH and inhibition of normal

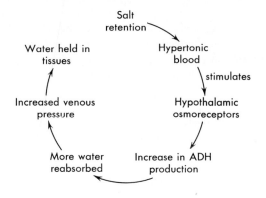

water diuresis. This is represented in the above diagram, which at the same time illustrates how water may be held in the tissues.

The mineralocorticoids of the adrenal cortex (aldosterone) promote the excretion of potassium ions and the reabsorption of sodium ions, which then electrostatically attract chloride ions and cause their reabsorption throughout most of the tubule. In this way, water and sodium reabsorption and elimination by the kidneys are rigorously controlled. Eighty to ninety per cent of the tubule water is reabsorbed by osmosis as a result of increased osmotic pressure created by the reabsorption of these electrolytes and, to a lesser extent, other solutes.

The following table compares the concentrations of the various substances in blood plasma and in urine and indicates the number of times *each substance is concentrated by the kidney*. It will be noted that proteins, fats, and other colloids are not filtered.

When the kidney is unable to secrete nitrogenous wastes and to regulate pH and electrolyte concentrations of the plasma (as in kidney disease) artificial control may be instituted. Hemodialysis by means of an artificial kidney involves removal of blood from an artery, transporting it through a lengthy coiled cellophane tube immersed in a "bath water," and returning the blood to the

Substance	Blood Plasma %	Urine %	Number of Times Concentrated by Kidney
Water	90–93	95	—
Proteins, fats, and other colloids	7–9	—	—
Glucose	0.1	—	—
Urea	0.03	2	60
Creatinine	0.001	0.075	75
Uric acid	0.004	0.05	12
Sodium ions	0.32	0.35	1
Potassium ions	0.02	0.15	7
Ammonium ions	0.001	0.04	40
Calcium ions	0.008	0.015	2
Magnesium ions	0.0025	0.006	2
Chloride ions	0.37	0.6	2
Phosphate ions	0.009	0.15	16
Sulfate ions	0.002	0.18	90

body via a vein. The radial artery and the cephalic or basilic veins are often used. The cellophane tube functions as a semipermeable membrane, and the mixture of ions in the "bath water" is calculated so that the ions *diffuse out* of the plasma. If, for example, the patient has a high serum potassium or urea level, there will be little or no potassium and *no* urea in the "bath water." Since the substances are in higher concentration in blood plasma than they are in the bath water, they are dialyzed *out* of the plasma into the bath, thereby lowering plasma concentrations.

Peritoneal dialysis is now frequently used instead of the artificial kidney. In this technique the *peritoneal cavity* is used, the dense capillary network of the entire peritoneal cavity functioning as a dialyzing membrane. A sterile solution of the desired mixture of substances is introduced into the abdominal cavity by means of a tube inserted through a small incision in the abdominal wall. The fluid usually remains for about an hour to allow for sufficient time for dialysis and is then permitted to flow out through the tube. The process may be repeated any number of times until normal plasma concentrations of the various substances have been attained.

Urine

Physical Characteristics of Urine. Normal urine is usually a yellow, transparent liquid with an aromatic odor. Cloudy urine is not necessarily pathological, for turbidity may be caused by mucin secreted by the lining membrane of the urinary tract; this, however, if present in excess does denote abnormal conditions. If urine is alkaline, especially after a meal, turbidity may be due to phosphates and carbonates. The color of urine varies with the changing ratios of water and substances in solution and may, of course, be affected by the presence of abnormal materials such as those produced by disease or certain drugs.

Urine is usually slightly acid, though its pH may vary between 5.5 and 7.5. Diet affects this reaction; a high-protein diet increases acidity, while a vegetable diet increases alkalinity. This variation is due to the difference in the end products of metabolism in each case. If human urine is allowed to stand, it will eventually become alkaline due to the decomposition of urea with production of ammonia, and many solutes will precipitate.

In health the specific gravity of urine may vary from 1.008 to 1.030, depending upon the relative proportions of solids and water. When the solids are dissolved in a large amount of water, the specific gravity will naturally be lower than when urine is more concentrated.

The average quantity of urine excreted by a normal adult in 24 hours varies from 1,200 to 1,500 ml (40 to 50 oz). Much wider variations may occur for short periods of time without pathological significance, as, for example, when a rise in environmental temperature or unusual muscular activity increases perspiration and so lessens the urinary output. The quantity of urine may be affected by the amount of fluid taken in by the body; the amount of fluid lost in perspiration, respiration, or in vomiting, diarrhea, or hemorrhage; the health of the organs concerned, the kidneys, heart, blood vessels; and the action of certain drugs such as diuretics.

The amount of urine excreted by children in 24 hours is great in proportion to their body weight.

Age	Weight	Amount	
6 months–2 years	17–26 lb	18–20 oz	540–600 ml
2–5 years	26–38 lb	16–26 oz	500–780 ml
5–8 years	38–55 lb	20–40 oz	600–1,200 ml
8–14 years	55–103 lb	32–48 oz	1,000–1,500 ml

Thus fluid intake in children must be closely observed for adequacy.

Chemical Composition of Urine. Water forms about 95 per cent of urine. The solutes (on chemical examination, precipitated as solids—some 60 gm in 1,500 ml of urine) are organic and inorganic waste products.

Urine 1,500 ml daily	Organic wastes 35 gm	Urea	30 gm
		Creatinine	1–2 gm
		Ammonia	1–2 gm
		Uric acid	1 gm
		etc.	1 gm

Solutes (solids) 60 gm	Inorganic salts 25 gm	Chlorides, sulfates, phosphates of	Sodium Potassium Magnesium Calcium

Sodium chloride is the chief inorganic salt, about 15 gm being excreted daily by the kidneys; however, sodium chloride excretion will vary with intake.

Origin of Constituents of Urine. The substances excreted in the urine are both exogenous and endogenous in origin; i.e., they are derived from the diet as well as from the metabolism within cells. Urea excretion, for example, closely parallels the protein intake in the diet. It is derived in part from the amino acids which were absorbed from the intestinal tract, but not built into tissues, and in part from the destruction of amino acids released from the cells in the continuous exchange process between the blood and tissues. The table below shows these types. Urea, it is seen, is an example of exogenous waste, varying greatly with

high- and low-protein intake. Creatinine, on the other hand, is probably endogenous, varying little with high and low protein intake.

Nitrogen Output as Influenced by Level of Protein Intake

	High-Protein Diet (Free from Meat)	Low-Protein Diet (Starch and Cream)
Total nitrogen	16.8 gm	3.6 gm
Urea nitrogen	14.7 gm, or 87.5%	2.2 gm, or 61.7%
Ammonia nitrogen	0.49 gm, or 2.9%	0.42 gm, or 11.3%
Uric acid nitrogen	0.18 gm, or 1.1%	0.09 gm, or 2.5%
Creatinine nitrogen	0.58 gm, or 3.6%	0.60 gm, or 17.2%
Undetermined nitrogen	0.85 gm, or 4.9%	0.27 gm, or 7.3%
Water output	Normal	Diminished

Note that urea nitrogen decreased 12.5 gm when the low-protein diet was used. The creatinine nitrogen varied
only 0.02 gm. These diets were similar in all respects, except for protein intake.

An understanding of the physiology of urine formation, with filtration of deproteinized blood plasma through the glomerular capsule and concentration in the
renal tubule, helps to explain the varying symptoms of glomerular nephritis and
tubular nephritis, respectively. When the glomerulus is impaired, proper filtration
does not occur; nonprotein nitrogenous substances are retained in the blood, edema
may be present, and a small amount of highly concentrated urine containing albumin
may be passed. Acidosis is probable, owing to the retention of acid substances in the
blood. In tubular nephritis, the usual dilute, plasmalike fluid is pressed through the
epithelium of the capsule, but it cannot be concentrated because of tubular impairment and so is excreted as such. Acidosis, however, is likely to be present in this type
of nephritis also, owing to the lack of ammonia production and absence of reabsorption of sodium ions by the tubules.

Diuretics are substances which increase the volume of urine excreted, causing a
condition known as *diuresis*. For example, mercurial diuretics prevent reabsorption
of sodium ions by the tubular cells, which in turn causes water to remain in the filtrate. Careful regulation of these drugs is necessary to prevent fluid and electrolyte
imbalances.

Nonprotein nitrogen constituents of normal urine are creatinine, urea, ammonia,
hippuric acid, and purine bodies.

Creatinine is always present in the urine, and in amounts independent of the
proteins of the diet. It is thought, therefore, to be an endogenous substance resulting from cellular metabolism of certain protoplasmic constituents. About 1
to 2 gm of creatinine are excreted in the urine daily, the amount being stable for
the individual. Thus it serves as a check for the adequate recording of urine
output. The source of creatinine in urine is creatine and creatine phosphate of
muscle. It is not yet known whether this change from creatine to creatinine,
which involves a loss of water, is accomplished in the blood or in the kidney.
Creatine is not excreted as such in the urine of the adult male, but it is constantly
present in the urine of children and perhaps in that of women after menstruation,
during pregnancy, and in the puerperium. Creatine is also present in the urine
during starvation or fever, probably because the body tissues are being utilized
at a rate too high for all the creatine to be changed to creatinine. It is markedly
increased in the urine of individuals who have muscular diseases.

Urea constitutes about one half (30 gm daily) of all the solids excreted in the urine. It is made by the liver cells from NH_2 radicals released on the deaminization of amino acids. Normally 27 to 28 mg of urea are contained in each 100 ml of blood. The kidneys constantly remove the urea as it is formed, keeping the amount in the blood stream at its normal level.

Ammonia in the urine is formed by the kidney from amino acids, especially glutamine. The amount of ammonia produced by the kidney may depend upon the general need of the body for conserving sodium ions to offset acid substances in the blood and tissues.

Hippuric acid is thought to be the means by which benzoic acid, a toxic substance occurring in food and from body processes, is eliminated from the body. A vegetable diet increases the quantity of hippuric acid excreted, probably because fruit and vegetables contain benzoic acid.

Purine bodies (*uric acid, etc.*)[5] are derived from foods containing nucleic acid (exogenous) and from the catabolism of the body cells (endogenous). The exogenous purines excreted depend upon the quantity eaten of purine-containing foods such as meat; the endogenous purine waste depends upon the health and activities of the body and is normally fairly constant.

Some abnormal constituents appearing in urine are albumin, glucose, indican, acetone bodies, casts, calculi, pus, blood, and bile pigments.

Albumin. Serum albumin is a normal constituent of the blood plasma, but it is not usually filtered into the renal capsule. Its presence in the urine is spoken of as *albuminuria* and is usually due to increased permeability of the glomerular membrane.

Certain conditions favoring albuminuria are:

Organic disease of the kidney, with injury to the glomerular membrane.

Increased blood pressure, which may be due to (1) stimulation of the vasoconstrictor mechanism, (2) vigorous muscular exercise, (3) inelastic arteries due to arteriosclerosis, (4) congestion of the kidneys because of interference with circulation through the renal vein, such as might result from pressure of tumors or a pregnant uterus.

Irritation of the kidney cells by poisons such as bacterial toxins, ether, turpentine, or heavy metals.

In abnormal conditions of the kidneys associated with albumin in the urine, there is usually retention of the inorganic salts and protein waste. In consequence, some of the salts may pass from the blood into the tissues and, by raising the osmotic pressure, promote excessive transudation of fluid into the tissues, thereby causing edema, or dropsy. Failure of the kidney to eliminate protein wastes may result in a condition known as uremia.

Glucose. Normal urine contains so little sugar that for clinical purposes it may be considered absent. In health the amount of glucose present in the blood varies from 80 to 120 mg per cent. When the quantity of sugar eaten is greater than the system can promptly change to glycogen and fat, the kidneys excrete it.

---

[5] Foods particularly rich in purine bodies include brain, sweetbreads, liver, kidney, meat extracts, and certain vegetables.

When glucose is found in the urine from this cause, the condition is called *temporary glycosuria*. Frequent or continuous elimination of glucose shows that the body has not the usual power to oxidize it, e.g., as in diabetes mellitus, or that the tubular cells of the kidney are unable to reabsorb it.

Indican. Indican (indoxyl potassium sulfate) is a potassium salt that is formed from indole. Indole results from the putrefaction of protein food in the large intestine. It is absorbed by the blood and carried to the liver, where it is probably changed to indican, a less poisonous substance. Traces of indican are found in normal urine, but its presence in larger amounts is abnormal and denotes excessive putrefaction of protein food in the intestines, or putrefaction in the body itself, as in abscess formation. Excessive putrefaction may be due to a diseased condition of the intestine that interferes with absorption, to a diet containing too much protein food, or to constipation.

Ketone Bodies. The ketone bodies, acetoacetic acid, beta hydroxybutric acid, and acetone, normally appear in the urine in very small amounts. But, when excessive quantities of fatty acids are oxidized in the liver, as in acute starvation, or in insulin deficiency of diabetes, these "ketones" are excreted in the urine in appreciable quantities. In normal individuals they may appear in the urine during periods of fasting.

Casts. In some abnormal conditions the kidney tubules become lined with substances which harden and form a mold or cast inside the tube. Later these casts are washed out by the urine, and their presence can be detected by the aid of a microscope. They are named either from the substances composing them or from their appearance. Thus there are pus casts, blood casts, epithelial casts from the walls of the tubes, granular casts from cells which have decomposed and form masses of granules, fatty casts from cells which have become fatty, and hyaline casts which are formed from coagulable elements of the blood.

Calculi. Mineral salts in the urine may precipitate and form calculi, or stones. Calculi may be formed in any part of the urinary tract from the tubules to the external orifice of the urethra. The causes which lead to their formation are an excessive amount of salts, a decrease in the amount of water, and abnormally acid or abnormally alkaline urine.

Pus. In suppurative conditions of any of the urinary organs, pus cells are present in the urine.

Blood. In cases of acute inflammation of any of the urinary organs, caused by tuberculosis, cancer, or renal stones, blood may be present in the urine, a condition known as *hematuria*. Blood imparts a smoky or reddish color to urine.

Bile pigments in the urine may be caused by obstructive jaundice, when bile has been reabsorbed from the biliary tract into the blood stream, or by diseases in which an abnormal number of erythrocytes are destroyed. Bile pigments give the urine a greenish-yellow or golden-brown color.

Elimination of Toxic Substances. During illness it is the function of the kidneys to eliminate toxic substances that find their way into the blood, whether these substances result from defective metabolism, from bacterial activity, or from chemical poisons. This may account for the fact that after a severe illness the kidneys are often left in a damaged condition and suggests the desirability of a copious intake of water in order to decrease the concentration of toxic materials and thereby lessen the chances of injury to the tissues.

The Ureters

The ureters are two tubes which convey the urine from the kidneys to the bladder. Each ureter commences as a number of cuplike tubes, or *calyces*, which surround the renal papillae. The calyces (varying in number from 7 to 13) join and form two or three short tubes, which unite and form a funnel-shaped dilatation called the *renal pelvis*. From the pelvis to the ureter proper, a cylindrical tube, passes to the fundus of the bladder. Each tube is about 25 to 30 cm long (10 to 12 in.) and about 4 to 5 mm (1/5 in.) in diameter. Each consists of three coats: an outer fibrous coat, a muscular coat, and an inner mucous lining. The contractions of the muscular coat produce peristaltic waves, which commence at the kidney end of the ureter and progress downward.

The Bladder

The bladder is a hollow muscular organ situated in the pelvic cavity behind the pubes, in front of the rectum in the male, and in front of the anterior wall of the vagina, and the neck of the uterus, in the female. It is a freely movable organ but is held in position by folds of peritoneum and fascia. During infancy it is

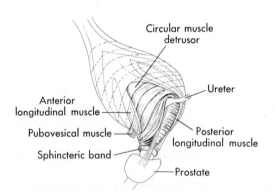

Figure 23–7. Lateral view of the male bladder. (Modified from McCrea.)

conical in shape and projects above the upper border of the pubes into the hypogastric region. In the adult, when quite empty, it is placed deeply in the pelvis; when slightly distended, it has a round form; but when greatly distended, it is ovoid in shape and rises to a considerable height in the abdominal cavity. It has four coats: (1) The *serous* coat is a reflection of the peritoneum and covers only the superior surface and the upper part of the lateral surfaces. (2) The *muscular* coat has three layers, an inner longitudinal, middle circular, and outer longitudinal. The fibers of the outer layer are arranged in a more or less longitudinal manner, up the inferior surface of the bladder, over its vertex, and descending along the fundus. They are attached in the male to the prostate, and in the female in front of the vagina. At the sides of the bladder the fibers are arranged obliquely and intersect one another. This layer is called the *detrusor urinae* muscle. The circular fibers are collected into a layer of some thickness around the opening

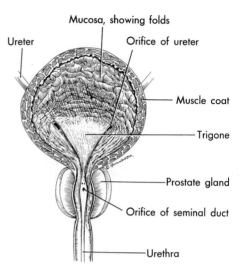

Figure 23–8. Diagram of the bladder opened ventrally to show bladder wall, orifices of ureters, and urethra. The orifices of the ureters and urethra form a triangle—the trigone. Note that the ureters enter the bladder wall from the posterior and run obliquely downward for about 2 cm. (Modified from Pansky and House.)

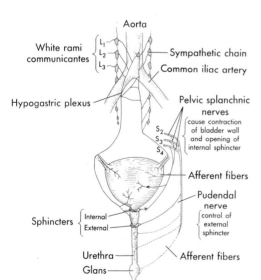

Figure 23–9. Innervation of bladder and urethra. (Modified from Grant.)

of the bladder into the urethra. These circular fibers form a sphincter muscle, which is normally in a state of contraction, relaxing only when the accumulation of urine within the bladder renders its expulsion necessary. (3) The *submucous* coat consists of areolar connective tissue and connects the mucous and muscular coats. (4) The *mucous* membrane of transitional epithelium lining the bladder is like that lining the ureters and the urethra. This coat is thrown into folds, or rugae, when the bladder is empty, with the exception of a small triangular area formed by the two uretal orifices and the internal orifice of the urethra where the mucous membrane is firmly attached to the muscular coat. This area is called the *trigonum vesicae.*

There are three openings into the bladder. The two ureters open into the lower part about ½ in. from the median plane. The ureters take an oblique course through the wall of the bladder, downward and medialward. The urethra leads from the bladder, its vesical opening lying in the median plane below and in front of the openings of the ureters.

Nerve Supply. The bladder is supplied by nerves from both the craniosacral and thoracolumbar divisions of the autonomic nervous system. The sacral fibers bring about contraction of the muscles of the bladder and relaxation of the internal sphincter. It is believed that the reflex centers for these fibers are located in the midbrain, anterior pons, and posterior hypothalamus. The function of the thoracolumbar fibers seems to be primarily related to blood supply to the bladder wall. Spinal nerves are important as well, because they innervate the muscles of the pelvic floor and perineum and aid in conscious control of the external sphincter.

Blood Supply. The superior, middle, and inferior vesical arteries (branches of the hypogastric artery) supply the bladder. In the female, branches of the uterine and vaginal arteries also supply the bladder.

Function. The bladder serves as a reservoir for the reception of urine. Its capacity varies. When moderately distended, it holds about ½ liter (about 1 pt).

The Urethra. In the female the urethra is a narrow membranous canal which extends from the bladder to the external orifice, the meatus urinarius. It is placed behind the symphysis pubis and is embedded in the anterior wall of the vagina. Its diameter, when undilated, is about 6 mm (¼ in.), and its length is about 3.8 cm (1½ in.). Its direction is obliquely downward and forward, its course being slightly curved, with the concavity directed forward and upward. Its external orifice is the narrowest part and is located between the clitoris and the opening of the vagina.

The walls of the urethra consist of three coats: (1) an outer muscular coat, which is continuous with that of the bladder; (2) a thin layer of spongy tissue, containing a plexus of veins; and (3) a mucous coat, which is continuous internally with that lining the bladder and externally with that of the vulva.

The male urethra is about 20 cm (8 in.) long. It is divided into three portions: (1) the prostatic, which runs vertically through the prostate; (2) the membranous, which extends between the apex of the prostate and the bulb of the urethra; and (3) the cavernous portion, which extends from the membranous to the external orifice.

The male urethra is composed of (1) mucous membrane, which is continuous with the mucous membrane of the bladder and is prolonged into the ducts of the glands that open into the urethra; and (2) a submucous tissue, which connects the urethra with the structures through which it passes.

Physiology of Micturition. The act by which the urine is expelled from the bladder is called micturition. The desire to urinate is due to stimulation of pressure receptors in the bladder itself caused by pressure of urine. As the bladder fills, pressure is exerted against the detrusor muscle. This reflexly causes the muscle to contract, and the internal sphincter to relax. The reflex is sustained until the bladder is completely empty. The act of micturition is started by voluntary relaxation of the external sphincter and surrounding muscles of the perineum.

While the emptying of the bladder is reflexly controlled, it may be initiated voluntarily and may be started or stopped at will. The average capacity of the bladder is about 700 to 800 ml.

Involuntary Micturition, or Incontinence. In young infants incontinence of urine is normal. The infant voids whenever the bladder is sufficiently distended to arouse a reflex stimulus. Children vary markedly in the ease with which they learn to control micturition and defecation. During the first year, some children can be taught to associate the act with the proper time and place. By the second year, regular training in habit formation and proper feeding should enable the child to inhibit the normal stimulus and control micturition, at least during the day. Control of micturition at night is a habit requiring longer practice and is usually formed by the end of the second year. When involuntary voiding occurs at night with any degree of regularity after the third year, it is called enuresis. If this is not caused by emotional stress or irritation of the bladder, it will usually yield to proper training.

Involuntary micturition may occur as the result of a lack of consciousness or as the result of injury to the spinal centers which control the bladder. If the spinal cord is transected, all bladder controls are abolished and loss of voluntary control is permanent. If there is injury to the sympathetic fibers, no significant effects result, but frequency may be present for a short time. There may be difficulty in initiating the act of voiding, where there is injury to the brain cortex.

Involuntary micturition may also result from some irritation due to abnormal substances in the urine, or to disease of the bladder (cystitis). Emotional stress may provoke the desire to urinate when there is only a small amount of urine in the bladder, due to failure of the detrusor muscles to relax. This desire may also be aroused by visual and auditory impressions, such as the sight and sound of running water.

Retention of Urine. Retention, or failure to void urine, may be due to: (1) some obstruction in the urethra or in the neck of the bladder, (2) nervous contraction of the urethra, or (3) lack of sensation to void. In the last two conditions retention is often overcome by measures which induce reflexes, i.e., pouring warm water over the vulva, or the sound of running water. If micturition does not occur and the bladder is not catheterized, distention of the organ may become extreme, and there is likely to be constant leakage, or involuntary voiding of small amounts of urine without emptying the bladder. This condition is described as retention with overflow.

Suppression of Urine. A far more serious condition than retention is the failure of the kidneys to secrete urine. This is spoken of as suppression, or *anuria*. Unless suppression is relieved, a toxic condition known as uremia will develop. When the secretion of urine is decreased below the normal amount, the condition is spoken of as *oliguria*.

QUESTIONS FOR DISCUSSION

1. Explain the functions of the glomerulus and renal tubule in relation to volume and composition of urine.
2. Which hormones affect kidney function? What is the specific action of each?
3. Explain the relationship of arterial blood pressure to kidney function.
4. What is the trigone? How does it differ from the rest of the bladder? Is this important?
5. Explain how the two divisions of the autonomic nervous system regulate micturition.
6. What is the normal composition of urine?
7. Would it be possible to remove excessive fluid from an edematous patient by use of the artificial kidney? Explain the principles involved.

SUMMARY

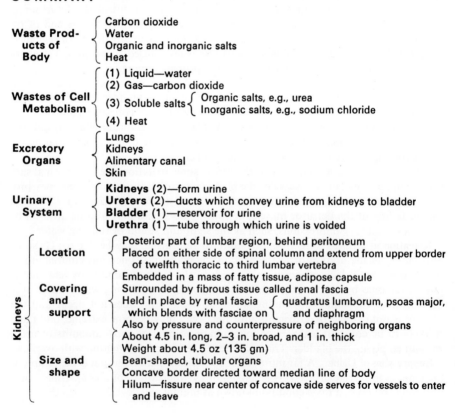

Waste Products of Body
{ Carbon dioxide
Water
Organic and inorganic salts
Heat

Wastes of Cell Metabolism
{ (1) Liquid—water
(2) Gas—carbon dioxide
(3) Soluble salts { Organic salts, e.g., urea
Inorganic salts, e.g., sodium chloride
(4) Heat

Excretory Organs
{ Lungs
Kidneys
Alimentary canal
Skin

Urinary System
{ Kidneys (2)—form urine
Ureters (2)—ducts which convey urine from kidneys to bladder
Bladder (1)—reservoir for urine
Urethra (1)—tube through which urine is voided

Kidneys

Location
{ Posterior part of lumbar region, behind peritoneum
Placed on either side of spinal column and extend from upper border of twelfth thoracic to third lumbar vertebra

Covering and support
{ Embedded in a mass of fatty tissue, adipose capsule
Surrounded by fibrous tissue called renal fascia
Held in place by renal fascia { quadratus lumborum, psoas major, which blends with fasciae on { and diaphragm
Also by pressure and counterpressure of neighboring organs

Size and shape
{ About 4.5 in. long, 2–3 in. broad, and 1 in. thick
Weight about 4.5 oz (135 gm)
Bean-shaped, tubular organs
Concave border directed toward median line of body
Hilum—fissure near center of concave side serves for vessels to enter and leave

Kidneys (cont.)

Gross structure
- **Pelvis**—upper expanded end of ureter
- **Calyces**—cuplike cavities of the pelvis that receive papillae of pyramids
- **Medulla**—inner striated portion, made up of cone-shaped masses
  - **Pyramids**—8–18
  - **Bases** directed toward circumference of kidney
  - **Papillae**—apices of pyramids, directed into pelvis
- **Cortex**—outer portion of kidney
  - **Renal columns**—extensions of cortical substance between pyramids

Unit pattern
- **Nephron**—consists of a renal tubule with its blood supply
- **Renal tubules**—begin as capsules enclosing capillary tufts—glomeruli—in the cortex, and after a tortuous course open into straight collecting tubes which pour their contents into calyces of kidney pelvis

Blood supply
- **Renal artery**—direct from aorta
- Before entering kidney divides into several branches
- **Arterial arches**
  - Lateral branches at the boundary zone between cortex and medulla
  - Send branches to cortex
- **Venous arches**
  - Lateral branches at level of base of pyramids
  - Receive blood from cortex
  - Receive blood from medulla
- Veins empty into renal vein, leave kidney at hilus, and empty into inferior vena cava

Autonomic Nerves
- Nerves derived from renal plexus, and from the lesser and lowest splanchnic nerves
- Vasomotor, by regulating size of blood vessels, influences blood pressure

Physiology of Kidneys
- Regulation of osmotic pressure of extracellular fluids
- Regulation of electrolytic pattern of extracellular fluids
- Excretion of metabolic wastes
- Regulation of acid-base ratio
- Regulation of the volume of extracellular fluid
- In shock the kidneys produce a vasoexcitatory material (VEM)

Hormonal Control
- ADH—reabsorption of water in the kidney tubule
- Mineralocorticoids (aldosterone)

Urine

Physical characteristics
- An aqueous solution of organic and inorganic substances
- **Color** and **transparency** depend upon concentration, diet, etc.
- **Reaction**, usually slightly acid, pH 5.5–7.5
- **Specific gravity** 1.010–1.030, depending upon proportions of solids and water
- **Quantity**—1,200–1,500 ml daily. Affected by :
  - Amount of fluid ingested
  - Amount of fluid lost in other excretions than urine, e.g., perspiration
  - Ability of organs to function—heart, blood vessels, kidneys, etc.
  - Action of specific substances, as diuretics

Composition of urine
- 95% water
- Remainder, about 3.7% organic and 1.3% inorganic wastes
  - May be exogenous or endogenous
- **Exogenous**, e.g., urea
  - Amount excreted varies with diet
- **Endogenous**, e.g., creatinine
  - Amount excreted does not vary with diet

Physiology of Urine Formation

- Efferent vessel is smaller than afferent, making blood pressure in glomerulus high
- Deproteinized plasma filters through capsule into tubule
- Efferent vessel, with others, forms plexuses about tubule
- Urine is concentrated in tubule by diffusion of water and some salts back into the blood
- Secretion of H^+, NH_3, or K^+, reabsorption of Na^+ to maintain acid-base balance
- Hormones (ADH, aldosterone) important in reabsorption

Some Constituents of Normal Urine

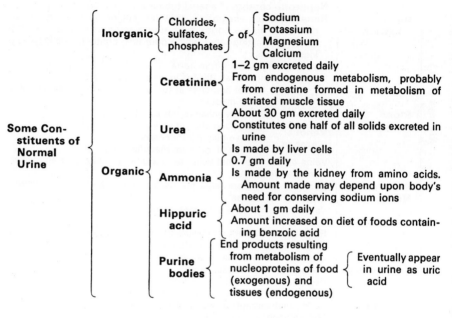

Inorganic — Chlorides, sulfates, phosphates — of — Sodium, Potassium, Magnesium, Calcium

Organic —

Creatinine —
- 1–2 gm excreted daily
- From endogenous metabolism, probably from creatine formed in metabolism of striated muscle tissue

Urea —
- About 30 gm excreted daily
- Constitutes one half of all solids excreted in urine
- Is made by liver cells

Ammonia —
- 0.7 gm daily
- Is made by the kidney from amino acids. Amount made may depend upon body's need for conserving sodium ions

Hippuric acid —
- About 1 gm daily
- Amount increased on diet of foods containing benzoic acid

Purine bodies —
- End products resulting from metabolism of nucleoproteins of food (exogenous) and tissues (endogenous) — Eventually appear in urine as uric acid

Some Abnormal Constituents of Urine

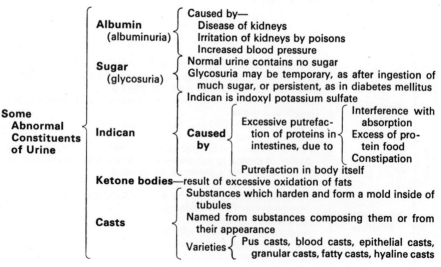

Albumin (albuminuria) —
Caused by—
- Disease of kidneys
- Irritation of kidneys by poisons
- Increased blood pressure

Sugar (glycosuria) —
- Normal urine contains no sugar
- Glycosuria may be temporary, as after ingestion of much sugar, or persistent, as in diabetes mellitus

Indican —
- Indican is indoxyl potassium sulfate
- Caused by — Excessive putrefaction of proteins in intestines, due to — Interference with absorption, Excess of protein food, Constipation
- Putrefaction in body itself

Ketone bodies—result of excessive oxidation of fats

Casts —
- Substances which harden and form a mold inside of tubules
- Named from substances composing them or from their appearance
- Varieties — Pus casts, blood casts, epithelial casts, granular casts, fatty casts, hyaline casts

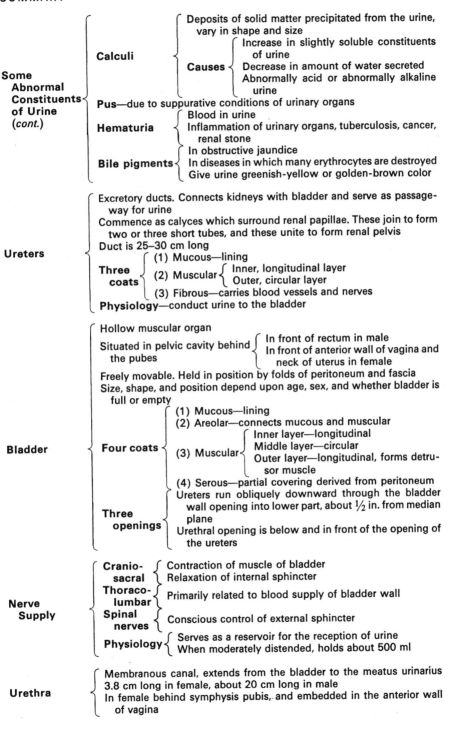

Some Abnormal Constituents of Urine (*cont.*)

Calculi — Deposits of solid matter precipitated from the urine, vary in shape and size

Causes — Increase in slightly soluble constituents of urine / Decrease in amount of water secreted / Abnormally acid or abnormally alkaline urine

Pus — due to suppurative conditions of urinary organs

Hematuria — Blood in urine / Inflammation of urinary organs, tuberculosis, cancer, renal stone

Bile pigments — In obstructive jaundice / In diseases in which many erythrocytes are destroyed / Give urine greenish-yellow or golden-brown color

Ureters

Excretory ducts. Connects kidneys with bladder and serve as passage-way for urine

Commence as calyces which surround renal papillae. These join to form two or three short tubes, and these unite to form renal pelvis

Duct is 25–30 cm long

Three coats — (1) Mucous—lining / (2) Muscular — Inner, longitudinal layer / Outer, circular layer / (3) Fibrous—carries blood vessels and nerves

Physiology — conduct urine to the bladder

Bladder

Hollow muscular organ

Situated in pelvic cavity behind the pubes — In front of rectum in male / In front of anterior wall of vagina and neck of uterus in female

Freely movable. Held in position by folds of peritoneum and fascia

Size, shape, and position depend upon age, sex, and whether bladder is full or empty

Four coats — (1) Mucous—lining / (2) Areolar—connects mucous and muscular / (3) Muscular — Inner layer—longitudinal / Middle layer—circular / Outer layer—longitudinal, forms detrusor muscle / (4) Serous—partial covering derived from peritoneum

Three openings — Ureters run obliquely downward through the bladder wall opening into lower part, about $\frac{1}{2}$ in. from median plane / Urethral opening is below and in front of the opening of the ureters

Nerve Supply

Cranio-sacral — Contraction of muscle of bladder / Relaxation of internal sphincter

Thoraco-lumbar — Primarily related to blood supply of bladder wall

Spinal nerves — Conscious control of external sphincter

Physiology — Serves as a reservoir for the reception of urine / When moderately distended, holds about 500 ml

Urethra

Membranous canal, extends from the bladder to the meatus urinarius

3.8 cm long in female, about 20 cm long in male

In female behind symphysis pubis, and embedded in the anterior wall of vagina

Urethra
(cont.)
{ **Three coats** { (1) Mucous—lining
(2) Submucous—supports network of veins
(3) Muscular { Inner—longitudinal
External—circular
Meatus urinarius—external orifice located between clitoris and vagina

Micturition { Act of expelling urine from bladder
Reflex act—controlled by voluntary effort

Retention { Failure to void urine
Due to { (1) Obstruction in urethra or neck of bladder
(2) Nervous contraction of urethra
(3) Lack of sensation
May be accompanied by constant leakage, or involuntary voiding of small amounts

Suppression, or Anuria—Failure of the kidneys to secrete urine
Oliguria—Deficient secretion of urine

The Structural and Functional Relationships for Human Reproduction and Development

24

The Anatomy and Physiology of Reproduction

SEX CELLS, or *gametes*, grow and develop within the reproductive organs. These organs are especially adapted for the maturation of spermatozoa in the male and ova in the female. Gonadal, hypophyseal, and thyroid hormones are essential influences in all aspects of reproduction. Once the ovum has been fertilized by a spermatozoon, it travels to the uterus, where it implants. Slowly and miraculously the *zygote* develops into an *embryo* and then a *fetus* and finally enters the external world, takes its first breath of air, and becomes a newborn baby.

MATURATION OF THE REPRODUCTIVE ORGANS

Although the sex of the embryo is determined at the time of fertilization, the reproductive organs do not acquire their morphological characteristics until the end of the second month of embryological development. Functional maturity is attained at the time of puberty. *Puberty* may be defined as the period when the gonads or sex glands attain normal adult function. In temperate climates, the age at which boys usually attain puberty is between 14 and 16 years; in girls, it is signaled by the beginning of the menses and occurs between the ages of 13 and 15. In warmer climates, puberty often occurs earlier, and in the arctic regions, one or two years later. However, there is no fixed rule, as the time of puberty varies from individual to individual. Psychological factors producing stress at the time of puberty may cause physiological changes that induce early puberty or impede its progress. It is believed that increased secretion of gonadotropic hormones several years before the onset of puberty brings about gonadal maturation.

The onset of puberty is signaled in the male by production of functional spermatozoa and in the female by the beginning of ovulation and menstruation. At birth, the testes contain thousands of immature spermatocytes and the ovaries contain thousands of partially developed germ cells, but these cells do not mature until the onset of puberty. Puberty is also marked by the gradual appearance of the secondary sex characteristics induced by the increasing amounts of circulating sex hormones in the body. In the male, increased secretion of testosterone by the testes causes the increased development of skeletal muscle, enlargement of the external genitals, and hair growth in the axillae and on the face, pubes, and to a varying degree on the extremities. The male larynx increases in size and accentuates the prominence called the "Adam's apple." The vocal folds become thickened, and the male voice becomes lower. The girl undergoes a gradual change of figure; the pelvis widens, and fat deposits increase around the hips, thighs, and buttocks. Hair grows on the pubes and in the axillae. Subcutaneous fat deposition increases in the breasts. The menstrual cycle is initiated, and rhythmical changes begin to occur in the ovaries, uterus, and vagina. Increased production of estrogens and progesterone by the ovaries and their homeostatic feedback effects upon pituitary gonadotropic secretion bring about these changes in the female figure and reproductive organs.

These secondary sex alterations begin at puberty and continue to develop over a number of years. This period is known as *adolescence*, and it extends from puberty until the age of 17 to 20 years in the female and until the age of 18 to 21 years in the male. At the age of 20 or 21, in the average man and woman the rapid increase in height characteristic of adolescence comes to an end due to the closure of the epiphyseal bone plates. The complete development of all secondary characteristics has also been achieved.

MALE ORGANS OF REPRODUCTION

The male reproductive organs include two *testes* that produce spermatozoa and testosterone and the following bilateral accessory organs: the *seminal vesicles*, *seminal ducts* (vas or ductus deferens), *ejaculatory ducts*, *epididymides* (singular *epididymis*), *bulbourethral* (Cowper's) *glands*, as well as the following single structures: the *prostate gland*, the *penis*, the *urethra*, and the *scrotum*.

The testes are two glandular organs suspended from the inguinal region by the *spermatic cord*. The *spermatic cord* is made up of sheets of fascia derived from the abdominal muscles and contains the ductus or vas deferens, spermatic artery and veins, lymph vessels, and autonomic nerve fibers. It is formed just above the internal inguinal ring and passes through the inguinal canal into the scrotum. Each testis is about the shape and size of an egg and is attached to an overlying structure called the epididymis. It is covered exteriorly by fibrous tissue which sends incomplete partitions into the central portion of the gland, dividing it into communicating cavities. In these cavities are winding seminiferous tubules surrounded by blood vessels and held together by interstitial tissue. The *seminiferous tubules* provide for production of spermatozoa, and the interstitial or Leydig cells produce testosterone. These tubules intertwine and join together in a sort of mesh of exiting small ducts called the rete testis and finally all unite in the epididymis.

The *epididymides* are long bilateral narrow bodies that lie upon the superior portions of the testes and are composed of a multitude of tortuous tubules. These tubules contain smooth muscle cells in their walls and are lined with mucous membrane. They connect the testes with the seminal ducts and serve as areas for final maturation of the spermatozoa.

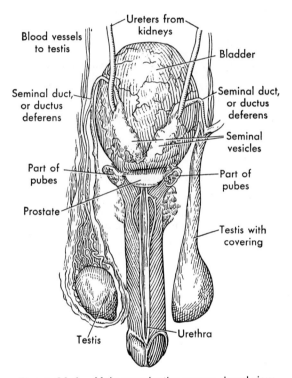

Figure 24–1. Male reproductive organs, dorsal view.

Descent of the Testes. The testes are formed and develop in the abdomen slightly inferior to the kidneys but within the peritoneal cavity. During growth and development of the fetus, they migrate downward and through the inguinal canal into the scrotum. Shortly before birth or soon afterward, the testes are found in the scrotum. Sometimes, particularly in premature infants, a testis has not descended and is found in the inguinal canal or even in the abdominal cavity. As a rule, it soon descends, but if it does not, the condition is referred to as *cryptorchidism* and may be either unilateral or bilateral. If the testis remains inside the abdomen after puberty, spermatogenesis is depressed owing to the slightly higher intra-abdominal temperature, and eventually it ceases altogether. It can be treated successfully prior to puberty with testosterone or, if this is ineffective, with surgery.

The scrotum is a thin pouch of skin, muscle, and fascia that contains and supports the testes, the epididymides, and parts of the spermatic cords. The smooth muscle layer of the scrotum that is covered by a thin layer of skin disposed in folds or rugae is called the *dartos muscle* and contracts reflexly with the cord to raise the testes closer to body warmth. The tissues of the scrotum are continuous with those of the groin and perineum.

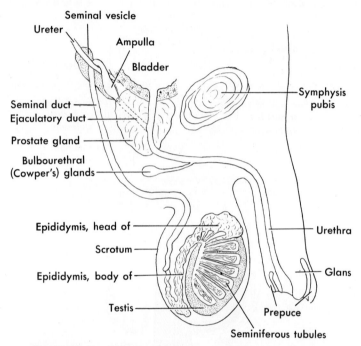

Figure 24–2. Diagram of the male organs of reproduction.

The seminal ducts (vas deferens or ductus deferens), which are bilateral continuations of the epididymides, are important storage sites for spermatozoa and are the excretory ducts of the testes. Each duct conveys the spermatozoa along a devious course, from the scrotum into the pelvic cavity and to the ejaculatory duct through the layers of the inguinal ligament known as the inguinal canal.

The seminal vesicles are two membranous pouches located posterior to the bladder, between this organ and the rectum. The seminal vesicles were originally thought to be important for the storage of spermatozoa or the various glandular secretions containing the spermatozoa known as *semen.* That is how the name seminal vesicle was derived. More recently it has been shown that the seminal vesicles produce secretions containing fructose, amino acids, mucus, and small amounts of some vitamins. During ejaculation, these substances are added to the semen at the same time that the seminal ducts transport spermatozoa to the ejaculatory ducts. The fructose and other substances contained in the seminal fluid provide nutrients and protection for the spermatozoa. All the various secretions added to the semen increase its bulk.

The ejaculatory ducts are narrow bilateral passageways less than an inch long formed by the union of the seminal vesicles with the seminal ducts. They descend, one on each side, from each of the seminal vesicles between the lobes of the prostate gland to the urethra, into which they open and discharge their contents.

The prostate gland is situated immediately inferior to the bladder and internal urethral orifice. It surrounds the first portion of the urethra, referred to as the *prostatic urethra*, and is comparable to a chestnut in shape, size, and consistency. The prostate is covered by a dense fibrous capsule and consists of glandular units surrounded by fibromuscular tissue that contracts only during ejaculation. The glandular tissue consists of tubules which communicate with the urethra by minute orifices. The function of the prostate gland is to secrete a thin, milky alkaline fluid that precedes the exit of the spermatozoa and enhances their motility. The fluid in the seminal duct is quite acidic due to the presence of the metabolic end products of the stored sperm. The secretions of the female vagina are also quite acidic. Therefore, it is probable that alkaline prostatic fluid neutralizes the acidity of the semen and vaginal secretions and thereby greatly increases the motility and fertility of the spermatozoa.

Age Changes in the Prostate. The prostate enlarges during adolescence along with the other reproductive organs owing to the effect of androgens secreted by the interstitial cells of the testes. The interstitial cells are stimulated by the anterior pituitary gonadotropins. The prostate attains full size during the twenties. In older age, for reasons not yet understood, frequently the prostate increases in size so that two out of every three men reaching the age of 70 suffer from some degree of obstruction to urination. This condition may be due to cancerous growth of the prostate but more frequently is due to nonmalignant enlargement called benign prostatic hypertrophy (BPH). Enlargement of the prostate is a serious condition due to the resulting urinary retention caused by the obstruction of the urethra and is usually treated by partial or complete surgical removal of the gland.

The bulbourethral glands (Cowper's glands) are two small bodies about the size of peas situated on either side of the membranous portion of the urethra a little inferior to the prostate gland. Each small gland is provided with a short duct which empties its mucous secretion into the urethra. These glands secrete an alkaline viscid fluid which adds lubricating and protective mucus to the semen. The secretion of these glands precedes ejaculation and removes any urine residues that may be injurious to the spermatozoa.

The semen is the fluid that is ejaculated during the male sexual act. It is composed of the combined fluids from the testes, epididymides, seminal vesicles, prostate gland, and bulbourethral glands. It is a grayish-white viscid liquid that contains carbohydrates, mucin, proteins, salt, and about 100,000,000 spermatozoa per milliliter. At each ejaculation, 2 to 5 ml of semen are usually expressed through the urethra. *Ejaculation,* or the discharge of semen to the exterior, is initiated by peristaltic waves moving along the tubes leading from the testes and by rhythmical contractions of the smooth muscle layers of the testes, epididymides, seminal vesicles, and prostate gland. Increased pressure upon all these structures causes expulsion of the semen. The bulbourethral glands discharge

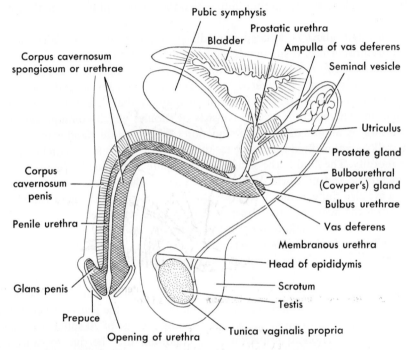

Figure 24–3. Diagram of midsagittal section of male reproductive organs to show glands, ducts, urethra, and corpora cavernosa. (Modified from Bloom and Fawcett.)

additional quantities of mucus into the urethra at this time. The process to this point is called *emission* and is brought about by rhythmical sympathetic impulses which leave the spinal cord at L_1 and L_2 and then pass through the hypogastric plexus to the genital organs. Ejaculation proper is brought about by contraction of the skeletal muscles that encase the base of the erectile tissue of the penis and that are innervated by fibers traveling in the pudendal nerves. In some stages of sexual life, especially during the teens, the male may have nocturnal emissions during dreams.

The penis, or organ of copulation of the male, is a short, cylindrical, pendulous body that is suspended from the front and sides of the pubic arch. It is composed of three cylindrical masses of cavernous erectile tissue bound together by fibrous strands and covered with skin. The lateral two masses are known as the *corpora cavernosa penis.* The third, known as the *corpus cavernosum urethrae* or *spongiosum*, makes up the ventral surface and contains the urethra. The term "cavernous" is used because of the relatively large venous spaces present within its structure. It is also described as erectile tissue because the venous spaces may become distended with blood during sexual excitement, and the penis then becomes firm and erect. *Erection* is the first effect of male sexual stimulation, and it is brought about by parasympathetic impulses that pass from the sacral portion of the spinal cord via the *nervi erigentes* (pelvic splanchnic nerves) to the penis. These impulses cause dilatation of the penile arteries which results in

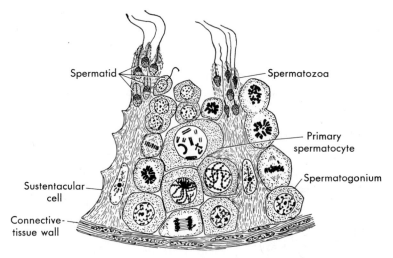

Figure 24–4. Section of the wall of a portion of a seminiferous tubule to show spermatogenesis, or the development of spermatozoa. (Modified from Walter, after Arey.)

compression of the exiting veins. Increased blood supply that is under high pressure and unable to leave the area results in filling of the erectile tissue and erection of the organ.

At the end of the penis there is a slight enlargement known as the *glans penis* that contains the urethral orifice (meatus) and the sensory end organs that are stimulated during sexual intercourse. These end organs convey impulses to the spinal cord via the pudendal nerves. Their endings synapse on the sacral preganglionic cell bodies of the parasympathetic nervous system to produce erection and upon preganglionic cell bodies of the sympathetic nervous system to produce emission of the semen. The loose integument of the penis forms the *prepuce*, or *foreskin*. Sometimes the foreskin may cover the glans too tightly causing restricted circulation to the area and a collection of the sebaceous secretion called *smegma* which provides a good environment for microbial multiplication and inflammation. Constriction of the foreskin is known as *phimosis* and is often prevented and treated by the operation known as *circumcision*, or surgical removal of the foreskin.

The male urethra is an S-shaped tube lined with mucous membrane about 17.5 to 20 cm (8 in.) long that extends from the internal to the external urethral orifice. It serves, at separate times, as conveyor of both urine and semen to the exterior. It is divided into three parts, the *prostatic*, the *membranous*, and the *cavernous*, or *penile*, portions.

Spermatogenesis. Beginning at about the age of 12, spermatozoa begin to be produced in the seminiferous tubules of the testis of the male under the influence of the pituitary gonadotropic hormones. Spermatogenesis, or the production and maturation of sperm, continues throughout adult life. Germ cells called spermatogonia, formed during fetal life, now begin to proliferate and differentiate through definite stages to form spermatozoa. As these cells divide, increase in number, and move toward the center of the tubule, they become *primary spermatocytes*. Primary spermatocytes then go through two meiotic, or reduction, divisions during which the number of chromosomes of the developing cells is halved from 46, or diploid number, to 23, or haploid number. The process and significance of meiosis are discussed in detail in the following chapter. Each primary spermatocyte divides into two *secondary spermatocytes*, each of which contains 23 double chromosomes. The secondary spermatocytes each divide again to form two *spermatids* with 23 single chromosomes contained within each one. In summary then, from every primary spermatocyte, four spermatids are derived. The process of meiosis apportions the sex chromosomes so that each spermatozoon receives one. One half of the spermatozoa carry the X chromosome, and one half carry the Y chromosome. The sex of the fertilized ovum is determined by the sex chromosome contributed by the spermatozoon because all ova normally contain one X chromosome. When a spermatozoon enters an ovum at fertilization, the original complement of 46 chromosomes is re-established.

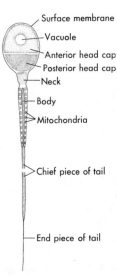

Surface membrane
Vacuole
Anterior head cap
Posterior head cap
Neck
Body
Mitochondria
Chief piece of tail
End piece of tail

Figure 24–5. Diagram of spermatozoon.

The *spermatid* develops into a *spermatozoon* when a tail or flagellum is formed, and the cytoplasm has contracted around the cell nucleus to form the head. Between the head and the tail, the neck and the body are found. The body contains many mitochondria that produce large amounts of adenosine triphosphate. ATP provides energy for movement of the flagellum.

Two other factors besides the gonadotropins, FSH and LH (called ICSH in the male), seem necessary for normal spermatogenesis to take place. The first factor is the presence of *Sertoli*, or *sustentacular*, *cells* which line the basement membrane of the tubules. They contain considerable amounts of glycogen in their cytoplasm and in some way are thought to serve as nutrient cells for the germinal epithelium during the formation of spermatozoa from spermatids. The second factor is the production of adequate amounts of *testosterone.* Under the influence of LH (ICSH) *testosterone* is secreted by the interstitial Leydig cells of the testis. These cells are found interspersed in groups between the seminiferous tubules. The specific role of this androgen in spermatogenesis is not clear, but without normal adult levels of this hormone, adequate formation of spermatozoa cannot take place.

Spermatozoa are formed at the edge of the lumen of the seminiferous tubules and reach the epididymis via a series of excretory ducts called the *tubuli recti,* the *rete testes,* and the *efferent ductules.* They are conveyed by the motion of ciliated epithelium, for at this stage of their development they are nonmotile. Sperm most probably mature within the epididymis, since after they have remained there for one-half day or more, they have developed the power of motility and the capability of fertilizing the ovum. They are stored in the seminal ducts, where they remain dormant within the acid medium resulting from their own metabolism. Viable sperm may be stored in the epididymis and vas deferens for as long as six weeks, but once ejaculated to the exterior, they survive at normal body temperature for only 24 to 72 hours.

Male Climacteric. Testicular function usually does not significantly decline at a particular period in the life of the male as it does in the female. If and when testosterone production by testicular Leydig cells does decrease, symptoms may appear that are similar to those observed in menopausal women. In addition to the increased irritability, episodes of depression, inability to concentrate, and perhaps "hot flashes," diminished libido, or sexual desire, and decreased spermatogenesis may also develop. This syndrome has been designated as the *male climacteric* and may occur between the ages of 45 and 60 as a result of interstitial cell failure. These symptoms can usually be relieved by the administration of testosterone or synthetic methyl testosterone. Too often symptoms of the male climacteric go untreated because the public is less knowledgeable about androgen withdrawal problems in the male than they are about menopausal symptoms in the female.

FEMALE ORGANS OF REPRODUCTION

The female organs of reproduction include the bilateral *ovaries,* the bilateral *uterine (fallopian) tubes,* or *oviducts,* the *uterus,* the *vagina,* and the *external genitals.*

The ovaries produce the ova and the sex hormones, progesterone and estrogens. Each ovary is a slightly flattened, almond-shaped body measuring from 2.5 to 5 cm. (1 to 2 inches) in length. One is located on each side of the pelvis, lateral to the uterus, inferior to the uterine tube and attached to the posterior surface of the broad ligament. The *broad ligament* is a reflection of the peritoneum that supports the uterus, and fixes the ovaries and uterine tubes to the posterior pelvic wall. Each ovary is attached to the lateral angle of the uterus by a short *ovarian ligament,* a fibrous cord within the broad ligament, and to the tubal end of the uterine tube by the largest one of the fringelike processes of the tubal fimbriated extremity.

The uterine (fallopian) tubes, or oviducts, ~~are bilateral muscular ducts~~, lined with mucosa containing ciliated epithelium, that pass from the upper angles of the uterus in a somewhat tortuous course between the folds and along the superior margin of the broad ligament toward the sides of the pelvis. They are

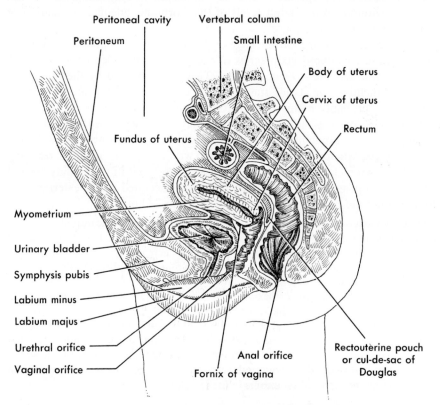

Peritoneal cavity Vertebral column
Peritoneum Small intestine
Body of uterus
Cervix of uterus
Fundus of uterus Rectum
Myometrium
Urinary bladder
Symphysis pubis
Labium minus
Labium majus
Urethral orifice Rectouterine pouch
or cul-de-sac of
Anal orifice Douglas
Vaginal orifice Fornix of vagina

Figure 24–6.   Median sagittal section of female pelvis.

about 4 inches long, and the margin of the dilated end, or ampulla, is surrounded by a number of fringelike processes called *fimbriae.* One of these processes is attached to the ovary.

The functions of the uterine tubes are ~~to convey the ova from the ovaries to the uterus, to aid in the upward passage of the spermatozoa~~, and ~~to provide circular folds within which the ovum is nourished and delayed for fertilization~~. The sequestration of the fertilized ovum within these tubes allows adequate time to elapse between fertilization and implantation so that the uterine wall will be properly prepared for growth and development of the embryo.

The uterus, or womb, is a hollow thick-walled, pear-shaped muscular organ about 3 inches long, situated in the pelvic cavity between the rectum and the bladder. Three parts of the uterus can be distinguished: (1) the *body*, or *corpus uteri*, with its superior expanded portion called the *fundus* extending above the entrance of the uterine tubes; (2) the *isthmus*, or middle, slightly constricted portion; and (3) the cervix, or cylindrical lower part, that surrounds the *cervical canal* and projects into the vagina. The *internal orifice* or *os* is located at the entrance of the cervical canal and the *external orifice* or *os* is located at the termination of the cervix. The short cervical canal extends for a distance of about 2.5 cm (1 inch) between these two openings.

The cavity of the uterus is small because of the thickness of its walls. The part of the cavity within the body is triangular and has three openings, one very small one at each upper angle communicating with the uterine tubes, and the third, the *internal os*, opening into the cavity of the cervix below. The uterus is the organ of the reproductive tract in which the embryo grows and develops until the time of delivery.

Structure of the Uterus. The walls of the uterus are thick and consist of three layers:

1. THE EXTERNAL, OR SEROUS, layer is derived from the peritoneum and covers the superior part of the uterus. It adheres intimately to the outer surface of the fundus and surfaces of the uterine body and is reflected from the body to the bladder as the *vesicouterine* pouch. Posteriorly it may descend as far as the upper part of the vagina before reflection to the rectum as the *rectouterine pouch* (of Douglas).

2. THE MIDDLE, OR MUSCULAR, layer is about 2 cm (¾ inch) thick, forms the bulk of the uterine wall, and is called the *myometrium*. It consists of three ill-defined layers of smooth muscle disposed longitudinally, circularly, and spirally. Peristalsislike movements of the muscle are thought to be increased around the time of ovulation. It is believed that these contractions assist the ascension of spermatozoa by the suction they produce within the organ. The larger blood vessels are found deep within the myometrium. Intense rhythmical contractions of the myometrium, probably under the influence of the posterior pituitary hormone, *oxytocin*, result in cervical dilatation and expulsion of the fetus during labor and delivery.

3. THE INNER, OR MUCOUS, layer called the *endometrium* is continuous with the mucous membrane that lines the vagina and uterine tubes. The endometrium is highly vascular and is provided with numerous uterine glands. It is lined with ciliated and secretory epithelium, except for the lower third of the cervical canal, where it gradually changes to stratified squamous epithelium similar to that lining the vagina. In the sexually mature, nonpregnant female, the uterine mucosa is subject to cyclical menstrual changes that are influenced by ovarian hormonal secretions. Four phases of activity can be identified in the endometrial cycle: (1) the follicular, or growth, phase, which makes up the first half and is concurrent with the developing graafian follicle; (2) the lutein, or secretory, phase, which is associated with the actively secreting corpus luteum and endometrial glands; (3) the ischemic phase, which occurs when the uterine mucosa

becomes necrotic owing to deficient blood flow through the myometrium to the inner layers of the endometrium; and (4) the menstrual, or sloughing-off, stage, which is associated with involution of the corpus luteum and the extravasation and expulsion of the necrotic mucosa.

The *blood supply of the uterus* is abundant and reaches it by means of the *uterine arteries*, branches from the internal iliac (hypogastric) arteries, and the *ovarian arteries*, which are branches from the aorta. Where the cervix joins the body of the uterus, the arteries from both sides are united by a branch called the circumflex artery. The arteries are remarkable for their tortuous course and frequency of anastomoses. The veins are large and correspond to the arteries in

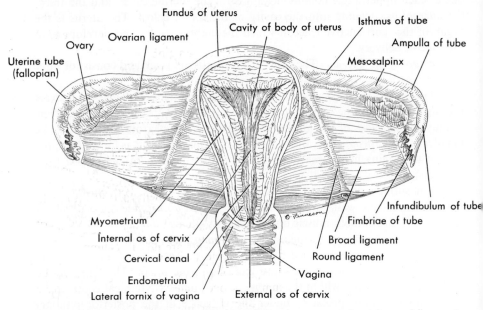

Figure 24–7. Uterus in section showing relation to ovary, uterine tube, and ligaments. Anterior view. (Modified from Pansky and House.)

size and frequency of anastomoses. The uterine veins empty into the internal iliac (hypogastric) veins. The right ovarian vein empties into the inferior vena cava but the left one empties into the left renal vein.

Position of the Uterus. The uterus is not firmly attached or adherent to any part of the skeleton. It is suspended in the pelvic cavity by fibrous cords and folds of peritoneum called *ligaments*. Normally the fundus is inclined forward, and the general line of the uterus is almost at right angles to that of the vagina. A full bladder tilts it backward, and a full rectum pushes it forward. During gestation the uterus becomes enormously enlarged and extends into the epigastric region of the abdominal cavity.

Minor variations in position of the uterus occur with alterations in posture or with changes in bladder content. If the uterus becomes fixed or rests habitually in a position beyond the limits of normal variation, it is said to be displaced. *Retroversion* signifies a backward turning of the whole uterus without a change in the relationship of the body to the cervix. *Retroflexion* signifies a bending backward of the body on the cervix at the level of the internal os. *Anteversion* means a forward turning of the whole uterus, and *anteflexion* a forward bend of the body at the isthmus which brings the fundus under the symphysis pubis.

Ligaments. The main support of the uterus is supplied by the *levator ani* and *coccygeus* muscles. Several fibrous cords covered with mesothelium and peritoneal folds, all called *ligaments*, assist in holding the internal reproductive organs in normal position and in anchoring them to the wall and floor of the pelvis. The ligaments of the uterus are two *broad ligaments*, two *round ligaments*, two *cardinal ligaments*, two *uterosacral*, and one *anterior* and one *posterior ligament*. The *broad ligaments* are the largest and the most important, and they provide the reproductive organs with the greatest support. They are wide peritoneal folds that are slung over the anterior and posterior surfaces of the uterus, ovaries, and uterine tubes, and extend laterally to the walls of the pelvis. Other important structures found between the layers of the broad ligaments are the ligaments of the ovary, nerves, blood vessels, and lymphatics and the cardinal and round ligaments. The part of the broad ligament containing the ovarian vessels is called the *suspensory ligament of the ovary.* The *round ligaments* are flattened fibrous cords that extend from the lateral borders of the uterus within the broad ligaments to the connective tissue and skin of the labia majora via the inguinal canals of their respective sides. They help to hold the fundus forward in a slightly anteflexed position. The *uterosacral ligaments* are peritoneal folds that pass from the cervix to the sacrum, one extending on each side of the rectum. The *cardinal*, or *Mackenrodt's, ligaments* are not very important supporting structures of the uterus. They are enveloping bands of fascia that surround the uterine blood vessels as they pass to the vagina and cervix from the lateral pelvis. Folds of peritoneum that contribute little or no support to the pelvic viscera, but which are frequently included in the list of ligaments, are the *anterior* and *posterior ligaments*. The sheath of peritoneum that extends from the urinary bladder to the anterior surface of the uterus is called the *anterior ligament*. The *posterior ligament* is the reflection of the peritoneum from the anterior surface of the rectum upon the posterior surface of the uterus and vagina. The *cul-de-sac*, or *pouch of Douglas*, is the deep recess formed by this peritoneal reflection between the uterus and the rectum.

The vagina is a fibromuscular tube, 7.5 to 10 cm. (3 to 4 inches) in length, situated anterior to the rectum and anal canal and posterior to the bladder and urethra. It is parallel to the direction of the urethra; that is to say, it is directed upward and backward. It is the organ of copulation, for the deposition of semen in the female, and during parturition it serves as the exit from the uterus. The cervix projects into the vault of the vagina, and the vaginal recesses are formed around it. These recesses are known as the *anterior, posterior*, and *lateral fornices* (singular, *fornix*).

The vaginal wall consists of fascial, muscular, and mucous coats. The mucous coat is composed of stratified squamous epithelium with glycogen stored within its cells. The inner surface of mucous membrane is thrown into two longitudinal folds and transverse folds, or rugae. The circular and longitudinal smooth muscle layers hypertrophy during pregnancy, and these layers, together with the rugae of the mucous coat and the interstitial elastic connective tissue, allow for extreme distensibility of the canal during parturition.

The vagina normally has a pH of between 4 and 6. This acidic environment impedes the growth of microorganisms and thus functions to prevent infection of the pelvic organs. Estrogen secretion during the menstrual cycle and pregnancy seems to cause an increase in glycogen stores and keratinization of the surface epithelium. The mucus that lubricates the vagina originates from the glands of the cervix. This mucus is acidified by the fermenting action of the vaginal bacteria, mainly lactobacilli, upon the glycogen from the vaginal epithelium. Striated muscle fibers form a ring-shaped sphincter around the introitus or external orifice of the vagina. This opening may be partially occluded in the virgin by a fold of mucous membrane containing squamous epithelium with a thin connective tissue core called the *hymen*.

The External Female Genitals. The external organs, often grouped together under the name of *vulva*, include the *mons pubis*, the *labia majora*, the *labia minora*, the *clitoris*, the *vestibule of the vagina*, and the *greater vestibular glands* (Bartholin's glands).

The mons pubis is a pad of fat making up an eminence situated anterior to the symphysis pubis. After puberty it is covered with hair.

The labia majora are two prominent longitudinal folds which begin at the mons pubis anteriorly and extend posteriorly to within 1 inch of the anus. The labia majora are homologues of the scrotum in the male and, like the scrotum, contain large sebaceous glands and become pigmented after puberty. They protect the perineum and help to maintain its secretions. Within their substance lie the terminations of the round ligaments.

The labia minora are two thin longitudinal folds of skin bordering the vestibule of the vagina. They are situated between the labia majora, are united anteriorly in the hood or prepuce of the clitoris, and form the boundaries of the vestibule, which is the area between them.

The clitoris is a small protuberance more or less hidden by the folds of skin called the prepuce, situated at the apex of the triangle formed by the junction of the labia minora. It is the homologue of the penis in the male and, like it, contains erectile tissue, venous cavernous spaces, and specialized sensory corpuscles that are stimulated during intercourse.

The vestibule of the vagina is the area situated posterior to the clitoris and between the labia minora. The urethra opens into this space anteriorly, and the vagina opens into it posteriorly. Several glands open into the floor of the vestibule.

Bartholin's glands, or the *greater vestibular glands*, open on either side of the vaginal orifice. These glands together with the smaller lesser vestibular glands and paraurethral glands have a moistening function and are of clinical diagnostic importance because they may become infected with microorganisms, particularly the gonococcus, which causes the venereal disease known as gonorrhea.

The perineum is the external surface of the floor of the pelvis, extending from the pubic arch to the coccyx and including the underlying muscles and fascia. In the female it is perforated by the vagina as well as by the urethra and anus. A wedge-shaped upward extension of the perineum, forming a septum between the vagina and rectum, is called the perineal body.

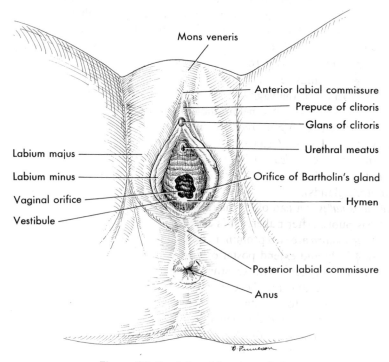

Figure 24–8.   External female genitalia.

The perineum is distensible and is stretched to a remarkable degree during parturition. Nevertheless, it may be lacerated during delivery and, if not surgically repaired, may cause weakening of the muscular and fascial supports of the pelvic floor. Without adequate support the bladder may push downward through the anterior vaginal wall to form a hernia known as a *cystocele.* The herniation of the rectum through the posterior vaginal wall is known as a *rectocele.* This condition can often be prevented if the trauma of delivery is alleviated by making a lateral or midline incision in the perineal body (episiotomy) to enlarge the vaginal opening. If an *episiotomy* is not performed at the time of delivery, the traumatized tissues should be surgically repaired after childbirth or in later years, after many deliveries, as early symptoms of prolapse become evident.

Histology of the Ovary. The ovaries embryologically are derived from the bilateral germinal ridges located in close proximity to the kidneys on the posterior wall of the abdominal cavity. The ovaries move into the pelvis during fetal life but descend a shorter distance than do the testes.

The peripheral layer, or cortex, of the ovary is covered by germinal epithelium which is derived from the epithelium of the germinal ridges. The primordial ova are believed to be differentiated from the germinal epithelium during fetal life and migrate, together with surrounding epithelioid granulosa cells, into the ovarian cortex. There they make up the approximately 500,000 primordial follicles that are present in the two ovaries at birth. During the sexual life of the female only about 400 of these follicles become mature, while the rest regress in size throughout life. At menopause they are hard to find and only the scars remain. The medulla or central part of the ovary consists of loose connective tissue that contains a large number of blood vessels.

The Menstrual Cycle. At the time of puberty the ovaries enlarge and become very vascular, and the normal sex life of the female, characterized by cyclical hormonal, ovarian, uterine, and vaginal changes, begins. This cycle is regulated by hormonal feedback mechanisms and averages 28 days, although its length may vary greatly.

The adenohypophysis begins secreting more and more hormones beginning at the age of about seven years until the beginning of adult sexual life at puberty, or between the ages of 11 and 13 years. At this time *follicle-stimulating hormone* (FSH) from the anterior pituitary begins to be secreted in large quantity. This causes growth and development of the *primordial follicle* and of its surrounding layer of cells, the *theca interna*, which then begins to produce increasing amounts of *estrogens*. FSH causes the ovum to enlarge with concurrent development of follicular fluid encompassing it. Several follicles begin to develop under this stimulation, but normally only one fully matures while the theca interna produces estrogens. *Estrogenic hormones* cause increased development of the inner lining of the uterus, the endometrium, and increases its vascularity and glandular secretions. This stage continues over approximately one half of the menstrual cycle and is often referred to as the *estrogenic, follicular,* or *proliferative phase.* As the blood level of estrogens rises, this has a feedback effect on the adenohypophysis by stimulating the secretion of *luteinizing hormone* (LH). This hormone, together with luteotropic or lactogenic hormone (LTH) also secreted by the adenohypophysis, seems to be necessary for final follicular growth and for ovulation. Secretion of FSH, LH, and LTH is regulated by hypothalamic factors (p. 277). No matter how long the menstrual cycle, ovulation is believed to occur between the thirteenth and fifteenth day before the beginning of menstrual bleeding.

Ovulation can be defined as the extrusion of the ovum surrounded by a mass of granulosa cells, into the abdominal cavity. As the fluid content of the follicular antrum increases, the blood supply is decreased, and it is perhaps, although by no means certain, for this reason that the follicle ruptures and releases the ovum. In its mature state the follicle is known as the *graafian follicle* and is about 10 to 12 mm ($\frac{2}{5}$ inch) in diameter.

At birth the primordial follicles are already formed and the *primary oocytes* have begun the first *meiotic*, or *chromosomal reduction*, division. They then enter a resting stage until sexual maturity is achieved. Under the influence of FSH, during the first portion of the menstrual cycle, the *primary oocyte* finishes its first meiotic division which was started a long time previously during prenatal life and a thick membrane, the *zona pellucida*, develops around it. From the first meiotic division two daughter cells of unequal size, each with 23 double chromosomes, are formed. The larger of the two cells is known as the *secondary oocyte* and the second, much smaller cell, containing very little cytoplasm is called *the first polar body*. The secondary oocyte then begins a second maturation division. A *mature ovum* containing 23 single chromosomes and another polar body result from this division. The secondary oocyte is extruded from the ovary before the second maturation division is completed. This division may never be terminated unless fertilization takes place. The first polar body may or may not undergo a second division. Three or four polar bodies may be formed during the two maturation divisions, but they are reabsorbed and do not serve any reproductive function. (See Fig. 25–2, p. 734.) The mature ovum is globular, almost 0.2 mm ($^{1}/_{125}$ inch) in diameter. It is much larger than the spermatozoon, whose elliptical head is only about 0.003 mm long and whose tail measures about 0.06 mm in length, or one half the diameter of the human ovum. If it is not fertilized within approximately 24 hours, it is no longer viable and is usually reabsorbed from the peritoneal cavity or genital tract.

After ovulation the remaining granulosa and theca cells of the follicle and the cells of the theca interna undergo a process of luteinization, or cellular accumulation of yellow, lipid inclusions. Under the continued stimulation of LH and LTH the mass of lutein cells becomes the *corpus luteum*, a secretory organ producing a large quantity of progesterone and, to a lesser degree, some estrogens. This phase of the menstrual cycle, usually comprising the 13 to 15 days before the commencement of menstrual bleeding, is most commonly referred to as the *progestational*, or *secretory*, stage.

The function of *progesterone* secreted under the influence of LH and LTH is to increase the secretory function of the endometrium, and to bring about the formation of glycogen and lipid stores within its structure. It also inhibits contractility of the uterine smooth muscle layers, the myometrium, thereby preventing expulsion of the embryo. In these ways progesterone functions to prepare the uterus for the implantation, early growth, and development of the fertilized ovum or zygote. High blood levels of progesterone also prepare the breasts for lactation, inhibit the secretion of FSH, and therefore the development of other follicles, while there is feasibility of fertilization of the extruded ovum.

The increasing production of progesterone toward the end of the cycle has a feedback inhibitory effect on the anterior pituitary production of LH and perhaps upon the production of LTH. This causes the corpus luteum to involute and become a *corpus albicans,* or scar, and results in decreasing production of progesterone and estrogens. About two days before the end of the cycle the ovarian hormone secretion decreases sharply to low levels and *menstruation* ensues. Inadequate amounts of ovarian hormones probably are the cause of vasospasm of blood vessels to the mucosal layers of the endometrium, and necrosis, or death, of the inner layers of endometrium. The dead tissues and released blood initiate uterine contractions which expel the sloughed-off uterine contents. Approximately 40 ml of blood and about the same amount of serous fluid are lost during menstruation. Small amounts of *fibrinolysin* released from the desquamated tissues prevent clotting of this blood and fluid. Menstruation usually ceases after four to six days and the endometrium becomes com-

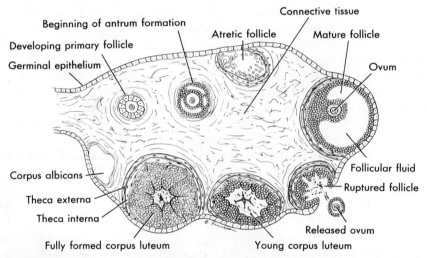

Figure 24–9. Microscopic view of the ovary showing ovum in various stages of maturation.

pletely re-epithelialized. FSH secretion, no longer inhibited by progesterone and estrogens at this time, resumes in increasingly larger amounts, the endometrium proliferates, another follicle begins to mature, and a new menstrual cycle has begun.

If fertilization of the ovum occurs, menstruation does not take place. The fertilized ovum or zygote completes its maturation division and implants within the uterus after about a week following fertilization, and the developing placenta secretes a hormone called *chorionic gonadotropin* which has much the same function as the pituitary hormones, LH and LTH. It prevents the involution of the corpus luteum at the end of the menstrual cycle and causes it to enlarge considerably and to continue to secrete large amounts of progesterone and estrogens. Desquamation of the endometrium, or menstruation, is thus prevented if pregnancy occurs.

Summary of Hormonal Changes and Influences During the Menstrual Cycle.
1. The anterior pituitary begins the secretion of *FSH* during the time of menstrual flow. This causes follicles to grow and develop in the ovary. At the end of about two weeks *one follicle* reaches maturity. Under the influence of

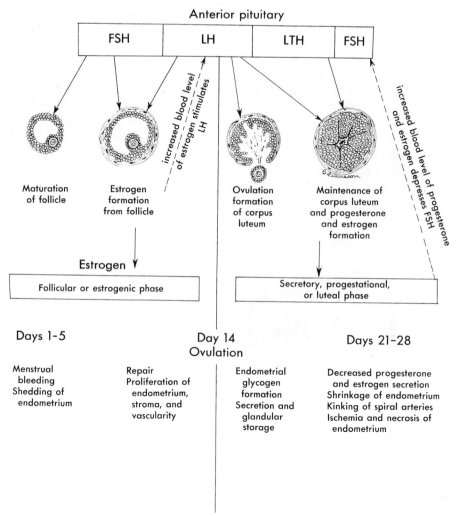

Figure 24–10.   Summary of hormonal effects upon the ovary and uterus.

FSH the *theca interna* begins to secrete gradually increasing amounts of *estrogens*. This is often referred to as the *estrogenic* or *proliferative phase of the cycle* and it lasts, usually, about two weeks.
2. The estrogens aid in the repair and proliferation of the endometrium of the uterus. They cause an increased thickening, keratinization, and glycogen

storage of the vaginal epithelium and also probably aid *libido*. The rising blood levels of estrogens stimulate the secretion of *LH* toward the end of the two-week period.

3. LH in some way helps to cause ovulation or rupture of the mature follicle and release of the ovum about 13 to 15 days before the beginning of the next menstrual flow. Together with *LTH*, now also released from the anterior pituitary, it causes the remains of the ruptured follicle to be transformed into an endocrine gland known as a *corpus luteum* that secretes increasingly large amounts of *progesterone* and some *estrogens* during the second, *progestational* or *secretory*, phase of the cycle.

4. *Progesterone* has a secretory effect on the uterine endometrium. That is to say, it causes increased secretions and a nutrient storage within the uterine mucosa in preparation for the reception and nourishment of a fertilized ovum. It also appears to have a quieting effect upon uterine musculature which favors implantation of the embryo. As the level of *progesterone increases* toward the

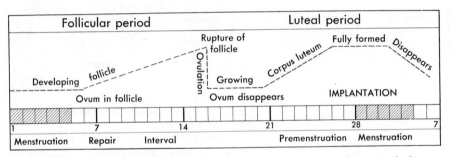

Figure 24–11. Diagram to show sequence of events in ovary and in uterus in human menstrual cycle. (Modified from Corner.)

end of the cycle, it appears to have a feedback effect upon the anterior pituitary by causing it to secrete *less* and *less LH* and *LTH*. When the production of LH and LTH are thus inhibited, the *corpus luteum involutes* and ceases to secrete progesterone.

5. *Menstruation* is believed to be caused by the resulting low levels of progesterone and estrogens. Lack of sufficient amounts of estrogens is thought to cause vasospasm of the spiral arteries to the endometrium. This results in inadequate nutrition of the superficial layers of endometrium, which then become necrotic and slough off.

6. The *decreased* blood level of *progesterone* is no longer sufficient to *inhibit* the anterior pituitary production of *FSH*, so it is *again secreted* and the cycle resumes.

7. If *fertilization* and *implantation* occur, the *corpus luteum persists* and continues to secrete large amounts of *estrogens* and *progesterone* under the stimulating influence of *chorionic gonadotropin* produced by the developing placenta. The action of chorionic gonadotropin is similar to that of LH and LTH.

Parturition takes place, normally, at about 280 days from the beginning of the last menstrual period and results in the birth of the child. It is brought about by the periodic contractions of the smooth muscles of the wall of the uterus, aided by contractions of the skeletal muscles of the wall of the abdomen.

Various investigations into the causes of the onset of parturition at the end of the ninth month and into the process of *labor* have been carried on. At present, however, no single factor or sequence of groups of factors is certainly known to initiate and control the processes. There is widespread belief in the theory of hormonal control of parturition, but this theory is not without its opponents. Immediately preceding delivery, there is an increase in excretion of free estrogen and an abrupt decrease in the amount of combined estrogen excreted. This may indicate that the presence of estrogen controls parturition. It is known that injection of estrogen may lead to abortion in pregnant animals. Although the oxytocic factor of pituitary extract is widely used to bring on rhythmical contractions of the uterus in labor, removal of the pituitary in laboratory animals interferes in no way with the onset of normal labor and parturition. Therefore, it is not known whether the pituitary *normally* plays a part in parturition in the human.

The duration of labor is variable, but the average length of time is about 12 to 18 hours. During the first stage, or *stage of dilation*, the cervix of the uterus is dilated, and as a rule the amnion is ruptured and the amniotic fluid expelled; during the second stage, or *stage of descent*, the child descends through the vagina and is expelled; during the third stage, or *placental stage*, the fetal membranes are expelled.

Involution is the process of rapid decrease in the size of the uterus. It is brought about by a gradual autolysis, or "self-digestion," of the uterine wall and requires from six to eight weeks. During this time the uterus resumes its original position in the pelvic cavity and approximately its original size.

The menopause, or female climacteric, is the period during which there is a physiological cessation of the menstrual flow, the termination of development of the follicles in the ovaries, a decrease in estrogen production, and consequently the end of the childbearing period. It is usually marked by atrophy of the breasts, uterus, uterine tubes, and ovaries. The onset of menopause usually occurs somewhere between the ages of 45 and 50 and may or may not be indicated by a number of troublesome symptoms that include insomnia, irregular menstruation with its eventual cessation, nervous irritability, palpitations, increased sweating, periods of depression, and intolerance to heat. These symptoms may be short-lived or they may continue over a period of years. One of the most disturbing complaints is that of "hot flashes," which consist of a flushing of the skin and a feeling of warmth and increased sweating especially about the head and neck. The exact cause of these symptoms has been ill-defined, although they presumably follow the reduction of blood and tissue levels of estrogens. It is probable that the estrogen deficiency itself is not the sole cause of emotional disturbances that may become evident at this time, but rather that the events associated with the climacteric amplify or bring about latent potentialities. Treatment of many of these disturbing signs and symptoms of the menopause may be effectively carried out with the administration of gradually diminishing doses of synthetic estrogens.

Other menopausal problems may include obesity, believed to result from decreasing caloric expenditure as a result of estrogen deficiency, and *osteoporosis* due to decreasing protein anabolism, causing a loss of protein matrix particularly of the vertebral column. *Osteoporosis* causes softening and decalcification of bones which may result in bone compression fractures.

Mammary Glands. The two mammary glands, or breasts, are structurally and developmentally closely related to the integument but function as accessory organs of the reproductive system since they secrete milk for nourishment of the infant.

The mammary gland is contained entirely within the superficial fascia and is composed of 15 to 20 glandular tissue lobes, divided by connective tissue bands and arranged radially about the centrally located *nipple*. The glandular tissue

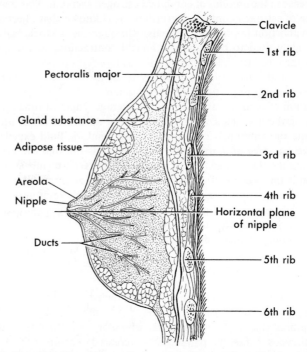

Pectoralis major

Gland substance

Adipose tissue

Areola

Nipple

Ducts

Clavicle

1st rib

2nd rib

3rd rib

4th rib

Horizontal plane of nipple

5th rib

6th rib

Figure 24–12.   Right breast in sagittal section, inner surface of outer segment.

occupies only a small portion of the breast in the nonpregnant or nonnursing breast. A variable but usually considerable amount of adipose tissue is contained between and around the lobules and makes up most of the peripheral part of the structure.

Each breast covers a nearly circular space anterior to the pectoralis muscles extending from the second to the sixth ribs and from the sternum into the axilla. The increase in the size and the shape of the mammary glands at the time of puberty and adolescence is due to increased amount of glandular tissue and adipose tissue brought about under the influence of estrogens and progesterone. The glandular tissue remains underdeveloped unless conception takes place.

The nipple is perforated at the tip by the 15 to 20 minute openings of the lactiferous ducts, each one of which is an excretory duct from one of the lobules to the surface. The skin of the nipple extends outward on the surface of the breast for 1 to 2 cm to form a pink- or brown-colored *areola*. The areola contains numerous large sebaceous glands that secrete a lipoid material which protects and lubricates the nipple during nursing of the infant.

During pregnancy *estrogens* probably stimulate the growth of the glandular duct system, whereas *progesterone* is considered to be the stimulus for glandular cell or acini formation. Complete development of the mammary system for lactation requires the concerted action of estrogens, progesterone, lactogenic hormone, and somatotropin. Before parturition lactation is presumably held in abeyance by the high titers of placental sex steroids which suppress secretion of *lactogenic* or *luteotropic hormone*, otherwise known as *prolactin*. After delivery and the expulsion of the placenta, the anterior pituitary is no longer inhibited by progesterone and estrogens, and lactogenic hormones begin to be secreted in increasingly large amounts. These hormones are especially important for their major role in the initiation and maintenance of lactation.

Oxytocin is secreted by the posterior pituitary by a reflex action induced by the infant's sucking on the breast. The milk letdown principle of this hormone causes contraction of the myoepithelial cells of the mammary alveoli and ductules, which forces the milk into collecting ducts to be expelled.

The mammary glands are well supplied with blood brought to them by the thoracic branches of the axillary, internal mammary, and intercostal arteries. The nerve fibers are derived from the ventral and lateral cutaneous branches of the fourth, fifth, and sixth thoracic nerves.

An understanding of the *lymphatic drainage* of the breasts is of the greatest importance in relation to malignant conditions of the breast. Malignant cells may readily spread from the affected breast to other areas of the body via the lymphatic vessels and nodes that drain the adjacent regions. Direct paths of lymph drainage follow the blood vessels and are primarily to the nodes within the pectoral muscles, the axillary nodes, and the internal mammary nodes. Some lymph also drains into the subcutaneous plexus and into the deep cervical nodes posterior to the clavicle.

In the surgical removal of malignant disease of the breast the entire breast, all of the underlying subcutaneous tissue, the pectoralis muscles of that side, and all of the aforementioned lymph nodes are removed *en bloc*, or *in one piece*, in an operation called a radical mastectomy. This massive area is removed with the hope of preventing the spread of the tumor to other areas of the body, either by direct extension into adjacent tissue, or by spread of some of the cells via lymph or blood systems.

QUESTIONS FOR DISCUSSION

1. Define the terms "puberty" and "adolescence." In temperate climates at what age do they occur in the male? In the female? Discuss secondary sex changes and their causes in the male and in the female.
2. Describe the pathway of the descent of the testes before or soon after birth. If the testis remains within the abdominal cavity, how will its function be affected? Explain.

3. What stimulates the production of LH? What are the functions of LH and LTH?

4. Where is progesterone produced and what are its functions? What is believed to be the cause of menstruation? Why does menstruation not take place if the ovum becomes fertilized?

5. Explain the pathway of the spermatozoa from the seminiferous tubules to the urinary meatus. What secretions are added to the semen and what are thought to be the special functions of each fluid that is added?

SUMMARY

Reproduction
{ Means by which new life is brought into existence
Sexual type depends upon the union of two cells, one of which is produced by the male and one by the female organism }

Puberty
{ Age at which sex organs attain normal adult function
Male begins to produce functional spermatozoa in temperate climates between ages 14–16 years
Female begins to ovulate and menstruation commences in temperate climate between ages 13–15 years
Period marked by gradual appearance of secondary sex characteristics in both sexes }

Adolescence
{ Period from puberty to early twenties during which complete development of all secondary sex characteristics have been achieved—epiphyseal plates close at age of 20–21 years }

Male Organs of Reproduction and Functions
{ 2 testes—contained in the scrotum—produce spermatozoa and testosterone

2 epididymides (singular, epididymis)—lie superior and posterior to testes—spermatozoa mature here

2 seminal ducts (vas or ductus deferens)—storage sites for spermatozoa—convey them from epididymides to seminal vesicles

2 seminal vesicles—membranous pouches—lie posterior to bladder—produce nutritious secretions added to semen

2 ejaculatory ducts—short passageways within prostate gland—convey semen from seminal ducts to urethra

Prostate gland—size of chestnut situated immediately inferior to internal urethral sphincter—surrounds proximal urethra—secretes alkaline fluid—increases motility of spermatozoa—prostate may increase in size in old age causing urinary retention

2 bulbourethral glands (Cowper's)—small bodies on either side of membranous urethra—secrete lubricating and protective mucus—remove urine residues prior to ejaculation

Penis—organ of copulation suspended from front and sides of pubic arch—consists of 3 bodies of cavernous tissue—2 lateral corpora cavernosa penis—and 1 corpus cavernosum urethrae—these erectile bodies become distended with blood to produce erection of organ—glans penis, expansion at lower portion of penis, contains sensory end organs and urethral orifice—covered by foreskin or prepuce

Semen { Fluid derived from the various sex glands in the male—contains approximately 100,000,000 spermatozoa per milliliter }

Nervous control { Parasympathetic nerves (sacral 2, 3, 4) control erection of penis
Sympathetic nerves (lumbar 1, 2, 3) control emission and ejaculation of semen } }

Spermatogenesis—begins at about age 12—continues throughout adult life

Spermatogonia—formed in seminiferous tubules of testes during fetal life

Primary spermatocytes—at puberty primary spermatocytes develop from spermatogonia
Primary spermatocytes undergo first maturation division of meiosis—46 or diploid number of chromosomes reduced to 23 double chromosomes in each of two secondary spermatocytes formed

Secondary spermatocytes—each secondary spermatocyte undergoes second maturation division of meiosis to form a spermatid containing 23 single chromosomes

Spermatids—a spermatid develops into a spermatozoon when it develops a head and tail, or flagellum

Spermatozoa—half of the spermatozoa contain X chromosomes; other half contain Y chromosomes
At fertilization original complement of 46 chromosomes is re-established—sex chromosome of spermatozoon determines sex of fertilized ovum

Male urethra—S-shaped tube—extends from internal urethral orifice to external urethral orifice of glans penis—20 cm (8 in.) in length—divided into 3 parts: prostatic, membranous, and penile urethra

Male climacteric—Decline of testicular function in some males occurring as result of Leydig cell failure after surgery, disease, or testicular atrophy between ages of 45 and 60 years. Symptoms may include increased irritability, episodes of depression, and diminished libido

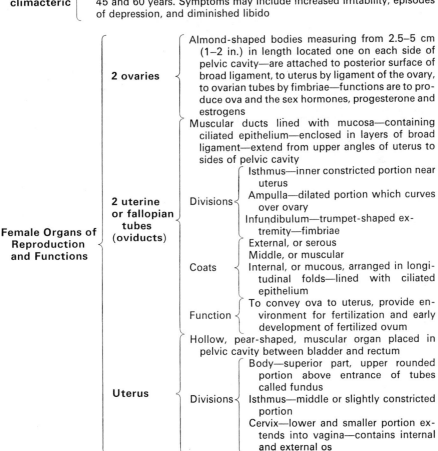

Female Organs of Reproduction and Functions

2 ovaries—Almond-shaped bodies measuring from 2.5–5 cm (1–2 in.) in length located one on each side of pelvic cavity—are attached to posterior surface of broad ligament, to uterus by ligament of the ovary, to ovarian tubes by fimbriae—functions are to produce ova and the sex hormones, progesterone and estrogens

2 uterine or fallopian tubes (oviducts)—Muscular ducts lined with mucosa—containing ciliated epithelium—enclosed in layers of broad ligament—extend from upper angles of uterus to sides of pelvic cavity

Divisions—
Isthmus—inner constricted portion near uterus
Ampulla—dilated portion which curves over ovary
Infundibulum—trumpet-shaped extremity—fimbriae

Coats—
External, or serous
Middle, or muscular
Internal, or mucous, arranged in longitudinal folds—lined with ciliated epithelium

Function—To convey ova to uterus, provide environment for fertilization and early development of fertilized ovum

Uterus—Hollow, pear-shaped, muscular organ placed in pelvic cavity between bladder and rectum

Divisions—
Body—superior part, upper rounded portion above entrance of tubes called fundus
Isthmus—middle or slightly constricted portion
Cervix—lower and smaller portion extends into vagina—contains internal and external os

Female Organs of Reproduction and Functions (*cont.*)

Uterus

- **Three coats**
  - External, or serous, derived from peritoneum, covers intestinal surface and anterior surfaces to beginning of cervix
  - Muscular or myometrium
    - Circular layer
    - Longitudinal layer — Interlaced
    - Spiral layer
  - Mucous membrane, or endometrium { Lines internal aspect

- **Blood vessels**
  - Uterine arteries from hypogastrics
  - Ovarian arteries from aorta
  - Remarkable for tortuous course and frequent anastomoses

- **Ligaments**
  - Broad—two large layers of serous membrane—from uterus to walls of pelvic cavity
  - Round—two fibromuscular cords from sides of uterus to labia majora
  - Anterior—peritoneal fold from bladder to uterus
  - Posterior—peritoneal fold from uterus to rectum
  - Uterosacral—two partly serous, partly muscular ligaments from cervix to sacrum
  - Cardinal, or Mackenrodt's—fascia surrounding uterine vessels from pelvic wall to cervix and vagina

- **Function**
  - To receive fertilized ovum, provide for implantation, nourishment, and environment for growth and development of fetus until parturition

Vagina

- Extends from uterus to vulva—about 7.5–10 cm (3–4 in.)
- **Coats**
  - Internal mucous lining arranged in rugae
  - Layer of submucous connective tissue
  - Muscular coat
- Location—placed anterior to rectum, posterior to bladder and urethra
- Function—for deposition of semen, serves as exit of birth canal

External genitals

- Mons pubis—cushion of areolar, fibrous, and adipose tissue in front of pubic symphysis, covered with skin and after puberty covered also with hair
- Labia majora—two folds that extend from mons pubis to within an inch of anus—protect perineum—maintain secretions
- Labia minora—two folds situated between labia majora
- Clitoris—small protuberance at apex of triangle formed by junction of labia minora—well supplied with nerves and blood vessels
- Vestibule—cleft between labia minora
- Hymen—fold of mucous membrane partly covering and surrounding vaginal orifice
- Glands—greater vestibular or Bartholin's—oval bodies situated on either side of vagina—secretions have moistening function
- Perineum—external surface of floor of pelvis, extends from pubic arch to coccyx

Histology of the Ovary	Embryonic development		Ovaries derived from bilateral germinal ridges located in close proximity to the kidneys Descend into pelvis during fetal life Primordial ova are differentiated from germinal epithelium, migrate into ovarian cortex, approximately 500,000 primordial follicles present at birth
	Structure		Outer layer of germinal epithelium Inner layer of connective tissue or stroma, also containing developing graafian follicles that are derived from primordial follicles—one graafian follicle matures during each menstrual cycle from puberty to menopause
	Menstrual cycle		Regulated by hormonal feedback mechanisms—begins at puberty—development of a mature ovum, ovulation, and endometrial changes occur during this cycle **Menstruation** or desquamation of the endometrium is thought to be due to ischemia of this tissue following drop in blood levels of progesterone and estrogens prior to beginning of cycle. In menstruation about 40 ml of blood and about the same amount of serous fluid are lost—cycle begins on first day of menstruation *FSH* secreted at beginning of cycle causes development of a graafian follicle and production of estrogens by follicle and theca interna
		Estrogenic follicular or proliferative stage	*Estrogens* cause increase in thickness, vascularity, and secretions of endometrium—high blood levels of estrogens stimulate production of LH *LH* assists production of ovulation or extrusion of ovum into peritoneal cavity usually between 13th–15th day before beginning of menstrual bleeding. One mature ovum derived from each primary oocyte. Each ovum contains $22 +$ one X chromosomes. Polar bodies disintegrate
		Progestational or secretory stage	*LH and LTH* stimulate luteinization of follicle after ovulation with formation of a corpus luteum, a secretory body that produces large quantities of progesterone and smaller amount of estrogens *Progesterone* increases secretory function of endometrium, causes formation of glycogen, and lipid stores within endometrium, inhibits contractility of uterine smooth muscle. Increased blood levels of progesterone depress production of FSH by anterior pituitary. Corpus luteum involutes as a result of diminished FSH, and menstruation ensues

**Histology of
the Ovary**
(cont.)
 { **Hormonal changes
in pregnancy** { If fertilization occurs, menstruation does not take place—placenta secretes hormone called chorionic gonadotropin that is similar to LH which causes continuation and enlargement of corpus luteum—large amounts of estrogens and progesterone are secreted, and thick, vascular secretory endometrium is maintained for implantation and development of embryo

Parturition { About 280 days from beginning of last menses
Stages of labor { Stage of cervical dilation
Stage of descent
Placental stage

Involution { Return of uterus to approximately normal size following parturition

Menopause { Female climacteric—the period of physiological cessation of menstrual flow, termination of follicular development, decrease in sex hormones, and the end of the childbearing period—occurs between the ages of 45–50 and may or may not cause troublesome symptoms such as increased irritability, hot flashes, insomnia, depression, and osteoporosis

**Mammary
glands**
 { Composition { Made up of 15–20 lobes of glandular tissue divided by connective tissue bands and embedded in superficial fascia
Location { Anterior to pectoralis muscles, extending from 2nd–6th ribs and from sternum into the axilla
Size and shape { Increased size at puberty under influence of increased hormones produced, especially estrogens and progesterones
Pregnancy and postpartum { Increase in size and numbers of glands mainly under influence of pituitary hormones and estrogens and progesterone. Lactation depends on concerted action of progesterone, estrogen, prolactin, and somatotropin
After delivery and expulsion of placenta, decrease in female sex steroids allows prolactin to be released from anterior pituitary. Milk letdown principle of oxytocin causes expulsion of milk
Blood supply—from thoracic branches of axillary, internal mammary, and intercostal arteries
Nerve supply—from lateral and cutaneous branches of fourth, fifth, and sixth thoracic nerves
Lymphatic drainage—follows pathway of blood vessels—drains into nodes within pectoral muscles, into axillary nodes and internal mammary nodes. Some lymph drains into deep cervical nodes

25

Maturation of Reproductive Cells, Fertilization, and Embryonic Development

THE HUMAN ORGANISM begins life as a single cell derived from the fusion of two parental cells, the ovum and the spermatozoon. This fertilized egg, or zygote, undergoes mitotic cell division and cells become differentiated into tissues, organs, and systems forming the multicellular, highly organized replica of its species. The purpose of this chapter is to discuss the maturation of the sex cells, the process of fertilization, and the development of a fetus from the zygote, or fertilized egg.

DEVELOPMENT OF GERMINAL TISSUES

In an embryo of about six weeks the germinal tissues that will develop into reproductive glands may be distinguished from the somatic tissues that will form the remaining portions of the body. The germinal tissues make their appearance as a pair of genital folds in the dorsal region of the embryo, and by about the tenth or eleventh week these are differentiated into the reproductive organs called *gonads*. Primordial germ cells that have migrated to the gonads during their embryological development remain dormant in a resting stage until puberty when, under the influence of gonadotropic hormones, their further growth and maturity are achieved.

Maturation of the germ cells is the process whereby the male and female reproductive cells grow and are prepared for fertilization. The process of egg

731

formation is referred to as *oogenesis* and the process of sperm formation is termed *spermatogenesis.*

Formation of the Oogonia and Primary Oocytes. In the embryo, once the primordial germ cells enter the developing ovary, they divide rapidly and form the most primitive female germ cells, the *oogonia.* The oogonia are arranged in clusters and are located in the cortical part of the ovary. They are surrounded by a layer of flat epithelial cells. It is believed that each group or cluster is formed by the descendants of a single primordial germ cell and that the cells that surround them are derived from the surface epithelium. From the fourth through the seventh months of fetal development each *oogonium,* or primitive sex cell, may differentiate into a larger cell known as a *primary oocyte,* which then enters the prophase of the first *meiotic,* or *reduction, division.*

Development of the Ovum from the Oogonium, Meiosis, and Its Two Maturation Divisions. *Meiosis* is a special kind of cell division which achieves a reduction in the number of chromosomes and genes within the germ cell to one half. Otherwise, with the fusion of sex cells, or *gametes* in fertilization, each carrying a full complement of chromosomes, there would be a doubling of chromosomes each generation. The number of chromosomes before meiosis is 46 and is referred to as the *diploid* number. The reduced number following meiosis is 23, or the *haploid* number.

As a sex cell goes into the prophase of the *first maturation division,* there is an important difference from the prophase of a typical mitotic division. The chromosomes begin to pair. *Homologous chromosomes* face each other and often entwine around one another in the center of the cell. This is referred to as a *synapsis.* Each chromosome reduplicates itself so that it becomes doubled. Such doubled chromosomes are termed *dyads* and are held together by a band called the *kinetocore* or *centromere.* In the late prophase, these paired, doubled chromosomes can be seen as four *chromatids* grouped together to form *tetrads.*

The work of Bateson[1] and Punnet[2] has shown that during the first maturation division of meiosis there is some method of transfer and recombination of genes that lie on *homologous chromosomes.* As the tetrads are formed there may be simultaneous breakage and reattachment between *homologous chromatids.* This process creates a new association of genes and is known as *crossing over.* As the chromosomes go into the later part of the prophase and separate from one another slightly, it is possible to see crosses between chromatids of the homologous chromosomes, forming *chiasmata.* It is generally concluded that the chiasmata (singular, chiasma) represent regions where crossing over has taken place.

Each tetrad, in the cell undergoing its first maturation division, goes into typical metaphase, anaphase, and telophase, and then the cell divides. Each daughter cell has 23 dyads, or *double chromosomes.* The reduction in chromosome number has been achieved, but the chromosomes are still double. There is

---

[1] William Bateson, British naturalist (1861–1926).
[2] Reginald C. Punnet, English geneticist (1875–   ).

a *second maturation division* of meiosis, to be discussed later, which permits separation of these dyads into single chromosomes and provides for increased numbers of cells.

By the end of the seventh month of fetal development when the oogonia have disappeared and the oocytes have started meiosis, each primary oocyte is surrounded by a layer of flat epithelial cells. At birth the primary oocytes have finished the prophase of the first maturation division and remain in a resting stage until sexual maturity of the female, when this first division is then finally completed.

Although the total number of primary oocytes present at birth is estimated to be between 40,000 and 500,000, the major portion of these cells degenerate gradually during lifetime. After puberty, under the influence of FSH and estrogens, a number of oocytes begin to enlarge during each ovarian cycle. Usually

Figure 25–1. Diagrams to illustrate the phenomenon of *crossing over*. *A*. Shows the breakage and reattachments between homologous chromosomes where genes *A* and *B* on one chromosome and *a* and *b* on its mate are located at opposite ends of the chromosomes. When the chromosomes are reattached, *crossing over* has taken place, with an exchange of the depicted genes, between the two chromosomes. *B*. Shows the adjacent location of *A* and *B* genes on one chromosome and *a* and *b* on the other. When *crossing over* occurs, the genes, because of their close relationship on the chromosome, are not exchanged between the two partners.

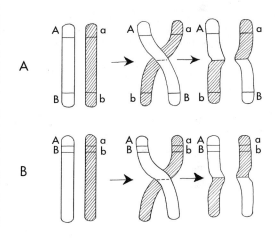

only one achieves full maturity. As the primary oocyte forms two daughter cells, the greater part of the cytoplasm goes to one of the two cells. This results in the formation of a *secondary oocyte* that is almost as large as the primary oocyte and a very much smaller cell called a *polar body*. The second maturation division of the oocyte may never take place, or it may occur after ovulation and be completed during fertilization. The secondary oocyte divides into an *ovum*, which is almost as large as the primary oocyte, and a *second polar body*. During this second maturation division the dyad chromosomes separate so that each cell has a single set of haploid chromosomes. The first polar body may also divide. Its dyad chromosomes separate so that each of the two cells formed has a single set of 23 chromosomes. The three polar bodies degenerate and have no role in reproduction. Their function seems to be to provide the setting for rearrangement of the chromosomes and genes and to bring about the great variety in the offspring of the species.

Spermatogenesis. Spermatogenesis has been discussed in detail in the previous chapter. Four spermatozoa are formed from each primary spermatocyte produced by the spermatogonium. Two of these cells carry X chromosomes, and the other two carry Y chromosomes, as has been previously stated. Some crossing over has undoubtedly taken place during the first reduction division.

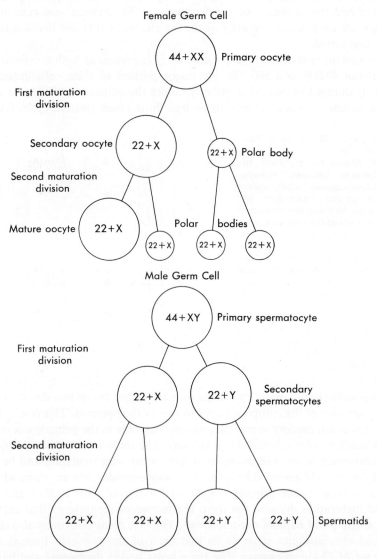

Figure 25–2. Diagrams to show the two maturation divisions in the male and female germ cells. Note that one ovum is formed from one primary oocyte, and four spermatids are formed from one primary spermatocyte. Two of the spermatids have X chromosomes, and two have Y chromosomes.

Genes and Heredity. *Heredity* is a term applied to the transmission of potential traits, physical or mental, from parents to their offspring. An individual receives one chromosome of each pair from each of his parents. Each member of the pair (except the sex chromosomes) carries the same general set of hereditary genes as its mate and is called an *autosome*. For example, each of the paired chromosomes may carry a gene for eye color, for hair form, or for length of fingers. These genes may be the same or different, depending on the genetic contribution of each parent. If the offspring has received a gene for brown eyes from each parent, we say he is *homozygous* for brown eyes. On the other hand, if he has received a gene for brown eyes from one parent and a gene for blue eyes from the other, we say he is *heterozygous* for eye color, and his eye color will be brown. Some traits, such as brown eye color, are *dominant* under usual conditions, and are bound to appear. Other traits are *recessive*, such as blue eye color, and will not *usually* appear unless two recessive genes are received by the offspring.

Two genes are *alleles* when they carry the same trait and occupy the same position or locus on the chromosome and will come together when the two chromosomes enter into synapsis during the first maturation division of meiosis. Other genes affecting eye color that are located on other positions on the chromosomes are not alleles.

The system of using letters as symbols for genes as well as the whole development of the gene concept was devised by the Austrian monk Gregor Mendel,[3] the "father of modern genetics," and it is utilized almost universally today. A small letter stands for a recessive gene, the capitalized form of the same letter for the gene which is dominant over this recessive. For instance, *B* might represent the dominant brown eye color and *b* the recessive color blue. The term *genotype* means the type of genes present in the individual. *Phenotype* refers to the expression of the genes. The person with one gene for blue eyes and one for brown eyes might be said to have the genotype for eye color of heterozygous brown, but the phenotype of brown since this is the color of this individual's eyes.

Dominance may be complete, partial, or absent. A gene that is dominant to one gene may be recessive to another one. Certain abnormalities are inherited as dominants over the normal condition, e.g., extra digits or excessively short digits. Others such as albinism may be recessive to the normal. Some abnormalities appear as sex-linked recessives, becoming evident in males with a single factor but in females only when there are two, e.g., red-green color blindness and hemophilia.

It used to be thought that all characteristics were caused by either heredity or environment. Modern genetic understanding has shown that there is rarely a clear-cut line of distinction between inherited and environmentally induced characteristics. It is the blending of heredity and environment that results in the total final expression of an individual's characteristics.

[3] Gregor Johann Mendel, Austrian monk and geneticist (1822–1884).

Significance of Meiosis. What is the significance of this process of selection and exchange of genes during meiosis? The reducing divisions of meiosis separate each pair of chromosomes; thus it halves the number of chromosomes, but chance alone decides the actual distribution of the maternal or paternal member of any pair to any particular daughter cell. Meiosis also provides an opportunity for reshuffling of the genes from one chromosome to another as the result of the *crossing over* or interchange of chromosome parts. In man, reduction to the haploid number of chromosomes during meiosis makes possible nearly 17 million final combinations of chromosomes. A further increase in new heredity combinations is made possible by the phenomenon of *crossing over*. Each child carries the genes inherited from his parents and their ancestors, but each child has a different inheritance and different appearance from every other person in the world because of the infinite variety provided by reduction and the recombination of chromosomes produced during meiosis.

FERTILIZATION AND DEVELOPMENT OF THE EMBRYO

A newborn individual is a sum of his genetic and environmental heritage. Much of his "magical" development from a tiny one-celled structure into an integrated, highly complex machine of tissues, organs, and systems is still not understood. A comprehension of some of the important aspects of developmental anatomy prepares the student for a better understanding of the essential aspects of prenatal care and some of the factors that may cause congenital defects in the newborn.

Fertilization occurs when the nucleus of the spermatozoon, or male gamete, fuses with the nucleus of the ovum, or female gamete, to form the *zygote*. Soon after extrusion into the peritoneal cavity, the ovum, surrounded by the follicular cells that make up the corona radiata, passes into the fallopian, or uterine, tube. It is apparently carried into the infundibulum, or funnel, of the tube by currents in the peritoneal fluid created by the fimbriae and the cilia of the infundibulum and tubular mucosa. It is possible that an ovum from one ovary can pass to the opposite uterine tube. Rhythmical muscular contractions of the uterine tube also aid the passage of the ovum toward the uterus.

Fertilization normally occurs in the ampulla of the uterine tube or at least in the distal third. It is believed that tubular and uterine musculature contractions cause aspiration of spermatozoa into the uterus and tubes. The flagella, or tails, of the sperm probably contribute only slightly to their ascent into the female reproductive tract, since they enable them to move only from 1 to 4 mm per minute. The main function of these flagella seems to be to aid in the penetration of the corona radiata and the surrounding membranes of the ovum, the zona pellucida and the vitelline membrane.

Only one spermatozoon of the 200 to 300 million spermatozoa deposited in the female reproductive tract is necessary for fertilization of the ovum. It is believed that other surrounding spermatozoa release enzymes such as hyaluronidase that detach the layer of corona radiata and thereby aid the penetration of the fertilizing cell. In the human being both the head and tail enter the ovum. If two ova mature at the same time and both are fertilized, fraternal twins result.

As soon as the spermatozoon enters the ovum, the female germ cell finishes its second maturation division, and its 22 plus 1 X chromosomes make up the *female pronucleus*. The spermatozoon moves toward the female pronucleus, and its swollen head becomes the *male pronucleus*. The two pronuclei meet and join, thus restoring the complete 46, or diploid number of, chromosomes in the

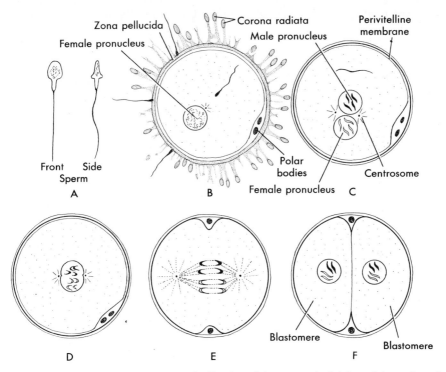

Figure 25–3. Diagrams showing the fertilization of the ovum, the joining of the male and female pronuclei, the chromosomes organized on the spindle, and the two-cell stage of blastomeres.

human somatic cell. The tail that had been detached from the head immediately following fertilization contributes to the formation of the centrosome, which soon divides into two halves, each half moving to the opposite pole of the spindle, thus forming two new cells. Each cell of the rapidly forming individual contains 46 chromosomes, that is, the original diploid number.

Fertilization determines the sex of the zygote, restores the diploid number of chromosomes, and causes the initiation of mitotic, cleavage division, all of which result in the formation of the embryo. The ovum remains viable and capable of being fertilized for approximately 12 to 24 hours. If during this interval it is not fertilized, degeneration rapidly ensues. Spermatozoa may survive for as long as four days within the female genital tract, but the majority of them probably do not maintain fertilizing power for more than 36 hours. Acid secretions of the vagina reduce the motility of many spermatozoa.

Fertility depends upon normal functioning of both mature male and female reproductive organs, as well as upon the coordination of many other essential contributing factors at the time of insemination. A few of the many important factors include the following: (1) the length of time the ovum remains viable, (2) the length of time between ovulation and insemination, (3) the presence of a sufficient quantity of the enzyme hyaluronidase in the spermatozoa or semen,

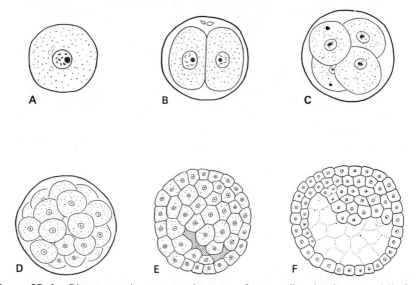

Figure 25–4.   Diagram to show very early stages of mammalian development. (*A*) One-celled embryo; (*B*) two-celled embryo; (*C*) four-celled embryo; (*D*) berrylike ball of cells or *morula*; (*E*) beginning formation of the blastocyst; (*F*) well-developed blastocyst, consisting of a hollow ball of *trophoblast* cells and an inner mass of cells known as the *embryoblast*.

(4) the length of the time during which the sperm retain their fertilizing power, (5) the number of normal spermatozoa in the semen, (6) the pH of the vagina and of the semen, and (7) the motility of the uterus, tubes, and spermatozoa.

Cleavage Formation of Morula and Blastocyst. *Cleavage* consists of a number of rapid mitotic divisions which result in the production of a number of increasingly smaller cells that are known as *blastomeres*. Cleavage is not really a growth process since there is no increase in protoplasmic volume despite the progressive increase in cell number.

As the zygote passes down the fallopian tube, cleavage continues. When the 16- to 20-cell stage is attained, it is known as a *morula* (a hollow ball of cells). The morula is divided into two parts, the inner cell mass, which is composed of a group of centrally located cells, and the surrounding layer, called the outer cell mass. The inner cell mass gives rise to the tissues that make up the embryo itself, but it also contributes to the formation of embryonic membranes called the amnion and yolk sac. The outer cell mass forms the trophoblast from which the outer embryonic membrane known as the *chorion* and the *placenta* are developed. The morula reaches the uterine cavity about five to six days after ovulation, the zona pellucida disappears, and the zygote absorbs uterine fluid, thus forming a single cavity between the inner and outer cell masses, resulting in the formation of the *blastocyst*.

Occasionally, as the inner cell mass develops in this early period prior to tissue differentiation, it separates into two groups of cells, each of which then matures

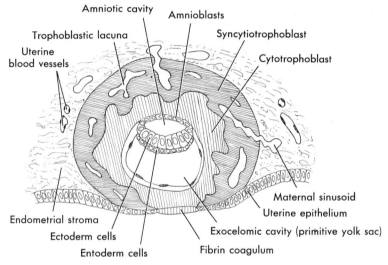

Figure 25–5. Diagram of a 9- to 12-day blastocyst to show developing ectoderm, entoderm, layers of the trophoblast, and the beginning of the uteroplacental circulation. The amniotic cavity is well defined, and the original uterine surface defect is closed by a fibrin coagulum. (Modified from Langman.)

in the normal fashion as described below. Should this occur, *identical* twins result—"identical" because each has developed from one fertilized ovum, therefore they have the same genetic inheritance.

Implantation of the Blastocyst. *Implantation*, or uterine attachment, of the blastocyst probably occurs between the seventh and ninth days after ovulation. It is thought that the penetration and erosion of the epithelial cells of the uterine mucosa necessary for implantation result from the combined effects of proteolytic enzymes produced by the trophoblast and by the vascular changes in the endometrium. In any case, the blastocyst normally implants in the endometrium of the body of the uterus. The erosion in the uterine mucosa brought about by the penetration of the blastocyst is gradually obliterated by the growth of adjacent epithelium and by the formation of a *fibrin coagulum*. If the blastocyst implants abnormally in close proximity to the cervical internal os, a condition known as *placenta previa* occurs and causes severe bleeding in the latter part of pregnancy and during delivery. Implantation in the uterine tube results in a tubal pregnancy, which is dangerous because it causes severe internal hemorrhage, rupture of the tube, and death of the embryo during the second or third month of pregnancy. Implantations anywhere outside the uterus are known as *extrauterine*, or *ectopic*, *pregnancies*.

During pregnancy, the uterine mucosa is highly modified and is called the *decidua*. The glands become extremely convoluted and hyperactive, and stromal cells become differentiated into decidual cells which possess variable amounts of glycogen, lipids, and increasing numbers of mitochondria. After implantation of the blastocyst and until the fourth month of gestation, three parts of the decidua can be recognized; the *decidua basalis* at the base of the placenta, the *decidua capsularis* that surrounds the surface of the implanted chorionic sac, and that portion that lines the rest of the uterus, the *decidua parietalis*, or *vera*.

Major Events in the Development of the Blastocyst.   The blastocyst becomes firmly embedded in the uterine mucosa during the second and third weeks of development and its two parts, the *embryoblast* and the *trophoblast*, begin to grow and differentiate. The embryoblast gives rise to the three basic layers of the embryo proper, the *ectoderm*, the *entoderm*, and the *mesoderm*. The cells of the trophoblast grow deeply into the endometrium and form the *placenta*.

By the eighth day of development, the embryoblastic cells differentiate into two distinct cell layers, the inner *entodermal* germ layer, which is composed of flattened polyhedral cells facing the lumen of the blastocyst, and the outer *ectodermal* germ layer, which is composed of a layer of tall columnar cells.

The trophoblast forms an inner pale layer, the *cytotrophoblast*, and an outer, darker zone referred to as the *syncytiotrophoblast*, or *syncytium*. The endometrial stroma at the implantation site is highly vascular and edematous, and its enlarged glands secrete mucus and glycogen. Between the ectoderm cells and the trophoblast an opening begins to form, called the *amniotic cavity*, and its outer portion is lined with flattened cells, the *amnioblasts*. The amniotic cavity becomes filled with a thin, clear fluid which serves as a protective cushion to absorb shock, to maintain fetal environmental temperature, to prevent adherence of the embryo to the surrounding surface, and to allow for fetal movements. The gradually enlarging cavity extending toward the lumen of the uterus forms the *exocelomic* cavity, or *primitive yolk sac*.

Maternal capillaries become dilated and congested and begin to extend into the syncytiotrophoblast. Maternal blood begins to enter the *lacunar system* as the syncytial cells begin to erode the endothelial lining of the maternal sinusoids. Thus the future uteroplacental circulation begins to be established. Owing to the great differences in blood pressures between the arterial and venous capillaries, maternal blood begins to flow through the trophoblastic lacunar system. Bleeding may occasionally occur at the implantation site around the thirteenth day of development owing to increased blood flow into the trophoblastic lacunar spaces at this time, although the epithelial surface has usually healed by then. This bleeding may be confused with normal menstrual bleeding since it occurs at about the twenty-eighth day of the menstrual cycle and the anticipated delivery date may be estimated inaccurately.

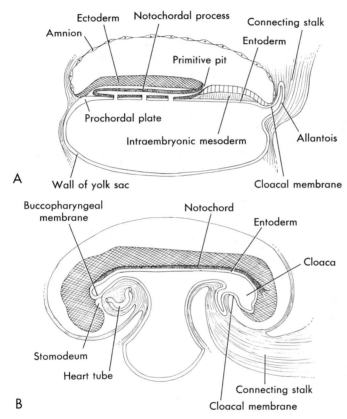

Figure 25–6. Diagrams of midsagittal sections through embryos to show: (*A*) Extension of notochordal process and fusion with the entoderm in 18-day embryo. The newly formed intermediate mesodermal layer is shown. It is thought to be derived from modified ectodermal cells. (*B*) Fourteen-somite embryo with developing heart and buccopharyngeal and cloacal membranes.

Cells of the inner surface of the cytotrophoblast delaminate and differentiate to form the loose network of tissue known as the *extraembryonic mesoderm.* This mesoderm fills the expanding space between the amnion and primitive yolk sac internally and the trophoblast externally. When large cavities develop in this tissue and become confluent, a new space, the *extraembryonic celom,* is formed. This cavity surrounds the blastocyst except between the germ disk and trophoblast, where the attachment remains.

The extraembryonic celomic cavity enlarges, and by the twentieth day the embryo is attached to the surrounding trophoblast by a narrow *connecting body stalk*, which later develops into the *umbilical cord* and attaches the embryo to the placenta.

During the second and third weeks, ectodermal cells in the caudal region of the germ disk begin to multiply and to migrate toward the midline, forming a narrow groove, the *primitive streak*. It is believed that modified ectodermal cells proliferate and migrate between the ectodermal and entodermal germ layers and spread laterally at this time, forming the intermediate cell layer known as the *mesoderm*. The *notochord* now is formed along a longitudinal axis and the entodermal layer establishes firm contact with the ectoderm making up the *posterior cloacal membrane* from which *urogenital* and *anal membranes* are derived. The *buccopharyngeal* membrane is later developed from the *prochordal* plate, which now begins to appear at the anterior ectodermal attachment. An outpocketing called the *allantois*, or *allantoenteric diverticulum*, appears about the sixteenth day and extends from the posterior wall of the yolk sac into the connecting stalk. This structure in some lower vertebrates becomes a large reservoir for urine storage, but in man it is normally rudimentary and gradually disappears during further embryonic development.

The Embryonic Period.   The first two months of development are known as the *embryonic period*. During this interval, the shape and the appearance of the embryo are greatly altered, and by the end of the second month of development, all the important features of the external body may be recognized. Each germ layer starts a course of differentiation into specific tissues, organs, and systems, and by the end of the embryonic period, all the major body systems have been formed.

Ectodermal Germ Layer.   The ectoderm gives rise to the formation of the *central nervous system* during the *somite period*. During the third and fourth week the *neural* plate, posterior to the *notochord*, is formed from ectoderm cells, and it soon invaginates to form the *neural groove* lined by the *neural fold*. When the folds approach each other and fuse, the groove becomes the *neural tube*. This fusion begins in the future neck region and proceeds simultaneously in cephalic and caudal directions. The tube does not close off entirely at this time but temporarily remains open for some time at the anterior and posterior neuropores. The brain begins to enlarge and develop at the cephalic end of the neural tube, while the spinal cord and peripheral nerves develop from the remainder of the tube. At the end of the first month the *otic vesicle* and *optic vesicle*, outpocketings of the brain, are formed. From the former, parts of the ear are derived and from the latter, the retina and optic nerve develop.

From the ectodermal germ layer the following parts of the body are derived: (1) the central nervous system and hypophysis, (2) the peripheral nervous system including the autonomic nervous system, (3) the sensory epithelium of the sense organs, (4) the enamel of the teeth, and (5) the epidermis including hair, nails, and subcutaneous glands.

Mesodermal Germ Layer. The mesoderm is formed between the ectoderm and the entoderm. The mesodermal cells form a thin layer on each side of the midline, until the end of the third week when the mass begins to thicken immediately lateral to the notochord, to become the *paraxial mesoderm* (the future somites), the *intermediate mesoderm* (the future excretory units), and the *lateral plate*, which splits into somatic and visceral layers.

By the end of the third week, the paraxial mesoderm becomes segmented into approximately 40 pairs of somites. These *somites* mold the contours of the embryo, and from them are formed the *mesenchyme*, which gives rise to con-

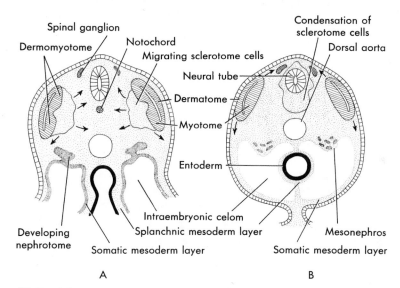

Spinal ganglion

Condensation of sclerotome cells

Dermomyotome

Notochord

Dorsal aorta

Migrating sclerotome cells

Neural tube

Dermatome

Myotome

Entoderm

Intraembryonic celom

Developing nephrotome

Splanchnic mesoderm layer

Mesonephros

Somatic mesoderm layer

Somatic mesoderm layer

A   B

Figure 25–7. (*A*) Transverse section through a 26-day embryo to show migration of cells of *sclerotome*, or ventromedial part of the somite. The remaining cells form the *dermomyotome*. The intermediate mesoderm has proliferated to form *nephrotomes*, the excretory units of the urinary system. The *arrows* indicate the direction of the migrating cells of the *dermatome* and *sclerotome*.

(*B*) Transverse section through a 28-day embryo to show condensation of sclerotome cells around the neural tube to form the axial skeleton. (J. Langman, *Medical Embryology.* Courtesy of Williams & Wilkins Co.)

nective tissue, cartilage, and bone, and *myoblasts*, which give rise to striated muscle cells. Some of the cells from the somites become mesenchymatous and spread under the ectoderm to form the subcutaneous tissue of the skin (integumentary system).

The *cardiovascular system* is derived from the mesodermal germ layer during the third week. Blood islands, lined by endothelial cells, become arranged in isolated clusters which then fuse and give rise to small blood vessels. During the fourth week, a single *primitive heart tube* is formed and is suspended in the pericardial cavity. *Extraembryonic blood vessels* are also formed in a similar manner during this time and become the *umbilical* and *vitelline vessels* which, as they develop, begin to penetrate the embryo proper where they reach the independently developing intraembryonic vascular system. The pharyngeal arches give rise to the maxillary, mandibular, hyoid bones, and ossicles of the ear, as well as other ligaments, muscles, and bones.

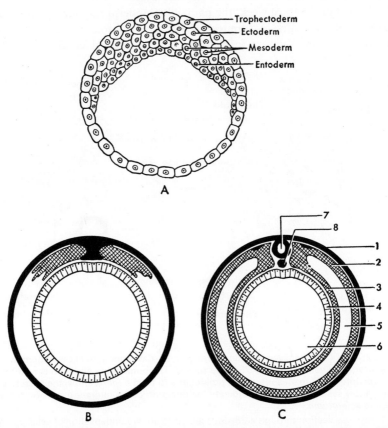

Figure 25–8. Diagram of a section of an embryo, showing the beginning of tissue formation. (*A*) The embryonic disk shows the cells arranged in layers. (*B, C*) Two diagrams of sections of embryos showing later stages of tissue formation. *Ectoderm* is shown in black, *entoderm* as cells; the two layers of *mesoderm* are cross-hatched. (*1*) Ectoderm, (*2*) parietal mesoderm, (*3*) visceral mesoderm, (*4*) entoderm, (*5*) future body cavity, (*6*) enteron, (*7*) neural tube, (*8*) notochord.

The lateral plate of the mesoderm separates into two layers, the *somatic*, or *parietal*, *layer* lying next to the ectoderm, and the *splanchnic*, or *visceral*, *layer* lying next to the entoderm. The ectoderm and the somatic mesoderm form the *somatopleure*, and from this the body wall is developed. The entoderm and the splanchnic mesoderm form the *splanchnopleure*, and from this the viscera are developed. The *celom* is a cavity between the two layers of mesoderm which develops into the body cavity. The peritoneal, pleural, and pericardial cavities develop from the celom and are lined with mesothelium derived from mesoderm encompassing them.

The important structures that are considered to be derivatives of the mesodermal layer are (1) cartilage, joints, and bones; (2) connective tissue; (3) blood and lymph cells, walls of blood and lymph vessels, and the heart; (4) the spleen; (5) serous membranes; and (6) kidneys, gonads, and their ducts.

Entodermal Germ Layer. As the embryo folds and its head comes closer to the tail, a portion of the yolk sac, lined with entoderm, becomes incorporated

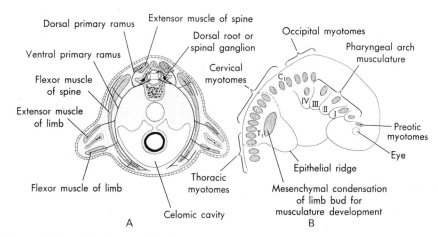

Figure 25–9. (*A*) Cross section through embryo in region of the limb bud attachment. Muscle tissue has penetrated limb bud and has divided into ventral (flexor) portion and dorsal (extensor) components. The spinal nerves follow a similar orientation but eventually unite to form large dorsal (radial) and ventral (median and ulnar) nerves in upper extremity. (*B*) Longitudinal view to show *myotomes* in head, neck, and thoracic regions of embryo at seven weeks. The tissue of the somite that remains after the migration of the cells of the *sclerotome* and *dermatome* makes up the *myotome*. *Myoblasts* of three of the four *occipital myotomes* migrate forward to form muscles of the tongue. The upper extremity is budding opposite the lower cervical and upper thoracic segments. (Modified from Langman.)

into the embryo proper and forms the *primitive foregut* and *hindgut* which are lined with epithelium of entodermal origin. The *buccopharyngeal* membrane ruptures at the end of the third week, and thus an open connection between the primitive gut and the amniotic cavity is established. The primitive gut located between the fore- and hindgut remains temporarily in open connection with the yolk sac by way of a wide duct, the *omphalomesenteric* or *vitelline duct*.

Important structures that are subsequently derived from the entodermal germ layer are (1) the epithelial lining of the digestive and respiratory tracts and part of the bladder and urethra, (2) the epithelial lining of the tympanic cavity and eustachian tube, and (3) the main cellular portions of the tonsils, parathyroids, thymus and liver, pancreas, and gallbladder.

Development of the Extremities. The fore- and hindlimbs appear as buds at the beginning of the second month. The *forelimb buds* arise quite high, at the level of the fourth cervical to the first thoracic somites, and this explains their subsequent innervation by the *brachial plexus.* The *hindlimbs* appear at the level of the lumbar and sacral somites just below the attachment of the umbilical stalk and are later innervated by nerves from the *lumbosacral plexus.* As the limb buds grow, they undergo a 90-degree rotation but in opposite directions, so that the elbow points dorsally and the knee points ventrally.

The Fetal Period. The interval from the beginning of the third month to the end of intrauterine life is known as the *fetal period.* During this time some differentiation of tissues does continue, but the major changes are brought about by the rapid growth of the body. At the beginning of the third month the head constitutes approximately one half of the crown-rump (CR) length, or sitting height, but at birth the proportion has diminished to one fifth. The eyes are initially directed laterally, but during the third month the eyes are located on the ventral aspect of the face, the ears reach their final position, and the limbs their relative length in comparison to the rest of the body, although the lower limbs remain a little shorter and slightly less developed than the upper extremities. The *external genitals* have developed by the end of the second month, so that the sex of the fetus can be determined by external appearance.

During the fourth and fifth months, at the end of the first half of intrauterine life, the fetus lengthens rapidly and its CH, or crown-heel length, is approximately 23 cm (9 inches). This is about one half of the total length of the newborn.

There are many presumptive signs of pregnancy, but the three positive signs occur during the fetal period and include hearing the fetal heart between the eighteenth and twentieth weeks, visibility of the fetal skeleton by x-ray during the fourteenth to sixteenth weeks, and the physician's observance of fetal movement during the fifth month. The mother is usually able to discern fetal movements during the fifth month.

The weight of the fetus increases considerably during the second half of intrauterine life, from 500 gm at the end of the fifth month to 3,200 gm by the end of the ninth month. Subcutaneous fat is formed during the last months before birth so that the fetus loses much of its former wrinkled appearance. At birth the fetus is approximately 50 cm (20 inches) long, and the skull still has the largest circumference of the body. At birth the testes have usually descended through the inguinal canal and into the scrotum.

The Placenta, Its Development and Functions. The placenta is composed of an embryonic portion, the *chorion frondosum,* and a maternal portion, the *decidua basalis.* Each portion has its own blood supply, and there is no direct connection between them. Exchange of substances between the two systems takes place by diffusion.

The *trophoblast* develops a great number of *secondary villi* or *cytotrophic projections* that extend into and are attached to the *maternal decidua.* They are now referred to as the *chorionic villi.* The portion of the chorion that contains the expanding villi and is adherent to the decidua basalis is called the *chorion frondosum* (bushy chorion), and the portion projecting into the lumen of the uterus is smooth and almost nonvascular and is known as the *chorion laeve*.

The *decidua basalis*, the endometrial layer adjacent to the embryonic *chorion frondosum*, consists of a compact layer that is tightly connected to the chorion and a spongy layer that contains dilated glands and the spiral arteries. The compact layer is often referred to as the *decidual plate*. The *decidua capsularis* is the decidual layer adjacent to the chorion laeve which projects into the uterine lumen. During the third month, as the fetus increases in size, the decidua capsularis degenerates, and the *chorion laeve* fuses with the *decidua parietalis* on the opposite side of the uterus. Most of the uterine cavity is now obliterated and the chorion

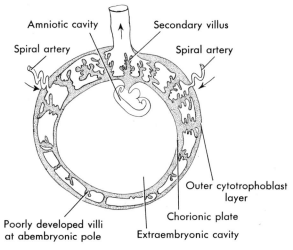

Figure 25–10.   Diagram of embryo at beginning of second month of development to show numerous well-formed secondary villi. (Modified from Langman.)

frondosum remains the only functional part of the chorion. The *placenta* is composed of the chorion frondosum, its fetal portion, and the decidua basalis, its maternal portion. The placenta enlarges greatly as the fetus and uterus increase in size, and it amounts to about 25 per cent of the internal surface of the uterus. The main functions of the placenta are the exchange of gaseous and metabolic products as well as nutrients between the maternal and fetal blood streams, and the production of hormones to maintain pregnancy.

There are intervillous spaces between the chorionic and decidual plates. These spaces are filled with maternal blood and are lined with *syncytium* of fetal origin. Fetal villous capillaries derived from umbilical arteries and veins project into these intervillous spaces, where they are bathed by approximately 150 ml of oxygenated blood from the maternal spiral arteries. Blood from the intervillous lakes is returned to the maternal circulation via venous openings from these spaces.

The placental barrier, or dividing membrane, is made up entirely of fetal tissue. Until the fourth month the barrier is composed of four layers, but then it becomes much thinner and retains only two, the endothelial lining of the

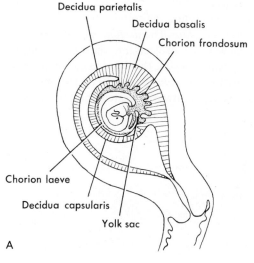

Decidua parietalis

Decidua basalis

Chorion frondosum

Chorion laeve

Decidua capsularis

Yolk sac

A

Amniotic cavity

Placenta

Fusion of amnion
and chorion

B

Figure 25–11. (*A*) Schematic drawing to show the decidua and fetal membranes in embryo at the end of the second month. Villi have disappeared at the abembryonic pole. (*B*) Schematic drawing of embryo at the end of the third month to show obliteration of the decidua capsularis and chorion laeve. Fusion of the amnion and chorion has also occurred.

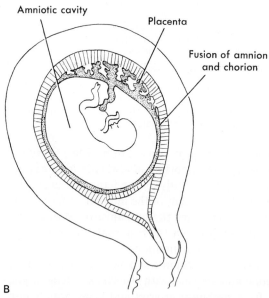

capillaries and the syncytial covering that lies in intimate contact with them. The thinner layer allows for more rapid exchange of substances such as nutrients, gases, and other metabolic products between the two blood systems. Hormones and antibodies also pass across the placental barrier, although it is not known just how the high-molecular-weight substances such as proteins and maternal gamma globulins can pass through the barrier. The fetus acquires some of the antibodies that the mother has produced against such infectious diseases as scarlet fever, measles, smallpox, and diphtheria. The precise mechanism whereby these antibodies reach the fetus is unknown, but it has been suggested that they may be transferred by the process of *pinocytosis.*

The placenta produces sufficient amounts of gonadotropins and progesterone by the end of the fourth month of pregnancy so that the ovarian corpus luteum is no longer needed and it therefore begins to degenerate. Estrogenic hormones are also produced by the placenta in increasing amounts until a maximum level is reached just before the end of pregnancy.

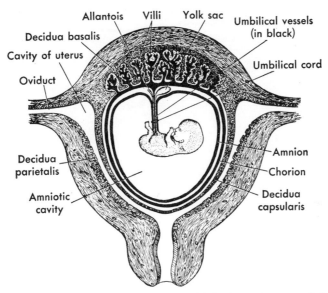

Figure 25–12. Sectional view of human uterus with fetal membranes and their relationship to the uterus and the embryo. (A. F. Huettner, *Fundamentals of Comparative Embryology of the Vertebrates,* 1st ed. Courtesy of The Macmillan Company.)

The presence of chorionic gonadotropin in the urine early in pregnancy is used as an indicator in some varieties of pregnancy tests. When this urine is injected into the immature mouse, it causes ovarian hyperemia, and in the young female rabbit it causes ovulation. If young male frogs are injected with urine or blood serum containing these gonadotropins, it will cause their ejection of spermatozoa.

Some Congenital Malformations and Their Causes. *Congenital malformations,* or "gross structural defects," present at birth may be caused by a great variety of viral infections or chromosomal and genetic factors. It is estimated that approximately 10 per cent are caused by environmental factors, 10 per cent are due to genetic and chromosomal factors, and the remaining 80 per cent are due to some combination of both genetic and environmental factors.

Malformations of the fetus have been known to follow maternal infection with measles, mumps, chickenpox, hepatitis, poliomyelitis, and German measles (rubella). At present it is well established that rubella virus affecting pregnant women during the first three and perhaps four months of gestation can cause malformations of the eye, internal ear, and heart and may also be responsible for some cases of mental retardation and brain abnormalities. Damage to the nervous system, cleft palate, damage to fetal extremities, or mutations which may later lead to the occurrence of

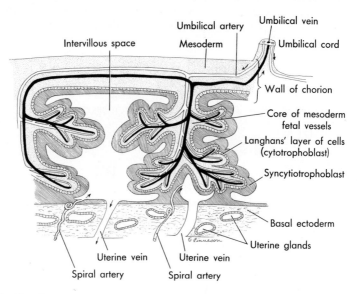

Figure 25–13. Schematic drawing of the structure of the villi at an early stage of development. The capillaries of the fetal circulation are separated from maternal blood in the intervillous spaces by surrounding layers of mesoderm, cytotrophoblast and syncytiotrophoblast. After the fifth month only a single layer, that of the syncytiotrophoblast lies between the fetal capillary wall and the maternal blood. Note the umbilical cord containing one umbilical vein and two arteries. Two uterine spiral arteries emptying into the intervillous spaces and two veins returning maternal blood are shown.

congenital malformations in succeeding generations may result from treating pregnant women with large doses of roentgen rays or radium. Mothers who have taken thalidomide, an antinauseant and hypnotic, have had babies with total or partial absence of the extremities. Other defects produced by thalidomide are intestinal atresia and cardiac anomalies. Other drugs such as quinine and the antimetabolite aminopterin and excessively large amounts of progestins may cause congenital malformations. Factors such as nutritional deficiencies, abnormal maternal antibodies, hypoxia, and maternal diabetes are under investigation for their role in the incidence of congenital abnormalities.

An abnormal number or configuration of chromosomes of the fetus may result in congenital malformation. The majority of mongoloid idiots have three number 21 chromosomes. Mental retardation, congenital heart defects, deafness, cleft lip and palate, or other defects may be found in the child with extra chromosomes numbers 13 to 15 and 17 to 18.

Abnormalities in the sex chromosomes may cause congenital defects. If, during meiosis of the female sex cell, the two homologous X chromosomes fail to separate and move instead into one daughter cell, the resultant ovum has either two X chromosomes or none. If an ovum with two X chromosomes combines with a sperm containing a Y chromosome, the result is a male with an XXY complement (Klinefelter's

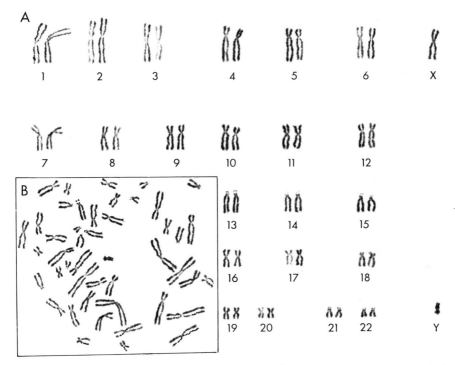

Figure 25–14. Normal human male chromosomes as they appear during metaphase. Cell division has been arrested by treatment with colchicine; hypotonic salt solution then is added to swell and disperse the chromosomes and make them more visible. (*B*) Inset: chromosomes as they appear under the microscope following this treatment. (*A*) Karyotype: chromosomes are paired and arranged according to a standard classification based on the size, position of the centromere, and other characteristics. The normal human has 22 somatic pairs plus two sex chromosomes (an X and Y in males, two X's in females). (Courtesy of Dr. James L. German, III, Cornell University Medical College, New York City.)

syndrome). Some of the important features of this syndrome are testicular atrophy, sterility, and mental retardation. If the ovum without sex chromosomes is fertilized by a sperm containing an X chromosome, the result is an individual with an XO complement (Turner's syndrome). This condition found in women is characterized by the absence of ovaries. Lastly, if an ovum containing two X chromosomes combines with an X sperm, the result is an XXX individual. Women with the triple-X syndrome have some degree of mental retardation, are infantile, and have scant menses.

Many congenital malformations in man are inherited and in many cases may be due to a change in a single gene. Malformations may be caused by autosomal dominant or recessive inheritance or by abnormal genes carried by the X chromosome. A mutation or sudden and persistent change in the expression of a gene may also cause congenital malformation.

Many different factors may cause congenital malformations, and they must be considered in the plan for pregnancy and maternal care during gestation, especially during the first four months of embryonic differentiation of tissues.

Fetal Circulation Before Birth. The umbilical cord unites the placenta with the navel of the fetus. The cord is made up of two arteries and one large vein. These vessels are surrounded and protected by soft mucous connective tissue known as *Wharton's jelly*. Nutrients and oxygenated blood are conveyed to the fetus via the umbilical vein, which travels to the liver within the anterior peritoneal attachment, the *falciform ligament*. The main portion of the blood to the fetus bypasses the liver. It flows from the umbilical vein into the short vessel called the *ductus venosus* and from there into the inferior vena cava. Since the liver, at this time, is only partially functional, there is no need for the major portion of blood to perfuse it. Only a small amount of blood enters the sinusoids of the liver and mixes with the blood from the portal circulation. There is a sphincter mechanism in the ductus venosus near the entrance of the umbilical vein. When venous return is too great because of the additional pressure caused by a uterine contraction, this sphincter, it is believed, closes so that the heart will not be overloaded with blood.

Blood from the inferior vena cava enters the right atrium and is directed toward the *foramen ovale* by the valve of the inferior vena cava. As a result the largest portion of the returning blood bypasses the nonfunctioning lungs and passes directly into the left atrium. This blood will supply the coronary vessels of the heart and the carotid arteries to the brain with well-oxygenated blood.

A small portion of blood from the inferior vena cava joins the desaturated blood from the superior vena cava which flows into the right ventricle and out into the pulmonary artery. During fetal life resistance in the pulmonary vascular system is very high, causing the blood to pass through the *ductus arteriosus* into the descending thoracic aorta, where it mixes with blood from the left heart. The *umbilical arteries*, branches of the hypogastric arteries, return the fetal blood to the placenta, where it is reoxygenated, receives nutrients diffused from the mother's blood, and discharges the excess carbon dioxide and nitrogenous metabolic wastes into her circulation. The capillary networks of fetal and maternal circulation are not directly connected, as has previously been stated, but are in close association within the placenta so that diffusion of products between the two separate systems is feasible. At the end of pregnancy a small portion of blood may be carried by the pulmonary artery through the fetal lungs.

Changes in the Blood Circulation After Birth. At birth a number of changes occur in the newborn due to the cessation of the placental flow and the beginning of lung respiration. When the amniotic fluid in the alveolar sacs and bronchial tree is replaced by air at birth and when the pressure in the right atrium decreases as a result of interruption of the placental blood flow, many of the fetal vascular structures are no longer needed and they cease functioning. The *ductus arteriosus* closes because of muscular contraction of its wall. The amount of blood flowing through the lung increases as the fluid is expelled and as breathing fills the lungs with air. Since the blood pressure within the right atrium has decreased as a result of the interrupted placental flow and the pulmonary pressure increases as a result of the increased pulmonary blood flow, the pressure becomes equalized on both sides of the *foramen ovale*. The *septum primum* is then apposed to the *septum secundum*, and the interatrial opening closes functionally. In 20 per cent of all adults perfect anatomical closure of the foramen ovale may

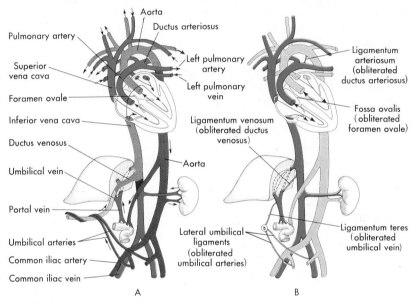

Figure 25–15. (*A*) Fetal circulation. (*B*) Circulation after birth. Highly oxygenated blood, *pink;* mixed oxygenated and desaturated blood (mainly oxygenated), *red;* desaturated blood, *blue;* mixed oxygenated and desaturated blood (mainly desaturated), *purple.*

never be obtained, although there may be no flow of blood from one atrium directly into the other. Anatomic fusion of the two septa is usually completed at the end of the first year of life.

The umbilical arteries, umbilical vein, and ductus venosus close shortly after birth owing to contraction of smooth muscle of the vessel walls as a result of the ligation of the umbilical cord and the thermal and mechanical stimuli, as well as a change in oxygen tension. Following their obliteration, the umbilical arteries become the *lateral vesicoumbilical ligaments*, while the umbilical vein becomes the connective tissue band, the *ligamentum teres hepatis*, in the margin of the *falciform ligament*. The ductus arteriosus closes almost immediately after birth following the contraction of its muscular wall and becomes the fibrous band known as the *ligamentum arteriosum.* If either the foramen ovale or the ductus arteriosus does not become entirely obliterated, the affected child may suffer from inadequate oxygenation of his blood, resulting in a bluish appearance of the skin, known as cyanosis, especially after exertion.

Complete anatomical closure of all these structures by proliferation of vessel wall intima and fibrous tissues takes anywhere from several months to a year.

QUESTIONS FOR DISCUSSION

1. Explain why no two children in the same family (unless they are identical twins) have exactly the same physical appearance despite the fact that every child has received twenty-three chromosomes from each of his parents.
2. Explain how the diploid number of chromosomes is reduced to the haploid number of single chromosomes during meiosis.
3. How many spermatozoa are formed from one primary spermatocyte? What percentage of the spermatozoa will carry X chromosomes?
4. What is crossing over and when may it occur?
5. How many ova are produced from each primary oocyte? When do the first and second maturation divisions occur? What are polar bodies and what happens to them after meiosis is completed?
6. If one parent is homozygous for brown eyes (B brown, B brown) and the other parent is heterozygous for brown eyes (B brown, b blue), can any of their children have blue eyes? Explain.
7. What important structures are developed from the embryoblast and from the trophoblast of the blastocyst?
8. Explain the development and functions of the placenta. What is the placental barrier, how is it formed, and what are its functions?
9. Describe fetal circulation before birth. Explain the causes of circulatory changes in the newborn infant.
10. What important parts of the body are developed from the ectoderm? The mesoderm? The entoderm?

SUMMARY

Development of Germinal Tissues
- Germinal tissues can be distinguished in six-week embryo, become genital folds in dorsal region of embryo
- Gonads are formed from genital folds at 10–11 weeks
- Primordial germ cells that have migrated to gonads remain dormant until puberty

Maturation of Germ Cells
- Process whereby male and female reproductive cells grow, develop, reduce their number of chromosomes to 23, and are prepared for fertilization
- **Oogenesis** { Process of egg formation
- **Spermatogenesis** { Process of sperm formation

Meiosis
- Special type of cell division which achieves a reduction in chromosomes from 46, or diploid number, to 23, or haploid number. Meiosis is composed of two maturation divisions

Meiosis (*cont.*)	**First maturation division**	Chromosomes of primary oocyte begin to pair; synapsis—entwining of homologous chromosomes in center of cell
		Each chromosome reduplicates itself and becomes doubled, or dyad
		Kinetocore or centromere—band binding dyad, constriction in chromosome
		Tetrad-paired double chromosomes or chromatids
		Crossing over—transfer and recombination of genes that lie on homologous chromosomes
		Chiasmata—represent regions where crossing over has occurred
		Cell completes prophase, metaphase, anaphase, and telophase, divides into secondary oocyte and a polar body
		Secondary oocyte and polar body each have 23 dyads
	Second maturation division	Secondary oocyte goes through second maturation division forming ovum and second polar body. Polar body may also divide
		Each cell now has single set of 23 chromosomes
		Polar bodies degenerate, have no role in reproduction

Genes and Heredity

Heredity—term applied to transmission of potential traits, physical or mental, from parents to their offspring; offspring receives one chromosome of a homologous pair from each of his parents

Autosome—chromosome that carries same general set of genes as its mate

Heterozygous—having alternative genes for the same trait, e.g., one gene for blue and one for brown eyes

Homozygous—having two similar genes for the same trait, e.g., two genes for brown eyes

Dominant gene—gene whose trait is bound to appear under usual circumstances

Recessive gene—gene whose trait will not appear usually unless two of them are present or dominance is not complete

Dominance may be complete, partial, or absent

Alleles—genes that carry the same trait and occupy the same position or locus on the chromosomes—come together during synapsis

Gregor Mendel—"father of modern genetics," responsible for whole development of the gene concept—capital letter usually used to denote dominant trait, small letter for recessive trait

Genotype—refers to type of genes present in individual

Phenotype—refers to expression of genes present

Total final expression of individual's characteristics due to blending of hereditary and environmental factors

Genetic abnormalities

Abnormalities may be inherited as dominants over normal condition, e.g., extra digits or excessively short digits, or may be recessive to the normal, e.g., albinism

Some abnormalities appear as sex-linked recessives evident in males with only one factor, but in females only when two factors are present, e.g., red-green color blindness or hemophilia

Spermatogenesis

Discussed in detail in previous chapter

Four spermatozoa formed from each primary spermatocyte

Two of these cells carry an X chromosome

Two of these cells carry a Y chromosome

Two maturation divisions of meiosis take place in the formation of spermatozoa from primary spermatocytes

Some crossing over undoubtedly occurs during first maturation division

Significance of Meiosis {
Halves number of chromosomes
Provides opportunity for crossing over and reshuffling of genes
Provides offspring with infinite variations resulting in greater individuality
}

Fertilization {
Fertilization—normally occurs when nucleus of spermatozoon fuses with nucleus of ovum to form *zygote*

Ovum conveyed to uterine tube by currents created in peritoneal fluid by fimbriae and cilia of tubular mucosa

Fertilization normally occurs in distal third of uterine tube

Flagella of spermatozoa propel them only 1–4 mm per minute, their ascent in female tract believed to be assisted by aspiration following tubular and uterine contractions

Only one out of 200–300 million deposited sperm necessary for fertilization—penetration of ovum assisted by enzyme, hyaluronidase, released by one or more sperm

Head and tail of sperm enter ovum

Pronuclei of sperm and ovum join to restore 46 or diploid number of chromosomes

Ovum remains viable for approximately 12–24 hours

Sperm survive up to four days, fertilizing power probably not longer than 36 hours and often not that long

Fertility depends on normal functioning of male and female reproductive organs, the time of insemination, as well as many other factors
}

Early Development of the Embryo—Cleavage Formation of Morula and Blastocyst {
Cleavage—consists of a number of rapid mitotic divisions which result in an increasing number of smaller cells known as *blastomeres*

Morula—16–20-cell stage of cleavage resulting in hollow ball of cells—inner cell mass forms embryo and embryonic membranes, the amnion and yolk sac—outer cell mass forms the trophoblast from which the chorion is developed

Morula reaches uterine cavity 5–6 days after ovulation

Blastocyst—formed when zygote absorbs uterine fluid
}

Implantation of Blastocyst {
Implantation—uterine attachment of the blastocyst—occurs 7–9 days after ovulation and normally in the endometrium

Decidua—modified uterine mucosa during pregnancy—can be divided into three parts : *decidua basalis* at base of placenta, *decidua capsularis* portion surrounding surface of chorionic sac, and *decidua parietalis* that lines the rest of the uterus
}

Major Events in Development of Blastocyst {
Blastocyst—made up of *trophoblast* and *embryoblast*

Embryoblast gives rise to *ectoderm*, *entoderm*, and *mesoderm*

Trophoblast has inner layer, *cytotrophoblast*, and outer layer, *syncytiotrophoblast*

Amniotic cavity—forms between trophoblast and ectoderm—fills with fluid to protect and nourish the embryo

Connecting stalk—later becomes umbilical cord, attaches embryo to placenta

Primitive streak and notochord (embryonic backbone) formed in midline from modified ectodermal cells; notochord later replaced by segmented vertebral column

Posterior cloacal membrane—formed from joining of ectoderm and entoderm, urogenital and anal membranes formed from it

Prochordal plate—appears at anterior ectodermal attachment—buccopharyngeal membrane formed from this plate

Allantois and yolk sac—pocketlike extensions of ventral side of embryo—they can be seen in umbilical cord of young embryo

Neural tube—developed from ectoderm—gives rise to brain, spinal cord, autonomic and spinal nerves

Embryonic period—the first two months of development during which all major body systems are formed
}

Portions of the Body Derived from Ectoderm	(1) Central nervous system and hypophysis (2) Peripheral nervous system (3) Sensory epithelium of sense organs (4) Enamel of teeth (5) Epidermis including hair, nails, and subcutaneous glands
Portions of the Body Derived from Mesoderm	(1) Cartilage, joints, and bones (2) Connective tissue (3) Heart, blood, and lymph cells and vessels (4) Spleen (5) Serous membranes (6) Kidneys, gonads, and their ducts
Portions of the Body Derived from Entoderm	(1) Epithelial lining of digestive and respiratory tracts and parts of bladder and urethra (2) Epithelial lining of tympanic cavity and eustachian tube (3) Main cellular portions of tonsils, parathyroids, thymus, liver, pancreas, and gallbladder
Development of Extremities	Fore- and hindlimbs appear as buds at beginning of second month—as buds grow, they undergo 90° rotation in opposite directions—elbow points dorsally, knee ventrally
The Fetal Period	Interval from beginning of third month to end of intrauterine life—major changes are brought about by rapid body growth—at end of 4th–5th month the CH length is approximately 23 cm and the weight 500 gm At birth the fetus is approximately 50 cm long and the weight is about 3,200 gm
Placental Development and Functions	Chorion frondosum—embryonic portion of placenta Decidua basalis—maternal portion of placenta Chorion laeve—portion of chorion that is smooth, almost non-vascular, and projects into uterus Main functions of placenta—exchange of gaseous and metabolic products between fetus and mother and production of hormones
Development of Blood Circulation Within Placenta	Intervillous spaces between chorionic and decidual plates are filled with maternal blood and are lined with syncytium of fetal origin Fetal villous capillaries derived from umbilical arteries and veins project into these spaces where they are bathed with oxygenated blood from maternal circulation Placental barrier—is made up of fetal tissue starting with four layers, but retaining only two after fourth month—endothelial lining of capillaries and syncytial covering—thinner layer allows for more rapid exchange of nutrients, gases, metabolic products, hormones, and antibodies
Fetal Circulation	Umbilical cord—unites the placenta with the navel of the fetus—contains *two umbilical arteries*, extensions from fetal hypogastric arteries, and one umbilical vein that travels in falciform ligament of fetus to the ductus venosus—these vessels are surrounded by soft mucous connective tissue called *Wharton's jelly* Direct communication between right and left atrium by means of *foramen ovale*

Fetal Circulation
(cont.)

Direct communication between pulmonary artery and aorta known as *ductus arteriosus*

Direct communication between umbilical vein and inferior vena cava through *ductus venosus*

Oxygen and nutritive substances diffuse from maternal blood in placenta across placental barrier to fetal blood. Carbon dioxide and metabolic wastes diffuse from fetal capillaries in placenta across the same barrier into maternal blood

Changes in Circulation of Infant Following Birth

Infant respiration stimulates pulmonary circulation ; this causes a rise in blood pressure in left atrium—pressure is equalized across atrial septum and connective tissue begins to close over foramen ovale—will become *fossa ovalis*

Ductus arteriosus becomes fibrous cord—*ligamentum arteriosum*

Umbilical vein becomes fibrous cord—*ligamentum teres*, or round ligament, in edge of falciform ligament

Ductus venosus becomes fibrous cord—*ligamentum venosum*

Umbilical arteries are obliterated to become *lateral vesico-umbilical ligaments*, their most proximal portions remain as *hypogastric* arteries

Complete anatomical closure of all these structures takes from several months to a year

Reference Books and Books for Further Study

GROSS ANATOMY

Callander, C. Latimer: *Surgical Anatomy*, 4th ed., edited by Barry J. Anson and Walter J. Maddock. Philadelphia: W. B. Saunders Company, 1958.

Cunningham's Textbook of Anatomy, 9th ed., edited by J. C. Brash and E. B. Jamieson. New York: Oxford University Press, 1951.

Grant, J. C. B.: *An Atlas of Anatomy*, 5th ed. Baltimore: The Williams and Wilkins Company 1962.

————: *A Method of Anatomy*, 6th ed. Baltimore: The Williams and Wilkins Company, 1958.

Gray's Anatomy of the Human Body, 28th ed., edited by C. M. Goss. Philadelphia: Lea & Febiger, 1966.

Hamilton, W. J. (ed.): *Textbook of Human Anatomy*. New York: St. Martin's Press, Inc., 1956.

Lockhart, R. D.; Hamilton, G. F.; and Fyfe, F. W.: *Anatomy of the Human Body*. Philadelphia: J. B. Lippincott Company, 1959.

Netter, Frank H.: "The Digestive System." *The Ciba Collection of Medical Illustrations*. Summit, N.J.: Ciba Pharmaceutical Products, Inc., 1957. Vol. 3, parts 1, 2, 3.

Pansky, Ben, and House, Earl L.: *Review of Gross Anatomy*. New York: The Macmillan Company, 1964.

———— and ————: *Study Wheels in Human Anatomy*. New York: The Macmillan Company, 1965.

Quiring, D. P.: *Collateral Circulation. Anatomical Aspects*. Philadelphia: Lea & Febiger, 1949.

759

Quiring, D. P.: *The Head, Neck and Trunk*, 2nd ed. Philadelphia: Lea & Febiger, 1960.

————: *The Extremities*, 2nd ed. Philadelphia: Lea & Febiger, 1960.

Schaeffer, J. Parsons (ed.): *Morris' Human Anatomy*, 11th ed. New York: The Blakiston Division, McGraw-Hill Book Company, 1953.

Sobotta, J., and McMurrich, J. P.: *Atlas of Human Anatomy*, 3rd ed. New York: G. E. Stechert and Company, 1933. 3 vols.

Spalteholz, W.: *Hand Atlas of Human Anatomy*, 7th ed. Philadelphia: J. B. Lippincott Company, 1937.

Toldt, C.: *An Atlas of Human Anatomy*. New York: The Macmillan Company, 1919. 2 vols.

Wischnitzer, Saul: *Outline of Human Anatomy*. New York: The Blakiston Division, McGraw-Hill Book Company, 1963.

Woodburne, Russell T.: *Essentials of Human Anatomy*, 2nd ed. New York: Oxford University Press, 1961.

Zuckerman, Sir Solly: *A New System of Anatomy*. New York: Oxford University Press, 1962.

HISTOLOGY—MICROSCOPIC ANATOMY

Arey, Leslie Brainerd: *Human Histology*, 3rd ed. Philadelphia: W. B. Saunders Company, 1965.

Bailey's Textbook of Histology, 15th ed., edited by W. M. Copenhaver and D. D. Johnson. Baltimore: The Williams and Wilkins Company, 1964.

Bloom, W., and Fawcett, D. W.: *Textbook of Histology*, 8th ed. Philadelphia: W. B. Saunders Company, 1962.

Clark, W. E. L.: *The Tissues of the Body: An Introduction to the Study of Anatomy*, 4th ed. New York: Oxford University Press, 1958.

Cowdry, E. V., and Finerty, J. C.: *A Textbook of Histology*, 5th ed. Philadelphia: Lea & Febiger, 1960.

Cruickshank, Bruce; Dodds, T. C.; and Gardner, D. L.: *Human Histology*. Baltimore: The Williams and Wilkins Company, 1964.

Greep, Roy O.: *Histology*, 2nd ed. New York: The Blakiston Division, McGraw-Hill Book Company, 1965.

Ham, A. W., and Leeson, T. S.: *Histology*, 4th ed. Philadelphia: J. B. Lippincott Company, 1961.

Jordan, H. E.: *Textbook of Histology*, 9th ed. New York: D. Appleton Company, 1952.

Windle, W. F.: *Textbook of Histology*, 3rd ed. New York: McGraw-Hill Book Company, 1960.

NEUROANATOMY AND NEUROPHYSIOLOGY

Alpers, Bernard J.: *Clinical Neurology*, Philadelphia: F. A. Davis Company, 1963.

Alvarez, W. C.: *Nervousness, Indigestion and Pain*, New York: Paul B. Hoeber, Inc., 1954.

Crosby, E. C.; Humphrey, T.; and Lauer, E. W.: *Correlative Anatomy of the Nervous System*. New York: The Macmillan Company, 1962.

Elliott, H. C.: *Textbook of Neuroanatomy*. Philadelphia: L. B. Lippincott Company, 1963.

Fulton, J. F.: *Physiology of the Nervous System*, 3rd ed. New York: Oxford University Press, 1949.

Gardner, E.: *Fundamentals of Neurology*, 4th ed. Philadelphia: W. B. Saunders Company, 1963.

House, E. Lawrence, and Pansky, Ben: *A Functional Approach to Neuroanatomy*. New York: The Blakiston Division, McGraw-Hill Book Company, 1960.

Magoun, H. W.: *The Waking Brain*, 2nd ed. Springfield, Ill.: Charles C Thomas, Publisher, 1963.

Millen, J. W., and Woollam, D. H. M.: *The Anatomy of Cerebrospinal Fluid*. New York: Oxford University Press, 1962.

Netter, F. H.: *The Nervous System*, 5th ed. Summit, N.J.: Ciba Pharmaceutical Products, Inc., 1962. Vol. I.

Penfield, W., and Rasmussen, T.: *The Cerebral Cortex of Man*. New York: The Macmillan Company, 1950.

Ranson, S. W., and Clark, S. L.: *Anatomy of the Nervous System*, 10th ed. Philadelphia: W. B. Saunders Company, 1959.

Rasmussen, A. T.: *Principal Nervous Pathways*, 4th ed. New York: The Macmillan Company, 1952.

Strong and Elwyn's Human Neuro-anatomy, 5th ed., revised by R. C. Truex and M. B. Carpenter. Baltimore: The Williams and Wilkins Company, 1964.

Wyburn, G. M.: *The Nervous System*. New York: Academic Press, Inc., 1960.

DEVELOPMENTAL ANATOMY AND GENETICS

Allan, Frank D.: *Essentials of Human Embryology*. New York: Oxford University Press, 1960.

Arey, L. B.: *Developmental Anatomy*, 6th ed. Philadelphia: W. B. Saunders Co., 1965.

Colin, E. C.: *Elements of Genetics: Mendel's Laws of Heredity with Special Application to Man*, 3rd ed. New York: McGraw-Hill Book Company, 1956.

Hamilton, W. J.; Boyd, J. D.; and Mossman, H. W.: *Human Embryology* (*Prenatal Development of Form and Function*), 3rd ed. Baltimore: The Williams and Wilkins Company, 1962.

Harrison, R. J.: *The Child Unborn*. New York: The Macmillan Company, 1951.

Kempthorne, O.: *Biometrical Genetics*. New York: The Macmillan Company, 1960.

Kormondy, Edward J.: *Introduction to Genetics*. New York: The Blakiston Division, McGraw-Hill Book Company, 1964.

Langman, Jan: *Medical Embryology*. Baltimore: The Williams and Wilkins Company, 1963.

Levine, R. P.: *Genetics*. New York: Holt, Rinehart, and Winston, Inc., 1962.

Li, C. C.: *Human Genetics*. New York: The Blakiston Division, McGraw-Hill Book Company, 1961.

Moore, John A.: *Heredity and Development*. New York: Oxford University Press, 1963.

Patten Bradley M.: *Foundations of Embryology*, 2nd ed. New York: The Blakiston Division, McGraw-Hill Book Company, 1964.

Roberts, J. A. Fraser: *An Introduction to Medical Genetics*, 2nd ed. New York: Oxford University Press, 1959.

Scheinfeld, Amram: *The Human Heredity Handbook*. Philadelphia: J. B. Lippincott Company, 1956.

————: *The New You and Heredity*. Philadelphia: J. B. Lippincott Company, 1950.

————: *Your Heredity and Environment*. Philadelphia: J. B. Lippincott Company, 1965.

PHYSIOLOGY

Bard, P. (ed.): *Medical Physiology*, 11th ed. St. Louis: The C. V. Mosby Company 1961.

Best, C. H., and Taylor, N. B. (eds.): *The Physiological Basis of Medical Practice*, 7th ed. Baltimore: The Williams and Wilkins Company, 1961.

Browse, Norman L.: *The Physiology and Pathology of Bed Rest*. Springfield, Ill.: Charles C Thomas, Publisher, 1965.

Cannon, W. B.: *Bodily Changes in Pain, Hunger, Fear, and Rage*, 2nd ed. New York: Appleton-Century-Crofts, Inc., 1929.

————: *The Wisdom of the Body*. New York: W. W. Norton and Company, 1963.

Davson, Hugh (ed.): *Principles of Human Physiology*, 13th ed. London: J. & A. Churchill, Ltd., 1962.

Ganong, William F.: *Review of Medical Physiology*. Los Altos, Calif.: Lange Medical Publications, 1963.

Gregg, D. E.: *Coronary Circulation in Health and Disease*. Philadelphia: Lea & Febiger, 1950.

Guyton, A. C.: *Textbook of Medical Physiology*, 2nd ed. Philadelphia: W. B. Saunders Company, 1961.

Hardy, James D. (ed.): *Physiological Problems in Space Exploration*. Springfield, Ill.: Charles C Thomas, Publisher, 1964.

Korenchevsky, V.: *Physiological and Pathological Aging*. New York: Hafner Publishing Company, 1961.

Leavell, Byrd, and Thorup, Oscar: *Fundamentals of Clinical Hematology*, 2nd ed. Philadelphia: W. B. Saunders Company, 1965.

McDowall, R. J. S.: *Handbook of Physiology*, 43rd ed. New York: The Blakiston Division, McGraw-Hill Book Company, 1960.

Mitchell, P. H.: *A Textbook of General Physiology*, 5th ed. New York: McGraw-Hill Book Company, 1956.

Montagna, W., *et al.*: *Advances in Biology of Skin, Volume II, Blood Vessels and Circulation*. New York: The Macmillan Company, 1961.

Ruch, T. C., and Fulton, J. F. (eds.): *Medical Physiology and Biophysics*, 18th ed. of Howell's *Textbook of Physiology*. Philadelphia: W. B. Saunders Company, 1960.

Schoenheimer, R.: *Dynamic State of Body Constituents*. Cambridge, Mass.: Harvard University Press, 1942.

Selkurt, Ewald E. (ed.): *Physiology*. Boston: Little, Brown and Company, 1963.

Sodeman, William A., and Sodeman, W. A., Jr. (eds.): *Pathologic Physiology*, 4th ed. Philadelphia: W. B. Saunders Company, 1966.

Starling, E. H., and Lovatt, Evans: *Principles of Human Physiology*, 13th ed. by Hugh Davson and M. Grace Eggleton. Philadelphia: Lea & Febiger, 1962.

Tuttle, W. W., and Schottelius, Byron A.: *Textbook of Physiology*, 14th ed. St. Louis: The C. V. Mosby Company, 1961.

Wiggers, C. J.: *Circulatory Dynamics*. New York: Grune & Stratton, Inc., 1952.

————: *Physiology in Health and Disease*, 5th ed. Philadelphia: Lea & Febiger, 1949.

Winton, F. R., and Bayliss, L. E.: *Human Physiology*, 5th ed. London: J. & A. Churchill, Ltd., 1962.

Wright, S.: *Applied Physiology*, 11th ed. revised by Cyril A. Keele and Eric Neil. New York: Oxford University Press, 1965.

Youmans, William B.: *Fundamentals of Human Physiology for Students in the Medical Sciences*, 2nd ed. Chicago: Year Book Medical Publishers, Inc., 1961.

STRESS

Selye, Hans: *The Story of the Adaptation Syndrome*. Montreal: Acta, Inc., 1952.

————: *Stress*. Montreal: Acta, Inc., 1950.

————: *The Stress of Life*. New York: McGraw-Hill Book Company, 1956.

ENDOCRINOLOGY

Grollman, Arthur: *Principles of Endocrinology*. Philadelphia: J. B. Lippincott Company, 1964.

Hall, Peter F.: *The Functions of the Endocrine Glands*. Philadelphia: W. B. Saunders Company, 1959.

Williams, R. H. (ed.): *Textbook of Endocrinology*, 3rd ed. Philadelphia: W. B. Saunders Company, 1962.

CELLS AND BODY FLUIDS

American Association for the Advancement of Science: *Cell and Protoplasm*, edited, by F. R. Moulton. Publication No. 14. New York: Science Press, 1940.

Andrew, W.: *Cellular Changes with Age*. Springfield, Ill.: Charles C Thomas, Publisher, 1952.

Asimov, Isaac: *The Living River*. New York: Abelard-Schuman, 1959.

————: *The Wellsprings of Life*. New York: The New American Library, 1960.

Bland, John H.: *Clinical Metabolism of Body Water and Electrolytes*. Philadelphia: W. B. Saunders Company, 1963.

Bowsher, David: *Cerebrospinal Fluid Dynamics in Health and Disease*. Springfield, Ill.: Charles C Thomas, Publisher, 1960.

Butler, J. A. V.: *Inside the Living Cell*. New York: Basic Books, Inc., 1959.

Christensen, H. N.: *Body Fluids and the Acid-Base Balance: A Learning Program for Students of the Biological and Medical Sciences*. Philadelphia: W. B. Saunders Company, 1964.

————: *Body Fluids and Their Neutrality*. New York: Oxford University Press, 1963.

DeRoberts, E. D.; Nowinski, W. W.; and Saly, F. A.: *Cell Biology*, 4th ed. Philadelphia: W. B. Saunders Company, 1965.

Elkinton, J. R., and Danowski, T. S.: *The Body Fluids*. Baltimore: The Williams and Wilkins Company, 1956.

Freeman, James A.: *Cellular Fine Structure*. New York: The Blakiston Division, McGraw-Hill Book Company, 1964.

Gamble, J. L.: *Chemical Anatomy, Physiology and Pathology of Extracellular Fluid: A Lecture Syllabus*, 6th ed. Cambridge, Mass.: Harvard University Press, 1954.

Gerard, R. W. (ed.): *Food for Life*. Chicago: University of Chicago Press, 1952.

Gerard, R. W.: *Unresting Cells*, new ed. New York: Harper & Brothers, 1949.

Giese, Arthur C.: *Cell Physiology*, 2nd ed. Philadelphia: W. B. Saunders Company, 1962.

Grace, W. J.: *Practical Clinical Management of Electrolyte Disorders*. New York: Appleton-Century-Crofts, Inc., 1960.

Heilbrunn, L. V.: *The Dynamics of Living Protoplasm*. New York: Academic Press, Inc., 1956.

Hill, Fontaine S.: *Practical Fluid Therapy in Pediatrics*. Philadelphia: W. B. Saunders Company, 1954.

Hutchins, Carleen M.: *Life's Key—DNA*. New York: Coward-McCann, Inc., 1961.

Loewy, Ariel G., and Siekevitz, Philip: *Cell Structure and Function*. New York: Holt, Rinehart and Winston, 1963.

McElroy, Wm. D.: *Cell Physiology and Biochemistry*, 2nd ed. Englewood Cliffs, N.J.: Prentice-Hall, Inc., 1964.

Mazia, Daniel, and Tyler, Albert (eds.): *General Physiology of Cell Specialization*. New York: The Blakiston Division, McGraw-Hill Book Company, 1963.

Snively, William D., Jr.: *Sea Within: Story of our Body Fluid*. Philadelphia: J. B. Lippincott Company, 1960.

Statland, Harry: *Fluid and Electrolytes in Practice*, 3rd ed. Philadelphia: J. B. Lippincott Company, 1963.

Strauss, Maurice B.: *Body Water in Man*. Boston: Little, Brown and Company, 1957.

Swanson, Carl P.: *The Cell*. Englewood Cliffs, N.J.: Prentice-Hall, Inc., 1960.

Welt, Louis G.: *Clinical Disorders of Hydration and Acid-Base Equilibrium*, 2nd ed. Boston: Little, Brown & Co., 1959.

Wilson, G. B., and Morrison, J. H.: *Cytology*. New York: Reinhold Publishing Corporation, 1961.

Yoffey, J. M., and Courtice, F. C.: *Lymphatics, Lymph and Tissue Fluid*. Cambridge, Mass.: Harvard University Press, 1956.

CHEMISTRY, BIOCHEMISTRY, AND NUTRITION

Bell, G. H.; Davidson, J. N.; and Scarborough, H.: *Textbook of Physiology and Biochemistry*, 5th ed. Baltimore: The Williams and Wilkins Company, 1961.

Fruton, Joseph S., and Simmonds, Sofia: *General Biochemistry*, 2nd ed. New York: John Wiley and Sons, 1958.

Harrow, Benjamin: *One Family: Vitamins, Enzymes and Hormones*. Minneapolis: Burgess Publishing Company, 1950.

Hawk's Physiological Chemistry, 14th ed., edited by Bernard L. Oser. New York: The Blakiston Division, McGraw-Hill Book Company, 1965.

Hodgman, Charles D. (ed.-in-chief): *Handbook of Chemistry and Physics*, revised annually. Cleveland, Ohio: Chemical Rubber Publishing Co.

Kleiner, Israel S., and Orten, James M.: *Biochemistry*, 6th ed. St. Louis: The C. V. Mosby Company, 1962.

Sherman, Henry C., and Lanford, Caroline Sherman: *Essentials of Nutrition*, 4th ed. New York: The Macmillan Company, 1957.

Sunderman, F. W., and Boerner, F.: *Normal Values in Clinical Medicine*. Philadelphia: W. B. Saunders Company, 1949.

Taylor, C. M., and Pye, O. F.: *Foundations of Nutrition*, 6th ed. New York: The Macmillan Company, 1966.

Weber, G.: *Regulation of Enzyme Activity.* New York: The Macmillan Company, 1965.

West, E. S.: *Textbook of Biophysical Chemistry,* 3rd ed. New York: The Macmillan Company, 1963.

West, E. S.; Todd, W. R.; Mason, H. S.; and Van Bruggen, J. T.: *Textbook of Biochemistry,* 4th ed. New York: The Macmillan Company, 1966.

White, Abraham; Handler, P.; Smith, E.; and Stetten, D., Jr.: *Principles of Biochemistry,* 3rd ed. New York: McGraw-Hill Book Company, 1964.

Wohl, Michael, and Robert Goodhart: *Modern Nutrition in Health and Disease,* 3rd ed. Philadelphia: Lea & Febiger, 1964.

GENERAL BIOLOGY

Bushbaum, R. M., *et al.: Lower Animals, Living Invertebrates of the World.* Garden City, N.Y.: Doubleday and Company, 1960.

Hegner, R. W., and Stiles, K. A.: *College Zoology,* 7th ed. New York: The Macmillan Company, 1959.

Mavor, J. W.: *General Biology,* 5th ed. New York: The Macmillan Company, 1959.

Swanson, C. P., *et al.: Foundations of Modern Biology Series,* 2nd ed. Englewood Cliffs, N. J.: Prentice-Hall, Inc., 1965.

Walter, H. E., and Sayles, L. P.: *Biology of the Vertebrates,* 3rd ed. New York: The Macmillan Company, 1949.

Weisz, P. B.: *The Elements of Biology.* New York: The McGraw-Hill Book Co., 1961.

Woodruff, L. L., and Baitsell, G. A.: *Foundations of Biology,* 7th ed. New York: The Macmillan Company, 1951.

LABORATORY MANUALS—ANATOMY AND PHYSIOLOGY

Bensley, B. A.: *Practical Anatomy of the Rabbit,* revised ed. by E. Horne Craigie. New York: The Blakiston Division, McGraw-Hill Book Company, 1957.

Booth, E. S.: *Laboratory Anatomy of the Cat.* College Place, Wash.: Walla Walla College, 1949.

Greene, E. G.: *Anatomy of the Rat.* Philadelphia: American Philosophical Society, 1935.

Leavell, L. C.; Chapin, F. M.; and Miller, M. A.: *Laboratory Manual and Workbook in Anatomy and Physiology,* 4th ed. New York: The Macmillan Company, 1964.

Reighard, J.; Jennings, H. S.; and Elliott, R.: *Anatomy of the Cat,* 3rd ed. New York: Henry Holt and Company, 1935.

Tuttle, W. W., and Schottelius, B. A.: *Physiology Laboratory Manual.* St. Louis: C. V. Mosby Company, 1963.

Visscher, M. B., *et al.: Experimental Physiology,* 2nd ed. Minneapolis: Burgess Publishing Company, 1950.

Zoethout, W. D.: *Laboratory Experiments in Physiology,* 6th ed. St. Louis: The C. V. Mosby Company, 1963.

DICTIONARIES

Asimov, Isaac: *Words of Science.* Boston: Houghton Mifflin Company, 1959.

Blakiston's New Gould Medical Dictionary, 2nd ed. New York: The Blakiston Division McGraw-Hill Book Company, 1956.

Chambers's Technical Dictionary, 3rd ed. New York: The Macmillan Company, 1958.

Dorland's Illustrated Medical Dictionary, 23rd ed. Philadelphia: W. B. Saunders Company, 1957.

Jaeger, Edmund C.: *A Source-Book of Biological Names and Terms*, 3rd ed. Springfield, Ill.: Charles C Thomas, Publisher, 1962.

The Macmillan Medical Dictionary. New York: The Macmillan Company, 1954.

Stedman's Medical Dictionary, 20th ed. Baltimore: The Williams and Wilkins Company, 1961.

Van Nostrand's Scientific Encyclopedia, 3rd ed. Princeton, N. J.: D. Van Nostrand Company, 1958.

Metric System

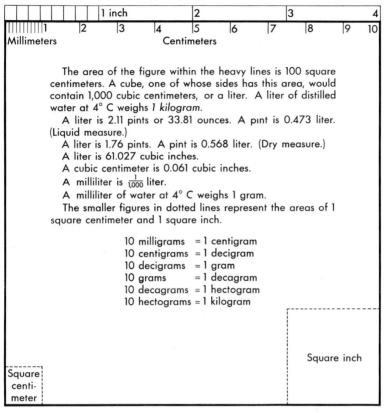

1 inch	2	3	4
1 2 3 4 5 6 7 8 9 10			

Millimeters   Centimeters

The area of the figure within the heavy lines is 100 square centimeters. A cube, one of whose sides has this area, would contain 1,000 cubic centimeters, or a liter. A liter of distilled water at 4° C weighs 1 *kilogram.*

A liter is 2.11 pints or 33.81 ounces. A pint is 0.473 liter. (Liquid measure.)

A liter is 1.76 pints. A pint is 0.568 liter. (Dry measure.)

A liter is 61.027 cubic inches.

A cubic centimeter is 0.061 cubic inches.

A milliliter is $\frac{1}{1,000}$ liter.

A milliliter of water at 4° C weighs 1 gram.

The smaller figures in dotted lines represent the areas of 1 square centimeter and 1 square inch.

10 milligrams	=	1 centigram
10 centigrams	=	1 decigram
10 decigrams	=	1 gram
10 grams	=	1 decagram
10 decagrams	=	1 hectogram
10 hectograms	=	1 kilogram

Square inch

Square centi- meter

1 millimeter	=	0.039 inch	1 decigram	=	1.543 grains
1 centimeter	=	0.393 inch	1 gram	=	15.432 grains
1 decimeter	=	3.937 inches	1 decagram	=	154.323 grains
1 meter	=	39.370 inches	1 hectogram	=	1,543.235 grains
			1 kilogram	=	15,432.350 grains
1 milligram	=	0.015 grain	1 kilogram	=	35.274 ounces
1 centigram	=	0.154 grain	1 kilogram	=	2.204 pounds
1 micron (μ)	=	0.001 millimeter			
1 millimicron (mμ or μμ)	=	0.000001 millimeter			
1 Å, or Angstrom unit	=	0.0001 μ, or 10^{-7} millimeters			

Avoirdupois weights are used in weighing the organs of the body. One ounce avoirdupois = 28.35 grams. For the sake of simplicity in converting figures in the text from one system to the other, we have assumed

1 in. to equal 25 mm
1 in. to equal 2.5 cm

1 in. to equal 25,000 microns (μ)
1 cm to equal 0.4 in.

1 ml to equal 15 minims
30 ml to equal 1 oz

767

Glossary

Terms adequately defined in the body of the text are not always included in the Glossary. They may be located through the Index.

acetab′ulum. "Shallow vinegar cup"; the depression in the innominate bone which receives the head of the femur

ac′etone. $(CH_3)_2CO$. A simple ketone with a sweetish odor, present in blood and in body excretions whenever fats are used in metabolism without the presence of sufficient carbohydrate

acro′mion. Point of the shoulder. The spine of the scapula terminates in the acromion process

adsorption. The attachment of one substance to the surface of another

adventi′tia. The outermost layer of the organs which are not bounded by a serous coat, the outer areolar connective tissue being continuous with that of the other organs; e.g., blood vessels have no outer limiting membrane but lie in the common areolar tissue. Often called the *externa*

agglu′tinins. Substances which induce adhesion or clumping together of cells

al′binism. Congenital absence of the pigment melanin in the skin, iris, and hair. It may be partial or complete

albu′mins. Thick, viscous substances containing nitrogen; soluble in water, dilute acids, dilute salines, and concentrated solutions of magnesiom sulfate and sodium chloride. They are coagulated by heat. Examples: egg albumin and serum albumin of blood

ampul'la. A flasklike dilatation of a canal

an'aerobe. Any microorganism which is able to live without free air or oxygen

anom'aly. Anything unusual, irregular, or contrary to the general rule

an'tigens. Name given to foreign proteins and certain other substances which upon entering the blood stream cause the formation of antibodies in the serum

antimetab'olite. A substance which resembles chemically a normal metabolite but is foreign to the body and competes with, replaces, or antagonizes the latter. These substances may be used to prevent growth of cancer cells

a'pex. The top or pointed extremity of a body

arach'noid. Resembling a cobweb

arboriza'tion. A branching distribution of veinlets or of nerve filaments, especially the branched, terminal ramifications of neurofibrils

au'ricle. Ear. The *pinna* of the ear which with the *external meatus* constitutes the external ear

autonom'ic. Performed without the will; automatic

az'ygos. Without a fellow; single; unpaired

bas'al metab'olism. Rate of energy metabolism of a person at rest 12 to 18 hours after eating, as measured by the calorimeter or a BMR machine

bas'ilar. Pertaining to the base of an object; e.g., basilar artery located at the base of the brain

bicip'ital. Referring to the biceps

blas'tula. A hollow sphere of embryonic cells; the last stage in development before the embryo divides into two layers

brachiocephal'ic. Pertaining to both the upper arm and head, as the brachiocephalic (innominate) artery and veins

cal'cify. Harden by deposit of salts of calcium; petrify

cal'culus, pl., **cal'culi.** A stone

cal'orie. The Calorie is the amount of heat required to raise the temperature of 1 kg of water 1°C. The small calorie is the amount of heat required to raise the temperature of 1 gm of water 1°C

canalic'ulus, pl., **canalic'uli.** A minute channel or vessel

car'dia. The heart. The esophageal orifice of the stomach

castra'tion. Removal of the testes in the male or the ovaries in the female

catacrot'ic. Referring to an irregularity of the pulse in which the beat is marked by two or more expansions of the artery. A tracing of this pulse shows one or more abnormal elevations on the downward stroke

catal'ysis. A changing of the speed of a reaction, produced by the presence of a substance which does not itself enter the final products

celluli'tis. Inflammation of connective tissue, most commonly of superficial fascia

chi'asm. An X-shaped crossing or decussation, especially that of the fibers of the optic nerve

choa'na. Any funnel-shaped cavity, such as the posterior nares

cholere'tic. Any substance that stimulates secretion and flow of bile

choles'terol. A sterol, $C_{27}H_{43}OH$, found in small quantities in the protoplasm of all cells, especially in nerve tissue, blood cells, and bile. Same as cholesterin

chor'da tym'pani. The tympanic cord, a branch of the facial (seventh cranial) nerve, which traverses the tympanic cavity and joins the gustatory (lingual) nerve

chro'maffin. Certain cells, occurring in the adrenal medulla, along the sympathetic nerves, and in various organs, stain deeply with chrome salts (brownish-yellow), hence the name chromaffin. The whole system of such tissue throughout the body is named the chromaffin or chromaphil system

chro'matin. Portions of the nucleus which stain deeply with basic dyes, e.g., methylene blue

chro'mosomes. Segments of chromatin in the nucleus of cells, concerned with the transmission of hereditary characteristics and the direction of the embryo's development

cica'trix. The mark or scar left after the healing of a wound

cister'na mag'na, or **cister'na cerebel'lo med'ullaris.** That portion of the subarachnoid cavity between the cerebellum and the medulla

clea'vage. The process of division of the fertilized ovum before differentiation into layers occurs

coen'zymes. Nonprotein substances produced by living cells, which are essential for action of certain enzymes

col'loid. A state of matter in which particles having a diameter of 0.1 to 0.001 μ are dispersed in a medium such as water, etc.

com'missure. A joining. A bundle of nerve fibers passing from one side of the brain or spinal cord to the other side. The corner or angle of the eyes or lips

congen'ital. Existing from or before birth

cor'acoid. Shaped like a crow's beak; a process of the scapula

cor'pus. A body or mass

cor'tex. The bark or outer layer; the outer portion of an organ

cre'nated. Notched on the edge (indented)

crepita'tion. A grating or crackling sound or sensation, like that produced by fragments of a fractured bone rubbing together

crib'riform. Perforated like a sieve

cu'neiform. Wedge-shaped

cyano'sis. Blueness of the skin, resulting from insufficient oxygenation of the blood

cysti'tis. Inflammation of the bladder

deaminiza'tion. Removal of the amino group, NH_2, from an amino compound

dec'ibel. Unit of loudness, tenth of a bel. Used for measuring loudness, differences of sounds

decid'uous. That which falls off; not permanent

dehydra'tion. Removal of water as from a tissue

del'toid. Triangular; resembling in shape the Greek letter Δ, delta

diapede'sis. Passing of any of the formed elements of the blood through vessel walls without rupture

diath'esis. A predisposition to certain kinds of disease

dichot'omous. Divided into two; consisting of a pair or pairs

diffu'sion. Continual movement of molecules among each other in liquid or in gases. The passage of a substance through a membrane. The diffusing substance always diffuses from an area of high concentration to an area of lesser concentration (of that particular substance)

dura mater. "Hard mother"; the tough outer membrane enveloping the brain and spinal cord

dyne. Unit of force which, when acting on a mass of 1 gm for 1 second, will cause an acceleration of 1 cm per second

dyspha′gia. Difficulty in swallowing

ectop′ic. Out of place. *Ectopic gestation* refers to pregnancy when the fecundated ovum, instead of entering the uterus, remains in either a fallopian tube or the abdominal cavity

ede′ma. Swelling due to abnormal effusion of serous fluid into the tissues

empir′ical. Founded on experience; relating to the treatment of disease according to symptoms alone, without regard to scientific knowledge

emul′sion. A mixture of two fluids insoluble in each other, where one is dispersed through the other in the form of finely divided globules

endergon′ic. A reaction characterized by absorption of energy; this is characteristic of many anabolic processes, such as synthesis

endochon′dral ossifica′tion. Ossification in which cartilage is formed first and then is gradually replaced with bone

endog′enous. Originating within the organism. Opposite of exogenous

endother′mic. In a reacting system, if heat is absorbed the reaction is said to be endothermic

en′ergy. Capacity or ability to do work, activity, exertion of power

equilib′rium. The balanced condition resulting when opposing forces are exactly equal. The term may refer to the maintenance of correct concentration of constituents of the body fluids or to the harmonious action of the organs of the body as in standing, etc.

erg. A unit of work. The work done in moving a body 1 cm against a force of 1 dyne

eth′moid. Resembling a sieve.

evagina′tion. Protrusion of some part or organ from its normal position

evapora′tion. The changing of a liquid into a vapor. Heat is necessary for evaporation, and if not otherwise supplied it is taken from near objects. Thus, the heat necessary for the evaporation of perspiration is taken from the body

exergon′ic. A reaction characterized by release of free energy; this is characteristic of catabolic reactions

exog′enous. Originating outside of the organism; opposite of endogenous

exophthal′mic. Pertaining to abnormal protrusion of the eyeball

exother′mic. In a reacting system if heat is formed, the reaction is said to be exothermic

exten′sile. Capable of being stretched

ex′udate. A fluid or semifluid which has oozed through the tissues into a cavity or upon the body surface

fal′ciform. Sickle-shaped

fal′ciform ligament. Fold of peritoneum between the liver and the anterior abdominal wall in which the umbilical vein (ligamentum teres) is contained

fascic′ulus, pl., **fascic′uli.** A bundle of close-set fibers, usually muscle or nerve fibers

fecunda′tion. Fertilization; impregnation

fenes′trated. Having windowlike openings; perforated

fibril'la, pl., **fibril'lae**. A small fiber or filament

fim'bria, pl., **fim'briae**. A fringe

flat'ulence. Distention due to generation of gases in the stomach and intestine

fontanel'. "Little fountain"; the rise and fall of the pulse can be observed through the membranous interspaces of fontanels in the infant's cranium

gastrocne'mius. "Belly of the leg"; one of the calf muscles

gas'troepiplo'ic. Pertaining to the stomach and greater omentum

gen'erative. Having the power of function of reproduction

genes. The factors on chromosomes which determine certain hereditary characteristics

gesta'tion. Pregnancy

gli'a. Neuroglia

glob'ulins. Protein substances (myosin, fibrinogen, etc.) similar to albumins but insoluble in water and soluble in dilute solutions of neutral salts

glycogen'esis. The production of glycogen

glycogenol'ysis. Splitting of glycogen into glucose by the liver, or into pyruvic or lactic acid in other tissues

glycol'ysis. Splitting of glucose into carbon dioxide and water

glyconeogen'esis. Formation of glucose or glycogen from noncarbohydrate substances

gon'ad. Gamete-producing gland; e.g., testis, ovary

hem'atin. An iron-containing compound derived from heme, the colored nonprotein constituent of hemoglobin

hemorrhoi'dal. Pertaining to hemorrhoids, small tumors caused by dilation of the veins of the anal region

hi'lus or **hi'lum**. The depression, usually on the concave surface of a gland, where vessels and ducts enter or leave

homeos'tasis. Constancy of the internal environment

homoge'neous. Of the same kind or quality throughout; uniform in nature; the reverse of heterogeneous

hy'aline. Glassy; translucent

hydrostatic pressure. A pressure exerted uniformly and perpendicularly to all surfaces as by a homogeneous liquid

hyperglyce'mia. An abnormally high amount of glucose in the blood

in'guinal. Pertaining to the groin

interme'diary meta'bolism. Refers to metabolism taking place after absorption and before excretion from the excretory organs, that is, either in cells or in the body fluids—tissue fluid, lymph, or blood

internun'cial. Acting as a medium between two nerve centers

intersti'tial. In the interspaces of a tissue; refers to the connective-tissue framework of organs

ionize. To form ions which are atoms, or groups of atoms, bearing electric charges

ische'mia. Local anemia due to mechanical obstruction (mainly arterial narrowing) to the blood supply

is'chium, pl., **is'chia**. The lower portion of the os innominatum; that upon which the body is supported in a sitting posture

isoagglu'tinin. A substance present in the blood serum which can agglutinate or clump together the erythrocytes of other individuals of the same species

isoagglutin'ogen. A substance in blood cells which stimulates the action of agglutinins

i'sotope. Isotopes are atoms that have different numbers of neutrons in their nuclei, but have the same number of protons. They weigh differently but behave alike chemically. Some of them are radioactive and can be used as tracers in the body; for instance, iron, iodine, etc.

ketogen'ic. Tending to produce "ketone bodies," acetone, acetoacetic acid, and beta hydroxybutyric acid

lacta'tion. The secretion of milk

lacu'na, pl., **lacu'nae**. A minute, hollow space

lambdoi'dal. Resembling the Greek letter Λ, lambda

lamel'la, pl., **lamel'lae**. A thin plate, or layer

lam'ina. A thin plate; a germinal layer

laryn'goscope. The instrument by which the larynx may be examined in the living subject

libi'do. Conscious or unconscious sexual desire

lin'ea as'pera. A rough, longitudinal line on the back of the femur

lymphangi'tis. Inflammation of a lymphatic vessel

ly'sin. Lysis, "to dissolve." An antibody which can dissolve cells, etc.

macera'tion. The softening of the parts of a tissue by soaking

macroscop'ic. That which can be viewed with the naked eye

manom'eter. An instrument for measuring the pressure or tension of liquids or gases

maras'mus. Progressive wasting and emaciation, especially in young infants

matura'tion. Cell division in which the number of chromosomes in the germ cells is reduced to one half the number usual for the species

medul'la. The central portions of an organ. Marrow. The medulla oblongata of the spinal cord

mesoco'lon. A process of the peritoneum by which the colon is attached to the posterior abdominal wall

methemoglo'bin. A transformation product of oxyhemoglobin found in the circulating blood after poisoning with acetanilid, potassium chlorate, etc.; the iron is oxidized from ferrous to ferric form; this compound does not carry oxygen

microceph'alus. An idiot or fetus with a very small head

mononu'clear. Having but one nucleus

mo'tor. Producing or subserving motion. A muscle, nerve, or center that affects or produces movement

mu'cin. A glycoprotein, a constituent of mucus

muta'tion. A distinctive character appearing for the first time in a pure line which is transmitted through succeeding generations. It is due to some change in the chromosomes

my'elocyte. A bone-marrow cell giving rise to granulocytes

myogen'ic. Originating in muscular tissue

myoneu'ral. Pertaining to both muscle and nerve

my'osin. A globulin, chief protein substance of muscle

na'ris, pl., **na'res.** A nostril

navic'ular. Boatlike

ner'vus er'igens, pl., **ner'vi erigen'tes.** A nerve fiber supplying the bladder, genitals, and rectum; derived from the second and third sacral nerves

neurogen'ic. Originating in nerve tissue

no'tochord. The primitive backbone in the embryo

nystag'mus. Rhythmical oscillation of the eyeballs, either horizontal, rotary, or vertical. A symptom seen sometimes in disease of the inner ear or cerebellum

odon'toid. Toothlike

o'ocyte. The primitive ovum in the cortex of the ovary, before maturation takes place

os, pl., **o'ra.** A mouth

os, pl., **os'sa.** A bone

osmo'sis. The passage of fluids and solutions, separated by a membrane or other porous septum, through the partition, so as to become mixed or diffused through each other

os'sa innomina'ta, pl. of **os innomina'tum.** "Unnamed bones." The irregular bones of the pelvis, unnamed on account of their nonresemblance to any known object

os'teoblasts. The cells forming or developing into bone

os'teoclast. A large cell found in the bone marrow, believed to be capable of absorbing bone

o'tic. Pertaining to the ear

o'toliths. Particles of calcium carbonate and phosphate found in the internal ear on the hair cells

papil'la, pl., **papil'lae.** A small eminence; a nipplelike process

paranas'al si'nuses. Sinuses which communicate with the cavity of the nose. They are often called air sinuses of the head

patel'la. A small pan; the kneecap

ped'icle. A stalk

pedun'cle. A narrow part acting as a support

pet'rous. Stonelike

phlebot'omy. The surgical opening of a vein; venesection

phren'ic. Pertaining to the diaphragm

pi'a ma'ter. "Tender mother"; the innermost membrane closely enveloping the brain and spinal cord

pir'iform. Pear-shaped

pis'iform. Pea-shaped

polar-ity. Tendency of a body to exhibit opposite properties in opposite directions; referring to the possession of positive and negative poles

poles. Points having opposite properties, occurring at the opposite extremities of an axis. Either end of a spindle in mitosis

precip'itins. Antibodies in the blood serum which are capable of precipitating antigens

psy′chical. Pertaining to the mind

ptery′goid. Wing-shaped

pyogen′ic. Producing pus

pyrex′ia. Elevation of temperature; fever

quadrigem′inal. Consisting of four parts

recep′tor. This word is used with various meanings. One dictionary defines it as a sense organ; another as "nerve endings in organs of sense." Others would define it as the "ends of an afferent nerve fiber." It should be used and interpreted with care

rec′tus, pl., **rec′ti.** Straight. Name given to certain straight muscles of the eye and abdomen

regurgita′tion. The casting up of undigested food from the stomach. A backward flowing of blood through a cardiac valve because of imperfect closure of a valve leaflet

rhe′obase. Minimal electric current required to excite a tissue, e.g., nerve or muscle

rhom′boid. A quadrilateral figure whose opposite sides and angles are equal but which is neither equilateral nor equiangular

saliva′tion. An excessive secretion of saliva

saponifica′tion. Alkaline hydrolysis; when fats are thus hydrolized, soaps are produced

sig′moid. Shaped like the letter S

ska′tole. A strong-smelling crystalline substance from human feces, produced by decomposition of proteins in the intestine

sol′ute. A dissolved substance

sol′vent. A substance, usually liquid, which is capable of dissolving another substance

somat′ic. Pertaining to the body, especially the body wall

specif′ic grav′ity. A comparison between the weight of a substance and the weight of an equal volume of some other substance taken as a standard. The standards usually referred to are air for gases, and water for liquids and solids. For instance, the specific gravity (s.g.) of carbon dioxide (air standard) is 1.5, meaning that is is 1.5 times as heavy as an equal volume of air. Again, the specific gravity of mercury (water standard) is 13.6, meaning that mercury is 13.6 times as heavy as an equal volume of water. The specific gravity of solutions, as a salt solution, will necessarily vary with the concentration

sphe′noid. Wedge-shaped

sphinc′ter. A circular muscle which contracts the aperture to which it is attached

splanch′nic. Pertaining to the viscera

summa′tion. Addition; finding of total or sum

sur′face ten′sion. The force which exists in the surface film of liquids which tends to bring the contained volume into a form having the least superficial area. It is due to the fact that the particles in the film are not equally acted on from all sides but instead are attracted inward by the pull of molecules below them

su′ture. That which is sewn together, a seam; the synarthrosis between two cranial bones

syner′gic or **synerget′ic.** Acting in harmonious cooperation, said especially of certain muscles

ten'do achil'lis. "Tendon of Achilles." The tendon attached to the heel, so named because Achilles is supposed to have been held by the heel when his mother dipped him in the river Styx to render him invulnerable

tet'any. A disease characterized by painful tonic and symmetrical spasm of the muscles of the extremities

the'nar. Mound at base of thumb

thermotax'is. The normal adjustment of the bodily temperature. The movement of organisms in response to heat

trabec'ula, pl., **trabec'ulae.** A supporting fiber; a prolongation of fibrous membrane which forms septa or partitions

troch'lear. Pertaining to a pulley. The trochlear nerve supplies the superior oblique muscle

u'vula. "Little grape"; the soft mass which projects downward from the posterior middle of the soft palate

vac'uole. A space or cavity within the protoplasm of a cell, containing nutritive or waste substances

vas'cular. Latin, *vasculum,* a small tube. Refers to tubes conveying liquids, as blood vascular and lymph vascular systems

ve'na co'mes, pl., **ve'nae com'itantes.** A deep vein following the same course as the corresponding artery

ver'miform. Worm-shaped

vo'lar. Pertaining to the palm of the hand or the sole of the foot

Index

Auditory meatus, **329**
Auditory (acoustic) nerve, **274, 289, 329**
Auditory tube, **52,** 325, 326, **517**
Auerbach's plexus, 305
Auricula of ear, 324-25
Auricular appendage, **389, 391, 405**
Auricularis muscles, **162**
Autologous tissue, 82
Autonomic nervous system, 222, 298-313
  craniosacral (parasympathetic), 229-301
  enteric, 305
  hypothalamus and, 276
  interdependence of craniosacral and tho-
    racolumbar, 310-11
  neural transmission in, 308-9
  pathways of, **306**
  physiology of, 305, 308-11
  plexuses of, 304-5
  thoracolumbar (sympathetic), 301-5
Autosome, 735
Axillary artery, **183, 403,** 417, **418**
Axillary lymph nodes, **478, 479**
Axillary nerve, **182**
Axillary vein, 427
Axis, 108, **110,** 137
Axis cylinder, 227
Axodendritic synapse, **241**
Axon, **223, 224,** 225, **237, 239**
Axoplasm, 227, 237
Azygos vein, **187, 392, 406, 428,** 429, **474,
  478**

Bacteriolysins, 364
Ball-and-socket joints, 137-39
Barometric pressure, respiration and, 546-
  547
Baroreceptors, 451-52
Bartholin's glands, 716, **717**
Basal metabolism, 645-47
Basal nuclei, 268, 273-75
Base-acid balance, 669-73, 684
Basement membrane, 48
Basilar artery, 415, **416**
Basilar membrane of inner ear, 328
Basilic vein, **177,** 427
Basophils, **364, 494**
Bath, heat regulation and, 654-55
Beriberi, 599
Beta cells of pancreas, 508
Bicarbonate of acid-base balance, 671
Biceps brachii, **118, 137, 160, 177,** 178, **183**
Biceps femoris, **161,** 194, **195**
Bicipital groove, 120
Bicuspid teeth, 560
Bicuspid valve, **387,** 388-89, **391**
Bile, 581-82, 615-16
  ducts, **411, 574, 576,** 578, **580**
  pigment in urine, 691
Biological sciences, 4
Biotin, 600

Bipolar neurons, 225
Bishydroxycoumarin, 375
Bladder, **6, 54, 55, 408,** 692-93, **705, 706,
  708, 712**
Blastocyst, 738-42
Blastomere, **737,** 738
Bleeding time, 375
Blind spot, 341
Blood, 357-71
  antibodies in, 370-71
  appearance of, 358-59
  carbon dioxide in, 537, 539-42
  clotting of, 372-76
  corticosteroid effect on, 502
  cross matching of, 377
  functions of, 371
  gases in, 370, 537, 539-42
  Hr factor in, 378
  liver function and, 579
  nutrients in, 370
  oxygen in, 537, 539-42
  pH of, 358
  plasma, 369-71
  proteins in, 369-70
  regeneration of, after hemorrhage, 375-
    376
  Rh factor in, 377-78
  specific gravity of, 357
  tissue fluid compared to, 42, 43
  transfusion, 376
  typing of, 376-78
  in urine, 691
  velocity of flow of, 459
  volume of, 358
  water in, 369
Blood cells, **364**
  platelets (thrombocytes), **364,** 368-69
  red, 359-62, **364**
    in anemia, 362
    color index of, 361
    function of, 361-62
    hemoglobin of, 360-61
    hemolysis of, 361
    maturation factors of, 359
    number of, 360
    origin of (hematopoiesis), 359-60
    in polycythemia, 362
    spleen and, 480
  white, 15, 362-68
    ameboid movement of, 363
    functions of, 364-65, 368
    inflammation and, 368
    life cycle of, 365-68
    varieties of, 362-63
Blood pressure, 460-66
  kidneys and, 458
  methods of determination of, 462-64
  normal degree of, 464-66
  pulse and, 464
Blood vessels, 405-6. *See also* Artery

Blood vessels [*Cont.*]
(arteries), Capillaries, Veins, and
specific names
of adrenal gland, **500,** 501
of bladder, 694
of bone, 73-75
development of, 743-44
of esophagus, 562
of heart, **389,** 390-91, **392, 405, 406,**
443-44
of hypophysis, 491, 493
of kidney, 682
of large intestine, 573
of liver, 577
of lungs, 406-8, 525-27
of nose, 518
of pharynx, 561
of pituitary, **491, 494**
of salivary glands, 558
of skin, 59-60
of small intestine, 570
of spleen, 480
of stomach, 565-66
systemic, 408-9
of thyroid gland, **497**
tonus of, 455-56
of uterus, 714
in visceral organ wall, **147**
Body, anatomical position of, 8-9
area and weight, basal metabolism and,
646
back view of, **10**
blood distribution to parts of, 454
cavities, 5-8
lining of, 51-53
chemical analysis of, 18
cross section (thoracic), 8
fluids, 39-43. *See also* Fluids
front view of, **10**
heat production, size and, 654
regions of, 8-9
terminology of, 9-10
transverse section of, **9**
wall, 5, 8, **478**
water distribution in, 664
Bolus of food, 606
Bone(s), 71-78
blood vessels and nerves of, 73-75
canaliculi, **72,** 73, **74**
cancellous (spongy), 72, **75, 135**
cells, 73-74
compact, 72, **74, 75, 79, 135**
of cranium, 96-108
decalcified, 71
development of, 76-77
endosteum of, 73
of extremities, lower, **126, 127**
upper, **119, 120, 122**
flat, 95
of foot, **128, 129**

fracture of, 78, 121, 128
of hand, **121**
hormonal influences on, 77-78
irregular, 95
long, **75,** 95
marrow of, 73, 360, **482**
of middle ear, 325-26
of nose, 516
periosteum of, 73
processes and depressions of, 95. *See
also* Process(es)
regeneration of, 78, 84
rickets and, 78
short, 95
of skeleton, 93
structure of, 71-73
of thorax, **116**
Bony levers, muscles and, 157
Bowman's capsule, 680, 681, **682**
Boyle's law, 537
Brachial artery, **177, 183, 403,** 417-18, 460
Brachial muscle, **119, 120,** 177-78
Brachial plexus, **182,** 219, 261-62, 746
Brachial vein, **427**
Brachiocephalic (innominate) artery, **403,
405, 407,** 409, **474**
Brachiocephalic veins, **426,** 428, **497, 629**
Brachioradialis, **160, 183**
Brain, 265-85. *See also* specific parts
association fibers of, **273**
cerebrospinal fluid of, 284-85
circulation of base of, **416**
development of, 265
forebrain, 266-78
hindbrain, 279-83
localization of functions of, 270-71
medial aspects of, **319**
meninges of, 283-84
midbrain, 278
parts of, 265-66
ventricles of, 268, **269,** 270
weight of, 265
Brain stem, **267,** 278, **287, 288**
reflexes involving, 235
Breastbone, 116
Breasts, 724-25
Breathing, 529-30
advantages of nasal, 518
Bregma, 105-6, 134
Broad ligament, 711, 715
Bronchial arteries, 410, 527
Bronchial veins, 429
Bronchioles, 522, 523, 525, **527**
Bronchus, 52, 406, 407, 522-23
Brunner's glands, 569
Buccal (mouth) cavity, **5,** 8, **517,** 555-60
Buccal glands, 557
Buccinator muscle, 162
Buccopharyngeal membrane, **741,** 742, 745
Buffer systems, 670-71

Bulb of eye, 337-42
Bulbar autonomics, 299
Bulbourethral glands, **706, 707, 708**
Bundle of His, 385, **446**
Bursae 53, **135**

Calcaneus, 128, **129**
Calcium, 372, 594-95
   muscle contraction and, 155
   rickets and, 78
Calculi in urine, 691
Calories, 645
   daily requirement of, 647-48
Calyces of kidney, **54, 55, 678**
Canal, 95
   alimentary, **5,** 54, 272, 554, 555
   anal, 619
   cervical, 713
   haversian, **72,** 73, **74, 79**
   inguinal, **6, 189**
   of Schlemm, 337
   semicircular, 330, 332-33
   Volkmann's, 73
Canaliculi of bone, **72,** 73, **74**
Cancellous bone, 72, **75, 135**
Canines, 560
Caninus muscle, **162**
Canthi of eye, 334
Capillaries, **396,** 397-99, **451**
   distribution of, 397
   function of, 397-98
   of glomerulus, 682
   lymph, **41,** 472, 473
   network of, **405**
   pressure of, 40-41, 464
   structure of, 397
   tissue fluid formation and, 40-41
Capitate bone, **121**
Capitulum, **119,** 120
Capsule, adipose, of kidney, 677
   articular, 134-35
   Glisson's, 578
   renal, 680, 681, **682**
   of Tenon, 336
Carbohydrases, 38
Carbohydrates, 589-90
   metabolism of, 634-39
      glucocorticoids and, 502
      liver function and, 579
Carbon dioxide, carriage of, in blood, 539-42
   oxygen and, exchange, 537-39
   respiratory depth and increase of, 534
Carbonic acid, 671
Carbonic anhydrase, 38, 541
Carboxypeptidases, 38
Cardia of stomach, 563, 564
Cardiac artery and vein, **391, 392**
Cardiac cycle, 447-48
Cardiac glands, 564

Cardiac muscle, **79,** 148, 154, 385, **386,** 449, 453
Cardiac output, 448, 458, 459
Cardiac plexus, 282, 304, **393**
Cardinal ligaments, 715
Carotid arteries, **393, 403, 405, 407, 410,** 415, **416, 417, 450,** 460, **474, 497**
Carotid body, 415
Carotid foramen, external, 99
Carotid sinus, 415, **450,** 452
Carpus, **94,** 121-22
   movement of, 179-80
Cartilage, 69-71
   articular, **75, 135**
   arytenoid, **517,** 519, **520**
   corniculate, 519
   costal, 117
   cricoid, **517,** 519, **520, 523**
   cuneiform, 519, **520**
   elastic, **70,** 71
   fibrous, **70,** 71
   hyaline, 69-70, **79**
   laryngeal, 518-19
   nasal, **516**
   repair of, 83
   thyroid, **517,** 519, **520, 523**
   tracheal, **523**
Caruncula lacrimalis, 334, **335**
Casts in urine, 691
Catabolism, 28, 633
Catacrotic limb, **456**
Catecholamines, 503
Cauda equina, **250**
Caudal, definition of, **9**
Caudate nucleus, **273, 274,** 275
Cavity (cavities), abdominal, **5, 6,** 7
   amniotic, 740
   body, 5-8, 51-53
   bone, 95
   buccal, 555-60
   cotyloid, 124
   dorsal, **5,** 8, **9**
   exocelomic, 740
   glenoid, 119
   lining of, 51-53
   mouth, 555-60
   nasal, 516-18
   orbital, 8, 336-37
   pleural, **6,** 7
   subarachnoid, **251**
   thoracic, 529-30
   throat, 560-61
Cecum, **7, 52, 562,** 570, **571, 632**
   veins of, **433**
Celiac artery, **408,** 411, **574, 580,** 629
Celiac plexus, 304
Cells, acid-base balance and, 669, 670-71
   active transport in, 36-37
   alpha and beta, 508
   astrocytes, 222

Cells [*Cont.*]
blood, *See* Blood cells
bone, 73-74
centrioles of, 23-24
centrosomes of, **19, 737**
chromosomes of. *See* Chromosomes
circulation of, 28
connective tissue, 65
diffusion of, 35
division of, **27,** 28-29, 719, 732-33, 736
endoplasmic reticulum of, **19, 20,** 24
enzyme action and, 37-39
ependymal, 222
excretion and secretion of, 28
fibrils of, 25
germinal, 731-36
glial, 222
Golgi apparatus of, **19,** 23
glycogen particles of, 20
inclusions of, 23
irritability of, 28
Kupffer, **482, 576,** 577, 580
lysosome of, **19, 23,** 24
mast, 65, **370**
membrane of, 19, **20, 21,** 37
microbodies of, 24-25
microglial, 222
mitochondria of, **19, 20, 21, 22**
motion of, 27-28
muscle. *See* Muscle tissue
nerve, *See* Neurons
nucleolus, **19, 20**
nucleus of, **19, 20,** 25
nutrients of, 28
organelles of, 23
osmosis of, 35-36
physiology of, 32-45
pinocytosis of, **19,** 37
protoplasm constituents of, 18-19
respiration of, 28
reticuloendothelial, 482-83
ribosomes of, **19, 24**
secretory granule of, 19
Sertoli, 710-11
shape of, 15-16
size of, 16-18
stomach, 564, 610, 611
surface area and volume of, 17
tissue fluid and, 39-43
visible microscopic structures, **19**
water in, 19, 33
Cellulitis, 69
Cellulose, 590
Celom, 5, 741, 744-45
Cement of tooth, 558
Center, nerve, 231, 240
Central nervous system, 220, **264,** 742. *See also* Brain, Spinal cord
Centrioles, 23-24
Centromere, 732

Centrosome, **19, 737**
Centrum, **251**
Cephalic vein, 427
Ceratocricoid ligament, **519**
Cerebellum, **264, 267, 274,** 279-81, **286**
Purkinje cells of, 226
reflexes involving, 235
spinal pathways to, 255
Cerebral arteries, 415-16
Cerebral peduncle, **274, 286**
Cerebrosides, 591
Cerebrospinal fluid, 284-85
Cerebrum, **264, 267**
acoustic center of, 330-31
association areas of, 273
autonomic nervous control by, 311
axodendritic synapse of, 241
basal nuclei of, 273-75
cerebellar connections with, **279, 280**
diencephalon of, 275-77
fissures and convolutions of, 266-67
functional areas of, **269,** 270-71, **272**
hemispheres of, 266
hypothalamus, 276-77
lobes of, 267-68, 330
mammillary bodies of, 275
motor area of, 271-72
pathways to, 255, **279**
physiology of, 270
reflexes involving, 235
reticular formation of, 277
rhinencephalon, 275
sensory area of, 272-73
thalamus, 275-76
ventricles of, 268, 270
Ceruminous glands, 63
Cervical canal, 713
Cervical nerves, 219, **249,** 258-59, 261, **302**
Cervical vertebrae, **94,** 108-9, **110, 111, 712**
Cervix of uterus, **713, 714**
Chalazion, 334
Charles's law, 537
Cheeks, 556
Chemoreceptors, 230, 452
Chest, 6
arteries of, 409-11
Cheyne-Stokes respiration, 543-44
Chiasmata, chromosomal, 732-33
Chief cells, 564
Chloride ion, 501, 541
Cholecystokinin, 581, 615, 617
Cholesterol, 370, 616, 641
Choline, 601, 640, 642
Cholinergic fibers, 308-9
Cholinesterase, 38, 150
Chordae tendineae, **387,** 388
Chorion, 739, 746, 747, **748, 749**
Chorionic gonadotropin, 720, 722, 749
Choroid, **335,** 338
Choroid plexus, **274, 284,** 285, **651**

Connective tissue [*Cont.*]
  submucous, 55
Consciousness, cerebrum and, 270
Constipation, 619
Contraction of muscles, 142, 149-57
  cardiac muscle, 453
  chemical changes in, 154-57
  conditions of, 151
  contractile phase, 154
  energy source for, 155
  excitation and, 149-51
  fatigue and exercise and, 156-57
  heat formation in, 155, 652
  isometric and isotonic, 152-53
  latent period in, 151
  oxygen debt and, 156
  refractory periods in, 152
  relaxation and, 151
  response to stimuli in, 151-52
  skeletal, 153-54
  tone and, 149
  types of, 152-53
Conus medullaris, 248, **250**
Convergence, 344
Convolutions, cerebral, 266
Copper, 596
Coracobrachialis muscle, **119**, 173, **183**
Coracoid process, **118**
Corium, 58-59
Cornea, **335,** 337
  repair of, 83
Corniculate cartilages, 519
Corona radiata, **274, 737**
Coronal plane, definition of, 9
Coronal suture, **96, 97, 105, 133,** 134
Coronary circulation, **389,** 390-91, **392,
    405, 406,** 443-44
Coronary sinus, **446**
Coronary (gastric) vein, **432, 433, 632**
Coronoid fossa, **119**
Coronoid process, **104, 120,** 121
Corpora arantii, **388, 389,** 390
Corpora cavernosa, **708,** 709
Corpora quadrigemina, **267,** 278
Corpus albicans, 720
Corpus callosum, 268, **273, 274, 284, 651**
Corpus luteum, 719, **720, 721,** 722
  hormone, 506
Corpus uteri, 713
Corpuscles, blood. *See* Blood cells
  malpighian, 680
Corrugator muscle, 162
Corti, organ of, 329
Cortical blood vessels (kidney), **681**
Cortical substance of kidney, 679
Corticosteroids, 501, 502
Corticotropin, 502
Cortisol, 502
Costae, 117
Costocervical artery, 417

Cotyloid cavity, 124
Cowper's glands, **706,** 707, **708**
Cranial, definition of, 9
Cranial nerves, 286, **289, 302**
  digestion and, 573
  numbers and names of, 286-91
  table of, 296-97
Craniosacral nervous system, 299-301
Cranium, 96-108
Creatine, 154-55, 689
Creatinine, 689
Crest, definition of, 95
Cretinism, 498-99
Cribriform lamina, **98**
Cricoid cartilage, **517,** 519, **520, 523**
Cricothyroid, **519, 520**
Crista galli, **98,** 100-101, **102, 516**
Crossing over, 732, **733,** 736
Cross matching of blood, 377
Cross-striped muscle tissue, 142-46
Crown of tooth, 558
Cruciate ligaments of knee, **136**
Crura of diaphragm, 184, **187**
Cryptorchidism, 705
Crypts of Lieberkühn, 568
Cubital vein, median, **427**
Cuboid bones, **128**
Cul-de-sac, uterine, **712,** 715
Cuneatus, nucleus, 282
Cuneiform bones, **128, 129**
Cuneiform cartilages, 519, **520**
Cutaneous nerve, anterior, **200**
Cuticle, 60
Cyanocobalamin, 600
Cystic artery, **411,** 412
Cystic duct, **411, 574,** 578, **580**
Cystocele, 717
Cytoplasm, 19, 33
Cytotrophoblast, **739,** 740, 741, **747, 750**

Dartos muscle, 706
Decalcified bone, 71
Decarboxylases, 38
Decidual membranes, 740, 746, 747, **748,
    749**
Deciduous teeth, 559
Defecation, 619
Deglutition, 607-8
Dehydrogenases, 38
Deltoid muscle, **118, 119, 160, 161,** 174,
    176, 183
Demifacet, **117**
Dendrites, **223,** 224-25
Dental nerve, 105
Dentin, 558
Deoxyribonucleic acid, 25-27, 29
Depressions, bone, 95
Depressor fibers of heart, 394
Depressor septi, **162**
Derma, 58-59

Dermatome, **743, 745**
Desoxycorticosterone acetate (DOCA), 501
Detoxication, by kidney, 691-92
    by liver, 579-80
Detrusor urinae muscle, 693
Deuteranope, 343
Dextrins, 590
Diabetes, 496, 638-39
Dialysis, 36, 686-87
Diaphragm, 5, **6, 7,** 181-85, **187, 530**
Diaphysis, 76
Diarrhea, 672
Diarthroses, 134-39
Diastole, 447, 463
Dichromats, 343
Dicumarol, 375
Diencephalon, 275-77
    reflexes involving, 235
Diet, accessory factors of, 604
Diffusion, 35
    oxygen and carbon dioxide, 539-41
    tissue fluid and, 40, 42
Digestion, 604-27
    absorption of end products of, 631-32
    accessory organs of, 573-82
    blood transport to liver and, **632**
    chemical, 605
    cranial nerves related to, 573
    enzymes in, 605-6
    in large intestine, 617-19
    mechanical, 605
    in mouth, 606-7
    in small intestine, 612-16
    in stomach, 608-12
    swallowing in, 607-8
Digestive system, 13, 553-87
Digestive tube. *See* Alimentary canal
Digital veins, **427**
Dilator pupillae, 339
Diploid number, 732
Disaccharides, 589
Disk, intervertebral, 110, 112
Dislocation, 139
Distal, definition of, 9-10
Diuretics, 689
Dominant genes, 735
Dorsal, definition of, 9
Dorsal cavity, **5,** 8, **9**
Dorsal root, **226, 252**
Dorsal (thoracic) vertebrae, **7, 94,** 109, 111
Dorsalis pedis artery, **403, 420, 421,** 422
Dorsum sellae, **98**
Dorsum of tongue, **166**
Douglas, pouch of, **712,** 715
Duct(s), bile, 578
    endolymphatic, 327
    lacrimal, 334
    lymphatic, 472
    pancreatic, 574
    semicircular, 330

seminal, **705,** 706
spermatic, 711
thoracic, **428,** 472, **474, 478, 629**
vitelline, 745
Wharton's, 558
Ductus arteriosus, 753
Ductus choledochus, 578
Ductus cochlearis, 329
Ductus deferens, **705,** 706
Ductus venosus, 752, **753**
Duodenum, **7, 52, 79,** 566, **580, 632**
    veins of, **433**
Dura mater, 249, **251,** 283, **284**
Dyspnea, 543

Ear, equilibrium and, 332-33
    external, 324-25
    internal, 53, 324, 326-30, 332-33
    middle, **324,** 325
    ossicles of, 325-26
Ectoderm, **739,** 740, **741,** 742, **744, 750**
Edema, 477-78
Edematous respiration, 544
Effector cells, 230-31
Efferent (motor) fibers, **79,** 222, **224,** 225, **226, 233, 239, 252**
Ejaculation, 708
Ejaculatory duct, **54, 706,** 707
Elastic arteries, 395, 457
Elastic cartilage, **70,** 71
Elastic connective tissue, 67-68, 83
Elasticity of muscles, 142
Elbow bone, 120-21
Elbow muscles, **177, 185**
Electrocardiogram, 445-47
Electrolytes, 667-73
    in cellular and interstitial fluid, 32
    kidneys and, 683-84
Elimination, materials for, 676
Embolus, 375
Embryo, development of, 736-54
Embryoblast, **738,** 740
Embryology, 4
Embryonal connective tissue, 64
Embryonic period, 742
Enamel, 558
Endocardium, 383, 385
Endochondrial ossification, 76-77
Endocrine glands, 13, 486, 489-510
Endoderm, 47*n.*
Endoenzymes, 37, 38, 39
Endolymph, 333
Endolymphatic duct, 327
Endometrium, 713, **714, 739**
Endomysium, **145**
Endoneurium, 232
Endoplasmic reticulum, **19, 20,** 24
End organs, 228-31
Endosteum, 73
Endothelial cells, 360

renal, 677
superficial and deep, 69
Fasciculi, **142,** 144, **146,** 252
Fasciculus cuneatus, 254-55
Fasciculus gracilis, 254
Fat(s), 590, 591
body, origin of, 640
cells, **58, 66**
enzymes and, 606
metabolism of, 639-42
glucocorticoids and, 502
liver function and, 579
Fatigue, 156-57, 239, 243-44
Fatty acids, 632
Fauces, 556, 560
Feces, 619
Feedback in glands, 490
Femoral arteries, **403,** 419-21, **430,** 460
Femoral nerves, 200
Femoral ring, 189
Femoral veins, **421, 430,** 431
Femur, **94, 122,** 125-26, **135, 138**
muscles of, **126,** 190-94
Fenestra cochleae, 325, **326**
Fenestra vestibuli, 325, **326**
Fertilization, 736-38
Fetal malformations, 749-52
Fetal membranes, **748**
Fetal period, 746
Fever, 656
Fibrillated cell, **64**
Fibrillation, 447
Fibrils, cell, 25
Fibrin, 372, 373, 374, 740
Fibrinogen, 372, 373
Fibrinolysin, 720
Fibroblasts, 65
Fibrous astrocytes, 222
Fibrous cartilage, **70,** 71
Fibrous connective tissue, 68-69, 83
Fibrous tunic of eyeball, 337
Fibrous union, 78
Fibula, **94, 122,** 127-28, **135, 136**
Filum terminale, 248, **250, 302**
Fimbriae, 712
Finger, bones of, 123
muscles of, 180
Fisher-Race concept, 377
Fissure, cerebral, 266-67
definition of, 95
palpebral, 333-34
Fixation, muscle, 159
Flexion, 138
reflex, 235
Flexor carpi radialis, 179
Flexor carpi ulnaris, 179
Flexor digitorum longus, **199**
Flexor digitorum profundus, **120, 180**
Flexor hallucis longus, **199**
Flexor pollicis longus, **120, 181**

Flocculus, 274
Fluids, 39-43, 65-66
cerebrospinal, 284-85
extracellular, kidneys and, 683
formation of, 40-41
intake and output of, 665-67
interstitial, 32
Fluorine, 596
Folic acid, 600
Follicles, malpighian, 480
ovarian, 718, 719, **720, 721**
Follicle-stimulating hormone, 492, 495,
718, 720, 721, 722
Fontanels, 105-6
Foods, acid-base balance and, 669-70
classification of, 589
energy of, 645
intake, regulation of, 277, 319
Foot, arteries of, **420, 421, 422**
bones of, 128-29
muscles of, 196-99, **202**
Foramen, 95
jugular, 259
of Luschka, 270
of Magendie, 270
magnum, 97
mental, 105
of Monro, **269,** 270
obturator, 124
ovale, **98, 99,** 388, 752, 753
rotundum, **98**
spinosum, **99**
transversarium, **110, 111**
Forearm, 120n.
Forebrain, 266-78
Foregut, primitive, 745
Forelimb buds, 746
Foreskin, 709
Fornices, brain, **284, 651**
vaginal, 715
Fossa(e), 95
intercondyloid, 125
of liver, 575
mandibular, 99
ovalis, **387, 753**
Fovea capitis, **126**
Fovea centralis, 341
Fractures, 78, 121, 128
Frontal bone, **96,** 97-98, **102**
Frontal lobe, 268, **269, 286**
Frontal plane, definition of, 9
Frontal sinuses, 98, 106, **107, 516, 517**
Frontal suture, 134
Frontalis muscle, **162**
Fructose, 589
Functional unit, definition of, 14
Fundic glands, 564
Fundus, of stomach, 564
of uterus, 713
Funiculi, 232, 251-53

Galactose, 589
Gallbladder, **6,** 52, 411, **562, 574,** 580-82, **632**
  stones of, 616
  veins of, 432
Gametes, 732
Ganglion, 231, 303, 329, 331. *See also* specific names
Gases, blood, 370
  exchange of, in lung, 537-39
Gasserian ganglion, **287**
Gastric arteries, **411,** 412, **629**
Gastric secretions, 507-8, 564-65, 610-11
Gastrin, 507-8, 565, 616
Gastrocnemius muscle, **126, 160, 161,** 197
Gastroduodenal artery, **411,** 412
Gastroepiploic arteries, **411**
Gastroepiploic veins, **432, 433, 632**
Gastropulmonary mucous membrane, 54
Gay-Lussac's law, 537
Gels, 34
Gemellus muscles, 194
Genes, allelic, 377-78, 735
  heredity and, 735
  ovum and, 732
Genicular arteries, **420, 421**
Genicular ligament, **136**
Geniculate body, 345
Genioglossus muscle, **166,** 167, **517**
Geniohyoideus muscle, **166, 517**
Genitals, female, 711-25
  fetal period, 746
  hypothalamic control of, 277
  male, 704-11
Genitofemoral nerve, **200**
Genitourinary mucous membrane, 54, **55**
Genotype, 735
Germinal tissue development, 731-36
Gingiva, **556**
Gladiolus, 116
Gland(s), 486. *See also* specific names
  alveolar, 488-89
  ceruminous, 63
  compound, 488
  endocrine, 486, 489-510, 635, 722
  epithelial, 61-63, 487
  exocrine, 486
  of external secretion, 487-89
  feedback in, 490
  heterocrine, 486-87
  lacrimal, 334-35
  lymphoid, 487
  mammary, 724-25
  mucous, 487
  multicellular, 487
  reproductive organ, 707, 716-17
  salivary, 557-58, 606
  sebaceous, 61-62, 334
  serous, 487
  simple, 487-88
  small intestine, 568-69

  stomach, 610-11
  sweat, 62-63, 652-53
  tubuloalveolar, 488
  unicellular, 487
Glans of clitoris, **717**
Glans penis, **706, 708,** 709
Glenoid fossa, **118,** 119, **137**
Glial cells, 222
Gliding joints, 135
Glisson's capsule, 578
Globulin, 369
Globus pallidus, **274**
Glomerulus, 680, 682, 685
Glossopalatine arch, 556
Glossopalatine nerve, **289**
Glossopharyngeal nerve, **274, 289,** 291, 450
Glottis, 519, **522, 523**
Glucagon, 508, 635
Glucocorticoids, 501, 502-3, 505, 506
Glucose, 508, 589, 634-35, 637
  in urine, 690-92
Gluteal arteries, **422**
Gluteal nerve, **201**
Gluteus maximus, **126, 160, 161, 190,** 192, **193**
Gluteus medius, **126, 191,** 192, **193**
Gluteus minimus, 192, **193**
Glycerol, 591, 632
Glycine, 592, 643
Glycogen, **20,** 590, 634-35, 636
Glycolipids, 591
Glycolysis, 635
Goblet cell, **49,** 50
Goiter, 498
Golgi apparatus, **19,** 23, **229**
Gonadal hormones, 495, 502, 710, 720, 722, 749
Gonads, 506-7, 731
Graafian follicle, 719
Gracilis, nucleus, 282
Gracilis muscle, **160, 195,** 196
Gray matter, 231-32, 249-51
Gristle, 69. *See also* Cartilage
Granulation tissue, 80, 81
Groove, definition of, 95
Growth hormone, 493-94
Gullet (esophagus), **7, 52, 116,** 187, **407, 517,** 561-62
Gyri, cerebral, 266

H band, 143
Hageman factor, 373
Hair, **59,** 60-61, **229**
  cells of inner ear, 329, 330, 332, 333
Hamate bone, **121**
Hamulus, **101**
Hand, arteries of, **418**
  bones of, **121,** 122-23
  muscles of, 178-79
  veins of, **427**
Haploid number, 732

Haustral churning, 617
Haversian canals, **72,** 73, **74, 79**
Head, arteries of, 415-16
  bones of, 96-108
  muscles of, **162,** 167-68
  sinuses of, 106-7
Head of bone, definition of, 95
Hearing, 324-33
  cerebral center for, 330-31
  physiology of, 331-32
Heart, 8, 383-94
  apex of, **6**
  atria, **6,** 386, **387, 391, 392, 405, 406, 441, 448**
  beat of, 449-50, 452-54, 548
  block, 447
  cavities of, 386-88
  circulation of, 390-91, **392, 405, 406,** 443-44
  cycle, 447-48
  front view of, **389**
  inhibition of, 282, **450**
  longitudinal section of, **387**
  lymph vessels, 394
  muscle, **79,** 148, 154, 385, **386,** 449, 453
  nerve supply of, 393-94, 449-50
  orifices of, 388
  pain, neural path for, **317**
  as a pump, 445
  reflex, 451-52
  sounds and murmurs, 449
  valves, 388-90, **391, 441, 444**
  wall, 383-85
Heat, loss, 649-50, 652-53
  production, 155, 649, 651-52
  receptors, 60, **229,** 230, **651**
Heel bone, 128
Helicotrema, **329**
Helmholtz resonance theory, 332
Hematopoiesis, 359-60
Heme, 360
Hemiazygos vein, **428,** 429, **474, 478**
Hemodialysis, 686-87
Hemoglobin, 360-61, 541
Hemolysis, 361
Hemorrhage, clotting and, 375-76
Hemorrhoidal arteries, **414**
Hemorrhoidal veins, **432, 433, 632**
Henle, loop of, **679, 680,** 681
Heparin, 370, 372, 375, 510, 642
Hepatic artery, 411, 412, 577, **580, 629**
Hepatic duct, **574,** 578
Hepatic veins, 431, 577
Heredity, 378, 735
Hering-Breuer reflex, 532
Hernia, 189-90, 717
Herophili, torcular, 424
Heterocrine glands, 486-87
Heterozygosity, 735
Hexokinases, 38, 635
Highmore, antrum of, 103, 106

Hilum, of kidney, 677
  of lung, 524
Hilus, lymph node, 473
Hindbrain, 279-83
Hindgut, primitive, 745
Hindlimbs, embryonic, 746
Hinge joints, 135-36
Hip, bones of, 123-25, **138**
  muscles of, **202**
Hippuric acid, 690
His, bundle of, 385, **446**
Histamine, 510
Histiocyte, **64,** 65
Histology, 4
Homeostasis, 4
Homeothermic animals, 649
Homologous tissue, 82
Homozygosity, 735
Horizontal plane, definition of, 9
Hormones. *See also* specific names
  bone influences of, 77-78
  intestinal, 616-17
  kidney function and, 686-87
  local, 489-90
  menstrual cycle and, 718, 719, 720, 721-722
  metabolism and, 489-90, 498, 502, 565, 635
  in pregnancy, 720, 725
Hr factor, 378
Humerus, **94,** 120, **122, 137, 177**
  muscles of, **119,** 173-78, **185**
Humors of eyeball, 341
Hunger, 319
Hyaline cartilage, 69-70, **79**
Hyaluronidase, 38
Hydrases, 38
Hydrochloric acid, 611
Hydrogen ions, 671, 684
Hydrolases, 38
Hydroxybutyric acid, 640, 691
Hymen, 716, **717**
Hyoglossus, **166**
Hyoid bone, 107-8, **166, 517, 519, 520, 523**
Hyperglycemia, 508, 510, 638
Hypermetropia, 347
Hyperparathyroidism, 499-500
Hyperpnea, 543
Hyperthyroidism, 499
Hypertonic solution, 36
Hypogastric artery, **403**
Hypogastric plexus, **693**
Hypoglossal nerve, **249,** 282, **289,** 291
Hypoglycemia, 508
Hypoparathyroidism, 499
Hypophyseal arteries, 491, 493, **494**
Hypophyseal vein, 494
Hypophysis, 102, **286, 287,** 490-99, **651**
  stress and, 504-6
Hypothalamic artery, **494**
Hypothalamus, 258, **267,** 276, 310, **492**

Hypothalamus [*Cont.*]
kidney function and, 686
Hypothermia, 656
Hypothyroidism, 498
Hypotonic solution, 36
Hypoxia, 544

Ileocolic artery, **412**
Ileum, 566, **569**, 632
Iliac arteries, **403**, 414-15, 419, 693, 753
Iliac lymph nodes, **478**
Iliac spine, 124
Iliac veins, 431, **433, 753**
Iliacus muscle, **190,** 191
Iliocostalis muscle, 170, 531
Iliohypogastric nerve, **200**
Ilioinguinal nerve, **200**
Ilium, **6, 7, 94, 122, 123,** 124, **170, 176**
Image inversion, 346
Incisive canal, **99**
Inclusions, cell, 23
Incontinence, 695
Incus, 325, 326
Indican in urine, 691
Inferior, definition of, 9
Inflammation, 368
Infraorbital foramen, **97, 99**
Infusion, intravenous, 376
Infraspinatus muscle, **118, 161,** 175, **176**
Infundibulum, **267, 286, 287,** 495
Inguinal canal, **6, 189**
Inguinal lymph nodes, **478, 479**
Inhibition, of gastric digestion, 612
of heart, 282, 393
neuron, 242-43
Innominate (brachiocephalic) artery, **403,
405, 407,** 409, **474**
Innominate bone, 124
Innominate (brachiocephalic) vein, **426,
428, 497, 629**
Inorganic compounds of protoplasm, 19
Inositol, 601
Inspiration, 530-31
Instep of foot, 128
Insula, cerebral, 268, **274**
Insulin, 508, 635
Intercostal arteries, 410-11
Intercostal lymph nodes, **474, 478**
Intercostal muscles, 186, **187**
Intercostal spaces, 117
Interlobar arteries, 682
Internal, definition of, 9
Internal os of uterus, 713
Interstitial-cell-stimulating hormone, 495,
710, 711
Interstitial fluid, 32, **663,** 664, **666, 668**
Interventricular septum, **387**
Intervertebral disks, **112**
Intestinal lymphatics, **487**
Intestinal secretions, 507-8, **509, 569**

Intestine. *See* Large intestine, Small intes-
tine
Intra-alveolar pressure, 536
Intracellular fluid, **663,** 664, **666**
Intrapleural pressure, **536-37**
Intrinsic factor, 360
Inversion of images, 346
Involution, 723
Iodine, 497, 596
Ionic concentration, nerve impulse and,
237-38
Iris, **335,** 338-39
Iron, 595
Irritability, of cardiac muscle, 453
of cells, 28
of muscle tissue, 142
of nerve fiber, 236
Ischium, **122, 123,** 124, **138**
Islets of Langerhans, 508, 574-75
Isomerases, 38
Isometric and isotonic contractions, 152-53
Isotonic solution, 36
Isotropic (I) bands, 143
Isthmus of uterus, 713

Jaundice, 616
Jawbones, 103-5
Jejunum, **52,** 566
Joints, 132-39. *See also* specific names
ball-and-socket, 137-39
condyloid, 136-37
freely movable, 134-39
gliding, 135, **138**
hinge, 135
immovable, 132-34
lining of, 53
opposing action at, muscles of, 173-88
saddle, 137
slightly movable, 113, 134
structure of, 132
Jugular foramen, **98, 99**
Jugular lymph vessels, **478**
Jugular veins, 425-26, **428, 474, 497, 629**
Juxtaglomerular apparatus, 685

Karyokinesis, 28-29
Karyoplasm, 25
Keratin, 57
Ketone bodies, 640, 641, 691
Kidney, **7, 9, 408,** 677-87
ammonia formation by, 684
arterial pressure and, 458
blood supply of, 682
calyces of, **54, 55, 678**
cortical substance of, **678,** 679
dialysis of, 686-87
filtering process of, 685-86
function of, 683-86
hormonal control of, 686-87
medullary substance of, 678

nephrons of, 680-81
nerves of, 682-83
pelvis, **54, 55,** 677, **678**
Kinetocore, 732
Knee joint, 135-36
ligaments, **136**
muscles of, 194-96, **202**
Kneecap, 126
Krause, end bulb of, **59,** 228, **229**
Kupffer cell, **482, 576,** 577, 580
Kymograph, **151**
Kyphosis, 115

Labia majora and minora, **712, 716, 717**
Labyrinth of ear, 53, 326-30, **328**
Lacrimal bone, **96, 97,** 103
Lacrimal apparatus, **52,** 334-36
Lactase, 614
Lacteals, 473, 576
Lactoflavin, 599
Lactogenic hormone, 492, 725
Lacunae, bone, **72, 74**
Lacunar system, 470
Laking, 361
Lambda, 134
Lambdoidal suture, **96, 105, 133,** 134
Lamellae of bone, **72**
Lamina propria, 55
Laminae, vertebral, 108
Landsteiner blood typing, 376
Langerhans, islets of, 508, 574-75
Langhans' layer of cells, 750
Large intestine, 570-73
absorption in, 630-31
action of organisms in, 618-19
coats of, 572-73
digestion in, 617-19
function of, 573
movements of, 617
nerves and blood vessels of, 573
secretion of, 617-18
Laryngeal nerves, **497,** 521
Laryngeal pharynx, 560
Larynx, **52, 517,** 518-21, **522, 524**
Late teeth, 560
Latent period in muscle, 151
Lateral, definition of, 9
Lateral fissure, 286
Latissimus dorsi, **118, 119, 161, 175,** 176-177
Leg, 127n. See also Extremities, lower
Lens, of eye, **335,** 341
Leukocytes. See Blood cells, white
Levator ani, **572,** 715
Levator palpebrae superioris, 165, 333
Levator scapulae, **118, 162,** 170-71, **176**
Levatores costarum, 187-88
Levers, 157-58
Lieberkühn, crypts of, 568, **569**
Lien. See Spleen

Ligament(s), 69
annular, 145, **160, 161**
cardinal, 715
falciform, 752, 753
inguinal, **6, 189**
of knee, **136**
of liver, 575
of uterus, 711, 714, 715
vertebral, 113, 114, **134, 251**
vesicolumbar, 753
Ligamentum arteriosum, **753,** 754
Ligamentum flavum, **134, 251**
Ligamentum nuchae, **111,** 115, **176**
Ligamentum teres hepatis, 753
Ligamentum venosum, **753**
Light perception, 342
Linea alba, 189
Linea aspera, **126**
Lipases, 38, 611, 614
Lipids, 590-91
Lipolytic enzymes, 606, 614
Lipotropic factors, 640
Lips, 555
Liquid tissue. See Blood, Lymph
Liver, **6, 52, 79, 562,** 575-80
cell of rat, **20**
clotting factors and, 372-73
fat metabolism and, 640
fossae of, 575
histology of, 577
ligaments of, 575
lobes of, 575, 577
nerves and blood vessels of, **432, 433,** 575-78
nutrient transport to, **632**
Lobes, of cerebrum, 267-68, 330
of hypophysis, 493
of liver, 575, 577
of lungs, 524, 525
of pancreas, 574
Locomotor ataxia, 253
Longissimus capitis, **167,** 168
Longissimus cervicus, **170**
Longissimus dorsi, 170
Longitudinal fissure, 286
Loop, Henle's, 681
Lordosis, 115
Lumbar arteries, **408,** 413
Lumbar lymph vessels, **478**
Lumbar nerves, **200,** 219, **249,** 262, **302,** 746
Lumbar veins, **408, 428,** 429
Lumbar vertebrae, **7, 94, 109,** 110
muscles of, **169**
Lumbocostal arches, 183-84
Lunate bone, **121**
Lung, **6, 7, 8, 52,** 524
blood vessels of, 442-43, 525-27
gas exchange of, 537-39
lobes of, 524, 525

Lung [*Cont.*]
  nerves of, 525
  pleura of, 527-29
Lunule, 60
Luschka, foramina of, 270
Luteinizing hormone, 492, 495, 718, 719, 720
Luteotropic hormone, 495, 718, 719, 720, 722, 725
Lymph, 40, 470-72
  composition of, 470
  corticosteroid influence on, 502
  edema and, 477-78
  flow, factors controlling, 476-77
  physiology of, 471-72
  sources of, 470-71
  spleen and, 478-81
  thymus and, 481-82
Lymph vessels, 472
  of bone, 75
  of breasts, 725
  capillaries, **41,** 472, 473
  distribution of, 473
  of heart, 394
  of liver, 577
  of skin, 60
  structure of, 472-73
  valves of, **476**
Lymphoblasts, **475**
Lymphocytes, **364, 475,** 476
Lymphoid tissue (nodes), 67, 473-76, 487
  adenoid, 561
  of ileum, **569**
  location of, 474-76, **477**
  physiology of, 476
  reticular tissue in, **67**
  of small intestine, 569-70
  tonsillar, 482, 556-57
Lysosome, **19, 23,** 24

Mackenrodt's ligaments, 715
Macrophage, **64, 65, 482**
Macula lutea, 341
Magendie, foramen of, 270
Magnesium, 569
Malar bones, 103
Malleolar arteries, **420, 421**
Malleoli of tibia, 127, 128
Malleus, 325, 326
Malpighian corpuscle, 680, **682**
Malpighian follicles of spleen, 480
Maltase, 614
Mammary artery, 416-17
Mammary glands, 724-25
Mammary vein, **426**
Mammillary body, **267, 274,** 275, **286**
Mandible, **96, 97,** 104-5
Mandibular fossa, 99, **100**
Mandibular nerve, 290
Mandibular notch, **104,** 105

Manganese, 596
Manometer, water, 462
Manubrium, 116
Marginal veins, 430
Marrow, bone, 73, 360
Masseter muscle, **162,** 165
Mast cells, 65, 370
Mastication, 606
  muscles of, 165-67
Masticator nerve, 289
Mastoid cells, **100,** 106
Mastoid fontanel, 106
Mastoid portion of temporal bone, **96, 99, 100**
Matrix, areolar connective tissue, 64
  intercellular, 33
  of skin cells, 60, 61
Maxilla, **96, 97, 99, 102,** 103-4, **516**
Maxillary artery, **403,** 460
Maxillary nerve, 290
Maxillary sinus, 103, **104,** 106, **107**
Maxillary vein, **426**
Meatus, definition of, 95
Mechanoreceptors, 228
Medial, definition of, 9
Median nerve, **182, 183**
Mediastinal arteries, 410
Mediastinum, 7, **8, 528,** 529
Medulla, hair, 60-61
Medulla oblongata, **264, 267, 274,** 281-83, **284, 286,** 299, **393, 651**
  respiratory center of, 531-32
  spinal pathways and, 256, 257
Medullary artery, 74
Medullary canal, bone, **75, 95**
Medullary membrane, **72**
Medullary substance of kidney, 678
Medullary veins, **681,** 682
Meibomian glands, 488
Meiosis, 719, 732-33, 736
Meissner's corpuscles, 60, 228, **229**
Meissner's plexus, 305
Membranes, 51-56, 69
  basement, 48
  basilar, 328
  choroid, **335,** 338
  cloacal, 742
  decidual, 740, 746, 747, **748, 749**
  embryonic, 742, 745
  mucous, 54-56, 507-8
  retinal, 339
  serous, 51-53
  spinal cord, 248-49
  synovial, 53-54
  tympanic, 325
  vestibular, 329
Memory, cerebrum and, 270
Meninges, 248-49, 283-84
Meniscus of knee, **135, 136**
Menopause, 723

Menstrual cycle, 718-21
Mental foramen, **97, 104,** 105
Mentalis muscle, 163
Mesencephalon, 278
Mesenchyme, 48, 743
Mesenteric arteries, **408, 412,** 413, **414, 629**
Mesenteric plexus, 304-5
Mesenteric veins, 432, **433, 629, 632**
Mesentery, **9,** 554
Mesoderm, 64, 740, 741, 742, 743-45, **750**
Mesonephros, **743**
Mesosalpinx, **714**
Mesothelium, 51, 83
Metabolism, 28, 633-47
   basal, 645-47
   carbohydrate, 634-39
   fat, 639-42
   hormones and, 489, 498, 502
   hypothalamus and, 276
   liver function and, 579
   mineral, 594-97
   protein, 642-47
Metacarpal bones, **94, 121,** 122-23
Metaphase, **751**
Metatarsal bones, **94, 122,** 128-29
Methionine, 640, 642, 643
Metric system, 767
Microbodies, **20,** 24-25
Microglial cells, 222
Micturition, 243, 695
Midbrain, **264,** 278, 299
   spinal pathway to, 256-57
Midsagittal plane, definition of, **9**
Mineral metabolism, 594-97
Mineral salts, absorption of, 631
Mineralocorticoids, 501-2, 505, 506, 686
Minimal air, 535
Minute volume, 448
Mitochondria, **19, 20, 21, 22,** 23, **241**
Mitosis, **27,** 28-29
Mitral valve, **387**
Moderator band, 387
Modiolus, 328, **329**
Molars, 560
Molding of skull, 106
Monocytes, **364**
Monosaccharides, 589
Monro, foramen of, **269,** 270
Mons pubis, 716, **717**
Morula, 738-39
Motor area, 271-72
Motor autonomic system, 222
Motor neurons, 225, **226, 233, 237, 239, 252**
Mouth (buccal) cavity, **5,** 8, **517,** 555-60
   digestion in, 606-7
   muscles of, **162,** 163-64
Mucin, 487
Mucous glands, 487
Mucous membranes, 54-56

functions of, 55-56
gastropulmonary, **52,** 54, 507-8
genitourinary, 54, **55**
structure of, 54-55
Mucous sheaths, 53
Multangular bones, **121**
Multipolar neurons, 225
Muscle(s), 158-218. *See also* specific names
   of abdomen, 188-90
   of ankle, **202**
   blood distribution and, 42-43
   bony levers and, 157-58
   of elbow, 185
   exercise of, 453-54, 652
   of expiration, 531
   of expression, 159-64
   of eye and lids, 164-65, 336
   fatigue of, **153**
   of femur, **126,** 190-94
   of fingers, 180
   of foot, 196-99, **202**
   functions of, 146, 148, 207-18
   of hand, 178-79
   of head and neck, **162,** 167-68
   of hip, 202
   of humerus, **119,** 173-77, **185**
   insertion of, 145, 207-18
   of inspiration, 530-31
   of knee joint, 194-96, **202**
   of larynx, 520-21
   lymph flow and, 476
   of mastication, **162,** 165-67
   of opposing action at joints, 173-88
   origin of, 145, 207-18
   of radioulnar joint, 178-79
   of shoulder, **118,** 170-73, **176, 184**
   of thumb, 180-81
   of toes, 199
   of tongue, **166**
   of vertebral column, 169-70, **201**
   of wrist, 179-80, **186**
Muscle tissue, 141-48
   cardiac, **79,** 148, 154, 385, **386,** 387, 449, 453
   cell, **17**
   contractions of. *See* Contraction of muscles
   elasticity of, 142
   excitation of, 149-51, 152
   fibers, 142, 144
   irritability of, 142
   repair of, 83
   smooth, 146-48, **394**
   spindles, 230
   striated, **79,** 142-46
   tendon junction with, **145**
   tetanus of, **153**
   types of, 142-48
Muscular system, definition of, 12
Muscularis mucosae, 55, **565, 567, 568, 618**

Musculocutaneous nerve, **182, 183**
Myelinated fiber, 227, 303
Myelocytes, 73
Myenteric plexus, 305
Mylohyoideus, **166**
Myoblasts, 743, **745**
Myocardium, 383, 385
Myofibrils, 143, 144, 148
Myogenic theory, 449
Myometrium, **712,** 713, **714**
Myopia, 346-47
Myosin, **143,** 144, 154
Myotomes, **745**
Myxedema, 499

Nails, 60
Nares, 516, 517, 560
Nasal bones, **96, 97,** 102, **104, 107, 516**
Nasal cavity, **5, 8, 322**
Nasal conchae, **97,** 102-3, **166**
Nasal muscles, **162,** 163
Nasolacrimal duct, **335**
Nasopharynx, 560
Nausea, 320
Navicular bones, **121, 129**
Neck, arteries of, 415-16
    muscles of, **162**
    veins of, 425-26
Neck of bone, definition of, 95
Nephron, 680-81
Nephrotomes, **743**
Nerve(s), of adrenal gland, 501
    arterial, 395-96
    of bladder and urethra, **693,** 694
    of bone, 75
    of bronchi, 523
    cranial. *See* Cranial nerves
    degeneration and regeneration of, 263, 265
    of digestive system, **581**
    of esophagus, 562
    of eye, 336
    of heart, 393-94, 449-50
    of kidney, 682-83
    of large intestine, 573
    of liver, 575, 577
    of lungs, 525
    mixed, 259-61
    of nose, 518
    peripheral, 263
    of pharynx, 561
    physiology of, 239-40
    of salivary gland, 558
    of skin, **58, 59,** 60
    of small intestine, 570
    spinal, 219. *See also* Spinal nerves
    of stomach, 565
    of tongue, 167, 321
    of trachea, 232-33
Nerve fibers, 232-33

afferent, 222, 225, 309
    association, 266, 273
    commissural, 266
    fatigue of, 239
    funicular, 232
    of heart, 282, 393-94
    impulse and, 236-40
    muscle contraction and, 150-51
    myelinated, 227, 303
    nonmyelinated, 227-28
    postganglionic, **299,** 308, 309
    preganglionic, **299,** 308-9
    pressor, 282, 394
    projection, 266
    refractory period of, 238, 239
    vasomotor, 282, 395-96
    as white matter, 232, 303-4
Nerve impulses, 236-43
    adaptation and, 236
    autonomic, 308-9
    convergence of, 241
    energy production and, 243
    frequency of, 239
    inhibition of, 242-43
    neuromuscular junction and, 238
    speed of, 242
    spreading of, 240-41
    synapse and, 238, 240
Nervi erigentes, 709
Nervous system, 12, 220*ff.*
    autonomic, 222, 276, 298. *See also* Autonomic nervous system
    central, 220, **264,** 742. *See also* Brain; Spinal cord, nerves
    cerebrospinal, 221-22
    development of, 742
    enteric, 305
    parasympathetic, 299-301, **306, 307,** 310-311
    sympathetic, 301-5, **306, 307,** 309, 310-311
    visceral, 220, 222
Neural groove, 742
Neurilemma, **224,** 227
Neuroblasts, 223
Neuroepithelium, 50-51
Neurofibrils, 223
Neuroglial tissue, 222
Neurohypophysis, 493, 495-96
Neuromuscular junction, impulses at, 328
Neurons, 222-33
    afferent, 222, 225, 309
    association, 225, 266, 273
    axon of, **223, 224,** 225, **237, 239**
    bipolar, 225
    cell body of, 223-24
    cell processes of, 224-25
    central, 225
    classification of, 225
    connecting, 225

stomach, 609-10
Peritoneal dialysis, 687
Peritoneum, **9,** 53, 554, 555
Permanent teeth, **559-60**
Peroneal artery, **420, 421,** 422
Peroneal nerve, **200, 201**
Peroneus brevis, **198,** 199
Peroneus longus, 198
Peroneus tertius, **197,** 198
Perspiration, 62-63, 652-53
Petrosal sinuses, 424, **425**
Petrous portion of temporal bone, 98-99
Peyer's patches, 569-70
pH, **670, 672**
  of bile, 615
  of blood, 358
  of saliva, 606
  of urine, 687
  of vagina, 716
Phagocytes, **482**
Phalanges, of foot, **122, 128,** 129
  of hand, **121, 122,** 123
Pharyngeal tubercle, **99**
Pharyngopalatine arch, 556
Pharynx, **517, 556,** 560-61
Phenotype, 735
Phimosis, 709-10
Phonation, 521
Phosphatases, 38
Phospholipids, 591, 641
Phosphorus, 595
  rickets and, 78
Phosphorylases, 38
Phrenic arteries, **408,** 411, 413, 431
Physical sciences, 4
Physiological integration, 42, 43
Physiology, 4
Pia mater, 249, **251,** 284
Pili, 60
Pineal gland, **267, 509,** 510, 651
Pinna of ear, 324-25
Pinocytic channel and vesicles, **19**
Pinocytosis, **27,** 37, 749
Piriformis, 192, **193,** 194
Pisiform bone, **121**
Pituitary gland, **267,** 490-99, **509,** 635
  stress and, 504-6
Pivot joints, 137
Placenta, 507, 739, 740, 746-49
Plantar arteries, **420,** 421-22
Plasma, 369-71
  buffers, 670
  cell, **64,** 65
  clotting factors of, 373
  membrane, 19
  tissue fluid formed from, 40
  volume, **663,** 664-65, **668**
Platelets, blood, **364,** 368-69
Platysma, **162,** 163
Pleurae, **6, 7,** 51, 527-29

Pleural cavity, **6,** 7
Pleurisy, 529
Plexus, arterial, 404
  choroid, **274, 284,** 285, **651**
  nerve, Auerbach's, 305
    brachial, **182,** 219, 261-62, 746
    cardiac, 282, 304, **393**
    celiac, 304
    lumbosacral, 746
    Meissner's, 305
    mesenteric, 304-5
    renal, 682
Pneumothorax, 529
Podocytes, 681, **682**
Poikilothermic animals, 649
Polar bodies, 719, 733, **734, 737**
Poliomyelitis, 253
Polycythemia, 362
Polysaccharides, 589-90
Pons, **249, 264, 267,** 274, 281, **284, 286, 651**
Popliteal artery, **403, 420,** 421, **422,** 460
Popliteal vein, **430,** 431
Popliteus muscle, 195-96
Portal system, 432-34, 577, **580, 629, 632**
  fetal, **753**
  hypophyseal, **491**
  pituitary, **494**
Posterior, definition of, 9
Posterior ligament of uterus, 715
Postganglionic fibers, 299, 308, 309
Posture, 115, 453
Potassium, 596
  mineralocorticoids and, 501
  nerve impulse and, 237-38
Pott's fracture, 128
Pouch of Douglas, 713, 715
Preganglionic fibers, 299, 308-9
Pregnancy, embryo development and, 736-754
  extrauterine, 740
  hormones and, 720, 725
Premolars, 560
Prepuce, **706, 708,** 709, **717**
Presbyopia, 347
Pressor fibers, 282, 394
Pressoreceptors, 451-52
Pressure, gas, 537-39
  intra-alveolar, 536
  intrapleural, 536-37
  lymph flow and, 476
  receptors, **59,** 60, 228, **229**
Primitive streak, 742
Primordial follicle, 718
Proaccelerin, 372
Procerus muscle, **162**
Process(es), 95
  acromion, **118,** 119, **137**
  coronoid, **104, 120,** 121
  ensiform, 116

Process(es) [*Cont.*]
ethmoid, 516
iliac, 124
odontoid, 109, 137
olecranon, 120, 121
spinous, 95, 115
styloid, **99,** 100
vertebral, 108, 109, 110
xiphoid, 116
Prochordal plate, 742
Proconvertin, 372
Proenzyme, 39
Profunda brachii artery, **418**
Profunda femoris artery, **420**
Progesterone, 506, 507, 719, 722, 725
Progestin, 502
Projection fibers, 266
Prolactin, 495
Pronation, 137
Pronator quadratus muscle, **120, 178,** 179
Pronator teres muscle, **119,** 178-79, **183**
Pronucleus, 737
Proprioceptors, **229,** 230
Prosecretin, 508
Prosencephalon, 266-78
Prostate, **692, 693, 705, 706, 707, 708**
Proteases, 38, 611
Proteins, 591-93
blood, 369
bound with iodine, 497
enzymes and, 606
metabolism of, 642-45
glucocorticoids and, 502
liver and, 579
nitrogen output and, 689
nutritive value of, 593
Prothrombin, 370, 372, 373
Protopathic sensation, 316
Protoplasm, cilia of, 28
conductivity of, 149
constituents of, 18-19, 33-34
Protoplasmic astrocytes, 222
Proximal, definition of, 9
Pseudopodia, 27
Psoas major muscle, **126, 190,** 191
Pteroylglutamic acid, 600
Pterygoid hamulus, **99**
Pterygoid muscles, 165-66
Pterygoid plates, **101**
Puberty, 703-4
Pubis, **6, 122, 123,** 124
Pudendal arteries, **421, 422**
Pudendal nerve, **201, 693**
Pulmonary arteries, **6, 387, 391, 392, 405,** 406-7, **441,** 526-27
fetal, **753**
Pulmonary circulation, 441
Pulmonary valve, 389
Pulmonary veins, **387, 391, 392, 405,** 407-8, 424, **441**

fetal, **753**
Pulp cavity of tooth, 559
Pulse, 452, 459-60
pressure, 464
Puncta lacrimalia, **335**
Pupil, **338,** 339, 345-46
Purine bodies, 690
Purkinje cells, **226**
Pus, 368
in urine, 691
Putamen, **274,** 275
Pyloric glands, 564
Pylorus of stomach, 564
sphincter of, 563, 610
Pyramid, **249, 274**
Pyramidal cell, **226**
Pyramidal pathways, 255-56
Pyridoxine, 600
Pyrophosphatases, 38
Pyruvic acid, 645

Quadratus labii muscles, **162,** 163
Quadratus lumborum muscle, 169
Quadriceps femoris muscle, **135, 160,** 194, 196

Reaction time, 242
Receptors, **59,** 60, 228-30
adaptation of, 236
aortic arch, **450**
chemoreceptors, 452
cold, 60, 228, 651
encapsulated, 228
free, 230
heat, 60, 230, 651
pain, 230
pressure, 60, 228, 451-52
stimuli for, 236
tactile, 58, 60, 228
Recessive genes, 735
Recovery phase, 154
Rectocele, 717
Rectouterine pouch, **712,** 713
Rectum, **6, 7, 52,** 571, **632, 712**
veins of, **433**
Rectus abdominis muscle, **188,** 189
Rectus femoris muscle, **193, 195**
Rectus muscles of eye, **164,** 336
Red blood cells. *See* Blood cells, red
Red nucleus, 256, 275
Referred pain, 218
Reflex(es), 233-44
aortic, 452
arc, 233-35
brain and, 235
carotid sinus, 452
facilitation of, 242
heart, right, 451-52
Hering-Breuer, 532

physiology of, 236-44
response, 233-34
Refraction in eyeball, 341-42, 343, 346
Refractory phase, of heart, 449
in muscle contraction, 152
of nerve fiber, 238, 239
Reil, island of, 268
Reissner's membrane, 329
Relaxation of muscle, 151
Relaxin, 507
Remak, fibers of, 227-28
Renal arteries, **408,** 413, **500,** 682
Renal capsule, 680, 681
Renal columns, 679
Renal fascia, 677
Renal plexus, 682
Renal tubules, 680
Renal veins, 429, **500,** 682
Renin, 685
Reproductive system, 13
female, 711-25
male, 704-11
maturation of, 703-4
Residual air, 535
Resolution in inflammation, 368
Resonance theory of Helmholtz, 332
Respiration, 529-44
atmospheric changes and, 546-47
of cell, 28
Cheyne-Stokes, 543-44
depth of, 534
disorders of, 543-44
edematous, 543-44
external, 534-35
first, cause of, 533-34
internal, 536
lymph flow and, 477
muscles of, 530-31
pressure and, 536-37
rate of, control of, 532-34
types of, 531
Respiratory center, 282-83, 531-32
Respiratory system, 13, 515-53
Respiratory tract, 518-23
Rete testes, 711
Reticular formation, 277, **278**
Reticular tissue, 58-59, **67**
Reticulocytes, 364
Reticuloendothelial cells, **475,** 482-83
Retina, **335,** 339-41
Retro-occipital fissure, **98**
Radial artery, **183, 403,** 418, 460
Radial nerve, **182, 183**
Radioulnar muscles, 178-79
Radius, **94, 120,** 121, **122,** 137
tuberosity of, 121
Rami communicantes, 250-51, 303
Ranvier, node of, **224,** 227
Rh factor, 377, 378
Rhinencephalon, 275

Rhodopsin, 340
Rhombencephalon, 279-83
Rhomboideus major and minor, **118,** 171,
176
Rib(s), **116,** 117, **138, 170**
muscles of, 186-88
Riboflavin, 599
Ribonucleic acid, 25-27
Ribosomes, **19, 24**
Rickets, 78
Rigor mortis, 156
Risorius muscle, **162,** 163
Rods and cones, 339-41
Root of tooth, 558
Rotation, 139
Rouget cells, 397
Round ligaments, 715
Rubrospinal pathways, 256-57
Ruffini end organ, **59, 229,** 230
Rugae of stomach, 564

Saccule of ear, **324,** 327, **328**
Sacral artery, 413-14
Sacral lymph nodes, **478**
Sacral nerves, **200,** 219, **249,** 263, 300-301
Sacrosciatic ligament, **7**
Sacrospinalis muscle, 169-70
Sacrovertebral joint, **109**
Sacrum, **94, 109,** 110, **113, 124, 250**
Saddle joints, 137
Sagittal plane, definition of, 9
Sagittal sinus, **284,** 424, **425**
Sagittal suture, **105, 133,** 134
Saliva, 606-7
Salivary glands, **52,** 557-58
Salts, mineral, 631
Saphenous nerve, 200
Saphenous veins, 430-31
Sarcolemma, 142, **143**
Sarcomere, **143**
Sarcoplasm, **142,** 143
Sartorius muscle, **160, 193, 195,** 196
Satellite cells, 222
Scalae of internal ear, 328, 329
Scalenus muscles, **162,** 531
Scaphoid fossa, **99**
Scapula, **7, 94,** 119, **122, 137, 176**
muscles of, **118**
Scapular circumflex artery, **418**
Scarpa's triangle, 419
Schlemm, canal of, **335,** 337
Schwann cell, **224, 226,** 227
Sciatic nerve, **200, 201, 232**
Sclera, **335,** 337, **338**
Sclerotome, **743, 745**
Scoliosis, 115
Scratch reflex, 235
Scrotum, 706, **708**
Scurvy, 601
Sebaceous gland, **59,** 61-62, 334

Sebum, 62
Secretin, 508, 570, 617
Secretions, 486
  cell, 28
  external, 487-89
  heartbeat and, 454
  intestinal, 507-8, 569, 570, 614-15, 617-18
  liver, 579, 615-16
  pancreatic, 575, 613
  regulation of, 489
  salivary, 557-58, 606
  stomach, 507-8, 564-65, 610
  tears, 334, 336
Secretory granule, 19
Sella turcica, 102, 516, 517
Semen, 706, 707-8
Semicircular canal, 324, 328, 330, 332-33
Semilunar notch of luna, 120
Semilunar valve, 387, 389, 391
Semimembranosus, 193, 195
Seminal duct, 693, 705, 706, 708
Seminal vesicle, 54, 706-7, 708
Seminiferous tubules, 705
Semispinalis capitis, 167, 168, 170
Semitendinosus, 194, 195
Sensations, 314-15
Sensory area, 272-73
Sensory epithelium, 50-51
Sensory fibers, 222, 225, 233
Septum, nasal, 516
Septum lucidum, 274
Septum pellucidum, 267, 651
Septum primum and secundum, 753
Serotonin, 510
Serous glands, 487
Serous membranes, 51-53
Serratus anterior, 160, 172-73, 188
Serratus posticus inferior, 531
Sertoli cells, 710-11
Serum, clotting and, 372
  in gland secretions, 487
  proteins, 369
  typing, 376
Sesamoid bone, 129
Sex cells, 732
Sex hormones, 502, 506-7
Shinbone, 127
Shoulder blade, 119
Shoulder girdle, 118-19, 137
  muscles of, 170-73, 176, 184
  veins of, 427
Sigmoid colon, 414, 562, 571
Sinews, 69
Sinoatrial node, 445, 446
Sinus(es), bone, definition of, 95
  carotid, 415, 452
  ethmoid, 52, 101, 106, 107
  frontal, 52, 98, 102, 106, 107, 516, 517
  of head, 52, 106-7, 425
  maxillary, 52, 103, 104, 106, 107

petrosal, 424
sagittal, 424
sphenoid, 52, 102, 106, 107, 516, 517
straight, 424, 425
transverse, 424, 425
of Valsalva, 391
venous, 337, 424
Sinusitis, 106
Sinusoids, liver, 577
Skeletal muscle, 142-46
Skeletal system, definition of, 12
Skeleton, 93-131
  appendicular, 118-29
  axial, 96-118
  body mechanics and, 114
  classification of bones of, 95
  divisions of, 96
  front and side views of, 94
  processes and depressions of, 96
Skin, 56-63
  appendages of, 60-63
  area of, 57
  blood vessels and lymphatics of, 59-60
  corium of, 58-59
  epidermis of, 57-58
  functions of, 56
  receptors of, 59, 228-30
  structure of, 58
Skull, 96-108
  base of, 98, 99
  at birth, 105, 106, 107, 133
  fontanels of, 105-6
  front view of, 97
  side view of, 96
  sinuses of, 425. See also Sinus(es)
  sutures, 96, 97, 105, 133
  as a whole, 105
Sleep-waking mechanisms, 276
Small intestine, 9, 52, 562, 566-70, 632
  absorption of, 628-30
  action of organisms in, 616
  coats of, 566-68, 631
  digestion in, 612-16
  glands and nodes of, 568-70, 614-15
  movements of, 612-13
  nerves and blood vessels of, 432, 433, 570
Smegma, 709
Smell, 322-24
Smooth muscle tissue, 146-48
Sodium bicarbonate, 671
Sodium ions, kidney and, 684
  mineralocorticoids and, 501
  nerve impulses and, 237-38
Sole of foot, 128
Soleus muscle, 160, 197
Sols, 34
Solutions, 36
Somatic layer of mesoderm, 744
Somatopleure, 744
Somatotropic hormone, 77, 492, 493-94, 635

Sublobular veins, **577**
Submaxillary gland, **557**, 558
Submucous plexus, 305
Subscapular artery, **417**
Subscapular nerve, **182**
Subscapularis, **119**
Substantia nigra, 275
Substrate, enzyme, 37-38
Subthalamic nuclei, 275
Succus entericus, 569, 614-15
Sucrase, 614
Sucrose, 589
Sudoriferous glands, 62-63
Sugars, 589-90, 606, 632
Sulci, cerebral, 266
Sulcus, definition of, 95
Superior, definition of, 9
Supination, 137
Supinator muscle, **120**, 178
Supplementary channel, 429
Suppuration, 368
Supraorbital foramen, **97**
Suprarenal arteries, 413, **500**
Suprarenal glands. *See* Adrenal glands
Suprarenal vein, 431, **500**
Supraspinatus muscle, **118**, 174
Supratrochlear lymph node, **479**
Surface area, height and weight calculated from, **647**
Surgical neck, 120
Sustentacular cells, **709**, 710-11
Sutures, skull, **96, 97, 105, 133**, 134
Swallowing, 607-8
Sweat glands, **58, 59**, 62-63, 652-53
Sylvius, aqueduct of, **267**, 270, 278, **284**
Sympathetic nervous system, 301-5, **306, 307, 693**
  heart and, 282
  interdependence with parasympathetic system, 310-11
Sympathomimetic amines, 503
Symphysis pubis, 124, 134, **706, 708, 712**
Synapse, 228, 238, **241**
  impulses and, 240
  meiotic, 732
Synarthroses, 132-34
Syncytiotrophoblast, **739**, 740, 747, **750**
Syndesmosis, 134
Synergists, 159
Synovial membranes, 53-54, **135**
System, definition of, 12
Systemic circulation, 408-9, 424-25, 441-42
Systole, 447, 448, 463

Tabes dorsalis, 253
Tactile receptors, 58, **59**, 60, 228, **229**
Taenia coli, **571**, 572
Talus, **128, 129**
Tarsal arteries, **421**

Tarsal bones, **94, 122**, 128, 333
  muscles of, 196-99
Taste, 320-22
  area of brain, 272
  buds, **229**, 320-21
Tectal autonomics, 299
Tectorial membrane, **329**
Tectospinal pathways, 257
Teeth, **99**, 558-60
Tela choroidea, **267**
Temperature, body, 648-50
  pulse rate and, 452-53
  regulation of, 277, 310, 650-55
  variations in, 655-56
Temporal artery, **403**, 460
Temporal bone, **96, 97**, 98-100, **324**
Temporal lobe, 268, **286**, 330-31
Temporal muscle, **162**, 165
Tendocalcaneus, **160**, 197
Tendons, 69, 145, **229**
Tenon, capsule of, 336
Tensor fascia latae, **160, 191**, 192
Tentorium cerebelli, 267, 279, **425**
Teres major, 118, 173-74, **176**
Teres minor, 118, **175-76**
Testes, **54, 509**, 704-6, **708**
Testicular artery, **408**
Testosterone, 78, 507, 711
Tetanus, 152, **153**
Tetrads, 732
Thalamus, 255, **267, 273, 274**, 275-76, 651
Theca interna, 718, **720**, 721
Thermoreceptors, 228, 230
Thiamine, 599
Thigh, 127*n.*
  arteries of, **421, 422**
  bone, 125-26. *See also* Femur
  muscles of, **191, 193**
Thirst, 320
Thoracic arteries, **410, 416, 417**
  aorta, **7, 407**, 409, **410**
Thoracic duct, **428**, 472, **474, 478, 629**
Thoracic nerves, **182, 183**, 219, **249, 261**
Thoracic veins, **426**, 428-29
Thoracic vertebrae, **7, 94**, 109, **111**
Thoracodorsal nerve, **182**
Thoracolumbar nervous system, 301-5, **306, 307**, 309
Thorax (thoracic cavity), **5, 6, 7, 8, 528**, 530
  bones of, 115-17
  muscles of, **187**
Thrombin, 372, 373
Thrombocytes, 368-69
Thromboplastin, 372, 373
Thrombus, 375
Thumb, muscles of, 180-81
Thymus, 481-82, 500, **509**
Thyroarytenoid, **520**
Thyrocervical trunk, **497**

Valsalva, sinus of, **391**
Valves, colic, 617
  heart, 388-90, **391, 441, 444**
  lymph, 476
  vein, 398
Valvulae conniventes, 55, **567**
Vas deferens, **693, 705,** 706, **708**
Vasa vasorum, 395
Vascular system, definition of, 13
Vasoconstrictor center, 282
Vasodilator fibers, 282
Vasomotor nerves, 395-96, 456
Vastus intermedius, **126, 195**
Vastus lateralis, **126, 161, 193, 195**
Vastus medialis, 195
Vater, ampulla of, 574
Veins, 423-34
  of abdomen and pelvis, 431-34
  cross section of, **394**
  deep, 424, 431
  of extremities, lower, 429-31
    upper, 426-27
  of neck, 425-26
  pulmonary, **387, 391, 392, 405,** 407-8,
    424, **441**
  structure and function of, 398
  superficial, 424, 426, 430
  systemic, 424-25
  of thorax, 428-29
  valves of, 398
Vena cava, inferior, **187, 387, 392, 406,**
    407, 408, 425, 429, 431, **441,** 577,
    629, 678, 753
  superior, **6, 387, 389, 391, 392, 405, 406,**
    407, 425, **426,** 428-29, **441, 474,**
    497, 629, 753
Venous circulation, factors maintaining,
    458-59
Venous pressure, 464
Ventilation, 529-30
Ventral, definition of, 9
Ventral cavity, **9**
Ventricles, of brain, 268, **269,** 270
  of heart, 386, 387, **391, 392, 405, 406,**
    441
Ventricular cycle, **448**
Ventricular fibrillation, 447
Ventricular folds of larynx, **517, 520, 522**
Venule, **396**
Vermis, **267,** 279
Vernix caseosa, 62
Vertebrae, **9, 94,** 108-12, **176**
  bodies of, 108, 109, 110
  cervical, **94,** 108-9, **110, 111**
  coccygeal, **109,** 110
  demifacet for, **117**
  disks between, 110, 112
  laminae of, 108, **110, 111,** 115
  lumbar, **7, 94, 109,** 110
  processes of, 108, 109, 115

  rib joint with, **138**
  sacral, 110, **250**
  symphyses, **134**
  thoracic, 7, **94,** 109, **111**
Vertebral arteries, 415, **416**
Vertebral column, 108, 112-15
  muscles of, 169-70
  relation to spinal cord, **259**
Vesicoumbilical ligaments, 753
Vesicouterine pouch, 713
Vestibular glands, 716-17
Vestibular membrane, 329
Vestibular nerve, 290-91, **329,** 331
Vestibule, of labyrinth, **326,** 327, 332
  of mouth cavity, 555
  of vagina, 716
Vestibulospinal pathway, 256
Villi, embryonic, 746, **747, 749, 750**
  intestinal, 567-68, **631**
Visceral, definition of, 10
Visceral membrane, 51-53
Visceral muscle tissue, **146-48**
Visceral nerves, 231, 298, 309
Visceral pain, **317,** 318
Visceral pericardium, 384
Visceral peritoneum, 554
Visceral pleura, 527
Vision, 333-47. *See also* Eye
  abnormal, 346-47
  binocular, 344-46
  of light and color, 342-43
  physiology of, 343
  refraction and, 341-42, 343, 346
Visual area, 272
Visual pathways, **345**
Vital capacity, 535
Vitamins, 597
  A, 597-98
  B complex, 81, 360, 599-601
  C, 81, 601
  D, 81, 598
  E, 598
  fat-soluble, 597-99, 602
  K, 81, 374, 598-99
  water-soluble, 599-601, 603
Vitelline duct, 745
Vitelline vessels, 744
Vitreous body, **335,** 341
Vocal folds, **517,** 520, **522**
Voice, 521-22
Volar arteries, **418**
Volkmann's canals, 73
Vomer, **97, 99,** 102, **516**
Vomiting, 608
Vulva, **55,** 716

Warm receptors, 60, **229,** 230, **651**
Water, 589, 662-67
  absorption of, 631
  in cells, 19, 33